The CHILDREN'S SHAKESPEARE

ARRANGED BY

ARTHUR MEE

Editor of The Children's Newspaper

With Colour Frontispiece

LONDON

THE AMALGAMATED PRESS LIMITED

FLEETWAY HOUSE

Published by arrangement with
Hodder & Stoughton Limited and
Made and Printed by
Hazell, Watson & Viney, Limited, London and Aylesbury

CONTENTS OF THIS BOOK

SHAKESPEARE IN OLD SAINT PAUL'S

The King of the World

There was once a Warwickshire boy who walked to London. He came from the heart of England, the very centre of the glory of our Little Treasure Island. He was twenty-one, and he was leaving home with a heavy heart, for he had left a wife and three small children, and a father sinking into poverty ; and he was walking to an unknown world.

He loved the quiet country roads, and the fields that had been green a thousand years, for he was born among them. He came into the world in the lovely little town of Stratford on the Avon, as restful a river as England has. We can see the cottage he was born in ; we can creep up into the attic where he slept with his brothers very near the old oak rafters ; we can sit where he sat at school ; we can walk about in gardens that he used to love ; we can stand in the place where he died ; and we know that all his country life was spent amid lovely scenes. He lived half his life in the quiet beauty of the country round the Avon, and half in the wonderful city that was growing up by the Thames.

It was a wonderful time that he lived through. Before he reached the noonday of his life the gates of a new world had been opened. Francis Drake and Walter Raleigh and Philip Sidney had thrilled the minds of men with deeds that rang out everywhere. The Golden Hind had been round the world. Sir Walter Raleigh had dreamed of a British Empire. The bitter power of Spain was broken on the seas. The ships of the Great Armada were lying on the ocean bed. The proud Elizabeth was on the throne. It was to such a world that Shakespeare came.

Like Dreaming John of Grafton he came to London Town. Like Dreaming John he came from the leafy lanes round Grafton. But Dreaming John went back into his fields to find his crown : Shakespeare took home with him the crown of the world.

There has been no man like him since Time began. Of half his life we know next to nothing, one or two things and no more ; but of the other half we know almost everything that matters. If we fix the year 1600 in our minds, and think of the twelve years before it and the twelve years after, we can easily remember the time when Shakespeare did the most wonderful thing that has ever been done by one man. In 24 years he wrote 36 plays. He went back to Stratford and saved his father's fortunes. He bought the best house in the town. He made his mother proud to see her son among the greatest in the land.

We can only say that it was all a miracle, for in these short years this boy from Stratford Grammar School had built up for himself imperishable fame, had created a new dramatic force in the life of the English people, had given his country a glory greater than all her kings, and had set in the world something that would march along the ages and help to shape the minds of millions yet unborn.

Thousands of books have been written about him, and men are never tired of him. No other man has equalled him in the power to interest mankind. If we take his comedies and fantasies, there is nothing like them; if we take his histories, we seem to be looking on at the pageantry of England passing by; if we take his tragedies, we feel that there is something in them far beyond the power of words.

We may divide his work into four great phases and two great periods: there were twelve years of gaiety and romance, and twelve years of strength and peace; and from the beginning to the end Shakespeare was growing in power and moving nearer to perfection. He laid down his work before his genius began to fail. He had begun to feel that we are such stuff as dreams are made of, but his strength was not failing; he was still like Moses when they laid him in a valley in the land of Moab: his eye was not dimmed, nor his natural force abated.

If we ask ourselves the secret of Shakespeare we are asking a question that all men ask in vain. We can only take the words of another poet and say that he bore unquenched for fifty years a spark of the eternal God. What is genius if it is not that? How is it that a Warwickshire lad could walk to London, struggle a little while as an actor, and then sit down to produce the greatest piece of work that has ever come from the brain of a single man? What is that power that makes us laugh and cry across the centuries? What is it in a man that can move as he will people of every land and every age long after he is in his grave? From what fathomless recesses of the brain comes such a mighty host of characters as move across this stage that Shakespeare gave the world?

Who put into this single mind these hundreds of figures that never lived and will never die, but move like immortal shadows falling across the path of men? In one of the pathetic visions of History we see Abraham Lincoln sitting round a table with that Cabinet of plain men who held in their hands for four years the lives and deaths of millions of their countrymen; and in his pocket is a worn-out copy of Shakespeare, with a mark at the passage about the cloud-capped towers, the gorgeous palaces. We see this man again on the deck of a steamer; he is taking back to White House the good news that the war is over and the slaves are free, and he takes this worn-out Shakespeare from his pocket and reads aloud:

Duncan is in his grave;
After life's fitful fever he sleeps well;
Treason has done his worst; nor steel, nor poison,
Malice domestic, foreign levy, nothing
Can touch him further.

A few more hours, and Abraham Lincoln too, after life's fitful fever, was sleeping well. In his most solemn hours, and in his last, Shakespeare was with him.

So, in that wondrous way he has, Shakespeare comes into the life of thinking men. Michael Angelo has given us statues that will crumble; Holbein and Rembrandt and Van Dyck have given us pictures in colours that will fade; but Shakespeare is the greatest artist of them all, for he has given us images in words that are stronger than marble, visions that time itself will not destroy. Time will roll on, but who can imagine a generation that will not think sometimes of Duncan in his grave; of Lady Macbeth walking in her sleep; of Juliet waking in her tomb; of Lear on the heath; of Arthur pleading that Hubert will not put out his eyes; of Wolsey's fall; of Mark Antony's

Imperious Caesar, dost thou lie so low,
Are all thy conquests, glories, triumphs, spoils,
Shrunk to this little measure?

of Caliban creeping about his island; of King Richard asking for a little, little grave; of John o' Gaunt dying with a broken heart for love of this dear, dear land, this realm, this England; of Hamlet wondering what to do; of Falstaff gathering his ragged troops or babbling of green fields; of Ariel performing his wonders in a twink; of Laertes at Ophelia's grave, with that cry on his lips to the churlish priest:

Lay her i' the earth,
And from her fair and unpolluted flesh
May violets spring! I tell thee, churlish priest,
A ministering angel shall my sister be
When thou liest howling.

After God, said a famous Frenchman, Shakespeare has created most; and if we measure a man's work by its influence on other men it must be true. Shakespeare goes through the centuries with the winds and the trees and the babbling brooks, and men will not tire of him.

He can touch any time and make it live again. He can raise up any spirit and make it walk abroad. He can take us into any land or make another world if this world has not lands enough. Ancient history and modern history, faery worlds and real lands, are all alike to him. His Ariel is as real as Caesar. His plays are as real as the life about us. His visions all come true.

What book can stand beside Shakespeare and not seem a poor dull thing? Where are such tales as his? Where is such tenderness, such humour, such play of good and evil, such love and hate, such tears of laughter and of sorrow, such cruelty and gentleness, such depths of grief, such heights of power, such a touch of the divinity within a man, such an understanding of the range of human life and the working of the human mind? Where is there to be found so big a world in little as in these plays?

Here are the best of them, with Shakespeare's words and all the wonder of his magic made easy for all to understand. The full plays make up a big and heavy book, set in small type and spoilt by things belonging to Shakespeare's age but not in keeping with ours. Much of it is coarse and gross. But enshrined in this matchless monument of the human mind is the spirit of the greatest Englishman who ever walked in our green fields. Never were words set to such majestic music, and this wondrous thing is ours, the heritage of every child who speaks our tongue, of every child who loves a tale. The English Bible and the English Shakespeare are the deathless glory of our race.

We must believe of Shakespeare that he and his kingdom were not wholly of this world. He believed in hidden powers and destinies, and he was part of them. In him the human mind ascended to its summit. Yet how modest he was! So rarely does he put himself into his plays that we leap with excitement when we fancy that a little bit of him is here. He must have been like his poor Yorick, a fellow of infinite jest, of most excellent fancy. We know that his greatest rivals came to love him, and that the greatest of them all confessed that he thought of him "only on this side of idolatry."

When Edmund Spenser died the poets gathered round his grave in the Abbey and dropped into it their pens; Shakespeare's pen may still be there. When Shakespeare died they gathered together his plays and printed them; they made them into such a book as Shakespeare never saw. Now it is ours, and here are some of the plays from it: comedy, fantasy, history, tragedy, what you will. There is nothing better that a man has left in the world for you, though you shall search the whole world for it.

Explanation of Words in Shakespeare

Many words and phrases found in Shakespeare have now passed out of use; some words have changed their meaning; and some Shakespeare uses at times in a special sense. Frequently the meaning is plain; where it is not this list will be helpful.

A', he
Achieve me, gain me
Addressed, equipped
Admiration, astonishment
Admitted, included
Advertisement, warning
Advise, reflect
Aediles, officials keeping order
Affected, disposed
Affined, bound
Allottery, portion
Amerce, punish
Amort, dejected
Amuraths, Turkish kings
An, if
Ancient, standard-bearer
Antic face, mask
Appeach, to impeach or denounce
Appeal, accuse
Apple-John, withered apple
Aqua-vitae, water of life
Argal, therefore
Aroint thee, begone
Arras, curtain
Aspics, asps
Atomies, tiny like atoms
Attach, detain
Augurs, diviners; studying signs and omens
Avouch, avow, confirm
Awful, reverential

Badged, marked
Baned, poisoned
Banked, sailed past
Barful, difficult
Basilisk, large cannon
Bass, boom
Bavin, brush-wood
Bawcock, endearing term
Beadsmen, pensioners
Became, adorned
Bedlam, lunatic
Beholding, beholden, obliged
Behoveful, suitable, fitting
Beldam, an old lady ancestor; later, any plain old woman
Benison, blessing
Bermoothes, Bermudas
Beshrew, curse or blame
Beteem, allow; pour forth
Betid, befell
Biggen, nightcap
Bills, halberds
Bird-bolts, arrows
Bobbed, stole, filched
Bodements, forecasts
Bolted, sifted
Boot, booty, profit
Bootless, unavailing
Boots, helps
Bounds of feed, pastures
Bourn, boundary
Brake, thicket
Brave, brag, defy
Braves, taunts
Brooched, adorned
Bruising irons, maces
Bugle eyeball, beady eye
Bully, a chum
Burden, chorus
Burgonet, a helmet
By interims, at intervals

Canon from the, contrary to the rule
Cantle, projecting piece
Capon, chicken
Carded his state, debased his sovereignty
Careful, full of care
Carlot, a rustic
Cates, delicacies
Catiff, despicable
Cautelous, crafty, cunning
Caveto, an empty phrase
Censure, judge
Century, centurion's troop
Chaces, pursuits
Champain, open country
Chares, odd jobs
Chaudron, entrails
Checking at, halting at
Chewet, jackdaw
Childing, fruitful
Choler, anger, temper
Choughs, crows
Christendom, Christian faith
Clept, called
Clip, embrace
Clogs, fetters
Cock-shut time, twilight
Cog, speak deceitfully; cheat
Coil, turmoil, trouble
Collied, pitch dark
Colour, pretence
Come from thy ward, lower thy sword
Commodity, self-interest
Conceit, fanciful notions
Contemned, scorned
Contestation, quarrel
Continent, used in the sense of containing
Convents, make convenient
Conversations, habits
Convertite, a convert
Cope, encounter; grapple with
Cote, cottage
Coystrill, knave
Coz, cousin
Cozened, cheated
Crants, garlands
Cross-row, the alphabet
Crusadoes, Portuguese gold coin
Crystals, eyes
Culling, collecting
Culverin, gun

Cursorary, cursory, casual
Curst, bad tempered
Curtle-axe, cutlass
Cynthia, the moon

Dam, mother
Dear, great
Dearth, shortage
Delivered, known
Demuring, pretending to be modest
Denay, denial
Dernier, a coin of small value
Descant, comment
Diable, devil
Dieu des batailles, God of Battles
Discandy, unsweeten
Discase, undress
Discontents, discontented people
Discover, tell
Dissension of a doit, a quarrel about a farthing
Distain, sully, dishonour
Distracted globe, head
Doit, smallest coin; a Dutch coin; a farthing
Dole, sorrow

Earing, ploughing
Egyptian, gipsy
Eisel, vinegar
Elysium, pagan paradise
Embarquements, firm restraints
Embossed, infuriated
Enfeoffed, devoted to
Enlarge, set free
Enow, enough
Epilogue, something after
Estates, bestows
Eterne, eternal
Et tu, Brute! And thou, Brutus!
Even, plain
Even o'er the time, bridge over the time
Expedience, going
Expedient, swift
Expiate, expired
Extent upon his house, seizure, or distraint
Extern, exterior, outside
Eye of heaven, the sun
Eyne, eyes

Fadge, work out
Fardels, burdens
Fardingales, crinolines, hoops
Fatigate, fatigued
Favour, features
Feather, coward
Featly, cleverly
Fet, fetched
Fetches, deceptions
Few, brief
Figo, a mere nothing
Filed, defiled
Fleer, gibe or mock
Flexure, bending
Florentius, a knight in one of John Gower's tales
Flote, flood
Flux, flow
Foison, plenty
Fond, foolish
Footing, landing
Forage, range about
Fordone, killed
Forfend, prevent
Frame of things, the earth
Franchised, free
Fraught, freighted or cargo
Fumiter, fumitor plant

Gage, gauntlet of defiance
Galliard, dance
Gallow, frighten
Garish, glaring
Gaud, plaything
Gaultree Forest, former royal forest, near York
Geck, dupe
General gender, general public
Germens, seeds of life
Ghostly, spiritual
Glasses, pours
Gleeking, scoffing
Glose, speak deceitfully
God 'ild you, God yield (or reward) you
God's Minister, the King
Good-den, Good-evening
Goss, gorse
Gossip of the air, echo
Gravelled, perplexed
Green, new
Grim ferryman, Charon, boatman of the pagan dead
Grizzle on thy case, a beard; hairs on thy skin
Gulls, people who are easily deceived

Habit, clothes
Hap, happening, position
Hatch, a half-door
Have after, follow after
Havoc, spare not
Heap, throng
Hebenon, poisonous herb
Hecate, goddess of witchery
Heinous, sinful
Help of your good hands, applause
Henchman, an attendant, page
Hent, opportunity
Hest, command
Hilding, a low person
Hoist with his own petar, blown up by his own explosive
Holidame, an oath; by all that is sacred
Household coat, coat-of-arms
Hull, lie waiting
Hulling, floating at the mercy of the waves
Humour, caprice
Hydra, many-headed monster
Hyperion, pagan god

Ild, yield
Immoment, trifling
Importance, importunity; urgent request
Inch-meal, inch by inch
Inconstant toy, capricious fancy
Indifferent, impartial
Indigest, confusion
Infection, plague
In few, in brief
Inhabitable, not habitable

Inheritor, possessor
Inhooped, enclosed in a hoop
Insane root, henbane
Intending, pretending
Intentively, consecutively
Interessed, concerned in
Interrogatories, questions
Intrinsicate, intricate
Irks, grieves

Jointstool, used for carving
Jump at this hour, just at this hour
Jumps with, agrees with
Juvenal, youth

Kerns and gallowglasses, types of fighting men
Knave, boy (affectionately)
Knots, flower-beds

Languish, slow suffering
Lanked, emaciated
Latch, catch
Latched, smeared
Lated, belated
Let, hinder
Lethe, river of oblivion
Levelled at, guessed
Lien, lain
Like well, look well
List, boundaries
Loofed, luffed (nautical)
Lour, frown
Love-in-idleness, pansy
Lurched, deprived
Lusty, valiant

Maggot pies, magpies
Make from the shaft, avoid obvious danger
Malapert, cheeky
Mammet, puppet
Marry, by St Mary
Mars, god of war
Martlet, swallow
Maugre, notwithstanding
Mechanical, artisan
Medicine potable, a supposed magic remedy
Meed, reward
Mewed, caged, imprisoned
Misgraffèd, badly matched
Misprised, mistaken
Misprision, mistake, or misunderstanding
Module, mould
Mop and mow, grimacing
Mortal, fatal
Mort de ma vie, Death of my Life
Mortal coil, troubled life
Moved, angry
Murrain, diseased
Mutines in the bilboes, mutineers in fetters

Nature's piece, something fine; a masterpiece
Neat, old word for cattle
Ne'er the near, never nearer
Nemean lion, lion whose skin resisted weapons
Nether, lower
News is used by Shakespeare as plural
Nice, finicking
Nicked, notched
Nole, head
Nonpareil, best of all
Nook-shotten, indented with bays or nooks
Nuncio, ambassador

Occident, West as opposed to Orient—East
O'er-posting, getting away from
Opinion, repute
Original, origin
Orisons, prayers
Ousel, blackbird
Out three, quite three
Owe, own
Owed, owned

Pains, services
Painted, feigned
Pantaloon, dotard
Pantler, pantry-man
Parcel, add up
Pard, leopard
Parle, parley, conference, talk
Partisan, an old weapon
Passage, passers-by
Pass upon, make fun of
Patches, countrymen, clowns
Patines, plates
Peak, to look sickly
Peascod, pea-pod
Peise, weigh
Peize, prolong
Pelting, petty, small
Pent-up guilt, hidden crime
Perdurable, enduring
Perseus, Greek god
Persevér, persist
Pert, lively
Phoebus, the sun
Pickers and stealers, hands
Pickthanks, gossips
Play the touch, touchstone
Pleached, trimmed
Pleached arms, folded arms
Poke, bonnet
Points, one that ties his, his valet
Port, bearing, appearance
Portance, bearing
Possets, evening drink
Potch, thrust
Pranks, decorates
Precedent, agreement, draft
Prefer, promote
Prick him, enrol him
Procreant cradle, nest
Project, state, argue
Prologue, introduction; something before
Proper stuff, spoken in bitter sarcasm
Proportioned, harmonious
Propose, suppose
Puissance, power
Pursuivant, heraldic officer
Put it to the foil, spoiled it
Pyx, case containing consecrated bread

Quail, fail
Quat, a pimple
Quiblets, quibbles

Rack dislimns, cloud disperses
Rascal counter, base coin
Raught, reached
Ravelled sleeve, a tangle
Ravin up, devour
Rayed, soiled
Razed, torn off
Razes, roots
Recks, cares
Recks not his own rede, takes not his own advice
Recorder, an old musical instrument
Recountments, stories
Recure, redress
Regreets, greetings
Remorse, mercifulness
Replenished, fully furnished
Requital, return
Rere-mice, bats
Respective, careful
Returns us, replies to us
Reverbs, reverberates
Rheum, tears ; watery fluid
Rigol, crown or circle
Rivage, shore
Rivals, partners
Rive your concealing continents, tear from hiding
Ronyon, abusive term for a woman
Roynish, rough
Rub, difficulty
Rubbed, hindered
Rubious, red as a ruby
Rudesby, a rough fellow
Runagate, scapegrace

Saba, Queen of Sheba
Sagittary, probably an inn
St Nicholas Clerks, footpads and highwaymen
Sans, without
Saw, proverb
Scald, scabby, shabby
Scamels, sea birds
Seeling, blindfolding
Semblable coherence, a close resemblance
Semblable import, of like kind
Se'nnight, seven nights
Serpent's tongue, hissing
Setter, a thief's tout
Shefalus, Cephalus
Shent, punished
Shrewd, bitter, sharp
Shrift, confession
Simony, making a profit out of sacred things
Simples, herbs
Sirrah, form of address to a decided inferior
Sleeking, scoffing
Slug, sluggard
Snuff part of nature, end of life ; snuffing a candle
Sociable to, in sympathy
Soldier's pole, the North Star
Sooth, truth
Sooth'st up, flatters
Sort, set
Sot, fool
Souse, sweep down on
Sped, slain
Square, square up, quarrel
Stale, a laughing-stock
Stale, a lure, or bait
Steaded, helped
Stomach, pride, boldness
Strike, influence for harm
Sufferance, suffering
Superflux, overflow
Suspects, suspicious
Swinge, to whip smartly
Swounded, swooned

Takes, bewitches
Tall, competent
Tarre, tease or annoy
Tassel-gentle, male falcon
Tender, prize or cherish
Tent him, probe him
Testril, sixpence
Thane, lord
Thorough, through
Thou's, thou shalt
Three-nooked world, Roman Empire
Thrift, profit
Tight and yare, sound, fit
Timeless, untimely
Touch, stroke
Touch noble, high quality
Tresses, hair
Triumph, festivity, procession
True blank, middle of the target
Trusted home, trusted to the utmost
Tun, cask

Umbered, darkened
Undeeded, unused
Urchins, sprites
Usances, usuries ; interest on money

Valanced, bearded
Valour's minion, favoured servant
Vanities forespent, follies of former days
Varlet, low fellow
Vaward, vanguard
Ventages, stops on a wind instrument
Vice's dagger, a man of lath ; in miracle plays Vice had a lath sword
Voucher, votes

Wassails, festivities
Watch case, sentry-box
Weasand, windpipe
Weather-fend, shelters
What time, then
Whiles, until
Whist, hush ! listen !
Womby vaultages, great caverns
Wooden O, the oval theatre
Woo't, wilt
Worth the whistle, worth while
Wot, know
Wotting, knowing

Yarely, handily, quickly
Yerk, kick or stab
Yesty, yeasty, frothy
Yew, double-fatal, poisonous

Zanies, buffoons

The Story of As You Like It

In the last year of the century in which he was born a great change came over Shakespeare. His magic pen was touched with gaiety still, but the pure joy of life that had marked his comedies up till then was mixed with something serious. At the beginning of the seventeenth century, when Shakespeare was 36 years old, something seems to have passed over his life like a shadow, and the shadow runs across his plays.

He gave us As You Like It at this time; it may have been the last of his pure comedies. It sparkles with delight; it keeps us merry all the time we read. It is perhaps the finest picture in English literature of English outdoor life.

Who would think that such a bright and joyous thing could begin in the mind of a West Ham boy? West Ham is one of our dark spots today, but there was a boy named Thomas Lodge born there when West Ham stood amid green fields; and it was he, grown up into a sailor and a dramatist, who wrote a romance called Rosalynde, which Shakespeare took and fashioned into As You Like It. In those days writers took each other's stories as men would never think of doing now, and Lodge had founded his romance on a story older still. But both these stories were in prose, and it was the genius of Shakespeare that gave them immortality, transfusing prose with poetry, and adding to it something rich and strange that was to send it rippling through the centuries.

All the world loves the charming character of Rosalind, made up, as somebody said, of "sportive gaiety and natural tenderness." The freedom of an open-air life in the heart of a forest, amid wild dumb things and simple rural folk, is pictured with a fascinating fidelity. The world forgetting, by the world forgot, this little band of Shakespeare folk is contented with its lot, willing to let the world go by, caring for nothing save the joyous life of the passing hour. Shakespeare added two characters that were not in the old romances, Touchstone and Jaques, and the play owes much to the humour of the one and the philosophy of the other. In a speech of Jaques is one of the first expressions found in English literature of compassion toward dumb creatures.

It is a weakness of the play that it hurries to its close; we can hardly help feeling that it winds up in a sort of hasty huddle for a play of quiet leisured scenes like these. But its interest does not flag; its wit does not fail; it is faithful to life to the end.

THE PLAYERS

Duke, living in banishment in a forest, with careless ease, surrounded by his friends.

Frederick, his brother, who has supplanted him, but in the end repents.

Amiens, a lord who has followed the Duke, in attendance on him.

Jaques, another lord, a moralising dreamer who lives to watch men's ways and comment on them.

Le Beau, a courtier in attendance on the usurper Frederick.

Charles, a wrestler performing at Frederick's Court.

Oliver, the eldest son of the late Sir Rowland de Boys.

Jaques de Boys, the second son of Sir Rowland de Boys, educated for his position.

Orlando, youngest son of Sir Rowland de Boys, who, left uneducated by his brother Oliver, educates himself and becomes the hero.

Adam, an aged servant of Oliver. He and Orlando go forth into the world together.

Dennis, another servant of Oliver.

Touchstone, a clown at the court of Frederick who accompanies Celia and Rosalind into the forest.

Sir Oliver Martext, a rural vicar.

Corin, an old shepherd who buys a sheep-run for Silvius.

Silvius, a young shepherd in love with Phebe.

Rosalind, daughter of the Duke, and herself banished. The chief figure in the play.

Celia, daughter of Frederick, accompanying Rosalind in her banishment.

Phebe, a shepherdess.

Audrey, a plain country girl.

Lords, attendants, messengers, a forester, and a page.

SCENES

Oliver's house; Duke Frederick's Court; and the Forest of Arden.

As You Like It

ACT 1

Scene 1—The Orchard of Oliver's House

ORLANDO. As I remember, Adam, it was upon this fashion bequeathed me by will but poor a thousand crowns, and, as thou sayest, charged my brother, on his blessing, to breed me well; and there begins my sadness. My brother Jaques he keeps at school, and report speaks goldenly of his profit; for my part, he keeps me rustically at home, or, to speak more properly, stays me here at home unkept; for call you that keeping for a gentleman of my birth that differs not from the stalling of an ox? His horses are bred better. He lets me feed with his hinds, bars me the place of a brother, and, as much as in him lies, mines my gentility with my education. This is it, Adam, that grieves me; and the spirit of my father, which I think is within me, begins to mutiny against this servitude. I will no longer endure it.

ADAM. Yonder comes my master, your brother.

ORLANDO. Go apart, Adam, and thou shalt hear how he will shake me up.

OLIVER (*entering*). Now, sir! what make you here?

ORLANDO. Nothing: I am not taught to make anything.

OLIVER. What mar you then, sir?

ORLANDO. Marry, sir, I am helping you to mar that which God made, a poor unworthy brother of yours, with idleness. Shall I keep your hogs and eat husks with them? What prodigal portion have I spent, that I should come to such penury?

OLIVER. Know you where you are, sir?

ORLANDO. O, sir, very well: here in your orchard.

OLIVER. Know you before whom, sir?

ORLANDO. Ay, better than him I am before knows me. I know you are my eldest brother; and, in the gentle condition of blood, you should so know me. The courtesy of nations allows you my better, in that you are the firstborn; but the same tradition takes not away my blood, were there twenty brothers betwixt us.

OLIVER. What, boy! Wilt thou lay hands on me, villain?

ORLANDO. I am no villain; I am the youngest son of Sir Rowland de Boys. Wert thou not my brother I would not take this hand from thy throat till this other had pulled out thy tongue for saying so: thou hast railed on thyself.

ADAM. Sweet masters, be patient; for your father's remembrance, be at accord.

OLIVER. Let me go, I say.

ORLANDO. I will not, till I please: you shall hear me. My father charged you in his will to give me good education: you have trained me like a peasant, obscuring and hiding from me all gentleman-like qualities. The spirit of my father grows strong in me, and I will no longer endure it: therefore allow me such exercises as may become a gentleman, or give me the poor allottery my father left me by testament; with that I will go buy my fortunes.

OLIVER. And what wilt thou do? Beg, when that is spent? Well, sir, get you in: I will not long be troubled with you; you shall have some part of your will: I pray you, leave me. Get you with him, you old dog.

ADAM. Is *old dog* my reward? Most true, I have lost my teeth in your service. God be with my old master! He would not have spoke such a word.

OLIVER. Is it even so? Begin you to grow upon me? I will physic your rankness, and yet give no thousand crowns neither. Holla, Dennis! (*The others leave*)

DENNIS. Calls your worship?

OLIVER. Was not Charles, the duke's wrestler, here to speak with me? Call him in. Twill be a good way, and tomorrow the wrestling is.

CHARLES. Good-morrow to your worship.

OLIVER. Good Monsieur Charles, what's the news at the court?

CHARLES. There's no news at the court, sir, but the old news: that is, the old duke is banished by his younger brother the new duke; and three or four loving lords have put themselves into voluntary exile with him, whose lands and revenues enrich the new duke; therefore he gives them good leave to wander.

OLIVER. Can you tell if Rosalind, the duke's daughter, be banished with her father?

CHARLES. O, no; for the duke's daughter, her cousin, so loves her, being ever from their cradles bred together, that she would have followed her exile, or have died to stay behind her. She is at the court, and no less beloved of her uncle than his own daughter; and never two ladies loved as they do.

OLIVER. Where will the old duke live?

CHARLES. They say he is already in the Forest of Arden, and a many merry men with him; and there they live like the old Robin Hood of England. They say many young gentlemen flock to him every day, and fleet the time carelessly, as they did in the golden world.

OLIVER. What, you wrestle tomorrow before the new duke?

CHARLES. Marry, do I, sir; and I came to acquaint you with a matter. I am given, sir, secretly to understand that your younger brother Orlando hath a disposition to come in disguised against me to try a fall. Tomorrow, sir, I wrestle for my credit; and he that escapes me without some broken limb shall acquit him well. Your brother is but young and tender, and, for your love, I would be loth to foil him, as I must, for my own honour, if he come in: therefore, out of my love to you, I came hither to acquaint you withal, that you might stay him from such disgrace as he shall run into.

OLIVER. Charles, I thank thee for thy love to me, which thou shalt find I will most kindly requite. I had myself notice of my brother's purpose herein, and have by underhand means laboured to dissuade him from it, but he is resolute. I'll tell thee, Charles: it is the stubbornest young fellow of France, full of ambition, an envious emulator of every man's good parts, a secret and villainous contriver against me his natural brother: therefore use thy discretion; I had as lief thou didst break his neck as his finger.

CHARLES. I am heartily glad I came hither to you. If he come tomorrow I'll give him his payment: if ever he go alone again, I'll never wrestle for prize more; and so God keep your worship!

OLIVER. Farewell, good Charles. Now will I stir this gamester: I hope I shall see an end of him, for my soul (yet I know not why) hates nothing more than he. Yet he's gentle, never schooled and yet learned, full of noble device, of all sorts enchantingly beloved. But it shall not be so long; this wrestler shall clear all. Nothing remains but that I kindle the boy thither; which now I'll go about.

Scene 2—The Lawn before the Palace

CELIA. I pray thee, Rosalind, sweet my coz, be merry.

ROSALIND. Dear Celia, I show more mirth than I am mistress of; and would you yet I were merrier?

CELIA. Herein I see thou lovest me not with the full weight that I love thee. If my uncle, thy banished father, had banished thy uncle, the duke my father, so thou hadst been still with me, I could have taught my love to take thy father for mine: so wouldst thou, if the truth of thy love to me were so righteously tempered as mine is to thee.

ROSALIND. Well, I will forget the condition of my estate, to rejoice in yours.

CELIA. You know my father hath no child but me, nor none is

like to have: and, truly, when he dies, thou shalt be his heir, for what he hath taken away from thy father perforce I will render thee again in affection; by mine honour, I will: therefore, my sweet Rose, my dear Rose, be merry.

ROSALIND. From henceforth I will, coz, and devise sports. Let me see; what think you of falling in love?

CELIA. Marry, I prithee, do, to make sport withal: but love no man in good earnest.

ROSALIND. What shall be our sport, then?

CELIA. Let us sit and mock the good housewife Fortune from her wheel, that her gifts may henceforth be bestowed equally.

ROSALIND. I would we could do so, for her benefits are mightily misplaced, and the bountiful blind woman doth most mistake in her gifts to women.

CELIA. Tis true; for those that she makes fair she scarce makes honest, and those that she makes honest she makes very ill-favouredly. Here comes Monsieur Le Beau.

ROSALIND. With his mouth full of news.

CELIA. *Bon jour*, Monsieur Le Beau: what's the news?

LE BEAU. Fair princess, you have lost much good sport.

CELIA. Sport! Of what colour?

LE BEAU. I will tell you the beginning, and if it please your ladyships you may see the end, for the best is yet to do; and here, where you are, they are coming to perform it. There comes an old man and his three sons, three proper young men, of excellent growth and presence. The eldest of the three wrestled with Charles, the duke's wrestler, who in a moment threw him and broke three of his ribs, that there is little hope of life in him; so he served the second, and so the third. Yonder they lie; the poor old man, their father, making such pitiful dole over them that all the beholders take his part with weeping.

ROSALIND. Alas! Shall we see this wrestling, cousin?

LE BEAU. You must, if you stay here; for here is the place appointed for the wrestling, and they are ready to perform it.

CELIA. Yonder, sure, they are coming: let us now stay and see it.

ROSALIND. Is yonder the man?

LE BEAU. Even he, madam.

CELIA. Alas, he is too young! yet he looks successfully.

FREDERICK (*entering*). How now, daughter and cousin! Are you crept hither to see the wrestling?

ROSALIND. Ay, my liege, so please you give us leave.

FREDERICK. You will take little delight in it, I can tell you; there is such odds in the man. In pity of the challenger's youth I would fain dissuade him, but he will not be entreated. Speak to him, ladies; see if you can move him. I'll not be by.

ROSALIND. Young man, have you challenged Charles the wrestler?

ORLANDO. No, fair princess; he is the general challenger; I come but in, as others do, to try with him the strength of my youth.

CELIA. Young gentleman, your spirits are too bold for your years. You have seen cruel proof of this man's strength: if you saw yourself with your eyes or knew yourself with your judgment, the fear of your adventure would counsel you to a more equal enterprise. We pray you, for your own sake, to embrace your own safety and give over this attempt.

ROSALIND. Do, young sir; your reputation shall not therefore be misprised: we will make it our suit to the duke that the wrestling might not go forward.

ORLANDO. I beseech you, punish me not with your hard thoughts; wherein I confess me much guilty, to deny so fair and excellent ladies anything. But let your fair eyes and gentle wishes go with me to my trial, wherein if I be foiled there is but one shamed that was never gracious; if killed, but one dead that is willing to be so. I shall do my friends no wrong, for I have none to lament me; the world no injury, for in it I have nothing.

ROSALIND. The little strength that I have, I would it were with you.

CELIA. And mine, to eke out hers.

ROSALIND. Fare you well: pray heaven I be deceived in you!

CELIA. Your heart's desires be with you!

CHARLES (*entering*). Come, where is this young gallant that is so desirous to lie with his mother earth?

ORLANDO. Ready, sir; but his will hath in it a more modest working.

FREDERICK. You shall try but one fall.

CHARLES. No, I warrant your grace, you shall not entreat him to a second, that have so mightily persuaded him from a first.

ORLANDO. An you mean to mock me after, you should not have mocked me before: but come your ways.

ROSALIND. Now Hercules be thy speed, young man!

CELIA. I would I were invisible, to catch the strong fellow by the leg. (*They wrestle and Charles is thrown*)

ROSALIND. O excellent young man!

FREDERICK. No more, no more.

ORLANDO. Yes, I beseech your grace: I am not yet well breathed.

FREDERICK. How dost thou, Charles?

LE BEAU. He cannot speak, my lord.

FREDERICK. Bear him away. What is thy name, young man?

ORLANDO. Orlando, my liege; son of Sir Rowland de Boys.

FREDERICK. I would thou hadst been son to some man else:
The world esteemed thy father honourable,
But I did find him still mine enemy:
Thou shouldst have better pleased me with this deed
Hadst thou descended from another house.
But fare thee well; thou art a gallant youth:
I would thou hadst told me of another father. (*He leaves*)

CELIA. Were I my father, coz, would I do this?

ORLANDO. I am more proud to be Sir Rowland's son,
His youngest son, and would not change that calling
To be adopted heir to Frederick.

ROSALIND. My father loved Sir Rowland as his soul,
And all the world was of my father's mind:
Had I before known this young man his son,
I should have given him tears unto entreaties,
Ere he should thus have ventured.

CELIA. Gentle cousin,
Let us go thank him and encourage him:
My father's rough and envious disposition
Sticks me at heart. Sir, you have well deserved:
If you do keep your promises in love
But justly, as you have exceeded all promise,
Your mistress shall be happy.

ROSALIND (*giving him a chain*). Gentleman,
Wear this for me, one out of suits with fortune,
That could give more, but that her hand lacks means
Shall we go, coz?

CELIA. Ay. Fare you well, fair gentleman.

ORLANDO. Can I not say, *I thank you*?

ROSALIND. He calls us back: my pride fell with my fortunes;
I'll ask him what he would. Did you call, sir?
Sir, you have wrestled well and overthrown
More than your enemies.

CELIA. Will you go, coz?

ROSALIND. Have with you. Fare you well.

ORLANDO. What passion hangs these weights upon my tongue?
I cannot speak to her, yet she urged conference.
O poor Orlando, thou art overthrown!
Or Charles or something weaker masters thee.

LE BEAU (*entering*). Good sir, I do in friendship counsel you
To leave this place. Albeit you have deserved
High commendation, true applause, and love,

Yet such is now the duke's condition
That he mis*con*strues all that you have done.

ORLANDO. I thank you, sir: and, pray you, tell me this;
Which of the two was daughter of the duke
That here was at the wrestling?

LE BEAU. Neither his daughter, if we judge by manners;
But yet indeed the lesser is his daughter:
The other is daughter to the banished duke,
And here detained by her usurping uncle,
To keep his daughter company; whose loves
Are dearer than the natural bond of sisters.
But I can tell you that of late this duke
Hath ta'en displeasure 'gainst his gentle niece,
Grounded upon no other argument
But that the people praise her for her virtues
And pity her for her good father's sake;
And, on my life, his malice 'gainst the lady
Will suddenly break forth. Sir, fare you well:
Hereafter, in a better world than this,
I shall desire more love and knowledge of you.

ORLANDO. I rest much bounden to you: fare you well.
Thus must I from the smoke into the smother;
From tyrant duke unto a tyrant brother:
But heavenly Rosalind!

Scene 3—A Room in the Palace

CELIA. Why, cousin! Cupid have mercy! not a word?

ROSALIND. Not one to throw at a dog.

CELIA. No, thy words are too precious to be cast away upon curs; throw some of them at me.

ROSALIND. O, how full of briars is this working-day world!

CELIA. They are but burs, cousin, thrown upon thee in holiday foolery: if we walk not in the trodden paths our very petticoats will catch them.

ROSALIND. I could shake them off my coat: these burs are in my heart.

CELIA. Come, come, wrestle with thy affections.

ROSALIND. O, they take the part of a better wrestler than myself!

CELIA. Turning these jests out of service, let us talk in good earnest: is it possible, on such a sudden, you should fall into so strong a liking with old Sir Rowland's youngest son?

ROSALIND. The duke my father loved his father dearly.

CELIA. Doth it therefore ensue that you should love his son

dearly? By this kind of chase I should hate him, for my father hated his father dearly; yet I hate not Orlando.

ROSALIND. No, faith, hate him not, for my sake.

CELIA. Why should I not? Doth he not deserve well?

ROSALIND. Let me love him for that, and do you love him because I do. Look, here comes the duke.

CELIA. With his eyes full of anger.

FREDERICK. Mistress, dispatch you with your safest haste
And get you from our court.

ROSALIND. Me, uncle?

FREDERICK. You, cousin:
Within these ten days if that thou be'st found
So near our public court as twenty miles,
Thou diest for it.

ROSALIND. I do beseech your grace,
Let me the knowledge of my fault bear with me:
Never so much as in a thought unborn
Did I offend your highness.

FREDERICK. Thus do all traitors:
Let it suffice thee that I trust thee not.

ROSALIND. Yet your mistrust cannot make me a traitor:
Tell me whereon the likelihood depends.

FREDERICK. Thou art thy father's daughter; there's enough.

ROSALIND. So was I when your highness took his dukedom;
So was I when your highness banished him:
Treason is not inherited, my lord;
Or, if we did derive it from our friends,
What's that to me? My father was no traitor:
Then, good my liege, mistake me not so much
To think my poverty is treacherous.

CELIA. Dear sovereign, hear me speak.

FREDERICK. Ay, Celia: we stayed her for your sake,
Else had she with her father ranged along.

CELIA. I did not then entreat to have her stay;
It was your pleasure and your own remorse:
I was too young that time to value her;
But now I know her: if she be a traitor,
Why so am I; we still have slept together,
Rose at an instant, learned, played, ate together,
And wheresoe'er we went, like Juno's swans,
Still we went coupled and inseparable.

FREDERICK. She is too subtle for thee; and her smoothness,
Her very silence, and her patience,
Speak to the people, and they pity her.
Thou art a fool: she robs thee of thy name;

And thou wilt show more bright and seem more virtuous
When she is gone. Then open not thy lips:
Firm and irrevocable is my doom
Which I have passed upon her; she is banished.

CELIA. Pronounce that sentence then on me, my liege:
I cannot live out of her company.

FREDERICK. You are a fool. You, niece, provide yourself:
If you outstay the time, upon mine honour,
And in the greatness of my word, you die. (*He leaves*)

CELIA. O my poor Rosalind, whither wilt thou go?
Wilt thou change fathers? I will give thee mine.
I charge thee, be not thou more grieved than I am.
Shall we be sundered? shall we part, sweet girl?
No: let my father seek another heir.
Therefore devise with me how we may fly,
Whither to go and what to bear with us;
And do not seek to take your change upon you,
To bear your griefs yourself and leave me out;
For, by this heaven, now at our sorrows pale,
Say what thou canst, I'll go along with thee.

ROSALIND. Why, whither shall we go?

CELIA. To seek my uncle in the Forest of Arden.

ROSALIND. Alas, what danger will it be to us,
Maids as we are, to travel forth so far!
Beauty provoketh thieves sooner than gold.

CELIA. I'll put myself in poor and mean attire
And with a kind of umber smirch my face;
The like do you: so shall we pass along
And never stir assailants.

ROSALIND. Were it not better,
Because that I am more than common tall,
That I did suit me all points like a man?
A gallant curtle-axe upon my thigh,
A boar-spear in my hand; and (in my heart
Lie there what hidden woman's fear there will)
We'll have a swashing and a martial outside,
As many other mannish cowards have
That do outface it with their semblances.

CELIA. What shall I call thee when thou art a man?

ROSALIND. I'll have no worse a name than Jove's own page;
And therefore look you call me Ganymede.
But what will you be called?

CELIA. Something that hath a reference to my state;
No longer Celia, but Aliena.

ROSALIND. But, cousin, what if we assayed to steal

The clownish fool out of your father's court?
Would he not be a comfort to our travel?

CELIA. He'll go along o'er the wide world with me;
Leave me alone to woo him. Let's away,
And get our jewels and our wealth together,
Devise the fittest time and safest way
To hide us from pursuit that will be made
After my flight. Now go we in content
To liberty and not to banishment.

ACT 2

Scene 1—The Banished Duke in the Forest

DUKE. Now, my co-mates and brothers in exile,
Hath not old custom made this life more sweet
Than that of painted pomp? Are not these woods
More free from peril than the envious court?
Here feel we but the penalty of Adam,
The season's difference, as the icy fang
And churlish chiding of the winter's wind,
Which, when it bites and blows upon my body,
Even till I shrink with cold, I smile and say:
This is no flattery; these are counsellors
That feelingly persuade me what I am.
Sweet are the uses of adversity,
Which, like the toad, ugly and venomous,
Wears yet a precious jewel in his head;
And this our life, exempt from public haunt,
Finds tongues in trees, books in the running brooks,
Sermons in stones, and good in everything.
I would not change it.

AMIENS. Happy is your grace
That can translate the stubbornness of fortune
Into so quiet and so sweet a style.

DUKE. Come, shall we go and kill us venison?
And yet it irks me the poor dappled fools,
Being native burghers of this desert city,
Should in their own confines with forkèd heads
Have their round haunches gored.

FIRST LORD. Indeed, my lord,
The melancholy Jaques grieves at that,
And, in that kind, swears you do more usurp
Than doth your brother that hath banished you.
Today my Lord of Amiens and myself
Did steal behind him as he lay along
Under an oak whose antique root peeps out
Upon the brook that brawls along this wood:

To the which place a poor sequestered stag,
That from the hunter's aim had ta'en a hurt,
Did come to languish, and indeed, my lord,
The wretched animal heaved forth such groans
That their discharge did stretch his leathern coat
Almost to bursting; and the big round tears
Coursed one another down.

DUKE. But what said Jaques?
Did he not moralize this spectacle?

FIRST LORD. O, yes, into a thousand similes.
First, for his weeping into the needless stream:
Poor deer (quoth he), *thou makest a testament*
As worldlings do, giving thy sum of more
To that which had too much: then, being there alone,
Left and abandoned of his velvet friends,
Tis right (quoth he), *thus misery doth part*
The flux of company. Anon a careless herd,
Full of the pasture, jumps along by him
And never stays to greet him: *Ay* (quoth Jaques),
Sweep on, you fat and greasy citizens;
Tis just the fashion: wherefore do you look
Upon that poor and broken bankrupt there?
Thus most invectively he pierceth through
The body of the country, city, court,
Yea, and of this our life, swearing that we
Are mere usurpers, tyrants and what's worse,
To fright the animals and to kill them up
In their assigned and native dwelling-place.

DUKE. And did you leave him in this contemplation?

SECOND LORD. We did, my lord, weeping and commenting
Upon the sobbing deer.

DUKE. Show me the place:
I love to cope him in these sullen fits,
For then he's full of matter.

FIRST LORD. I'll bring you to him straight.

Scene 2—A Room in the Palace: Rosalind and Celia missing

FREDERICK. Can it be possible that no man saw them?
It cannot be: some villains of my court
Are of consent and sufferance in this.

FIRST LORD. I cannot hear of any that did see her.
The ladies, her attendants of her chamber,
Saw her a-bed, and in the morning early
They found the bed untreasured of their mistress.

SECOND LORD. My lord, the roynish clown, at whom so oft

Your grace was wont to laugh, is also missing.
Hisperia, the princess' gentlewoman,
Confesses that she secretly o'erheard
Your daughter and her cousin much commend
The parts and graces of the wrestler
That did but lately foil the sinewy Charles;
And she believes, wherever they are gone,
That youth is surely in their company.

FREDERICK. Send to his brother; fetch that gallant hither;
If he be absent, bring his brother to me;
I'll make him find him: do this suddenly,
And let not search and inquisition quail
To bring again these foolish runaways.

Scene 3—Before Oliver's House

ORLANDO. Who's there?

ADAM. What, my young master? O my gentle master!
O my sweet master! O you memory
Of old Sir Rowland! Why, what make you here?
Why are you virtuous? Why do people love you?
And wherefore are you gentle, strong, and valiant?
Your praise is come too swiftly home before you.
Know you not, master, to some kind of men
Their graces serve them but as enemies?
No more do yours: your virtues, gentle master,
Are sanctified and holy traitors to you.
O, what a world is this, when what is comely
Envenoms him that bears it!

ORLANDO. Why, what's the matter?

ADAM. O unhappy youth!
Come not within these doors; within this roof
The enemy of all your graces lives:
Your brother (no, no brother); yet the son
(Yet not the son, I will not call him son
Of him I was about to call his father)
Hath heard your praises, and this night he means
To burn the lodging where you use to lie
And you within it: if he fail of that,
He will have other means to cut you off.
I overheard him and his practices.
This is no place; this house is but a butchery:
Abhor it, fear it, do not enter it.

ORLANDO. Why, whither, Adam, wouldst thou have me go?

ADAM. No matter whither, so you come not here.

ORLANDO. What, wouldst thou have me go and beg my food?

ADAM. I have five hundred crowns,

The thrifty hire I saved under your father,
Which I did store to be my foster-nurse
When service should in my old limbs lie lame,
And unregarded age in corners thrown:
Take that, and He that doth the ravens feed,
Yea, providently caters for the sparrow,
Be comfort to my age! Here is the gold;
All this I give you. Let me be your servant:
Though I look old, yet I am strong and lusty;
For in my youth I never did apply
Hot and rebellious liquors in my blood,
Nor did not with unbashful forehead woo
The means of weakness and debility;
Therefore, my age is as a lusty winter,
Frosty, but kindly: let me go with you;
I'll do the service of a younger man
In all your business and necessities.

ORLANDO. O good old man, how well in thee appears
The constant service of the antique world,
When service sweat for duty, not for meed!
Thou art not for the fashion of these times,
Where none will sweat but for promotion,
But, poor old man, thou prun'st a rotten tree,
That cannot so much as a blossom yield
In lieu of all thy pains and husbandry.
But come thy ways; we'll go along together,
And ere we have thy youthful wages spent,
We'll light upon some settled low content.

ADAM. Master, go on, and I will follow thee,
To the last gasp, with truth and loyalty.
From seventeen years till now almost fourscore
Here livèd I, but now live here no more.
At seventeen years many their fortunes seek;
But at fourscore it is too late a week:
Yet fortune cannot recompense me better
Than to die well and not my master's debtor.

Scene 4—The Forest of Arden

Enter Rosalind as Ganymede, Celia as Aliena, and Touchstone.

ROSALIND. O Jupiter, how weary are my spirits!

TOUCHSTONE. I care not for my spirits, if my legs were not weary.

ROSALIND. I could find in my heart to disgrace my man's apparel and to cry like a woman; but I must comfort the weaker vessel, as doublet and hose ought to show itself courageous to petticoat: therefore courage, good Aliena!

CELIA. I pray you, bear with me; I can go no further.

ROSALIND. Well, this is the Forest of Arden.

TOUCHSTONE. Ay, now am I in Arden; the more fool I; when I was at home I was in a better place: but travellers must be content.

ROSALIND. Ay, be so, good Touchstone. Look you, who comes here; a young man and an old in solemn talk. (*Enter Corin and Silvius*)

CORIN. That is the way to make her scorn you still.

SILVIUS. O Corin, that thou knew'st how I do love her!

CORIN. I partly guess; for I have loved ere now.

SILVIUS. No, Corin, being old, thou canst not guess,
Though in thy youth thou wast as true a lover
As ever sighed upon a midnight pillow:
But if thy love were ever like to mine,
(As sure I think did never man love so),
How many actions most ridiculous
Hast thou been drawn to by thy fantasy?

CORIN. Into a thousand that I have forgotten.

SILVIUS. O, thou didst then ne'er love so heartily!
If thou remember'st not the slightest folly
That ever love did make thee run into,
Thou hast not loved:
Or if thou hast not sat as I do now,
Wearying thy hearer in thy mistress' praise,
Thou hast not loved:
Or if thou hast not broke from company
Abruptly, as my passion now makes me,
Thou hast not loved.
O Phebe, Phebe, Phebe! (*He leaves*)

ROSALIND. Alas, poor shepherd! searching of thy wound, I have by hard adventure found mine own.

TOUCHSTONE. And I mine. We true lovers run into strange capers.

ROSALIND. Thou speakest wiser than thou art ware of.

CELIA. I pray you, one of you question yond man
If he for gold will give us any food:
I faint almost to death.

TOUCHSTONE. Holla, you clown!

CORIN. Who calls?

ROSALIND. Good-even to you, friend.

CORIN. And to you, gentle sir, and to you all.

ROSALIND. I prithee, shepherd, if that love or gold
Can in this desert place buy entertainment,
Bring us where we may rest ourselves and feed.
Here's a young maid with travel much oppressed
And faints for succour.

CORIN. Fair sir, I pity her

And wish, for her sake more than for mine own,
My fortunes were more able to relieve her ;
But I am shepherd to another man
And do not shear the fleeces that I graze :
My master is of churlish disposition
And little recks to find the way to heaven
By doing deeds of hospitality :
Besides, his cote, his flocks and bounds of feed,
Are now on sale, and at our sheepcote now,
By reason of his absence, there is nothing
That you will feed on ; but what is, come see,
And in my voice most welcome shall you be.

ROSALIND. What is he that shall buy his flock and pasture ?

CORIN. That young swain that you saw here but erewhile,
That little cares for buying anything.

ROSALIND. I pray thee, if it stand with honesty,
Buy thou the cottage, pasture, and the flock,
And thou shalt have to pay for it of us.

CELIA. And we will mend thy wages. I like this place,
And willingly could waste my time in it.

CORIN. Assuredly the thing is to be sold :
Go with me : if you like upon report
The soil, the profit, and this kind of life,
I will your very faithful feeder be
And buy it with your gold right suddenly.

Scene 5—The Forest

AMIENS (*singing*).
Under the greenwood tree
Who loves to lie with me,
And turn his merry note
Unto the sweet bird's throat,
Come hither, come hither, come hither :
Here shall he see no enemy
But winter and rough weather.

JAQUES. More, more, I prithee, more.

AMIENS. It will make you melancholy, Monsieur Jaques.

JAQUES. I thank it. More, I prithee, more. I can suck melancholy out of a song as a weasel sucks eggs. More, I prithee, more.

AMIENS. My voice is ragged : I know I cannot please you.

JAQUES. I do not desire you to please me ; I do desire you to sing.

AMIENS. More at your request than to please myself.

JAQUES. Well then, if ever I thank any man I'll thank you.

AMIENS. Well, I'll end the song. Sirs, cover the while ; the duke will drink under this tree. He hath been all this day to look you.

JAQUES. And I have been all this day to avoid him. He is too disputable for my company: I think of as many matters as he, but I give heaven thanks and make no boast of them. Come, warble.

The Song of Amiens

Who doth ambition shun
And loves to live i' the sun,
Seeking the food he eats
And pleased with what he gets,
Come hither, come hither, come hither:
Here shall he see no enemy
But winter and rough weather.

Scene 6—The Forest

ADAM. Dear master, I can go no further: O, I die for food! Here lie I down, and measure out my grave. Farewell, kind master.

ORLANDO. Why, how now, Adam! no greater heart in thee? Live a little; comfort a little; cheer thyself a little. If this uncouth forest yield anything savage, I will either be food for it or bring it for food to thee. For my sake be comfortable; hold death awhile at the arm's end: I will here be with thee presently; and if I bring thee not something to eat I will give thee leave to die: but if thou diest before I come thou art a mocker of my labour. Come, I will bear thee to some shelter, and thou shalt not die for lack of a dinner if there live anything in this desert. Cheerly, good Adam!

Scene 7—A Dinner in the Forest

The Duke and his lords are seated at dinner, dressed like outlaws, and the Duke calls for the missing Jaques, who suddenly approaches.

DUKE. Why, how now, monsieur! what a life is this,
That your poor friends must woo your company?
What, you look merrily!

JAQUES. A fool, a fool! I met a fool i' the forest,
A motley fool; a miserable world!
As I do live by food, I met a fool
Who laid him down and basked him in the sun,
And railed on Lady Fortune in good terms,
In good set terms; and yet a motley fool.
Good-morrow, fool, quoth I. *No, sir,* quoth he,
Call me not fool till heaven hath sent me fortune:
And then he drew a dial from his poke,
And, looking on it with lack-lustre eye,
Says very wisely, *It is ten o'clock:*
Thus we may see (quoth he) *how the world wags:*
'Tis but an hour ago since it was nine,
And after one hour more 'twill be eleven;
And so from hour to hour we ripe and ripe,

And then from hour to hour we rot and rot;
And thereby hangs a tale. When I did hear
The motley fool thus moral on the time,
My lungs began to crow like chanticleer,
That fools should be so deep-contemplative,
And I did laugh sans intermission
An hour by his dial. O noble fool!
A worthy fool! Motley's the only wear.

DUKE. What fool is this?

JAQUES. O worthy fool! One that hath been a courtier,
And says, if ladies be but young and fair,
They have the gift to know it: and in his brain,
Which is as dry as the remainder biscuit
After a voyage, he hath strange places crammed
With observation, the which he vents
In mangled forms. O that I were a fool!
I am ambitious for a motley coat.

DUKE. Thou shalt have one.

JAQUES. It is my only suit;
Provided that you weed your better judgments
Of all opinion that grows rank in them
That I am wise. I must have liberty
Withal, as large a charter as the wind,
To blow on whom I please; for so fools have;
And they that are most gallèd with my folly,
They most must laugh.
Invest me in my motley; give me leave
To speak my mind, and I will through and through
Cleanse the foul body of the infected world,
If they will patiently receive my medicine.

ORLANDO (*entering fiercely*). Forbear, and eat no more.

JAQUES. Why, I have ate none yet.

ORLANDO. Nor shalt not, till necessity be served.

JAQUES. Of what kind should this cock come of?

DUKE. Art thou thus boldened, man, by thy distress,
Or else a rude despiser of good manners,
That in civility thou seem'st so empty?

ORLANDO. You touched my vein at first: the thorny point
Of bare distress hath ta'en from me the show
Of smooth civility: yet am I inland bred
And know some nurture. But forbear, I say:
He dies that touches any of this fruit
Till I and my affairs are answered.

JAQUES. An you will not be answered with reason, I must die.

DUKE. What would you have? Your gentleness shall force

More than your force move us to gentleness.

ORLANDO. I almost die for food; and let me have it.

DUKE. Sit down and feed, and welcome to our table.

ORLANDO. Speak you so gently? Pardon me, I pray you:
I thought that all things had been savage here;
And therefore put I on the countenance
Of stern commandment. But whate'er you are
That in this desert inaccessible,
Under the shade of melancholy boughs,
Lose and neglect the creeping hours of time;
If ever you have looked on better days,
If ever been where bells have knolled to church,
If ever sat at any good man's feast,
If ever from your eyelids wiped a tear
And know what tis to pity and be pitied,
Let gentleness my strong enforcement be:
In the which hope I blush, and hide my sword.

DUKE. True is it that we have seen better days,
And have with holy bell been knolled to church,
And sat at good men's feasts, and wiped our eyes
Of drops that sacred pity hath engendered;
And therefore sit you down in gentleness
And take upon command what help we have
That to your wanting may be ministered.

ORLANDO. Then but forbear your food a little while,
Whiles, like a doe, I go to find my fawn
And give it food. There is an old poor man,
Who after me hath many a weary step
Limped in pure love: till he be first sufficed,
Oppressed with two weak evils, age and hunger,
I will not touch a bit.

DUKE. Go find him out,
And we will nothing waste till you return.

ORLANDO. I thank ye; and be blest for your good comfort!

DUKE (*to Jaques*). Thou seest we are not all alone unhappy:
This wide and universal theatre
Presents more woeful pageants than the scene
Wherein we play in.

JAQUES. All the world's a stage,
And all the men and women merely players:
They have their exits and their entrances;
And one man in his time plays many parts,
His acts being seven ages. At first the infant,
Mewling and puking in the nurse's arms.
And then the whining schoolboy, with his satchel

And shining morning face, creeping like snail
Unwillingly to school. And then the lover,
Sighing like furnace, with a woeful ballad
Made to his mistress' eyebrow. Then a soldier,
Full of strange oaths and bearded like the pard,
Jealous in honour, sudden and quick in quarrel,
Seeking the bubble reputation
Even in the cannon's mouth. And then the justice,
In fair round belly with good capon lined,
With eyes severe and beard of formal cut,
Full of wise saws and modern instances ;
And so he plays his part. The sixth age shifts
Into the lean and slippered pantaloon,
With spectacles on nose and pouch on side,
His youthful hose, well saved, a world too wide
For his shrunk shanks ; and his big manly voice,
Turning again toward childish treble, pipes
And whistles in his sound. Last scene of all,
That ends this strange eventful history,
Is second childishness and mere oblivion,
Sans teeth, sans eyes, sans taste, sans everything.

Orlando comes in with Adam

DUKE. Welcome. Set down your venerable burthen,
And let him feed.

ORLANDO. I thank you most for him.

ADAM. So had you need :
I scarce can speak to thank you for myself.

DUKE. Welcome ; fall to : I will not trouble you
As yet, to question you about your fortunes.
Give us some music ; and, good cousin, sing.

Song of Amiens

Blow, blow, thou winter wind,
Thou art not so unkind
As man's ingratitude ;
Thy tooth is not so keen,
Because thou art not seen,
Although thy breath be rude.

Freeze, freeze, thou bitter sky,
That dost not bite so nigh
As benefits forgot :
Though thou the waters warp,
Thy sting is not so sharp
As friend remembered not.

Heigh-ho ! sing, heigh-ho ! unto the green holly :
Most friendship is feigning, most loving mere folly ;
Then, heigh-ho, the holly !
This life is most jolly.

DUKE. If that you were the good Sir Rowland's son,
As you have whispered faithfully you were,
Be truly welcome hither : I am the duke
That loved your father : the residue of your fortune,

Go to my cave and tell me. Good old man,
Thou art right welcome as thy master is.
Support him by the arm. Give me your hand,
And let me all your fortunes understand.

ACT 3

Scene 1—A Room in the Palace: Oliver before Frederick

FREDERICK. Not see him since? Sir, sir, that cannot be.
Find out thy brother, wheresoe'er he is;
Seek him with candle; bring him dead or living
Within this twelvemonth, or turn thou no more
To seek a living in our territory.
Thy lands and all things that thou dost call thine
Worth seizure do we seize into our hands,
Till thou canst quit thee by thy brother's mouth
Of what we think against thee.

OLIVER. O that your highness knew my heart in this!
I never loved my brother in my life.

FREDERICK. More villain thou. Well, push him out of doors;
And let my officers of such a nature
Make an extent upon his house and lands:
Do this expediently and turn him going.

Scene 2—The Forest

ORLANDO. Hang there, my verse, in witness of my love:
And thou, thrice-crownèd queen of night, survey
With thy chaste eye, from thy pale sphere above,
Thy huntress' name that my full life doth sway.
O Rosalind! these trees shall be my books
And in their barks my thoughts I'll character;
That every eye which in this forest looks
Shall see thy virtue witnessed everywhere.
Run, run, Orlando; carve on every tree
The fair, the chaste, and unexpressive she.

CORIN (*entering with Touchstone*). And how like you this shepherd's life, Master Touchstone?

TOUCHSTONE. Truly, shepherd, in respect of itself, it is a good life; but in respect that it is a shepherd's life, it is naught. In respect that it is solitary, I like it very well; but in respect that it is private, it is a very vile life. Now, in respect it is in the fields, it pleaseth me well; but in respect it is not in the court, it is tedious. As it is a spare life, look you, it fits my humour well; but as there is no more plenty in it, it goes much against my stomach. Hast any philosophy in thee, shepherd?

CORIN. No more but that I know the more one sickens the worse at ease he is; and that he that wants money, means, and content is without three good friends; that the property of rain is to wet, and fire to burn; that good pasture makes fat sheep, and that a great cause of the night is lack of the sun; that he that hath learned no wit by nature nor art may complain of good breeding or comes of a very dull kindred.

TOUCHSTONE. Such a one is a natural philosopher. Wast ever in court, shepherd?

CORIN. No, truly. I am a true labourer: I earn that I eat, get that I wear, owe no man hate, envy no man's happiness, glad of other men's good, content with my harm, and the greatest of my pride is to see my ewes graze and my lambs suck. Here comes young Master Ganymede, my new mistress's brother.

Rosalind comes reading a paper

From the east to western Ind,
No jewel is like Rosalind.
Her worth, being mounted on the wind,
Through all the world bears Rosalind.
All the pictures fairest lined
Are but black to Rosalind.
Let no fair be kept in mind
But the fair of Rosalind.

TOUCHSTONE. I'll rhyme you so eight years together, dinners and suppers and sleeping-hours excepted. This is the very false gallop of verses: why do you infect yourself with them?

ROSALIND. Peace, you dull fool! I found them on a tree.

TOUCHSTONE. Truly the tree yields bad fruit.

ROSALIND. Peace!
Here comes my sister, reading: stand aside.

Celia reading a paper

Why should this a desert be?
For it is unpeopled? No;
Tongues I'll hang on every tree,
That shall civil sayings show:
Some, of violated vows
Twixt the souls of friend and friend:
But upon the fairest boughs,
Or at every sentence end,
Will I Rosalinda write,
Teaching all that read to know
The quintessence of every sprite
Heaven would in little show.
Therefore Heaven Nature charged
That one body should be filled
With all graces wide-enlarged:
Nature presently distilled
Helen's cheek, but not her heart,
Cleopatra's majesty,
Atalanta's better part,
Sad Lucretia's modesty.
Thus Rosalind of many parts
By heavenly synod was devised,
Of many faces, eyes, and hearts,
To have the touches dearest prized.
Heaven would that she these gifts should have,
And I to live and die her slave.

ROSALIND. O most gentle pulpiter! What tedious homily of love have you wearied your parishioners withal, and never cried *Have patience, good people!*

CELIA. How now! back, friends! Shepherd, go off a little.

TOUCHSTONE. Come, shepherd, let us make an honourable retreat; though not with bag and baggage, yet with scrip and scrippage.

CELIA (*to Rosalind*). Didst thou hear these verses?

ROSALIND. O, yes, I heard them all, and more too.

CELIA. But didst thou hear without wondering how thy name should be hanged and carved upon these trees?

ROSALIND. I was seven of the nine days out of the wonder before you came; for look here what I found on a palm-tree.

CELIA. Trow you who hath done this?

ROSALIND. Is it a man?

CELIA. And a chain, that you once wore, about his neck. Change you colour?

ROSALIND. Nay, but who is it?

CELIA. Is it possible?

ROSALIND. Nay, I prithee now with most petitionary vehemence, tell me who it is.

CELIA. O wonderful, wonderful, and most wonderful wonderful! and yet again wonderful, and after that out of all whooping!

ROSALIND. I prithee, tell me who is it quickly, and speak apace. Is he of God's making? What manner of man? Is his head worth a hat, or his chin worth a beard?

CELIA. It is young Orlando, that tripped up the wrestler's heels and your heart both in an instant.

ROSALIND. Orlando? Alas the day! What shall I do with my doublet and hose? What did he when thou sawest him? What said he? How looked he? Wherein went he? What makes he here? Did he ask for me? Where remains he? How parted he with thee? and when shalt thou see him again? Answer me in one word.

CELIA. You must borrow me Gargantua's mouth first: tis a word too great for any mouth of this age's size.

ROSALIND. Doth he know that I am in this forest and in man's apparel? Looks he as freshly as he did the day he wrestled?

CELIA. I found him under a tree, like a dropped acorn.

ROSALIND. It may well be called Jove's tree, when it drops forth such fruit.

CELIA. Give me audience, good madam.

ROSALIND. Proceed.

CELIA. There lay he, stretched along, like a wounded knight.

ROSALIND. Though it be pity to see such a sight, it well becomes the ground.

CELIA. Cry *Holla* to thy tongue, I prithee; it curvets unseasonably. He was furnished like a hunter.

ROSALIND. O, ominous! he comes to kill my heart.

CELIA. I would sing my song without a burden: thou bringest me out of tune.

ROSALIND. Do you not know I am a woman? When I think, I must speak. Sweet, say on.

CELIA. You bring me out. Soft! comes he not here?

ROSALIND. Tis he: slink by, and note him.

JAQUES (*entering with Orlando*). I thank you for your company; but, good faith, I had as lief have been myself alone.

ORLANDO. And so had I; but yet, for fashion sake, I thank you, too, for your society.

JAQUES. God be wi' you: let's meet as little as we can.

ORLANDO. I do desire we may be better strangers.

JAQUES. I pray you, mar no more trees with writing love-songs in their barks.

ORLANDO. I pray you, mar no more of my verses with reading them ill-favouredly.

JAQUES. Rosalind is your love's name?

ORLANDO. Yes, just.

JAQUES. I do not like her name.

ORLANDO. There was no thought of pleasing you when she was christened.

JAQUES. What stature is she of?

ORLANDO. Just as high as my heart.

JAQUES. You have a nimble wit: I think twas made of Atalanta's heels. Will you sit down with me, and we two will rail against our mistress the world and all our misery?

ORLANDO. I will chide no breather in the world but myself, against whom I know most faults.

JAQUES. The worst fault you have is to be in love.

ORLANDO. Tis a fault I will not change for your best virtue. I am weary of you.

JAQUES. By my troth, I was seeking for a fool when I found you.

ORLANDO. He is drowned in the brook: look but in, and you shall see him.

JAQUES. I'll tarry no longer with you: farewell, good Signior Love.

ORLANDO. I am glad of your departure: adieu, good Monsieur Melancholy.

ROSALIND (*aside*). I will speak to him like a saucy lackey, and under that habit play the knave with him. Do you hear, forester?

Orlando. Very well: what would you?

Rosalind. I pray you, what is't o'clock?

Orlando. You should ask me what time o' day: there's no clock in the forest.

Rosalind. Then there is no true lover in the forest; else sighing every minute and groaning every hour would detect the lazy foot of Time as well as a clock.

Orlando. And why not the swift foot of Time? Had not that been as proper?

Rosalind. By no means, sir. Time travels in divers paces with divers persons. I'll tell you who Time ambles withal, who Time trots withal, who Time gallops withal, and who he stands still withal.

Orlando. I prithee, who doth he trot withal?

Rosalind. Marry, he trots hard with a young maid between the contract of her marriage and the day it is solemnised: if the interim be but a sennight, Time's pace is so hard that it seems the length of seven year.

Orlando. Who ambles Time withal?

Rosalind. With a priest that lacks Latin and a rich man that hath not the gout, for the one sleeps easily because he cannot study and the other lives merrily because he feels no pain, the one lacking the burden of lean and wasteful learning, the other knowing no burden of heavy tedious penury; these Time ambles withal.

Orlando. Who doth he gallop withal?

Rosalind. With a thief to the gallows, for though he go as softly as foot can fall he thinks himself too soon there.

Orlando. Who stays it still withal?

Rosalind. With lawyers in the vacation; for they sleep between term and term and then they perceive not how Time moves.

Orlando. Where dwell you, pretty youth?

Rosalind. With this shepherdess, my sister; here in the skirts of the forest, like fringe upon a petticoat.

Orlando. Are you native of this place? Your accent is something finer than you could purchase in so removed a dwelling.

Rosalind. I have been told so of many: but indeed an old religious uncle of mine taught me to speak, who was in his youth an inland man; one that knew courtship too well, for there he fell in love. I have heard him read many lectures against it, and I thank God I am not a woman, to be touched with so many giddy offences as he hath generally taxed their whole sex withal.

Orlando. Can you remember any of the principal evils that he laid to the charge of women?

Rosalind. There were none principal; they were all like one

another as halfpence are, every one fault seeming monstrous till his fellow-fault came to match it.

Orlando. I prithee, recount some of them.

Rosalind. No, I will not cast away my physic, but on those that are sick. There is a man haunts the forest that abuses our young plants with carving *Rosalind* on their barks; hangs odes upon hawthorns and elegies on brambles, all, forsooth, deifying the name of Rosalind: if I could meet that fancy-monger I would give him some good counsel.

Orlando. I am he that is so love-shaked: I pray you, tell me your remedy.

Rosalind. There is none of my uncle's marks upon you: he taught me how to know a man in love; in which cage of rushes I am sure you are not prisoner.

Orlando. What were his marks?

Rosalind. A lean cheek, which you have not; a blue eye and sunken, which you have not; an unquestionable spirit, which you have not; a beard neglected, which you have not. Then your hose should be ungartered, your bonnet unbanded, your sleeve unbuttoned, your shoe untied, and everything about you demonstrating a careless desolation; but you are no such man.

Orlando. Fair youth, I would I could make thee believe I love.

Rosalind. Me believe it! You may as soon make her that you love believe it; which, I warrant, she is apter to do than to confess she does. But, in good sooth, are you he that hangs the verses on the trees, wherein Rosalind is so admired?

Orlando. I swear to thee, youth, by the white hand of Rosalind, I am that he, that unfortunate he.

Rosalind. But are you so much in love as your rhymes speak?

Orlando. Neither rhyme nor reason can express how much.

Rosalind. Love is merely a madness, and, I tell you, deserves as well a dark house and a whip as madmen do: and the reason why they are not so punished and cured is that the lunacy is so ordinary that the whippers are in love too. Yet I profess curing it by counsel.

Orlando. Did you ever cure any so?

Rosalind. Yes, one, and in this manner. He was to imagine me his love, his mistress; and I set him every day to woo me: at which time would I grieve, being effeminate, changeable, longing and liking, proud, fantastical, apish, shallow, inconstant, full of tears, full of smiles, for every passion something and for no passion truly anything, as boys and women are for the most part cattle of this colour; would now like him, now loathe him; then entertain him, then forswear him; now weep for him, then spit at him; that I drave my suitor from his mad humour of love to a living humour of madness. Thus I cured him; and this way I would cure you if you would but call me Rosalind and come every day to my cote and woo me. Will you?

ORLANDO. With all my heart, good youth.

ROSALIND. Nay, you must call me Rosalind. Come, sister.

Scene 3—The Forest

TOUCHSTONE. Come apace, good Audrey; I will fetch up your goats, Audrey. And how, Audrey? am I the man yet? Doth my simple feature content you?

AUDREY. Your features! Lord warrant us! what features?

TOUCHSTONE. Truly, I would the gods had made thee poetical.

AUDREY. I do not know what poetical is: is it honest in deed and word? Is it a true thing?

TOUCHSTONE. No, truly; for the truest poetry is the most feigning; and lovers are given to poetry, and what they swear in poetry may be said as lovers they do feign.

AUDREY. Do you wish, then, that the gods had made me poetical?

TOUCHSTONE. I do, truly.

AUDREY. Would you not have me honest?

TOUCHSTONE. No, truly, unless thou wert hard-favoured; for honesty coupled to beauty is to have honey a sauce to sugar.

AUDREY. Well, I am not fair; and therefore I pray the gods make me honest.

TOUCHSTONE. But be it as it may be, I will marry thee, and to that end I have been with Sir Oliver Martext, the vicar of the next village, who hath promised to meet me in this place of the forest, and to couple us.

JAQUES (*aside*). I would fain see this meeting.

AUDREY. Well, the gods give us joy!

TOUCHSTONE. Here comes Sir Oliver. Sir Oliver Martext, you are well met: will you dispatch us here under this tree, or shall we go with you to your chapel?

SIR OLIVER MARTEXT. Is there none here to give the woman?

TOUCHSTONE. I will not take her on gift of any man.

SIR OLIVER. Truly, she must be given, or the marriage is not lawful.

JAQUES (*advancing*). Proceed, proceed: I'll give her.

TOUCHSTONE. Good-even, good Master What-ye-call't: how do you, sir?

JAQUES. Will you be married, motley?

TOUCHSTONE. As the ox hath his bow, sir, the horse his curb, and the falcon her bells, so man hath his desires; and as pigeons bill, so wedlock would be nibbling.

JAQUES. And will you, being a man of your breeding, be married under a bush like a beggar? Get you to church, and have a good priest that can tell you what marriage is: this fellow will but join you together as they join wainscot; then one of you will prove a shrunk panel and, like green timber, warp, warp. Go thou with me, and let me counsel thee.

TOUCHSTONE. Come, sweet Audrey: farewell, good Master Oliver.

SIR OLIVER MARTEXT. Tis no matter: ne'er a fantastical knave of them all shall flout me out of my calling.

Scene 4—The Forest

Scene Four shows Celia teasing Rosalind about her growing interest in Orlando, when Corin enters and invites them to observe another love scene between the scornful shepherdess Phebe and her lover Silvius.

Scene 5—The Forest

Enter Silvius and Phebe, followed by Rosalind, Celia, and Corin

SILVIUS. Sweet Phebe, do not scorn me; do not, Phebe;
Say that you love me not, but say not so
In bitterness. The common executioner,
Whose heart the accustomed sight of death makes hard,
Falls not the axe upon the humbled neck
But first begs pardon.

PHEBE. I would not be thy executioner:
I fly thee, for I would not injure thee.
Thou tell'st me there is murder in mine eye.
Lie not, to say mine eyes are murderers!
There is no force in eyes that can do hurt.

SILVIUS. O dear Phebe,
If ever (as that ever may be near),
You meet in some fresh cheek the power of fancy,
Then shall you know the wounds invisible
That love's keen arrows make.

PHEBE. But till that time
Come not thou near me: and when that time comes,
Afflict me with thy mocks, pity me not;
As till that time I shall not pity thee.

ROSALIND. And why, I pray you? Who might be your mother,
That you insult, exult, and all at once,
Over the wretched? What though you have no beauty?
Must you be therefore proud and pitiless?
Why, what means this? Why do you look on me?
(I think she means to tangle my eyes too!)
No, faith, proud mistress, hope not after it:
Tis not your inky brows, your black silk hair,
Your bugle eyeballs, nor your cheek of cream,
That can entame my spirits to your worship.

You foolish shepherd, wherefore do you follow her,
Like foggy south puffing with wind and rain ?
You are a thousand times a properer man
Than she a woman : tis such fools as you
That makes the world full of ill-favoured children :
Tis not her glass, but you, that flatters her.
But, mistress, know yourself : down on your knees,
And thank heaven, fasting, for a good man's love :
For I must tell you friendly in your ear,
Sell when you can : you are not for all markets.
Cry the man mercy ; love him ; take his offer :
Foul is most foul, being foul to be a scoffer.
So take her to thee, shepherd : fare you well.

PHEBE. Sweet youth, I pray you, chide a year together :
I had rather hear you chide than this man woo.

ROSALIND. I pray you, do not fall in love with me.

PHEBE. Dead shepherd, now I find thy saw of might :
Who ever loved that loved not at first sight ?

SILVIUS. Sweet Phebe, pity me.

PHEBE. Why, I am sorry for thee, gentle Silvius.

SILVIUS. Wherever sorrow is, relief would be.

PHEBE. Thou hast my love : is not that neighbourly ?
Silvius, the time was that I hated thee,
And yet it is not that I bear thee love ;
But since that thou canst talk of love so well,
Thy company, which erst was irksome to me,
I will endure, and I'll employ thee too :
But do not look for further recompense
Than thine own gladness that thou art employed.

SILVIUS. So holy and so perfect is my love,
And I in such a poverty of grace,
That I shall think it a most plenteous crop
To glean the broken ears after the man
That the main harvest reaps : loose now and then
A scattered smile, and that I'll live upon.

PHEBE. Knowest thou the youth that spoke to me erewhile ?

SILVIUS. Not very well, but I have met him oft ;
And he hath bought the cottage and the bounds
That the old carlot once was master of.

PHEBE. Think not I love him, though I ask for him ;
Tis but a peevish boy ; yet he talks well ;
(But what care I for words ? yet words do well
When he that speaks them pleases those that hear).
It is a pretty youth : not very pretty :
But, sure, he's proud, and yet his pride becomes him :

He'll make a proper man : the best thing in him
Is his complexion ; and faster than his tongue
Did make offence his eye did heal it up.
He is not very tall ; yet for his years he's tall :
His leg is but so so ; and yet tis well :
There was a pretty redness in his lip,
A little riper and more lusty red
Than that mixed in his cheek ; 'twas just the difference
Betwixt the constant red and mingled damask.
There be some women, Silvius, had they marked him
In parcels as I did, would have gone near
To fall in love with him ; but, for my part,
I love him not nor hate him not ; and yet
I have more cause to hate him than to love him :
For what had he to do to chide at me ?
He said mine eyes were black and my hair black ;
And, now I am remembered, scorned at me :
I marvel why I answered not again :
But that's all one ; omittance is no quittance.
I'll write to him a very taunting letter,
And thou shalt bear it : wilt thou, Silvius ?

SILVIUS. Phebe, with all my heart.

ACT 4

Scene 1—The Forest

JAQUES (*to Rosalind*). I prithee, pretty youth, let me be better acquainted with thee.

ROSALIND. They say you are a melancholy fellow.

JAQUES. I am so ; I do love it better than laughing. Tis good to be sad and say nothing.

ROSALIND. Why then, tis good to be a post.

JAQUES. I have neither the scholar's melancholy, which is emulation, nor the musician's, which is fantastical, nor the courtier's, which is proud, nor the soldier's, which is ambitious, nor the lawyer's, which is politic, nor the lady's, which is nice, nor the lover's, which is all these ; but it is a melancholy of mine own, compounded of many simples, extracted from many objects, and indeed the sundry contemplation of my travels, in which my rumination wraps me in a most humorous sadness.

ROSALIND. A traveller ! By my faith, you have great reason to be sad : I fear you have sold your own lands to see other men's ; then, to have seen much and to have nothing, is to have rich eyes and poor hands.

JAQUES. Yes, I have gained my experience.

ROSALIND. And your experience makes you sad : I had rather

have a fool to make me merry than experience to make me sad; and to travel for it too!

JAQUES. Nay, then, God be wi' you, an you talk in blank verse.

ROSALIND. Farewell, Monsieur Traveller. Look you lisp and wear strange suits, disable all the benefits of your own country, be out of love with your nativity and almost chide God for making you that countenance you are, or I will scarce think you have swam in a gondola. (*Orlando approaches*) Why, how now, Orlando! Where have you been all this while? You a lover! An you serve me such another trick, never come in my sight more.

ORLANDO. My fair Rosalind, I come within an hour of my promise.

ROSALIND. Break an hour's promise in love! He that will divide a minute into a thousand parts and break but a part of the thousandth part of a minute in the affairs of love, it may be said of him that Cupid hath clapped him o' the shoulder, but I'll warrant him heart-whole.

ORLANDO. Pardon me, dear Rosalind.

ROSALIND. Nay, an you be so tardy, come no more in my sight: I had as lief be wooed of a snail. Come, woo me, woo me, for now I am in a holiday humour and like enough to consent. What would you say to me now, an I were your very very Rosalind?

ORLANDO. I would kiss before I spoke.

ROSALIND. Nay, you were better speak first, and when you were gravelled for lack of matter you might take occasion to kiss. Am not I your Rosalind?

ORLANDO. I take some joy to say you are.

ROSALIND. Well, in her person I say I will not have you.

ORLANDO. Then in mine own person I die.

ROSALIND. No, faith, die by attorney. The poor world is almost six thousand years old, and in all this time there was not any man died in his own person in a love-cause. Men have died from time to time and worms have eaten them, but not for love.

ORLANDO. I would not have my right Rosalind of this mind, for, I protest, her frown might kill me.

ROSALIND. By this hand, it will not kill a fly. But come, now I will be your Rosalind in a more coming-on disposition, and ask me what you will, I will grant it.

ORLANDO. Then love me, Rosalind.

ROSALIND. Yes, faith, will I, Fridays and Saturdays and all.

ORLANDO. And wilt thou have me?

ROSALIND. Ay, and twenty such.

ORLANDO. What sayest thou?

ROSALIND. Are you not good?

ORLANDO. I hope so.

ROSALIND. Why then, can one desire too much of a good thing? Come, sister, you shall be the priest and marry us. Give me your hand, Orlando. What do you say, sister?

ORLANDO. Pray thee, marry us.

CELIA. I cannot say the words.

ROSALIND. You must begin, *Will you, Orlando—*

CELIA. Go to. Will you, Orlando, have to wife this Rosalind?

ORLANDO. I will.

ROSALIND. Then you must say, *I take thee, Rosalind, for wife.*

ORLANDO. I take thee, Rosalind, for wife.

ROSALIND. I might ask you for your commission, but I do take thee, Orlando, for my husband; there's a girl goes before the priest; and certainly a woman's thought runs before her actions.

ORLANDO. So do all thoughts; they are winged.

ROSALIND. Now tell me how long you would have her after you have possessed her.

ORLANDO. For ever and a day.

ROSALIND. Say a day without the ever. No, no, Orlando; men are April when they woo, December when they wed: maids are May when they are maids, but the sky changes when they are wives. I will be more jealous of thee than a Barbary cock-pigeon over his hen, more clamorous than a parrot against rain, more new-fangled than an ape, more giddy than a monkey: I will weep for nothing, like Diana in the fountain, and I will do that when you are disposed to be merry; I will laugh like a hyena, and that when thou art inclined to sleep.

ORLANDO. But will my Rosalind do so?

ROSALIND. By my life, she will do as I do.

ORLANDO. O, but she is wise.

ROSALIND. Or else she could not have the wit to do this: the wiser, the waywarder: make the doors upon a woman's wit and it will out at the casement; shut that and 'twill out at the keyhole; stop that, 'twill fly with the smoke out at the chimney.

ORLANDO. For these two hours, Rosalind, I will leave thee.

ROSALIND. Alas! dear love, I cannot lack thee two hours.

ORLANDO. I must attend the duke at dinner: by two o'clock I will be with thee again.

ROSALIND. Ay, go your ways, go your ways; I knew what you would prove: my friends told me as much, and I thought no less. That flattering tongue of yours won me: tis but one cast away, and so, come, death! Two o'clock is your hour?

ORLANDO. Ay, sweet Rosalind.

ROSALIND. By my troth, and in good earnest, and so God mend me, and by all pretty oaths that are not dangerous, if you break one jot of your promise or come one minute behind your hour, I will think you the most pathetical break-promise and the most hollow lover and the most unworthy of her you call Rosalind that may be chosen out of the gross band of the unfaithful: therefore beware my censure and keep your promise.

ORLANDO. With no less religion than if thou wert indeed my Rosalind: so adieu.

ROSALIND. Well, Time is the old justice that examines all such offenders, and let Time try: adieu.

CELIA. You have simply misused our sex in your love-prate.

ROSALIND. O coz, coz, coz, my pretty little coz, that thou didst know how many fathom deep I am in love! But it cannot be sounded. I'll tell thee, Aliena, I cannot be out of the sight of Orlando: I'll go find a shadow and sigh till he come.

CELIA. And I'll sleep.

Scene 2—The Forest

In this brief scene Jaques, the philosopher of the Duke's party, calls on a forester for a song of victory to one who killed the deer.

Scene 3—The Forest

ROSALIND. How say you now? Is it not past two o'clock, and here much Orlando!

CELIA. I warrant you, with pure love and troubled brain, he hath ta'en his bow and arrows and is gone forth to sleep. Look, who comes here.

SILVIUS. My errand is to you, fair youth;
My gentle Phebe bid me give you this:
I know not the contents; but, as I guess
By the stern brow and waspish action
Which she did use as she was writing of it,
It bears an angry tenour: pardon me;
I am but as a guiltless messenger.

ROSALIND. Patience herself would startle at this letter
And play the swaggerer; bear this, bear all:
She says I am not fair, that I lack manners;
She calls me proud, and that she could not love me
Were man as rare as Phoenix.
Why writes she so to me? Well, shepherd, well,
This is a letter of your own device.

SILVIUS. No, I protest, I know not the contents:
Phebe did write it.

ROSALIND. This is a man's invention, and his hand.
Why, tis a boisterous and a cruel style,
A style for challengers; why, she defies me,
Like Turk to Christian: women's gentle brain
Could not drop forth such giant-rude invention,

Such Ethiope words, blacker in their effect
Than in their countenance.

CELIA. Alas, poor shepherd.

ROSALIND. Do you pity him? No, he deserves no pity. Wilt thou love such a woman? What, to make thee an instrument and play false strains upon thee! Not to be endured! Well, go your way to her, and say: if she love me I charge her to love thee; if she will not I will never have her unless thou entreat for her. If you be a true lover, hence, and not a word; for here comes more company.

OLIVER (*entering*). Good-morrow, fair ones: pray you, if you know,
Where in the purlieus of this forest stands
A sheep-cote fenced about with olive trees?

CELIA. West of this place, down in the neighbour bottom:
The rank of osiers by the murmuring stream
Left on your right hand brings you to the place.
But at this hour the house doth keep itself;
There's none within.

OLIVER. If that an eye may profit by a tongue,
Then should I know you by description;
Such garments and such years: *The boy is fair,*
Of female favour, and bestows himself
Like a ripe sister: the woman low
And browner than her brother. Are not you
The owner of the house I did inquire for?

CELIA. It is no boast, being asked, to say we are.

OLIVER. Orlando doth commend him to you both,
And to that youth he calls his Rosalind
He sends this blood-stained napkin. Are you he?

ROSALIND. I am: what must we understand by this?

OLIVER. Some of my shame; if you will know of me
What man I am, and how, and why, and where
This handkercher was stained.

CELIA. I pray you, tell it.

OLIVER. When last the young Orlando parted from you
He left a promise to return again
Within an hour, and pacing through the forest,
Chewing the food of sweet and bitter fancy,
Lo, what befel! he threw his eye aside,
And mark what object did present itself:
Under an oak, whose boughs were mossed with age
And high top bald with dry antiquity,
A wretched ragged man, o'ergrown with hair,
Lay sleeping on his back: about his neck
A green and gilded snake had wreathed itself,
Who with her head nimble in threats approached

The opening of his mouth : but suddenly,
Seeing Orlando, it unlinked itself,
And with indented glides did slip away
Into a bush : under which bush's shade
A lioness, with udders all drawn dry,
Lay couching, head on ground, with catlike watch,
When that the sleeping man should stir ; for tis
The royal disposition of that beast
To prey on nothing that doth seem as dead :
This seen, Orlando did approach the man
And found it was his brother, his elder brother.

CELIA. O, I have heard him speak of that same brother ;
And he did render him the most unnatural
That lived amongst men.

OLIVER. And well he might so do,
For well I know he was unnatural.

ROSALIND. But, to Orlando : did he leave him there,
Food to the sucked and hungry lioness ?

OLIVER. Twice did he turn his back and purposed so ;
But kindness, nobler ever than revenge,
And nature, stronger than his just occasion,
Made him give battle to the lioness,
Who quickly fell before him : in which hurtling
From miserable slumber I awaked.

CELIA. Are you his brother ?

ROSALIND. Was't you he rescued ?

CELIA. Was't you that did so oft contrive to kill him ?

OLIVER. Twas I ; but tis not I : I do not shame
To tell you what I was, since my conversion
So sweetly tastes, being the thing I am.

ROSALIND. But, for the napkin ?

OLIVER. By and by.
When from the first to last betwixt us two
Tears our recountments had most kindly bathed,
As how I came into that desert place :
In brief, he led me to the gentle duke,
Who gave me fresh array and entertainment,
Committing me unto my brother's love ;
Who led me instantly unto his cave,
There stripped himself, and here upon his arm
The lioness had torn some flesh away,
Which all this while had bled ; and now he fainted
And cried, in fainting, upon Rosalind.
Brief, I recovered him, bound up his wound ;
And, after some small space, being strong at heart,

He sent me hither, stranger as I am,
To tell this story, that you might excuse
His broken promise, and to give this napkin,
Dyed in his blood, unto the shepherd youth
That he in sport doth call his Rosalind. (*Rosalind swoons*)

CELIA. Why, how now, Ganymede! sweet Ganymede!

OLIVER. Many will swoon when they do look on blood.

CELIA. There is more in it. Cousin Ganymede!

OLIVER. Look, he recovers.

ROSALIND. I would I were at home.

CELIA. We'll lead you thither.
I pray you, will you take him by the arm?

OLIVER. Be of good cheer, youth: you a man! You lack a man's heart.

ROSALIND. I do so, I confess it. Ah, sirrah, a body would think this was well counterfeited! I pray you, tell your brother how well I counterfeited.

OLIVER. This was not counterfeit; there is too great testimony in your complexion that it was a passion of earnest.

ROSALIND. Counterfeit, I assure you.

OLIVER. Well then, take a good heart and counterfeit to be a man.

ROSALIND. So I do: but, i' faith, I should have been a woman by right.

CELIA. Come, you look paler and paler; pray you, draw homewards. Good sir, go with us.

OLIVER. That will I, for I must bear answer back how you excuse my brother, Rosalind.

ROSALIND. I shall devise something: but, I pray you, commend my counterfeiting to him. Will you go?

ACT 5

Scene 1—The Forest

This scene pictures Touchstone and Audrey encountering William, a rustic youth who is in love with Audrey. Touchstone confuses his rival with talk he cannot understand, and frightens him with threats so that he hastily departs.

Scene 2—The Forest

ORLANDO. Is't possible that on so little acquaintance you should like her? that, but seeing, you should love her? and, loving, woo? and, wooing, she should grant?

OLIVER. Neither call the giddiness of it in question, the poverty of her, the small acquaintance, my sudden wooing, nor her sudden consenting; but say with me, I love Aliena; say with her that she loves me; it shall be to your good; for my father's house and all the revenue that was old Sir Rowland's will I estate upon you, and here live and die a shepherd.

ORLANDO. You have my consent. Let your wedding be tomorrow: thither will I invite the duke and his contented followers. Go you and prepare Aliena; for look you, here comes my Rosalind.

ROSALIND. God save you, brother.

OLIVER (*leaving*). And you, fair sister.

ROSALIND. O, my dear Orlando, how it grieves me to see thee wear thy heart in a scarf!

ORLANDO. It is my arm.

ROSALIND. I thought thy heart had been wounded with the claws of a lion.

ORLANDO. Wounded it is, but with the eyes of a lady.

ROSALIND. Did your brother tell you how I counterfeited to swoon when he showed me your handkercher?

ORLANDO. Ay, and greater wonders than that.

ROSALIND. O, I know where you are: nay, tis true, for your brother and my sister no sooner met but they looked, no sooner looked but they loved, no sooner loved but they sighed, no sooner sighed but they asked one another the reason, no sooner knew the reason but they sought the remedy; and in these degrees have they made a pair of stairs to marriage which they will climb.

ORLANDO. They shall be married tomorrow, and I will bid the duke to the nuptial. But, O, how bitter a thing it is to look into happiness through another man's eyes! By so much the more shall I tomorrow be at the height of heart-heaviness, by how much I shall think my brother happy in having what he wishes for.

ROSALIND. Why, then, tomorrow I cannot serve your turn for Rosalind?

ORLANDO. I can live no longer by thinking.

ROSALIND. I will weary you then no longer with idle talking. Know of me, then, for now I speak to some purpose, that I know you are a gentleman of good conceit. Believe, then, that I can do strange things: I have, since I was three year old, conversed with a magician, most profound in his art. If you do love Rosalind so near the heart as your gesture cries it out, when your brother marries Aliena shall you marry her: I know into what straits of fortune she is driven; and it is not impossible to me, if it appear not inconvenient to you, to set her before your eyes tomorrow human as she is and without any danger.

ORLANDO. Speakest thou in sober meanings?

ROSALIND. By my life, I do; which I tender dearly, though I say I am a magician. Therefore, put you in your best array; bid your friends; for if you will be married tomorrow you shall, and to Rosalind, if you will. Look, here comes a lover of mine and a lover of hers. (*Enter Silvius and Phebe*)

PHEBE. Youth, you have done me much ungentleness
To show the letter that I writ to you.

ROSALIND. I care not if I have: it is my study
To seem despiteful and ungentle to you:
You are there followed by a faithful shepherd;
Look upon him, love him; he worships you.

PHEBE. Good shepherd, tell this youth what tis to love.

SILVIUS. It is to be all made of sighs and tears;
And so am I for Phebe.

PHEBE. And I for Ganymede.

ORLANDO. And I for Rosalind.

ROSALIND. And I for no woman.

SILVIUS. It is to be all made of faith and service;
And so am I for Phebe.

PHEBE. And I for Ganymede.

ORLANDO. And I for Rosalind.

ROSALIND. And I for no woman.

SILVIUS. It is to be all made of fantasy,
All made of passion and all made of wishes,
All adoration, duty, and observance,
All humbleness, all patience and impatience,
All purity, all trial, all observance;
And so am I for Phebe.

PHEBE. And so am I for Ganymede.

ORLANDO. And so am I for Rosalind.

ROSALIND. And so am I for no woman.

PHEBE. If this be so, why blame you me to love you?

SILVIUS. If this be so, why blame you me to love you?

ORLANDO. If this be so, why blame you me to love you?

ROSALIND. Whom do you speak to, *Why blame you me to love you?*

ORLANDO. To her that is not here, nor doth not hear.

ROSALIND. Pray you, no more of this; tis like the howling of Irish wolves against the moon. (*To Silvius*) I will help you, if I can. (*To Phebe*) I would love you, if I could. I will marry you if ever I marry woman, and I'll be married tomorrow. (*To Orlando*) I will satisfy you if ever I satisfied man, and you shall be married tomorrow. (*To Silvius*) I will content you, if what pleases you contents you, and you shall be married tomorrow. (*To Orlando*) As you love Rosalind, meet. (*To Silvius*) As you love Phebe, meet; and as I love no woman, I'll meet. So fare you well: I have left you commands.

SILVIUS. I'll not fail, if I live.

PHEBE and ORLANDO. Nor I.

Scene 3—The Forest

TOUCHSTONE. Tomorrow is the joyful day, Audrey; tomorrow will we be married.

AUDREY. I do desire it with all my heart; and I hope it is no dishonest desire to desire to be a woman of the world. Here come two of the banished duke's pages.

PAGE. Well met, honest gentleman.

TOUCHSTONE. By my troth, well met. Come, sit, sit, and a song.

PAGE. We are for you: sit i' the middle.

It was a lover and his lass,
With a hey, and a ho, and a hey nonino,
That o'er the green cornfield did pass
In the spring time, the only pretty ring time,
When birds do sing, hey ding a ding, ding:
Sweet lovers love the spring.

TOUCHSTONE. Truly, young gentlemen, though there was no great matter in the ditty, yet the note was very untuneable.

PAGE. You are deceived, sir: we kept time, we lost not our time.

TOUCHSTONE. By my troth, yes; I count it but time lost tc hear such a foolish song. God be wi' you; and God mend your voices! Come, Audrey.

Scene 4—All Meet in the Forest

DUKE. Dost thou believe, Orlando, that the boy
Can do all this that he hath promised?

ORLANDO. I sometimes do believe, and sometimes do not;
As those that fear they hope, and know they fear.

ROSALIND. Patience once more, while our compact is urged:
You say, if I bring in your Rosalind,
You will bestow her on Orlando here?

DUKE. That would I, had I kingdoms to give with her.

ROSALIND. And you say you will have her, when I bring her?

ORLANDO. That would I, were I of all kingdoms king.

ROSALIND. You say, you'll marry me, if I be willing?

PHEBE. That will I, should I die the hour after.

ROSALIND. But if you do refuse to marry me,
You'll give yourself to this most faithful shepherd?

PHEBE. So is the bargain.

ROSALIND. You say that you'll have Phebe, if she will?

SILVIUS. Though to have her and death were both one thing.

ROSALIND. I have promised to make all this matter even.
Keep you your word, O duke, to give your daughter;
You yours, Orlando, to receive his daughter:
Keep your word, Phebe, that you'll marry me,

Or else, refusing me, to wed this shepherd:
Keep your word, Silvius, that you'll marry her,
If she refuse me, and from hence I go
To make these doubts all even.

DUKE. I do remember in this shepherd boy
Some lively touches of my daughter's favour.

ORLANDO. My lord, the first time that I ever saw him
Methought he was a brother to your daughter:
But, my good lord, this boy is forest-born,
And hath been tutored in the rudiments
Of many desperate studies by his uncle,
Whom he reports to be a great magician,
Obscured in the circle of this forest.

JAQUES. There is, sure, another flood toward, and these couples are coming to the ark. Here comes a pair of very strange beasts, which in all tongues are called fools. *(Enter Touchstone and Audrey)*

TOUCHSTONE. Salutation and greeting to you all!

JAQUES. Good my lord, bid him welcome: this is the motley-minded gentleman that I have so often met in the forest. He hath been a courtier, he swears.

TOUCHSTONE. If any man doubt that, let him put me to my purgation. I have trod a measure; I have flattered a lady; I have been politic with my friend, smooth with mine enemy; I have undone three tailors; I have had four quarrels, and like to have fought one.

JAQUES. And how was that ta'en up?

TOUCHSTONE. Faith, we met, and found the quarrel was upon the seventh cause.

JAQUES. How seventh cause? Good my lord, like this fellow.

DUKE. I like him very well.

TOUCHSTONE. God shield you, sir; I desire you of the like. I press in here, sir, amongst the rest to swear and to forswear; a poor virgin, sir, an ill-favoured thing, sir, but mine own; a poor humour of mine, sir, to take that that no man else will: rich honesty dwells like a miser, sir, in a poor house; as your pearl in your foul oyster.

DUKE. By my faith, he is very swift and sententious.

JAQUES. But, for the seventh cause; how did you find the quarrel on the seventh cause?

TOUCHSTONE. Upon a lie seven times removed (bear your body more seeming, Audrey); as thus, sir. I did dislike the cut of a certain courtier's beard: he sent me word, if I said his beard was not cut well, he was in the mind it was: this is called the Retort Courteous. If I sent him word again it was not well cut, he would send me word he cut it to please himself: this is called the Quip Modest. If again it was not well cut, he disabled my judgment: this is called the Reply Churlish. If again it was not well cut, he would answer I spake not true: this is called the Reproof Valiant. If again it was not well cut, he would say I lied: this is called the Countercheck Quarrelsome: and so to the Lie Circumstantial and the Lie Direct.

JAQUES. And how oft did you say his beard was not well cut?

TOUCHSTONE. I durst go no further than the Lie Circumstantial, nor he durst not give me the Lie Direct; and so we measured swords and parted.

JAQUES. Can you nominate in order now the degrees of the lie?

TOUCHSTONE. O sir, we quarrel in print, by the book; as you have books for good manners: I will name you the degrees. The first the Retort Courteous; the second the Quip Modest; the third the Reply Churlish; the fourth the Reproof Valiant; the fifth the Countercheck Quarrelsome; the sixth the Lie with Circumstance; the seventh the Lie Direct. All these you may avoid but the Lie Direct; and you may avoid that too, with an If. I knew when seven justices could not take up a quarrel, but when the parties were met themselves, one of them thought but of an If, as, *If you said so, then I said so*; and they shook hands and swore brothers. Your *If* is the only peace-maker; much virtue in If.

JAQUES. Is not this a rare fellow, my lord? He's as good at anything, and yet a fool.

DUKE. He uses his folly like a stalking-horse, and under the presentation of that he shoots his wit.

Rosalind enters with the Spirit of Hymen, soft music playing

HYMEN. Then is there mirth in heaven,
When earthly things made even
Atone together.
Good duke, receive thy daughter:
Hymen from heaven brought her,
Yea, brought her hither,
That thou mightst join her hand with his
Whose heart within his bosom is.

ROSALIND (*to Duke*). To you I give myself, for I am yours.
(*To Orlando*) To you I give myself, for I am yours.

DUKE. If there be truth in sight you are my daughter.

ORLANDO. If there be truth in sight you are my Rosalind.

PHEBE. If sight and shape be true,
Why then, my love adieu!

ROSALIND. I'll have no father if you be not he:
I'll have no husband if you be not he:
Nor ne'er wed woman if you be not she.

HYMEN. Peace, ho! I bar confusion:
Tis I must make conclusion

Of these most strange events:
Here's eight that must take hands
To join in Hymen's bands,
If truth holds true contents.
You and you no cross shall part:
You and you are heart in heart:
You to his love must accord,
Or have a woman to your lord:
You and you are sure together,
As the winter to foul weather.
Whiles a wedlock-hymn we sing,
Feed yourselves with questioning;
That reason wonder may diminish,
How thus we met, and these things finish.

Wedding is great Juno's crown:
O blessed bond of board and bed!
Tis Hymen peoples every town;
High wedlock then be honourèd:
Honour, high honour and renown,
To Hymen, god of every town!

DUKE. O my dear niece, welcome thou art to me!
Even daughter, welcome, in no less degree.

PHEBE. I will not eat my word, now thou art mine;
Thy faith my fancy to thee doth combine.

Enter Jaques de Boys

JAQUES DE BOYS. Let me have audience for a word or two:
I am the second son of old Sir Rowland,
That bring these tidings to this fair assembly.
Duke Frederick, hearing how that every day
Men of great worth resorted to this forest,
Addressed a mighty power: which were on foot,
In his own conduct, purposely to take
His brother here and put him to the sword:
And to the skirts of this wild wood he came;
Where meeting with an old religious man,
After some question with him, was converted
Both from his enterprise and from the world,
His crown bequeathing to his banished brother,
And all their lands restored to them again
That were with him exiled. This to be true,
I do engage my life.

DUKE. Welcome, young man;
Thou offerest fairly to thy brothers' wedding;
To one his lands withheld, and to the other
A land itself at large, a potent dukedom.
First, in this forest let us do those ends
That here were well begun and well begot;
And, after, every of this happy number

That have endured shrewd days and nights with us
Shall share the good of our returnèd fortune,
According to the measure of their states.
Meantime, forget this new-fallen dignity
And fall into our rustic revelry.
Play, music ! And you, brides and bridegrooms all,
With measure heaped in joy, to the measures fall.

JAQUES. Sir, by your patience. If I heard you rightly,
The duke hath put on a religious life
And thrown into neglect the pompous court ?

JAQUES DE BOYS. He hath.

JAQUES. To him will I : out of these convertites
There is much matter to be heard and learned.
(*To Duke*) You to your former honour I bequeath ;
Your patience and your virtue well deserves it.
(*To Orlando*) You to a love that your true faith doth merit.
(*To Oliver*) You to your land and love and great allies.
(*To Silvius*) You to a long and well-deservèd bed.
(*To Touchstone*) And you to wrangling ; for thy loving voyage
Is but for two months victualled. So, to your pleasures :
I am for other than for dancing measures.

DUKE. Stay, Jaques, stay.

JAQUES. To see no pastime I : what you would have
I'll stay to know at your abandoned cave.

DUKE. Proceed, proceed : we will begin these rites,
As we do trust they'll end, in true delights.

EPILOGUE

ROSALIND. It is not the fashion to see the lady the Epilogue ; but it is no more unhandsome than to see the lord the Prologue.

If it be true that good wine needs no bush, tis true that a good play needs no epilogue ; yet to good wine they do use good bushes, and good plays prove the better by the help of good epilogues. What a case am I in then, that am neither a good epilogue nor cannot insinuate with you in the behalf of a good play ! I am not furnished like a beggar, therefore to beg will not become me : my way is to conjure you, and I 'll begin with the women.

I charge you, O women, for the love you bear to men, to like as much of this play as please you ; and I charge you, O men, for the love you bear to women (as I perceive by your simpering, none of you hates them), that between you and the women the play may please. If I were a woman I would kiss as many of you as had beards that pleased me, complexions that liked me, and breaths that I defied not ; and, I am sure, as many as have good beards or good faces or sweet breaths will, for my kind offer, when I make curtsey, bid me farewell.

The Story of Romeo and Juliet

OUT of the mind of a Dominican monk came the old tale which Shakespeare has transformed into one of the great love stories of the world.

HE was thirty when he gave us this lyrical drama of life, and we find in it an interesting milestone on the poet's pathway. He seems to be dropping some early tricks of style, and finding his way to smoothness with strength. He is become a master of melodious verse. As scene after scene unfolded in the lives of these young lovers, Shakespeare was caught up by his theme and swept along on a surge as strong as the passion of Romeo, as deep as the pure delight of Juliet.

IT is a tale of love and hate, and therefore it appeals to all the world, for these two things have made the history of the world. We have to throw ourselves back to a medieval society in Verona where life is enslaved by social customs and family feuds, ever seeking a quarrel and a fight. They were days when love was a wishy-washy sentiment with the young, and marriage a heartless business traffic with the old.

INTO this atmosphere Romeo and Juliet came. It was their duty to their houses to hate each other, but they burst into these hostile camps with the love of two ardent souls, defiant and careless of all opposition. The clash is tragic for both, but in the end the life of Verona is purified by love and sacrifice. The cruelties of the feud are swept away, the cynical old men of both houses stand abashed, and the love that fears no sacrifice is enthroned on golden monuments.

IT is because it deals with human things that the play has always been popular. The characters are vivid, and the scenes move swiftly. Perhaps old Matteo Bandello would hardly recognise his Romeo and Juliet if he met them in Shakespeare, but Shakespeare took his story from Bandello's collection of two hundred tales and transformed it into this matchless thing. He wrote it about 1592.

IT has been said that the young people in this play are mad and the old people foolish, but it was the heaped-up foolishness of the old that hemmed in the love of the young and left it no chance of natural expression. The crowning glory of the play is the innocence and purity of Juliet, who passes through the crisis of her life without tarnish and without one understanding word from any woman. Even her dear Romeo is all too lightly swayed, too easily controlled by his emotion rather than his brain.

ON and on through the ages this story goes, and it has this great lesson for us all—that hate is the affliction of all who cherish it, and that love is the only way to happiness and peace.

THE PLAYERS

Prince of Verona, Escalus, a moderate, sensible man who does his best to keep his quarrelsome people quiet.

Montague, head of a family that has a fierce feud with the Capulets.

Capulet, head of a family that has a fierce feud with the Montagues. An unsentimental tyrant.

Romeo, son of Montague. At first absurdly in love with love, and then really in love with Juliet Capulet.

Paris, a young nobleman mildly in love with Juliet, and encouraged by her autocratic father.

Mercutio, a kinsman of the Prince and a friend of Romeo; lightheartedly impetuous and a great talker.

Benvolio, a cousin and friend of Romeo.

Tybalt, a brawling hothead, nephew of Lady Capulet.

Balthasar, Romeo's servant.

Friar Laurence, a Franciscan monk, the only level-headed person in the play except the Prince.

Friar John, a Franciscan who fails in his one task.

Sampson and Gregory, brawling servants of Capulet.

Peter, attendant on Juliet's nurse.

Abraham, servant of Montague.

Lady Montague, wife of Montague.

Lady Capulet, wife of Capulet.

Juliet, daughter of Capulet, in love with Romeo, without discretion but with purity of heart.

Juliet's Nurse, a comedy character without true womanliness.

An apothecary, musicians, pages, officers, watchmen, and citizens.

SCENES—Verona and Mantua, cities in Italy.

Romeo and Juliet

ACT 1

Scene 1—A Public Place in Verona

Enter servants of the House of Capulet

SAMPSON. I strike quickly, being moved.

GREGORY. But thou art not quickly moved to strike.

SAMPSON. A dog of the house of Montague moves me.

GREGORY. To move is to stir; and to be valiant is to stand: therefore, if thou art moved, thou runn'st away.

SAMPSON. A dog of that house shall move me to stand.

GREGORY. The quarrel is between our masters and us their men.

SAMPSON. Tis all one, I will show myself a tyrant. Me they shall feel while I am able to stand.

GREGORY. Draw thy tool; here come two of the house of the Montagues.

SAMPSON. My naked weapon is out: quarrel, I will back thee. Let us take the law of our sides; let them begin.

GREGORY. I will frown as I pass by, and let them take it as they list.

SAMPSON. Nay, as they dare. I will bite my thumb at them; which is a disgrace to them if they bear it. (*All draw near*)

ABRAHAM. Do you bite your thumb at us, sir?

SAMPSON. I do bite my thumb, sir.

ABRAHAM. Do you bite your thumb at us, sir?

SAMPSON. No, sir, I do not bite my thumb at you, sir, but I bite my thumb, sir.

GREGORY. Do you quarrel, sir?

ABRAHAM. Quarrel, sir? no, sir.

SAMPSON. If you do, sir, I am for you: I serve as good a man as you.

ABRAHAM. No better.

SAMPSON. Well, sir.

GREGORY. Say *better*: here comes one of my master's kinsmen.

SAMPSON. Yes, better, sir.

ABRAHAM. You lie.

SAMPSON. Draw, if you be men. (*They fight*)

BENVOLIO (*approaching*). Part, fools!
Put up your swords; you know not what you do.

Enter Tybalt, followed by citizens

TYBALT. What, art thou drawn among these heartless hinds?
Turn thee, Benvolio; look upon thy death.

BENVOLIO. I do but keep the peace: put up thy sword,
Or manage it to part these men with me.

TYBALT. What, drawn, and talk of peace! I hate the word,
As I hate hell, all Montagues, and thee:
Have at thee, coward! (*They fight*)

CITIZEN. Clubs, bills, and partisans! strike! beat them down!
Down with the Capulets! Down with the Montagues!

Enter the Capulets and Montagues, the Prince following

CAPULET. What noise is this? Give me my long sword, ho!

LADY CAPULET. A crutch, a crutch! why call you for a sword?

CAPULET. My sword, I say! Old Montague is come,
And flourishes his blade in spite of me.

PRINCE (*approaching*). Rebellious subjects, enemies to peace,
Profaners of this neighbour-stainèd steel,
Will they not hear? What, ho! you men, you beasts,
That quench the fire of your pernicious rage
With purple fountains issuing from your veins,
Throw your mistempered weapons to the ground,
And hear the sentence of your movèd prince.
Three civil brawls, bred of an airy word,
By thee, old Capulet, and Montague,
Have thrice disturbed the quiet of our streets:
If ever you disturb our streets again
Your lives shall pay the forfeit of the peace.
For this time all the rest depart away.
You, Capulet, shall go along with me;
And, Montague, come you this afternoon,
To know our further pleasure in this case.
Once more, on pain of death, all men depart.

All leave except Benvolio and the Montagues

LADY MONTAGUE. O, where is Romeo? Saw you him today?
Right glad I am he was not at this fray.

BENVOLIO. Madam, an hour before the worshipped sun
Peered forth the golden window of the east,
A troubled mind drave me to walk abroad;

Where, underneath the grove of sycamore
That westward rooteth from the city's side,
So early walking did I see your son.
Towards him I made, but he was ware of me
And stole into the covert of the wood:
I, measuring his affections by my own,
That most are busied when they're most alone,
Pursued my humour not pursuing his,
And gladly shunned who gladly fled from me.

MONTAGUE. Many a morning hath he there been seen,
With tears augmenting the fresh morning's dew,
Adding to clouds more clouds with his deep sighs;
But all so soon as the all-cheering sun
Should in the furthest east begin to draw
The shady curtains from Aurora's bed,
Away from light steals home my heavy son,
And private in his chamber pens himself,
Shuts up his windows, locks fair daylight out,
And makes himself an artificial night:
Black and portentous must this humour prove,
Unless good counsel may the cause remove.

BENVOLIO. My noble uncle, do you know the cause?

MONTAGUE. I neither know it nor can learn of him.
Could we but learn from whence his sorrows grow,
We would as willingly give cure as know.

BENVOLIO. See, where he comes: so please you, step aside;
I'll know his grievance, or be much denied.

BENVOLIO. Good-morrow, cousin.

ROMEO. Is the day so young?

BENVOLIO. But new struck nine.

ROMEO. Ay me! sad hours seem long.
Was that my father that went hence so fast?

BENVOLIO. It was. What sadness lengthens Romeo's hours?

ROMEO. Not having that which, having, makes them short.

BENVOLIO. In love?

ROMEO. Out of her favour where I am in love.

BENVOLIO. Tell me in sadness, who is that you love.

ROMEO. In sadness, cousin, I do love a woman.

BENVOLIO. I aimed so near, when I supposed you loved.

ROMEO. A right good markman! And she's fair I love.

BENVOLIO. A right fair mark, fair coz, is soonest hit.

ROMEO. Well, in that hit you miss: she'll not be hit
With Cupid's arrow; she hath Dian's wit;
And, in strong proof of chastity well armed,

From love's weak childish bow she lives unharmed.
O, she is rich in beauty, only poor
That when she dies with beauty dies her store.
She hath forsworn to love, and in that vow
Do I live dead that live to tell it now.

BENVOLIO. Be ruled by me, forget to think of her.

ROMEO. O, teach me how I should forget to think.

BENVOLIO. By giving liberty unto thine eyes;
Examine other beauties.

ROMEO. Tis the way
To call hers exquisite, in question more:
He that is stricken blind cannot forget
The precious treasure of his eyesight lost.
Farewell: thou canst not teach me to forget.

Scene 2—A Street

CAPULET (*to Paris*). But Montague is bound as well as I,
In penalty alike; and tis not hard, I think,
For men so old as we to keep the peace.

PARIS. Of honourable reckoning are you both;
And pity tis you lived at odds so long.
But now, my lord, what say you to my suit?

CAPULET. But saying o'er what I have said before.
My child is yet a stranger in the world;
She hath not seen the change of fourteen years;
Let two more summers wither in their pride
Ere we may think her ripe to be a bride.

PARIS. Younger than she are happy mothers made.

CAPULET. And too soon marred are those so early made.
The earth hath swallowed all my hopes but she,
She is the hopeful lady of my earth:
But woo her, gentle Paris, get her heart;
My will to her consent is but a part.
This night I hold an old accustomed feast,
Whereto I have invited many a guest,
Such as I love; and you, among the store,
One more, most welcome, makes my number more.
Go, sirrah (*to servant*), trudge about
Through fair Verona; find those persons out
Whose names are written there, and to them say
My house and welcome on their pleasure stay.

SERVANT. Find them out whose names are written here! It is written that the shoemaker should meddle with his yard and the tailor with his last, the fisher with his pencil, and the painter with his nets; but I am sent to find those persons whose names are here writ, and can never find what names the writing person hath here writ. I must to the learned. In good time. (*Enter Benvolio and Romeo, talking*)

BENVOLIO. Tut, man, one fire burns out another's burning,
One pain is lessened by another's anguish;
Turn giddy, and be helped by backward turning;
One desperate grief cures with another's languish:
Take thou some new infection to thy eye,
And the rank poison of the old will die.

SERVANT. I pray, sir, can you read?

ROMEO. Ay, mine own fortune in my misery.

SERVANT. Perhaps you have learned it without book: but, I pray, can you read anything you see?

ROMEO. Ay, if I know the letters and the language.

SERVANT. Ye say honestly: rest you merry!

ROMEO. Stay, fellow; I can read.

He reads out the names

Signior Martino and his wife and daughters; County Anselme and his beauteous sisters; the lady widow of Vitruvio; Signior Placentio and his lovely nieces; Mercutio and his brother Valentine; mine uncle Capulet, his wife, and daughters; my fair niece Rosaline; Livia; Signior Valentio and his cousin Tybalt; Lucio and the lively Helena.

A fair assembly: whither should they come?

SERVANT. To supper; to our house.

ROMEO. Whose house?

SERVANT. My master's. My master is the great rich Capulet, and, if you be not of the house of Montagues, I pray, come and crush a cup of wine. Rest you merry!

BENVOLIO. At this same ancient feast of Capulet's
Sups the fair Rosaline whom thou so lovest,
With all the admired beauties of Verona:
Go thither; and, with unattainted eye,
Compare her face with some that I shall show,
And I will make thee think thy swan a crow.

ROMEO. When the devout religion of mine eye
Maintains such falsehood, then turn tears to fires.
One fairer than my love! The all-seeing sun
Ne'er saw her match since first the world begun.

BENVOLIO. Tut, you saw her fair, none else being by,
Herself poised with herself in either eye:
But in that crystal scales let there be weighed
Your lady's love against some other maid
That I will show you shining at this feast,
And she shall scant show well that now shows best.

ROMEO. I'll go along, no such sight to be shown,
But to rejoice in splendour of mine own.

Scene 3—A Room in Capulet's House

LADY CAPULET. Nurse, where's my daughter? Call her forth to me.

JULIET. Madam, I am here. What is your will?

LADY CAPULET. Nurse, give leave awhile,
We must talk in secret: nurse, come back again;
I have remembered me, thou's hear our counsel.
Thou know'st my daughter's of a pretty age.

NURSE. Faith, I can tell her age unto an hour.

LADY CAPULET. She's not fourteen.

NURSE. I'll lay fourteen of my teeth,
(And yet, to my teen be it spoken, I have but four)
She is not fourteen. How long is it now
To Lammas-tide?

LADY CAPULET. A fortnight and odd days.

NURSE. Even or odd, of all days in the year,
Come Lammas-eve at night shall she be fourteen.
Susan and she (God rest all Christian souls!)
Were of an age: well, Susan is with God;
She was too good for me: but, as I said,
On Lammas-eve at night shall she be fourteen;
That shall she, marry; I remember it well. . . .

LADY CAPULET. Enough of this; I pray thee, hold thy peace.

NURSE. Peace, I have done. God mark thee to his grace!
Thou wast the prettiest babe that e'er I nursed:
An I might live to see thee married once
I have my wish.

LADY CAPULET. Marry, that *marry* is the very theme
I came to talk of. Tell me, daughter Juliet,
How stands your disposition to be married?

JULIET. It is an honour that I dream not of.

LADY CAPULET. Well, think of marriage now.
The valiant Paris seeks you for his love.

NURSE. A man, young lady! lady, such a man
As all the world—why, he's a man of wax.

LADY CAPULET. Verona's summer hath not such a flower.

NURSE. Nay, he's a flower; in faith, a very flower.

LADY CAPULET. What say you? can you love the gentleman?
This night you shall behold him at our feast;
Read o'er the volume of young Paris' face
And find delight writ there with beauty's pen;
Speak briefly, can you like of Paris' love?

JULIET. I'll look to like, if looking liking move:
But no more deep will I endart mine eye
Than your consent gives strength to make it fly.

SERVANT. Madam, the guests are come, supper served up, you called, my young lady asked for, the nurse cursed in the pantry, and everything in extremity. I must hence to wait; I beseech you, follow straight.

LADY CAPULET. We follow thee.

Scene 4—A Street; Romeo on his Way to the Feast

ROMEO. We mean well in going to this mask,
But tis no wit to go.

MERCUTIO. Why, may one ask?

ROMEO. I dreamed a dream tonight.

MERCUTIO. And so did I.

ROMEO. Well, what was yours?

MERCUTIO. That dreamers often lie.

ROMEO. In bed asleep, while they do dream things true.

MERCUTIO. O, then, I see Queen Mab hath been with you.
She is the fairies' midwife, and she comes
In shape no bigger than an agate-stone
On the fore-finger of an alderman,
Drawn with a team of little atomies
Athwart men's noses as they lie asleep;
Her waggon-spokes made of long spinners' legs,
The cover of the wings of grasshoppers,
The traces of the smallest spider's web,
The collars of the moonshine's watery beams,
Her whip of cricket's bone, the lash of film,
Her waggoner a small grey-coated gnat;
Her chariot is an empty hazel-nut
Made by the joiner squirrel or old grub,
Time out o' mind the fairies' coachmakers.
And in this state she gallops night by night
Through lovers' brains, and then they dream of love;
O'er courtiers' knees, that dream on courtsies straight;
O'er lawyers' fingers, who straight dream on fees;
O'er ladies' lips, who straight on kisses dream.
Sometime she gallops o'er a courtier's nose,
And then dreams he of smelling out a suit;
And sometime comes she with a tithe-pig's tail
Tickling a parson's nose as a' lies asleep;
Then dreams he of another benefice.
Sometime she driveth o'er a soldier's neck,
And then dreams he of cutting foreign throats,
Of breaches, ambuscadoes, Spanish blades,
Of healths five-fathom deep; and then anon
Drums in his ear, at which he starts and wakes,

And being thus frighted swears a prayer or two
And sleeps again. This is she—

ROMEO. Peace, peace, Mercutio, peace!
Thou talk'st of nothing.

MERCUTIO. True, I talk of dreams,
Which are the children of an idle brain,
Begot of nothing but vain fantasy,
Which is as thin of substance as the air
And more inconstant than the wind.

BENVOLIO. This wind you talk of blows us from ourselves;
Supper is done, and we shall come too late.

ROMEO. I fear, too early: for my mind misgives
Some consequence yet hanging in the stars
Shall bitterly begin his fearful date
With this night's revels.
But He that hath the steerage of my course
Direct my sail! On, lusty gentlemen.

Scene 5—A Hall in Capulet's House

CAPULET. Welcome, gentlemen! ladies that have their toes
Unplagued with corns will have a bout with you.
Welcome, gentlemen! I have seen the day
That I have worn a visor and could tell
A whispering tale in a fair lady's ear,
Such as would please: tis gone, tis gone, tis gone:
You are welcome, gentlemen! Come, musicians, play.
More light, you knaves; and turn the tables up,
And quench the fire—the room is grown too hot.
Ah, sirrah, this unlooked-for sport comes well.
Nay, sit, nay, sit, good cousin Capulet;
For you and I are past our dancing days.

ROMEO. What lady is that, which doth enrich the hand
Of yonder knight?

SERVANT. I know not, sir.

ROMEO. O, she doth teach the torches to burn bright!
It seems she hangs upon the cheek of night
Like a rich jewel in an Ethiop's ear;
Beauty too rich for use, for earth too dear!
So shows a snowy dove trooping with crows,
As yonder lady o'er her fellows shows.
The measure done, I'll watch her place of stand,
And, touching hers, make blessèd my rude hand.
Did my heart love till now? Forswear it, sight!
For I ne'er saw true beauty till this night.

TYBALT. This, by his voice, should be a Montague.
Fetch me my rapier, boy. What! dares the slave

Come hither, covered with an antic face,
To fleer and scorn at our solemnity ?
Now, by the stock and honour of my kin,
To strike him dead I hold it not a sin.

CAPULET. Why, how now, kinsman ! wherefore storm you so ?

TYBALT. Uncle, this is a Montague, our foe,
A villain that is hither come in spite,
To scorn at our solemnity this night.

CAPULET. Young Romeo is it ?

TYBALT. Tis he, that villain Romeo.

CAPULET. Content thee, gentle coz, let him alone ;
He bears him like a portly gentleman ;
And, to say truth, Verona brags of him
To be a virtuous and well governed youth :
I would not for the wealth of all the town
Here in my house do him disparagement :
Therefore be patient, take no note of him :
It is my will, the which if thou respect,
Show a fair presence and put off these frowns,
An ill-beseeming semblance for a feast.

TYBALT. It fits when such a villain is a guest ;
I'll not endure him.

CAPULET. He shall be endured :
What, goodman boy ! I say, he shall : go to ;
Am I the master here, or you ? Go to.
You'll not endure him ! Go to, go to ;
You are a saucy boy. . . . More light ! For shame !
I'll make you quiet. What, cheerly, my hearts !

TYBALT. I will withdraw ; but this intrusion shall,
Now seeming sweet, convert to bitter gall.

ROMEO (*to Juliet*). If I profane with my unworthiest hand
This holy shrine, the gentle fine is this :
My lips, two blushing pilgrims, ready stand
To smooth that rough touch with a tender kiss.

JULIET. Good pilgrim, you do wrong your hand too much,
Which mannerly devotion shows in this ;
For saints have hands that pilgrims' hands do touch,
And palm to palm is holy palmers' kiss.

ROMEO. Have not saints lips, and holy palmers too ?

JULIET. Ay, pilgrim, lips that they must use in prayer.

ROMEO. O, then, dear saint, let lips do what hands do ;
They pray, grant thou, lest faith turn to despair.

JULIET. Saints do not move, though grant for prayer's sake.

ROMEO. Then move not, while my prayer's effect I take.
Thus from my lips, by yours, my sin is purged.

JULIET. Then have my lips the sin that they have took.

ROMEO. Sin from my lips ? O trespass sweetly urged !
Give me my sin again.

NURSE. Madam, your mother craves a word with you.

ROMEO. What is her mother ?

NURSE. Marry, bachelor,
Her mother is the lady of the house,
And a good lady, and a wise and virtuous :
I nursed her daughter, that you talked withal.

ROMEO. Is she a Capulet ?
O dear account ! my life is my foe's debt.

BENVOLIO. Away, be gone ; the sport is at the best.

ROMEO. Ay, so I fear ; the more is my unrest.

All leave but Juliet and Nurse

JULIET. Come hither, nurse. What is yond gentleman ?

NURSE. The son and heir of old Tiberio.

JULIET. What's he that now is going out of door ?

NURSE. Marry, that, I think, be young Petrucio.

JULIET. What's he that follows there, that would not dance ?

NURSE. His name is Romeo, and a Montague ;
The only son of your great enemy.

JULIET. My only love sprung from my only hate !
Too early seen unknown, and known too late !
Prodigious birth of love it is to me,
That I must love a loathèd enemy.

NURSE. What's this ? what's this ?

JULIET. A rhyme I learned even now
Of one I danced withal.

NURSE. Come, let's away ; the strangers all are gone.

ACT 2

Scene 1—A Lane by the Wall of Capulet's Orchard

ROMEO. Can I go forward when my heart is here ?
Turn back, dull earth, and find thy centre out.

He leaps over the wall, and Benvolio and Mercutio enter

BENVOLIO. Romeo ! my cousin Romeo !

MERCUTIO. He is wise ;
And, on my life, hath stolen him home to bed.

BENVOLIO. He ran this way, and leaped this orchard wall :
Call, good Mercutio.

MERCUTIO. Nay, I'll conjure too.
Romeo ! humours ! madman ! passion ! lover !

Appear thou in the likeness of a sigh,
Speak but one rhyme, and I am satisfied.
He heareth not, he stirreth not, he moveth not;
The ape is dead, and I must conjure him.
I conjure thee by Rosaline's bright eyes,
That in thy likeness thou appear to us!

BENVOLIO. Come, he hath hid himself among these trees,
To be consorted with the humorous night:
Blind is his love and best befits the dark.

MERCUTIO. If love be blind, love cannot hit the mark.
Romeo, Good-night: I'll to my truckle-bed.

BENVOLIO. Go, then; for tis in vain
To seek him here that means not to be found.

Scene 2—Capulet's Orchard

ROMEO. He jests at scars that never felt a wound.
But, soft! what light through yonder window breaks?
It is the east, and Juliet is the sun.
Arise, fair sun, and kill the envious moon.
Who is already sick and pale with grief,
That thou, her maid, art far more fair than she:
Be not her maid, since she is envious;
Her vestal livery is but sick and green
And none but fools do wear it; cast it off.
It is my lady, O, it is my love!
O, that she knew she were!
She speaks, yet she says nothing: what of that?
Her eye discourses; I will answer it.
I am too bold, tis not to me she speaks:
Two of the fairest stars in all the heaven,
Having some business, do entreat her eyes
To twinkle in their spheres till they return.
What if her eyes were there, they in her head?
The brightness of her cheek would shame those stars,
As daylight doth a lamp; her eyes in heaven
Would through the airy region stream so bright
That birds would sing and think it were not night.
See, how she leans her cheek upon her hand!
O, that I were a glove upon that hand,
That I might touch that cheek!

JULIET (*thinking herself alone*). Ay me!

ROMEO. She speaks:
O, speak again, bright angel! for thou art
As glorious to this night, being o'er my head,
As is a wingèd messenger of heaven
Unto the white-upturnèd wondering eyes
Of mortals that fall back to gaze on him

When he bestrides the lazy-pacing clouds
And sails upon the bosom of the air.

JULIET. O Romeo, Romeo! wherefore art thou Romeo?
Deny thy father and refuse thy name;
Or, if thou wilt not, be but sworn my love,
And I'll no longer be a Capulet.

ROMEO (*aside*). Shall I hear more, or shall I speak at this?

JULIET. Tis but thy name that is my enemy;
Thou art thyself, though not a Montague.
What's Montague? It is nor hand, nor foot,
Nor arm, nor face, nor any other part
Belonging to a man. O, be some other name!
What's in a name? That which we call a rose
By any other name would smell as sweet;
So Romeo would, were he not Romeo called,
Retain that dear perfection which he owes
Without that title. Romeo, doff thy name,
And for that name which is no part of thee
Take all myself.

ROMEO. I take thee at thy word:
Call me but love, and I'll be new baptised;
Henceforth I never will be Romeo.

JULIET. What man art thou that, thus bescreened in night,
So stumblest on my counsel?

ROMEO. By a name
I know not how to tell thee who I am:
My name, dear saint, is hateful to myself
Because it is an enemy to thee;
Had I it written, I would tear the word.

JULIET. My ears have not yet drunk a hundred words
Of that tongue's utterance, yet I know the sound:
Art thou not Romeo, and a Montague?

ROMEO. Neither, fair saint, if either thee dislike.

JULIET. How camest thou hither, tell me, and wherefore?
The orchard walls are high and hard to climb,
And the place death, considering who thou art,
If any of my kinsmen find thee here.

ROMEO. With love's light wings did I o'er-perch these walls,
For stony limits cannot hold love out;
And what love can do that dares love attempt:
Therefore thy kinsmen are no let to me.

JULIET. If they do see thee they will murder thee.

ROMEO. Alack, there lies more peril in thine eye
Than twenty of their swords: look thou but sweet,
And I am proof against their enmity.

JULIET. I would not for the world they saw thee here.

ROMEO. I have night's cloak to hide me from their sight;
And but thou love me, let them find me here:
My life were better ended by their hate,
Than death proroguèd, wanting of thy love.

JULIET. By whose direction found'st thou out this place?

ROMEO. By love, who first did prompt me to inquire;
He lent me counsel and I lent him eyes.
I am no pilot; yet, wert thou as far
As that vast shore washed with the farthest sea,
I would adventure for such merchandise.

JULIET. Thou know'st the mask of night is on my face,
Else would a maiden blush bepaint my cheek
For that which thou hast heard me speak tonight.
Fain would I dwell on form, fain, fain deny
What I have spoke. But farewell compliment!
Dost thou love me? I know thou wilt say *Ay*,
And I will take thy word: yet, if thou swear'st,
Thou mayst prove false; at lovers' perjuries,
They say, Jove laughs. O gentle Romeo,
If thou dost love, pronounce it faithfully:
Or if thou think'st I am too quickly won,
I'll frown and be perverse and say thee nay,
So thou wilt woo; but else, not for the world.
In truth, fair Montague, I am too fond,
And therefore thou mayst think my 'haviour light.
But trust me, gentleman, I'll prove more true
Than those that have more cunning to be strange.
I should have been more strange, I must confess,
But that thou overheard'st, ere I was ware,
My true love's passion: therefore pardon me,
And not impute this yielding to light love,
Which the dark night hath so discovered.

ROMEO. Lady, by yonder blessed moon I swear,
That tips with silver all these fruit-tree tops—

JULIET. O, swear not by the moon, the inconstant moon,
That monthly changes in her circled orb,
Lest that thy love prove likewise variable.

ROMEO. What shall I swear by?

JULIET. Do not swear at all;
Or, if thou wilt, swear by thy gracious self,
Which is the god of my idolatry,
And I'll believe thee.

ROMEO. If my heart's dear love—

JULIET. Well, do not swear; although I joy in thee,

I have no joy of this contract tonight:
It is too rash, too unadvised, too sudden;
Too like the lightning, which doth cease to be
Ere one can say *It lightens*. Sweet, Good-night!
This bud of love, by summer's ripening breath,
May prove a beauteous flower when next we meet.
Good-night, Good-night! as sweet repose and rest
Come to thy heart as that within my breast!

ROMEO. O, wilt thou leave me so unsatisfied?

JULIET. What satisfaction canst thou have tonight?

ROMEO. The exchange of thy love's faithful vow for mine.

JULIET. I gave thee mine before thou didst request it:
And yet I would it were to give again.

ROMEO. Wouldst thou withdraw it? For what purpose, love?

JULIET. But to be frank, and give it thee again.
And yet I wish but for the thing I have:
My bounty is as boundless as the sea,
My love as deep; the more I give to thee,
The more I have, for both are infinite.
I hear some noise within; dear love, adieu!
Anon, good nurse! Sweet Montague, be true.
Stay but a little, I will come again.

ROMEO. O blessed, blessed night! I am afeard,
Being in night, all this is but a dream,
Too flattering-sweet to be substantial.

JULIET. Three words, dear Romeo, and Good-night indeed.
If that thy bent of love be honourable,
Thy purpose marriage, send me word tomorrow,
By one that I'll procure to come to thee,
Where and what time thou wilt perform the rite;
And all my fortunes at thy foot I'll lay
And follow thee my lord throughout the world.

NURSE (*within*). Madam!

JULIET. I come, anon (But if thou mean'st not well,
I do beseech thee . . .)

NURSE (*within*). Madam!

JULIET. By and by, I come:
(To cease thy suit, and leave me to my grief:
Tomorrow will I send).

ROMEO. So thrive my soul.

JULIET. A thousand times Good-night! (*Juliet goes*)

ROMEO. A thousand times the worse, to want thy light.
Love goes toward love as schoolboys from their books,
But love from love toward school with heavy looks.

JULIET (*returning*). Hist! Romeo, hist! O, for a falconer's voice,
To lure this tassel-gentle back again!
Bondage is hoarse, and may not speak aloud;
Else would I tear the cave where Echo lies,
And make her airy tongue more hoarse than mine,
With repetition of my Romeo's name.

ROMEO. It is my soul that calls upon my name:
How silver-sweet sound lovers' tongues by night,
Like softest music to attending ears!

JULIET. Romeo!

ROMEO. My dear?

JULIET. At what o'clock tomorrow
Shall I send to thee?

ROMEO. At the hour of nine.

JULIET. I will not fail: tis twenty years till then.
I have forgot why I did call thee back.

ROMEO. Let me stand here till thou remember it.

JULIET. I shall forget, to have thee still stand there,
Remembering how I love thy company.

ROMEO. And I'll still stay, to have thee still forget,
Forgetting any other home but this.

JULIET. 'Tis almost morning; I would have thee gone:
And yet no further than a wanton's bird;
Who lets it hop a little from her hand,
Like a poor prisoner in his twisted gyves,
And with a silk thread plucks it back again,
So loving-jealous of his liberty.

ROMEO. I would I were thy bird.

JULIET. Sweet, so would I:
Yet I should kill thee with much cherishing.
Good-night, Good-night! parting is such sweet sorrow,
That I shall say Good-night till it be morrow.

ROMEO. Sleep dwell upon thine eyes, peace in thy breast!
Would I were sleep and peace, so sweet to rest!
Hence will I to my ghostly father's cell,
His help to crave, and my dear hap to tell.

Scene 3—Friar Laurence's Cell

Enter the friar with a basket for gathering flowers

FRIAR. The grey-eyed morn smiles on the frowning night,
Chequering the eastern clouds with streaks of light,
And fleckèd darkness like a drunkard reels
From forth day's path and Titan's fiery wheels:
Now, ere the sun advance his burning eye,
The day to cheer and night's dank dew to dry,

I must up-fill this osier cage of ours
With baleful weeds and precious-juicèd flowers.
O, mickle is the powerful grace that lies
In herbs, plants, stones, and their true qualities :
For nought so vile that on the earth doth live
But to the earth some special good doth give,
Nor aught so good but strained from that fair use
Revolts from true birth, stumbling on abuse :
Virtue itself turns vice, being misapplied ;
And vice sometimes by action dignified.
Within the infant rind of this small flower
Poison hath residence and medicine power :
For this, being smelt, with that part cheers each part ;
Being tasted, slays all senses with the heart.
Two such opposèd kings encamp them still
In man as well as herbs, grace and rude will ;
And where the worser is predominant,
Full soon the canker death eats up that plant.

ROMEO (*approaching*). Good-morrow, father.

FRIAR. *Benedicite !*
What early tongue so sweet saluteth me ?
Young son, it argues a distempered head
So soon to bid Good-morrow to thy bed :
Care keeps his watch in every old man's eye,
And where care lodges sleep will never lie ;
But where unbruisèd youth with unstuffed brain
Doth couch his limbs, there golden sleep doth reign :
Therefore thy earliness doth me assure
Thou art up-roused by some distemperature ;
Or if not so, then here I hit it right,
Our Romeo hath not been in bed tonight.

ROMEO. That last is true ; the sweeter rest was mine.

FRIAR. God pardon sin ! wast thou with Rosaline ?

ROMEO. With Rosaline, my ghostly father ? no ;
I have forgot that name, and that name's woe.

FRIAR. That's my good son : but where hast thou been, then ?

ROMEO. I'll tell thee, ere thou ask it me again.
I have been feasting with mine enemy,
Where on a sudden one hath wounded me,
That's by me wounded : both our remedies
Within thy help and holy physic lies :
I bear no hatred, blessèd man, for, lo,
My intercession likewise steads my foe.

FRIAR. Be plain, good son, and homely in thy drift ;
Riddling confession finds but riddling shrift.

ROMEO. Then plainly know my heart's dear love is set
On the fair daughter of rich Capulet:
As mine on hers, so hers is set on mine;
And all combined, save what thou must combine
By holy marriage: when and where and how
We met, we wooed, and made exchange of vow,
I'll tell thee as we pass; but this I pray,
That thou consent to marry us today.

FRIAR. Holy Saint Francis, what a change is here!
Is Rosaline, whom thou didst love so dear,
So soon forsaken? Young men's love then lies
Not truly in their hearts, but in their eyes.
The sun not yet thy sighs from heaven clears,
Thy old groans ring yet in my ancient ears;
Lo, here upon thy cheek the stain doth sit
Of an old tear that is not washed off yet:
If e'er thou wast thyself and these woes thine,
Thou and these woes were all for Rosaline:
And art thou changed? Pronounce this sentence then,
Women may fall, when there's no strength in men.

ROMEO. Thou chid'st me oft for loving Rosaline.

FRIAR. For doting, not for loving, pupil mine.

ROMEO. I pray thee, chide not: she whom I love now
Doth grace for grace and love for love allow;
The other did not so.

FRIAR. O, she knew well.
Thy love did read by rote and could not spell.
But come, young waverer, come, go with me,
In one respect I'll thy assistant be;
For this alliance may so happy prove,
To turn your households' rancour to pure love.

ROMEO. O, let us hence; I stand on sudden haste.

FRIAR. Wisely and slow; they stumble that run fast.

Scene 4—A Street

Romeo greets Mercutio and Benvolio, and Nurse approaches with Peter

MERCUTIO. A sail, a sail!

BENVOLIO. Two, two; a shirt and a smock.

NURSE. Peter!

PETER. Anon!

NURSE. My fan, Peter. God ye Good-morrow, gentlemen.

MERCUTIO. God ye Good-den, fair gentlewoman.

NURSE. Gentlemen, can any of you tell me where I may find the young Romeo?

Romeo. I can tell you; but young Romeo will be older when you have found him than he was when you sought him: I am the youngest of that name, for fault of a worse.

Nurse. You say well. If you be he, sir, I desire some confidence with you.

Romeo. I will follow you.

Mercutio. Farewell, ancient lady; farewell, (*singing*) *lady, lady, lady.*

Nurse. Marry, farewell! I pray you, sir, what saucy merchant was this.

Romeo. A gentleman, nurse, that loves to hear himself talk, and will speak more in a minute than he will stand to in a month.

Nurse. An a' speak anything against me I'll take him down, an a' were lustier than he is, and twenty such Jacks; and, if I cannot, I'll find those that shall. And thou must stand by, too, and suffer every knave to use me at his pleasure!

Peter. I saw no man use you at his pleasure; if I had my weapon should quickly have been out, I warrant you: I dare draw as soon as another man if I see occasion in a good quarrel, and the law on my side.

Nurse. Now, afore God, I am so vexed that every part about me quivers. Scurvy knave! Pray you, sir, a word; and as I told you, my young lady bade me inquire you out. What she bade me say I will keep to myself; but first let me tell ye, if ye should lead her into a fool's paradise it were a very gross kind of behaviour, for the gentlewoman is young; and, therefore, if you should deal double with her, truly it were an ill thing to be offered to any gentlewoman, and very weak dealing.

Romeo. Nurse, commend me to thy lady and mistress. I protest unto thee—

Nurse. Good heart, and, i' faith, I will tell her as much: Lord, Lord, she will be a joyful woman.

Romeo. What wilt thou tell her, nurse? Thou dost not mark me.

Nurse. I will tell her, sir, that you do protest; which, as I take it, is a gentlemanlike offer.

Romeo. Bid her devise
Some means to come to shrift this afternoon;
And there she shall, at Friar Laurence' cell,
Be shrived and married.

Nurse. This afternoon, sir? Well, she shall be there.

Romeo. And stay, good nurse, behind the abbey wall:
Within this hour my man shall be with thee,
And bring thee cords made like a tackled stair;
Which to the high top-gallant of my joy

Must be my convoy in the secret night.
Farewell; be trusty, and I'll quit thy pains:
Farewell; commend me to thy mistress.

NURSE. Ay, a thousand times.
Peter, take my fan, and go before, and apace.

Scene 5—Capulet's Orchard

JULIET. The clock struck nine when I did send the nurse;
In half an hour she promised to return.
Perchance she cannot meet him: that's not so.
O, she is lame! Love's heralds should be thoughts,
Which ten times faster glide than the sun's beams,
Driving back shadows over louring hills:
Therefore do nimble-pinioned doves draw love,
And therefore hath the wind-swift Cupid wings.
Now is the sun upon the highmost hill
Of this day's journey, and from nine till twelve
Is three long hours, yet she is not come.
O God! She comes! O honey nurse, what news?
Hast thou met with him? Send thy man away.

NURSE. Peter, stay at the gate.

JULIET. Now, good sweet nurse—O Lord, why look'st thou sad?
Though news be sad, yet tell them merrily;
If good, thou shamest the music of sweet news
By playing it to me with so sour a face.

NURSE. I am a-weary, give me leave awhile:
Fie, how my bones ache! What a jaunt have I had!

JULIET. I would thou hadst my bones, and I thy news.
Nay, come, I pray thee, speak; good, good nurse, speak.

NURSE. Jesu, what haste! Can you not stay awhile?
Do you not see that I am out of breath?

JULIET. How art thou out of breath, when thou hast breath
To say to me that thou art out of breath?
The excuse that thou dost make in this delay
Is longer than the tale thou dost excuse.
Is thy news good, or bad? Answer to that;
Say either, and I'll stay the circumstance.
Let me be satisfied; is't good or bad?

NURSE. Well, you have made a simple choice; you know not how to choose a man. Romeo! no, not he; though his face be better than any man's, yet his leg excels all men's; and for a hand, and a foot, and a body, though they be not to be talked on, yet they are past compare. He is not the flower of courtesy, but, I'll warrant him, as gentle as a lamb. Go thy ways, wench; serve God. What, have you dined at home?

JULIET. No, no: but all this did I know before.
What says he of our marriage? what of that?

NURSE. Lord, how my head aches! what a head have I!
It beats as it would fall in twenty pieces.
My back o' t'other side. O, my back, my back!
Beshrew your heart for sending me about,
To catch my death with jaunting up and down!

JULIET. I' faith, I am sorry that thou art not well.
Sweet, sweet, sweet nurse, tell me, what says my love?

NURSE. Have you got leave to go to shrift today?

JULIET. I have.

NURSE. Then hie you hence to Friar Laurence' cell;
There stays a husband to make you a wife.
Now comes the wanton blood up in your cheeks,
They'll be in scarlet straight at any news.
Hie you to church; I must another way,
To fetch a ladder, by the which your love
Must climb a bird's nest soon when it is dark:
I am the drudge and toil in your delight.
Go; I'll to dinner; hie you to the cell.

JULIET. Hie to high fortune! Honest nurse, farewell.

Scene 6—Friar Laurence's Cell

FRIAR. So smile the heavens upon this holy act,
That after hours with sorrow chide us not!

ROMEO. Amen, amen! but come what sorrow can,
It cannot countervail the exchange of joy
That one short minute gives me in her sight:
Do thou but close our hands with holy words,
Then love-devouring death do what he dare;
It is enough I may but call her mine.

FRIAR. These violent delights have violent ends
And in their triumph die, like fire and powder,
Which as they kiss consume. The sweetest honey
Is loathsome in his own deliciousness,
And in the taste confounds the appetite.
Therefore love moderately; long love doth so:
Too swift arrives as tardy as too slow.
Here comes the lady: O, so light a foot
Will ne'er wear out the everlasting flint.
A lover may bestride the gossamer
That idles in the wanton summer air,
And yet not fall; so light is vanity.

JULIET. Good-even to my ghostly *con*fessor.

FRIAR. Romeo shall thank thee, daughter, for us both.

JULIET. As much to him, else is his thanks too much.

ROMEO. Ah, Juliet, if the measure of thy joy
Be heaped like mine, and that thy skill be more
To blazon it, then sweeten with thy breath
This neighbour air, and let rich music's tongue
Unfold the imagined happiness that doth
Receive in either by this dear encounter.

JULIET. Conceit, more rich in matter than in words,
Brags of his substance, not of ornament:
They are but beggars that can count their worth;
But my true love is grown to such excess
I cannot sum up sum of half my wealth.

FRIAR. Come, come with me, and we will make short work;
For, by your leave, you shall not stay alone
Till holy church incorporate two in one.

ACT 3

Scene 1—A Public Place

BENVOLIO. I pray thee, good Mercutio, let's retire:
The day is hot, the Capulets abroad,
And, if we meet, we shall not scape a brawl;
For now, these hot days, is the mad blood stirring.

MERCUTIO. Come, come, thou art as hot a Jack in thy mood as any in Italy. An there were two such we should have none shortly, for one would kill the other. Thou! why, thou wilt quarrel with a man that hath a hair more or a hair less in his beard than thou hast; thou wilt quarrel with a man for cracking nuts, having no other reason but because thou hast hazel eyes. Thy head is as full of quarrels as an egg is full of meat, and yet thy head hath been beaten as addle as an egg for quarrelling. Thou hast quarrelled with a man for coughing in the street, because he hath wakened thy dog that hath lain asleep in the sun. Didst thou not fall out with a tailor for wearing his new doublet before Easter? with another for tying his new shoes with old riband? And yet thou wilt tutor me from quarrelling!

BENVOLIO. An I were so apt to quarrel as thou art, any man should buy the fee-simple of my life for an hour and a quarter. . . . By my head, here come the Capulets.

MERCUTIO. By my heel, I care not.

TYBALT. Gentlemen, Good-den: a word with one of you.

MERCUTIO. And but one word with one of us? Couple it with something; make it a word and a blow.

TYBALT. You shall find me apt enough to that, sir, an you will give me occasion.

MERCUTIO. Could you not take some occasion without giving?

TYBALT. Mercutio, thou consort'st with Romeo.

BENVOLIO. We talk here in the public haunt of men.
Either withdraw unto some private place,
And reason coldly of your grievances,
Or else depart; here all eyes gaze on us.

MERCUTIO. Men's eyes were made to look, and let them gaze;
I will not budge for no man's pleasure, I. (*Romeo approaches*)

TYBALT. Well, peace be with you, sir: here comes my man.
Romeo, the hate I bear thee can afford
No better term than this: thou art a villain.

ROMEO. Tybalt, the reason that I have to love thee
Doth much excuse the appertaining rage
To such a greeting: villain am I none;
Therefore farewell; I see thou know'st me not.

TYBALT. Boy, this shall not excuse the injuries
That thou hast done me; therefore turn and draw.

ROMEO. I do protest, I never injured thee,
But love thee better than thou canst devise,
Till thou shalt know the reason of my love:
And so, good Capulet (which name I tender
As dearly as my own) be satisfied.

MERCUTIO. O calm, dishonourable, vile submission!
Tybalt, you rat-catcher, will you walk?

TYBALT. What wouldst thou have with me?

MERCUTIO. Good king of cats, nothing but one of your nine lives.

TYBALT. I am for you. (*They fight*)

ROMEO. Gentle Mercutio, put thy rapier up.
Draw, Benvolio; beat down their weapons.
Gentlemen, for shame, forbear this outrage!
Tybalt, Mercutio, the prince expressly hath
Forbidden bandying in Verona streets:
Hold, Tybalt! good Mercutio!

Tybalt stabs Mercutio and disappears

MERCUTIO. I am hurt.
A plague o' both your houses! I am sped.
Is he gone, and hath nothing?

BENVOLIO. What, art thou hurt?

MERCUTIO. Ay, ay, a scratch, a scratch; marry, tis enough.
Where is my page? Go, villain, fetch a surgeon.

ROMEO. Courage, man; the hurt cannot be much.

MERCUTIO. No, tis not so deep as a well, nor so wide as a church door, but tis enough; 'twill serve. Ask for me tomorrow and you shall find me a grave man. I am peppered, I warrant, for this world.

A plague o' both your houses! Zounds, a dog, a rat, a mouse, a cat, to scratch a man to death! a braggart, a rogue, a villain, that fights by the book of arithmetic! Help me into some house, Benvolio, or I shall faint. A plague o' both your houses! They have made worm's meat of me. (*Mercutio and Benvolio go*)

ROMEO. This gentleman, the prince's near ally,
My very friend, hath got his mortal hurt
In my behalf; my reputation stained
With Tybalt's slander—Tybalt, that an hour
Hath been my kinsman! O sweet Juliet,
Thy beauty hath made me effeminate
And in my temper softened valour's steel!

BENVOLIO (*returning*). O Romeo, Romeo, brave Mercutio's dead!
That gallant spirit hath aspired the clouds,
Which too untimely here did scorn the earth.

ROMEO. This day's black fate on more days doth depend:
This but begins the woe others must end.

BENVOLIO. Here comes the furious Tybalt back again.

ROMEO. Alive, in triumph! and Mercutio slain!
Away to heaven, respective lenity,
And fire-eyed fury be my conduct now!
Now, Tybalt, take the *villain* back again
That late thou gavest me; for Mercutio's soul
Is but a little way above our heads,
Staying for thine to keep him company:
Either thou or I, or both, must go with him.

TYBALT. Thou, wretched boy, that didst consort him here,
Shalt with him hence. (*They fight and Tybalt falls*)

BENVOLIO. Romeo, away, be gone!
The citizens are up, and Tybalt slain.
Stand not amazed: the Prince will doom thee death,
If thou art taken: hence, be gone, away!

ROMEO. O, I am fortune's fool!

BENVOLIO. Why dost thou stay?

Romeo flees and the Prince appears, with the Montagues and Capulets

PRINCE. Where are the vile beginners of this fray?

BENVOLIO. O noble Prince, I can discover all
The unlucky manage of this fatal brawl:
There lies the man, slain by young Romeo,
That slew thy kinsman, brave Mercutio.

LADY CAPULET. Tybalt, my cousin! O my brother's child!
O Prince! O cousin! husband! O, the blood is spilt
Of my dear kinsman! Prince, as thou art true,
For blood of ours, shed blood of Montague.

PRINCE. Benvolio, who began this fray?

BENVOLIO. Tybalt, here slain, whom Romeo's hand did slay.
Romeo that spoke him fair, bade him bethink
How nice the quarrel was, and urged withal
Your high displeasure: all this uttered
With gentle breath, calm look, knees humbly bowed,
Could not take truce with the unruly spleen
Of Tybalt deaf to peace.
An envious thrust from Tybalt hit the life
Of stout Mercutio, and then Tybalt fled,
But by and by comes back to Romeo,
Who had but newly entertained revenge,
And to 't they go like lightning, for, ere I
Could draw to part them, was stout Tybalt slain,
And, as he fell, did Romeo turn and fly.
This is the truth, or let Benvolio die.

LADY CAPULET. He is a kinsman to the Montague;
Affection makes him false; he speaks not true.
I beg for justice, which thou, Prince, must give;
Romeo slew Tybalt, Romeo must not live.

PRINCE. Romeo slew him, he slew Mercutio;
Who now the price of his dear blood doth owe?

MONTAGUE. Not Romeo, Prince, he was Mercutio's friend;
His fault concludes but what the law should end,
The life of Tybalt.

PRINCE. And for that offence
Immediately we do exile him hence:
I have an interest in your hate's proceeding,
My blood for your rude brawls doth lie a-bleeding;
But I'll amorce you with so strong a fine
That you shall all repent the loss of mine:
I will be deaf to pleading and excuses;
Nor tears nor prayers shall purchase out abuses:
Therefore use none: let Romeo hence in haste,
Else, when he's found, that hour is his last.
Bear hence this body and attend our will:
Mercy but murders, pardoning those that kill.

Scene 2—Capulet's Orchard; Juliet at the Window

JULIET. Come, night; come, Romeo; come, thou day in night;
For thou wilt lie upon the wings of night
Whiter than new snow on a raven's back.
Come, gentle night, come, loving, black-browed night,
Give me my Romeo; and, when he shall die,
Take him and cut him out in little stars,
And he will make the face of heaven so fine

That all the world will be in love with night
And pay no worship to the garish sun.
O, I have bought the mansion of a love,
But not possessed it; so tedious is this day
As is the night before some festival
To an impatient child that hath new robes
And may not wear them. O, here comes my nurse,
And she brings news; and every tongue that speaks
But Romeo's name speaks heavenly eloquence.
Now, nurse, what news? What hast thou there? the cords
That Romeo bid thee fetch?

NURSE. Ay, ay, the cords.

JULIET. Ay me! what news? why dost thou wring thy hands?

NURSE. Ah, well-a-day! he's dead, he's dead, he's dead!
We are undone, lady, we are undone!
Alack the day! he's gone, he's killed, he's dead!

JULIET. Can heaven be so envious?

NURSE. Romeo can,
Though heaven cannot: O Romeo, Romeo!
Who ever would have thought it? Romeo!

JULIET. What devil art thou, that dost torment me thus?
Hath Romeo slain himself?

NURSE. I saw the wound, I saw it with mine eyes,
(God save the mark!) here on his manly breast:
A piteous corse: I swounded at the sight.

JULIET. O, break, my heart! poor bankrupt, break at once!
To prison, eyes, ne'er look on liberty!
Vile earth, to earth resign; end motion here;
And thou and Romeo press one heavy bier!

NURSE. O Tybalt, Tybalt, the best friend I had!
O courteous Tybalt! honest gentleman!
That ever I should live to see thee dead!

JULIET. What storm is this that blows so contrary?
Is Romeo slaughtered, and is Tybalt dead?
My dear-loved cousin and my dearer lord?
Then, dreadful trumpet, sound the general doom!
For who is living if those two are gone?

NURSE. Tybalt is gone, and Romeo banishèd;
Romeo that killed him, he is banishèd.

JULIET. O God! did Romeo's hand shed Tybalt's blood?

NURSE. It did, it did: alas the day, it did!

JULIET. O serpent heart, hid with a flowering face!
Did ever dragon keep so fair a cave?
Beautiful tyrant! Fiend angelical!

Dove-feathered raven! Wolvish-ravening lamb!
Despisèd substance of divinest show!
Just opposite to what thou justly seem'st!
Was ever book containing such vile matter
So fairly bound? O, that deceit should dwell
In such a gorgeous palace!

NURSE. There's no trust,
No faith, no honesty in men.
These griefs, these woes, these sorrows make me old.
Shame come to Romeo!

JULIET. Blistered be thy tongue
For such a wish! He was not born to shame:
Upon his brow shame is ashamed to sit;
For tis a throne where honour may be crowned
Sole monarch of the universal earth
O, what a beast was I to chide at him!

NURSE. Will you speak well of him that killed your cousin?

JULIET. Shall I speak ill of him that is my husband?
Ah, poor my lord, what tongue shall smooth thy name,
When I, thy three-hours wife, have mangled it?
But, wherefore, villain, didst thou kill my cousin?
That villain cousin would have killed my husband:
Back, foolish tears, back to your native spring;
Your tributary drops belong to woe,
Which you, mistaking, offer up to joy.
My husband lives, that Tybalt would have slain;
And Tybalt's dead, that would have slain my husband:
All this is comfort; wherefore weep I then?
Some word there was, worser than Tybalt's death,
That murdered me: I would forget it fain;
But, O, it presses to my memory,
Tybalt is dead, and Romeo banishèd;
That *banishèd*, that one word *banishèd*,
Hath slain ten thousand Tybalts.
There is no end, no limit, measure, bound,
In that word's death; no words can that woe sound.
Where is my father, and my mother, nurse?

NURSE. Weeping and wailing over Tybalt's corse:
Will you go to them? I will bring you thither.

JULIET. Wash they his wounds with tears: mine shall be spent,
When theirs are dry, for Romeo's banishment.
Take up those cords: poor ropes, you are beguiled,
Both you and I; for Romeo is exiled.

NURSE. Hie to your chamber: I'll find Romeo
To comfort you: I wot well where he is.

Hark ye, your Romeo will be here at night:
I'll to him; he is hid at Laurence' cell.

JULIET. O, find him! Give this ring to my true knight,
And bid him come to take his last farewell.

Scene 3—Friar Laurence's Cell

FRIAR. Romeo, come forth; come forth, thou fearful man:
Affliction is enamoured of thy parts,
And thou art wedded to calamity.

ROMEO. Father, what news? what is the Prince's doom?
What sorrow craves acquaintance at my hand,
That I yet know not?

FRIAR. Too familiar
Is my dear son with such sour company:
I bring thee tidings of the Prince's doom.

ROMEO. What less than Doomsday is the Prince's doom?

FRIAR. A gentler judgment vanished from his lips,
Not body's death, but body's banishment.

ROMEO. Ha, banishment! be merciful, say *death*;
For exile hath more terror in his look,
Much more than death: do not say *banishment.*

FRIAR. Hence from Verona art thou banishèd:
Be patient, for the world is broad and wide.

ROMEO. There is no world without Verona walls,
But purgatory, torture, hell itself.
Hence banishèd is banished from the world,
And world's exile is death: then banishèd,
Is death mis-termed: calling death banishment
Thou cutt'st my head off with a golden axe,
And smil'st upon the stroke that murders me.

FRIAR. O deadly sin! O rude unthankfulness!
Thy fault our law calls death; but the kind Prince,
Taking thy part, hath rushed aside the law,
And turned that black word death to banishment:
This is dear mercy, and thou seest it not.

ROMEO. Tis torture, and not mercy: heaven is here,
Where Juliet lives; and every cat and dog
And little mouse, every unworthy thing,
Live here in heaven and may look on her;
But Romeo may not; he is banishèd.
And say'st thou yet that exile is not death?
Hadst thou no poison mixed, no sharp-ground knife,
No sudden mean of death, though ne'er so mean,
But *banishèd* to kill me?—*banishèd?*
How hast thou the heart,

Being a divine, a ghostly *con*fessor,
A sin-absolver, and my friend professed,
To mangle me with that word *banishèd* ?

FRIAR. Thou fond mad man, hear me but speak a word.

ROMEO. O, thou wilt speak again of banishment.

FRIAR. I'll give thee armour to keep off that word;
Adversity's sweet milk, philosophy,
To comfort thee, though thou art banishèd.

ROMEO. Yet *banishèd* ? Hang up philosophy!
Unless philosophy can make a Juliet,
Displant a town, reverse a prince's doom,
It helps not, it prevails not: talk no more.

FRIAR. O, then I see that madmen have no ears.

ROMEO. How should they, when that wise men have no eyes?

FRIAR. Let me dispute with thee of thy estate.

ROMEO. Thou canst not speak of that thou dost not feel:
Wert thou as young as I, Juliet thy love,
An hour but married, Tybalt murdered,
Doting like me and like me banishèd,
Then mightst thou speak, then mightst thou tear thy hair,
And fall upon the ground, as I do now,
Taking the measure of an unmade grave.

FRIAR. Arise; one knocks; good Romeo, hide thyself.

ROMEO. Not I; unless the breath of heart-sick groans,
Mist-like, infold me from the search of eyes.

FRIAR. Hark, how they knock! Who's there? Romeo, arise;
Run to my study. By and by! God's will,
What simpleness is this! I come, I come!
Who knocks so hard? whence come you? what's your will?

NURSE. Let me come in, and you shall know my errand;
I come from Lady Juliet.

FRIAR. Welcome, then.

NURSE. O holy friar, O, tell me, holy friar,
Where is my lady's lord, where's Romeo?

FRIAR. There on the ground, with his own tears made drunk.

NURSE. O! he is even in my mistress' case,
Just in her case. O woeful sympathy!
Piteous predicament! Even so lies she,
Blubbering and weeping, weeping and blubbering.
Stand up, stand up; stand, an you be a man:

ROMEO. Spak'st thou of Juliet? how is it with her?
Doth she not think me an old murderer,
Now I have stained the childhood of our joy
With blood removed but little from her own?

Where is she ? and how doth she ? and what says
My concealed lady to our cancelled love ?

NURSE. O, she says nothing, sir, but weeps and weeps;
And now falls on her bed ; and then starts up,
And Tybalt calls ; and then on Romeo cries,
And then down falls again.

ROMEO. As if that name,
Shot from the deadly level of a gun,
Did murder her ; as that name's cursèd hand
Murdered her kinsman. O, tell me, friar, tell me,
In what vile part of this anatomy
Doth my name lodge ? Tell me, that I may sack
The hateful mansion.

FRIAR. Hold thy desperate hand :
Art thou a man ? Thy form cries out thou art :
Thy tears are womanish ; thy wild acts denote
The unreasonable fury of a beast :
Unseemly woman in a seeming man !
Or ill-beseeming beast in seeming both !
Thou hast amazed me : by my holy order,
I thought thy disposition better tempered.
Hast thou slain Tybalt ? wilt thou slay thyself ?
Why rail'st thou on thy birth, the heaven, and earth ?
Since birth, and heaven, and earth, all three do meet
In thee at once ; which thou at once wouldst lose.
Fie, fie, thou sham'st thy shape, thy love, thy wit.
Thy noble shape is but a form of wax,
Digressing from the valour of a man ;
Thy dear love sworn but hollow perjury,
Killing that love which thou hast vowed to cherish.
What, rouse thee, man ! Thy Juliet is alive,
For whose dear sake thou wast but lately dead ;
There art thou happy. Tybalt would kill thee,
But thou slew'st Tybalt ; there art thou happy too.
The law that threatened death becomes thy friend
And turns it to exile ; there art thou happy.
A pack of blessings lights upon thy back ;
Happiness courts thee in her best array ;
But, like a misbehaved and sullen wench,
Thou pout'st upon thy fortune and thy love.
Take heed, take heed, for such die miserable.
Go, get thee to thy love, as was decreed,
Ascend her chamber, hence and comfort her :
But look thou stay not till the watch be set,
For then thou canst not pass to Mantua,
Where thou shalt live, till we can find a time

To blaze your marriage, reconcile your friends,
Beg pardon of the Prince, and call thee back
With twenty hundred thousand times more joy
Than thou went'st forth in lamentation.
Go before, nurse: commend me to thy lady;
And bid her hasten all the house to bed,
Which heavy sorrow makes them apt unto:
Romeo is coming.

NURSE. O Lord, I could have stayed here all the night
To hear good counsel: O, what learning is!
My lord, I'll tell my lady you will come.

ROMEO. Do so, and bid my sweet prepare to chide.

NURSE. Here, sir, a ring she bid me give you, sir:
Hie you, make haste, for it grows very late.

ROMEO. How well my comfort is revived by this!

FRIAR. Go hence; Good-night; and here stands all your state:
Either be gone before the watch be set,
Or by the break of day disguised from hence.
Sojourn in Mantua. I'll find out your man,
And he shall signify from time to time
Every good hap to you that chances here.
Give me thy hand; tis late: farewell; Good-night.

ROMEO. But that a joy past joy calls out on me,
It were a grief so brief to part with thee:
Farewell.

Scene 4—In Capulet's House

CAPULET (*to Paris*). Things have fallen out, sir, so unluckily,
That we have had no time to move our daughter.
Look you, she loved her kinsman Tybalt dearly,
And so did I. Well, we were born to die.
Tis very late, she'll not come down tonight.

PARIS. These times of woe afford no time to woo.
Madam, Good-night: commend me to your daughter.

LADY CAPULET. I will, and know her mind early tomorrow.

CAPULET. Sir Paris, I will make a desperate tender
Of my child's love: I think she will be ruled
In all respects by me; nay, more, I doubt it not.
Wife, go you to her ere you go to bed;
Acquaint her here of my son Paris' love;
And bid her, mark you me, on Wednesday next—
But, soft! what day is this?

PARIS. Monday, my lord.

CAPULET. Monday! ha, ha! Well, Wednesday is too soon,
O' Thursday let it be; o' Thursday, tell her,

She shall be married to this noble earl.
Will you be ready ? do you like this haste ?
We'll keep no great ado—a friend or two ;
For, hark you, Tybalt being slain so late,
It may be thought we held him carelessly,
Being our kinsman, if we revel much :
Therefore we'll have some half-a-dozen friends,
And there an end. But what say you to Thursday ?

PARIS. My lord, I would that Thursday were tomorrow

CAPULET. Well, get you gone : o' Thursday be it, then.
Go you to Juliet ere you go to bed,
Prepare her, wife, against this wedding-day.
Farewell, my lord. Light to my chamber, ho !

Scene 5—Juliet's Chamber

Romeo and Juliet on the Balcony

JULIET. Wilt thou be gone ? It is not yet near day :
It was the nightingale, and not the lark,
That pierced the fearful hollow of thine ear ;
Nightly she sings on yon pomegranate-tree :
Believe me, love, it was the nightingale.

ROMEO. It was the lark, the herald of the morn,
No nightingale : look, love, what envious streaks
Do lace the severing clouds in yonder east ;
Night's candles are burnt out, and jocund day
Stands tiptoe on the misty mountain tops.
I must be gone and live, or stay and die.

JULIET. Yon light is not daylight, I know it, I :
It is some meteor that the sun exhales,
To be to thee this night a torchbearer,
And light thee on thy way to Mantua :
Therefore stay yet : thou need'st not to be gone.

ROMEO. Let me be ta'en, let me be put to death ;
I am content, so thou wilt have it so.
I'll say yon grey is not the morning's eye,
Tis but the pale reflex of Cynthia's brow ;
Nor that is not the lark, whose notes do beat
The vaulty heaven so high above our heads :
I have more care to stay than will to go :
Come, death, and welcome ! Juliet wills it so.
How is't, my soul ? let's talk ; it is not day.

JULIET. It is, it is : hie hence, be gone, away !
It is the lark that sings so out of tune,
Straining harsh discords and unpleasing sharps.
O, now be gone ; more light and light it grows.

ROMEO. More light and light ; more dark and dark our woes !

NURSE (*calling*). Your lady mother is coming to your chamber:
The day is broke; be wary, look about.

JULIET. Then, window, let day in, and let life out.

ROMEO. Farewell, farewell! one kiss, and I'll descend.

JULIET. Art thou gone so? love, lord, ay, husband, friend!
I must hear from thee every day in the hour,
For in a minute there are many days:
O, by this count I shall be much in years
Ere I again behold my Romeo!

ROMEO. Farewell!
I will omit no opportunity
That may convey my greetings, love, to thee.

JULIET. O, think'st thou we shall ever meet again?

ROMEO. I doubt it not; and all these woes shall serve
For sweet discourses in our time to come.

JULIET. O God, I have an ill-divining soul!
Methinks I see thee, now thou art below,
As one dead in the bottom of a tomb:
Either my eyesight fails, or thou look'st pale.

ROMEO. And trust me, love, in my eye so do you:
Dry sorrow drinks our blood. Adieu, adieu!

JULIET. O fortune, fortune! all men call thee fickle:
If thou art fickle, what dost thou with him
That is renowned for faith? Be fickle, fortune;
For then, I hope, thou wilt not keep him long,
But send him back.

LADY CAPULET (*calling*). Ho, daughter! are you up?

JULIET. Who is't that calls? is it my lady mother?

LADY CAPULET (*entering*). Why, how now, Juliet!

JULIET. Madam, I am not well.

LADY CAPULET. Evermore weeping for your cousin's death?
What, wilt thou wash him from his grave with tears?
An if thou couldst, thou couldst not make him live;
Therefore, have done: some grief shows much of love;
But much of grief shows still some want of wit.

JULIET. Yet let me weep for such a feeling loss.

LADY CAPULET. Well, girl, thou weep'st not so much for his death,
As that the villain lives which slaughtered him.

JULIET. What villain, madam?

LADY CAPULET. That same villain, Romeo.

JULIET. God pardon him! I do, with all my heart;
And yet no man like he doth grieve my heart.

LADY CAPULET. That is because the traitor murderer lives.

JULIET. Ay, madam, from the reach of these my hands:
Would none but I might venge my cousin's death!

LADY CAPULET. We will have vengeance for it, fear thou not:
Then weep no more. I'll send to one in Mantua,
Where that same banished runagate doth live,
Shall give him such an unaccustomed dram
That he shall soon keep Tybalt company:
And then, I hope, thou wilt be satisfied.

JULIET. Madam, if you could find out but a man
To bear a poison, I would temper it;
That Romeo should, upon receipt thereof,
Soon sleep in quiet.

LADY CAPULET. Find thou the means, and I'll find such a man.
But now I'll tell thee joyful tidings, girl.

JULIET. And joy comes well in such a needy time:
What are they, I beseech your ladyship?

LADY CAPULET. Well, well, thou hast a careful father, child;
One who, to put thee from thy heaviness,
Hath sorted out a sudden day of joy,
That thou expect'st not nor I looked not for.
Marry, my child, early next Thursday morn,
The gallant, young, and noble gentleman,
The County Paris, at Saint Peter's Church,
Shall happily make thee there a joyful bride.

JULIET. Now, by Saint Peter's Church and Peter too,
He shall not make me there a joyful bride.
I wonder at this haste; that I must wed
Ere he, that should be husband, comes to woo.
I pray you, tell my lord and father, madam,
I will not marry yet; and, when I do, I swear,
It shall be Romeo, whom you know I hate,
Rather than Paris. These are news indeed!

LADY CAPULET. Here comes your father; tell him so yourself,
And see how he will take it at your hands.

CAPULET. When the sun sets, the air doth drizzle dew:
But for the sunset of my brother's son
It rains downright.
How now! a conduit, girl? what, still in tears?
Evermore showering? In one little body
Thou counterfeit'st a bark, a sea, a wind;
For still thy eyes, which I may call the sea,
Do ebb and flow with tears. How now, wife!
Have you delivered to her our decree?

LADY CAPULET. Ay, sir; but she will none, she gives you thanks:
I would the fool were married to her grave!

CAPULET. How! will she none? doth she not give us thanks?
Is she not proud? doth she not count her blest,
Unworthy as she is, that we have wrought
So worthy a gentleman to be her bridegroom?

JULIET. Not proud you have, but thankful that you have:
Proud can I never be of what I hate;
But thankful even for hate that is meant love.

CAPULET. How now, how now, chop-logic! What is this?
Proud, and *I thank you*, and *I thank you not*;
And yet *not proud*: mistress, minion you,
Thank me no thankings, nor proud me no prouds,
But fettle your fine joints 'gainst Thursday next,
To go with Paris to Saint Peter's Church,
Or I will drag thee on a hurdle thither.
Out, you green-sickness carrion! Out, you baggage!
You tallow-face!

LADY CAPULET. Fie, fie! What, are you mad?

JULIET. Good father, I beseech you on my knees,
Hear me with patience but to speak a word.

CAPULET. Hang thee, young baggage! disobedient wretch!
I tell thee what: get thee to church o' Thursday,
Or never after look me in the face:
Speak not, reply not, do not answer me;
My fingers itch. Wife, we scarce thought us blest
That God had lent us but this only child;
But now I see this one is one too much,
And that we have a curse in having her.

NURSE. God in heaven bless her!
You are to blame, my lord, to rate her so.

CAPULET. And why, my lady wisdom? Hold your tongue,
Good prudence; smatter with your gossips, go.

NURSE. I speak no treason.

CAPULET. Peace, you mumbling fool!
Utter your gravity o'er a gossip's bowl;
For here we need it not.

LADY CAPULET. You are too hot.

CAPULET. God's bread! it makes me mad:
Day, night, hour, tide, time, work, play,
Alone, in company, still my care hath been
To have her matched: and having now provided
A gentleman of noble parentage,
Of fair demesnes, youthful, and nobly trained,
Proportioned as one's thought would wish a man;
And then to have a wretched puling fool,
A whining mammet, in her fortune's tender,

To answer *I'll not wed; I cannot love,*
I am too young: I pray you, pardon me!
But, an you will not wed, I'll pardon you:
Graze where you will, you shall not house with me:
Look to't, think on't, I do not use to jest.
Thursday is near; lay hand on heart, advise,
An you be mine, I'll give you to my friend;
An you be not, hang, beg, starve, die in the streets,
For, by my soul, I'll ne'er acknowledge thee. (*He goes*)

JULIET. Is there no pity sitting in the clouds,
That sees into the bottom of my grief?
O, sweet my mother, cast me not away!
Delay this marriage for a month, a week;
Or, if you do not, make the bridal bed
In that dim monument where Tybalt lies.

LADY CAPULET. Talk not to me, for I'll not speak a word:
Do as thou wilt, for I have done with thee. (*She goes*)

JULIET. O God! O nurse, how shall this be prevented?
Alack, alack, that heaven should practise stratagems
Upon so soft a subject as myself!
What say'st thou? Hast thou not a word of joy?
Some comfort, nurse.

NURSE. Faith, here it is.
Romeo is banished; and all the world to nothing
That he dares ne'er come back to challenge you;
Or, if he do, it needs must be by stealth.
Then, since the case so stands as now it doth,
I think it best you married with the county.
O, he's a lovely gentleman!
Romeo's a dishclout to him: an eagle, madam,
Hath not so green, so quick, so fair an eye
As Paris hath. Beshrew my very heart,
I think you are happy in this second match,
For it excels your first: or if it did not,
Your first is dead; or 'twere as good he were,
As living here and you no use of him.

JULIET. Speakest thou from thy heart?

NURSE. And from my soul too,
Or else beshrew them both.

JULIET. Well, thou hast comforted me marvellous much.
Go in; and tell my lady I am gone,
Having displeased my father, to Laurence' cell,
To make confession and to be absolved.

NURSE. Marry, I will; and this is wisely done.

JULIET (*alone*). O most wicked fiend!

Is it more sin to wish me thus forsworn,
Or to dispraise my lord with that same tongue
Which she hath praised him with above compare
So many thousand times ? Go, counsellor ;
Thou and my bosom henceforth shall be twain.
I'll to the friar, to know his remedy :
If all else fail, myself have power to die.

ACT 4

Scene 1—Friar Laurence's Cell

FRIAR (*to Paris*). On Thursday, sir ? the time is very short.

PARIS. My father Capulet will have it so ;
And I am nothing slow to slack his haste.

FRIAR. You say you do not know the lady's mind :
Uneven is the course, I like it not.

PARIS. Immoderately she weeps for Tybalt's death,
And therefore have I little talked of love,
For Venus smiles not in a house of tears.
Now, sir, her father counts it dangerous
That she doth give her sorrow so much sway,
And in his wisdom hastes our marriage,
To stop the inundation of her tears ;
Which, too much minded by herself alone,
May be put from her by society.
Now do you know the reason of this haste.

FRIAR (*aside*). I would I knew not why it should be slowed.
Look, sir, here comes the lady towards my cell.

PARIS (*advancing to Juliet*). Happily met, my lady and my wife !

JULIET. That may be, sir, when I may be a wife.

PARIS. That may be must be, love, on Thursday next.

JULIET. What must be shall be.

FRIAR. That's a certain text.

PARIS. Come you to make confession to this father ?

JULIET. To answer that I should confess to you.

PARIS. Do not deny to him that you love me.

JULIET. I will confess to you that I love him.

PARIS. So will ye, I am sure, that you love me.

JULIET. If I do so, it will be of more price
Being spoke behind your back than to your face.

PARIS. Poor soul, thy face is much abused with tears.

JULIET. The tears have got small victory by that,
For it was bad enough before their spite.
Are you at leisure, holy father, now,

Or shall I come to you at evening mass?

FRIAR. My leisure serves me, pensive daughter, now.
My lord, we must entreat the time alone.

PARIS. God shield I should disturb devotion!
Juliet, on Thursday early will I rouse ye:
Till then, adieu; and keep this holy kiss. (*He goes*)

JULIET. O, shut the door! and when thou hast done so,
Come weep with me; past hope, past cure, past help!

FRIAR. Ah, Juliet, I already know thy grief;
It strains me past the compass of my wits:
I hear thou must, and nothing may prorogue it,
On Thursday next be married to this county.

JULIET. Tell me not, friar, that thou hear'st of this,
Unless thou tell me how I may prevent it:
If, in thy wisdom, thou canst give no help,
Do thou but call my resolution wise,
And with this knife I'll help it presently.
God joined my heart and Romeo's, thou our hands;
And ere this hand, by thee to Romeo sealed,
Shall be the label to another deed,
Or my true heart with treacherous revolt
Turn to another, this shall slay them both.
Be not so long to speak; I long to die
If what thou speak'st speak not of remedy.

FRIAR. Hold, daughter: I do spy a kind of hope
Which craves as desperate an execution
As that is desperate which we would prevent.
If, rather than to marry County Paris,
Thou hast the strength of will to slay thyself,
Then is it likely thou wilt undertake
A thing like death to chide away this shame
That copest with death himself to scape from it;
And, if thou darest, I'll give thee remedy.

JULIET. O, bid me leap, rather than marry Paris,
From off the battlements of yonder tower;
Or walk in thievish ways; or bid me lurk
Where serpents are; chain me with roaring bears;
Or shut me nightly in a charnel-house,
O'er-covered quite with dead men's rattling bones;
Or bid me go into a new-made grave
And hide me with a dead man in his shroud:
Things that, to hear them told, have made me tremble;
And I will do it without fear or doubt,
To live an unstained wife to my sweet love.

FRIAR. Hold, then; go home, be merry, give consent

To marry Paris. Wednesday is tomorrow :
Tomorrow night look that thou lie alone ;
Let not thy nurse lie with thee in thy chamber.
Take thou this vial, being then in bed,
And this distillèd liquor drink thou off ;
When presently through all thy veins shall run
A cold and drowsy humour, for no pulse
Shall keep his native progress, but surcease :
No warmth, no breath, shall testify thou livest ;
The roses in thy lips and cheeks shall fade
To paly ashes, thy eyes' windows fall
Like death, when he shuts up the day of life :
Each part, deprived of supple government,
Shall, stiff and stark and cold, appear like death :
And in this borrowed likeness of shrunk death
Thou shalt continue two-and-forty hours,
And then awake as from a pleasant sleep.
Now, when the bridegroom in the morning comes
To rouse thee from thy bed, there art thou dead ;
Then, as the manner of our country is,
In thy best robes uncovered on the bier
Thou shalt be borne to that same ancient vault
Where all the kindred of the Capulets lie.
In the meantime, against thou shalt awake,
Shall Romeo by my letters know our drift,
And hither shall he come : and he and I
Will watch thy waking, and that very night
Shall Romeo bear thee hence to Mantua.
And this shall free thee from this present shame,
If no inconstant toy, nor womanish fear,
Abate thy valour in the acting it.

JULIET. Give me, give me ! O, tell not me of fear !

FRIAR. Hold ; get you gone, be strong and prosperous
In this resolve : I'll send a friar with speed
To Mantua, with my letters to thy lord.

JULIET. Love give me strength ! and strength shall help afford
Farewell, dear father !

Scene 2—In Capulet's House

CAPULET (*to Servant*). So many guests invite as here are writ.
Sirrah, go hire me twenty cunning cooks.
We shall be much unfurnished for this time.
What, is my daughter gone to Friar Laurence ?

NURSE. See where she comes from shrift with merry look.

CAPULET (*advancing to Juliet*). How now, my headstrong ! Where have you been gadding ?

JULIET. Where I have learned me to repent the sin
Of disobedient opposition
To you and your behests, and am enjoined
By holy Laurence to fall prostrate here,
And beg your pardon: pardon, I beseech you!
Henceforward I am ever ruled by you.

CAPULET. Send for the county; go tell him of this:
I'll have this knot knit up tomorrow morning.

JULIET. I met the youthful lord at Laurence' cell;
And gave him what becomèd love I might,
Not stepping o'er the bounds of modesty.

CAPULET. Why, I am glad on't; this is well: stand up:
This is as't should be. Let me see the county;
Ay, marry, go, I say, and fetch him hither.
Now, afore God! this reverend holy friar,
All our whole city is much bound to him.

JULIET. Nurse, will you go with me into my closet,
To help me sort such needful ornaments
As you think fit to furnish me tomorrow?

LADY CAPULET. No, not till Thursday; there is time enough.

CAPULET. Go, nurse, go with her: we'll to church tomorrow.

LADY CAPULET. We shall be short in our provision:
Tis now near night.

CAPULET. Tush, I will stir about,
And all things shall be well, I warrant thee, wife:
Go thou to Juliet, help to deck up her;
I'll not to bed tonight; let me alone;
I'll play the housewife for this once. What, ho!
They are all forth. Well, I will walk myself
To County Paris, to prepare him up
Against tomorrow: my heart is wondrous light,
Since this same wayward girl is so reclaimed.

Scene 3—Juliet's Chamber

JULIET. Ay, those attires are best: but, gentle nurse,
I pray thee, leave me to myself tonight;
For I have need of many orisons
To move the heavens to smile upon my state,
Which, well thou know'st, is cross and full of sin.

LADY CAPULET (*entering*). What, are you busy, ho? need you my help?

JULIET. No, madam; we have culled such necessaries
As are behoveful for our state tomorrow:
So please you, let me now be left alone,
And let the nurse this night sit up with you;

For I am sure you have your hands full all,
In this so sudden business.

LADY CAPULET (*leaving with Nurse*). Good-night:
Get thee to bed and rest, for thou hast need.

JULIET. Farewell! God knows when we shall meet again.
I have a faint cold fear thrills through my veins,
That almost freezes up the heat of life:
I'll call them back again to comfort me:
Nurse! What should she do here?
My dismal scene I needs must act alone.
Come, vial.
What if this mixture do not work at all?
Shall I be married then tomorrow morning?
No, no: this shall forbid it: lie thou there.

She lays down a dagger

What if it be a poison, which the friar
Subtly hath ministered to have me dead,
Lest in this marriage he should be dishonoured,
Because he married me before to Romeo?
I fear it is: and yet, methinks, it should not,
For he hath still been tried a holy man.
How if, when I am laid into the tomb,
I wake before the time that Romeo
Come to redeem me? There's a fearful point!
Shall I not, then, be stifled in the vault,
To whose foul mouth no healthsome air breathes in,
And there die strangled ere my Romeo comes?
Or, if I live, is it not very like
The horrible conceit of death and night,
Together with the terror of the place,
(As in a vault, an ancient receptacle,
Where, for these many hundred years, the bones
Of all my buried ancestors are packed:
Where Tybalt, yet but green in earth,
Lies festering in his shroud; where, as they say,
At some hours in the night spirits resort)
Alack, alack, is it not like that I,
So early waking, what with loathsome smells,
And shrieks like mandrakes' torn out of the earth,
That living mortals, hearing them, run mad:
Oh, if I wake, shall I not be distraught,
Environèd with all these hideous fears,
And madly play with my forefathers' joints,
And pluck the mangled Tybalt from his shroud,
And, in this rage, with some great kinsman's bone,
As with a club, dash out my desperate brains?

O, look! methinks I see my cousin's ghost,
Seeking out Romeo, that did spit his body
Upon a rapier's point: stay, Tybalt, stay!
Romeo, I come! this do I drink to thee.

She falls upon her bed within the curtain

Scene 4—Capulet's House

LADY CAPULET. Hold, take these keys, and fetch more spices, nurse.

NURSE. They call for dates and quinces in the pastry.

CAPULET. Come, stir, stir, stir! the second cock hath crowed,
The curfew-bell hath rung, tis three o'clock:
Look to the baked meats, good Angelica:
Spare not for cost. Now, fellow, what's there?

SERVANT. Things for the cook, sir; but I know not what.

CAPULET. Make haste, make haste. Sirrah, fetch drier logs.
Nurse! Wife! What, ho! What, nurse, I say!
Go waken Juliet, go and trim her up;
I'll go and chat with Paris: hie, make haste.

Scene 5—Juliet's Chamber

NURSE. Mistress! what, mistress! Juliet, fast, I warrant her, she:
Why, lamb! why, lady! fie, you slug-a-bed!
Why, love, I say! madam! sweetheart! why, bride!
What, not a word? God forgive me,
Marry, and amen, how sound is she asleep!
I must needs wake her. Madam, madam, madam!

She draws back the curtain

What, dressed! and in your clothes! and down again!
I must needs wake you: Lady! lady! lady!
Alas, alas! Help, help! my lady's dead!
O, well-a-day, that ever I was born!
Some *aqua vitae*, ho! My lord! my lady!

LADY CAPULET (*approaching*). What noise is here?

NURSE. O lamentable day!

LADY CAPULET. What is the matter?

NURSE. Look, look! O heavy day!

LADY CAPULET. O me, O me! My child, my only life,
Revive, look up, or I will die with thee!
Help, help! Call help. (*Capulet approaches*)

CAPULET. For shame, bring Juliet forth; her lord is come.

NURSE. She's dead, deceased, she's dead; alack the day!

LADY CAPULET. Alack the day, she's dead, she's dead, she's dead!

CAPULET. Ha! let me see her: out, alas! she's cold;
Her blood is settled, and her joints are stiff;

Life and these lips have long been separated :
Death lies on her like an untimely frost
Upon the sweetest flower of all the field.

NURSE. O lamentable day !

LADY CAPULET. O woeful time !

CAPULET. Death, that hath ta'en her hence to make me wail,
Ties up my tongue, and will not let me speak.

Enter Friar Laurence and Paris, with musicians

FRIAR. Come, is the bride ready to go to church ?

CAPULET. Ready to go, but never to return.
O son ! the night before thy wedding-day
Hath Death lain with thy wife. There she lies,
Death is my son-in-law, Death is my heir ;
My daughter he hath wedded : I will die,
And leave him all ; life, living, all is Death's.

PARIS. Have I thought long to see this morning's face,
And doth it give me such a sight as this ?

LADY CAPULET. Accursed, unhappy, wretched, hateful day !
Most miserable hour that e'er Time saw
In lasting labour of his pilgrimage !
But one, poor one, one poor and loving child,
But one thing to rejoice and solace in,
And cruel death hath catched it from my sight !

NURSE. O woe ! O woeful, woeful, woeful day !
Most lamentable day, most woeful day
That ever, ever, I did yet behold !
O day ! O day ! O day ! O hateful day !

PARIS. Beguiled, divorced, wronged, spited, slain !
Most detestable death, by thee beguiled,
By cruel cruel thee quite overthrown !
O love ! O life ! not life, but love in death !

CAPULET. Despised, distressèd, hated, martyred, killed !
Uncomfortable time, why cam'st thou now
To murder, murder our solemnity ?
O child ! O child ! my soul, and not my child !
Dead art thou ! Alack, my child is dead ;
And with my child my joys are burièd.

FRIAR. Peace, ho, for shame ! confusion's cure lives not
In these confusions. Heaven and yourself
Had part in this fair maid ; now heaven hath all,
And all the better is it for the maid :
Your part in her you could not keep from death,
But heaven keeps his part in eternal life.
The most you sought was her promotion ;
For 'twas your heaven she should be advanced :

And weep ye now, seeing she is advanced
Above the clouds, as high as heaven itself?
Dry up your tears, and stick your rosemary
On this fair corse; and, as the custom is,
In all her best array bear her to church:
or though fond nature bids us all lament,
Yet nature's tears are reason's merriment.

CAPULET. All things that we ordainèd festival
Turn from their office to black funeral;
Our instruments to melancholy bells,
Our wedding cheer to a sad burial feast,
Our solemn hymns to sullen dirges change,
Our bridal flowers serve for a buried corse,
And all things change them to the contrary.

FRIAR. Sir, go you in; and, madam, go with him;
And go, Sir Paris; everyone prepare
To follow this fair corse unto her grave:
The heavens do lour upon you for some ill;
Move them no more by crossing their high will.

MUSICIAN. Faith, we may put up our pipes, and be gone.

NURSE. Honest good fellows, ah, put up, put up;
For, well you know, this is a pitiful case.

ACT 5

Scene 1—A Street in Mantua

ROMEO. If I may trust the flattering truth of sleep,
My dreams presage some joyful news at hand:
My bosom's lord sits lightly in his throne;
And all this day an unaccustomed spirit
Lifts me above the ground with cheerful thoughts.
I dreamt my lady came and found me dead
(Strange dream, that gives a dead man leave to think!)
And breathed such life with kisses in my lips,
That I revived, and was an emperor.
Ah me! how sweet is love itself possessed,
When but love's shadows are so rich in joy!

Enter Romeo's servant Balthasar

News from Verona! How now, Balthasar!
Dost thou not bring me letters from the friar?
How doth my lady? Is my father well?
How fares my Juliet? That I ask again;
For nothing can be ill if she be well.

BALTHASAR. Then she is well, and nothing can be ill:
Her body sleeps in Capel's monument,
And her immortal part with angels lives.

I saw her laid low in her kindred's vault,
And presently took post to tell it you:
O, pardon me for bringing these ill news,
Since you did leave it for my office, sir.

ROMEO. Is it even so? then I defy you, stars!
Thou know'st my lodging: get me ink and paper,
And hire post-horses; I will hence tonight.

BALTHASAR. I do beseech you, sir, have patience:
Your looks are pale and wild, and do import
Some misadventure.

ROMEO. Tush, thou art deceived:
Leave me, and do the thing I bid thee do.
Hast thou no letters to me from the friar?

BALTHASAR. No, my good lord.

ROMEO. No matter: get thee gone,
And hire those horses; I'll be with thee straight.
Well, Juliet, I will lie with thee tonight.
Let's see for means: O mischief, thou art swift
To enter in the thoughts of desperate men!
I do remember an apothecary,
And hereabouts he dwells, which late I noted
In tattered weeds, with overwhelming brows,
Culling of simples; meagre were his looks,
Sharp misery had worn him to the bones:
And in his needy shop a tortoise hung,
An alligator stuffed, and other skins
Of ill-shaped fishes; and about his shelves
A beggarly account of empty boxes,
Green earthen pots, bladders and musty seeds,
Remnants of packthread and old cakes of roses,
Were thinly scattered to make up a show.
Noting this penury, to myself I said:
An if a man did need a poison now,
Whose sale is present death in Mantua,
Here lives a caitiff wretch would sell it him.
O, this same thought did but forerun my need;
And this same needy man must sell it me.
As I remember, this should be the house.
What, ho, apothecary!

APOTHECARY. Who calls so loud?

ROMEO. Come hither, man, I see that thou art poor:
Hold, there is forty ducats: let me have
A dram of poison, such soon-speeding gear
As will disperse itself through all the veins
That the life-weary taker may fall dead,
And that the trunk may be discharged of breath

As violently as hasty powder fired
Doth hurry from the fatal cannon's womb.

APOTHECARY. Such mortal drugs I have; but Mantua's law
Is death to any he that utters them.

ROMEO. Art thou so bare and full of wretchedness,
And fear'st to die? Famine is in thy cheeks,
Need and oppression starveth in thine eyes,
Contempt and beggary hang upon thy back;
The world is not thy friend, nor the world's law;
The world affords no law to make thee rich;
Then be not poor, but break it, and take this.

APOTHECARY. My poverty, but not my will, consents.

ROMEO. I pay thy poverty, and not thy will.

APOTHECARY. Put this in any liquid thing you will,
And drink it off; and, if you had the strength
Of twenty men, it would dispatch you straight.

ROMEO. There is thy gold, worse poison to men's souls,
Doing more murders in this loathsome world,
Than these poor compounds that thou mayst not sell.
I sell thee poison; thou hast sold me none.
Farewell: buy food, and get thyself in flesh.
Come, cordial and not poison, go with me
To Juliet's grave; for there must I use thee.

Scene 2—Friar Laurence's Cell

FRIAR JOHN. Holy Franciscan friar! brother, ho!

FRIAR. This same should be the voice of Friar John.
Welcome from Mantua: what says Romeo?
Or, if his mind be writ, give me his letter.

FRIAR JOHN. Going to find a barefoot brother out,
One of our order, to associate me,
Here in this city visiting the sick,
And finding him, the searchers of the town,
Suspecting that we both were in a house
Where the infectious pestilence did reign,
Sealed up the doors, and would not let us forth;
So that my speed to Mantua there was stayed.

FRIAR. Who bare my letter, then, to Romeo?

FRIAR JOHN. I could not send it (here it is again)
Nor get a messenger to bring it thee,
So fearful were they of infection.

FRIAR. Unhappy fortune! by my brotherhood,
The letter was not nice but full of charge
Of dear import, and the neglecting it
May do much danger. Friar John, go hence;

Get me an iron crow, and bring it straight
Unto my cell.

FRIAR JOHN. Brother, I'll go and bring it thee.

FRIAR. Now must I to the monument alone;
Within this three hours will fair Juliet wake:
She will beshrew me much that Romeo
Hath had no notice of these accidents;
But I will write again to Mantua,
And keep her at my cell till Romeo come.
Poor living corse, closed in a dead man's tomb!

Scene 3—The Churchyard at Night

Enter Paris, his Page bearing flowers

PARIS. Give me thy torch, boy: hence, and stand aloof:
Yet put it out, for I would not be seen.
Under yond yew-trees lay thee all along,
Holding thine ear close to the hollow ground;
So shall no foot upon the churchyard tread,
Being loose, unfirm, with digging up of graves,
But thou shalt hear it: whistle then to me,
As signal that thou hear'st something approach.
Give me those flowers. Do as I bid thee, go.
Sweet flower, with flowers thy bridal bed I strew,—
O woe! thy canopy is dust and stones,—
Which with sweet water nightly I will dew,
Or, wanting that, with tears distilled by moans:
The obsequies that I for thee will keep
Nightly shall be to strew thy grave and weep. (*A whistle*)
The boy gives warning something doth approach.
What cursèd foot wanders this way tonight,
To cross my obsequies and true love's rite?
What, with a torch! muffle me, night, awhile.

Enter Romeo and Balthasar, with a torch and tools

ROMEO. Give me that mattock and the wrenching iron.
Hold, take this letter; early in the morning
See thou deliver it to my lord and father.
Give me the light: upon thy life, I charge thee,
Whate'er thou hear'st or seest, stand all aloof,
And do not interrupt me in my course.
Why I descend into this bed of death,
Is partly to behold my lady's face;
But chiefly to take thence from her dead finger
A precious ring, a ring that I must use
In dear employment: therefore hence, be gone:
But if thou, jealous, dost return to pry
In what I further shall intend to do,

By heaven, I will tear thee joint by joint
And strew this hungry churchyard with thy limbs.
The time and my intents are savage-wild,
More fierce and more inexorable far
Than empty tigers or the roaring sea.

BALTHASAR. I will be gone, sir, and not trouble you.

ROMEO. So shalt thou show me friendship. Take thou that:
Live, and be prosperous: and farewell, good fellow.

BALTHASAR (*aside*). For all this same, I'll hide me hereabout:
His looks I fear, and his intents I doubt.

ROMEO. Thou detestable maw, thou womb of death,
Gorged with the dearest morsel of the earth,
Thus I enforce thy rotten jaws to open,
And, in despite, I'll cram thee with more food!

Romeo forces open the tomb

PARIS. This is that banished haughty Montague
That murdered my love's cousin, with which grief
It is supposèd the fair creature died;
And here is come to do some villainous shame
To the dead bodies: I will apprehend him.
Stop thy unhallowed toil, vile Montague!
Can vengeance be pursued further than death?
Condemnèd villain, I do apprehend thee:
Obey, and go with me; for thou must die.

ROMEO. I must indeed; and therefore came I hither.
Good gentle youth, tempt not a desperate man;
Fly hence, and leave me: think upon these gone;
Let them affright thee. I beseech thee, youth,
Put not another sin upon my head
By urging me to fury: O, begone!
By heaven, I love thee better than myself;
For I come hither armed against myself:
Stay not, be gone; live, and hereafter say
A madman's mercy bade thee run away.

PARIS. I do defy thy conjurations,
And apprehend thee for a felon here.

ROMEO. Wilt thou provoke me? then have at thee, boy!

PAGE. O Lord, they fight! I will go call the watch.

PARIS (*dying*). O, I am slain! If thou be merciful,
Open the tomb, lay me with Juliet.

ROMEO. In faith, I will. Let me peruse this face.
Mercutio's kinsman, noble County Paris!
What said my man, when my betossèd soul
Did not attend him as we rode? I think
He told me Paris should have married Juliet:

Said he not so? or did I dream it so?
Or am I mad, hearing him talk of Juliet,
To think it was so? O, give me thy hand,
One writ with me in sour misfortune's book!
I'll bury thee in a triumphant grave;
A grave? O, no! a lantern, slaughtered youth,
For here lies Juliet, and her beauty makes
This vault a feasting presence full of light.
Death, lie thou there, by a dead man interred.
How oft when men are at the point of death
Have they been merry! which their keepers call
A lightning before death: O, how may I
Call this a lightning? O my love! my wife!
Death, that hath sucked the honey of thy breath,
Hath had no power yet upon thy beauty:
Thou art not conquered; beauty's ensign yet
Is crimson in thy lips and in thy cheeks,
And death's pale flag is not advancèd there.
Tybalt, liest thou there?
O, what more favour can I do to thee
Than with that hand that cut thy youth in twain
To sunder his that was thine enemy?
Forgive me, cousin! Ah, dear Juliet,
Why art thou yet so fair? I still will stay with thee;
And never from this palace of dim night
Depart again: here, here will I remain
With worms that are thy chamber-maids; O, here
Will I set up my everlasting rest,
And shake the yoke of inauspicious stars
From this world-wearied flesh. Eyes, look your last!
Arms, take your last embrace, and, lips, O you,
The doors of breath, seal with a righteous kiss
A dateless bargain to engrossing death!
Come, bitter conduct, come, unsavoury guide!
Thou desperate pilot, now at once run on
The dashing rocks thy sea-sick weary bark!
Here's to my love! O true apothecary!
Thy drugs are quick. Thus with a kiss I die.

As Romeo dies, the Friar enters with a lantern, crow, and spade

FRIAR. Saint Francis be my speed! how oft tonight
Have my old feet stumbled at graves! Who's there?

BALTHASAR. Here's one, a friend, and one that knows you well.

FRIAR. Bliss be upon you! Tell me, good my friend,
What torch is yond, that vainly lends his light
To grubs and eyeless skulls? As I discern,
It burneth in the Capel's monument.

BALTHASAR. It doth so, holy sir; and there's my master,
One that you love.

FRIAR. How long hath he been there?

BALTHASAR. Full half an hour.

FRIAR. Go with me to the vault.

BALTHASAR. I dare not, sir:
My master knows not but I am gone hence
And fearfully did menace me with death,
If I did stay to look on his intents.

FRIAR. Stay, then; I'll go alone. Fear comes upon me:
O, much I fear some ill unlucky thing.

BALTHASAR. As I did sleep under this yew-tree here,
I dreamt my master and another fought,
And that my master slew him.

FRIAR. Romeo!
Alack, alack, what blood is this, which stains
The stony entrance of this sepulchre?
Romeo! O, pale! Who else? What, Paris too?
And steeped in blood? Ah, what an unkind hour
Is guilty of this lamentable chance!
The lady stirs.

JULIET (*waking*). O comfortable friar! where is my lord?
I do remember well where I should be,
And there I am. Where is my Romeo?

FRIAR. I hear some noise. Lady, come from that nest
Of death, contagion, and unnatural sleep:
A greater power than we can contradict
Hath thwarted our intents. Come, come away.
Thy husband in thy bosom there lies dead;
And Paris too. Come, I'll dispose of thee
Among a sisterhood of holy nuns:
Stay not to question, for the watch is coming;
Come, go, good Juliet, I dare no longer stay.

JULIET. Go, get thee hence, for I will not away.
What's here? A cup, closed in my true love's hand?
Poison, I see, hath been his timeless end:
O churl! drunk all, and left no friendly drop
To help me after? I will kiss thy lips;
Haply some poison yet doth hang on them,
To make me die with a restorative.
Thy lips are warm.

FIRST WATCH (*within*). Lead, boy: which way?

JULIET. Yea, noise? then I'll be brief. O happy dagger!
This is thy sheath; there rust, and let me die.

As Juliet kills herself, the Watch enters with the Page of Paris

PAGE. This is the place ; there, where the torch doth burn.

FIRST WATCH. Go, some of you, whoe'er you find attach.
Pitiful sight ! here lies the county slain ;
And Juliet bleeding, warm, and newly dead,
Who here hath lain these two days buriѐd.
Go, tell the Prince ; run to the Capulets ;
Raise up the Montagues ; some others search.

Some of the Watch return, with Balthasar

SECOND WATCH. Here's Romeo's man ; we found him in the churchyard.

FIRST WATCH. Hold him in safety, till the Prince come hither.

THIRD WATCH. Here is a friar, that trembles, sighs, and weeps :
We took this mattock and this spade from him,
As he was coming from this churchyard side.

FIRST WATCH. A great suspicion ; stay the friar, too.

PRINCE (*approaching suddenly*). What misadventure is so early up
That calls our person from our morning's rest ?

CAPULET. What should it be, that they so shriek abroad ?

LADY CAPULET. The people in the street cry *Romeo*,
Some *Juliet*, and some *Paris* ; and all run,
With open outcry, toward our monument.

PRINCE. What fear is this which startles in our ears ?

FIRST WATCH. Sovereign, here lies the County Paris slain ;
And Romeo dead ; and Juliet, dead before,
Warm, and new killed.

PRINCE. Search, seek, and know how this foul murder comes.

FIRST WATCH. Here is a friar, and slaughtered Romeo's man ;
With instruments upon them, fit to open
These dead men's tombs.

CAPULET. O heavens ! O wife, look how our daughter bleeds !

LADY CAPULET. O me ! this sight of death is as a bell
That warns my old age to a sepulchre. (*Here Montague comes*)

PRINCE. Come, Montague ; for thou art early up,
To see thy son and heir more early down.

MONTAGUE. Alas, my liege, my wife is dead tonight ;
Grief of my son's exile hath stopped her breath :
What further woe conspires against mine age ?

PRINCE. Look, and thou shalt see.

MONTAGUE. O thou untaught ! what manners is in this,
To press before thy father to a grave ?

PRINCE. Seal up the mouth of outrage for a while,
Till we can clear these ambiguities,
And know their spring, their head, their true descent ;

And then will I be general of your woes,
And lead you even to death: meantime forbear,
And let mischance be slave to patience.
Bring forth the parties of suspicion.

FRIAR. I am the greatest, able to do least,
Yet most suspected, as the time and place
Doth make against me, of this direful murder;
And here I stand, both to impeach and purge
Myself condemnèd and myself excused.

PRINCE. Then say at once what thou dost know in this.

FRIAR. I will be brief, for my short date of breath
Is not so long as is a tedious tale.
Romeo, there dead, was husband to that Juliet;
And she, there dead, that Romeo's faithful wife.
I married them; and their stolen marriage-day
Was Tybalt's doomsday, whose untimely death
Banished the new-made bridegroom from this city,
For whom, and not for Tybalt, Juliet pined.
You, to remove that siege of grief from her,
Betrothed and would have married her perforce
To County Paris: then comes she to me
And, with wild looks, bids me devise some mean
To rid her from this second marriage,
Or in my cell there would she kill herself.
Then gave I her, so tutored by my art,
A sleeping potion, which so took effect
As I intended, for it wrought on her
The form of death: meantime I writ to Romeo,
That he should hither come as this dire night,
To help to take her from her borrowed grave,
Being the time the potion's force should cease.
But he which bore my letter, Friar John,
Was stayed by accident, and yesternight
Returned my letter back. Then, all alone,
At the prefixèd hour of her waking,
Came I to take her from her kindred's vault;
Meaning to keep her closely at my cell
Till I conveniently could send to Romeo;
But when I came, some minute ere the time
Of her awaking, here untimely lay
The noble Paris and true Romeo dead.
She wakes; and I entreated her come forth,
And bear this work of heaven with patience:
But then a noise did scare me from the tomb;
And she, too desperate, would not go with me,
But, as it seems, did violence on herself.

All this I know; and to the marriage
Her nurse is privy: and, if aught in this
Miscarried by my fault, let my old life
Be sacrificed, some hour before his time,
Unto the rigour of severest law.

PRINCE. We still have known thee for a holy man.
Where's Romeo's man? What can he say in this?

BALTHASAR. I brought my master news of Juliet's death;
And then in post he came from Mantua.
This letter he early bid me give his father,
And threatened me with death, going in the vault,
If I departed not and left him there.

PRINCE. Give me the letter; I will look on it.
Where is the county's page that raised the watch?
Sirrah, what made your master in this place?

PAGE. He came with flowers to strew his lady's grave;
And bid me stand aloof, and so I did.
Anon comes one with light to ope the tomb;
And by and by my master drew on him;
And then I ran away to call the watch.

PRINCE. This letter doth make good the friar's words,
Their course of love, the tidings of her death:
And here he writes that he did buy a poison
Of a poor 'pothecary, and therewithal
Came to this vault to die, and lie with Juliet.
Where be these enemies? Capulet! Montague!
See, what a scourge is laid upon your hate,
That heaven finds means to kill your joys with love.
And I for winking at your discords too
Have lost a brace of kinsmen: all are punished.

CAPULET. O brother Montague, give me thy hand:
This is my daughter's jointure, for no more
Can I demand.

MONTAGUE. But I can give thee more,
For I will raise her statue in pure gold,
That, while Verona by that name is known,
There shall no figure at such rate be set
As that of true and faithful Juliet.

CAPULET. As rich shall Romeo's by his lady's lie;
Poor sacrifices of our enmity!

PRINCE. A glooming peace this morning with it brings;
The sun for sorrow will not show his head:
Go hence, to have more talk of these sad things;
Some shall be pardoned and some punishèd:
For never was a story of more woe
Than this of Juliet and her Romeo.

The Story of Julius Caesar

HERE Shakespeare sets the foremost man in all the world in the centre of his stage. He has made Julius Caesar the hero of the Roman Empire for all time.

HE wrote this play when his genius was at its height. He was not yet forty. His materials were ready for him in Plutarch's Lives; but, though he followed them closely, he shaped his course with splendid originality, and set a new standard for historic tragedy.

IT is a man's play; only two women come into it, and these two but to show a wifely anxiety for husbands oppressed by public cares. It is all on the level of heroic history, depending on the sternest motives that come into the working of men's minds. It raises the murder of Caesar to the height of a great event.

WE may doubt if Julius Caesar was the central figure in the mind of Shakespeare as he wrote this play. He gives the play its name, and his power over men's minds is felt throughout, but if we knew nothing of Caesar except from this play it would not seem to us that he was what Brutus called him, the foremost man in all this world. He does not appear as a man of strength; he seems to us a sort of demi-god by virtue of his rank rather than his character. We may think Shakespeare does him some injustice when we remember how splendid Caesar was, but the truth is probably that Shakespeare rendered Caesar less than justice in order to raise to a high plane the man who most appealed to him, Marcus Brutus, Caesar's friend.

WHAT a figure he is, this great and splendid Brutus, allowing himself to become the tool of baser men about him! Honest, patriotic, public-spirited, free from all selfishness, noble in heart and mind, tender and considerate, loving Caesar and loving Rome, he believed all men like himself. He could allow himself to believe that small men, moved by petty jealousy, were men of equal honesty with Brutus, acting for the good of Rome. He could allow himself to be drawn into a crime his nature loathed. A tragedy indeed is this, but the tragedy of Brutus more than Caesar.

OF all the conspirators, only he was truly honourable, and his virtues could not save him. Caesar's friend Mark Antony was more than a match for the bluff sincerity of Brutus, the craft of Cassius, and the bitter hate of Casca. Is not Mark Antony's speech perhaps the cleverest thing in Shakespeare? It is noble and tender and eloquent, but it is cunning, and it does its work: it wins over the fickle Roman crowd from the side of the conspirators. There is no authority in Plutarch for this; it is Shakespeare's own invention.

A GREAT array of vivid characters moves across this stage, and the play brings us to the triumph of Octavius, the Augustus who ordered the census to be taken in Bethlehem when Christ was born. But, of all these characters, Brutus only sets himself firmly in our hearts. He was the noblest Roman of them all.

THE PLAYERS

Julius Caesar, ruler of Rome, whom some would crown as Emperor, but whose greatness is resented and feared by others.

Brutus, an honest Republican patriot, who objects to one-man rule, and whose support is eagerly sought by the conspirators, all less noble than he.

Cassius, a clever plotting friend of Brutus, who persuades him to join in a conspiracy.

Casca, Trebonius, and Ligarius, conspirators.

Cinna, Decius Brutus, and Metellus Cimber, conspirators.

Mark Antony, a friend of Caesar, who after his death shares the rule with Octavius and Lepidus. He raises Rome against Caesar's murderers.

Octavius, a young man whom Caesar chose as his successor. He becomes (but not in the play) first Roman Emperor, Augustus. It was he who ordered the counting of the people at the time when Jesus was born in Bethlehem.

Flavius and Marullus, tribunes unfriendly to Caesar, seeking to check public admiration of him.

Cicero, a senator who is kept out of the conspiracy; showing a mind above the superstitions of the day.

Artemidorus, friendly to Caesar, seeking in vain to warn him.

Publius and Popilius, onlooking senators.

Lepidus, a triumvir (one of three united rulers) with Octavius and Antony, after Caesar's death.

Calpurnia, wife of Julius Caesar.

Portia, wife of Brutus.

Lucilius, Titinius, and Messala, friends of the conspirators.

Young Cato and Volumnius, friends of Brutus and Cassius.

Varro, Clitus, and Claudius, servants of Brutus.

Strato and Dardanius, servants of Brutus.

Lucius, the young page of Brutus.

Pindarus, servant of Cassius.

A soothsayer.

Citizens, guards, and attendants.

Scenes—In Rome; near Sardis; and near Philippi.

Julius Caesar

ACT 1

Scene 1—A Street in Rome

FLAVIUS. Hence ! home, you idle creatures, get you home :
Is this a holiday ? What ! know you not,
Being mechanical, you ought not walk
Upon a labouring day without the sign
Of your profession ? Speak, what trade art thou ?

COMMONER. Why, sir, a carpenter.

MARULLUS. Where is thy leather apron and thy rule ?
What dost thou with thy best apparel on ?
You, sir, what trade are you ?

ANOTHER COMMONER. A trade, sir, that I hope I may use with a safe conscience ; which is indeed, sir, a mender of bad soles. If you be out, sir, I can mend you.

MARULLUS. What meanest thou—mend me, thou saucy fellow ?

COMMONER. Why, sir, cobble you.

FLAVIUS. Thou art a cobbler, art thou ?

COMMONER. Truly, sir, all that I live by is with the awl : I meddle with no tradesman's matters, nor women's matters, but with awl. I am, indeed, sir, a surgeon to old shoes ; when they are in great danger I recover them. As proper men as ever trod upon neat's leather have gone upon my handiwork.

FLAVIUS. But wherefore art not in thy shop today ?
Why dost thou lead these men about the streets ?

COMMONER. Truly, sir, to wear out their shoes, to get myself into more work. But, indeed, sir, we make holiday to see Caesar, and to rejoice in his triumph.

MARULLUS. Wherefore rejoice ? What conquest brings he home ?
What tributaries follow him to Rome
To grace in captive bonds his chariot wheels ?
You blocks, you stones, you worse than senseless things !
O you hard hearts, you cruel men of Rome,
Knew you not Pompey ? Many a time and oft
Have you climbed up to walls and battlements,
To towers and windows, yea, to chimney-tops,
Your infants in your arms, and there have sat

The live-long day, with patient expectation,
To see great Pompey pass the streets of Rome;
And when you saw his chariot but appear,
Have you not made a universal shout,
That Tiber trembled underneath her banks?
And do you now put on your best attire?
And do you now cull out a holiday?
And do you now strew flowers in his way
That comes in triumph over Pompey's blood?
Be gone! Run to your houses, fall upon your knees,
Pray to the gods to intermit the plague
That needs must light on this ingratitude.

FLAVIUS. Go, go, good countrymen, and, for this fault,
Assemble all the poor men of your sort;
Draw them to Tiber banks, and weep your tears
Into the channel, till the lowest stream
Do kiss the most exalted shores of all.

All the Commoners go

See, whether their basest metal be not moved;
They vanish tongue-tied in their guiltiness.
Go you down that way towards the Capitol;
This way will I; let no images
Be hung with Caesar's trophies. I'll about,
And drive away the vulgar from the streets:
So do you too, where you perceive them thick.
These growing feathers plucked from Caesar's wing
Will make him fly an ordinary pitch,
Who else would soar above the view of men
And keep us all in servile fearfulness.

Scene 2—A Public Place

Enter Caesar and Senators, a crowd following

SOOTHSAYER. Caesar!

CAESAR. Ha! who calls?

CASCA. Bid every noise be still: peace yet again!

CAESAR. Who is it in the press that calls on me?
I hear a tongue, shriller than all the music,
Cry *Caesar*! Speak; Caesar is turned to hear.

SOOTHSAYER. Beware the ides of March.

CAESAR. What man is that?

BRUTUS. A soothsayer bids you beware the ides of March.

CAESAR. Set him before me; let me see his face.

CASSIUS. Fellow, come from the throng; look upon Caesar.

CAESAR. What say'st thou to me now? Speak once again.

SOOTHSAYER. Beware the ides of March.

CAESAR. He is a dreamer; let us leave him: pass.

CASSIUS (*staying behind*). Brutus, I do observe you now of late:
I have not from your eyes that gentleness
And show of love as I was wont to have:
You bear too stubborn and too strange a hand
Over your friend that loves you.

BRUTUS. Cassius,
Be not deceived: if I have veiled my look,
I turn the trouble of my countenance
Merely upon myself. Vexed I am
Of late with passions of some difference;
But let not therefore my good friends be grieved,
Nor construe any further my neglect,
Than that poor Brutus, with himself at war,
Forgets the shows of love to other men.

CASSIUS. Then, Brutus, I have much mistook your passion:
By means whereof this breast of mine hath buried
Thoughts of great value. I have heard,
Where many of the best respect in Rome,
Except immortal Caesar, speaking of Brutus
And groaning underneath this age's yoke,
Have wished that noble Brutus had his eyes.

BRUTUS. Into what dangers would you lead me, Cassius,
That you would have me seek into myself
For that which is not in me?

CASSIUS. Therefore, good Brutus, be prepared to hear.

BRUTUS. What means this shouting? I do fear the people
Choose Caesar for their king.

CASSIUS. Ay, do you fear it?
Then must I think you would not have it so.

BRUTUS. I would not, Cassius; yet I love him well.
But wherefore do you hold me here so long?
What is it that you would impart to me?
If it be aught toward the general good,
Set honour in one eye and death i' the other,
And I will look on both indifferently,
For let the gods so speed me as I love
The name of honour more than I fear death.

CASSIUS. I know that virtue to be in you, Brutus,
As well as I do know your outward favour.
Well, honour is the subject of my story.
I cannot tell what you and other men
Think of this life; but, for my single self,
I had as lief not be as live to be
In awe of such as thing as I myself.
I was born free as Caesar; so were you:
We both have fed as well, and we can both

Endure the winter's cold as well as he:
For once, upon a raw and gusty day,
The troubled Tiber chafing with her shores,
Caesar said to me *Darest thou, Cassius, now*
Leap in with me into this angry flood,
And swim to yonder point? Upon the word,
Accoutred as I was, I plungèd in
And bade him follow; so indeed he did.
But ere we could arrive the point proposed,
Caesar cried *Help me, Cassius, or I sink!*
This man is now become a god, and Cassius is
A wretched creature, and must bend his body
If Caesar carelessly but nod on him.
He had a fever when he was in Spain,
And when the fit was on him I did mark
How he did shake: tis true, this god did shake!
Ay, and that tongue of his that bade the Romans
Mark him and write his speeches in their books,
Alas, it cried *Give me some drink, Titinius,*
As a sick girl. Ye gods, it doth amaze me
A man of such a feeble temper should
So get the start of the majestic world
And bear the palm alone.

BRUTUS. Another general shout!
I do believe that these applauses are
For some new honours that are heaped on Caesar.

CASSIUS. Why, man, he doth bestride the narrow world
Like a Colossus, and we petty men
Walk under his huge legs and peep about
To find ourselves dishonourable graves.
Men at some time are masters of their fates:
The fault, dear Brutus, is not in our stars,
But in ourselves, that we are underlings.
Brutus and Caesar: what should be in that *Caesar*?
Why should that name be sounded more than yours?
Write them together, yours is as fair a name;
Sound them, it doth become the mouth as well;
Weigh them, it is as heavy; conjure with 'em,
Brutus will start a spirit as soon as Caesar.
Now, in the names of all the gods at once,
Upon what meat doth this our Caesar feed
That he is grown so great? Age, thou art shamed!
Rome, thou hast lost the breed of noble bloods!
When went there by an age, since the Great Flood,
But it was famed with more than with one man?
When could they say till now, that talked of Rome,
That her wide walls encompassed but one man?

O, you and I have heard our fathers say,
There was a Brutus once that would have brooked
The eternal devil to keep his state in Rome
As easily as a king.

BRUTUS. That you do love me, I am nothing jealous
What you would work me to, I have some aim;
How I have thought of this and of these times,
I shall recount hereafter; for this present,
I would not, so with love I might entreat you,
Be any further moved. What you have said
I will consider; what you have to say
I will with patience hear, and find a time
Both meet to hear and answer such high things.
Brutus had rather be a villager
Than to repute himself a son of Rome
Under these hard conditions as this time
Is like to lay upon us.

CASSIUS. I am glad that my weak words
Have struck but thus much show of fire from Brutus.

BRUTUS. The games are done and Caesar is returning.

CASSIUS. As they pass by, pluck Casca by the sleeve.

BRUTUS. I will do so. But, look you, Cassius,
The angry spot doth glow on Caesar's brow,
And all the rest look like a chidden train:
Calpurnia's cheek is pale; and Cicero
Looks with such ferret and such fiery eyes
As we have seen him in the Capitol,
Being crossed in conference by some senators.

CASSIUS. Casca will tell us what the matter is.

CAESAR (*passing by*). Antonius!

ANTONY. Caesar!

CAESAR. Let me have men about me that are fat:
Sleek-headed men and such as sleep o' nights:
Yond Cassius has a lean and hungry look;
He thinks too much: such men are dangerous.

ANTONY. Fear him not, Caesar; he's not dangerous;
He is a noble Roman and well given.

CAESAR. Would he were fatter! But I fear him not:
Yet, if my name were liable to fear,
I do not know the man I should avoid
So soon as that spare Cassius. He reads much;
He is a great observer, and he looks
Quite through the deeds of men; he loves no plays,
As thou dost, Antony; he hears no music;
Seldom he smiles, and smiles in such a sort
As if he mocked himself and scorned his spirit

That could be moved to smile at anything.
Such men as he be never at heart's ease
Whiles they behold a greater than themselves,
And therefore are they very dangerous.
I rather tell thee what is to be feared
Than what I fear.

Caesar passes on, and Brutus approaches Casca

CASCA. You pulled me by the cloak; would you speak with me?

BRUTUS. Ay, Casca; tell us what hath chanced today,
That Caesar looks so sad.

CASCA. Why, there was a crown offered him: and he put it by with the back of his hand, thus; and then the people fell a-shouting.

BRUTUS. What was the second noise for?

CASCA. Why, for that too.

CASSIUS. They shouted thrice: what was the last cry for?

CASCA. Why, for that too.

BRUTUS. Was the crown offered him thrice?

CASCA. Ay, and he put it by thrice, every time gentler than other, and at every putting-by mine honest neighbours shouted.

BRUTUS. Tell us the manner of it, gentle Casca.

CASCA. I can as well be hanged as tell the manner of it: it was mere foolery; I did not mark it. I saw Mark Antony offer him a crown; yet 'twas not a crown neither, 'twas one of these coronets; and, as I told you, he put it by once: but, for all that, to my thinking, he would fain have had it. Then he offered it to him again; then he put it by again: but, to my thinking, he was very loth to lay his fingers off it. And then he offered it the third time; he put it the third time by: and still the rabblement hooted and clapped their hands because Caesar refused the crown that it had almost choked Caesar; for he swounded and fell down at it.

CASSIUS. But, soft, I pray you: what, did Caesar swound?

CASCA. He fell down in the market-place. I could tell you more news too: Marullus and Flavius, for pulling scarfs off Caesar's images, are put to silence. Fare you well. There was more foolery yet, if I could remember it.

CASSIUS. Will you sup with me tonight, Casca?

CASCA. No, I am promised forth.

CASSIUS. Will you dine with me tomorrow?

CASCA. Ay, if I be alive, and your mind hold, and your dinner worth the eating. Farewell, both.

BRUTUS. What a blunt fellow is this grown to be!
He was quick mettle when he went to school.

CASSIUS. So is he now in execution
Of any bold or noble enterprise,

However he puts on this tardy form.
This rudeness is a sauce to his good wit,
Which gives men stomach to digest his words
With better appetite.

BRUTUS. And so it is. For this time I will leave you:
Tomorrow, if you please to speak with me,
I will come home to you; or, if you will,
Come home to me, and I will wait for you.

CASSIUS. I will do so: till then, think of the world.
(*To himself*) Well, Brutus, thou art noble; yet, I see,
Thy honourable metal may be wrought
From that it is disposed: therefore it is meet
That noble minds keep ever with their likes;
For who so firm that cannot be seduced?
Caesar doth bear me hard; but he loves Brutus:
If I were Brutus now and he were Cassius,
He should not humour me. I will this night,
In several hands, in at his windows throw,
As if they came from several citizens,
Writings all tending to the great opinion
That Rome holds of his name; wherein obscurely
Caesar's ambition shall be glancèd at:
And after this let Caesar seat him sure;
For we will shake him, or worse days endure.

Scene 3—A Street in Rome in a Thunderstorm

CICERO. Good even, Casca: brought you Caesar home?
Why are you breathless? and why stare you so?

CASCA. Are not you moved, when all the sway of earth
Shakes like a thing unfirm? O Cicero,
I have seen tempests, when the scolding winds
Have rived the knotty oaks, and I have seen
The ambitious ocean swell and rage and foam,
To be exalted with the threatening clouds:
But never till tonight, never till now,
Did I go through a tempest dropping fire.
Either there is a civil strife in heaven,
Or else the world, too saucy with the gods,
Incenses them to send destruction.

CICERO. Indeed, it is a strange-disposèd time:
But men may construe things after their fashion,
Clean from the purpose of the things themselves.
Comes Caesar to the Capitol tomorrow?

CASCA. He doth; for he did bid Antonius
Send word to you he would be there tomorrow.

CICERO. Good-night then, Casca: this disturbèd sky
Is not to walk in.

CASCA. Farewell, Cicero.
(*To Cassius, approaching*) Cassius, what night is this !
CASSIUS. A very pleasing night to honest men.
CASCA. Who ever knew the heavens menace so ?
CASSIUS. Those that have known the earth so full of faults.
For my part, I have walked about the streets,
Submitting me unto the perilous night,
And when the cross blue lightning seemed to open
The breast of heaven I did present myself
Even in the aim and very flash of it.
CASCA. But wherefore did you so much tempt the heavens ?
It is the part of men to fear and tremble,
When the most mighty gods by tokens send
Such dreadful heralds to astonish us.
CASSIUS. You are dull, Casca, and those sparks of life
That should be in a Roman you do want,
Or else you use not. You look pale, and gaze,
And put on fear, and cast yourself in wonder,
To see the strange impatience of the heavens.
Now could I, Casca, name to thee a man
Most like this dreadful night
That thunders, lightens, opens graves, and roars
As doth the lion in the Capitol,
A man no mightier than thyself or me
In personal action, yet prodigious grown
And fearful, as these strange eruptions are.
CASCA. Tis Caesar that you mean, is it not, Cassius ?
CASSIUS. Let it be who it is ; for Romans now
Have thews and limbs like to their ancestors ;
But, woe the while ! our fathers' minds are dead.
CASCA. Indeed, they say the senators tomorrow
Mean to establish Caesar as a king ;
And he shall wear his crown by sea and land,
In every place, save here in Italy.
CASSIUS. I know where I will wear this dagger then ;
Cassius from bondage will deliver Cassius.
CASCA. So every bondman in his own hand bears
The power to cancel his captivity.
CASSIUS. And why should Caesar be a tyrant then ?
Poor man ! I know he would not be a wolf,
But that he sees the Romans are but sheep :
He were no lion, were not Romans hinds.
But, O grief,
Where hast thou led me ? I perhaps speak this
Before a willing bondman.

CASCA. You speak to Casca, and to such a man
That is no fleering tell-tale. Hold, my hand:
And I will set this foot of mine as far
As who goes farthest.

CASSIUS. There's a bargain made.
Now know you, Casca, I have moved already
Some certain of the noblest-minded Romans
To undergo with me an enterprise
Of honourable-dangerous consequence;
And I do know, by this, they stay for me
In Pompey's porch: for now, this fearful night,
There is no stir or walking in the streets;
And the complexion of the element
In favour's like the work we have in hand,
Most fiery and most terrible.

CASCA. Stand close awhile, for here comes one in haste.

CINNA (*approaching*). What a fearful night is this!
There's two or three of us have seen strange sights.
O Cassius, if you could
But win the noble Brutus to our party—

CASSIUS. Be you content: good Cinna, take this paper,
And look you lay it in the praetor's chair,
Where Brutus may but find it; and throw this
In at his window. All this done,
Repair to Pompey's porch, where you shall find us.
Come, Casca, you and I will yet ere day
See Brutus at his house: three parts of him
Is ours already, and the man entire
Upon the next encounter yields him ours.

CASCA. O, he sits high in all the people's hearts,
And that which would appear offence in us,
His countenance, like richest alchemy,
Will change to virtue and to worthiness.

CASSIUS. Him and his worth and our great need of him
You have right well conceited. Let us go,
For it is after midnight; and ere day
We will awake him and be sure of him.

ACT 2

Scene 1—Brutus's Orchard

BRUTUS. What, Lucius, ho!

LUCIUS. Called you, my lord?

BRUTUS. Get me a taper in my study, Lucius:
When it is lighted, come and call me here.

LUCIUS. I will, my lord.

BRUTUS. It must be by his death: and for my part,
I know no personal cause to spurn at him,
But for the general. He would be crowned:
How that might change his nature, there's the question.
It is the bright day that brings forth the adder;
And that craves wary walking. Crown him? that—
And then, I grant, we put a sting in him
That at his will he may do danger with.
The abuse of greatness is when it disjoins
Remorse from power: and, to speak truth of Caesar,
I have not known when his affections swayed
More than his reason. But tis a common proof,
That lowliness is young ambition's ladder,
Whereto the climber-upward turns his face;
But when he once attains the upmost round
He then unto the ladder turns his back,
Looks in the clouds, scorning the base degrees
By which he did ascend. So Caesar may.
Then, lest he may, prevent.

LUCIUS (*entering*). The taper burneth in your closet, sir.
Searching the window for a flint, I found
This paper, thus sealed up; and, I am sure,
It did not lie there when I went to bed.

BRUTUS. Get you to bed again; it is not day.

Brutus opens the letter and reads it

Brutus, thou sleep'st: awake, and see thyself.
Shall Rome, etc. Speak, strike, redress!
Brutus, thou sleep'st: awake!
Such instigations have been often dropped
Where I have took them up.
Shall Rome, etc. Thus must I piece it out:
Shall Rome stand under one man's awe? What, Rome?
My ancestors did from the streets of Rome
The Tarquin drive, when he was called a king.
Speak, strike, redress! Am I entreated
To speak and strike? O Rome, I make thee promise;
If the redress will follow, thou receivest
Thy full petition at the hand of Brutus!
(*To Lucius*) Go to the gate; somebody knocks.
Since Cassius first did whet me against Caesar,
I have not slept.
Between the acting of a dreadful thing
And the first motion, all the interim is
Like a phantasma, or a hideous dream:
The Genius and the mortal instruments
Are then in council; and the state of man,

Like to a little kingdom, suffers then
The nature of an insurrection.

LUCIUS (*returning*). Sir, tis your brother Cassius at the door
Who doth desire to see you.

BRUTUS. Is he alone?

LUCIUS. No, sir, there are more with him.

BRUTUS. Do you know them?

LUCIUS. No, sir; their hats are plucked about their ears,
And half their faces buried in their cloaks,
That by no means I may discover them
By any mark of favour.

BRUTUS. Let 'em enter. O conspiracy,
Sham'st thou to show thy dangerous brow by night,
When evils are most free? O, then by day
Where wilt thou find a cavern dark enough
To mask thy monstrous visage?

CASSIUS. I think we are too bold upon your rest:
Good-morrow, Brutus; do we trouble you?

BRUTUS. I have been up this hour, awake all night.
Know I these men that come along with you?

CASSIUS. Yes, every man of them, and no man here
But honours you; and every one doth wish
You had but that opinion of yourself
Which every noble Roman bears of you.
This is Trebonius.

BRUTUS. He is welcome hither.

CASSIUS. This, Decius Brutus.

BRUTUS. He is welcome too.

CASSIUS. This, Casca; this, Cinna; and this, Metellus Cimber.

BRUTUS. They are all welcome.
What watchful cares do interpose themselves
Betwixt your eyes and night?

CASSIUS. Shall I entreat a word? (*They whisper*)

BRUTUS. Give me your hands all over, one by one.

CASSIUS. And let us swear our resolution.

BRUTUS. No, not an oath: if not the face of men,
The sufferance of our souls, the time's abuse—
If these be motives weak, break off betimes,
And every man hence to his idle bed;
So let high-sighted tyranny range on,
Till each man drop by lottery. But if these,
As I am sure they do, bear fire enough
To kindle cowards and to steel with valour
The melting spirits of women, then, countrymen,
What need we any spur but our own cause

To prick us to redress? What other bond
Than secret Romans, that have spoke the word
And will not palter? And what other oath
Than honesty to honesty engaged
That this shall be, or we will fall for it?
Swear priests and cowards and men cautelous,
Old feeble carrions and such suffering souls
That welcome wrongs; unto bad causes swear
Such creatures as men doubt; but do not stain
The even virtue of our enterprise,
Nor the insuppressive mettle of our spirits,
To think that or our cause or our performance
Did need an oath.

CASSIUS. But what of Cicero? Shall we sound him?
I think he will stand very strong with us.

CASCA. Let us not leave him out.

CINNA. No, by no means.

METELLUS. O, let us have him, for his silver hairs
Will purchase us a good opinion
And buy men's voices to commend our deeds:
It shall be said his judgment ruled our hands;
Our youths and wildness shall no whit appear,
But all be buried in his gravity.

BRUTUS. O, name him not: let us not break with him;
For he will never follow anything
That other men begin.

CASSIUS. Then leave him out.

DECIUS BRUTUS. Shall no man else be touched but only Caesar?

CASSIUS. Decius, well urged: I think it is not meet,
Mark Antony, so well beloved of Caesar,
Should outlive Caesar: we shall find of him
A shrewd contriver; which to prevent,
Let Antony and Caesar fall together.

BRUTUS. Our course will seem too fearful, Caius Cassius,
To cut the head off and then hack the limbs,
Like wrath in death and envy afterwards;
For Antony is but a limb of Caesar:
Let us be sacrificers, but not butchers, Caius.
We all stand up against the spirit of Caesar;
And in the spirit of men there is no blood:
O, that we then could come by Caesar's spirit,
And not dismember Caesar! But, alas,
Caesar must bleed for it! And, gentle friends,
Let's kill him boldly, but not wrathfully;
Let's carve him as a dish fit for the gods,

Not hew him as a carcass fit for hounds.
And for Mark Antony, think not of him;
For he can do no more than Caesar's arm
When Caesar's head is off.

CASSIUS. Yet I fear him,
For in the ingrafted love he bears to Caesar—

TREBONIUS. There is no fear in him; let him not die;
For he will live, and laugh at this hereafter.

CASSIUS. The morning comes upon 's: we'll leave you, Brutus.
And, friends, disperse yourselves; but all remember
What you have said, and show yourselves true Romans.

BRUTUS. Good gentlemen, look fresh and merrily:
Let not our looks put on our purposes,
But bear it as our Roman actors do,
With untired spirits and formal constancy:
And so Good-morrow to you every one.
Boy! Lucius! Fast asleep? It is no matter;
Enjoy the honey-heavy dew of slumber:
Thou hast no figures nor no fantasies,
Which busy care draws in the brains of men;
Therefore thou sleep'st so sound.

PORTIA (*entering*). Brutus, my lord!

BRUTUS. Portia, what mean you? wherefore rise you now?
It is not for your health thus to commit
Your weak condition to the raw cold morning.

PORTIA. Nor for yours neither. You've ungently, Brutus,
Stole from my bed: and yesternight, at supper,
You suddenly arose, and walked about,
Musing and sighing, with your arms across,
And when I asked you what the matter was
You stared upon me with ungentle looks,
Gave sign for me to leave you: so I did,
Fearing to strengthen that impatience
Which seemed too much enkindled, and, withal,
Hoping it was but an effect of humour,
Which sometime hath his hour with every man.
It will not let you eat, nor talk, nor sleep,
And could it work so much upon your shape
As it hath much prevailed on your condition
I should not know you, Brutus. Dear my lord,
Make me acquainted with your cause of grief.

BRUTUS. I am not well in health, and that is all.

PORTIA. Is Brutus sick? and is it physical
To walk unbracèd and suck up the humours
Of the dank morning? No, my Brutus;
You have some sick offence within your mind,

Which, by the right and virtue of my place,
I ought to know of; and, upon my knees,
I charm you, by my once-commended beauty,
That you unfold to me, yourself, your half,
Why you are heavy, and what men tonight
Have had resort to you: for here have been
Some six or seven who did hide their faces
Even from darkness.

BRUTUS. Kneel not, gentle Portia.
You are my true and honourable wife,
As dear to me as are the ruddy drops
That visit my sad heart.

PORTIA. If this were true, then should I know this secret.
I grant I am a woman; but, withal,
A woman that Lord Brutus took to wife:
I grant I am a woman; but, withal,
A woman well-reputed, Cato's daughter.
Tell me your counsels.

BRUTUS. O ye gods,
Render me worthy of this noble wife!
Hark, hark! one knocks: Portia, go in awhile;
And by and by thy bosom shall partake
The secrets of my heart.

Scene 2—Caesar's House during a Storm

CAESAR. Nor heaven nor earth have been at peace tonight:
Thrice hath Calpurnia in her sleep cried out,
Help, ho! they murder Caesar! Who's within?

SERVANT. My lord?

CAESAR. Go bid the priests do present sacrifice
And bring me their opinions of success.

CALPURNIA. What mean you, Caesar? Think you to walk forth?
You shall not stir out of your house today.

CAESAR. Caesar shall forth: the things that threatened me
Ne'er looked but on my back; when they shall see
The face of Caesar, they are vanishèd.

CALPURNIA. Caesar, I never stood on ceremonies,
Yet now they fright me. There is one within,
Besides the things that we have heard and seen,
Recounts most horrid sights seen by the watch.
And graves have yawned, and yielded up their dead;
Fierce fiery warriors fought upon the clouds.
O Caesar! these things are beyond all use,
And I do fear them.

CAESAR. What can be avoided
Whose end is purposed by the mighty gods?

Yet Caesar shall go forth, for these predictions
Are to the world in general as to Caesar.

CALPURNIA. When beggars die there are no comets seen;
The heavens themselves blaze forth the death of princes.

CAESAR. Cowards die many times before their deaths;
The valiant never taste of death but once.
Of all the wonders that I yet have heard,
It seems to me most strange that men should fear;
Seeing that death, a necessary end,
Will come when it will come. . . What say the augurers?

SERVANT. They would not have you to stir forth today.

CAESAR. The gods do this in shame of cowardice:
Caesar should be a beast without a heart
If he should stay at home today for fear.
Caesar shall go forth.

CALPURNIA. Alas, my lord,
Your wisdom is consumed in confidence.
Do not go forth today: call it my fear
That keeps you in the house, and not your own.
We'll send Mark Antony to the Senate House;
And he shall say you are not well today:
Let me, upon my knee, prevail in this.

CAESAR. Mark Antony shall say I am not well;
And, for thy humour, I will stay at home.
Here's Decius Brutus, he shall tell them so.

DECIUS BRUTUS. Caesar, all hail! Good-morrow, worthy Caesar:
I come to fetch you to the Senate House.

CAESAR. And you are come in very happy time,
To bear my greeting to the senators
And tell them that I will not come today.

CALPURNIA. Say he is sick.

CAESAR. Shall Caesar send a lie?
Have I in conquest stretched mine arm so far,
To be afeard to tell graybeards the truth?
Decius, go tell them Caesar will not come.

DECIUS BRUTUS. Most mighty Caesar, let me know some cause,
Lest I be laughed at when I tell them so.

CAESAR. The cause is in my will: I will not come;
That is enough to satisfy the Senate.
But for your private satisfaction,
Because I love you, I will let you know:
Calpurnia here, my wife, stays me at home:
She dreamt tonight she saw my statue,
Which, like a fountain with a hundred spouts,
Did run pure blood; and many lusty Romans

Came smiling, and did bathe their hands in it:
And these does she apply for warnings, and portents,
And evils imminent; and on her knee
Hath begged that I will stay at home today.

DECIUS BRUTUS. This dream is all amiss interpreted;
It was a vision fair and fortunate:
Your statue spouting blood in many pipes,
Signifies that from you great Rome shall suck
Reviving blood.
This by Calpurnia's dream is signified.

CAESAR. And this way have you well expounded it.

DECIUS BRUTUS. I have, when you have heard what I can say:
And know it now: the Senate have concluded
To give this day a crown to mighty Caesar.
If you shall send them word you will not come,
Their minds may change. Besides, it were a mock
Apt to be rendered, for some one to say:
Break up the Senate till another time,
When Caesar's wife shall meet with better dreams.
If Caesar hide himself, shall they not whisper
Lo, Caesar is afraid?
Pardon me, Caesar; for my dear dear love
To your proceeding bids me tell you this;
And reason to my love is liable.

CAESAR. How foolish do your fears seem now, Calpurnia!
I am ashamèd I did yield to them.
Give me my robe, for I will go. (*Enter conspirators*)
And look where Publius is come to fetch me.

PUBLIUS. Good-morrow, Caesar.

CAESAR. Welcome, Publius.
What, Brutus, are you stirred so early too?
Good-morrow, Casca. What is't o'clock?

BRUTUS. Caesar, tis strucken eight.

CAESAR. I thank you for your pains and courtesy.
See! Antony, that revels long o' nights,
Is notwithstanding up. Good-morrow, Antony.

ANTONY (*advancing*). So to most noble Caesar.

CAESAR. Bid them prepare within:
I am to blame to be thus waited for.
Now, Cinna: now, Metellus: what, Trebonius!
I have an hour's talk in store for you;
Remember that you call on me today:
Be near me, that I may remember you.
Good friends, go in, and taste some wine with me;
And we, like friends, will straightway go together.

BRUTUS (*aside*). That every like is not the same, O Caesar,
The heart of Brutus yearns to think upon!

Scene 3—A Street near the Capitol

ARTEMIDORUS (*reading a paper*). Caesar, beware of Brutus; take heed of Cassius; come not near Casca; have an eye to Cinna; trust not Trebonius; mark well Metellus Cimber: Decius Brutus loves thee not: thou hast wronged Caius Ligarius. There is but one mind in all these men, and it is bent against Caesar. If thou beest not immortal, look about you: security gives way to conspiracy. The mighty gods defend thee! Thy lover, ARTEMIDORUS

Here will I stand till Caesar pass along,
And as a suitor will I give him this.
If thou read this, O Caesar, thou mayst live;
If not, the Fates with traitors do contrive.

Scene 4—Before the House of Brutus

PORTIA (*to Lucius*). I prithee, boy, run to the Senate House;
Stay not to answer me, but get thee gone:
Why dost thou stay?

LUCIUS. To know my errand, madam.

PORTIA. I would have had thee there, and here again,
Ere I can tell thee what thou shouldst do there.
Art thou here yet?

LUCIUS. Madam, what should I do?
Run to the Capitol, and nothing else?
And so return to you, and nothing else?

PORTIA. Yes, bring me word, boy, if thy lord look well,
For he went sickly forth; and take good note
What Caesar doth, what suitors press to him.
Hark, boy! what noise is that?

LUCIUS. I hear none, madam.

PORTIA. Prithee, listen well;
I heard a bustling rumour, like a fray,
And the wind brings it from the Capitol.

LUCIUS. Sooth, madam, I hear nothing.

PORTIA. I must go in. Ay me, how weak a thing
The heart of woman is! O Brutus,
The heavens speed thee in thine enterprise!
Run, Lucius, and commend me to my lord;
Say I am merry: come to me again,
And bring me word what he doth say to thee.

ACT 3

Scene 1—Before the Capitol

ARTEMIDORUS. Hail, Caesar! read this schedule.

DECIUS BRUTUS. Trebonius doth desire you to o'er-read,

At your best leisure, this his humble suit.
ARTEMIDORUS. O Caesar, read mine first; for mine's a suit
That touches Caesar nearer: read it, great Caesar.
CAESAR. What touches us ourself shall be last served.
ARTEMIDORUS. Delay not, Caesar; read it instantly.
CAESAR. What, is the fellow mad?
PUBLIUS. Sirrah, give place.
CASSIUS. What, urge you your petitions in the street?
Come to the Capitol.

Caesar goes up to the Senate House

POPILIUS. I wish your enterprise today may thrive.
CASSIUS. What enterprise, Popilius?
POPILIUS. Fare you well. (*He advances to Caesar*)
BRUTUS. What said Popilius Lena?
CASSIUS. He wished today our enterprise might thrive.
I fear our purpose is discovered.
BRUTUS. Look, how he makes to Caesar: mark him.
CASSIUS. Casca, be sudden, for we fear prevention.
Brutus, what shall be done? If this be known,
Cassius or Caesar never shall turn back,
For I will slay myself.
BRUTUS. Cassius, be constant:
Popilius Lena speaks not of our purposes;
For, look, he smiles, and Caesar doth not change.
CASSIUS. Trebonius knows his time; for, look you, Brutus,
He draws Mark Antony out of the way.
DECIUS BRUTUS. Where is Metellus Cimber? Let him go,
And presently prefer his suit to Caesar.
BRUTUS. He is addressed: press near and second him.
CINNA. Casca, you are the first that rears your hand.
CAESAR. Are we all ready? What is now amiss
That Caesar and his Senate must redress?
METELLUS. Most high, most mighty, and most puissant Caesar,
Metellus Cimber throws before thy seat
A humble heart— (*Kneeling*)
CAESAR. I must prevent thee, Cimber.
Thy brother by decree is banishèd:
If thou dost bend and pray and fawn for him,
I spurn thee like a cur out of my way.
Know, Caesar doth not wrong, nor without cause
Will he be satisfied.
METELLUS. Is there no voice more worthy than my own,
To sound more sweetly in great Caesar's ear
For the repealing of my banished brother?

BRUTUS. I kiss thy hand, but not in flattery, Caesar ;
Desiring thee that Publius Cimber may
Have an immediate freedom of repeal.

CAESAR. What, Brutus !

CASSIUS. Pardon, Caesar ; Caesar, pardon :
As low as to thy foot doth Cassius fall,
To beg enfranchisement for Publius Cimber.

CAESAR. I could be well moved, if I were as you ;
If I could pray to move, prayers would move me ;
But I am constant as the northern star,
Of whose true-fixed and resting quality
There is no fellow in the firmament.
The skies are painted with unnumbered sparks,
They are all fire and every one doth shine,
But there's but one in all doth hold his place :
So in the world ; tis furnished well with men,
And men are flesh and blood, and apprehensive ;
Yet in the number I do know but one
That unassailable holds on his rank,
Unshaked of motion : and that I am he,
Let me a little show it, even in this :
That I was constant Cimber should be banished,
And constant do remain to keep him so.

CINNA. O Caesar—

CAESAR. Hence ! wilt thou lift up Olympus ?

DECIUS BRUTUS. Great Caesar—

CAESAR. Doth not Brutus bootless kneel ?

CASCA. Speak, hands, for me !

Casca first, then the others, and then Brutus, stab Caesar.

CAESAR. *Et tu, Brute !* Then fall, Caesar ! (*He dies*)

CINNA. Liberty ! Freedom ! Tyranny is dead !
Run hence, proclaim, cry it about the streets.

CASSIUS. Some to the common pulpits, and cry out
Liberty, Freedom, and Enfranchisement !

BRUTUS. People and senators, be not affrighted ;
Fly not ; stand still : ambition's debt is paid.

CASCA. Go to the pulpit, Brutus.

CASSIUS. Where is Antony ?

TREBONIUS. Fled to his house amazed :
Men, wives, and children stare, cry out, and run
As it were Doomsday.

BRUTUS. Fates, we will know your pleasures :
That we shall die, we know ; tis but the time
And drawing days out, that men stand upon.

CASSIUS. Why, he that cuts off twenty years of life
Cuts off so many years of fearing death.

BRUTUS. Grant that, and then is death a benefit:
So are we Caesar's friends, that have abridged
His time of fearing death.

STOP

BRUTUS. Soft! who comes here? A friend of Antony's.

SERVANT. Thus, Brutus, did my master bid me kneel;
Thus did Mark Antony bid me fall down;
And, being prostrate, thus he bade me say:
Brutus is noble, wise, valiant, and honest;
Caesar was mighty, bold, royal, and loving:
Say I love Brutus, and I honour him;
Say I feared Caesar, honoured him, and loved him.
If Brutus will vouchsafe that Antony
May safely come to him, and be resolved
How Caesar hath deserved to lie in death,
Mark Antony shall not love Caesar dead
So well as Brutus living; but will follow
The fortunes and affairs of noble Brutus
Thorough the hazards of this untrod state
With all true faith. So says my master Antony.

BRUTUS. Thy master is a wise and valiant Roman.
Tell him, so please him come unto this place,
He shall be satisfied.

SERVANT. I'll fetch him presently.

BRUTUS. I know that we shall have him well to friend.

CASSIUS. I wish we may: but yet have I a mind
That fears him much.

BRUTUS. But here comes Antony. Welcome, Mark Antony.

ANTONY. O mighty Caesar! dost thou lie so low?
Are all thy conquests, glories, triumphs, spoils,
Shrunk to this little measure? Fare thee well.
I know not, gentlemen, what you intend,
Who else must be let blood, who else is rank:
If I myself, there is no hour so fit
As Caesar's death-hour, nor no instrument
Of half that worth as those your swords, made rich
With the most noble blood of all this world.
I do beseech ye, if you bear me hard,
Now, whilst your purpled hands do reek and smoke,
Fulfil your pleasure. Live a thousand years,
I shall not find myself so apt to die:
No place will please me so, no mean of death,
As here by Caesar, and by you cut off,
The choice and master spirits of this age.

BRUTUS. O Antony, beg not your death of us.

Though now we must appear bloody and cruel,
As, by our hands and this our present act,
You see we do, yet see you but our hands
And this the bleeding business they have done:
Our hearts you see not; they are pitiful;
And pity to the general wrong of Rome
Hath done this deed on Caesar. For your part,
To you our swords have leaden points, Mark Antony:
Our arms, in strength of malice, and our hearts
Of brothers' temper, do receive you in
With all kind love, good thoughts, and reverence.

CASSIUS. Your voice shall be as strong as any man's
In the disposing of new dignities.

BRUTUS. Only be patient till we have appeased
The multitude, beside themselves with fear,
And then we will deliver you the cause,
Why I, that did love Caesar when I struck him,
Have thus proceeded.

ANTONY. I doubt not of your wisdom.
Let each man render me his hand:
First, Marcus Brutus, will I shake with you;
Next, Caius Cassius, do I take your hand;
Now, Decius Brutus, yours; now yours, Metellus;
Yours, Cinna; and, my valiant Casca, yours;
Though last, not least in love, yours, good Trebonius.
Gentlemen all—alas, what shall I say?
My credit now stands on such slippery ground,
That one of two bad ways you must conceit me,
Either a coward or a flatterer.
That I did love thee, Caesar, O, tis true:
Had I as many eyes as thou hast wounds,
Weeping as fast as they stream forth thy blood,
It would become me better than to close
In terms of friendship with thine enemies.
Pardon me, Julius! Here wast thou bayed, brave hart;
Here didst thou fall; and here thy hunters stand.
O world, thou wast the forest to this hart;
And this, indeed, O world, the heart of thee.
How like a deer, strucken by many princes,
Dost thou here lie!

CASSIUS. Mark Antony—

ANTONY. Pardon me, Caius Cassius:
The enemies of Caesar shall say this;
Then, in a friend, it is cold modesty.

CASSIUS. I blame you not for praising Caesar so;
But what compact mean you to have with us?

Will you be pricked in number of our friends;
Or shall we on, and not depend on you?

ANTONY. Therefore I took your hands, but was, indeed,
Swayed from the point by looking down on Caesar.
Friends am I with you all and love you all,
Upon this hope, that you shall give me reasons
Why and wherein Caesar was dangerous.

BRUTUS. Or else were this a savage spectacle.
Our reasons are so full of good regard
That were you, Antony, the son of Caesar,
You should be satisfied.

ANTONY. That's all I seek:
And am moreover suitor that I may
Produce his body to the market-place;
And in the pulpit, as becomes a friend,
Speak in the order of his funeral.

BRUTUS. You shall, Mark Antony.

CASSIUS. Brutus, a word with you.
(*Aside*) You know not what you do: do not consent
That Antony speak in his funeral:
Know you how much the people may be moved
By that which he will utter?

BRUTUS. By your pardon;
I will myself into the pulpit first,
And show the reason of our Caesar's death:
What Antony shall speak I will protest
He speaks by leave and by permission,
And that we are contented Caesar shall
Have all true rites and lawful ceremonies.
It shall advantage more than do us wrong.

CASSIUS. I know not what may fall; I like it not.

BRUTUS. Mark Antony, here, take you Caesar's body.
You shall not in your funeral speech blame us,
But speak all good you can devise of Caesar,
And say you do 't by our permission;
Else shall you not have any hand at all
About his funeral: and you shall speak
In the same pulpit whereto I am going,
After my speech is ended.

ANTONY. Be it so;
I do desire no more.

BRUTUS. Prepare the body then, and follow us.

All leave except Mark Antony

ANTONY. O, pardon me, thou bleeding piece of earth,
That I am meek and gentle with these butchers!

Thou art the ruins of the noblest man
That ever livèd in the tide of times.
Woe to the hand that shed this costly blood!
Over thy wounds now do I prophesy:
A curse shall light upon the limbs of men;
Domestic fury and fierce civil strife
Shall cumber all the parts of Italy;
And Caesar's spirit, ranging for revenge,
Shall in these confines with a monarch's voice
Cry *Havoc*, and let slip the dogs of war.
(*To servant, entering*) You serve Octavius Caesar, do you not?

SERVANT. I do, Mark Antony.

ANTONY. Caesar did write for him to come to Rome.

SERVANT. He did receive his letters, and is coming.
O Caesar! (*Seeing the body*)

ANTONY. Thy heart is big, get thee apart and weep.
Passion, I see, is catching; for mine eyes,
Seeing those beads of sorrow stand in thine,
Began to water. Is thy master coming?

SERVANT. He lies tonight within seven leagues of Rome.

ANTONY. Post back with speed, and tell him what hath chanced.
Here is a mourning Rome, a dangerous Rome,
No Rome of safety for Octavius yet;
Hie hence, and tell him so. Yet, stay awhile;
Thou shalt not back till I have borne this corse
Into the market-place.

Scene 2—The Forum

Enter Brutus and Cassius, and a throng of citizens.

CITIZENS. We will be satisfied; let us be satisfied.

BRUTUS. Then follow me, and give me audience, friends.
Cassius, go you into the other street,
And part the numbers.
Those that will hear me speak, let 'em stay here;
Those that will follow Cassius, go with him;
And public reasons shall be renderèd
Of Caesar's death.

FIRST CITIZEN. I will hear Brutus speak.

SECOND CITIZEN. I will hear Cassius; and compare their reasons.

Cassius leaves with some citizens—Brutus goes into the pulpit

THIRD CITIZEN. The noble Brutus is ascended: silence!

BRUTUS. Be patient till the last.
Romans, countrymen, and lovers! Hear me for my cause, and be silent, that you may hear: believe me for mine honour, and have

respect to mine honour, that you may believe: censure me in your wisdom, and awake your senses, that you may the better judge. If there be any in this assembly, any dear friend of Caesar's, to him I say that Brutus' love to Caesar was no less than his. If then that friend demand why Brutus rose against Caesar, this is my answer: *Not that I loved Caesar less, but that I loved Rome more.* Had you rather Caesar were living and die all slaves, than that Caesar were dead, to live all free men? As Caesar loved me I weep for him; as he was fortunate I rejoice at it; as he was valiant I honour him; but as he was ambitious I slew him. There is tears for his love; joy for his fortune; honour for his valour; and death for his ambition. Who is here so base that would be a bondman? If any, speak; for him have I offended. Who is here so rude that would not be a Roman? If any, speak; for him have I offended. Who is here so vile that will not love his country? If any, speak; for him have I offended. I pause for a reply.

ALL. None, Brutus, none.

BRUTUS. Then none have I offended. I have done no more to Caesar than you shall do to Brutus. The question of his death is enrolled in the Capitol; his glory not extenuated, wherein he was worthy, nor his offences enforced, for which he suffered death.

Enter Mark Antony with Caesar's body

Here comes his body, mourned by Mark Antony, who, though he had no hand in his death, shall receive the benefit of his dying, a place in the Commonwealth, as which of you shall not? With this I depart: that, as I slew my best lover for the good of Rome, I have the same dagger for myself when it shall please my country to need my death.

ALL. Live, Brutus! live, live!

FIRST CITIZEN. Bring him with triumph home unto his house.

SECOND CITIZEN. Give him a statue with his ancestors.

THIRD CITIZEN. Let him be Caesar.

BRUTUS. Good countrymen, let me depart alone,
And, for my sake, stay here with Antony:
Do grace to Caesar's corpse, and grace his speech
Tending to Caesar's glories; which Mark Antony,
By our permission, is allowed to make.
I do entreat you, not a man depart,
Save I alone, till Antony have spoke.

FIRST CITIZEN. Stay, ho! and let us hear Mark Antony.

THIRD CITIZEN. Let him go up into the public chair;
We'll hear him. Noble Antony, go up.

ANTONY. For Brutus' sake, I am beholding to you.

FOURTH CITIZEN. What does he say of Brutus?

THIRD CITIZEN. He says, for Brutus' sake,
He finds himself beholding to us all.

FOURTH CITIZEN. Twere best he speak no harm of Brutus here.

FIRST CITIZEN. This Caesar was a tyrant.

THIRD CITIZEN. Nay, that's certain:
We are blest that Rome is rid of him.

SECOND CITIZEN. Peace! let us hear what Antony can say.

ANTONY. Friends, Romans, countrymen, lend me your ears;
I come to bury Caesar, not to praise him.
The evil that men do lives after them;
The good is oft interrèd with their bones:
So let it be with Caesar. The noble Brutus
Hath told you Caesar was ambitious:
If it were so it was a grievous fault,
And grievously hath Caesar answered it.
Here, under leave of Brutus and the rest
(For Brutus is an honourable man;
So are they all, all honourable men),
Come I to speak in Caesar's funeral.
He was my friend, faithful and just to me:
But Brutus says he was ambitious;
And Brutus is an honourable man.
He hath brought many captives home to Rome,
Whose ransoms did the general coffers fill:
Did this in Caesar seem ambitious?
When that the poor have cried, Caesar hath wept;
Ambition should be made of sterner stuff:
Yet Brutus says he was ambitious;
And Brutus is an honourable man.
You all did see that on the Lupercal
I thrice presented him a kingly crown,
Which he did thrice refuse: was this ambition?
Yet Brutus says he was ambitious;
And, sure, he is an honourable man.
I speak not to disprove what Brutus spoke,
But here I am to speak what I do know.
You all did love him once, not without cause:
What cause withholds you then, to mourn for him?
O judgment! thou art fled to brutish beasts,
And men have lost their reason. Bear with me;
My heart is in the coffin there with Caesar,
And I must pause till it come back to me.

FIRST CITIZEN. Methinks there is much reason in his sayings.

SECOND CITIZEN. If thou consider rightly of the matter,
Caesar has had great wrong.

THIRD CITIZEN. Has he, masters?
I fear there will a worse come in his place.

Fourth Citizen. Marked ye his words? He would not take the crown;
Therefore tis certain he was not ambitious.

First Citizen. If it be found so, some will dear abide it.

Second Citizen. Poor soul! his eyes are red as fire with weeping.

Third Citizen. There's not a nobler man in Rome than Antony.

Fourth Citizen. Now mark him, he begins again to speak.

Antony. But yesterday the word of Caesar might
Have stood against the world; now lies he there,
And none so poor to do him reverence.
O masters, if I were disposed to stir
Your hearts and minds to mutiny and rage,
I should do Brutus wrong, and Cassius wrong,
Who, you all know, are honourable men.
I will not do them wrong; I rather choose
To wrong the dead, to wrong myself and you,
Than I will wrong such honourable men.
But here's a parchment with the seal of Caesar;
I found it in his closet, tis his will:
Let but the commons hear this testament
(Which, pardon me, I do not mean to read)
And they would go and kiss dead Caesar's wounds
And dip their napkins in his sacred blood,
Yea, beg a hair of him for memory,
And, dying, mention it within their wills,
Bequeathing it as a rich legacy
Unto their issue.

Citizen. We'll hear the will: read it, Mark Antony.

All. The will, the will! we will hear Caesar's will.

Antony. Have patience, gentle friends, I must not read it;
It is not meet you know how Caesar loved you.
You are not wood, you are not stones, but men;
And, being men, hearing the will of Caesar,
It will inflame you, it will make you mad:
Tis good you know not that you are his heirs;
For, if you should, O, what would come of it!

Citizen. Read the will; we'll hear it, Antony;
You shall read us the will, Caesar's will.

Antony. Will you be patient? will you stay awhile?
I have o'ershot myself to tell you of it:
I fear I wrong the honourable men
Whose daggers have stabbed Caesar; I do fear it.

Citizen. They were traitors: honourable men!

All. The will! the testament!

Citizen. They were villains, murderers: the will! read the will.

ANTONY. You will compel me, then, to read the will?
Then make a ring about the corpse of Caesar,
And let me show you him that made the will.
Shall I descend? and will you give me leave?

CITIZEN. A ring; stand round.

ANTONY. If you have tears, prepare to shed them now.
You all do know this mantle: I remember
The first time ever Caesar put it on;
Twas on a summer's evening, in his tent,
That day he overcame the Nervii:
Look, in this place ran Cassius' dagger through:
See what a rent the envious Casca made:
Through this the well-belovèd Brutus stabbed;
And as he plucked his cursèd steel away
Mark how the blood of Caesar followed it,
As rushing out of doors, to be resolved
If Brutus so unkindly knocked, or no;
For Brutus, as you know, was Caesar's angel:
Judge, O you gods, how dearly Caesar loved him!
This was the most unkindest cut of all,
For when the noble Caesar saw him stab,
Ingratitude, more strong than traitors' arms,
Quite vanquished him: then burst his mighty heart,
And, in his mantle muffling up his face,
Even at the base of Pompey's statue,
Which all the while ran blood, great Caesar fell.
O, what a fall was there, my countrymen!
Then I, and you, and all of us fell down,
Whilst bloodstained treason flourished over us.
O, now you weep; and, I perceive, you feel
The dint of pity: these are gracious drops.
Kind souls, what, weep you when you but behold
Our Caesar's vesture wounded? Look you here,
Here is himself, marred, as you see, with traitors.

FIRST CITIZEN. O piteous spectacle!

SECOND CITIZEN. O noble Caesar!

THIRD CITIZEN. O woeful day!

FOURTH CITIZEN. O traitors, villains!

ALL. Revenge! Seek! Burn! Kill! Let not a traitor live!

ANTONY. Stay, countrymen.
Good friends, sweet friends, let me not stir you up
To such a sudden flood of mutiny.
They that have done this deed are honourable:
What private griefs they have, alas, I know not,
That made them do it: they are wise and honourable,

And will, no doubt, with reasons answer you.
I come not, friends, to steal away your hearts :
I am no orator, as Brutus is,
But, as you know me all, a plain blunt man
That love my friend ; and that they know full well
That gave me public leave to speak of him :
For I have neither wit, nor words, nor worth,
Action nor utterance, nor the power of speech,
To stir men's blood : I only speak right on ;
I tell you that which you yourselves do know ;
Show you sweet Caesar's wounds, poor poor dumb mouths,
And bid them speak for me : but were I Brutus,
And Brutus Antony, there were an Antony
Would ruffle up your spirits and put a tongue
In every wound of Caesar that should move
The stones of Rome to rise and mutiny.

ALL. We'll mutiny.

CITIZEN. We'll burn the house of Brutus.

ANTONY. Yet hear me, countrymen ; yet hear me speak.

ALL. Peace, ho ! Hear Antony. Most noble Antony !

ANTONY. Why, friends, you go to do you know not what :
Wherein hath Caesar thus deserved your loves ?
Alas, you know not : I must tell you, then :
You have forgot the will I told you of.

ALL. Most true. The will ! Let's stay and hear the will.

ANTONY. Here is the will, and under Caesar's seal.
To every Roman citizen he gives,
To every several man, seventy-five drachmas.

SECOND CITIZEN. Most noble Caesar ! We'll revenge his death.

THIRD CITIZEN. O royal Caesar !

ANTONY Hear me with patience.

ALL. Peace, ho !

ANTONY. Moreover, he hath left you all his walks,
His private arbours and new-planted orchards,
On this side Tiber ; he hath left them you,
And to your heirs for ever, common pleasures,
To walk abroad, and recreate yourselves.
Here was a Caesar ! When comes such another ?

FIRST CITIZEN. Never, never. Come, away, away !
We'll burn his body in the holy place,
And with the brands fire the traitors' houses.

CITIZENS. Go fetch fire. Pluck down benches. Pluck down forms, windows, anything.

Citizens depart with the body of Caesar

ANTONY. Now let it work. Mischief, thou art afoot,

Take thou what course thou wilt!

SERVANT (*entering*). Sir, Octavius is already come to Rome.

ANTONY. Where is he?

SERVANT. He and Lepidus are at Caesar's house.

ANTONY. And thither will I straight to visit him:
He comes upon a wish. Fortune is merry,
And in this mood will give us anything.

SERVANT. I heard him say, Brutus and Cassius
Are rid like madmen through the gates of Rome.

ANTONY. Belike they had some notice of the people,
How I had moved them. Bring me to Octavius.

ACT 4

Scene 1—A Room in Mark Antony's House

This scene shows Antony, Octavius, and Lepidus choosing who shall be executed for their share in the conspiracy. Antony condemns the brother of Lepidus, and Lepidus condemns Antony's nephew; and each agrees. On Lepidus leaving, Antony expresses contempt for him, but Octavius reminds him that Lepidus is a valiant soldier. They then plan measures against Brutus and Cassius, who are in arms against them.

Scene 2—Camp near Sardis; Before Brutus's Tent

BRUTUS. What now, Lucilius! is Cassius near?

LUCILIUS. He is at hand; and Pindarus is come
To do you salutation from his master.

BRUTUS. He greets me well. Your master, Pindarus,
In his own change, or by ill officers,
Hath given me some worthy cause to wish
Things done, undone: but, if he be at hand,
I shall be satisfied.

PINDARUS. I do not doubt
But that my noble master will appear
Such as he is, full of regard and honour.

CASSIUS (*approaching*). Most noble brother, you have done me wrong.

BRUTUS. Judge me, you gods! wrong I mine enemies?
And, if not so, how should I wrong a brother?

CASSIUS. Brutus, this sober form of yours hides wrongs;
And when you do them—

BRUTUS. Cassius, be content;
Speak your griefs softly: I do know you well.
Before the eyes of both our armies here,
Which should perceive nothing but love from us,
Let us not wrangle: bid them move away;
Then in my tent, Cassius, enlarge your griefs,
And I will give you audience.

Scene 3—Brutus's Tent

CASSIUS. That you have wronged me doth appear in this:
You have condemned and noted Lucius Pella
For taking bribes here of the Sardians;
Wherein my letters, praying on his side,
Because I knew the man, were slighted off.

BRUTUS. You wronged yourself to write in such a case.

CASSIUS. In such a time as this it is not meet
That every nice offence should bear his comment.

BRUTUS. Let me tell you, Cassius, you yourself
Are much condemned to have an itching palm;
To sell and mart your offices for gold
To undeservers.

CASSIUS. I an itching palm!
You know that you are Brutus that speak this,
Or, by the gods, this speech were else your last.

BRUTUS. The name of Cassius honours this corruption,
And chastisement doth therefore hide his head.

CASSIUS. Chastisement!

BRUTUS. Remember March, the ides of March remember:
Did not great Julius bleed for justice sake?
What villain touched his body, that did stab,
And not for justice? What, shall one of us,
That struck the foremost man of all this world
But for supporting robbers, shall we now
Contaminate our fingers with base bribes,
And sell the mighty space of our large honours
For so much trash as may be graspèd thus?
I had rather be a dog, and bay the moon,
Than such a Roman.

CASSIUS. Brutus, bay not me; I'll not endure it.
Urge me no more, I shall forget myself;
Have mind upon your health; tempt me no farther.

BRUTUS. Away, slight man!
Shall I be frighted when a madman stares?

CASSIUS. O ye gods, ye gods! must I endure all this?

BRUTUS. All this! ay, more: fret till your proud heart break;
Go show your slaves how choleric you are,
And make your bondmen tremble. Must I budge?
Must I observe you? Must I stand and crouch
Under your testy humour? By the gods,
You shall digest the venom of your spleen,
Though it do split you; for, from this day forth,
I'll use you for my mirth, yea, for my laughter,
When you are waspish.

CASSIUS. Is it come to this?
When Caesar lived he durst not thus have moved me.

BRUTUS. Peace, peace! you durst not so have tempted him.

CASSIUS. Do not presume too much upon my love;
I may do that I shall be sorry for.

BRUTUS. You have done that you should be sorry for.
There is no terror, Cassius, in your threats,
For I am armed so strong in honesty
That they pass by me as the idle wind,
Which I respect not. I did send to you
For certain sums of gold, which you denied me:
For I can raise no money by vile means:
By heaven, I had rather coin my heart,
And drop my blood for drachmas, than to wring
From the hard hands of peasants their vile trash
By any indirection: I did send
To you for gold to pay my legions,
Which you denied me: was that done like Cassius?
Should I have answered Caius Cassius so?
When Marcus Brutus grows so covetous,
To lock such rascal counters from his friends,
Be ready, gods, with all your thunderbolts;
Dash him to pieces!

CASSIUS. I denied you not; he was but a fool that brought
My answer back. Brutus hath rived my heart:
A friend should bear his friend's infirmities,
But Brutus makes mine greater than they are.

BRUTUS. I do not, till you practise them on me.

CASSIUS. You love me not.

BRUTUS. I do not like your faults.

CASSIUS. A friendly eye could never see such faults.

BRUTUS. A flatterer's would not, though they do appear
As huge as high Olympus.

CASSIUS. Come, Antony, and young Octavius, come,
Revenge yourselves alone on Cassius,
For Cassius is aweary of the world;
Hated by one he loves; braved by his brother;
Checked like a bondman; all his faults observed,
Set in a note-book, learned, and conned by rote,
To cast into my teeth. O, I could weep
My spirit from mine eyes! There is my dagger,
And here my naked breast; within, a heart
Dearer than Plutus' mine, richer than gold:
If that thou be'st a Roman, take it forth;
I, that denied thee gold, will give my heart:

Strike, as thou didst at Caesar; for, I know,
When thou didst hate him worst thou lovedst him better
Than ever thou lovedst Cassius.

BRUTUS. Sheathe your dagger:
Be angry when you will, it shall have scope;
Do what you will, dishonour shall be humour.
O Cassius, you are yokèd with a lamb
That carries anger as the flint bears fire;
Who, much enforcèd, shows a hasty spark,
And straight is cold again.

CASSIUS. Hath Cassius lived
To be but mirth and laughter to his Brutus
When grief and blood ill-tempered vexeth him?

BRUTUS. When I spoke that I was ill-tempered too.

CASSIUS. Do you confess so much? Give me your hand.

BRUTUS. And my heart too.

CASSIUS. O Brutus!

BRUTUS. What's the matter?

CASSIUS. Have not you love enough to bear with me,
When that rash humour which my mother gave me
Makes me forgetful?

BRUTUS. Yes, Cassius; and, from henceforth,
When you are over-earnest with your Brutus,
He'll think your mother chides, and leave you so.

CASSIUS. I did not think you could have been so angry.

BRUTUS. O Cassius, I am sick of many griefs.

CASSIUS. Of your philosophy you make no use
If you give place to accidental evils.

BRUTUS. No man bears sorrow better. Portia is dead.

CASSIUS. Ha! Portia!

BRUTUS. She is dead.

CASSIUS. How scaped I killing when I crossed you so?
O insupportable and touching loss!
Upon what sickness?

BRUTUS. Impatient of my absence,
And grief that young Octavius with Mark Antony
Have made themselves so strong—for with her death
That tidings came.

CASSIUS. O ye immortal gods!

BRUTUS. Speak no more of her. Give me a bowl of wine.
In this I bury all unkindness, Cassius.

CASSIUS. My heart is thirsty for that noble pledge.
Fill, Lucius, till the wine o'erswell the cup;
I cannot drink too much of Brutus' love.

BRUTUS. Messala, I have here receivèd letters,
That young Octavius and Mark Antony
Come down upon us with a mighty power,
Bending their expedition toward Philippi.

MESSALA. Myself have letters of the selfsame tenour.

BRUTUS. With what addition ?

MESSALA. That by proscription and bills of outlawry,
Octavius, Antony, and Lepidus,
Have put to death a hundred senators.

BRUTUS. Therein our letters do not well agree ;
Mine speak of seventy senators that died
By their proscriptions, Cicero being one.

CASSIUS. Cicero one !

MESSALA. Cicero is dead.

BRUTUS. Well, to our work alive. What do you think
Of marching to Philippi presently ?
Our legions are brimfull, our cause is ripe :
The enemy increaseth every day ;
We, at the height, are ready to decline.
There is a tide in the affairs of men,
Which, taken at the flood, leads on to fortune ;
Omitted, all the voyage of their life
Is bound in shallows and in miseries.
On such a full sea are we now afloat,
And we must take the current when it serves,
Or lose our ventures.

CASSIUS. Then, with your will, go on ;
We'll along ourselves, and meet them at Philippi.

BRUTUS. The deep of night is crept upon our talk,
And nature must obey necessity ;
Which we will niggard with a little rest.
There is no more to say ?

CASSIUS. No more. Good-night :
Early tomorrow will we rise, and hence.

BRUTUS. Lucius ! My gown. Farewell, good Messala :
Good-night, Titinius. Noble, noble Cassius,
Good-night, and good repose.

CASSIUS. O my dear brother !
This was an ill beginning of the night :
Never come such division tween our souls !
Let it not, Brutus.

BRUTUS. Everything is well.

CASSIUS. Good-night, my lord.

BRUTUS. Good-night, good brother.
(*To Lucius*) Give me the gown. Where is thy instrument ?

LUCIUS. Here in the tent.

BRUTUS. What, thou speak'st drowsily?
Poor knave, I blame thee not; thou art o'er-watched.
Call Claudius and some other of my men;
I'll have them sleep on cushions in my tent.

LUCIUS. Varro and Claudius!

BRUTUS. I pray you, sirs, lie in my tent and sleep;
It may be I shall raise you by and by
On business to my brother Cassius.

VARRO. So please you, we will stand and watch your pleasure.

BRUTUS. I will not have it so: lie down, good sirs;
It may be I shall otherwise bethink me.
Look, Lucius, here's the book I sought for so;
I put it in the pocket of my gown.

LUCIUS. I was sure your lordship did not give it me.

BRUTUS. Bear with me, good boy, I am much forgetful.
Canst thou hold up thy heavy eyes awhile,
And touch thy instrument a strain or two?

LUCIUS. Ay, my lord, an't please you.

BRUTUS. It does, my boy:
I trouble thee too much, but thou art willing.
I will not hold thee long: if I do live
I will be good to thee. (*Music*)
This is a sleepy tune. O murderous slumber,
Lay'st thou thy leaden mace upon my boy,
That plays thee music? Gentle knave, Good-night;
I will not do thee so much wrong to wake thee:
If thou dost nod, thou break'st thy instrument;
I'll take it from thee; and, good boy, Good-night.
Let me see, let me see; is not the leaf turned down
Where I left reading? Here it is, I think.

Enter the Ghost of Caesar

How ill this taper burns! Ha! who comes here?
I think it is the weakness of mine eyes
That shapes this monstrous apparition.
It comes upon me. Art thou anything?
Art thou some god, some angel, or some devil,
That makest my blood cold and my hair to stare?
Speak to me what thou art.

GHOST. Thy evil spirit, Brutus.

BRUTUS. Why comest thou?

GHOST. To tell thee thou shalt see me at Philippi.

BRUTUS. Well, then I shall see thee again?

GHOST. Ay, at Philippi.

BRUTUS. Why, I will see thee at Philippi, then.

The Ghost vanishes

Now I have taken heart thou vanishest:
Ill spirit, I would hold more talk with thee.
Boy! Lucius! Varro! Claudius! Sirs, awake!

BRUTUS. Didst thou dream, Lucius, that thou so criedst out?

LUCIUS. My lord, I do not know that I did cry.

BRUTUS. Yes, that thou didst: didst thou see anything?

LUCIUS. Nothing, my lord.

BRUTUS. Sleep again, Lucius. Sirrah, Claudius!
Why did you so cry out, sirs, in your sleep?

VARRO and CLAUDIUS. Did we, my lord?

BRUTUS. Ay: saw you anything

VARRO. No, my lord, I saw nothing.

CLAUDIUS. Nor I, my lord.

BRUTUS. Go and commend me to my brother Cassius;
Bid him set on his powers betimes before,
And we will follow.

ACT 5

Scene 1—The Plains of Philippi

Octavius and Antony appear with their armies

MESSENGER. Prepare you, generals:
The enemy comes on in gallant show.

ANTONY. Octavius, lead your battle softly on,
Upon the left hand of the even field.

OCTAVIUS. Upon the right hand I; keep thou the left.

Armies of Brutus and Cassius appear

CASSIUS. Now, most noble Brutus,
The gods today stand friendly, that we may,
Lovers in peace, lead on our days to age!
But since the affairs of men rest still uncertain,
Let's reason with the worst that may befall.
If we do lose this battle, then is this
The very last time we shall speak together:
What are you then determinèd to do?

BRUTUS. Even by the rule of that philosophy
By which I did blame Cato for the death
Which he did give himself, I know not how,
But I do find it cowardly and vile,
For fear of what might fall, so to prevent
The time of life: arming myself with patience,
To stay the providence of some high powers
That govern us below.

CASSIUS. Then, if we lose this battle,
You are contented to be led in triumph
Through the streets of Rome?

BRUTUS. No, Cassius, no: think not, thou noble Roman,
That ever Brutus will go bound to Rome;
He bears too great a mind. But this same day
Must end that work the ides of March begun;
And whether we shall meet again I know not.
Therefore our everlasting farewell take:
For ever and for ever, farewell, Cassius!
If we do meet again, why, we shall smile;
If not, why then, this parting was well made.

CASSIUS. For ever and for ever, farewell, Brutus!
If we do meet again, we'll smile indeed:
If not, tis true this parting was well made.

BRUTUS. Why, then, lead on. O, that a man might know
The end of this day's business ere it come!
But it sufficeth that the day will end,
And then the end is known. Come, ho! away!

Scene 2—The Field of Battle

BRUTUS. Ride, ride, Messala, ride, and give these bills
Unto the legions on the other side.
Let them set on at once; for I perceive
But cold demeanour in Octavius' wing,
And sudden push gives them the overthrow.
Ride, ride, Messala: let them all come down.

Scene 3—Another Part of the Field

CASSIUS. O, look, Titinius, look, the villains fly!
Myself have to mine own turned enemy:
This ensign here of mine was turning back;
I slew the coward, and did take it from him.

TITINIUS. O Cassius, Brutus gave the word too early;
Who, having some advantage on Octavius,
Took it too eagerly: his soldiers fell to spoil,
Whilst we by Antony are all enclosed.

PINDARUS (*entering*). Fly farther off, my lord, fly farther off;
Mark Antony is in your tents, my lord:
Fly, therefore, noble Cassius, fly far off.

CASSIUS. This hill is far enough. Look, look, Titinius;
Are those my tents where I perceive the fire?

TITINIUS. They are, my lord.

CASSIUS. Titinius, if thou lovest me,
Mount thou my horse, and hide thy spurs in him
Till he have brought thee up to yonder troops,
And here again; that I may rest assured
Whether yond troops are friend or enemy.

TITINIUS. I will be here again, even with a thought.

CASSIUS. Go, Pindarus, get higher on that hill;

My sight was ever thick; regard Titinius,
And tell me what thou not'st about the field.
This day I breathèd first: time is come round,
And where I did begin, there shall I end;
My life is run his compass. Sirrah, what news?

PINDARUS (*above*). O my lord!

CASSIUS. What news?

PINDARUS (*above*). Titinius is enclosèd round about
With horsemen, that make to him on the spur;
Yet he spurs on. Now they are almost on him.
Now, Titinius! Now some light. O, he lights too.
He's ta'en. And, hark! they shout for joy.

CASSIUS. Come down, behold no more.
O, coward that I am, to live so long,
To see my best friend ta'en before my face!
Come hither, sirrah:
In Parthia did I take thee prisoner;
And then I swore thee, saving of thy life,
That whatsoever I did bid thee do,
Thou shouldst attempt it. Come now, keep thine oath;
Now be a freeman: and with this good sword,
That ran through Caesar's bowels, search this bosom.
Stand not to answer: here, take thou the hilts;
And, when my face is covered, as tis now,
Guide thou the sword. Caesar, thou art revenged,
Even with the sword that killed thee. (*Cassius falls*)

PINDARUS. So, I am free; yet would not so have been,
Durst I have done my will. O Cassius,
Far from this country Pindarus shall run,
Where never Roman shall take note of him.

Enter Titinius with Messala

MESSALA. It is but change, Titinius; for Octavius
Is overthrown by noble Brutus' power,
As Cassius' legions are by Antony.

TITINIUS. These tidings will well comfort Cassius.

MESSALA. Where did you leave him?

TITINIUS. All disconsolate,
With Pindarus his bondman, on this hill.

MESSALA. Is not that he that lies upon the ground?

TITINIUS. He lies not like the living. O my heart!

MESSALA. Is not that he?

TITINIUS. No, this was he, Messala.
But Cassius is no more. O setting sun,
As in thy red rays thou dost sink tonight,
So in his red blood Cassius' day is set;

The sun of Rome is set! Our day is gone!
Clouds, dews, and dangers come; our deeds are done!
Mistrust of my success hath done this deed.

MESSALA. Mistrust of good success hath done this deed.
O hateful error, melancholy's child,
Why dost thou show to the apt thoughts of men
The things that are not?

TITINIUS. What, Pindarus! Where art thou, Pindarus?

MESSALA. Seek him, Titinius, whilst I go to meet
The noble Brutus, thrusting this report
Into his ears; I may say *thrusting it*,
For piercing steel and darts envenomed
Shall be as welcome to the ears of Brutus
As tidings of this sight.

TITINIUS. Why didst thou send me forth, brave Cassius?
Did I not meet thy friends? and did not they
Put on my brows this wreath of victory,
And bid me give it thee? Didst thou not hear their shouts?
Alas, thou hast mis*con*strued everything!
But, hold thee, take this garland on thy brow;
Thy Brutus bid me give it thee, and I
Will do his bidding. Brutus, come apace,
And see how I regarded Caius Cassius.
By your leave, gods: this is a Roman's part:
Come, Cassius' sword, and find Titinius' heart.

BRUTUS (*approaching*). Where, where, Messala, doth his body lie?

MESSALA. Lo, yonder, and Titinius mourning it.

BRUTUS. O Julius Caesar, thou art mighty yet!
Thy spirit walks abroad.
Are yet two Romans living such as these?
The last of all the Romans, fare thee well!
It is impossible that ever Rome
Should breed thy fellow. Friends, I owe more tears
To this dead man than you shall see me pay.
I shall find time, Cassius, I shall find time.

Scene 4—The Field of Battle

Brutus continues the fight in another part of the field, his friends falling around him. Lucilius is captured, wounded. To aid his friend's escape he pretends to be Brutus, but is recognised by Antony. All is now lost.

Scene 5—Another Part of the Field

Enter Brutus, Dardanius, Clitus, Strato, and Volumnius.

BRUTUS. Come, poor remains of friends, rest on this rock.

CLITUS. Statilius showed the torch-light, but, my lord,
He came not back: he is or ta'en or slain.

BRUTUS. Sit thee down, Clitus: slaying is the word;
It is a deed in fashion. Hark thee, Clitus (*whispering*).

CLITUS. What, I, my lord? No, not for all the world.

BRUTUS. Peace then! no words.

CLITUS. I'll rather kill myself.

BRUTUS. Hark thee, Dardanius (*whispering*).

DARDANIUS. Shall I do such a deed?

CLITUS. O Dardanius!

DARDANIUS. O Clitus!

CLITUS. What ill request did Brutus make to thee?

DARDANIUS. To kill him, Clitus. Look, he meditates.

CLITUS. Now is that noble vessel full of grief,
That it runs over even at his eyes.

BRUTUS. Come hither, good Volumnius; list a word.

VOLUMNIUS. What says my lord?

BRUTUS. Why, this, Volumnius:
The ghost of Caesar hath appeared to me
Two several times by night; at Sardis once,
And, this last night, here in Philippi fields:
I know my hour is come.

VOLUMNIUS. Not so, my lord.

BRUTUS. Nay, I am sure it is, Volumnius.
Thou seest the world, Volumnius, how it goes;
Our enemies have beat us to the pit:
It is more worthy to leap in ourselves,
Than tarry till they push us. Good Volumnius,
Thou know'st that we two went to school together:
Even for that our love of old, I prithee,
Hold thou my sword-hilts, whilst I run on it.

VOLUMNIUS. That's not an office for a friend, my lord.

CLITUS. Fly, fly, my lord; there is no tarrying here.

BRUTUS. Farewell to you; and you; and you, Volumnius.
Strato, thou hast been all this while asleep;
Farewell to thee, too, Strato. Countrymen,
My heart doth joy that yet in all my life
I found no man but he was true to me.
I shall have glory by this losing day,
More than Octavius and Mark Antony
By this vile conquest shall attain unto.
So fare you well at once; for Brutus' tongue
Hath almost ended his life's history:
Night hangs upon mine eyes; my bones would rest,
That have but laboured to attain this hour.

Cry comes from within, Fly, fly, fly!

CLITUS. Fly, my lord, fly.

BRUTUS. Hence! I will follow.

Brutus and Strato are left alone

I prithee, Strato, stay thou by thy lord:
Thou art a fellow of a good respect;
Thy life hath had some smatch of honour in it:
Hold then my sword, and turn away thy face,
While I do run upon it. Wilt thou, Strato?

STRATO. Give me your hand first. Fare you well, my lord.

BRUTUS. Farewell, good Strato. Caesar, now be still;
I killed not thee with half so good a will. (*He dies*)

Enter Octavius, Antony, Messala, Lucilius, and the Army.

OCTAVIUS. What man is that?

MESSALA. My master's man. Strato, where is thy master?

STRATO. Free from the bondage you are in, Messala:
The conquerors can but make a fire of him,
For Brutus only overcame himself,
And no man else hath honour by his death.

LUCILIUS. So Brutus should be found. I thank thee, Brutus,
That thou hast proved Lucilius' saying true.

OCTAVIUS. All that served Brutus, I will entertain them.
Fellow, wilt thou bestow thy time with me?

STRATO. Ay, if Messala will prefer me to you.

OCTAVIUS. Do so, good Messala.

MESSALA. How died my master, Strato?

STRATO. I held the sword, and he did run on it.

MESSALA. Octavius, then take him to follow thee,
That did the latest service to my master.

ANTONY. This was the noblest Roman of them all:
All the conspirators save only he
Did that they did in envy of great Caesar;
He only, in a general honest thought
And common good to all, made one of them.
His life was gentle, and the elements
So mixed in him that Nature might stand up
And say to all the world *This was a man!*

OCTAVIUS. According to his virtue let us use him,
With all respect and rites of burial.
Within my tent his bones tonight shall lie,
Most like a soldier, ordered honourably.
So call the field to rest; and let's away,
To part the glories of this happy day.

The Story of Hamlet

A PROUD man must Shakespeare have been when Hamlet was staged, for it was the play which ranked him as the greatest writer of his day. It is counted as having in it the fullest evidence of his genius.

THE story has its beginning in an old Danish saga which was very widely known, and an English play with Hamlet in it had been known for ten years when Shakespeare took the old stories and made a new drama out of them. It leapt into popularity.

HAMLET marks the time when Shakespeare's mind became more serious. He found in this prince a type of mind to enthral him, and he fashioned him into a character that has fascinated and perplexed thinking men ever since. It is one of the greatest tributes to Shakespeare's genius that, though there is little action in the play, Hamlet holds the mind by a subtle spell, from the first romantic moment on the battlements of Elsinore to the final moment when four captains carry out his body to the muffled music of the drums.

IT is the character of Hamlet, the mysterious personality of a man who does not understand himself, which makes this the most famous of the matchless plays that Shakespeare left behind. Hamlet is a thinker whose thoughts hold him back from action rather than hurry him into it. A student dawdling at college at thirty, he allows an uncle to usurp his throne while he stands by moodily thinking about it. When his father's ghost appears, and tells him his uncle gained the throne by murder, he believes it but thinks himself into doubt. He settles the doubt, but would rather die than be the instrument of justice. He refuses to act, yet he is tortured by his indecision. It is not that he is a coward, for on the spur of the moment he is often prompt and brave, and he dies at last a man of action. But Hamlet's is a courage that will not survive thinking. Give him time for thought and he is paralysed.

WHO but Shakespeare could have made a play like this out of nothing but a mind like that? Hamlet is the problem of a man who cannot think and act, the problem of indecisive thought. What a wealth of imagination the whole situation brings out from Hamlet's troubled mind? And yet there is a rather grim humour, a sort of mockery of humour, running through it all.

IT is one of the greatest plays ever written. We must not think it a weakness that a ghost comes into it. There are no ghosts off the stage, but this pretence has always been allowed in plays, and Shakespeare uses it many times. Here the idea of the ghost is an essential part of this great play of a man who fails to be a hero.

THE PLAYERS

Hamlet, a dreamer and not a man of action, son of the dead King of Denmark and nephew of the reigning king.

Claudius, King of Denmark, who has murdered his brother the King, Hamlet's father, and seized the throne.

Horatio, a faithful friend of Hamlet.

Polonius, the Lord Chamberlain, a prosy, talkative old man.

Laertes, son of Polonius, a fiery-tempered young man of action, in contrast with Hamlet.

Rosencrantz and Guildenstern, student friends of Hamlet, but unfaithful to him. Called to court to serve the King.

Francisco, a soldier on sentinel duty by night.

Bernardo and Marcellus, officers, loyal to Hamlet. They see the dead King's Ghost and tell Hamlet.

Ghost of Hamlet's Father, seen only between midnight and sunrise.

Fortinbras, Prince of Norway, who at the end of the play succeeds Claudius as King of Denmark.

Gertrude, Queen of Denmark, mother of Hamlet, and the hastily-married wife of Claudius.

Ophelia, daughter of Polonius, a beautiful and pathetic figure. She and Hamlet love each other, but he gives her up to fulfil the mission demanded by the Ghost.

Osric, a young courtier, a fantastic coxcomb.

Reynaldo, servant to Polonius.

Two gravediggers, who represent rural character.

Ambassadors, a captain, actors, officials, a priest and soldiers.

Scene—Denmark

Hamlet

ACT 1

Scene 1—A Platform before the Castle at Elsinore

BERNARDO. Who's there ?

FRANCISCO. Nay, answer me ; stand, and unfold yourself.

BERNARDO. Long live the king !

FRANCISCO. Bernardo ?

BERNARDO. He.

FRANCISCO. You come most carefully upon your hour.

BERNARDO. Tis now struck twelve ; get thee to bed, Francisco.

FRANCISCO. For this relief much thanks : tis bitter cold,
And I am sick at heart.

BERNARDO. Have you had quiet guard ?

FRANCISCO. Not a mouse stirring.

BERNARDO. Well, Good-night.
If you do meet Horatio and Marcellus,
The rivals of my watch, bid them make haste.

FRANCISCO. I think I hear them. Stand, ho ! Who's there ?

HORATIO. Friends to this ground.

MARCELLUS. And liegemen to the Dane.

FRANCISCO. Give you Good-night.

MARCELLUS. O, farewell, honest soldier.

BERNARDO. What, is Horatio there ?

HORATIO. A piece of him.

BERNARDO. Welcome, Horatio : welcome, good Marcellus.

MARCELLUS. What, has this thing appeared again tonight ?

BERNARDO. I have seen nothing.

MARCELLUS. Horatio says tis but our fantasy,
And will not let belief take hold of him
Touching this dreaded sight, twice seen of us :
Therefore I have entreated him along
With us to watch the minutes of this night,
That if again this apparition come
He may approve our eyes and speak to it.

HORATIO. Tush, tush, 'twill not appear.

BERNARDO. Sit down awhile;
And let us once again assail your ears
What we have two nights seen. Last night of all,
When yond same star that's westward from the Pole
Had made his course to illume that part of heaven
Where now it burns, Marcellus and myself,
The bell then beating one— (*Here the Ghost enters*)

MARCELLUS. Peace, break thee off; look, where it comes again!

BERNARDO. In the same figure, like the king that's dead.

MARCELLUS. Thou art a scholar; speak to it, Horatio.

BERNARDO. Looks it not like the king? mark it, Horatio.

HORATIO. Most like: it harrows me with fear and wonder.

BERNARDO. It would be spoke to.

MARCELLUS. Question it, Horatio.

HORATIO. What art thou that usurp'st this time of night,
Together with that fair and warlike form
In which the majesty of buried Denmark
Did sometimes march? By heaven I charge thee, speak!

MARCELLUS. It is offended.

BERNARDO. See, it stalks away!

HORATIO. Stay! speak, speak! I charge thee, speak!

MARCELLUS. Tis gone, and will not answer.

BERNARDO. How now, Horatio! You tremble and look pale:
Is not this something more than fantasy?
What think you on't?

HORATIO. Before my God, I might not this believe
Without the sensible and true avouch
Of mine own eyes.

MARCELLUS. Is it not like the king?

HORATIO. As thou art to thyself. Tis strange.

MARCELLUS. Thus twice before, and jump at this dead hour,
With martial stalk hath he gone by our watch.

HORATIO. In what particular thought to work I know not,
But in the gross and scope of my opinion,
This bodes some strange eruption to our State.
A mote it is to trouble the mind's eye.
In the most high and palmy state of Rome,
A little ere the mightiest Julius fell,
The graves stood tenantless and the sheeted dead
Did squeak and gibber in the Roman streets:
But soft, behold! lo, where it comes again!
I'll cross it, though it blast me. Stay, illusion!
If thou hast any sound, or use of voice,
Speak to me:

If there be any good thing to be done
That may to thee do ease and grace to me,
Speak to me :
If thou art privy to thy country's fate,
Which, happily, foreknowing may avoid,
O, speak ! Stop it, Marcellus.

MARCELLUS. Shall I strike at it with my partisan ?

HORATIO. Do, if it will not stand.

MARCELLUS. Tis gone !
We do it wrong, being so majestical,
To offer it the show of violence.

BERNARDO. It was about to speak when the cock crew.

HORATIO. And then it started like a guilty thing
Upon a fearful summons. I have heard,
The cock, that is the trumpet to the morn,
Doth with his lofty and shrill-sounding throat
Awake the god of day ; and, at his warning,
Whether in sea or fire, in earth or air,
The extravagant and erring spirit hies
To his confine.

MARCELLUS. It faded on the crowing of the cock.
Some say that ever gainst that season comes
Wherein our Saviour's birth is celebrated,
The bird of dawning singeth all night long :
And then, they say, no spirit can walk abroad ;
The nights are wholesome ; then no planets strike,
No fairy takes, nor witch hath power to charm,
So hallowed and so gracious is the time.

HORATIO. So have I heard and do in part believe it.
But, look, the morn, in russet mantle clad,
Walks o'er the dew of yon high eastward hill :
Break we our watch up ; and by my advice
Let us impart what we have seen tonight
Unto young Hamlet ; for, upon my life,
This spirit, dumb to us, will speak to him.

Scene 2—A Room in the Castle

KING. Though yet of Hamlet our dear brother's death
The memory be green, and that it us befitted
To bear our hearts in grief, and our whole kingdom
To be contracted in one brow of woe,
Yet so far hath discretion fought with nature
That we with wisest sorrow think on him,
Together with remembrance of ourselves.
Therefore our sometime sister, now our queen,
The imperial jointress to this warlike State,

Have we, as 'twere with a defeated joy,
Taken to wife : nor have we herein barred
Your better wisdoms, which have freely gone
With this affair along. For all, our thanks.
Now follows, that you know, young Fortinbras,
Holding a weak supposal of our worth,
Or thinking by our late dear brother's death
Our State to be disjoint and out of frame,
Colleagued with the dream of his advantage,
He hath not failed to pester us with message,
Importing the surrender of those lands
Lost by his father, with all bonds of law,
To our most valiant brother. So much for him.
And now, Laertes, what's the news with you ?
You told us of some suit ; what wouldst thou beg, Laertes,
That shall not be my offer, not thy asking ?
The head is not more native to the heart,
The hand more instrumental to the mouth,
Than is the throne of Denmark to thy father.
What wouldst thou have, Laertes ?

LAERTES. My dread lord,
Your leave and favour to return to France;
From whence though willingly I came to Denmark,
To show my duty in your coronation,
Yet now, I must confess, that duty done,
My thoughts and wishes bend again toward France,
And bow them to your gracious leave and pardon.

KING. Have you your father's leave ? What says Polonius ?

POLONIUS. He hath, my lord, wrung from me my slow leave
By laboursome petition, and at last
I do beseech you, give him leave to go.

KING. Take thy fair hour, Laertes ; time be thine,
And thy best graces spend it at thy will !
But now, my cousin Hamlet, and my son,
How is it that the clouds still hang on you ?

HAMLET. Not so, my lord ; I am too much i' the sun.

QUEEN. Good Hamlet, cast thy nighted colour off,
And let thine eye look like a friend on Denmark.
Do not for ever with thy vailèd lids
Seek for thy noble father in the dust :
Thou know'st tis common ; all that lives must die,
Passing through nature to eternity.

HAMLET. Ay, madam, it is common.

QUEEN. If it be,
Why seems it so particular with thee ?

HAMLET. Seems, madam ! nay, it is ; I know not *seems*.

Tis not alone my inky cloak, good mother,
Nor customary suits of solemn black,
Nor windy suspiration of forced breath,
No, nor the fruitful river in the eye,
Nor the dejected 'haviour of the visage,
Together with all forms, moods, shapes of grief,
That can denote me truly : these indeed *seem*,
For they are actions that a man might play :
But I have that within which passeth show ;
These but the trappings and the suits of woe.

KING. Tis sweet and commendable in your nature, Hamlet,
To give these mourning duties to your father ;
But, you must know, your father lost a father ;
That father lost, lost his, and the survivor bound
In filial obligation for some term
To do obsequious sorrow ; but to persevere
In obstinate condolement is a course
Of impious stubbornness ; tis unmanly grief ;
It shows a will most incorrect to heaven,
A heart unfortified, a mind impatient,
An understanding simple and unschooled :
For what we know must be, and is as common
As any the most vulgar thing to sense,
Why should we in our peevish opposition
Take it to heart ? Fie ! tis a fault to heaven,
A fault against the dead, a fault to nature,
To reason most absurd—whose common theme
Is death of fathers, and who still hath cried,
From the first corse till he that died today :
This must be so. We pray you, throw to earth
This unprevailing woe, and think of us
As of a father : for, let the world take note,
You are the most immediate to our throne ;
And with no less nobility of love
Than that which dearest father bears his son
Do I impart toward you. For your intent
In going back to school in Wittenberg,
It is most retrograde to our desire ;
And we beseech you, bend you, to remain
Here, in the cheer and comfort of our eye,
Our chiefest courtier, cousin, and our son.

QUEEN. Let not thy mother lose her prayers, Hamlet :
I pray thee, stay with us ; go not to Wittenberg.

HAMLET. I shall in all my best obey you, madam.

KING. Why, tis a loving and a fair reply :
Be as ourself in Denmark. Madam, come ;

This gentle and unforced accord of Hamlet
Sits smiling to my heart.

HAMLET (*alone*). O, that this too too solid flesh would melt,
Thaw, and resolve itself into a dew!
Or that the Everlasting had not fixed
His canon gainst self-slaughter! O God! God!
How weary, stale, flat, and unprofitable
Seem to me all the uses of this world!
Fie on't! ah fie! tis an unweeded garden
That grows to seed; things rank and gross in nature
Possess it merely. That it should come to this!
But two months dead (nay, not so much, not two):
So excellent a king; so loving to my mother
That he might not beteem the winds of heaven
Visit her face too roughly. Heaven and earth!
Must I remember? Why, she would hang on him,
As if increase of appetite had grown
By what it fed on: and yet, within a month
(Let me not think on't—Frailty, thy name is woman!)
A little month, or ere those shoes were old
With which she followed my poor father's body,
Like Niobe, all tears:—why she, even she
(O God! a beast, that wants discourse of reason,
Would have mourned longer) married with my uncle,
My father's brother, but no more like my father
Than I to Hercules: within a month:
Ere yet the salt of most unrighteous tears
Had left the flushing in her gallèd eyes,
She married. O, most wicked speed!
It is not nor it cannot come to good.
But break, my heart, for I must hold my tongue.

Enter Horatio, Marcellus, and Bernardo

HORATIO. Hail to your lordship!

HAMLET. I am glad to see you well:
Horatio—or I do forget myself.

HORATIO. The same, my lord, and your poor servant ever.

HAMLET. Sir, my good friend; I'll change that name with you;
And what make you from Wittenberg, Horatio? Marcellus?

MARCELLUS. My good lord—

HAMLET. I am very glad to see you. Good-even, sir.
But what, in faith, make you from Wittenberg?

HORATIO. A truant disposition, good my lord.

HAMLET. I would not hear your enemy say so,
Nor shall you do mine ear that violence,
To make it truster of your own report

Against yourself: I know you are no truant.
But what is your affair in Elsinore?

HORATIO. My lord, I came to see your father's funeral.

HAMLET. I pray thee, do not mock me, fellow-student;
I think it was to see my mother's wedding.

HORATIO. Indeed, my lord, it followed hard upon.

HAMLET. Thrift, thrift, Horatio! the funeral baked meats
Did coldly furnish forth the marriage tables.
Would I had met my dearest foe in heaven
Or ever I had seen that day, Horatio!
My father!—methinks I see my father.

HORATIO. Where, my lord?

HAMLET. In my mind's eye, Horatio.

HORATIO. I saw him once; he was a goodly king.

HAMLET. He was a man, take him for all in all,
I shall not look upon his like again.

HORATIO. My lord, I think I saw him yesternight.

HAMLET. Saw? whom?

HORATIO. My lord, the king your father.

HAMLET. The king my father!
For God's love, let me hear.

HORATIO. Two nights together had these gentlemen,
Marcellus and Bernardo, on their watch,
In the dead vast and middle of the night,
Been thus encountered. A figure like your father,
Armed at point exactly, cap-a-pe,
Appears before them, and with solemn march
Goes slow and stately by them: thrice he walked
By their oppressed and fear-surprisèd eyes,
Within his truncheon's length; whilst they, distilled
Almost to jelly with the act of fear,
Stand dumb and speak not to him. This to me
In dreadful secrecy impart they did;
And I with them the third night kept the watch:
Where, as they had delivered, both in time,
Form of the thing, each word made true and good,
The apparition comes. I knew your father;
These hands are not more like.

HAMLET. But where was this?

MARCELLUS. My lord, upon the platform where we watched.

HAMLET. Did you not speak to it?

HORATIO. My lord, I did,
But answer made it none: yet once methought
It lifted up its head and did address
Itself to motion, like as it would speak;

But even then the morning cock crew loud,
And at the sound it shrunk in haste away,
And vanished from our sight.

HAMLET. Tis very strange.
Hold you the watch tonight?

MARCELLUS. We do, my lord.

HAMLET. Armed, say you?

MARCELLUS. Armed, my lord.

HAMLET. From top to toe?

MARCELLUS. My lord, from head to foot

HAMLET. Then saw you not his face?

HORATIO. O, yes, my lord; he wore his beaver up.

HAMLET. What looked he—frowningly?

HORATIO. A countenance more in sorrow than in anger.

HAMLET. I would I had been there.

HORATIO. It would have much amazed you.

HAMLET. Very like, very like. Stayed it long?

HORATIO. While one with moderate haste might tell a hundred.

HAMLET. I will watch tonight;
Perchance 'twill walk again.
If it assume my noble father's person,
I'll speak to it, though hell itself should gape
And bid me hold my peace. I pray you all,
If you have hitherto concealed this sight,
Give it an understanding, but no tongue:
I will requite your loves. So, fare you well:
Upon the platform, 'twixt eleven and twelve,
I'll visit you: farewell.
My father's spirit in arms! all is not well;
I doubt some foul play: would the night were come!
Till then sit still, my soul: foul deeds will rise,
Though all the earth o'erwhelm them, to men's eyes.

Scene 3—A Room in the House of Polonius

LAERTES. My necessaries are embarked: farewell!
And, sister, as the winds give benefit
And convoy is assistant, do not sleep,
But let me hear from you.

OPHELIA. Do you doubt that?

LAERTES. For Hamlet and the trifling of his favour,
Hold it a fashion and a toy in blood,
A violet in the youth of primy nature,
Forward, not permanent, sweet, not lasting,
The perfume and suppliance of a minute;
No more. Think it no more:

For he himself is subject to his birth :
He may not, as unvalued persons do,
Carve for himself ; for on his choice depends
The safety and health of this whole State ;
Fear it, Ophelia, fear it, my dear sister,
And keep you in the rear of your affection.

OPHELIA. I shall the effect of this good lesson keep,
As watchman to my heart. But, good my brother,
Do not, as some ungracious pastors do,
Show me the steep and thorny way to heaven ;
Whiles, like a puffed and reckless libertine,
Himself the primrose path of dalliance treads,
And recks not his own rede.

LAERTES. O, fear me not.
I stay too long : but here my father comes.

POLONIUS. Yet here, Laertes ! aboard, aboard, for shame !
The wind sits in the shoulder of your sail,
And you are stayed for. There ; my blessing with thee !
And these few precepts in thy memory.
See thou character. Give thy thoughts no tongue,
Nor any unproportioned thought his act.
Be thou familiar, but by no means vulgar.
Those friends thou hast, and their adoption tried,
Grapple them to thy soul with hoops of steel ;
But do not dull thy palm with entertainment
Of each new-hatched, unfledged comrade. Beware
Of entrance to a quarrel, but, being in,
Bear 't that the opposèd may beware of thee.
Give every man thine ear, but few thy voice ;
Take each man's censure, but reserve thy judgment.
Costly thy habit as thy purse can buy,
But not expressed in fancy ; rich, not gaudy,
For the apparel oft proclaims the man.
Neither a borrower nor a lender be ;
For loan oft loses both itself and friend,
And borrowing dulls the edge of husbandry.
This above all : to thine own self be true,
And it must follow, as the night the day,
Thou canst not then be false to any man.
Farewell : my blessing season this in thee !

LAERTES. Most humbly do I take my leave, my lord.
Farewell, Ophelia ; and remember well
What I have said to you.

OPHELIA. Tis in my memory locked,
And you yourself shall keep the key of it.

LAERTES. Farewell.

POLONIUS. What is't, Ophelia, he hath said to you ?

OPHELIA. So please you, something touching the Lord Hamlet.

POLONIUS. Marry, well bethought :
Tis told me he hath very oft of late
Given private time to you ; and you yourself
Have of your audience been most free and bounteous :
If it be so, as so tis put on me,
And that in way of caution, I must tell you,
You do not understand yourself so clearly
As it behoves my daughter and your honour.
What is between you ? Give me up the truth.

OPHELIA. He hath, my lord, of late made many tenders
Of his affection to me.

POLONIUS. Affection ! pooh ! you speak like a green girl,
Unsifted in such perilous circumstance.
Do you believe his tenders, as you call them ?

OPHELIA. I do not know, my lord, what I should think.

POLONIUS. Marry, I'll teach you : think yourself a baby
That you have ta'en these tenders for true pay,
Which are not sterling. Tender yourself more dearly.

OPHELIA. My lord, he hath importuned me with love
In honourable fashion.

POLONIUS. Ay, fashion you may call it ; go to, go to.

OPHELIA. And hath given countenance to his speech, my lord,
With almost all the holy vows of heaven.

POLONIUS. Ay, springes to catch woodcocks. From this time
Be somewhat scanter of your maiden presence ;
Set your entreatments at a higher rate
Than a command to parley.
In few, Ophelia,
Do not believe his vows.
I would not, in plain terms, from this time forth,
Have you so slander any moment's leisure
As to give words or talk with the Lord Hamlet.
Look to 't, I charge you : come your ways.

OPHELIA. I shall obey, my lord.

Scene 4—The Platform

HAMLET. The air bites shrewdly ; it is very cold.

HORATIO. It is a nipping and an eager air.
Look, my lord, it comes ! (*The Ghost appears*)

HAMLET. Angels and ministers of grace defend us !
Be thou a spirit of health or goblin damned,
Bring with thee airs from heaven or blasts from hell,

Be thy intents wicked or charitable,
Thou comest in such a questionable shape
That I will speak to thee : I'll call thee Hamlet,
King, father, royal Dane : O, answer me !
Let me not burst in ignorance ; but tell
Why thy canonized bones, hearsèd in death,
Have burst their cerements ; why the sepulchre,
Wherein we saw thee quietly inurned,
Hath oped his ponderous and marble jaws
To cast thee up again. What may this mean,
That thou, dead corse, again in complete steel
Revisit'st thus the glimpses of the moon,
Making night hideous ; and we fools of nature
So horridly to shake our disposition
With thoughts beyond the reaches of our souls ?
Say, why is this ? wherefore ? what should we do ?

HORATIO. It beckons you to go away with it,
As if it some impartment did desire
To you alone.

MARCELLUS. Look, with what courteous action
It waves you to a more removèd ground :
But do not go with it.

HORATIO. No, by no means.

HAMLET. It will not speak ; then I will follow it.

HORATIO. Do not, my lord.

HAMLET. Why, what should be the fear ?
I do not set my life at a pin's fee ;
And for my soul, what can it do to that,
Being a thing immortal as itself ?
It waves me forth again : I'll follow it.

HORATIO. What if it tempt you toward the flood, my lord,
Or to the dreadful summit of the cliff
That beetles o'er his base into the sea,
And there assume some other horrible form,
Which might deprive your sovereignty of reason
And draw you into madness ? Think of it :
The very place puts toys of desperation,
Without more motive, into every brain
That looks so many fathoms to the sea
And hears it roar beneath.

HAMLET. It waves me still.
Go on ; I'll follow thee.

MARCELLUS. You shall not go, my lord.

HAMLET. Hold off your hands.

HORATIO. Be ruled ; you shall not go.

HAMLET. My fate cries out,
And makes each petty artery in this body
As hardy as the Nemean lion's nerve.
Still am I called. Unhand me, gentlemen.
By heaven, I'll make a ghost of him that lets me!
I say, Away! Go on; I'll follow thee.

HORATIO. He waxes desperate with imagination.

MARCELLUS. Let's follow; tis not fit thus to obey him.

HORATIO. Have after. To what issue will this come?

MARCELLUS. Something is rotten in the state of Denmark.

HORATIO. Heaven will direct it.

MARCELLUS. Nay, let's follow him.

Scene 5—Another Part of the Platform

HAMLET. Where wilt thou lead me? Speak; I'll go no further.

GHOST. Mark me.

HAMLET. I will.

GHOST. My hour is almost come.

HAMLET. Alas, poor ghost!

GHOST. Pity me not, but lend thy serious hearing
To what I shall unfold.

HAMLET. Speak; I am bound to hear.

GHOST. So art thou to revenge, when thou shalt hear.
I am thy father's spirit,
Doomed for a certain term to walk the night,
And for the day confined to fast in fires,
Till the foul crimes done in my days of nature
Are burnt and purged away. But that I am forbid
To tell the secrets of my prison-house,
I could a tale unfold whose lightest word
Would harrow up thy soul, freeze thy young blood,
Make thy two eyes, like stars, start from their spheres,
Thy knotted and combinèd locks to part
And each particular hair to stand an end,
Like quills upon the fretful porcupine:
But this eternal blazon must not be
To ears of flesh and blood. List, list, O, list!
If thou didst ever thy dear father love,
Revenge his foul and most unnatural murder.

HAMLET. Murder!

GHOST. Murder most foul, as in the best it is;
But this most foul, strange, and unnatural.

HAMLET. Haste me to know 't, that I, with wings as swift
As meditation or the thoughts of love,
May sweep to my revenge.

GHOST. I find thee apt;
And duller shouldst thou be than the fat weed
That roots itself in ease on Lethe wharf,
Wouldst thou not stir in this. Now, Hamlet, hear:
Tis given out that, sleeping in my orchard,
A serpent stung me; so the whole ear of Denmark
Is by a forgèd process of my death
Rankly abused: but know, thou noble youth,
The serpent that did sting thy father's life
Now wears his crown.

HAMLET. O my prophetic soul! my uncle!

GHOST. But, soft! methinks I scent the morning air;
Brief let me be. Sleeping within my orchard,
My custom always of the afternoon,
Upon my secure hour thy uncle stole,
With juice of cursèd hebenon in a vial,
And in the porches of my ears did pour
The leperous distilment.
Thus was I, sleeping, by a brother's hand
Of life, of crown, of queen, at once dispatched:
Cut off even in the blossoms of my sin,
No reckoning made, but sent to my account
With all my imperfections on my head:
O, horrible! O, horrible! most horrible!
If thou hast nature in thee, bear it not;
But, howsoever thou pursuest this act,
Taint not thy mind, nor let thy soul contrive
Against thy mother aught; leave her to heaven
And to those thorns that in her bosom lodge,
To prick and sting her. Fare thee well at once!
The glow-worm shows the matin to be near,
And 'gins to pale his uneffectual fire.
Adieu, adieu! Hamlet, remember me.

HAMLET. O all you host of heaven! O earth! what else?
Hold, hold, my heart! Remember thee!
Ay, thou poor ghost, while memory holds a seat
In this distracted globe. Remember thee!
Yea, from the table of my memory
I'll wipe away all trivial fond records,
All saws of books, all forms, all pressures past,
That youth and observation copied there;
And thy commandment all alone shall live
Within the book and volume of my brain,
Unmixed with baser matter: yes, by heaven!
O most pernicious woman!
O villain, villain, smiling villain!

My tables,—meet it is I set it down,
That one may smile, and smile, and be a villain;
At least I'm sure it may be so in Denmark.

HORATIO (*advancing*). What news, my lord?

HAMLET. O, wonderful!
There's ne'er a villain dwelling in all Denmark
But he's an arrant knave.

HORATIO. There needs no ghost, my lord, come from the grave
To tell us this.

HAMLET. Why, right; you are i' the right;
And so, without more circumstance at all,
I hold it fit that we shake hands and part:
You, as your business and desire shall point you:
For every man has business and desire,
Such as it is; and for mine own poor part,
Look you, I'll go pray. . . . Touching this vision here,
It is an honest ghost; that let me tell you:
For your desire to know what is between us,
O'ermaster it as you may. And now, good friends,
As you are friends, scholars, and soldiers,
Never make known what you have seen tonight.

BOTH. My lord, we will not.

HORATIO. O day and night, but this is wondrous strange!

HAMLET. And therefore as a stranger give it welcome.
There are more things in heaven and earth, Horatio,
Than are dreamt of in your philosophy.
But come;
Here, as before, never, so help you mercy,
How strange or odd soe'er I bear myself,
As I perchance hereafter shall think meet
To put an antic disposition on,
That you, at such times seeing me, never shall,
With arms encumbered thus, or this head-shake,
Or by pronouncing of some doubtful phrase,
As *Well, well, we know*, or *We could, an if we would*,
Or *If we list to speak*, or *There be, an if they might*,
Or such ambiguous giving out, to note
That you know aught of me: this not to do,
So grace and mercy at your most need help you,
Swear. So, gentlemen,
With all my love I do commend me to you:
And what so poor a man as Hamlet is
May do to express his love and friending to you,
God willing, shall not lack. Let us go in together;
And still your fingers on your lips, I pray.

The time is out of joint: O cursèd spite,
That ever I was born to set it right!

ACT 2

Scene 1—A Room in the House of Polonius

In this scene Polonius sends one of his lackeys, Reynaldo, secretly to discover what his son Laertes is doing in France.

Scene 2—A Room in the Castle

KING. Welcome, dear Rosencrantz and Guildenstern!
Moreover that we much did long to see you,
The need we have to use you did provoke
Our hasty sending. Something have you heard
Of Hamlet's transformation; so call it,
Since nor the exterior nor the inward man
Resembles that it was. What it should be,
More than his father's death, that thus hath put him
So much from the understanding of himself,
I cannot dream of: I entreat you both,
That, being of so young days brought up with him,
That you vouchsafe your rest here in our court
Some little time, so by your companies
To draw him on to pleasures, and to gather
Whether aught to us unknown afflicts him thus,
That, opened, lies within our remedy.

QUEEN. Good gentlemen, he hath much talked of you;
And sure I am two men there are not living
To whom he more adheres.

GUILDENSTERN. We both obey,
And here give up ourselves, in the full bent
To lay our service freely at your feet.

KING. Thanks, Rosencrantz and gentle Guildenstern.

QUEEN. Thanks, Guildenstern and gentle Rosencrantz:
And I beseech you instantly to visit
My too much changèd son. Go, some of you,
And bring these gentlemen where Hamlet is.

POLONIUS. My liege, and madam, to expostulate
What majesty should be, what duty is,
Why day is day, night night, and time is time,
Were nothing but to waste night, day, and time.
Therefore, since brevity is the soul of wit,
And tediousness the limbs and outward flourishes,
I will be brief: your noble son is mad.
Mad call I it; for, to define true madness,
What is't but to be nothing else but mad?
But let that go.

QUEEN. More matter, with less art.

POLONIUS. Madam, I swear I use no art at all.
That he is mad, tis true: tis true tis pity;
And pity tis tis true: a foolish figure;
But farewell it, for I will use no art.
Mad let us grant him, then; and now remains
That we find out the cause of this effect.
I have a daughter (have while she is mine)
Who, in her duty and obedience, mark,
Hath given me this: now gather, and surmise:

To the celestial and my soul's idol, the most beautified Ophelia:
Doubt thou the stars are fire; Doubt that the sun doth move;
Doubt truth to be a liar; But never doubt I love.
O dear Ophelia, I am ill at these numbers; I have not art to reckon my groans: but that I love thee best, O most best, believe it. Adieu.
Thine evermore, most dear lady, whilst this machine is to him,
HAMLET

This, in obedience, hath my daughter shown me.
KING. But how hath she received his love?
POLONIUS. What do you think of me?
KING. As of a man faithful and honourable.
POLONIUS. I would fain prove so. I went round to work,
And my young mistress thus I did bespeak:
Lord Hamlet is a prince, out of thy star;
This must not be; and then I precepts gave her,
That she should lock herself from his resort,
Admit no messengers, receive no tokens.
Which done, she took the fruits of my advice;
And he, repulsèd (a short tale to make)
Fell into a sadness, then into a fast,
Thence to a watch, thence into a weakness,
Thence to a lightness, and by this declension,
Into the madness wherein now he raves,
And all we mourn for.
KING. Do you think tis this?
QUEEN. It may be, very likely.
POLONIUS. Hath there been such a time (I'd fain know that)
That I have positively said *Tis so,*
When it proved otherwise?
KING. Not that I know. How may we try it further?
POLONIUS. You know, sometimes he walks for hours together.
QUEEN. So he does indeed.
POLONIUS. At such a time I'll loose my daughter to him:
Be you and I behind an arras then;
Mark the encounter: if he love her not
And be not from his reason fallen thereon,

Let me be no assistant for a State,
But keep a farm and carters.

KING. We will try it.

QUEEN. But, look, where sadly the poor wretch comes reading.

POLONIUS. Away, I do beseech you, both away . . .
How does my good Lord Hamlet ?

HAMLET. Well, God-a-mercy.

POLONIUS. Do you know me, my lord ?

HAMLET. Excellent well ; you are a fishmonger.

POLONIUS. Not I, my lord.

HAMLET. Then I would you were so honest a man.

POLONIUS. Honest, my lord !

HAMLET. Ay, sir ; to be honest, as this world goes, is to be one man picked out of ten thousand.

POLONIUS. That's very true, my lord.

HAMLET. Have you a daughter ?

POLONIUS. I have, my lord.

HAMLET. Let her not walk i' the sun.

POLONIUS (*aside*). Still harping on my daughter : yet he knew me not at first ; he said I was a fishmonger : he is far gone, far gone : and truly in my youth I suffered much extremity for love ; very near this. I'll speak to him again. What do you read, my lord ?

HAMLET. Words, words, words.

POLONIUS. What is the matter, my lord ?

HAMLET. Between whom ?

POLONIUS. I mean the matter that you read, my lord.

HAMLET. Slanders, sir, for the satirical rogue says here that old men have grey beards, that their faces are wrinkled, and that they have a plentiful lack of wit.

POLONIUS (*aside*). Though this be madness, yet there is method in't. I will leave him, and suddenly contrive the means of meeting between him and my daughter. My honourable lord, I will most humbly take my leave of you.

HAMLET. You cannot, sir, take from me anything that I will more willingly part withal, except my life, except my life, except my life.

POLONIUS. Fare you well, my lord.

HAMLET. These tedious old fools !
My excellent good friends ! How dost thou, Guildenstern ? Ah, Rosencrantz ! Good lads, how do ye both ? What's the news ?

ROSENCRANTZ. None, my lord, but that the world's grown honest.

HAMLET. Then is Doomsday near. But your news is not true. Let me question more in particular : what have you, my good friends, deserved at the hands of fortune that she send you to prison hither ?

GUILDENSTERN. Prison, my lord!

HAMLET. Denmark's a prison.

ROSENCRANTZ. Then is the world one.

HAMLET. A goodly one, in which there are many confines, wards, and dungeons, Denmark being one of the worst.

ROSENCRANTZ. We think not so, my lord.

HAMLET. Why, then, tis none to you; for there is nothing either good or bad, but thinking makes it so: to me it is a prison.

ROSENCRANTZ. Why then, your ambition makes it one; tis too narrow for your mind.

HAMLET. O God, I could be bounded in a nutshell and count myself a king of infinite space, were it not that I have bad dreams. But, in the beaten way of friendship, what make you at Elsinore?

ROSENCRANTZ. To visit you, my lord; no other occasion.

HAMLET. Beggar that I am, I am even poor in thanks, but I thank you. Were you not sent for? Is it your own inclining? Is it a free visitation? Come, deal justly with me: come, come; speak.

GUILDENSTERN. What should we say, my lord?

HAMLET. Why, anything, but to the purpose. You were sent for; and there is a kind of confession in your looks which your modesties have not craft enough to colour: I know the good king and queen have sent for you.

ROSENCRANTZ. To what end, my lord?

HAMLET. That you must teach me. But let me conjure you, by the rights of our fellowship, by the consonancy of our youth, by the obligation of our ever-preserved love, be even and direct with me, whether you were sent for, or no?

GUILDENSTERN. My lord, we were sent for.

HAMLET. I will tell you why; so shall my anticipation prevent your discovery, and your secrecy to the king and queen moult no feather. I have of late (but wherefore I know not) lost all my mirth, foregone all custom of exercises; and indeed it goes so heavily with my disposition that this goodly frame, the earth, seems to me a sterile promontory; this most excellent canopy, the air, this brave o'erhanging firmament, this majestical roof fretted with golden fire, appears no other thing to me than a foul and pestilent congregation of vapours. What a piece of work is a man! How noble in reason, how infinite in faculty, in form and moving how express and admirable, in action how like an angel, in apprehension how like a god—the beauty of the world, the paragon of animals! And yet, to me, what is this quintessence of dust? Man delights not me; no, nor woman neither, though by your smiling you seem to say so.

ROSENCRANTZ. My lord, there was no such stuff in my thoughts.

HAMLET. Why did you laugh, then, when I said *Man delights not me?*

Rosencrantz. To think, my lord, if you delight not in man, what Lenten entertainment the players shall receive from you: we caught them on the way; and hither are they coming, to offer you service.

Hamlet. What players are they?

Rosencrantz. Even those you were wont to take delight in, the tragedians of the city.

Guildenstern (*at sound of trumpets*). There are the players.

Hamlet. Gentlemen, you are welcome to Elsinore. You are welcome; but my uncle-father and aunt-mother are deceived.

Guildenstern. In what, my dear lord?

Hamlet. I am but mad north-north-west: when the wind is southerly I know a hawk from a handsaw.

Polonius (*approaching*). Well be with you, gentlemen!

Hamlet. Hark you, Guildenstern; and you too; at each ear a hearer: that great baby you see there is not yet out of his swaddling-clouts. I will prophesy he comes to tell me of the players; mark it.

Polonius. My lord, I have news to tell you.

Hamlet. My lord, I have news to tell you. When Roscius was an actor in Rome—

Polonius. The actors are come hither, my lord.

Hamlet. You are welcome, masters; welcome, all. I am glad to see thee well. Welcome, good friends. O, my old friend! thy face is valanced since I saw thee last. What, my young lady and mistress! Masters, you are all welcome. Good my lord, will you see the players well bestowed? Let them be well used, for they are the abstract and brief chronicles of the time: after your death you were better have a bad epitaph than their ill report while you live.

Polonius. My lord, I will use them according to their desert.

Hamlet. God's bodykins, man, much better; use every man after his desert, and who should scape whipping? Use them after your own honour and dignity: the less they deserve, the more merit is in your bounty. Take them in. Follow him, friends: we'll hear a play tomorrow. Dost thou hear me, old friend; can you play the Murder of Gonzago?

First Player. Ay, my lord.

Hamlet. We'll ha't tomorrow night. You could, for a need, study a speech of some dozen or sixteen lines, which I would set down and insert in't, could you not?

First Player. Ay, my lord.

Hamlet. Very well. Follow that lord; and look you mock him not. My good friends, I'll leave you till night: you are welcome to Elsinore.

Hamlet (*alone*). O, what a rogue and peasant slave am I!

Is it not monstrous that this player here,
But in a fiction, in a dream of passion,
Could force his soul so to his own conceit
That from her working all his visage wanned,
Tears in his eyes, distraction in his aspect,
A broken voice, and his whole function suiting
With forms to his conceit ? and all for nothing !
What would he do,
Had he the motive and the cue for passion
That I have ? He would drown the stage with tears
And cleave the general ear with horrid speech,
Make mad the guilty and appal the free,
Confound the ignorant, and amaze indeed
The very faculties of eyes and ears.
Yet I,
A dull and muddy-mettled rascal, peak,
Like John-a-dreams, unpregnant of my cause,
And can say nothing ; no, not for a king.
Am I a coward ?
Who calls me villain ? breaks my pate across ?
Plucks off my beard, and blows it in my face ?
Tweaks me by the nose ? gives me the lie i' the throat,
As deep as to the lungs ? Who does me this ?
O, vengeance !
Why, what an ass am I ! This is most brave,
That I, the son of a dear father murdered,
Prompted to my revenge by heaven and hell,
Must, like a cur, unpack my heart with words,
And fall a-cursing like a scullion !
Fie upon 't ! foh ! About, my brain ! I have heard
That guilty creatures sitting at a play
Have by the very cunning of the scene
Been struck so to the soul that presently
They have proclaimed their malefactions ;
For murder, though it have no tongue, will speak
With most miraculous organ. I'll have these players
Play something like the murder of my father
Before mine uncle : I'll observe his looks ;
I'll tent him to the quick ; if he but blench,
I know my course. The spirit that I have seen
May be the devil : and the devil hath power
To assume a pleasing shape ; yea, and perhaps,
Out of my weakness and my melancholy,
Abuses me. I'll have grounds
More relative than this : the play's the thing
Wherein I'll catch the conscience of the king.

ACT 3

Scene 1—A Room in the Castle

KING (*to Rosencrantz*). And can you, by no drift of circumstance,
Get from him why he puts on this confusion,
Grating so harshly all his days of quiet
With turbulent and dangerous lunacy?

ROSENCRANTZ. He does confess he feels himself distracted;
But from what cause he will by no means speak.

GUILDENSTERN. Nor do we find him forward to be sounded,
But, with a crafty madness, keeps aloof,
When we would bring him on to some confession
Of his true state.

QUEEN. Did he receive you well?

ROSENCRANTZ. Most like a gentleman.

QUEEN. Did you assay him to any pastime?

ROSENCRANTZ. Madam, it so fell out that certain players
We o'er-raught on the way: of these we told him,
And there did seem in him a kind of joy
To hear of it: they are about the court,
And, as I think, they have already order
This night to play before him.

POLONIUS. Tis most true:
And he beseeched me to entreat your majesties
To hear and see the matter.

KING. With all my heart; and it doth much content me
To hear him so inclined.
Good gentlemen, give him a further edge,
And drive his purpose on to these delights.

ROSENCRANTZ. We shall, my lord. (*They leave*)

KING. Sweet Gertrude, leave us too;
For we have closely sent for Hamlet hither,
That he, as 'twere by accident, may here
Affront Ophelia:
Her father and myself, lawful espials,
Will so bestow ourselves that, seeing, unseen,
We may of their encounter frankly judge,
And gather by him, as he is behaved,
If't be the affliction of his love or no
That thus he suffers for.

QUEEN. I shall obey you.
And for your part, Ophelia, I do wish
That your good beauties be the happy cause
Of Hamlet's wildness: so shall I hope your virtues
Will bring him to his wonted way again,
To both your honours.

OPHELIA. Madam, I wish it may.

POLONIUS. Ophelia, walk you here. Read on this book;
That show of such an exercise may colour
Your loneliness.
I hear him coming: let's withdraw, my lord.

HAMLET. To be, or not to be: that is the question:
Whether tis nobler in the mind to suffer
The slings and arrows of outrageous fortune,
Or to take arms against a sea of troubles,
And by opposing end them? To die: to sleep;
No more; and by a sleep to say we end
The heart-ache and the thousand natural shocks
That flesh is heir to—tis a consummation
Devoutly to be wished. To die, to sleep;
To sleep: perchance to dream; ay, there's the rub;
For in that sleep of death what dreams may come
When we have shuffled off this mortal coil,
Must give us pause. There's the respect
That makes calamity of so long life;
For who would bear the whips and scorns of time,
The oppressor's wrong, the proud man's contumely,
The pangs of despised love, the law's delay,
The insolence of office and the spurns
That patient merit of the unworthy takes,
When he himself might his quietus make
With a bare bodkin? Who would fardels bear,
To grunt and sweat under a weary life,
But that the dread of something after death,
The undiscovered country from whose bourn
No traveller returns, puzzles the will
And makes us rather bear those ills we have
Than fly to others that we know not of?
Thus conscience does make cowards of us all;
And thus the native hue of resolution
Is sicklied o'er with the pale cast of thought,
And enterprises of great pith and moment
With this regard their currents turn away,
And lose the name of action. Soft you now!
The fair Ophelia! Nymph, in thy orisons
Be all my sins remembered.

OPHELIA. Good my lord,
How does your honour for this many a day?

HAMLET. I humbly thank you; well, well, well.

OPHELIA. My lord, I have remembrances of yours,
That I have longèd long to re-deliver;
I pray you, now receive them.

HAMLET. No, not I;
I never gave you aught.

OPHELIA. My honoured lord, you know right well you did;
And with them words of so sweet breath composed
As made the things more rich: their perfume lost,
Take these again: for to the noble mind
Rich gifts wax poor when givers prove unkind.

HAMLET. Ha, ha! are you honest?

OPHELIA. My lord?

HAMLET. Are you fair?

OPHELIA. What means your lordship?

HAMLET. That if you be honest and fair your honesty should admit no discourse to your beauty.

OPHELIA. Could beauty, my lord, have better commerce than with honesty?

HAMLET. Ay, truly, for the power of beauty will sooner transform honesty from what it is to a rogue than the force of honesty can translate beauty into his likeness. I did love you once.

OPHELIA. Indeed, my lord, you made me believe so.

HAMLET. You should not have believed me; for virtue cannot so inoculate our old stock but we shall relish of it: I loved you not.

OPHELIA. I was the more deceived.

HAMLET. Get thee to a nunnery. I am myself indifferent honest; but yet I could accuse me of such things that it were better my mother had not borne me. I am very proud, revengeful, ambitious, with more offences at my beck than I have thoughts to put them in, imagination to give them shape, or time to act them in. What should such fellows as I do crawling between earth and heaven? We are arrant knaves, all; believe none of us. Go thy ways to a nunnery. Where's your father?

OPHELIA. At home, my lord.

HAMLET. Let the doors be shut upon him, that he may play the fool nowhere but in his own house. Farewell.

OPHELIA. O, help him, you sweet heavens!

HAMLET. If thou dost marry I'll give thee this plague for thy dowry: be thou as chaste as ice, as pure as snow, thou shalt not escape calumny. Get thee to a nunnery, go: farewell. Or, if thou wilt needs marry, marry a fool, for wise men know well enough what monsters you make of them. To a nunnery, go, and quickly too. Farewell.

OPHELIA. O heavenly powers, restore him!

HAMLET. I have heard of your paintings, too, well enough; God has given you one face, and you make yourselves another: you jig, you amble, and you lisp, and nickname God's creatures, and make your wantonness your ignorance. Go to, I'll no more on't; it hath made me mad.

OPHELIA. O what a noble mind is here o'erthrown!
The courtier's, soldier's, scholar's, eye, tongue, sword;
The expectancy and rose of the fair State,
The glass of fashion and the mould of form,
The observed of all observers, quite, quite down!
And I, of ladies most deject and wretched,
That sucked the honey of his music vows,
Now see that noble and most sovereign reason,
Like sweet bells jangled, out of tune and harsh;
That unmatched form and feature of blown youth
Blasted with ecstasy: O, woe is me,
To have seen what I have seen, see what I see!

Enter King and Polonius

KING. Love! his affections do not that way tend;
Nor what he spake, though it lacked form a little,
Was not like madness. There's something in his soul,
O'er which his melancholy sits on brood;
And I do doubt the hatch and the disclose
Will be some danger. He shall with speed to England,
For the demand of our neglected tribute:
Haply the seas and countries different
With variable objects shall expel
This something-settled matter in his heart,
Whereon his brains still beating puts him thus
From fashion of himself. What think you on't?

POLONIUS. It shall do well; but yet do I believe
The origin and commencement of his grief
Sprung from neglected love. How now, Ophelia!
You need not tell us what Lord Hamlet said:
We heard it all. My lord, do as you please;
But, if you hold it fit, after the play
Let his queen mother all alone entreat him
To show his grief: let her be round with him;
And I'll be placed, so please you, in the ear
Of all their conference. If she find him not,
To England send him, or confine him where
Your wisdom best shall think.

KING. It shall be so:
Madness in great ones must not unwatched go.

Scene 2—A Hall in the Castle

HAMLET (*to players*). Speak the speech, I pray you, as I pronounced it to you, trippingly on the tongue: but if you mouth it, as many of your players do, I had as lief the town-crier spoke my lines. Nor do not saw the air too much with your hand, thus, but, use all gently; for in the very torrent, tempest, and, as I may say, the whirlwind of passion, you must acquire and beget a temperance that may give it smoothness. O, it offends me to the soul to hear a robustious periwig-pated fellow tear a passion to tatters, to very rags, to split the ears of the groundlings, who for the most part are capable of nothing but inexplicable dumb-shows and noise: I would have such a fellow whipped; it out-herods Herod: pray you, avoid it.

First Player. I warrant your honour.

Hamlet. Be not too tame neither, but let your own discretion be your tutor. Suit the action to the word, the word to the action, with this special observance, that you o'erstep not the modesty of nature: for anything so overdone is from the purpose of playing, whose end, both at the first and now, was, and is, to hold, as 'twere, the mirror up to nature; to show virtue her own feature, scorn her own image, and the very age and body of the time his form and pressure. Now this overdone, or come tardy off, though it make the unskilful laugh, cannot but make the judicious grieve. O, there be players that I have seen play, and heard others praise, that, neither having the accent of Christians nor the gait of Christian, pagan, nor man, have so strutted and bellowed that I have thought some of nature's journeymen had made men and not made them well, they imitated humanity so abominably.

First Player. I hope we have reformed that indifferently with us, sir.

Hamlet. O, reform it altogether. And let those that play your clowns speak no more than is set down for them; for there be of them that will themselves laugh, to set on some quantity of barren spectators to laugh too; though, in the meantime, some necessary question of the play be then to be considered. That's villainous, and shows a most pitiful ambition in the fool that uses it. Go, make you ready. (*Enter Polonius*) How now, my lord! will the king hear this piece of work?

Polonius. And the queen too, and that presently.

Hamlet. Bid the players make haste. What ho! Horatio!

Horatio. Here, sweet lord, at your service.

Hamlet. Horatio, thou art e'en as just a man
As e'er my conversation coped withal.

Horatio. O, my dear lord—

Hamlet. Nay, do not think I flatter;
For what advancement may I hope from thee
That no revenue hast but thy good spirits
To feed and clothe thee? Why should the poor be flattered?
No, let the candied tongue lick absurd pomp,

And crook the pregnant hinges of the knee
Where thrift may follow fawning. Dost thou hear?
Since my dear soul was mistress of her choice
And could of men distinguish, her election
Hath sealed thee for herself; for thou hast been
As one, in suffering all, that suffers nothing,
A man that fortune's buffets and rewards
Hast ta'en with equal thanks; and blest are those
Whose blood and judgment are so well commingled
That they are not a pipe for fortune's finger
To sound what stop she please. Give me that man
That is not passion's slave, and I will wear him
In my heart's core, ay, in my heart of heart,
As I do thee. (Something too much of this!)
There is a play tonight before the king;
One scene of it comes near the circumstance
Which I have told thee of my father's death:
I prithee, when thou seest that act afoot,
Even with the very comment of thy soul
Observe mine uncle. Give him heedful note;
For I mine eyes will rivet to his face,
And after we will both our judgments join
In censure of his seeming.

HORATIO. Well, my lord:
If he steal aught the whilst this play is playing,
And scape detecting, I will pay the theft.

HAMLET. They are coming to the play; I must be idle: Get you a place.

KING (*approaching*). How fares our cousin Hamlet?

HAMLET. Excellent, i' faith.

QUEEN. Come hither, my dear Hamlet, sit by me.

HAMLET. No, good mother, here's metal more attractive.

POLONIUS. O, ho! do you mark that?

HAMLET. Lady, shall I lie in your lap? (*Lying at Ophelia's feet*)

OPHELIA. No, my lord.

HAMLET. I mean, my head upon your lap?

OPHELIA. You are merry, my lord.

HAMLET. Who, I?

OPHELIA. Ay, my lord.

HAMLET. What should a man do but be merry? for, look you, how cheerfully my mother looks, and my father died within these two hours.

OPHELIA. Nay, tis twice two months, my lord.

HAMLET. So long? O heavens! die two months ago, and not forgotten yet? Then there's hope a great man's memory may outlive his life half a year: but, by our lady, he must build churches, then; or else shall he suffer not thinking on.

The Dumb Show enters

Enter a king and a queen very lovingly. She kneels. He takes her up, and rests upon a bank of flowers. She, seeing him asleep, leaves him. Anon comes a fellow up to him, takes off his crown, kisses it, and pours poison in the king's ear. The queen returns to find the king dead. The poisoner comes in again, seeming to lament with her. The body is carried away. The poisoner woos the queen with gifts, and she accepts his love.

OPHELIA. What means this, my lord?

HAMLET. Marry, it means mischief.

OPHELIA. Belike this show imports the argument of the play.

HAMLET (*as Prologue enters*). We shall know by this fellow: the players cannot keep counsel; they'll tell all.

PROLOGUE. *For us, and for our tragedy,*
Here stooping to your clemency,
We beg your hearing patiently.

PLAYER KING. Faith, I must leave thee, love, and shortly too;
My operant powers their functions leave to do:
And thou shalt live in this fair world behind,
Honoured, beloved; and haply one as kind
For husband shalt thou—

PLAYER QUEEN. O, confound the rest!
Such love must needs be treason in my breast:
In second husband let me be accurst!
None wed the second but who killed the first.

HAMLET (*aside*). Wormwood, wormwood.

PLAYER QUEEN. The instances that second marriage move
Are base respects of thrift, but none of love.

PLAYER KING. I do believe you think what now you speak;
But what we do determine oft we break.
Our wills and fates do so contrary run
That our devices still are overthrown;
Our thoughts are ours, their ends none of our own:
So think thou wilt no second husband wed;
But die thy thoughts when thy first lord is dead.

PLAYER QUEEN. Nor earth to me give food, nor heaven light!
Sport and repose lock from me day and night!
To desperation turn my trust and hope!
An anchor's cheer in prison be my scope!
Both here and hence pursue me lasting strife,
If, once a widow, ever I be wife!

HAMLET. If she should break it now!

PLAYER KING. Tis deeply sworn. Sweet, leave me here awhile;

My spirits grow dull, and fain I would beguile
The tedious day with sleep.

PLAYER QUEEN. Sleep rock thy brain;
And never come mischance between us twain!

HAMLET. Madam, how like you this play?

QUEEN. The lady protests too much, methinks.

HAMLET. O, but she'll keep her word.

KING. Have you heard the argument? Is there no offence in't?

HAMLET. No, no, they do but jest, poison in jest; no offence i' the world.

KING. What do you call the play?

HAMLET. The Mouse Trap. This play is the image of a murder done in Vienna. Gonzago is the duke's name; his wife, Baptista; you shall see anon. Tis a knavish piece of work, but what o' that? Your majesty and we that have free souls, it touches us not: let the galled jade wince; our withers are unwrung. (*Enter Lucianus*) This is one Lucianus, nephew to the king.

OPHELIA. You are as good as a chorus, my lord.

LUCIANUS (*pouring poison into the sleeper's ear*). Thoughts black,
hands apt, drugs fit, and time agreeing;
Confederate season, else no creature seeing;
Thou mixture rank, of midnight weeds collected,
With Hecate's ban thrice blasted, thrice infected,
Thy natural magic and dire property,
On wholesome life usurp immediately.

HAMLET. He poisons him i' the garden for his estate. His name's Gonzago. The story is extant, and writ in choice Italian. You shall see anon how the murderer gets the love of Gonzago's wife.

OPHELIA. The King rises.

HAMLET. What, frighted with false fire!

QUEEN. How fares my lord?

POLONIUS. Give o'er the play.

KING. Give me some light: away!

ALL. Lights, lights, lights! (*All but Hamlet and Horatio leave*)

HAMLET. Why, let the stricken deer go sleep,
The hart ungallèd play;
For some must watch, while some must weep:
So runs the world away.

O good Horatio, I'll take the ghost's word for a thousand pound. Didst perceive?

HORATIO. Very well, my lord.

HAMLET. Upon the talk of the poisoning?

HORATIO. I did very well note him.

HAMLET. Ah, ha! Come, some music! Come, the recorders!

Enter Rosencrantz, and Guildenstern soon after

GUILDENSTERN. Good my lord, vouchsafe me a word with you.

HAMLET. Sir, a whole history.

GUILDENSTERN. The king, sir—

HAMLET. Ay, sir, what of him?

GUILDENSTERN. Is in his retirement marvellous distempered.

HAMLET. With drinks, sir?

GUILDENSTERN. No, my lord, rather with choler.

HAMLET. Your wisdom should show itself more richer to signify this to his doctor.

GUILDENSTERN. Good my lord, start not so wildly from my affair. The queen, your mother, in most great affliction of spirit, hath sent me to you.

HAMLET. You are welcome.

GUILDENSTERN. Nay, good my lord, this courtesy is not of the right breed. If it shall please you to make me a wholesome answer I will do your mother's commandment: if not, your pardon and my return shall be the end of my business.

HAMLET. My mother, you say—

ROSENCRANTZ. Then thus she says; your behaviour hath struck her into amazement. She desires to speak with you ere you go to bed.

HAMLET. We shall obey, were she ten times our mother. Have you any further trade with us?

ROSENCRANTZ. My lord, you once did love me.

HAMLET. So I do still, by these pickers and stealers.

ROSENCRANTZ. Good my lord, what is your cause of distemper? You do, surely, bar the door upon your own liberty if you deny your griefs to your friend.

HAMLET. Sir, I lack advancement.

ROSENCRANTZ. How can that be, when you have the voice of the king himself for your succession in Denmark?

HAMLET. Ay, but sir, *While the grass grows*—the proverb is something musty. (*Enter Players with recorders*) O, the recorders! let me see one. Will you play upon this pipe?

GUILDENSTERN. My lord, I cannot.

HAMLET. I pray you.

GUILDENSTERN. Believe me, I cannot.

HAMLET. I do beseech you.

GUILDENSTERN. I know no touch of it, my lord.

HAMLET. Tis as easy as lying: govern these ventages with your fingers and thumb, give it breath with your mouth, and it will discourse most eloquent music. Look you, these are the stops.

GUILDENSTERN. But these cannot I command to any utterance of harmony; I have not the skill.

HAMLET. Why, look you now, how unworthy a thing you make of me! You would play upon me; you would seem to know my stops; you would pluck out the heart of my mystery; you would sound me from my lowest note to the top of my compass: and there is much music, excellent voice, in this little organ; yet cannot you make it speak. Do you think I am easier to be played on than a pipe? Call me what instrument you will, though you can fret me, yet you cannot play upon me. (*Enter Polonius*) God bless you, sir!

POLONIUS. My lord, the queen would speak with you.

HAMLET. Do you see yonder cloud that's almost in shape of a camel?

POLONIUS. By the mass, and tis like a camel, indeed.

HAMLET. Methinks it is like a weasel.

POLONIUS. It is backed like a weasel.

HAMLET. Or like a whale?

POLONIUS. Very like a whale.

HAMLET. Then I will come to my mother by and by. They fool me to the top of my bent. I will come by and by.

POLONIUS. I will say so.

HAMLET. By and by is easily said. Leave me, friends.
Tis now the very witching time of night,
When churchyards yawn and hell itself breathes out
Contagion to this world. Now could I drink hot blood,
And do such bitter business as the day
Would quake to look on. Soft! now to my mother.
O heart, lose not thy nature; let not ever
The soul of Nero enter this firm bosom;
Let me be cruel, not unnatural:
I will speak daggers to her, but use none;
My tongue and soul in this be hypocrites.

Scene 3—A Room in the Castle

KING (*to Guildenstern*). I like him not, nor stands it safe with us
To let his madness range. Therefore prepare you;
I your commission will forthwith dispatch,
And he to England shall along with you:
The terms of our estate may not endure
Hazard so dangerous as doth hourly grow
Out of his lunacies.

GUILDENSTERN. We will ourselves provide:
Most holy and religious fear it is
To keep those many many bodies safe
That live and feed upon your majesty.

KING. Arm you, I pray you, to this speedy voyage.

Polonius (*entering*). My lord, he's going to his mother's closet:
Behind the arras I'll convey myself,
To hear the process; I'll warrant she'll tax him home.

King (*alone*). O, my offence is rank, it smells to heaven;
It hath the primal eldest curse upon't,
A brother's murder. Pray can I not,
Though inclination be as sharp as will:
My stronger guilt defeats my strong intent;
And, like a man to double business bound,
I stand in pause where I shall first begin,
And both neglect. What if this cursèd hand
Were thicker than itself with brother's blood,
Is there not rain enough in the sweet heavens
To wash it white as snow? But, O, what form of prayer
Can serve my turn? *Forgive me my foul murder?*
That cannot be; since I am still possessed
Of those effects for which I did the murder,
My crown, mine own ambition, and my queen.
May one be pardoned and retain the offence?
In the corrupted currents of this world
Offence's gilded hand may shove by justice,
And oft tis seen the wicked prize itself
Buys out the law: but tis not so above;
There is no shuffling, there the action lies
In his true nature. What then? What rests?
Try what repentance can: what can it not?
Yet what can it when one cannot repent?
O wretched state! Help, angels! Make assay!
Bow, stubborn knees; and, heart with strings of steel,
Be soft as sinews of the new-born babe!
All may be well. (*He retires and kneels*)

Hamlet (*entering*). Now might I do it pat, now he is praying!
And now I'll do it; and so he goes to heaven;
And so am I revenged. That would be scanned:
A villain kills my father; and for that,
I, his sole son, do this same villain send
To heaven.
O, this is hire and salary, not revenge.
He took my father grossly, full of bread;
With all his crimes broad blown, as flush as May;
And how his audit stands who knows save heaven?
But in our circumstance and course of thought,
Tis heavy with him: and am I then revenged,
To take him in the purging of his soul,
When he is fit and seasoned for his passage?
No!
Up, sword; and know thou a more horrid hent

When he is drunk asleep, or in his rage,
At gaming, swearing, or about some act
That has no relish of salvation in't. My mother stays:
This physic but prolongs thy sickly days. (*He goes*)

KING (*rising*). My words fly up, my thoughts remain below:
Words without thoughts never to heaven go.

Scene 4—The Queen's Room ; enter Queen and Polonius

POLONIUS. He will come straight. Look you lay home to him:
Tell him his pranks have been too broad to bear with,
And that your grace hath screened and stood between
Much heat and him. Pray you, be round with him.

QUEEN. Fear me not: withdraw, I hear him coming.

Polonius hides behind the curtain

HAMLET (*entering*). Now, mother, what's the matter?

QUEEN. Hamlet, thou hast thy father much offended.

HAMLET. Mother, you have my father much offended.

QUEEN. Come, come, you answer with an idle tongue.

HAMLET. Go, go, you question with a wicked tongue.

QUEEN. Why, how now, Hamlet!

HAMLET. What's the matter now?

QUEEN. Have you forgot me?

HAMLET. No, by the rood, not so:
You are the queen, your husband's brother's wife;
And (would it were not so!) you are my mother.

QUEEN. Nay, then, I'll set those to you that can speak.

HAMLET. Come, come and sit you down; you shall not budge;
You go not till I set you up a glass
Where you may see the inmost part of you.

QUEEN. What wilt thou do? thou wilt not murder me?
Help, help, ho!

POLONIUS (*behind*). What, ho! help, help, help!

HAMLET. How now! a rat! Dead, for a ducat, dead!

He makes a pass with his sword through the curtain

POLONIUS. O, I am slain!

QUEEN. O me, what hast thou done?

HAMLET. Nay, I know not:
Is it the king?

QUEEN. O, what a rash and fearful deed is this!

HAMLET. A fearful deed! almost as bad, good mother,
As kill a king, and marry with his brother.

QUEEN. As kill a king!

HAMLET. Ay, lady, 'twas my word.

He lifts up the curtain and discovers Polonius

Thou wretched, rash, intruding fool, farewell!
I took thee for thy better: take thy fortune;
Thou find'st to be too busy is some danger.
Leave wringing of your hands: peace! sit you down,
And let me wring your heart; for so I shall,
If it be made of penetrable stuff,
If custom have not brassed it so
That it is proof and bulwark against sense.

QUEEN. What have I done, that thou darest wag thy tongue
In noise so rude against me?

HAMLET. Such an act
That blurs the grace and blush of modesty,
Calls virtue hypocrite, takes off the rose
From the fair forehead of an innocent love
And sets a blister there, makes marriage-vows
As false as dicers' oaths.

QUEEN. Ay me, what act, that roars so loud?

HAMLET. Look here, upon this picture, and on this,
The counterfeit presentment of two brothers.
See what a grace was seated on this brow;
Hyperion's curls; the front of Jove himself;
An eye like Mars, to threaten and command;
A station like the herald Mercury
New-lighted on a heaven-kissing hill;
A combination and a form indeed,
Where every god did seem to set his seal,
To give the world assurance of a man:
This was your husband. Look you now, what follows:
Here is your husband; like a mildewed ear,
Blasting his wholesome brother. Have you eyes?
Could you on this fair mountain leave to feed
And batten on this moor? Ha! have you eyes?
You cannot call it love; for at your age
The heyday in the blood is tame, it's humble,
And waits upon the judgment: and what judgment
Would step from this to this? What devil was't
That thus hath cozened you at hoodman-blind?
Eyes without feeling, feeling without sight,
Ears without hands or eyes, smelling sans all,
Or but a sickly part of one true sense
Could not so mope. O shame! where is thy blush?

QUEEN. O Hamlet, speak no more:
Thou turn'st mine eyes into my very soul.
These words, like daggers, enter in mine ears;
No more, sweet Hamlet!

HAMLET. A murderer and a villain;

A slave that is not twentieth part the tithe
Of your precedent lord; a vice of kings;
A cutpurse of the empire and the rule,
That from a shelf the precious diadem stole,
And put it in his pocket!

QUEEN. No more!

HAMLET. A king of shreds and patches.

Here the Ghost appears, visible to Hamlet only

Save me, and hover o'er me with your wings,
You heavenly guards! What would your gracious figure?

QUEEN. Alas, he's mad!

HAMLET. Do you not come your tardy son to chide,
That, lapsed in time and passion, lets go by
The important acting of your dread command?
O, say!

GHOST. Do not forget: this visitation
Is but to whet thy almost blunted purpose.
But, look, amazement on thy mother sits:
O, step between her and her fighting soul;
Speak to her, Hamlet.

HAMLET. How is it with you, lady?

QUEEN. Alas, how is't with you,
That you do bend your eye on vacancy
And with the incorporal air do hold discourse?
Forth at your eyes your spirits wildly peep;
O gentle son,
Upon the heat and flame of thy distemper
Sprinkle cool patience. Whereon do you look?

HAMLET. On him, on him! Look you, how pale he glares!

QUEEN. To whom do you speak this?

HAMLET. Do you see nothing there?

QUEEN. Nothing at all; yet all that is I see.

HAMLET. Nor did you nothing hear?

QUEEN. No, nothing but ourselves.

HAMLET. Why, look you there! look, how it steals away!
My father, in his habit as he lived!
Look, where he goes, even now, out at the portal!

QUEEN. This is the very coinage of your brain.

HAMLET. My pulse, as yours, doth temperately keep time,
And makes as healthful music: it is not madness
That I have uttered. Mother, for love of grace,
Lay not that flattering unction to your soul,
That not your trespass but my madness speaks:
Confess yourself to heaven;

Repent what's past; avoid what is to come;
And do not spread the compost on the weeds,
To make them ranker.

QUEEN. O Hamlet, thou hast cleft my heart in twain.

HAMLET. O, throw away the worser part of it,
And live the purer with the other half:
Assume a virtue if you have it not.
Once more, Good-night:
And when you are desirous to be blessed
I'll blessing beg of you. For this same lord
I do repent; but heaven hath pleased it so,
To punish me with this and this with me,
That I must be their scourge and minister.
I will bestow him, and will answer well
The death I gave him. So, again, Good-night.
I must be cruel, only to be kind:
Thus bad begins and worse remains behind.
One word more, good lady.
I must to England; you know that?

QUEEN. Alack, I had forgot: tis so concluded on.

HAMLET. There's letters sealed; and my two schoolfellows,
Whom I will trust as I will adders fanged,
They bear the mandate; they must sweep my way,
And marshal me to knavery. Let it work;
For tis the sport to have the engineer
Hoist with his own petar: and 't shall go hard
But I will delve one yard below their mines,
And blow them at the moon. O, tis most sweet,
When in one line two crafts directly meet.
Mother, Good-night.

ACT 4

Scene 1—A Room in the Castle

QUEEN. Ah, my good lord, what have I seen tonight!

KING. What, Gertrude? How does Hamlet?

QUEEN. Mad as the sea and wind, when both contend
Which is the mightier: in his lawless fit,
Behind the arras hearing something stir,
Whips out his rapier, cries, *A rat, a rat!*
And, in this brainish apprehension, kills
The unseen good old man.

KING. O heavy deed!
It had been so with us, had we been there:
His liberty is full of threats to all;
To you yourself, to us, to every one.
Alas, how shall this deed be answered?
Where is he gone?

QUEEN. To draw apart the body he hath killed,
O'er whom his very madness, like some ore
Among a mineral of metals base,
Shows itself pure ; he weeps for what is done.

KING. O Gertrude, come away !
The sun no sooner shall the mountains touch,
But we will ship him hence.
Ho, Guildenstern ! Go with some further aid :
Hamlet in madness hath Polonius slain,
And from his mother's closet hath he dragged him :
Go seek him out ; speak fair, and bring the body
Into the chapel. I pray you, haste in this.
Come, Gertrude, we'll call up our wisest friends,
And let them know both what we mean to do
And what's untimely done. O, come away !
My soul is full of discord and dismay.

Scene 2—In the Castle

Rosencrantz and Guildenstern are sent by the King to discover where Hamlet has placed the body of Polonius, but he dislikes and suspects them, and they gain no information from him.

Scene 3—A Room in the Castle

KING. I have sent to seek him, and to find the body.
How dangerous is it that this man goes loose !
Yet must not we put the strong law on him :
He's loved of the distracted multitude,
Who like not in their judgment, but their eyes :
This sudden sending him away must seem
Deliberate pause ; diseases desperate grown
By desperate appliance are relieved,
Or not at all. Bring him before us.

ROSENCRANTZ. Ho, Guildenstern ! bring in my lord.

KING. Hamlet, this deed, for thine especial safety
(Which we do tender, as we dearly grieve
For that which thou hast done) must send thee hence
With fiery quickness : therefore prepare thyself ;
The bark is ready, and the wind at help,
The associates tend, and everything is bent
For England.

HAMLET. Good.

KING. So is it, if thou knew'st our purposes.

HAMLET. I see a cherub that sees them. But come ; for England ! Farewell, dear mother. (*He leaves*)

KING. Follow him at foot ; tempt him with speed aboard ;
Delay it not ; I'll have him hence tonight :

Away! for everything is sealed and done
That else leans on the affair: pray you, make haste.
And, England, if my love thou hold'st at aught
Thou mayst not coldly set
Our sovereign process; which imports at full,
By letters congruing to that effect,
The present death of Hamlet. Do it, England;
For like the hectic in my blood he rages,
And thou must cure me: till I know tis done,
Howe'er my haps, my joys were ne'er begun.

Scene 4—A Plain in Denmark

Hamlet meets a Norwegian force crossing Danish territory to attack Poland for a worthless scrap of territory. The force is under the command of a nephew of King Fortinbras. That they should destroy thousands of lives for so little, while he cannot summon up resolution to avenge his father's wrongs, agitates Hamlet's mind afresh.

Scene 5—A Room in the Castle at Elsinore

Enter Queen, Horatio, and a Gentleman

QUEEN. I will not speak with her.

GENTLEMAN. She is importunate, indeed distract;
Her mood will needs be pitied.

QUEEN. What would she have?

GENTLEMAN. She speaks much of her father: says she hears
There's tricks i' the world; and hems, and beats her heart;
Spurns enviously at straws; speaks things in doubt
That carry but half-sense.

HORATIO. Twere good she were spoken with; for she may strew
Dangerous conjectures in ill-breeding minds.

QUEEN. Let her come in.
To my sick soul, as sin's true nature is,
Each toy seems prologue to some great amiss:
So full of artless jealousy is guilt,
It spills itself in fearing to be spilt.

OPHELIA. Where is the beauteous majesty of Denmark?

QUEEN. How now, Ophelia!

OPHELIA (*singing*). How should I your true love know
From another one?
By his cockle hat and staff,
And his sandal shoon.

He is dead and gone, lady,
He is dead and gone;
At his head a grass-green turf,
At his heels a stone.

QUEEN. Nay, but, Ophelia—

OPHELIA. Pray you, mark.

White his shroud as the mountain snow,
Larded with sweet flowers;
Which bewept to the grave did go
With true-love showers.

KING (*entering*). How do you, pretty lady?

OPHELIA. They say the owl was a baker's daughter. Lord, we know what we are, but know not what we may be. God be at your table!

KING. Conceit upon her father.

OPHELIA. Pray you, let's have no words of this; but when they ask you what it means, say you this:

Tomorrow is Saint Valentine's day,
All in the morning betime,
And I a maid at your window,
To be your Valentine.

KING. Pretty Ophelia. How long hath she been thus?

OPHELIA. I hope all will be well. We must be patient: but I cannot choose but weep, to think they should lay him i' the cold ground. My brother shall know of it; and so I thank you for your good counsel. Come, my coach! Good-night, ladies: Good-night, sweet ladies; Good-night, Good-night.

KING. Follow her close: give her good watch, I pray you.
O, this is the poison of deep grief; it springs
All from her father's death. O Gertrude, Gertrude,
When sorrows come, they come not single spies
But in battalions. First, her father slain:
Next, your son gone, and he most violent author
Of his own just remove: the people muddied,
Thick and unwholesome in their thoughts and whispers,
For good Polonius' death; and we have done but greenly,
In hugger-mugger to inter him: poor Ophelia,
Divided from herself and her fair judgment,
Without the which we are pictures, or mere beasts:
Last, and as much containing as all these,
Her brother is in secret come from France;
Feeds on his wonder, keeps himself in clouds,
And wants not buzzers to infect his ear
With pestilent speeches of his father's death.

QUEEN. Alack, what noise is this?

KING. Where are my Switzers? Let them guard the door.
What is the matter?

GENTLEMAN (*appearing*). Save yourself, my lord:
The ocean, overpeering of his list,
Eats not the flats with more impetuous haste

Than young Laertes, in a riotous head,
O'erbears your officers. The rabble call him lord;
And, as the world were now but to begin,
Antiquity forgot, custom not known,
They cry *Choose we: Laertes shall be king:*
Caps, hands, and tongues, applaud it to the clouds:
Laertes shall be king, Laertes king!

QUEEN. How cheerfully on the false trail they cry!

KING. The doors are broke. (*Laertes bursts in*)

LAERTES. Where is this king? Sirs, stand you all without.
I thank you; keep the door. O thou vile king,
Give me my father!

QUEEN. Calmly, good Laertes.

KING. Let him go, Gertrude; do not fear our person:
There's such divinity doth hedge a king,
That treason can but peep to what it would,
Acts little of his will. Tell me, Laertes,
Why thou art thus incensed.

LAERTES. Where is my father?

KING. Dead.

LAERTES. How came he dead? I'll not be juggled with:
Let come what comes; only I'll be revenged.

KING. Good Laertes. If you desire to know the certainty
Of your dear father's death, is 't writ in your revenge,
That, swoopstake, you will draw both friend and foe?

LAERTES. None but his enemies.

KING. Why, now you speak
Like a good child and a true gentleman.
That I am guiltless of your father's death,
And am most sensibly in grief for it,
It shall as level to your judgment pierce
As day does to your eye.

LAERTES. How now! What noise is that?

Ophelia enters

O heat, dry up my brains! tears seven times salt,
Burn out the sense and virtue of mine eye!
By heaven, thy madness shall be paid by weight,
Till our scale turn the beam. O rose of May!
Dear maid, kind sister, sweet Ophelia!
O heavens! is't possible, a young maid's wits
Should be as mortal as an old man's life?
Nature is fine in love, and where tis fine
It sends some precious instance of itself
After the thing it loves.

Ophelia sings

They bore him barefaced on the bier;
Hey non nonny, nonny, hey nonny;
And in his grave rained many a tear—

Fare you well, my dove!

LAERTES. Hadst thou thy wits, and didst persuade revenge,
It could not move thus.

OPHELIA. There's rosemary; that's for remembrance; pray, love, remember: and there is pansies; that's for thoughts. There's fennel for you, and columbines: there's rue for you; and here's some for me: we may call it herb-grace o' Sundays: O, you must wear your rue with a difference. There's a daisy: I would give you some violets, but they withered all when my father died: they say he made a good end—

For bonny sweet Robin is all my joy.

LAERTES. Thought and affliction, passion, hell itself,
She turns to favour and to prettiness.

Ophelia passes by singing

And will he not come again?
And will he not come again?
No, no, he is dead:
Go to thy deathbed:
He never will come again.

His beard was as white as snow,
All flaxen was his poll:
He is gone, he is gone,
And we cast away moan:
God ha' mercy on his soul!

And of all Christian souls, I pray God. God be wi' ye.

LAERTES. Do you see this, O God?

KING. Laertes, I must commune with your grief,
Or you deny me right. Go but apart,
Make choice of whom your wisest friends you will,
And they shall hear and judge 'twixt you and me:
If by direct or by collateral hand
They find us touched, we will our kingdom give,
Our crown, our life, and all that we call ours,
To you in satisfaction; but if not,
Be you content to lend your patience to us,
And we shall jointly labour with your soul
To give it due content.

LAERTES. Let this be so;
His means of death, his obscure funeral
(No trophy, sword, nor hatchment o'er his bones,
No noble rite nor formal ostentation)
Cry to be heard, as 'twere from heaven to earth,
That I must call 't in question.

KING. So you shall;
And where the offence is let the great axe fall.
I pray you, go with me.

Scene 6—A Room in the Castle

HORATIO. What are they that would speak with me ?

SERVANT. Sailors, sir : they say they have letters for you.

HORATIO. Let them come in.
I do not know from what part of the world
I should be greeted, if not from Lord Hamlet.

SAILOR (*entering*). God bless you, sir.

HORATIO. Let Him bless thee too.

SAILOR. He shall, sir, an't please Him. There's a letter for you, sir : it comes from the ambassador that was bound for England, if your name be Horatio. (*Horatio reads the letter*)

Horatio, when thou shalt have overlooked this, give these fellows some means to the king : they have letters for him. Ere we were two days old at sea, a pirate of very warlike appointment gave us chase. Finding ourselves too slow of sail, we put on a compelled valour, and in the grapple I boarded them. On the instant they got clear of our ship, so I alone became their prisoner. They have dealt with me like thieves of mercy, but they knew what they did ; I am to do a good turn for them. Let the king have the letters I have sent ; and repair thou to me with as much speed as thou wouldst fly death. I have words to speak in thine ear will make thee dumb. These good fellows will bring thee where I am. Rosencrantz and Guildenstern hold their course for England : of them I have much to tell thee. Farewell. He that thou knowest thine, HAMLET.

Come, I will make you way for these your letters ;
And do 't the speedier, that you may direct me
To him from whom you brought them.

Scene 7—A Room in the Castle

Enter the King and Laertes

KING. Now must your conscience my acquittance seal,
And you must put me in your heart for friend,
Since you have heard, and with a knowing ear,
That he which hath your noble father slain
Pursued my life.

LAERTES. It well appears ; but tell me
Why you proceeded not against these feats,
So crimeful and so capital in nature.

KING. O, for two special reasons. The queen his mother
Lives almost by his looks. The other motive
Is the great love the general gender bear him.

LAERTES. And so have I a noble father lost ;
A sister driven into desperate terms,
Whose worth, if praises may go back again,
Stood challenger on mount of all the age
For her perfections : but my revenge will come.

KING. Break not your sleeps for that; you must not think
That we are made of stuff so flat and dull
That we can let our beard be shook with danger
And think it pastime. You shortly shall hear more:
I loved your father, and we love ourself;
And that, I hope, will teach you to imagine—

Enter a Messenger

How now! what news?

MESSENGER. Letters, my lord, from Hamlet.
This to your majesty: this to the Queen.

KING. From Hamlet! Who brought them?

MESSENGER. Sailors, my lord, they say.

KING. Laertes, you shall hear them.

High and mighty, You shall know I am set naked on your kingdom. Tomorrow shall I beg leave to see your kingly eyes, when I shall, first asking your pardon thereunto, recount the occasion of my sudden and more strange return. HAMLET

What should this mean? Are all the rest come back?
Or is it some abuse, and no such thing?

LAERTES. I'm lost in it, my lord. But let him come;
It warms the very sickness in my heart,
That I shall live and tell him to his teeth,
Thus didest thou.

KING. If it be so, Laertes,
Will you be ruled by me?

LAERTES. Ay, my lord;
So you will not o'er-rule me to a peace.

KING. To thine own peace. If he be now returned,
As checking at his voyage, and that he means
No more to undertake it, I will work him
To an exploit, now ripe in my device,
Under the which he shall not choose but fall:
And for his death no wind of blame shall breathe,
But even his mother shall uncharge the practice
And call it accident.

LAERTES. My lord, I will be ruled;
The rather, if you could devise it so
That I might be the organ.

The King discloses a plot by which Laertes may avenge himself on Hamlet. He tells Laertes that the fame of his swordsmanship had made Hamlet wish to try his skill with him, and suggests a test of swordsmanship. The King suggests it would be easy, during the contest, to change a sword protected by a foil for one without a foil, and Laertes adds that he will also poison the point. To make sure, the King arranges a poisoned cup for Hamlet.

KING (*to Queen, entering*). How now, sweet queen!

QUEEN. One woe doth tread upon another's heel,
So fast they follow: your sister's drowned, Laertes.

LAERTES. Drowned! O, where?

QUEEN. There is a willow grows aslant a brook
That shows his hoar leaves in the glassy stream;
There with fantastic garlands did she come
Of crow-flowers, nettles, daisies, and long purples.
There, on the pendant boughs her coronet weeds
Clambering to hang, an envious sliver broke;
When down her weedy trophies and herself
Fell in the weeping brook. Her clothes spread wide;
And, mermaid-like, awhile they bore her up:
Which time she chanted snatches of old tunes,
As one incapable of her own distress,
Or like a creature native and indued
Unto that element: but long it could not be
Till that her garments, heavy with their drink,
Pulled the poor wretch from her melodious lay
To muddy death.

LAERTES. Alas, then, she is drowned?

QUEEN. Drowned, drowned.

LAERTES. Too much of water hast thou, poor Ophelia,
And therefore I forbid my tears: but yet
It is our trick; nature her custom holds,
Let shame say what it will.

KING. Let's follow, Gertrude:
How much I had to do to calm his rage!
Now fear I this will give it start again.

ACT V

Scene 1—A Churchyard

FIRST GRAVEDIGGER. Is she to be buried in Christian burial that wilfully seeks her own salvation?

SECOND GRAVEDIGGER. I tell thee she is; and therefore make her grave straight. The crowner hath sat on her and finds it Christian burial.

FIRST GRAVEDIGGER. How can that be, unless she drowned herself in her own defence. For here lies the point: if I drown myself wittingly, it argues an act: and an act hath three branches; it is, to act, to do, to perform: argal, she drowned herself wittingly.

SECOND GRAVEDIGGER. Nay, but hear you, goodman delver,—

FIRST GRAVEDIGGER. Give me leave. Here lies the water; good. Here stands the man; good. If the man go to this water and drown himself, it is, will he, nill he, he goes,—mark you that; but if the water come to him and drown him, he drowns not himself: argal, he that is not guilty of his own death shortens not his own life.

Second Gravedigger. But is this law?

First Gravedigger. Ay, marry, is't; crowner's quest law.

Second Gravedigger. If this had not been a gentlewoman she should have been buried out o' Christian burial.

First Gravedigger. Why, there thou say'st: and the more pity that great folk should have countenance in this world to drown or hang themselves more than their even Christian. Come, my spade. There is no ancient gentlemen but gardeners, ditchers, and grave-makers: they hold up Adam's profession. What is he that builds stronger than either the mason, the shipwright, or the carpenter?

Second Gravedigger. The gallows-maker; for that frame outlives a thousand tenants.

First Gravedigger. I like thy wit well, in good faith: the gallows does well; but cudgel thy brains no more about it, for your dull ass will not mend his pace with beating; and when you are asked this question next, say *a grave-maker*: the houses he makes last till Doomsday. Go, fetch me a stoup of liquor. (*He throws up a skull*)

Hamlet (*appearing with Horatio*). That skull had a tongue in it, and could sing once: how the knave jowls it to the ground, as if it were Cain's jaw-bone, that did the first murder! It might be the pate of a politician which this ass now o'er-reaches! one that would circumvent God, might it not?

Horatio. It might, my lord.

Hamlet. Or of a courtier; which could say *Good-morrow, sweet lord! How dost thou, good lord?* This might be my lord such-a-one, that praised my lord such-a-one's horse when he meant to beg it; might it not?

Horatio. Ay, my lord.

Hamlet. Why, e'en so: and now my Lady Worm's.

Gravedigger (*singing*).

A pick-axe, and a spade, a spade,
For and a shrouding sheet:
O, a pit of clay for to be made
For such a guest is meet.

Hamlet. There's another: why may not that be the skull of a lawyer? Where be his quiddities now, his quillets, his cases, his tenures, and his tricks? Why does he suffer this rude knave now to knock him about the sconce with a dirty shovel, and will not tell him of his action of battery. Hum! This fellow might be in's time a great buyer of land, with his statutes, his recognizances, his fines, his double vouchers, his recoveries. Is this the fine of his fines, and the recovery of his recoveries, to have his fine pate full of fine dirt? Will his vouchers vouch him no more of his purchases, and double ones too, than the length and breadth of a pair of indentures? The very conveyances of his lands will hardly lie in this box; and must the inheritor himself have no more, ha?

HORATIO. Not a jot more, my lord.

HAMLET. I will speak to this fellow. Whose grave's this, sirrah?

GRAVEDIGGER. Mine, sir.

O, a pit of clay for to be made
For such a guest is meet.

HAMLET. I think it be thine, indeed, for thou liest in't.

GRAVEDIGGER. You lie out on't, sir, and therefore it is not yours: for my part, I do not lie in't, and yet it is mine.

HAMLET. Thou dost lie in't, to be in't and say it is thine: tis for the dead, not for the quick; therefore thou liest.

GRAVEDIGGER. Tis a quick lie, sir; 'twill away again, from me to you.

HAMLET. What man dost thou dig it for?

GRAVEDIGGER. For no man, sir.

HAMLET. What woman, then?

GRAVEDIGGER. For none, neither.

HAMLET. Who is to be buried in't?

GRAVEDIGGER. One that was a woman, sir; but, rest her soul, she's dead.

HAMLET. How absolute the knave is! We must speak by the card, or equivocation will undo us. By the Lord, Horatio, these three years I have taken a note of it; the age is grown so picked that the toe of the peasant comes near the heel of the courtier. How long hast thou been a grave-maker?

GRAVEDIGGER. Of all the days i' the year, I came to 't that day that our last King Hamlet overcame Fortinbras.

HAMLET. How long is that since?

GRAVEDIGGER. Cannot you tell that? Every fool can tell that: it was the very day that young Hamlet was born; he that is mad, and sent into England.

HAMLET. Ay, marry, why was he sent into England?

GRAVEDIGGER. Why, because he was mad: he shall recover his wits there; or, if he do not, it's no great matter there.

HAMLET. Why?

GRAVEDIGGER. Twill not be seen in him there; there the men are as mad as he.

HAMLET. How came he mad ?

GRAVEDIGGER. Very strangely, they say ; e'en with losing his wits.

HAMLET. Upon what ground ?

GRAVEDIGGER. Why, here in Denmark : I have been sexton here, man and boy, thirty years.

HAMLET. How long will a man lie i' the earth ere he rot ?

GRAVEDIGGER. I' faith, if he be not rotten before he die, he will last you some eight year or nine year : a tanner will last you nine year.

HAMLET. Why he more than another ?

GRAVEDIGGER. Why, sir, his hide is so tanned with his trade that he will keep out water a great while. Here's a skull now ; this skull has lain in the earth three-and-twenty years.

HAMLET. Whose was it ?

GRAVEDIGGER. A mad fellow's it was : whose do you think it was ? A pestilence on him for a mad rogue ; a' poured a flagon of Rhenish on my head once. This, sir, was Yorick's skull, the king's jester.

HAMLET. This ?

GRAVEDIGGER. E'en that.

HAMLET (*taking the skull*). Let me see. Alas, poor Yorick ! I knew him, Horatio : a fellow of infinite jest, of most excellent fancy. He hath borne me on his back a thousand times ; and now how abhorred in my imagination it is ! my gorge rises at it. Here hung those lips that I have kissed I know not how oft. Where be your gibes now ? your gambols ? your songs ? your flashes of merriment, that were wont to set the table on a roar ? Not one now to mock your own grinning ! Now get you to my lady's chamber, and tell her, let her paint an inch thick, to this favour she must come ; make her laugh at that. Prithee, Horatio, tell me one thing.

HORATIO. What's that, my lord ?

HAMLET. Dost thou think Alexander looked o' this fashion i' the earth ?

HORATIO. E'en so, my lord.

HAMLET. To what base uses we may return, Horatio ! Why may not imagination trace the noble dust of Alexander till he find it stopping a bung-hole ?

HORATIO. Twere to consider too curiously, to consider so.

HAMLET. No, faith, not a jot ; but to follow him thither with modesty enough, and likelihood to lead it—as thus : Alexander died, Alexander was buried, Alexander returneth into dust : the dust is earth ; of earth we make loam ; and why of that loam, whereto he was converted, might they not stop a beer-barrel ?

Imperious Cæsar, dead and turned to clay,
Might stop a hole to keep the wind away:
O, that that earth, which kept the world in awe,
Should patch a wall to expel the winter's flaw!
But soft! but soft! aside: here comes the king.

Enter the Funeral Procession of Ophelia

The queen, the courtiers: Who is this they follow?
And with such maimèd rights? This doth betoken
The corse they follow did with desperate hand
Fordo its own life: 'twas of some estate.
Couch we awhile, and mark.

LAERTES. What ceremony else?

HAMLET. That is Laertes,
A very noble youth: mark.

LAERTES. What ceremony else?

PRIEST. Her obsequies have been as far enlarged
As we have warrant: her death was doubtful;
And, but that great command o'ersways the order,
She should in ground unsanctified have lodged
Till the last trumpet; for charitable prayers,
Shards, flints, and pebbles should be thrown on her:
Yet here she is allowed her virgin crants,
Her maiden strewments, and the bringing home
Of bell and burial.

LAERTES. Must there no more be done?

PRIEST. No more be done:
We should profane the service of the dead
To sing a requiem and such rest to her
As to peace-parted souls.

LAERTES. Lay her i' the earth,
And from her fair and unpolluted flesh
May violets spring! I tell thee, churlish priest,
A ministering angel shall my sister be
When thou liest howling.

HAMLET. What, the fair Ophelia!

QUEEN (*scattering flowers*). Sweets to the sweet: farewell!
I hoped thou shouldst have been my Hamlet's wife;
I thought thy bride-bed to have decked, sweet maid,
And not have strewed thy grave.

LAERTES. O, treble woe
Fall ten times treble on that cursèd head,
Whose wicked deed thy most ingenious sense
Deprived thee of! Hold off the earth awhile,
Till I have caught her once more in mine arms.

He leaps into the grave

Now pile your dust upon the quick and dead,
Till of this flat a mountain you have made,
To o'ertop Olympus.

HAMLET (*advancing*). What is he whose grief
Bears such an emphasis ? whose phrase of sorrow
Conjures the wandering stars, and makes them stand
Like wonder-wounded hearers ? This is I,
Hamlet the Dane. (*He leaps into the grave*)

LAERTES. The devil take thy soul ! (*Grappling with him*)

HAMLET. Thou pray'st not well.
I prithee, take thy fingers from my throat ;
For, though I am not splenitive and rash,
Yet have I something in me dangerous,
Which let thy wiseness fear : hold off thy hand.

KING. Pluck them asunder.

QUEEN. Hamlet, Hamlet !

HORATIO. Good my lord, be quiet.

The Attendants part them, and they come out of the grave

HAMLET. Why, I will fight with him upon this theme
Until my eyelids will no longer wag.

QUEEN. O my son, what theme ?

HAMLET. I loved Ophelia : forty thousand brothers
Could not, with all their quantity of love,
Make up my sum. What wilt thou do for her ?

KING. O, he is mad, Laertes.

QUEEN. For love of God, forbear him.

HAMLET. Swounds, show me what thou'lt do :
Woo't weep ? woo't fight ? woo't fast ? woo't tear thyself ?
Woo't drink up eisel ? eat a crocodile ?
I'll do't. Dost thou come here to whine ?
To outface me with leaping in her grave ?
Be buried quick with her, and so will I :
And, if thou prate of mountains, let them throw
Millions of acres on us. Nay, and thou'lt mouth,
I'll rant as well as thou.

QUEEN. This is mere madness :
And thus awhile the fit will work on him.

HAMLET. Hear you, sir ;
What is the reason that you use me thus ?
I loved you ever : but it is no matter ;
Let Hercules himself do what he may,
The cat will mew, and dog will have his day. (*Hamlet goes*)

KING. I pray you, good Horatio, wait upon him.
(*To Laertes*) Strengthen your patience in our last night's speech ;

We'll put the matter to the present push.
Good Gertrude, set some watch over your son.
This grave shall have a living monument:
An hour of quiet shortly shall we see;
Till then in patience our proceeding be.

Scene 2—A Hall in the Castle

HAMLET. So much for this, sir: now shall you see the other;
You do remember all the circumstance?

HORATIO. Remember it, my lord!

HAMLET. Sir, in my heart there was a kind of fighting
That would not let me sleep: methought I lay
Worse than the mutines in the bilboes. Rashly,
And praised be rashness for it, let us know,
Our indiscretion sometimes serves us well,
When our deep plots do pall: and that should teach us
There's a divinity that shapes our ends,
Rough-hew them how we will.

HORATIO. That is most certain.

Hamlet goes on to relate how, unable to sleep, he rose in the night and, being suspicious of the contents of a letter his companions were carrying, he searched for it and seized it. Opening the letter, he found it to be a command for his own execution immediately he arrived in England. Knowing that Rosencrantz and Guildenstern were aware of this treachery, he redrafted the letter so that it applied to them instead of to himself, and re-sealed it with the royal seal, of which he had had a model from his father.

So the two false friends were going to their own doom in his place.

HORATIO. Why, what a king is this!

HAMLET. Does it not, think'st thou, stand me now upon
To quit him with this arm?

HORATIO. It must be shortly known to him from England
What is the issue of the business there.

HAMLET. It will be short: the interim is mine;
And a man's life's no more than to say *One*.
But I am very sorry, good Horatio,
That to Laertes I forgot myself;
For, by the image of my cause, I see
The portraiture of his: I'll court his favours:
But, sure, the bravery of his grief did put me
Into a towering passion.

HORATIO. Peace! who comes here?

OSRIC. Your lordship is right welcome back to Denmark.

HAMLET. I humbly thank you, sir. Dost know this water-fly?

HORATIO. No, my good lord.

Hamlet. Thy state is the more gracious; for tis a vice to know him.

Osric. Sweet lord, if your lordship were at leisure, I should impart a thing to you from his majesty.

Hamlet. I will receive it, sir, with all diligence of spirit. Put your bonnet to his right use; tis for the head.

Osric. I thank your lordship; it is very hot.

Hamlet. No, believe me, tis very cold; the wind is northerly.

Osric. It is indifferent cold, my lord, indeed.

Hamlet. But yet methinks it is very sultry and hot for my complexion.

Osric. Exceedingly, my lord; it is very sultry. But, my lord, his majesty bade me signify to you that he has laid a great wager on your head: sir, this is the matter. Here is newly come to court Laertes; believe me, an absolute gentleman, full of most excellent differences, of very soft society and great showing: indeed, to speak feelingly of him, he is the card or calendar of gentry. You are not ignorant of what excellence Laertes is. The king, sir, hath wagered with him six Barbary horses; against the which he has imponed, as I take it, six French rapiers and poniards, with their assigns, as girdle, hangers, and so. The king hath laid that in a dozen passes between yourself and him he shall not exceed you three hits; and it would come to immediate trial if your lordship would vouchsafe the answer.

Hamlet. Sir, I will walk here in the hall: if it please his majesty, tis the breathing time of day with me; let the foils be brought, the gentleman willing, and the king hold his purpose, I will win for him an I can; if not, I will gain nothing but my shame and the odd hits.

A Lord. My lord, the king and queen and all are coming down. The queen desires you to use some gentle entertainment to Laertes before you fall to play.

Hamlet. She well instructs me.

Horatio. You will lose this wager, my lord.

Hamlet. I do not think so; since he went into France I have been in continual practice; I shall win at the odds. But thou wouldst not think how ill all's here about my heart: but it is no matter.

Horatio. Nay, good my lord. If your mind dislike anything, obey it; I will forestal their repair hither, and say you are not fit.

Hamlet. Not a whit; we defy augury: there's a special providence in the fall of a sparrow. If it be now, tis not to come; if it be not to come, it will be now; if it be not now, yet it will come: the readiness is all.

King and Queen enter, and join the hands of Hamlet and Laertes

KING. Come, Hamlet, come, and take this hand from me.

HAMLET. Give me your pardon, sir: I've done you wrong;
But pardon 't, as you are a gentleman.
This presence knows,
And you must needs have heard, how I am punished
With sore distraction. What I have done,
That might your nature, honour, and exception
Roughly awake, I here proclaim was madness.
Was't Hamlet wronged Laertes? Never Hamlet:
If Hamlet from himself be ta'en away,
And when he's not himself does wrong Laertes,
Then Hamlet does it not; Hamlet denies it.
Who does it, then? His madness: if 't be so,
Hamlet is of the faction that is wronged;
His madness is poor Hamlet's enemy.
Sir, in this audience,
Let my disclaiming from a purposed evil
Free me so far in your most generous thoughts,
That I have shot mine arrow o'er the house,
And hurt my brother.

LAERTES. I am satisfied in nature,
Whose motive, in this case, should stir me most
To my revenge: but in my terms of honour
I do receive your offered love like love,
And will not wrong it.

HAMLET. I embrace it freely;
And will this brother's wager frankly play.
Give us the foils. Come on,

KING. Give them the foils, young Osric. Cousin Hamlet,
You know the wager?

HAMLET. Very well, my lord;
Your grace hath laid the odds o' the weaker side.

KING. I do not fear it; I have seen you both:
But, since he is bettered, we have therefore odds.

LAERTES. This is too heavy, let me see another.

HAMLET. This likes me well. These foils have all a length?

OSRIC. Ay, my good lord.

KING. Set me the stoups of wine upon that table.
If Hamlet give the first or second hit,
Or quit in answer of the third exchange,
Let all the battlements their ordnance fire;
The king shall drink to Hamlet's better breath,
And in the cup a union shall he throw,
Richer than that which four successive kings
In Denmark's crown have worn. Give me the cups;

And let the kettle to the trumpet speak,
The trumpet to the cannoneer without,
The cannons to the heavens, the heavens to earth:
Now the king drinks to Hamlet. Come, begin.

They play. Hamlet hits Laertes and the King offers him a drink from the poisoned cup, which he refuses.

HAMLET. I'll play this bout first; set it by awhile.
Come. Another hit; what say you?

LAERTES. A touch, a touch, I do confess.

KING. Our son shall win.

QUEEN. He's fat, and scant of breath.
Here, Hamlet, take my napkin, rub thy brows:
The queen carouses to thy fortune, Hamlet.

HAMLET. Good madam!

KING. Gertrude, do not drink.

QUEEN. I will, my lord; I pray you, pardon me.

KING (*aside*). It is the poisoned cup: it is too late!

HAMLET. I dare not drink yet, madam; by and by.

QUEEN. Come, let me wipe thy face.

LAERTES. My lord, I'll hit him now.

KING. I do not think 't.

LAERTES (*aside*). And yet tis almost 'gainst my conscience.

HAMLET. Come, for the third, Laertes: you but dally;
I pray you, pass with your best violence;
I am afeard you make a wanton of me.

LAERTES. Say you so? Come on.

OSRIC. Nothing, neither way.

LAERTES. Have at you now!

Laertes wounds Hamlet with the poisoned blade. In scuffling they drop their weapons, and Hamlet, picking up the poisoned one, wounds Laertes.

KING. Part them; they are incensed.

HAMLET. Nay, come, again. (*The Queen falls*)

OSRIC. Look to the queen there, ho!
How is't, Laertes?

LAERTES. Why, as a woodcock to mine own springe, Osric;
I am justly killed with mine own treachery.

HAMLET. How does the queen?

KING. She swounds to see them bleed.

QUEEN. No, no, the drink, the drink: O my dear Hamlet!
The drink, the drink! I am poisoned. (*She dies*)

HAMLET. O villany! Ho! let the door be locked:
Treachery! Seek it out.

LAERTES. It is here, Hamlet: Hamlet, thou art slain;
No medicine in the world can do thee good;
In thee there is not half an hour of life;
The treacherous instrument is in thy hand,
Unbated and envenomed: the foul practice
Hath turned itself on me; lo, there I lie,
Never to rise again: thy mother's poisoned:
I can no more: the king, the king's to blame.

HAMLET. The point!—envenomed too!
Then, venom, to thy work. (*He stabs the King*)

ALL. Treason! treason!

KING. O, yet defend me, friends; I am but hurt. (*He dies*)

LAERTES. He is justly served;
It is a poison tempered by himself.
Exchange forgiveness with me, noble Hamlet:
Mine and my father's death come not upon thee,
Nor thine on me! (*He dies*)

HAMLET. Heaven make thee free of it! I follow thee.
I am dead, Horatio. Wretched queen, adieu!
You that look pale and tremble at this chance,
That are but mutes or audience to this act,
Had I but time, O, I could tell you—
But let it be. Horatio, I am dead;
Thou livest; report me and my cause aright
To the unsatisfied.

HORATIO. Never believe it:
I am more an antique Roman than a Dane:
Here's yet some liquor left.

HAMLET. As thou'rt a man,
Give me the cup: let go; by heaven, I'll have't.
O good Horatio, what a wounded name,
Things standing thus unknown, shall live behind me!
If thou didst ever hold me in thy heart,
Absent thee from felicity awhile,
And in this harsh world draw thy breath in pain,
To tell my story . . . What warlike noise is this?

OSRIC. Young Fortinbras, with conquest come from Poland,
To the ambassadors of England gives
This warlike volley.

HAMLET. O, I die, Horatio;
The potent poison quite o'er-crows my spirit:
I cannot live to hear the news from England;
But I do prophesy the election lights
On Fortinbras: he has my dying voice;
So tell him, with the occurrents, more and less,
Which have solicited. The rest is silence. (*He dies*)

HORATIO. Now cracks a noble heart. Good-night, sweet prince;
And flights of angels sing thee to thy rest!
Why does the drum come hither?

Enter Fortinbras and English Ambassadors

FORTINBRAS. Where is this sight?
HORATIO. What is it ye would see?
If aught of woe or wonder, cease your search.
FORTINBRAS. This quarry cries on havoc. O proud death,
What feast is toward in thine eternal cell,
That thou so many princes at a shot hast struck?
AMBASSADORS. The sight is dismal;
And our affairs from England come too late:
The ears are senseless that should give us hearing,
To tell him his commandment is fulfilled,
That Rosencrantz and Guildenstern are dead:
Where should we have our thanks?
HORATIO. Not from his mouth,
Had it the ability of life to thank you:
He never gave commandment for their death.
But let me speak to the yet unknowing world
How these things came about: so shall you hear
Of carnal and unnatural acts,
Of accidental judgments, casual slaughters,
Of deaths put on by cunning and forced cause,
And, in this upshot, purposes mistook
Fallen on the inventors' heads: all this can I
Truly deliver.
FORTINBRAS. Let us haste to hear it,
And call the noblest to the audience.
For me, with sorrow I embrace my fortune:
I have some rights of memory in this kingdom,
Which now to claim my vantage doth invite me.
HORATIO. Of that I shall have also cause to speak,
And from his mouth whose voice will draw on more:
But let this same be presently performed,
Even while men's minds are wild, lest more mischance
On plots and errors happen.
FORTINBRAS. Let four captains
Bear Hamlet, like a soldier, to the stage;
For he was likely, had he been put on,
To have proved most royally: and, for his passage,
The soldier's music and the rites of war
Speak loudly for him.
Take up the bodies: such a sight as this
Becomes the field, but here shows much amiss.
Go, bid the soldiers shoot.

The Story of The Merchant of Venice

SHAKESPEARE wrote more powerful plays, but he wrote nothing more popular than The Merchant of Venice. If has been appearing on the stage almost without ceasing since Shakespeare's day.

IT is perhaps the best of all the stories that he made immortal. It is as thrilling as a novel. It is well knit together, and the whole play is simple and easily understood. It has in it one of the most remarkable characters in the literature of the world, Shylock the Jew.

HE stands for all time raging like a storm against the persecution of his race. He has Antonio within his power, and the bitterness with which he leads the merchant to the edge of doom is Shakespeare's reflection of the age-old hatred of Christian and Jew. In these days it is good to feel that men are getting tired of hate, but in those days hate was undisguised and unashamed. Shakespeare has no more cruel figure than Shylock, and yet we feel that this strange, dark, and terrible old man hated the others no more than the others hated him. He has a heart like stone; he is as pitiless as an avalanche sweeping a village to its doom; and yet we feel that Shakespeare meant us to have a little secret sympathy for the Jew. Who can read unmoved that speech of Shylock in which he asks if Jews are not as other men?

SHYLOCK existed before Shakespeare's time; Shakespeare found him already in print, as he found most of his stories. He found the relentless Jew and the Christian's pound of flesh. He found the idea of the choice of a wife by opening a secret casket. All these appeared a hundred years before Shakespeare, in story and drama and ballad. But it was Shakespeare who gave Shylock his immortality. He took two old tales and wove them into one, and he crowded his stage with characters such as no one else could draw. He wrote the play about 1596, and it was well known in the theatres in 1598.

IT is reckoned among the comedies, and is decked with choicest poetry and romance; but we feel, as we read it, that it hovers on the very verge of tragedy. It is only the genial spirit of Shakespeare, so conspicuous at the period of his career when he wrote this play, which leaves us happy at the end. Shylock, baffled at every turn, retires into a tragic loneliness, but the rest of the characters are happily assorted, and we can share in their rejoicing that all is well.

IN Shakespeare's gallery of women the exquisite and resourceful Portia stands out with a majestic splendour, like one who foreshadows the character and capacity and independence of the women of our time.

THE PLAYERS

Duke of Venice, a fair-minded ruler, but unable to modify the law's demands.

Prince of Morocco, suitor for Portia's hand in marriage.

Prince of Arragon, another suitor for the hand of Portia.

Bassanio, a Venetian gentleman, also one of Portia's suitors, and favoured by her, though she has not the power of choice.

Antonio, a merchant of Venice, and a great friend of Bassanio.

Gratiano, active and talkative, friend of Bassanio and Antonio.

Salanio, Salarino, and Salerio, three friends in Venice.

Lorenzo, in love with Jessica the Jewess.

Shylock, a Jewish moneylender who deeply resents the treatment of his race by Christians, and specially dislikes Antonio.

Tubal, a Jewish friend of Shylock.

Launcelot Gobbo, servant of Shylock, afterwards of Bassanio.

Old Gobbo, Launcelot's father.

Balthasar and Stephano, servants in Portia's house at Belmont.

Portia, a rich heiress who has suitors from all parts of the world, but must be chosen in a certain way and cannot decide herself. A clever woman, and a sound judge of character.

Nerissa, Portia's maid.

Jessica, daughter of Shylock, in love with Lorenzo.

SCENE—In Venice and at Portia's country house at Belmont.

The Merchant of Venice

ACT 1

Scene 1—A Street in Venice: Antonio with his friends

ANTONIO. In sooth, I know not why I am so sad:
It wearies me; you say it wearies you;
But how I caught it, found it, or came by it,
What stuff tis made of, whereof it is born,
I am to learn;
And such a want-wit sadness makes of me,
That I have much ado to know myself.

SALARINO. Your mind is tossing on the ocean;
There, where your argosies with portly sail,
Like signiors and rich burghers on the flood,
Or, as it were, the pageants of the sea,
Do overpeer the petty traffickers,
That curtsey to them, do them reverence,
As they fly by them with their woven wings.

SALANIO. Believe me, sir, had I such venture forth,
The better part of my affections would
Be with my hopes abroad. I should be still
Plucking the grass, to know where sits the wind,
Peering in maps for ports and piers and roads;
And every object that might make me fear
Misfortune to my ventures, out of doubt
Would make me sad.

SALARINO. My wind cooling my broth
Would blow me to an ague, when I thought
What harm a wind too great at sea might do.
I should not see the sandy hour-glass run
But I should think of shallows and of flats,
And see my wealthy Andrew docked in sand,
Vailing her high-top lower than her ribs
To kiss her burial. Should I go to church
And see the holy edifice of stone,
And not bethink me straight of dangerous rocks,
Which touching but my gentle vessel's side,
Would scatter all her spices on the stream.

Enrobe the roaring waters with my silks,
And, in a word, but even now worth this,
And now worth nothing? I know Antonio
Is sad to think upon his merchandise.

ANTONIO. Believe me, no: I thank my fortune for it,
My ventures are not in one bottom trusted,
Nor to one place; nor is my whole estate
Upon the fortune of this present year:
Therefore my merchandise makes me not sad.

SALARINO. Why, then you are in love.

ANTONIO. Fie, fie!

SALARINO. Not in love neither? Then let's say you are sad
Because you are not merry.

SALANIO. Here comes Bassanio, your most noble kinsman,
Gratiano, and Lorenzo. Fare ye well:
We leave you now in better company.

ANTONIO. Your worth is very dear in my regard.
I take it your own business calls on you
And you embrace the occasion to depart.

GRATIANO. You look not well, Signior Antonio;
You have too much respect upon the world:
They lose it that do buy it with much care:
Believe me, you are marvellously changed.

ANTONIO. I hold the world but as the world, Gratiano;
A stage where every man must play a part,
And mine a sad one.

GRATIANO. Let me play the fool:
With mirth and laughter let old wrinkles come,
And let my liver rather heat with wine
Than my heart cool with mortifying groans.
Why should a man whose blood is warm within
Sit like his grandsire cut in alabaster?
Sleep when he wakes and creep into the jaundice
By being peevish? I tell thee what, Antonio,
(I love thee, and it is my love that speaks)
There are a sort of men whose visages
Do cream and mantle like a standing pond,
And do a wilful stillness entertain,
With purpose to be dressed in an opinion
Of wisdom, gravity, profound conceit,
As who should say *I am Sir Oracle,*
And when I ope my lips let no dog bark!
O, my Antonio, I do know of these
That therefore only are reputed wise

For saying nothing.
Come, good Lorenzo. Fare ye well awhile. (*They leave*)

BASSANIO. Gratiano speaks an infinite deal of nothing, more than any man in all Venice. His reasons are as two grains of wheat hid in two bushels of chaff; you shall seek all day ere you find them, and when you have them they are not worth the search.

ANTONIO. Well, tell me now, what lady is the same
To whom you swore a secret pilgrimage,
That you today promised to tell me of?

BASSANIO. Tis not unknown to you, Antonio,
How much I have disabled mine estate.
To you, Antonio,
I owe the most, in money and in love,
And from your love I have a warranty
To unburden all my plots and purposes
How to get clear of all the debts I owe.

ANTONIO. I pray you, good Bassanio, let me know it;
And if it stand, as you yourself still do,
Within the eye of honour, be assured,
My purse, my person, my extremest means,
Lie all unlocked to your occasions.

BASSANIO. In my schooldays, when I had lost one shaft,
I shot his fellow of the selfsame flight
The selfsame way, with more advisèd watch,
To find the other forth, and by adventuring both
I oft found both: I urge this childhood proof,
Because what follows is pure innocence.
I owe you much, and, like a wilful youth,
That which I owe is lost; but if you please
To shoot another arrow that self way
Which you did shoot the first, I do not doubt,
As I will watch the aim, or to find both
Or bring your latter hazard back again,
And thankfully rest debtor for the first.

ANTONIO. You know me well, and herein spend but time
To wind about my love with circumstance;
And out of doubt you do me now more wrong
In making question of my uttermost
Than if you had made waste of all I have:
Then do but say to me what I should do.

BASSANIO. In Belmont is a lady richly left;
And she is fair and, fairer than that word,
Of wondrous virtues: sometimes from her eyes
I did receive fair speechless messages:
Her name is Portia, nothing undervalued
To Cato's daughter, Brutus' Portia:

Nor is the wide world ignorant of her worth,
For the four winds blow in from every coast
Renownèd suitors, and her sunny locks
Hang on her temples like a golden fleece;
And many Jasons come in quest of her.
O my Antonio, had I but the means
To hold a rival place with one of them,
I have a mind presages me such thrift
That I should questionless be fortunate!

ANTONIO. Thou know'st that all my fortunes are at sea;
Neither have I money nor commodity
To raise a present sum: therefore go forth;
Try what my credit can in Venice do:
That shall be racked, even to the uttermost,
To furnish thee to Belmont, to fair Portia.
Go, presently inquire, and so will I,
Where money is, and I no question make
To have it of my trust or for my sake.

Scene 2—Portia's House at Belmont

PORTIA. By my troth, Nerissa, my little body is aweary of this great world.

NERISSA. You would be, sweet madam, if your miseries were in the same abundance as your good fortunes are: and yet, for aught I see, they are as sick that surfeit with too much as they that starve with nothing.

PORTIA. If to do were as easy as to know what were good to do, chapels had been churches and poor men's cottages princes' palaces. It is a good divine that follows his own instructions; I can easier teach twenty what were good to be done than be one of the twenty to follow mine own teaching. The brain may devise laws for the blood, but a hot temper leaps o'er a cold decree. But this reasoning is not in the fashion to choose me a husband. O me, the word Choose! I may neither choose whom I would nor refuse whom I dislike; so is the will of a living daughter curbed by the will of a dead father. Is it not hard that I cannot choose one nor refuse none?

NERISSA. Your father was ever virtuous, and holy men at their death have good inspirations: therefore the lottery that he hath devised in these three chests of gold, silver, and lead, whereof who chooses his meaning chooses you, will, no doubt, never be chosen by any rightly but one who shall rightly love. But what warmth is there in your affection towards any of these princely suitors that are already come? There is the Neapolitan prince.

PORTIA. Ay, that's a colt indeed, for he doth nothing but talk of his horse.

NERISSA. Then there is the County Palatine.

Portia. He doth nothing but frown, as who should say *If you will not have me, Choose:* he hears merry tales and smiles not. I had rather be married to a death's-head with a bone in his mouth than to either of these.

Nerissa. How say you by the French lord, Monsieur Le Bon?

Portia. God made him, and therefore let him pass for a man. In truth, I know it is a sin to be a mocker, but, he! why, he hath a horse better than the Neapolitan's, a better bad habit of frowning than the Count Palatine. He is every man in no man. If a throstle sing he falls straight a capering; he will fence with his own shadow. If I should marry him I should marry twenty husbands.

Nerissa. What say you, then, to Falconbridge, the young baron of England?

Portia. You know I say nothing to him, for he understands not me, nor I him: he hath neither Latin, French, nor Italian. He is a proper man's picture, but, alas, who can converse with a dumb-show? How oddly he is suited! I think he bought his doublet in Italy, his round hose in France, his bonnet in Germany, and his behaviour everywhere.

Nerissa. What think you of the Scottish lord, his neighbour?

Portia. That he hath a neighbourly charity in him, for he borrowed a box of the ear of the Englishman and swore he would pay him again when he was able.

Nerissa. How like you the young German?

Portia. Very vilely in the morning, when he is sober, and most vilely in the afternoon, when he is drunk. When he is best he is a little worse than a man, and when he is worst he is little better than a beast. I will do anything, Nerissa, ere I'll be married to a sponge.

Nerissa. You need not fear, lady, the having any of these lords; they have acquainted me with their determinations, which is, indeed, to return to their home and to trouble you with no more suit, unless you may be won by some other sort than your father's imposition depending on the caskets.

Portia. I am glad this parcel of wooers are so reasonable, for there is not one among them but I dote on his very absence, and I pray God grant them a fair departure.

Nerissa. Do you not remember, lady, in your father's time, a Venetian, a scholar and a soldier, that came hither in company of the Marquis of Montferrat?

Portia. Yes, yes, it was Bassanio; as I think he was so called.

Nerissa. True, madam: he, of all the men that ever my foolish eyes looked upon, was the best deserving a fair lady.

Portia. I remember him well, and I remember him worthy of thy praise.

Servant (*entering*). The four strangers seek for you, madam, to take their leave: and there is a forerunner come from a fifth, the Prince of Morocco, who brings word the prince his master will be here tonight.

PORTIA. If I could bid the fifth welcome with so good a heart as I can bid the other four farewell, I should be glad of his approach. Come, Nerissa. Sirrah, go before. Whiles we shut the gates upon one wooer, another knocks at the door.

Scene 3—A Public Place in Venice

SHYLOCK. Three thousand ducats; well.

BASSANIO. Ay, sir, for three months.

SHYLOCK. For three months; well.

BASSANIO. For the which, as I told you, Antonio shall be bound.

SHYLOCK. Antonio shall become bound; well.

BASSANIO. Will you pleasure me? Shall I know your answer?

SHYLOCK. Three thousand ducats for three months and Antonio bound.

BASSANIO. Your answer to that.

SHYLOCK. Antonio is a good man.

BASSANIO. Have you heard any imputation to the contrary?

SHYLOCK. Oh, no, no, no, no: my meaning in saying he is a good man is to have you understand me that he is sufficient. Yet his means are in supposition: he hath an argosy bound to Tripolis, another to the Indies; I understand, moreover, upon the Rialto, he hath a third at Mexico, a fourth for England, and other ventures he hath, squandered abroad. But ships are but boards, sailors but men: there be land-rats and water-rats, water-thieves and land-thieves (I mean pirates), and then there is the peril of waters, winds, and rocks. The man is, notwithstanding, sufficient. Three thousand ducats; I think I may take his bond. May I speak with Antonio?

BASSANIO. If it please you to dine with us.

SHYLOCK. Yes, to smell pork; to eat of the habitation which your prophet the Nazarite conjured the devil into. I will buy with you, sell with you, talk with you, walk with you, and so following, but I will not eat with you, drink with you, nor pray with you. What news on the Rialto? Who is he comes here?

BASSANIO. This is Signior Antonio.

SHYLOCK (*aside*). How like a fawning publican he looks!
I hate him for he is a Christian,
But more for that in low simplicity
He lends out money gratis and brings down
The rate of usance here with us in Venice.
If I can catch him once upon the hip
I will feed fat the ancient grudge I bear him.
He hates our sacred nation, and he rails,
Even there where merchants most do congregate,

On me, my bargains and my well-won thrift,
Which he calls interest. Cursèd be my tribe
If I forgive him!

BASSANIO. Shylock, do you hear?

SHYLOCK. I am debating of my present store,
And, by the near guess of my memory,
I cannot instantly raise up the gross
Of full three thousand ducats. What of that?
Tubal, a wealthy Hebrew of my tribe,
Will furnish me. But soft! how many months
Do you desire? (*To Antonio*) Rest you fair, good signior;
Your worship was the last man in our mouths.

ANTONIO. Shylock, although I neither lend nor borrow
By taking nor by giving of excess,
Yet, to supply the ripe wants of my friend,
I'll break a custom. Is he yet possessed
How much ye would?

SHYLOCK. Ay, ay, three thousand ducats.

ANTONIO. And for three months.

SHYLOCK. I had forgot; three months; you told me so.
Well then, your bond; and let me see; but hear you;
Methought you said you neither lend nor borrow
Upon advantage.

ANTONIO. I do never use it.

SHYLOCK. When Jacob grazed his uncle Laban's sheep. . .

ANTONIO. And what of him? Did he take interest?

SHYLOCK. No, not take interest, not, as you would say,
Directly interest. . .

ANTONIO. Mark you this, Bassanio,
The devil can cite Scripture for his purpose.
An evil soul producing holy witness
Is like a villain with a smiling cheek,
A goodly apple rotten at the heart:
O, what a goodly outside falsehood hath!

SHYLOCK. Three thousand ducats; tis a good round sum.
Three months from twelve; then, let me see! the rate. . .

ANTONIO. Well, Shylock, shall we be beholden to you?

SHYLOCK. Signior Antonio, many a time and oft
In the Rialto you have rated me
About my moneys and my usances:
Still have I borne it with a patient shrug,
For sufferance is the badge of all our tribe.
You call me misbeliever, cut-throat dog,
And spit upon my Jewish gaberdine,
And all for use of that which is mine own.

Well then, it now appears you need my help:
Go to, then; you come to me, and you say
Shylock, we would have moneys: you say so;
You, that did void your rheum upon my beard
And foot me as you spurn a stranger cur
Over your threshold: moneys is your suit.
What should I say to you? Should I not say
Hath a dog money? Is it possible
A cur can lend three thousand ducats? Or
Shall I bend low, and in a bondman's key,
With bated breath and whispering humbleness,
Say this:
Fair sir, you spit on me on Wednesday last
You spurned me such a day; another time
You called me dog; and for these courtesies
I'll lend you thus much moneys?

ANTONIO. I am as like to call thee so again,
To spit on thee again, to spurn thee too.
If thou wilt lend this money, lend it not
As to thy friends,
But lend it rather to thine enemy,
Who, if he break, thou mayst with better face
Exact the penalty.

SHYLOCK. Why, look you, how you storm!
I would be friends with you and have your love,
Forget the shames that you have stained me with,
Supply your present wants and take no doit
Of usance for my moneys, and you'll not hear me.

BASSANIO. This were kindness.

SHYLOCK. This kindness will I show.
Go with me to a notary, seal me there
Your single bond; and, in a merry sport,
If you repay me not on such a day,
In such a place, such sum or sums as are
Expressed in the condition, let the forfeit
Be nominated for an equal pound
Of your fair flesh, to be cut off and taken
In what part of your body pleaseth me.

ANTONIO. Content, i' faith: I'll seal to such a bond
And say there is much kindness in the Jew.

BASSANIO. You shall not seal to such a bond for me:
I'll rather dwell in my necessity.

ANTONIO. Why, fear not, man; I will not forfeit it:
Within these two months, that's a month before
This bond expires, I do expect return
Of thrice three times the value of this bond.

SHYLOCK. O father Abram, what these Christians are,
Whose own hard dealing teaches them suspect
The thoughts of others! Pray you, tell me this;
If he should break his day, what should I gain
By the exaction of the forfeiture?
A pound of man's flesh taken from a man
Is not so estimable, profitable neither,
As flesh of muttons, beefs, or goats. I say,
To buy his favour I extend this friendship:
If he will take it, so; if not, adieu;
And, for my love, I pray you wrong me not.

ANTONIO. Yes, Shylock, I will seal unto this bond.

SHYLOCK. Then meet me forthwith at the notary's;
Give him direction for this merry bond,
And I will go and purse the ducats straight,
See to my house, left in the fearful guard
Of an unthrifty knave, and presently
I will be with you.

ANTONIO. Hie thee, gentle Jew. (*Shylock goes*)
The Hebrew will turn Christian: he grows kind.

BASSANIO. I like not fair terms and a villain's mind.

ANTONIO. Come on: in this there can be no dismay;
My ships come home a month before the day.

ACT 2

Scene 1—Portia's House at Belmont

The Prince of Morocco enters to a flourish of cornets

PRINCE. Mislike me not for my complexion,
The shadowed livery of the burnished sun,
To whom I am a neighbour and near bred.
I tell thee, lady, this aspect of mine
Hath feared the valiant:
I would not change this hue,
Except to steal your thoughts, my gentle queen.

PORTIA. In terms of choice I am not solely led
By nice direction of a maiden's eyes;
Besides, the lottery of my destiny
Bars me the right of voluntary choosing.
But if my father had not scanted me
And hedged me by his wit, to yield myself
His wife who wins me by that means I told you,
Yourself, renownèd prince, then stood as fair
As any comer I have looked on yet
For my affection.

PRINCE. Even for that I thank you:
Therefore, I pray you, lead me to the caskets

To try my fortune. By this scimitar
That slew the Sophy and a Persian prince,
That won three fields of Sultan Solyman,
I would outstare the sternest eyes that look,
Outbrave the heart most daring on the earth,
Yea, mock the lion when he roars for prey,
To win thee, lady.

PORTIA. You must take your chance,
And either not attempt to choose at all
Or swear before you choose, if you choose wrong,
Never to speak to lady afterward
In way of marriage: therefore be advised.

PRINCE. Nor will not. Come, bring me unto my chance.

PORTIA. First, forward to the temple: after dinner
Your hazard shall be made.

PRINCE. Good fortune then!
To make me blest or cursed'st among men.

Scene 2—A Venice Street

LAUNCELOT. Certainly my conscience will serve me to run from this Jew my master. The fiend is at mine elbow and tempts me, saying *Gobbo, Launcelot Gobbo, use your legs, run away.* My conscience says *No; take heed, honest Launcelot; take heed, honest Gobbo; do not run; scorn running with thy heels.* Well, the most courageous fiend bids me pack. *Away!* says the fiend; *rouse up a brave mind, and run.* Well, my conscience says *Launcelot, budge not. Budge,* says the fiend. The fiend gives the more friendly counsel: I will run.

Enter Old Gobbo with a basket

LAUNCELOT (*aside*). O heavens, this is my true-begotten father, who, being more than sand-blind, high-gravel blind, knows me not: I will try confusions with him.

OLD GOBBO. Master young gentleman, I pray you, which is the way to master Jew's?

LAUNCELOT. Turn up on your right hand at the next turning, but, at the next turning of all, on your left; marry, at the very next turning, turn of no hand, but turn down indirectly to the Jew's house.

OLD GOBBO. Twill be a hard way to hit. Can you tell me whether one Launcelot, that dwells with him, dwell with him or no?

LAUNCELOT. Talk you of young Master Launcelot?

OLD GOBBO. No master, sir, but a poor man's son: his father, though I say it, is an honest exceeding poor man.

LAUNCELOT. Well, let his father be what a' will, talk not of Master Launcelot, father; for the young gentleman is, as you would say in plain terms, gone to heaven.

OLD GOBBO. Marry, God forbid! the boy was the very staff of my age, my very prop.

LAUNCELOT. Do I look like a prop? Do you know me, father?

OLD GOBBO. Alack the day, I know you not, young gentleman: but, I pray you, tell me, is my boy, God rest his soul, alive or dead?

LAUNCELOT. Do you not know me, father?

OLD GOBBO. Alack, sir, I am sand-blind; I know you not.

LAUNCELOT. Well, old man, I will tell you news of your son. Give me your blessing.

OLD GOBBO. I cannot think you are my son.

LAUNCELOT. I know not what I shall think of that: but I am Launcelot, the Jew's man, and Margery your wife is my mother.

OLD GOBBO. Her name is Margery, indeed: I'll be sworn, if thou be Launcelot, thou art mine own flesh and blood. How art thou changed? How dost thou and thy master agree? I have brought him a present. How 'gree you now?

LAUNCELOT. Well, well: but my master's a very Jew. Give him a present! Give him a halter: I am famished in his service. Father, I am glad you are come: give me your present to one Master Bassanio, who indeed gives rare new liveries; if I serve not him, I will run as far as God has any ground. O rare fortune! here comes the man: to him, father.

GOBBO. God bless your worship! Here's my son, sir, a poor boy.

LAUNCELOT. Not a poor boy, sir, but the rich Jew's man; that would, sir, as my father shall specify—

OLD GOBBO. I have here a dish of doves that I would bestow upon your worship, and my suit is—

BASSANIO. One speak for both. What would you?

LAUNCELOT. Serve you, sir.

BASSANIO. I know thee well. Go, father, with thy son.
Take leave of thy old master and inquire my lodging out.

Enter Gratiano

GRATIANO. Signior Bassanio, I must go with you to Belmont.

BASSANIO. Why, then you must. But hear thee, Gratiano;
Thou art too wild, too rude and bold of voice;
Parts that become thee happily enough
And in such eyes as ours appear not faults;
But where thou art not known, why, there they show
Something too liberal. Pray thee, take pain
To allay with some cold drops of modesty
Thy skipping spirit, lest through thy wild behaviour
I be mis*con*strued in the place I go to
And lose my hopes.

GRATIANO. If I do not put on a sober habit,
Talk with respect and swear but now and then,
Wear prayer-books in my pocket, look demurely,
Nay more, while grace is saying hood mine eyes
Thus with my hat, and sigh, and say *Amen*,
Never trust me more.

BASSANIO. Well, we shall see your bearing.
But fare you well: I have some business.

GRATIANO. And I must to Lorenzo and the rest:
But we will visit you at supper-time.

Scene 3—A Room in Shylock's House

JESSICA (*to Launcelot*). I am sorry thou wilt leave my father so:
Our house is hell, and thou, a merry devil,
Didst rob it of some taste of tediousness.
But fare thee well, there is a ducat for thee:
And, Launcelot, soon at supper shalt thou see
Lorenzo, who is thy new master's guest:
Give him this letter; do it secretly;
And so farewell: I would not have my father
See me in talk with thee.

LAUNCELOT. Adieu! Most beautiful pagan, most sweet Jew! these foolish drops do something drown my manly spirit: adieu.

JESSICA. Farewell, good Launcelot.
Alack, what heinous sin is it in me
To be ashamed to be my father's child!
But though I am a daughter to his blood,
I am not to his manners. O Lorenzo,
If thou keep promise I shall end this strife,
Become a Christian and thy loving wife.

Scene 4—A Street in Venice

LORENZO. Nay, we will slink away in supper-time,
Disguise us at my lodging and return,
All in an hour.

GRATIANO. We have not made good preparation.

LORENZO. Tis now but four o'clock: we have two hours
To furnish us. Friend Launcelot, what's the news?

LAUNCELOT (*delivering a letter*). An it shall please you to break up this, it shall seem to signify.

LORENZO. I know the hand: in faith, tis a fair hand;
And whiter than the paper it writ on
Is the fair hand that writ.

LAUNCELOT. By your leave, sir.

LORENZO. Whither goest thou?

LAUNCELOT. Marry, sir, to bid my old master the Jew to sup tonight with my new master the Christian.

LORENZO. Hold here, take this: tell gentle Jessica
I will not fail her; speak it privately.

GRATIANO. Was not that letter from fair Jessica?

LORENZO. I must needs tell thee all. She hath directed
How I shall take her from her father's house,
What gold and jewels she is furnished with,
What page's suit she hath in readiness.
If e'er the Jew her father come to heaven,
It will be for his gentle daughter's sake:
And never dare misfortune cross her foot,
Unless she do it under this excuse,
That she is issue to a faithless Jew.
Come, go with me; peruse this as thou goest:
Fair Jessica shall be my torch-bearer.

Scene 5—Before Shylock's House: Shylock and Launcelot

SHYLOCK. Well, thou shalt see, thy eyes shall be thy judge
The difference of old Shylock and Bassanio:
(*What, Jessica!*) Thou shalt not gormandise,
As thou hast done with me: (*What, Jessica!*)
And sleep and snore, and rend apparel out—
(*Why, Jessica, I say!*)

JESSICA (*appearing*). Call you? What is your will?

SHYLOCK. I am bid forth to supper, Jessica:
There are my keys. But wherefore should I go?
I am not bid for love; they flatter me:
But yet I'll go in hate, to feed upon
The prodigal Christian. Jessica, my girl,
Look to my house. I am right loth to go:
There is some ill a-brewing towards my rest,
For I did dream of money-bags tonight.

LAUNCELOT. I beseech you, sir, go: my young master doth expect your reproach.

SHYLOCK. So do I his. Hear you me, Jessica:
Lock up my doors; and when you hear the drum,
And the vile squealing of the wry-necked fife,
Clamber not you up to the casements then,
Nor thrust your head into the public street
To gaze on Christian fools with varnished faces,
But stop my house's ears, I mean my casements:
Let not the sound of shallow foppery enter
My sober house. By Jacob's staff, I swear,

I have no mind of feasting forth tonight:
But I will go. Go you before me, sirrah.

LAUNCELOT. I will go before, sir. Mistress, look out at window, for all this.

There will come a Christian by,
Will be worth a Jewess' eye.

SHYLOCK. What says that fool of Hagar's offspring, ha?

JESSICA. His words were *Farewell, Mistress*; nothing else.

SHYLOCK. The patch is kind enough, but a huge feeder;
Snail-slow in profit, and he sleeps by day
More than the wild cat: drones hive not with me;
Therefore I part with him, and part with him
To one that I would have him help to waste
His borrowed purse. Well, Jessica, go in:
Perhaps I will return immediately:
Do as I bid you; shut doors after you:
Fast bind, fast find;
A proverb never stale in thrifty mind.

JESSICA (*aside*). Farewell, and if my fortune be not crost,
I have a father, you a daughter, lost.

Scene 6—Before Shylock's House

Gratiano and Salarino meet Lorenzo before Shylock's house and witness Jessica's escape, dressed as a boy and acting as a torch-bearer to her lover Lorenzo. She carries off with her a casket of jewels and a store of ducats. They go to Bassanio's house for supper, and almost at once, the wind being favourable, Bassanio sails for Belmont, to see Portia, and to try his fortune with the caskets.

Scene 7—Prince of Morocco at Portia's House

PORTIA. Go draw aside the curtains and discover
The several caskets to this noble prince.
Now make your choice.

PRINCE. The first of gold, who this inscription bears:
Who chooseth me shall gain what many men desire.
The second, silver, which this promise carries:
Who chooseth me shall get as much as he deserves.
This third, dull lead, with warning all as blunt:
Who chooseth me must give and hazard all he hath.
How shall I know if I do choose the right?

PORTIA. The one of them contains my picture, prince:
If you choose that, then I am yours withal.

PRINCE. Some god direct my judgment!
What says this leaden casket?
Who chooseth me must give and hazard all he hath.
Must give: for what? For lead? Hazard for lead?

This casket threatens. Men that hazard all
Do it in hope of fair advantages :
A golden mind stoops not to shows of dross.
What says the silver with her virgin hue ?
Who chooseth me shall get as much as he deserves.
As much as he deserves ! Pause there, Morocco,
And weigh thy value with an even hand :
As much as I deserve ! Why, that's the lady :
I do in birth deserve her, and in fortunes,
In graces and in qualities of breeding ;
But, more than these, in love I do deserve.
What if I strayed no further, but chose here ?
Let's see once more this saying graved in gold :
Who chooseth me shall gain what many men desire.
Why, that's the lady ; all the world desires her ;
From the four corners of the earth they come
To kiss this shrine, this mortal-breathing saint :
The Hyrcanian deserts and the vasty wilds
Of wide Arabia are as throughfares now
For princes to come view fair Portia :
The watery kingdom, whose ambitious head
Spits in the face of heaven, is no bar
To stop the foreign spirits, but they come,
As o'er a brook, to see fair Portia.
One of these three contains her heavenly picture.
Is't like that lead contains her ? It were too gross.
Or shall I think in silver she's immured,
Being ten times undervalued to tried gold ?
O sinful thought ! Never so rich a gem
Was set in worse than gold. Deliver me the key :
Here do I choose, and thrive I as I may !

PORTIA. There, take it, prince ; and if my form lie there,
Then I am yours.

PRINCE (*unlocking the gold casket*). What have we here ?
A carrion Death, within whose empty eye
There is a written scroll : I'll read the writing.

All that glisters is not gold ;
Often have you heard that told :
Many a man his life hath sold
But my outside to behold :
Gilded tombs do worms infold.
Had you been as wise as bold,
Young in limbs, in judgment old,
Your answer had not been inscrolled :
Fare you well ; your suit is cold.

Cold, indeed, and labour lost :
Then, farewell heat, and welcome frost !

Portia, adieu. I have too grieved a heart
To take a tedious leave; thus losers part.

Scene 8—A Venice Street

SALARINO. Why, man, I saw Bassanio under sail:
With him is Gratiano gone along;
And in their ship I am sure Lorenzo is not.

SALANIO. The villain Jew with outcries raised the duke,
Who went with him to search Bassanio's ship.

SALARINO. He came too late, the ship was under sail:
But there the duke was given to understand
That in a gondola were seen together
Lorenzo and his amorous Jessica.

SALANIO. I never heard a passion so confused,
So strange, outrageous, and so variable,
As the dog Jew did utter in the streets:
My daughter! O my ducats! O my daughter!
Fled with a Christian! O my Christian ducats!
Justice! the law! my ducats and my daughter!

SALARINO. Why, all the boys in Venice follow him,
Crying, his stones, his daughter, and his ducats.

SALANIO. Let good Antonio look he keep his day,
Or he shall pay for this.

SALARINO. Marry, well remembered.
I reasoned with a Frenchman yesterday,
Who told me, in the narrow seas that part
The French and English, there miscarried
A vessel of our country richly fraught:
I thought upon Antonio when he told me,
And wished in silence that it were not his.
A kinder gentleman treads not the earth.
I saw Bassanio and Antonio part:
Bassanio told him he would make some speed
Of his return: he answered, *Do not so;*
Slubber not business for my sake, Bassanio,
But stay the very riping of the time;
And for the Jew's bond which he hath of me,
Let it not enter in your mind of love:
Be merry, and employ your chiefest thoughts
To courtship and such fair ostents of love
As shall conveniently become you there.
And even there, his eye being big with tears,
Turning his face, he put his hand behind him,
And with affection wondrous sensible
He wrung Bassanio's hand; and so they parted.

SALANIO. I think he only loves the world for him.

I pray thee, let us go and find him out
And quicken his embracèd heaviness
With some delight or other.

Scene 9—Prince of Arragon at Portia's House

NERISSA. Quick, quick, I pray thee; draw the curtain straight:
The Prince of Arragon hath ta'en his oath,
And comes to his election presently.

PORTIA. Behold, there stand the caskets, noble prince:
If you choose that wherein I am contained,
Straight shall our nuptial rites be solemnized:
But if you fail, without more speech, my lord,
You must be gone from hence immediately.

PRINCE. I am enjoined by oath to observe three things:
First, never to unfold to any one
Which casket 'twas I chose; next, if I fail
Of the right casket, never in my life
To woo a maid in way of marriage:
Lastly,
If I do fail in fortune of my choice,
Immediately to leave you and be gone.

PORTIA. To these injunctions every one doth swear
That comes to hazard for my worthless self.

PRINCE. And so have I addressed me. Fortune now
To my heart's hope! Gold, silver, and base lead.
Who chooseth me must give and hazard all he hath.
You shall look fairer, ere I give or hazard.
What says the golden chest? ha! let me see:
Who chooseth me shall gain what many men desire.
I will not choose what many men desire,
Because I will not jump with common spirits
And rank me with the barbarous multitudes.
Why, then to thee, thou silver treasure-house;
Tell me once more what title thou dost bear:
Who chooseth me shall get as much as he deserves.
And well said, too; for who shall go about
To cozen fortune and be honourable
Without the stamp of merit? Let none presume
To wear an undeservèd dignity.
O, that estates, degrees, and offices
Were not derived corruptly, and that clear honour
Were purchased by the merit of the wearer!
How many then should cover that stand bare!
How many be commanded that command!
How much low peasantry would then be gleaned
From the true seed of honour! and how much honour

Picked from the chaff and ruin of the times
To be new-varnished ! Well, but to my choice :
Who chooseth me shall get as much as he deserves.
I will assume desert. Give me a key for this,
And instantly unlock my fortunes here. (*He opens the silver casket*)

PORTIA. Too long a pause for that which you find there.

PRINCE. Did I deserve no more than a fool's head ?
Is that my prize ? Are my deserts no better ?
What is here ?

The fire seven times tried this :
Seven times tried that judgment is,
That did never choose amiss.
Some there be that shadows kiss ;
Such have but a shadow's bliss :
There be fools alive, I wis,
Silvered o'er ; and so was this.

Still more fool I shall appear
By the time I linger here :
With one fool's head I came to woo,
But I go away with two.
Sweet, adieu. I'll keep my oath,
Patiently to bear my wrath.

PORTIA (*watching the Prince depart*). Thus hath the candle singed the moth. Come, draw the curtain, Nerissa.

SERVANT (*entering*). Madam, there is alighted at your gate
A young Venetian, one that comes before
To signify the approaching of his lord,
From whom he bringeth sensible regreets,
To wit, besides commends and courteous breath,
Gifts of rich value. Yet I have not seen
So likely an ambassador of love :
A day in April never came so sweet,
To show how costly summer was at hand,
As this fore-spurrer comes before his lord.

PORTIA. Come, come, Nerissa ; for I long to see
Quick Cupid's post that comes so mannerly.

NERISSA. Bassanio, Lord Love, if thy will it be !

ACT 3

Scene 1—A Street in Venice

SALANIO. Now, what news on the Rialto ?

SALARINO. Why, yet it lives there unchecked that Antonio hath a ship of rich lading wrecked on the narrow seas ; the Goodwins, I think they call the place ; a very dangerous flat and fatal, where the carcases of many a tall ship lie buried, as they say, if my gossip Report be an honest woman of her word.

SALANIO. I would she were as lying a gossip in that as ever made her neighbours believe she wept for the death of a third husband. But it is true, without crossing the plain highway of talk, that the good Antonio, the honest Antonio, hath lost a ship.

SALARINO. I would it might prove the end of his losses.

SALANIO. Let me say *Amen* betimes, lest the devil cross my prayer, for here he comes in the likeness of a Jew. How now, Shylock! What news among the merchants?

SHYLOCK (*approaching*). You knew, none so well, none so well as you, of my daughter's flight.

SALARINO. That's certain: I, for my part, knew the tailor that made the wings she flew withal.

SHYLOCK. My own flesh and blood to rebel!

SALANIO. Out upon it, old carrion! rebels it at these years? There is more difference between thy flesh and hers than between jet and ivory. But tell us, do you hear whether Antonio have had any loss at sea or no?

SHYLOCK. There I have another bad match: a bankrupt, a prodigal, who dare scarce show his head on the Rialto: a beggar, that was used to come so smug upon the mart. Let him look to his bond. He was wont to call me usurer; let him look to his bond. He was wont to lend money for a Christian courtesy; let him look to his bond.

SALARINO. Why, I am sure, if he forfeit, thou wilt not take his flesh: what's that good for?

SHYLOCK. To bait fish withal: if it will feed nothing else it will feed my revenge. He hath disgraced me, and hindered me half a million; laughed at my losses, mocked at my gains, scorned my nation, thwarted my bargains, cooled my friends, heated mine enemies; and what's his reason? I am a Jew. Hath not a Jew eyes? hath not a Jew hands, organs, dimensions, senses, affections, passions? fed with the same food, hurt with the same weapons, subject to the same diseases, healed by the same means, warmed and cooled by the same winter and summer, as a Christian is? If you prick us, do we not bleed? if you tickle us, do we not laugh? if you poison us, do we not die? and if you wrong us, shall we not revenge? If we are like you in the rest, we will resemble you in that. If a Jew wrong a Christian, what is his humility? Revenge. If a Christian wrong a Jew, what should his sufferance be by Christian example? Why, revenge. The villainy you teach me I will execute, and it shall go hard but I will better the instruction.

SALANIO. Here comes another of the tribe: a third cannot be matched unless the devil himself turn Jew.

SHYLOCK. How now, Tubal! What news from Genoa? Hast thou found my daughter?

TUBAL. I often came where I did hear of her, but cannot find her.

SHYLOCK. Why, there, there, there, there! a diamond gone—cost me two thousand ducats in Frankfort! The curse never fell upon our nation till now; two thousand ducats and other precious, precious jewels. I would my daughter were dead at my foot, and the jewels in her ear! would she were hearsed at my foot, and the ducats in her coffin! No news of them? Why, so: and I know not what's spent in the search: why, thou loss upon loss! the thief gone with so much, and so much to find the thief; and no satisfaction, no revenge: nor no ill luck stirring but what lights on my shoulders.

TUBAL. Yes, other men have ill luck too: Antonio, as I heard in Genoa——

SHYLOCK. What, what, what? Ill luck, ill luck?

TUBAL. Hath an argosy cast away, coming from Tripolis.

SHYLOCK. I thank God, I thank God. Is't true, is't true?

TUBAL. I spoke with some of the sailors that escaped the wreck.

SHYLOCK. I thank thee, good Tubal: good news, good news! ha, ha! where? in Genoa?

TUBAL. Your daughter spent in Genoa, as I heard, in one night fourscore ducats.

SHYLOCK. Thou stickest a dagger in me: I shall never see my gold again: fourscore ducats at a sitting! fourscore ducats!

TUBAL. There came divers of Antonio's creditors in my company to Venice that swear he cannot choose but break.

SHYLOCK. I am very glad of it: I'll plague him; I'll torture him: I am glad of it.

TUBAL. One of them showed me a ring that he had of your daughter for a monkey.

SHYLOCK. Out upon her! Thou torturest me, Tubal: it was my turquoise; I had it of Leah when I was a bachelor: I would not have given it for a wilderness of monkeys.

TUBAL. But Antonio is certainly undone.

SHYLOCK. Nay, that's true, that's very true. Go, Tubal, fee me an officer. I will have the heart of him if he forfeit; for, were he out of Venice, I can make what merchandise I will. Go, go, Tubal, and meet me at our synagogue.

Scene 2—A Room in Portia's House

PORTIA (*to Bassanio*). I pray you, tarry: pause a day or two
Before you hazard; for, in choosing wrong,
I lose your company: therefore forbear awhile.
There's something tells me (but it is not love),
I would not lose you.
I would detain you here some month or two
Before you venture for me. I could teach you

How to choose right, but I am then forsworn;
So will I never be: so may you miss me;
But, if you do, you'll make me wish a sin,
That I had been forsworn.
I speak too long; but tis to peize the time,
To eke it and to draw it out.

BASSANIO. Let me choose;
For, as I am, I live upon the rack.

PORTIA. Upon the rack, Bassanio! then confess
What treason there is mingled with your love.

BASSANIO. None but that ugly treason of mistrust
Which makes me fear the enjoying of my love:
There may as well be amity and life
Tween snow and fire, as treason and my love.

PORTIA. Ay, but I fear you speak upon the rack,
Where men enforcèd do speak anything.

BASSANIO. Promise me life, and I'll confess the truth.

PORTIA. Well then, confess and live.

BASSANIO. *Confess and love*
Had been the very sum of my confession:
O happy torment, when my torturer
Doth teach me answers for deliverance!
But let me to my fortune and the caskets.

PORTIA. Away, then! I am locked in one of them:
If you do love me, you will find me out.
Nerissa and the rest, stand all aloof.
Let music sound while he doth make his choice;
Then, if he lose, he makes a swan-like end,
Fading in music. . . . Go, Hercules!
Live thou, I live: with much, much more dismay
I view the fight than thou that mak'st the fray.

Music while Bassanio surveys the caskets

Tell me where is fancy bred,
Or in the heart or in the head?
How begot, how nourishèd?
Reply, reply.
It is engendered in the eyes,
With gazing fed; and fancy dies
In the cradle where it lies.
Let us all ring fancy's knell:
I'll begin it—Ding, dong, bell.

BASSANIO. So may the outward shows be least themselves:
The world is still deceived with ornament.
In law, what plea so tainted and corrupt
But, being seasoned with a gracious voice,

Obscures the show of evil? In religion,
What monstrous error, but some sober brow
Will bless it and approve it with a text,
Hiding the grossness with fair ornament?
There is no vice so simple but assumes
Some mark of virtue on his outward parts.
Look on beauty,
And you shall see tis purchased by the weight;
Which therein works a miracle in nature,
Making them lightest that wear most of it.
Thus ornament is but the treacherous shore
To a most dangerous sea,
The seeming truth which cunning times put on
To entrap the wisest. Therefore, thou gaudy gold,
Hard food for Midas, I will none of thee;
Nor none of thee, thou pale and common drudge
Tween man and man: but thou, thou meagre lead,
Which rather threatenest than dost promise aught,
Thy paleness moves me more than eloquence;
And here choose I: joy be the consequence!

PORTIA (*aside*). O love, be moderate; allay thy ecstasy;
In measure rein thy joy; scant this excess.
I feel too much thy blessing: make it less,
For fear I surfeit.

BASSANIO (*opening the lead casket*). What find I here?
Fair Portia's counterfeit! What demi-god
Hath come so near creation?
Here's the scroll,
The continent and summary of my fortune:

> You that choose not by the view,
> Chance as fair and choose as true!
> Since this fortune falls to you,
> Be content and seek no new.
> If you be well pleased with this
> And hold your fortune for your bliss,
> Turn you where your lady is
> And claim her with a loving kiss.

A gentle scroll. Fair lady, by your leave:
I come by note, to give and to receive.
Like one of two contending in a prize,
That thinks he hath done well in people's eyes,
Hearing applause and universal shout,
Giddy in spirit, still gazing in a doubt
Whether those peals of praise be his or no;
So, thrice-fair lady, stand I, even so;
As doubtful whether what I see be true,
Until confirmed, signed, ratified by you.

PORTIA. You see me, Lord Bassanio, where I stand,
Such as I am: though for myself alone
I would not be ambitious in my wish,
To wish myself much better, yet, for you
I would be trebled twenty times myself,
A thousand times more fair, ten thousand times
More rich,
That, only to stand high in your account,
I might in virtues, beauties, livings, friends,
Exceed account; but the full sum of me
Is an unlessoned girl, unschooled, unpractised;
Happy in this, she is not yet so old
But she may learn; happier in this,
She is not bred so dull but she can learn;
Happiest of all is that her gentle spirit
Commits itself to yours to be directed,
As from her lord, her governor, her king.
Myself and what is mine to you and yours
Is now converted. But now I was the lord
Of this fair mansion, master of my servants,
Queen o'er myself; and even now, but now,
This house, these servants, and this same myself
Are yours, my lord: I give them with this ring,
Which when you part from, lose, or give away,
Let it presage the ruin of your love
And be my vantage to exclaim on you.

BASSANIO. Madam, you have bereft me of all words;
Only my blood speaks to you in my veins,
And there is such confusion in my powers,
As, after some oration fairly spoke
By a belovèd prince, there doth appear
Among the buzzing pleasèd multitude,
Where every something, being blent together,
Turns to a wild of nothing, save of joy,
Expressed and not expressed. But when this ring
Parts from this finger, then parts life from hence:
O, then be bold to say Bassanio's dead!

NERISSA. My lord and lady, it is now our time,
That have stood by and seen our wishes prosper,
To cry, Good joy: Good joy, my lord and lady!

GRATIANO. My lord Bassanio and my gentle lady,
I wish you all the joy that you can wish;
And when your honours mean to solemnize
The bargain of your faith, I do beseech you,
Even at that time I may be married too.

BASSANIO. With all my heart, so thou canst get a wife.

GRATIANO. I thank your lordship, you have got me one.
My eyes, my lord, can look as swift as yours:
You saw the mistress, I beheld the maid;
Your fortune stood upon the casket there,
And so did mine too, as the matter falls.

PORTIA. Is this true, Nerissa?

NERISSA. Madam, it is, so you stand pleased withal.

BASSANIO. And do you, Gratiano, mean good faith?

GRATIANO. Yes, faith, my lord.

BASSANIO. Our feast shall be much honoured in your marriage.
But who comes here? Lorenzo and his infidel?
What, and my old Venetian friend Salerio?

BASSANIO. Lorenzo and Salerio, welcome hither;
If that the youth of my new interest here
Have power to bid you welcome. By your leave,
I bid my very friends and countrymen,
Sweet Portia, welcome.

PORTIA. So do I, my lord: they are entirely welcome.

LORENZO. I thank your honour. For my part, my lord,
My purpose was not to have seen you here;
But, meeting with Salerio by the way,
He did intreat me, past all saying nay,
To come with him along.

SALERIO. I did, my lord;
And I have reason for it. Signior Antonio
Commends him to you. (*He gives Bassanio a letter*)

BASSANIO. Ere I ope his letter,
I pray you, tell me how my good friend doth.

SALERIO. Not sick, my lord, unless it be in mind;
Nor well, unless in mind: his letter there
Will show you his estate.

GRATIANO. Nerissa, cheer yon stranger; bid her welcome.
Your hand, Salerio: what's the news from Venice?
How doth that royal merchant, good Antonio?
I know he will be glad of our success;
We are the Jasons; we have won the fleece.

SALERIO. I would you had won the fleece that he hath lost.

PORTIA. There are some shrewd con*tents* in yon same paper,
That steals the colour from Bassanio's cheek:
Some dear friend dead—else nothing in the world
Could turn so much the constitution
Of any constant man. What, worse and worse!
With leave, Bassanio; I am half yourself,
And I must freely have the half of anything
That this same paper brings you.

BASSANIO. O sweet Portia,
Here are a few of the unpleasantest words
That ever blotted paper! Gentle lady,
When I did first impart my love to you,
I freely told you all the wealth I had
Ran in my veins. I was a gentleman,
And then I told you true. And yet, dear lady,
Rating myself at nothing, you shall see
How much I was a braggart. When I told you
My state was nothing I should then have told you
That I was worse than nothing; for, indeed,
I have engaged myself to a dear friend,
Engaged my friend to his mere enemy,
To feed my means. Here is a letter, lady;
The paper as the body of my friend,
And every word in it a gaping wound,
Issuing life-blood. But is it true, Salerio?
Have all his ventures failed? What, not one hit?
From Tripolis, from Mexico and England,
From Lisbon, Barbary, and India?
And not one vessel scape?

SALERIO. Not one, my lord.
Besides, it should appear that if he had
The present money to discharge the Jew,
He would not take it. Never did I know
A creature that did bear the shape of man
So keen and greedy to confound a man:
He plies the duke at morning and at night,
And doth impeach the freedom of the State
If they deny him justice: twenty merchants,
The duke himself, and the magnificoes
Of greatest port, have all persuaded with him;
But none can drive him from the envious plea
Of forfeiture, of justice, and his bond.

PORTIA. Is it your dear friend that is thus in trouble?

BASSANIO. The dearest friend to me, the kindest man,
The best-conditioned and unwearied spirit
In doing courtesies, and one in whom
The ancient Roman honour more appears
Than any that draws breath in Italy.

PORTIA. What sum owes he the Jew?

BASSANIO. For me three thousand ducats.

PORTIA. What, no more
Pay him six thousand and deface the bond;
Double six thousand, and then treble that,

Before a friend of this description
Shall lose a hair through Bassanio's fault.
First go with me to church and call me wife,
And then away to Venice to your friend;
For never shall you lie by Portia's side
With an unquiet soul. You shall have gold
To pay the petty debt twenty times over:
When it is paid, bring your true friend along.
My maid Nerissa and myself meantime
Will live as maids and widows. Come, away!
For you shall hence upon your wedding-day.
Bid your friends welcome, show a merry cheer:
Since you are dear bought, I will love you dear.
But let me hear the letter of your friend.

Bassanio reads the letter

Sweet Bassanio, my ships have all miscarried, my creditors grow cruel, my estate is very low, my bond to the Jew is forfeit; and since, in paying it, it is impossible I should live, all debts are cleared between you and me, if I might but see you at my death. Notwithstanding, use your pleasure: if your love do not persuade you to come, let not my letter.

PORTIA. O love, dispatch all business, and be gone!

BASSANIO. Since I have your good leave to go away,
I will make haste: but, till I come again,
No bed shall e'er be guilty of my stay,
No rest be interposer 'twixt us twain.

Scene 3—A Street in Venice

SHYLOCK. Gaoler, look to him: tell not me of mercy;
This is the fool that lent out money gratis:
Gaoler, look to him.

ANTONIO. Hear me yet, good Shylock.

SHYLOCK. I'll have my bond: speak not against my bond:
I have sworn an oath that I will have my bond.
Thou call'dst me dog before thou hadst a cause;
But, since I am a dog, beware my fangs:
The duke shall grant me justice.

ANTONIO. I pray thee, hear me speak.

SHYLOCK. I'll have my bond; I will not hear thee speak:
I'll have my bond; and therefore speak no more.
I'll not be made a soft and dull-eyed fool,
To shake the head, relent, and sigh, and yield
To Christian intercessors. Follow not;
I'll have no speaking: I will have my bond.

SALARINO (*as Shylock goes*). It is the most impenetrable cur
That ever kept with men.

ANTONIO. Let him alone:
I'll follow him no more with bootless prayers.
He seeks my life; his reason well I know:
I oft delivered from his forfeitures
Many that have at times made moan to me;
Therefore he hates me.

SALARINO. I am sure the duke
Will never grant this forfeiture to hold.

ANTONIO. The duke cannot deny the course of law,
For the commodity that strangers have
With us in Venice, if it be denied,
Will much impeach the justice of the State,
Since that the trade and profit of the city
Consisteth of all nations. Therefore, go:
These griefs and losses have so bated me
That I shall hardly spare a pound of flesh
Tomorrow to my creditor.
Well, gaoler, on. Pray God, Bassanio come
To see me pay his debt, and then I care not!

Scene 4—A Room in Portia's House

Enter Portia, Nerissa, Lorenzo, Jessica, and Balthasar

LORENZO. Madam, although I speak it in your presence,
You have a noble and a true conceit
Of god-like amity, which appears most strongly
In bearing thus the absence of your lord.
But if you knew to whom you show this honour,
How true a gentleman you send relief,
How dear a lover of my lord your husband,
I know you would be prouder of the work
Than customary bounty can enforce you.

PORTIA. No more of it: hear other things.
Lorenzo, I commit into your hands
The husbandry and manage of my house
Until my lord's return: for mine own part,
I have toward heaven breathed a secret vow
To live in prayer and contemplation,
Only attended by Nerissa here,
Until her husband and my lord's return.
There is a monastery two miles off;
And there will we abide.

LORENZO. Madam, with all my heart;
I shall obey you in all fair commands.
Fair thoughts and happy hours attend on you!

JESSICA. I wish your ladyship all heart's content.

PORTIA. I thank you for your wish, and am well pleased
To wish it back on you : fare you well, Jessica.
Now, Balthasar,
As I have ever found thee honest-true,
So let me find thee still. Take this same letter,
And use thou all the endeavour of a man
In speed to Padua : see thou render this
Into my cousin's hand, Doctor Bellario ;
And, look, what notes and garments he doth give thee,
Bring them, I pray thee, to the common ferry
Which trades to Venice.

PORTIA. Come on, Nerissa ; I have work in hand
That you yet know not of ; we'll see our husbands
Before they think of us.

NERISSA. Shall they see us ?

PORTIA. They shall, Nerissa ; but in such a habit
That they shall think we are accomplishèd
With that we lack. I'll hold thee any wager,
When we are both accoutred like young men,
I'll prove the prettier fellow of the two,
And wear my dagger with the braver grace,
And speak between the change of man and boy
With a reed voice, and turn two mincing steps
Into a manly stride, and speak of frays
Like a fine bragging youth, and tell quaint lies,
How honourable ladies sought my love,
Which I denying, they fell sick and died.
But come, I'll tell thee all my whole device
When I am in my coach, which stays for us
At the park gate ; and therefore haste away,
For we must measure twenty miles today.

ACT 4

Scene 1—A Venice Court of Justice

DUKE. What, is Antonio here ?

ANTONIO. Ready, so please your grace.

DUKE. I am sorry for thee : thou art come to answer
A stony adversary, an inhuman wretch,
Uncapable of pity, void and empty
From any dram of mercy.

ANTONIO. I have heard
Your grace hath ta'en great pains to qualify
His rigorous course ; but since he stands obdurate,
And that no lawful means can carry me
Out of his envy's reach, I do oppose
My patience to his fury, and am armed

To suffer, with a quietness of spirit,
The very tyranny and rage of his.

Duke. Go one, and call the Jew into the court.

Salerio. He is ready at the door: he comes, my lord.

Duke. Make room, and let him stand before our face.
Shylock, the world thinks, and I think so too,
That thou but lead'st this fashion of thy malice
To the last hour of act; and then tis thought
Thou'lt show thy mercy and remorse more strange
Than is thy strange apparent cruelty;
And where thou now exact'st the penalty,
Which is a pound of this poor merchant's flesh,
Thou wilt not only loose the forfeiture,
But, touched with human gentleness and love,
Forgive a moiety of the principal,
Glancing an eye of pity on his losses,
That have of late so huddled on his back,
Enow to press a royal merchant down
And pluck commiseration of his state
From brassy bosoms and rough hearts of flint,
From stubborn Turks and Tartars, never trained
To offices of tender courtesy.
We all expect a gentle answer, Jew.

Shylock. I have possessed your grace of what I purpose;
And by our holy Sabbath have I sworn
To have the due and forfeit of my bond:
If you deny it, let the danger light
Upon your charter and your city's freedom.
You'll ask me why I rather choose to have
A weight of carrion flesh than to receive
Three thousand ducats: I'll not answer that.
But say it is my humour: is it answered?
What if my house be troubled with a rat
And I be pleased to give ten thousand ducats
To have it baned? What, are you answered yet?
Some men there are love not a gaping pig;
Some, that are mad if they behold a cat.
As there is no firm reason to be rendered,
Why he cannot abide a gaping pig,
Why he, a harmless necessary cat,
So can I give no reason, nor I will not,
More than a lodged hate and a certain loathing
I bear Antonio, that I follow thus
A losing suit against him. Are you answered?

Bassanio. This is no answer, thou unfeeling man,
To excuse the current of thy cruelty.

SHYLOCK. I am not bound to please thee with my answers.

BASSANIO. Do all men kill the things they do not love?

SHYLOCK. Hates any man the thing he would not kill?

BASSANIO. Every offence is not a hate at first.

SHYLOCK. What, wouldst thou have a serpent sting thee twice?

ANTONIO. I pray you, think you question with the Jew:
You may as well go stand upon the beach
And bid the main flood bate his usual height;
You may as well use question with the wolf
Why he hath made the ewe bleat for the lamb;
You may as well forbid the mountain pines
To wag their high tops and to make no noise
When they are fretted with the gusts of heaven;
You may as well do anything most hard,
As seek to soften that (than which what's harder?)
His Jewish heart: therefore, I do beseech you,
Make no more offers, use no farther means,
But with all brief and plain conveniency
Let me have judgment and the Jew his will.

BASSANIO. For thy three thousand ducats here is six.

SHYLOCK. If every ducat in six thousand ducats
Were in six parts and every part a ducat,
I would not draw them; I would have my bond.

DUKE. How shalt thou hope for mercy, rendering none?

SHYLOCK. What judgment shall I dread, doing no wrong?
You have among you many a purchased slave,
Which, like your asses and your dogs and mules,
You use in abject and in slavish parts,
Because you bought them: shall I say to you,
Let them be free, marry them to your heirs?
Why sweat they under burthens? let their beds
Be made as soft as yours, and let their palates
Be seasoned with such viands? You will answer
The slaves are ours. So do I answer you:
The pound of flesh, which I demand of him,
Is dearly bought; tis mine and I will have it.
If you deny me, fie upon your law!
There is no force in the decrees of Venice.
I stand for judgment: answer; shall I have it?

DUKE. Upon my power I may dismiss this court,
Unless Bellario, a learnèd doctor,
Whom I have sent for to determine this,
Come here today.

SALERIO. My lord, here stays without

A messenger with letters from the doctor,
New come from Padua.

DUKE. Bring us the letters ; call the messenger.

BASSANIO. Good cheer, Antonio ! What, man, courage yet !
The Jew shall have my flesh, blood, bones, and all,
Ere thou shalt lose for me one drop of blood.

ANTONIO. I am a tainted wether of the flock,
Meetest for death : the weakest kind of fruit
Drops earliest to the ground ; and so let me :
You cannot better be employed, Bassanio,
Than to live still and write mine epitaph.

Enter Nerissa as a lawyer's clerk, presenting a letter

DUKE. Came you from Padua, from Bellario ?

NERISSA. From both, my lord. Bellario greets your grace.

BASSANIO (*to Shylock*). Why dost thou whet thy knife so earnestly ?

SHYLOCK. To cut the forfeiture from that bankrupt there.

GRATIANO. Can no prayers pierce thee ?

SHYLOCK. No, none that thou hast wit enough to make.

GRATIANO. O, be thou damned, inexorable dog !
And for thy life let justice be accused.
Thou almost makest me waver in my faith
To hold opinion with Py*thag*oras,
That souls of animals infuse themselves
Into the trunks of men : thy currish spirit
Governed a wolf, who, hanged for human slaughter,
Infused itself in thee, for thy desires
Are wolfish, starved, and ravenous.

SHYLOCK. Till thou canst rail the seal from off my bond
Thou but offend'st thy lungs to speak so loud :
Repair thy wit, good youth, or it will fall
To cureless ruin. I stand here for law.

DUKE. This letter from Bellario doth commend
A young and learned doctor to our court.
Some three or four of you
Go give him courteous conduct to this place.
Meantime the court shall hear Bellario's letter.

CLERK (*reading*). Your grace shall understand that at the receipt of your letter I am very sick, but in the instant that your messenger came, in loving visitation was with me a young doctor of Rome ; his name is Balthasar. I acquainted him with the cause in controversy between the Jew and Antonio the merchant ; we turned o'er many books together : he is furnished with my opinion ; which, bettered with his own learning, the greatness whereof I cannot enough commend, comes with him, at my importunity, to fill up your grace's request in my stead. I beseech you, let his lack of years be no impediment to let him lack a reverend estimation; for I never knew so young a body with so old a head.

DUKE. You hear the learned Bellario, what he writes:
And here, I take it, is the doctor come.

Enter Portia as a Doctor of Laws

DUKE. You are welcome: take your place.
Are you acquainted with the difference
That holds this present question in the court?

PORTIA. I am informèd thoroughly of the cause.
Which is the merchant here, and which the Jew?

DUKE. Antonio and old Shylock, both stand forth.

PORTIA. Is your name Shylock?

SHYLOCK. Shylock is my name.

PORTIA. Of a strange nature is the suit you follow,
Yet in such rule that the Venetian law
Cannot impugn you as you do proceed.
(*To Antonio*) You stand within his danger, do you not?

ANTONIO. Ay, so he says.

PORTIA. Do you confess the bond?

ANTONIO. I do.

PORTIA. Then must the Jew be merciful.

SHYLOCK. On what compulsion must I? Tell me that.

PORTIA. The quality of mercy is not strained,
It droppeth as the gentle rain from heaven
Upon the place beneath: it is twice blest;
It blesseth him that gives and him that takes:
Tis mightiest in the mightiest: it becomes
The thronèd monarch better than his crown;
His sceptre shows the force of temporal power,
The attribute to awe and majesty,
Wherein doth sit the dread and fear of kings;
But mercy is above this sceptred sway;
It is enthronèd in the hearts of kings,
It is an attribute to God himself,
And earthly power doth then show likest God's
When mercy seasons justice. Therefore, Jew,
Though justice be thy plea, consider this,
That, in the course of justice, none of us
Should see salvation: we do pray for mercy,
And that same prayer doth teach us all to render
The deeds of mercy. I have spoke thus much
To mitigate the justice of thy plea;
Which, if thou follow, this strict court of Venice
Must needs give sentence 'gainst the merchant there.

SHYLOCK. My deeds upon my head! I crave the law,
The penalty and forfeit of my bond.

PORTIA. Is he not able to discharge the money?

BASSANIO. Yes, here I tender it for him in the court;
Yea, twice the sum: if that will not suffice,
I will be bound to pay it ten times o'er,
On forfeit of my hands, my head, my heart:
If this will not suffice, it must appear
That malice bears down truth; and, I beseech you,
Wrest once the law to your authority:
To do a great right do a little wrong,
And curb this cruel devil of his will.

PORTIA. It must not be: there is no power in Venice
Can alter a decree establishèd:
Twill be recorded for a precedent,
And many an error by the same example
Will rush into the State: it cannot be.

SHYLOCK. A Daniel come to judgment! yea, a Daniel!
O wise young judge, how I do honour thee!

PORTIA. I pray you, let me look upon the bond.

SHYLOCK. Here tis, most reverend doctor, here it is.

PORTIA. Shylock, there's thrice thy money offered thee.

SHYLOCK. An oath, an oath, I have an oath in heaven:
Shall I lay perjury upon my soul?
No, not for Venice.

PORTIA. Why, this bond is forfeit;
And lawfully by this the Jew may claim
A pound of flesh, to be by him cut off
Nearest the merchant's heart. Be merciful:
Take thrice thy money; bid me tear the bond.

SHYLOCK. When it is paid according to the tenour.
It doth appear you are a worthy judge;
You know the law, your exposition
Hath been most sound: I charge you by the law,
Whereof you are a well-deserving pillar,
Proceed to judgment; by my soul I swear
There is no power in the tongue of man
To alter me: I stay here on my bond.

ANTONIO. Most heartily I do beseech the court
To give the judgment.

PORTIA. Why then, thus it is:
You must prepare your bosom for his knife.

SHYLOCK. O noble judge! O excellent young man!

PORTIA. For the intent and purpose of the law

Hath full relation to the penalty,
Which here appeareth due upon the bond.

SHYLOCK. Tis very true : O wise and upright judge !
How much more elder art thou than thy looks !

PORTIA. Therefore lay bare your bosom.

SHYLOCK. Ay, his breast :
So says the bond : doth it not, noble judge ?
Nearest his heart : those are the very words.

PORTIA. It is so. Are there balance here to weigh the flesh ?

SHYLOCK. I have them ready.

PORTIA. Have by some surgeon, Shylock, on your charge,
To stop his wounds, lest he do bleed to death.

SHYLOCK. Is it so nominated in the bond ?

PORTIA. It is not so expressed, but what of that ?
Twere good you do so much for charity.

SHYLOCK. I cannot find it ; tis not in the bond.

PORTIA. You, merchant, have you anything to say ?

ANTONIO. But little : I am armed and well prepared.
Give me your hand, Bassanio : fare you well !
Grieve not that I am fallen to this for you,
For herein Fortune shows herself more kind
Than is her custom : it is still her use
To let the wretched man outlive his wealth,
To view with hollow eye and wrinkled brow
An age of poverty ; from which lingering penance
Of such misery doth she cut me off.
Commend me to your honourable wife :
Tell her the process of Antonio's end ;
Say how I loved you, speak me fair in death ;
And, when the tale is told, bid her be judge
Whether Bassanio had not once a love.
Repent but you that you shall lose your friend,
And he repents not that he pays your debt ;
For if the Jew do cut but deep enough,
I'll pay it presently with all my heart.

BASSANIO. Antonio, I am married to a wife
Which is as dear to me as life itself ;
But life itself, my wife, and all the world,
Are not with me esteemed above thy life :
I would lose all, ay, sacrifice them all
Here to this devil, to deliver you.

PORTIA. Your wife would give you little thanks for that,
If she were by, to hear you make the offer.

GRATIANO. I have a wife, whom I protest I love :

I would she were in heaven, so she could
Entreat some power to change this currish Jew.

NERISSA. Tis well you offer it behind her back;
The wish would make else an unquiet house.

SHYLOCK. These be the Christian husbands. I have a daughter;
Would any of the stock of Barabbas
Had been her husband rather than a Christian!
We trifle time: I pray thee, pursue sentence.

PORTIA. A pound of that same merchant's flesh is thine:
The court awards it, and the law doth give it.

SHYLOCK. Most rightful judge!

PORTIA. And you must cut this flesh from off his breast:
The law allows it, and the court awards it.

SHYLOCK. Most learned judge! A sentence! Come, prepare!

PORTIA. Tarry a little; there is something else.
This bond doth give thee here no jot of blood;
The words expressly are *A pound of flesh*;
Take then thy bond, take thou thy pound of flesh;
But, in the cutting it, if thou dost shed
One drop of Christian blood, thy lands and goods
Are, by the laws of Venice, confiscate
Unto the State of Venice.

GRATIANO. O upright judge! Mark, Jew: O learned judge!

SHYLOCK. Is that the law?

PORTIA. Thyself shalt see the Act:
For, as thou urgest justice, be assured
Thou shalt have justice, more than thou desirest.

GRATIANO. O learned judge! Mark, Jew: a learned judge!

SHYLOCK. I take this offer, then; pay the bond thrice
And let the Christian go.

BASSANIO. Here is the money.

PORTIA. Soft!
The Jew shall have all justice; soft! no haste:
He shall have nothing but the penalty.

GRATIANO. O Jew! an upright judge! a learned judge!

PORTIA. Therefore prepare thee to cut off the flesh.
Shed thou no blood, nor cut thou less nor more
But just a pound of flesh: if thou cut'st more
Or less than a just pound, be it but so much
As makes it light or heavy in the substance,
Or the division of the twentieth part
Of one poor scruple (nay, if the scale do turn
But in the estimation of a hair),
Thou diest, and all thy goods are confiscate.

GRATIANO. A second Daniel, a Daniel, Jew!
Now, infidel, I have you on the hip.

PORTIA. Why doth the Jew pause? Take thy forfeiture.

SHYLOCK. Give me my principal, and let me go.

BASSANIO. I have it ready for thee; here it is.

PORTIA. He hath refused it in the open court:
He shall have merely justice and his bond.

GRATIANO. A Daniel still say I, a second Daniel!
I thank thee, Jew, for teaching me that word.

SHYLOCK. Shall I not have barely my principal?

PORTIA. Thou shalt have nothing but the forfeiture,
To be so taken at thy peril, Jew.

SHYLOCK. Why, then the devil give him good of it!
I'll stay no longer question.

PORTIA. Tarry, Jew:
The law hath yet another hold on you.
It is enacted in the laws of Venice,
If it be proved against an alien
That by direct or indirect attempts
He seek the life of any citizen,
The party 'gainst the which he doth contrive
Shall seize one half his goods; the other half
Comes to the privy coffer of the State;
And the offender's life lies in the mercy
Of the duke only, 'gainst all other voice.
In which predicament I say thou stand'st;
Down therefore and beg mercy of the duke.

GRATIANO. Beg that thou mayst have leave to hang thyself:
And yet, thy wealth being forfeit to the State,
Thou hast not left the value of a cord;
Therefore thou must be hanged at the State's charge.

DUKE. That thou shalt see the difference of our spirits,
I pardon thee thy life before thou ask it:
For half thy wealth, it is Antonio's;
The other half comes to the general State,
Which humbleness may drive unto a fine.

PORTIA. Ay, for the State, not for Antonio.

SHYLOCK. Nay, take my life and all; pardon not that:
You take my house when you do take the prop
That doth sustain my house; you take my life
When you do take the means whereby I live.

PORTIA. What mercy can you render him, Antonio?

GRATIANO. A halter gratis; nothing else, for God's sake.

ANTONIO. So please my lord the duke and all the court

To quit the fine for one half of his goods,
I am content, so he will let me have
The other half in use, to render it,
Upon his death, unto the gentleman
That lately stole his daughter :
Two things provided more, that, for this favour,
He presently become a Christian ;
The other, that he do record a gift,
Here in the court, of all he dies possessed,
Unto his son Lorenzo and his daughter.

DUKE. He shall do this, or else I do recant
The pardon that I late pronouncèd here.

PORTIA. Art thou contented, Jew ? What dost thou say ?

SHYLOCK. I am content.

PORTIA. Clerk, draw a deed of gift.

SHYLOCK. I pray you, give me leave to go from hence ;
I am not well : send the deed after me,
And I will sign it.

DUKE. Get thee gone, but do it.

GRATIANO. In christening shalt thou have two godfathers :
Had I been judge thou shouldst have had ten more,
To bring thee to the gallows, not the font. (*Shylock goes*)

DUKE. Sir, I entreat you home with me to dinner.

PORTIA. I humbly do desire your grace of pardon :
I must away this night toward Padua,
And it is meet I presently set forth.

DUKE (*departing*). I am sorry that your leisure serves you not.
Antonio, gratify this gentleman,
For, in my mind, you are much bound to him.

BASSANIO. Most worthy gentleman, I and my friend
Have by your wisdom been this day acquitted
Of grievous penalties ; in lieu whereof,
Three thousand ducats, due unto the Jew,
We freely cope your courteous pains withal.

ANTONIO. And stand indebted, over and above,
In love and service to you evermore.

PORTIA. He is well paid that is well satisfied ;
And I, delivering you, am satisfied
And therein do account myself well paid :
My mind was never yet more mercenary.
I pray you, know me when we meet again :
I wish you well, and so I take my leave.

BASSANIO. Dear sir, of force I must attempt you further :
Take some remembrance of us, as a tribute,

Not as a fee: grant me two things, I pray you,
Not to deny me, and to pardon me.

PORTIA. You press me far, and therefore I will yield.
(*To Antonio*) Give me your gloves, I'll wear them for your sake;
(*To Bassanio*) And, for your love, I'll take this ring from you:
Do not draw back your hand; I'll take no more;
And you in love shall not deny me this.

BASSANIO. This ring, good sir, alas, it is a trifle!
I will not shame myself to give you this.

PORTIA. I will have nothing else but only this;
And now methinks I have a mind to it.

BASSANIO. There's more depends on this than on the value.
The dearest ring in Venice will I give you,
And find it out by proclamation:
Only for this, I pray you, pardon me.

PORTIA. I see, sir, you are liberal in offers:
You taught me first to beg; and now methinks
You teach me how a beggar should be answered.

BASSANIO. Good sir, this ring was given me by my wife;
And when she put it on she made me vow
That I should neither sell nor give nor lose it.

PORTIA. That 'scuse serves many men to save their gifts.
An if your wife be not a mad woman,
And know how well I have deserved the ring,
She would not hold out enemy for ever,
For giving it to me. Well, peace be with you!

ANTONIO. My Lord Bassanio, let him have the ring:
Let his deservings and my love withal
Be valued 'gainst your wife's commandment.

BASSANIO. Go, Gratiano, run and overtake him;
Give him the ring, and bring him, if thou canst,
Unto Antonio's house: away! make haste.
Come, you and I will thither presently;
And in the morning early will we both
Fly toward Belmont: come, Antonio.

Scene 2—A Street in Venice

PORTIA. Inquire the Jew's house out, give him this deed
And let him sign it: we'll away tonight
And be a day before our husbands home:
This deed will be well welcome to Lorenzo.

GRATIANO (*approaching*). Fair sir, you are well o'ertaken:
My Lord Bassanio upon more advice
Hath sent you here this ring, and doth entreat
Your company at dinner.

PORTIA. That cannot be:
His ring I do accept most thankfully:
And so, I pray you, tell him: furthermore,
I pray you, show my youth old Shylock's house.

NERISSA (*aside*). I'll see if I can get my husband's ring,
Which I did make him swear to keep for ever.
(*Aloud*) Come, good sir, will you show me to this house?

ACT 5

Scene 1—Avenue to Portia's House

LORENZO. The moon shines bright: in such a night as this,
When the sweet wind did gently kiss the trees
And they did make no noise—in such a night
Troilus methinks mounted the Troyan walls
And sighed his soul toward the Grecian tents,
Where Cressid lay that night.

JESSICA. In such a night
Did Thisbe fearfully o'ertrip the dew,
And saw the lion's shadow ere himself,
And ran dismayed away.

LORENZO. In such a night
Stood Dido with a willow in her hand
Upon the wild sea banks and waft her love
To come again to Carthage.

JESSICA. In such a night
Medea gathered the enchanted herbs
That did renew old Aeson.

LORENZO. In such a night
Did Jessica steal from the wealthy Jew
And with an unthrift love did run from Venice
As far as Belmont.

JESSICA. In such a night
Did young Lorenzo swear he loved her well,
Stealing her soul with many vows of faith
And ne'er a true one.

LORENZO. In such a night
Did pretty Jessica, like a little shrew,
Slander her love, and he forgave it her.

JESSICA. I would out-night you, did nobody come;
But, hark, I hear the footing of a man.

STEPHANO. Stephano is my name; and I bring word
My mistress will before the break of day
Be here at Belmont.
I pray you, is my master yet returned?

LORENZO. He is not, nor we have not heard from him.
My friend Stephano, signify, I pray you,

Within the house, your mistress is at hand ;
And bring your music forth into the air.
How sweet the moonlight sleeps upon this bank !
Here will we sit and let the sounds of music
Creep in our ears : soft stillness and the night
Become the touches of sweet harmony.
Sit, Jessica. Look how the floor of heaven
Is thick inlaid with patines of bright gold :
There's not the smallest orb which thou behold'st
But in his motion like an angel sings,
Still quiring to the young-eyed cherubins.
Such harmony is in immortal souls,
But whilst this muddy vesture of decay
Doth grossly close it in, we cannot hear it.
Come, ho ! and wake Diana with a hymn :
With sweetest touches pierce your mistress' ear
And draw her home with music. (*Musicians play*)

JESSICA. I am never merry when I hear sweet music.

LORENZO. The reason is, your spirits are attentive ;
For do but note a wild and wanton herd,
Or race of youthful and unhandled colts,
Fetching mad bounds, bellowing and neighing loud ;
Which is the hot condition of their blood ;
If they but hear perchance a trumpet sound,
Or any air of music touch their ears,
You shall perceive them make a mutual stand,
Their savage eyes turned to a modest gaze .
By the sweet power of music : therefore the poet
Did feign that Orpheus drew trees, stones, and floods :
Since nought so stockish, hard, and full of rage,
But music for the time doth change his nature.
The man that hath no music in himself,
Nor is not moved with concord of sweet sounds,
Is fit for treasons, stratagems, and spoils ;
The motions of his spirit are dull as night
And his affections dark as Erebus :
Let no such man be trusted. Mark the music.

PORTIA (*approaching*). That light we see is burning in my hall.
How far that little candle throws his beams !
So shines a good deed in a naughty world.

NERISSA. When the moon shone we did not see the candle.

PORTIA. So doth the greater glory dim the less :
A substitute shines brightly as a king
Until a king be by, and then his state
Empties itself as doth an inland brook
Into the main of waters. Music ! hark !

NERISSA. It is your music, madam, of the house.

PORTIA. Methinks it sounds much sweeter than by day.

NERISSA. Silence bestows that virtue on it, madam.

PORTIA. The crow doth sing as sweetly as the lark
When neither is attended, and I think
The nightingale, if she should sing by day,
When every goose is cackling, would be thought
No better a musician than the wren.
How many things by season seasoned are
To their right praise and true perfection!
Peace, ho! the moon sleeps with Endymion
And would not be awaked.

LORENZO. Dear lady, welcome home.

PORTIA. We have been praying for our husbands' healths:
Are they returned?

LORENZO. Your husband is at hand; I hear his trumpet.

Enter Bassanio, Antonio, and Gratiano

BASSANIO. We should hold day with the Antipodes
If you would walk in absence of the sun.

PORTIA. Let me give light, but let me not be light;
For a light wife doth make a heavy husband,
And never be Bassanio so for me:
But God sort all! You are welcome home, my lord.

BASSANIO. I thank you, madam. Give welcome to my friend.
This is the man, this is Antonio,
To whom I am so infinitely bound.

PORTIA. You should in all sense be much bound to him,
For, as I hear, he was much bound for you.

ANTONIO. No more than I am well acquitted of.

PORTIA. Sir, you are very welcome to our house:
It must appear in other ways than words,
Therefore I scant this breathing courtesy.

GRATIANO (*to Nerissa*). By yonder moon I swear you do me wrong;
In faith, I gave it to the judge's clerk.
Would he were dead that had it, for my part,
Since you do take it, love, so much at heart.

PORTIA. A quarrel, ho, already! what's the matter?

GRATIANO. About a hoop of gold, a paltry ring
That she did give me, whose posy was
For all the world like cutler's poetry
Upon a knife, *Love me, and leave me not.*

NERISSA. What talk you of, the posy or the value?
You swore to me, when I did give it you,

That you would wear it till your hour of death
And that it should lie with you in your grave :
Though not for me, yet for your vehement oaths,
You should have been respective and have kept it.
Gave it a judge's clerk ! no, God's my judge,
The clerk will ne'er wear hair on's face that had it.

GRATIANO. He will, an if he live to be a man.

NERISSA. Ay, if a woman live to be a man.

GRATIANO. Now, by this hand, I gave it to a youth,
A kind of boy, a little scrubbèd boy,
No higher than thyself, the judge's clerk ;
A prating boy, that begged it as a fee :
I could not for my heart deny it him.

PORTIA. You were to blame (I must be plain with you)
To part so slightly with your wife's first gift,
A thing stuck on with oaths upon your finger
And riveted so with faith unto your flesh.
I gave my love a ring and made him swear
Never to part with it ; and here he stands ;
I dare be sworn for him he would not leave it,
Nor pluck it from his finger, for the wealth
That the world masters. Now, in faith, Gratiano,
You give your wife too unkind a cause of grief :
An 'twere to me, I should be mad at it.

BASSANIO (*aside*). Why, I were best to cut my left hand off
And swear I lost the ring defending it.

GRATIANO. My Lord Bassanio gave his ring away
Unto the judge that begged it—and indeed
Deserved it too ; and then the boy, his clerk,
That took some pains in writing, he begged mine ;
And neither man nor master would take aught
But the two rings.

PORTIA. What ring gave you, my lord ?
Not that, I hope, which you received of me.

BASSANIO. If I could add a lie unto a fault,
I would deny it ; but you see my finger
Hath not the ring upon it ; it is gone.

PORTIA. Even so void is your false heart of truth.

BASSANIO. Sweet Portia,
If you did know to whom I gave the ring,
If you did know for whom I gave the ring
And would conceive for what I gave the ring
And how unwillingly I left the ring,
When nought would be accepted but the ring,
You would abate the strength of your displeasure.

PORTIA. If you had known the virtue of the ring,
Or half her worthiness that gave the ring,
Or your own honour to contain the ring,
You would not then have parted with the ring.
What man is there so much unreasonable,
If you had pleased to have defended it
With any terms of zeal, wanted the modesty
To urge the thing held as a ceremony ?
Nerissa teaches me what to believe :
I'll die for 't but some woman had the ring.

BASSANIO. No, by my honour, madam, by my soul,
No woman had it, but a civil doctor,
Which did refuse three thousand ducats of me
And begged the ring ; the which I did deny him
And suffered him to go displeased away ;
Even he that did uphold the very life
Of my dear friend. What should I say, sweet lady ?
I was enforced to send it after him ;
I was beset with shame and courtesy ;
My honour would not let ingratitude
So much besmear it. Pardon me, good lady ;
For, by these blessèd candles of the night,
Had you been there, I think you would have begged
The ring of me to give the worthy doctor.

PORTIA. Let not that doctor e'er come near my house :
Since he hath got the jewel that I loved,
And that which you did swear to keep for me,
I will become as liberal as you ;
I'll not deny him anything I have.

NERISSA. And I his clerk.

ANTONIO. I am the unhappy subject of these quarrels.

PORTIA. Sir, grieve not you ; you are welcome notwithstanding.

BASSANIO. Portia, forgive me this enforcèd wrong ;
And, in the hearing of these many friends,
I swear to thee, even by thine own fair eyes,
Wherein I see myself—

PORTIA. Mark you but that !
In both my eyes he doubly sees himself ;
In each eye, one : swear by your double self,
And there's an oath of credit.

BASSANIO. Nay, but hear me :
Pardon this fault, and by my soul I swear
I never more will break an oath with thee.

ANTONIO. I once did lend my body for his wealth ;
Which, but for him that had your husband's ring,

Had quite miscarried: I dare be bound again,
My soul upon the forfeit, that your lord
Will never more break faith advisedly.

PORTIA. Then you shall be his surety. Give him this
And bid him keep it better than the other.

ANTONIO. Here, Lord Bassanio; swear to keep this ring.

BASSANIO. By heaven, it is the same I gave the doctor!

PORTIA. You are all amazed!
Here is a letter; read it at your leisure;
It comes from Padua, from Bellario:
There you shall find that Portia was the doctor,
Nerissa there her clerk: Lorenzo here
Shall witness I set forth as soon as you
And even but now returned; I have not yet
Entered my house. Antonio, you are welcome;
And I have better news in store for you
Than you expect: unseal this letter soon;
There you shall find three of your argosies
Are richly come to harbour suddenly:
You shall not know by what strange accident
I chancèd on this letter.

ANTONIO. I am dumb.

BASSANIO. Were you the doctor, and I knew you not?

GRATIANO. Were you the clerk!

BASSANIO. Sweet doctor!

ANTONIO. Sweet lady, you have given me life and living;
For here I read for certain that my ships
Are safely come to road.

PORTIA. How now, Lorenzo!
My clerk hath some good comforts too for you.

NERISSA. Ay, and I'll give them him without a fee.
There do I give to you and Jessica,
From the rich Jew, a special deed of gift,
After his death, of all he dies possessed of.

LORENZO. Fair ladies, you drop manna in the way
Of starvèd people.

PORTIA. It is almost morning,
And yet I am sure you are not satisfied
Of these events at full. Let us go in,
And charge us there upon interrogatories,
And we will answer all things faithfully.

GRATIANO. Well, while I live I'll fear no other thing
So sore as keeping safe Nerissa's ring.

The Story of King Lear

In King Lear grief reaches the utmost depths that Shakespeare plumbed. It is the most intense and powerful of all the plays. It carries emotion as far as words can carry it. It is agonising.

Shakespeare found the story in old legends of British kings. He wrote the play when he was forty, and it was acted before James the First in Whitehall during the Christmas of 1607. It is one of the least acted of the plays, because it is almost beyond the power of acting.

We are not to think of Lear as a hero. He endures with a patience that is marvellous to behold, but the sorrows heaped upon the heads of all concerned begin with the folly of this vain old king, parading showy sentiment while he shirks his duty, and keeping up an empty show of the power he has resigned. He gives away his kingdom but wants to keep his pomp; he calls pitifully upon his daughters to declare their love for him, and his pride rejects the only honest answer.

Out of all this comes the greatest clash of passions ever evoked in an English play. The tragedy of Lear and his daughters runs side by side with the tragedy of Gloucester and his sons, but while Lear fights against his doom with a frenzy that shatters his mind; Gloucester suffers his fate with almost uncomplaining patience. Lear fills us with pity; for Gloucester we feel an infinite pathos.

The strain of such a play must be relieved, and we have another contrast. We have the unfathomable love of Lear's youngest daughter and the fine fidelity of Gloucester's son. We have the loyalty of old Gloucester himself, who, though almost as unstable as Lear in fatherly feeling, is yet true to his king. We have the merry sadness of the Fool, and the king's tenderness for him. We have the uprightness of Albany in a position of very great trial, and the unshaken affection of one of the rarest characters in Shakespeare, the Earl of Kent. Flung out of court by the king, Kent follows Lear through all his miseries; he gives him all that he has.

So virtues balance vices in this play that fills the heart with pity and the eye with tears. Nature herself plays a stern accompaniment to these titanic scenes. The storm in the old man's soul matches the storm on the heath. There is nothing in books more stirring than all this rousing of the elements in man and in the world about him. Nor is there anything more tender than the love of Cordelia, and the meeting of these two in those last hours, when they would let the world go by and sing like birds i' the cage.

Running through the play is the filial feeling which strikes so deep a root in the human heart. Lear is blind to all except his own affections, and it is in them that he is wounded; yet he has a priceless love he does not deserve. It is all harrowing in its poignancy, and it is the greatest of Shakespeare's passionate plays.

THE PLAYERS

Lear, King of ancient Britain, aged, impulsive, romantic, hot-tempered, his judgment weakened by age and lack of control.

King of France, an honourable man who marries Cordelia, Lear's youngest daughter.

Duke of Burgundy, a selfish suitor for Cordelia.

Duke of Albany, husband of Goneril, Lear's eldest daughter; a quiet, retiring man, right-thinking and honourable.

Duke of Cornwall, husband of Regan, Lear's second daughter; a man of brutal nature, fit mate for his brutal wife.

Earl of Kent, a wise and brave courtier, but plain and blunt, serving Lear faithfully though the King treats him harshly.

Earl of Gloucester, a man easily deceived, but loyal, and honestly friendly to Lear.

Edgar, son of Gloucester, always faithful, adopting a madman's rags and actions as a disguise when driven into hiding.

Edmund, the low-born son of Gloucester, half-brother of Edgar, whom he schemes to supplant. He is the villain of the play, ever plotting for his own advantage.

Oswald, a man of insipid character; steward and messenger for Goneril.

Fool, Lear's attendant, who is allowed to say frankly whatever he likes, remaining faithful to his master but not sparing him.

Goneril and Regan, ungrateful and stony-hearted daughters of Lear; false and hypocritical, and both fascinated by Edmund.

Cordelia, Lear's youngest daughter, destined for tragedy, but always loyal, loving, and truthful.

A doctor, a gentleman, servants, soldiers, and messengers.

SCENE—Ancient Britain

King Lear

ACT 1

Scene 1—The King's Palace

LEAR. Attend the lords of France and Burgundy, Gloucester.

GLOUCESTER. I shall, my liege.

LEAR. Meantime we shall express our darker purpose.
Give me the map there. Know that we have divided
In three our kingdom: and tis our fast intent
To shake all cares and business from our age;
Conferring them on younger strengths, while we
Unburthened crawl toward death. Our son of Cornwall,
And you, our no less loving son of Albany,
We have this hour a constant will to publish
Our daughters' several dowers, that future strife
May be prevented now. The princes, France and Burgundy,
Great rivals in our youngest daughter's love,
Long in our court have made their amorous sojourn,
And here are to be answered. Tell me, my daughters
(Since now we will divest us, both of rule,
Interest of territory, cares of State),
Which of you shall we say doth love us most?
That we our largest bounty may extend
Where merit most doth challenge it.
Goneril, our eldest-born, speak first.

GONERIL. Sir, I love you more than words can wield the matter;
Dearer than eyesight, space, and liberty;
Beyond what can be valued, rich or rare;
No less than life, with grace, health, beauty, honour;
As much as child e'er loved, or father found;
A love that makes breath poor, and speech unable;
Beyond all manner of so much I love you.

CORDELIA (*aside*). What shall Cordelia do? Love, and be silent.

LEAR. Of all these bounds, even from this line to this,
With shadowy forests and with champains riched,
With plenteous rivers and wide-skirted meads,
We make thee lady: to thine and Albany's issue
Be this perpetual. What says our second daughter,
Our dearest Regan, wife to Cornwall? Speak.

REGAN. Sir, I am made of that same metal as my sister,
And prize me at her worth. In my true heart
I find she names my very deed of love,
Only she comes too short: that I profess
Myself an enemy to all other joys,
Which the most precious square of sense possesses;
And find I am alone felicitate
In your dear highness' love.

CORDELIA. (*Aside*) Then poor Cordelia!
And yet not so; since, I am sure, my love's
More richer than my tongue.

LEAR. To thee and thine hereditary ever
Remain this ample third of our fair kingdom;
No less in space, validity, and pleasure,
Than that conferred on Goneril. Now, our joy,
Although the last, not least; to whose young love
The vines of France and milk of Burgundy
Strive to be interessed; what can you say to draw
A third more opulent than your sisters? Speak.

CORDELIA. Nothing, my lord.

LEAR. Nothing! Nothing will come of nothing: speak again.

CORDELIA. Unhappy that I am, I cannot heave
My heart into my mouth: I love your majesty
According to my bond; nor more nor less.

LEAR. How, how, Cordelia! mend your speech a little,
Lest it may mar your fortunes.

CORDELIA. Good my lord,
You have begot me, bred me, loved me:
Return those duties back as are right fit,
Obey you, love you, and most honour you.
Why have my sisters husbands, if they say
They love you all? Haply, when I shall wed,
That lord whose hand must take my plight shall carry
Half my love with him, half my care and duty
Sure, I shall never marry like my sisters,
To love my father all.

LEAR. But goes thy heart with this?

CORDELIA. Ay, good my lord.

LEAR. So young, and so untender.

CORDELIA. So young, my lord, and true.

LEAR. Let it be so; thy truth, then, be thy dower:
For, by the sacred radiance of the sun,
By all the operation of the orbs
From whom we do exist, and cease to be,

Here I disclaim all my paternal care,
And as a stranger to my heart and me
Hold thee, from this, for ever.

KENT. Good my liege—

LEAR. Peace, Kent!
Come not between the dragon and his wrath.
I loved her most, and thought to set my rest
On her kind nursery. Hence, and avoid my sight!
So be my grave my peace, as here I give
Her father's heart from her! Call France: who stirs?
Call Burgundy. Cornwall and Albany,
With my two daughters' dowers digest this third:
Let pride, which she calls plainness, marry her.
I do invest you jointly with my power,
Pre-eminence, and all the large effects
That troop with majesty. Ourself, by monthly course,
With reservation of a hundred knights,
By you to be sustained, shall our abode
Make with you by due turns. Only we still retain
The name and all the additions to a king;
The sway, revenue, execution of the rest,
Belovèd sons, be yours: which to confirm,
This coronet part betwixt you.

KENT. Royal Lear,
Whom I have ever honoured as my king,
Loved as my father, as my master followed,
As my great patron thought on in my prayers—

LEAR. The bow is bent and drawn, make from the shaft.

KENT. Let it fall rather, though the fork invade
The region of my heart: be Kent unmannerly,
When Lear is mad. What wilt thou do, old man?
Think'st thou that duty shall have dread to speak,
When power to flattery bows? To plainness honour's bound
When majesty stoops to folly. Reserve thy state;
And, in thy best consideration, check
This hideous rashness: answer my life my judgment,
Thy youngest daughter does not love thee least;
Nor are those empty-hearted whose low sound
Reverbs no hollowness.

LEAR. Kent, on thy life, no more.

KENT. My life I never held but as a pawn
To wage against thy enemies; nor fear to lose it,
Thy safety being the motive.

LEAR. Out of my sight!

KENT. See better, Lear; and let me still remain
The true blank of thine eye,

Or, whilst I can vent clamour from my throat,
I'll tell thee thou dost evil.

LEAR. Hear me, recreant!
On thine allegiance hear me!
Since thou hast sought to make us break our vow,
Which we durst never yet, and with strained pride
To come between our sentence and our power,
Take thy reward.
Five days we do allot thee, for provision
To shield thee from diseases of the world;
And on the sixth to turn thy hated back
Upon our kingdom. If, on the tenth day following,
Thy banished trunk be found in our dominions,
The moment is thy death. Away! by Jupiter,
This shall not be revoked.

KENT. Fare thee well, king: since thus thou wilt appear,
Freedom lives hence, and banishment is here.
(*To Cordelia*) The gods to their dear shelter take thee, maid,
That justly think'st, and hast most rightly said!
(*To the others*) And your large speeches may your deeds approve,
That good effects may spring from words of love.
Thus Kent, O princes, bids you all adieu;
He'll shape his old course in a country new.

The King of France and the Duke of Burgundy now enter to sue for the hand of Cordelia, and Lear explains that she has lost her right to a marriage dower. Under the circumstances the Duke of Burgundy withdraws his proposal. The King of France gives a nobler answer.

FRANCE. Fairest Cordelia, that art most rich, being poor;
Most choice, forsaken; and most loved, despised!
Thee and thy virtues here I seize upon:
Be it lawful I take up what's cast away.
Thy dowerless daughter, king, thrown to my chance,
Is queen of us, of ours, and our fair France:
Not all the dukes of waterish Burgundy
Can buy this unprized precious maid of me.

LEAR. Thou hast her, France: let her be thine; for we
Have no such daughter, nor shall ever see
That face of hers again. Therefore be gone
Without our grace, our love, our benison.
Come, noble Burgundy. (*The King goes*)

FRANCE. Bid farewell to your sisters.

CORDELIA. The jewels of our father, with washed eyes
Cordelia leaves you: I know you what you are;
And like a sister am most loth to call
Your faults as they are named. Use well our father:
To your professèd bosoms I commit him:

But yet, alas, stood I within his grace,
I would prefer him to a better place.

REGAN. Prescribe not us our duties.

CORDELIA. Time shall unfold what plaited cunning hides:
Who cover faults, at last shame them derides.
Well may you prosper! (*Cordelia leaves with France*)

GONERIL. Sister, it is not a little I have to say of what most nearly appertains to us both. I think our father will hence tonight.

REGAN. That's most certain, and with you; next month with us.

GONERIL. You see how full of changes his age is; the observation we have made of it hath not been little: he always loved our sister most; and with what poor judgment he hath now cast her off appears too grossly.

REGAN. Tis the infirmity of his age; yet he hath ever but slenderly known himself.

GONERIL. The best and soundest of his time hath been but rash; then must we look to receive from his age the unruly waywardness that infirm years bring with them.

REGAN. We shall further think on't.

GONERIL. We must do something.

Scene 2—Outside Gloucester's Castle

Edmund discloses a plan for securing the estate. On his father appearing he pretends to hide a letter, and shows it with apparent reluctance, saying it is from Edgar, suggesting they should kill their father and divide the estate. The father, greatly distressed, dwells on the sadness of the time.

GLOUCESTER. Love cools, friendship falls off, brothers divide: in cities, mutinies; in countries, discord; in palaces, treason; and the bond cracked 'twixt son and father. We have seen the best of our time: machinations, hollowness, treachery, and all ruinous disorders, follow us to our graves. (Find out this villain, Edmund; it shall lose thee nothing; do it carefully.) And the noble and true-hearted Kent banished! his offence, honesty! Tis strange.

Edmund pretends to defend Edgar, and suggests that he should draw him into a talk which the father can overhear. Meeting Edgar, he tells him that his life is in danger from the anger of their father, and advises him to hide. The scene closes with Edmund meanly congratulating himself on the cleverness with which he has deceived his father:

A credulous father, and a brother noble,
Whose nature is so far from doing harms
That he suspects none.

Scene 3—The Duke of Albany's Palace

GONERIL. Did my father strike my gentleman for chiding his fool?

OSWALD. Yes, madam.

GONERIL. By day and night he wrongs me; every hour
He flashes into one gross crime or other,

That sets us all at odds: I'll not endure it:
His knights grow riotous, and himself upbraids us
On every trifle. When he returns from hunting,
I will not speak with him; say I am sick:
If you come slack of former services
You shall do well; the fault of it I'll answer.
Put on what weary negligence you please,
You and your fellows; I'd have it come to question:
If he dislike it, let him to our sister,
Whose mind and mine, I know, in that are one,
Not to be over-ruled. Idle old man,
That still would manage those authorities
That he hath given away! Now, by my life,
Old fools are babes again. Remember what I tell you.
And let his knights have colder looks among you;
What grows of it, no matter; advise your fellows so.

Scene 4—A Hall in Albany's Palace

KENT (*disguised*). Now, banished Kent,
If thou canst serve where thou dost stand condemned,
So may it come, thy master, whom thou lovest,
Shall find thee full of labours.

LEAR (*entering*). Let me not stay a jot for dinner; go get it ready. How now! what art thou?

KENT. A man, sir.

LEAR. What dost thou profess? What wouldst thou with us?

KENT. I do profess to be no less than I seem; to serve him truly that will put me in trust; to love him that is honest; to converse with him that is wise, and says little; to fear judgment; to fight when I cannot choose; and to eat no fish.

LEAR. What art thou?

KENT. A very honest-hearted fellow, and as poor as the king.

LEAR. If thou be as poor for a subject as he is for a king, thou art poor enough. What wouldst thou?

KENT. Service.

LEAR. Whom wouldst thou serve?

KENT. You.

LEAR. Dost thou know me, fellow?

KENT. No, sir; but you have that in your countenance which I would fain call master.

LEAR. What's that?

KENT. Authority.

LEAR. What services canst thou do?

KENT. I can keep honest counsel, ride, run, mar a curious tale in telling it, and deliver a plain message bluntly: that which ordinary men are fit for I am qualified in; and the best of me is diligence.

LEAR. How old art thou?

KENT. Not so young, sir, to love a woman for singing, nor so old to dote on her for anything: I have years on my back forty-eight.

LEAR. Follow me; thou shalt serve me: if I like thee no worse after dinner I will not part from thee yet. Dinner, ho, dinner! Where's my knave? my fool? You, you, sirrah, where's my daughter?

OSWALD (*entering*). So please you— (*He leaves*)

LEAR. What says the fellow there? Call the clotpoll back. (*Exit a knight*) Where's my fool, ho? I think the world's asleep. (*The knight returns*) How now! where's that mongrel?

KNIGHT. He says, my lord, your daughter is not well.

LEAR. Why came not the slave back to me when I called him?

KNIGHT. Sir, he answered me he would not.

LEAR. He would not!

KNIGHT. My lord, I know not what the matter is; but, to my judgment, your highness is not entertained with that ceremonious affection as you were wont.

LEAR. Ha! sayest thou so? Thou but rememberest me of mine own conception: I have perceived a most faint neglect of late; which I have rather blamed as mine own jealous curiosity than as a very pretence and purpose of unkindness: I will look further into't. But where's my fool? I have not seen him this two days.

KNIGHT. Since my young lady's going into France, sir, the fool hath much pined away.

LEAR. No more of that; I have noted it well. Go you, and tell my daughter I would speak with her. Call hither my fool. (*Enter Oswald*) O, you sir, you, come you hither, sir: who am I, sir?

OSWALD. My lady's father.

LEAR. *My lady's father!* my lord's knave: you dog! you slave!

OSWALD. I am none of these, my lord; I beseech your pardon.

LEAR. Do you bandy looks with me, you rascal? (*Striking him*)

OSWALD. I'll not be struck, my lord.

KENT (*tripping him*). Nor tripped neither, you base football player.

LEAR. I thank thee, fellow; thou servest me, and I'll love thee.

LEAR (*to Fool*). How now, my pretty knave! How dost thou?

FOOL. Sirrah, I'll teach thee a speech.

LEAR. Do.

FOOL. Mark it, nuncle:

Have more than thou showest,
Speak less than thou knowest,
Lend less than thou owest,
Ride more than thou goest,
Learn more than thou trowest,
Set less than thou throwest.

KENT. This is nothing, fool.

FOOL. Then tis like the breath of an unfee'd lawyer; you gave me nothing for't.

LEAR (*to Goneril, entering*). How now, daughter! Methinks you are too much of late i' the frown.

GONERIL. Not only, sir, this your all-licensed fool,
But other of your insolent retinue
Do hourly carp and quarrel; breaking forth
In rank and not-to-be-endurèd riots. Sir,
I had thought, by making this well known unto you,
To have found a safe redress; but now grow fearful,
By what yourself too late have spoke and done,
That you protect this course, and put it on
By your allowance.

LEAR. Are you our daughter?

GONERIL. Come, sir,
I would you would make use of that good wisdom,
Whereof I know you are fraught; and put away
These dispositions that of late transform you
From what you rightly are.

LEAR. Doth any here know me?
Who is it that can tell me who I am?

FOOL. Lear's shadow.

LEAR. I would learn that; for, by the marks of sovereignty, knowledge, and reason, I should be false persuaded I had daughters. Your name, fair gentlewoman?

GONERIL. This admiration, sir, is much o' the savour
Of other your new pranks. I do beseech you
To understand my purposes aright:
As you are old and reverend, you should be wise.
Here do you keep a hundred knights and squires;
Men so disordered, so deboshed and bold,
That this our court, infected with their manners,
Shows like a riotous inn.
The shame itself doth speak
For instant remedy: be then desired,
By her that else will take the thing she begs,
A little to disquantity your train;
And the remainder, that shall still depend,
To be such men as may besort your age,
And know themselves and you.

LEAR. Darkness and devils!
Saddle my horses; call my train together.
Yet have I left a daughter.

GONERIL. You strike my people; and your disordered rabble
Make servants of their betters.

LEAR (*to Albany, entering*). O, sir, are you come?
Is it your will? Speak, sir. Prepare my horses.
Ingratitude, thou marble-hearted fiend,
More hideous when thou show'st thee in a child
Than the sea-monster!

ALBANY. Pray, sir, be patient.

LEAR (*to Goneril*). Detested kite! thou liest:
My train are men of choice and rarest parts,
That all particulars of duty know,
And in the most exact regard support
The worships of their name. O most small fault,
How ugly didst thou in Cordelia show!
That, like an engine, wrenched my frame of nature
From the fixed place; drew from my heart all love,
And added to the gall. O Lear, Lear, Lear!
Beat at this gate, that let thy folly in (*striking his head*),
And thy dear judgment out! Go, go, my people.

ALBANY. My lord, I am guiltless, as I am ignorant
Of what hath moved you.

LEAR. It may be so, my lord.
How sharper than a serpent's tooth it is
To have a thankless child!

ALBANY. Now, gods that we adore, whereof comes this?

GONERIL. Never afflict yourself to know the cause;
But let this disposition have that scope
That dotage gives it.

LEAR. What, fifty of my followers at a clap!

ALBANY. What's the matter, sir?

LEAR. I'll tell thee. (*To Goneril*) Life and death! I am ashamed
That thou hast power to shake my manhood thus;
That these hot tears, which break from me perforce,
Should make thee worth them. Blasts and fogs upon thee!
The untented woundings of a father's curse
Pierce every sense about thee? Old fond eyes,
Beweep this cause again, I'll pluck ye out,
And cast you, with the waters that you lose,
To temper clay. Yea, is it come to this?
Let it be so: yet have I left a daughter,
Who, I am sure, is kind and comfortable:
When she shall hear this of thee, with her nails
She'll flay thy wolvish visage. Thou shalt find
That I'll resume the shape which thou dost think
I have cast off for ever: thou shalt, I warrant thee.

The King and Kent leave

GONERIL. Do you mark that, my lord?

ALBANY. I cannot be so partial, Goneril,
To the great love I bear you—

GONERIL. Pray you, content. How now, Oswald!
What, have you writ that letter to my sister?

OSWALD. Yes, madam.

GONERIL. Take you some company, and away to horse:
Inform her full of my particular fear;
And hasten your return. No, no, my lord,
This milky gentleness and course of yours
Though I condemn not, yet, under pardon,
You are much more attasked for want of wisdom
Than praised for harmful mildness.

ALBANY. How far your eyes may pierce I cannot tell:
Striving to better, oft we mar what's well.

ACT 2

Scene 1—A Court in Gloucester's Castle

While Edmund is advising Edgar to flee, Gloucester approaches, whereupon Edmund advises Edgar to draw his sword and defend himself, while he pretends to try to capture him. In the sham fight Edgar escapes, and Edmund, slightly wounding himself, pretends he was wounded by Edgar because he would not attack their father. Gloucester is completely deceived, and, on Cornwall approaching, the account of Edmund's bravery leads to his being taken into Cornwall's service.

Scene 2—Before Gloucester's Castle

OSWALD (*meeting Kent*). Good dawning to thee, friend: art of this house? Where may we set our horses?

KENT. I' the mire.

OSWALD. Prithee, if thou lovest me, tell me.

KENT. I love thee not.

OSWALD. Why, then, I care not for thee. Why dost thou use me thus? I know thee not.

KENT. Fellow, I know thee.

OSWALD. What dost thou know me for?

KENT. A knave; a rascal; an eater of broken meats; a base, proud, shallow, beggarly, three-suited, hundred-pound, filthy, worsted stocking knave.

OSWALD. Why, what a monstrous fellow art thou, thus to rail on one that is neither known of thee nor knows thee!

KENT. What a brazen-faced varlet art thou, to deny thou knowest me! Is it two days ago since I tripped up thy heels and beat thee before the king?

OSWALD. Away! I have nothing to do with thee.

KENT. Strike, you slave; stand, rogue, stand.

He is beating him when Cornwall, Regan, and Gloucester enter

CORNWALL. Keep peace, upon your lives:
He dies that strikes again. What is the matter?

REGAN. The messengers from our sister and the king.

CORNWALL. What is your difference? Speak.

OSWALD. I am scarce in breath, my lord.

KENT. His countenance likes me not.

CORNWALL. No more, perchance, does mine, nor his, nor hers.

KENT. Sir, tis my occupation to be plain:
I have seen better faces in my time
Than stands on any shoulder that I see
Before me at this instant.

CORNWALL. This is some fellow
Who, having been praised for bluntness, doth affect
A saucy roughness, and constrains the garb
Quite from his nature: he cannot flatter, he,
An honest mind and plain, he must speak truth!
An they will take it, so; if not, he's plain.
These kind of knaves I know, which in this plainness
Harbour more craft and more corrupter ends
Than twenty silly-ducking observants
That stretch their duties nicely.

CORNWALL. Fetch forth the stocks!
You stubborn ancient knave, you reverend braggart,
We'll teach you——

KENT. Sir, I am too old to learn:
Call not your stocks for me: I serve the king,
On whose employment I was sent to you:
You shall do small respect, show too bold malice
Against the grace and person of my master,
Stocking his messenger.

CORNWALL. Fetch forth the stocks! As I have life and honour,
There shall he sit till noon.

REGAN. Till noon! till night, my lord; and all night too.

KENT. Why, madam, if I were your father's dog,
You should not use me so.

REGAN. Sir, being his knave, I will.

CORNWALL. Come, bring away the stocks!

GLOUCESTER. Let me beseech your grace not to do so:
His fault is much, and the good king his master
Will check him for't: your purposed low correction
Is such as basest and contemned'st wretches
For pilferings and most common trespasses

Are punished with: the king must take it ill,
That he's so slightly valued in his messenger.

REGAN. My sister may receive it much more worse,
To have her gentleman abused, assaulted,
For following her affairs. Put in his legs.
Come, my good lord, away.

GLOUCESTER. I am sorry for thee, friend; tis the duke's pleasure,
Whose disposition, all the world well knows,
Will not be rubbed nor stopped: I'll entreat for thee.

KENT. Pray, do not, sir: I have watched and travelled hard;
Some time I shall sleep out, the rest I'll whistle.
A good man's fortune may grow out at heels:
Give you Good-morrow!

GLOUCESTER. The duke's to blame in this; 'twill be ill taken.

KENT (*alone*). Good king, that must approve the common saw,
Thou out of heaven's benediction comest
To the warm sun!
Approach, thou beacon to this under globe,
That by thy comfortable beams I may
Peruse this letter! Nothing almost sees miracles
But misery: I know tis from Cordelia,
Who hath most fortunately been informed
Of my obscurèd course.
All weary and o'erwatched,
Take vantage, heavy eyes, not to behold
This shameful lodging.
Fortune, Good-night: smile once more; turn thy wheel!

Scene 3—A Wood

EDGAR. I heard myself proclaimed;
And by the happy hollow of a tree
Escaped the hunt. No port is free; no place,
That guard, and most unusual vigilance,
Does not attend my taking. Whiles I may scape,
I will preserve myself; and am bethought
To take the basest and most poorest shape
That ever penury, in contempt of man,
Brought near to beast: my face I'll grime with filth;
Blanket my loins; elf all my hair in knots;
And with presented nakedness out-face
The winds and persecutions of the sky.
The country gives me proof and precedent
Of Bedlam beggars, who, with roaring voices,
Strike in their numbed and mortified bare arms
Pins, wooden pricks, nails, sprigs of rosemary;
And with this horrible object, from low farms,

Poor pelting villages, sheep-cotes, and mills,
Sometime with lunatic bans, sometime with prayers,
Enforce their charity. Poor Turlygod! poor Tom!
That's something yet: Edgar I nothing am.

Scene 4—Before Gloucester's Castle

KENT (*in the stocks*). Hail to thee, noble master!

LEAR (*astonished*). Ha! Makest thou this shame thy pastime?

KENT. No, my lord.

LEAR. What's he that hath so much thy place mistook
To set thee here?

KENT. It is both he and she; your son and daughter.

LEAR. No.

KENT. Yes.

LEAR. No, no; they would not.

KENT. Yes, they have.

LEAR. They durst not do't;
They could not, would not do't; tis worse than murder
To do upon respect such violent outrage.
O, how this swells up toward my heart!
Where is this daughter?

KENT. With the earl, sir, here within.

LEAR. Follow me not; stay here.

Lear goes and returns with Gloucester

LEAR. Deny to speak with me? They are sick? They are weary?
They have travelled all the night? Mere fetches;
The images of revolt and flying off.
Fetch me a better answer.

GLOUCESTER. My dear lord,
You know the fiery quality of the duke;
How unremoveable and fixed he is
In his own course.

LEAR. Vengeance! plague! death! confusion!
Fiery! What quality? Why, Gloucester, Gloucester,
I'd speak with the Duke of Cornwall and his wife.

GLOUCESTER. Well, my good lord, I have informed them so.

LEAR. Informed them! Dost thou understand me, man?

GLOUCESTER. Ay, my good lord.

LEAR. The king would speak with Cornwall; the dear father
Would with his daughter speak, commands her service:
Are they informed of this? My breath and blood!
Fiery? the fiery duke? Tell the hot duke that—
No, but not yet: may be he is not well;

Infirmity doth still neglect all office
Whereto our health is bound ; we are not ourselves
When nature, being oppressed, commands the mind
To suffer with the body : I'll forbear ;
And am fallen out with my more headier will,
To take the indisposed and sickly fit
For the sound man. Death on my state ! wherefore
(*Looking on Kent*) Should he sit here ?
Go tell the duke and's wife I'd speak with them,
Now, presently : bid them come forth and hear me,
Or at their chamber-door I'll beat the drum
Till it cry *Sleep to death.*

GLOUCESTER. I would have all well betwixt you.

LEAR. O me, my heart, my rising heart ! but, down !

Enter Cornwall, Regan, and Gloucester

LEAR. Good-morrow to you both.

CORNWALL. Hail to your grace ! (*Kent is set at liberty*)

REGAN. I am glad to see your highness.

LEAR. Regan, I think you are ; I know what reason
I have to think so. Belovèd Regan,
Thy sister's naught : O Regan, she hath tied
Sharp-toothed unkindness, like a vulture, here (*touching his heart*) :
I can scarce speak to thee.

REGAN. I pray you, sir, take patience : I have hope
You less know how to value her desert
Than she to scant her duty.

LEAR. Say, how is that ?

REGAN. I cannot think my sister in the least
Would fail her obligation : if, sir, perchance
She have restrained the riots of your followers,
Tis on such ground, and to such wholesome end,
As clears her from all blame.

LEAR. My curses on her !

REGAN. O, sir, you are old ;
Nature in you stands on the very verge
Of her confine : you should be ruled and led
By some discretion, that discerns your state
Better than you yourself. Therefore I pray you
That to our sister you do make return ;
Say you have wronged her, sir.

LEAR. Ask her forgiveness ?
Do you but mark how this becomes the house :
Dear daughter, I confess that I am old ;
Age is unnecessary : on my knees I beg
That you'll vouchsafe me raiment, bed, and food.

REGAN. Good sir, no more ; these are unsightly tricks :
Return you to my sister.

LEAR. Never, Regan :
She hath abated me of half my train ;
Looked black upon me ; struck me with her tongue,
Most serpent-like, upon the very heart :
All the stored vengeances of heaven fall
On her ingrateful top !

CORNWALL. Fie, sir, fie !

LEAR. You nimble lightnings, dart your blinding flames
Into her scornful eyes ! Infect her beauty,
You fen-sucked fogs, drawn by the powerful sun,
To fall and blast her pride !

REGAN. O the blest gods ! So will you wish on me
When the rash mood is on.

LEAR. No, Regan, thou shalt never have my curse :
Thy tender-hefted nature shall not give
Thee o'er to harshness : her eyes are fierce ; but thine
Do comfort and not burn. Tis not in thee
To grudge my pleasures, to cut off my train,
To bandy hasty words, to scant my sizes,
And in conclusion to oppose the bolt
Against my coming in : thou better know'st
The offices of nature, bond of childhood,
Effects of courtesy, dues of gratitude ;
Thy half o' the kingdom hast thou not forgot,
Wherein I thee endowed.

REGAN. Good sir, to the purpose.

LEAR. Who stocked my servant ? Regan, I have good hope
Thou didst not know on't. Who comes here ? O heavens,
If you do love old men, if your sweet sway
Allow obedience, if yourselves are old,
Make it your cause ; send down, and take my part !
(*To Goneril, entering*) Art not ashamed to look upon this beard ?
O Regan, wilt thou take her by the hand ?

GONERIL. Why not by the hand, sir ? How have I offended ?
All's not offence that indiscretion finds
And dotage terms so.

LEAR. O sides, you are too tough ;
Will you yet hold ? How came my man i' the stocks ?

CORNWALL. I set him there, sir : but his own disorders
Deserved much less advancement.

LEAR. You ! did you ?

REGAN. I pray you, father, being weak, seem so.
If, till the expiration of your month,

You will return and sojourn with my sister,
Dismissing half your train, come then to me :
I am now from home, and out of that provision
Which shall be needful for your entertainment.

LEAR. Return to her, and fifty men dismissed ?
No, rather I abjure all roofs, and choose
To wage against the enmity o' the air ;
To be a comrade with the wolf and owl,
Necessity's sharp pinch ! Return with her ?
Why, the hot-blooded France, that dowerless took
Our youngest born, I could as well be brought
To knee his throne, and, squire-like, pension beg
To keep base life afoot.

GONERIL. At your choice, sir.

LEAR. I prithee, daughter, do not make me mad :
I will not trouble thee, my child ; farewell :
We'll no more meet, no more see one another :
But yet thou art my flesh, my blood, my daughter
(Or rather a disease that's in my flesh,
Which I must needs call mine).
But I'll not chide thee ;
Let shame come when it will, I do not call it :
I do not bid the thunder-bearer shoot,
Nor tell tales of thee to high-judging Jove.
Mend when thou canst ; be better at thy leisure :
I can be patient ; I can stay with Regan,
I and my hundred knights.

REGAN. Not altogether so :
I looked not for you yet, nor am provided
For your fit welcome. Give ear, sir, to my sister.

LEAR. Is this well spoken ?

REGAN. I dare avouch it, sir : what, fifty followers ?
Is it not well ? What should you need of more ?
Yea, or so many, since that both charge and danger
Speak gainst so great a number ? How, in one house,
Should many people, under two commands,
Hold amity ? Tis hard ; almost impossible.

GONERIL. Why might not you, my lord, receive attendance
From those that she calls servants, or from mine ?

REGAN. Why not, my lord ? If then they chanced to slack you,
We could control them. If you will come to me
(For now I spy a danger) I entreat you
To bring but five-and-twenty : to no more
Will I give place or notice.

LEAR. I gave you all.

REGAN. And in good time you gave it.

LEAR. Made you my guardians, my depositaries;
But kept a reservation to be followed
With such a number. What, must I come to you
With five-and-twenty, Regan? Said you so?

REGAN. And speak't again, my lord; no more with me.

LEAR. Those wicked creatures yet do look well-favoured
When others are more wicked; not being the worst
Stands in some rank of praise. I'll go with thee (*to Goneril*):
Thy fifty yet doth double five-and-twenty,
And thou art twice her love.

GONERIL. Hear me, my lord:
What need you five-and-twenty, ten, or five,
To follow in a house where twice so many
Have a command to tend you?

REGAN. What need one?

LEAR. O, reason not the need: our basest beggars
Are in the poorest thing superfluous:
Allow not nature more than nature needs,
Man's life's as cheap as beast's: thou art a lady;
If only to go warm were gorgeous,
Why, nature needs not what thou gorgeous wear'st,
Which scarcely keeps thee warm. But, for true need—
You heavens, give me that patience, patience I need!
You see me here, you gods, a poor old man,
As full of grief as age; wretched in both!
If it be you that stir these daughters' hearts
Against their father, fool me not so much
To bear it tamely; touch me with noble anger,
And let not women's weapons, water-drops,
Stain my man's cheeks! No, you unnatural hags,
I will have such revenges on you both,
That all the world shall—I will do such things,
What they are yet I know not, but they shall be
The terrors of the earth. You think I'll weep;
No, I'll not weep:
I have full cause of weeping; but this heart
Shall break into a hundred thousand flaws
Or ere I'll weep. (*To his Jester*) O fool, I shall go mad!

He goes with Gloucester, Kent, and the Fool into the storm

CORNWALL. Let us withdraw; 'twill be a storm.

REGAN. This house is little, the old man and his people
Cannot be well bestowed.

GONERIL. Tis his own blame ; hath put himself from rest,
And must needs taste his folly.

GLOUCESTER (*returning*). The king is in high rage.

CORNWALL. Whither is he going ?

GLOUCESTER. He calls to horse ; but will I know not whither.

CORNWALL. Tis best to give him way ; he leads himself.

GONERIL. My lord, entreat him by no means to stay.

GLOUCESTER. Alack, the night comes on, and the bleak winds
Do sorely ruffle ; for many miles about
There's scarce a bush.

REGAN. O, sir, to wilful men,
The injuries that they themselves procure
Must be their schoolmasters. Shut up your doors :
He is attended with a desperate train ;
And what they may incense him to, being apt
To have his ear abused, wisdom bids fear.

CORNWALL. Shut up your doors, my lord ; tis a wild night :
My Regan counsels well : come out o' the storm.

ACT 3

Scene 1—A Heath in a Storm

KENT. Who's there, besides foul weather ?

GENTLEMAN. One minded like the weather, most unquietly.

KENT. I know you. Where's the king ?

GENTLEMAN. Contending with the fretful element ;
Bids the wind blow the earth into the sea,
Or swell the curlèd waters above the main,
That things might change or cease ; tears his white hair,
Which the impetuous blasts, with eyeless rage,
Catch in their fury, and make nothing of ;
Strives in his little world of man to out-scorn
The to-and-fro-conflicting wind and rain.
This night, wherein the cub-drawn bear would couch,
The lion and the belly-pinchèd wolf
Keep their fur dry, unbonneted he runs,
And bids what will take all.

KENT. But who is with him ?

GENTLEMAN. None but the fool ; who labours to outjest
His heart-struck injuries.

KENT. Sir, I do know you ;
And dare, upon the warrant of my note,
Commend a dear thing to you.
From France there comes a power
Into this scattered kingdom ; who already,
Wise in our negligence, have secret feet

In some of our best ports, and are at point
To show their open banner. Now to you:
If on my credit you dare build so far
To make your speed to Dover, you shall find
Some that will thank you, making just report
Of how unnatural and bemadding sorrow
The king hath cause to plain.
I am a gentleman of blood and breeding;
And, from some knowledge and assurance, offer
This office to you.
Open this purse and take
What it contains. If you shall see Cordelia
(As fear not but you shall), show her this ring;
And she will tell you who your fellow is
That yet you do not know. I will go seek the king.

GENTLEMAN. Give me your hand: have you no more to say?

KENT. Few words, but, to effect, more than all yet;
That, when we have found the king (in which your pain
That way, I'll this), he that first lights on him
Holla the other.

Scene 2—The Storm in another Part of the Heath

Lear appears with his Fool.

LEAR. Blow, winds, and crack your cheeks! rage! blow!
You cataracts and hurricanoes, spout
Till you have drenched our steeples, drowned the cocks!
You sulphurous and thought-executing fires,
Vaunt-couriers to oak-cleaving thunderbolts,
Singe my white head! And thou, all-shaking thunder,
Smite flat the thick rotundity o' the world!
Crack nature's moulds, all germens spill at once,
That make ingrateful man!

FOOL. O nuncle, court holy-water in a dry house is better than this rain-water out o' door. Good nuncle, in, and ask thy daughters' blessing: here's a night pities neither wise man nor fool.

LEAR. Rumble thy bellyful! Spit, fire! Spout, rain!
Nor rain, wind, thunder, fire, are my daughters:
I tax not you, you elements, with unkindness;
I never gave you kingdom, called you children,
You owe me no subscription: then let fall
Your horrible pleasure; here I stand, your slave,
A poor, infirm, weak, and despised old man:
But yet I call you servile ministers,
That have with two pernicious daughters joined
Your high-engendered battles gainst a head
So old and white as this. O! O! tis foul!

KENT (*entering*). Who's there ?

FOOL. Marry here's a wise man and a fool.

KENT. Alas, sir, are you here ? Things that love night
Love not such nights as these ; the wrathful skies
Gallow the very wanderers of the dark,
And make them keep their caves : since I was man
Such sheets of fire, such bursts of horrid thunder,
Such groans of roaring wind and rain, I never
Remember to have heard : man's nature cannot carry
The affliction nor the fear.

LEAR. Let the great gods,
That keep this dreadful pother o'er our heads,
Find out their enemies now. Tremble, thou wretch,
That hast within thee undivulgèd crimes,
Unwhipped of justice : caitiff, to pieces shake,
That under covert and convenient seeming
Hast practised on man's life : close pent-up guilts,
Rive your concealing continents, and cry
These dreadful summoners grace. I am a man
More sinned against than sinning.

KENT. Alack, bare-headed !
Gracious my lord, hard by here is a hovel ;
Some friendship will it lend you 'gainst the tempest :
Repose you there, while I to this hard house,
More harder than the stones whereof tis raised,
Return, and force their scanted courtesy.

LEAR. My wits begin to turn.
Come on, my boy : how dost, my boy ? art cold ?
I am cold myself. Where is this straw, my fellow ?
The art of our necessities is strange,
That can make vile things precious. Come, your hovel.
Poor fool and knave, I have one part in my heart
That's sorry yet for thee.

FOOL (*singing*). *He that has and a little tiny wit,*
With hey, ho, the wind and the rain,
Must make content with his fortunes fit,
For the rain it raineth every day.

LEAR. True, my good boy. Come, bring us to this hovel.

Scene 3—Gloucester's Castle

GLOUCESTER. Alack, alack, Edmund, I like not this unnatural dealing. When I desired their leave that I might pity him they took from me the use of mine own house ; charged me, on pain of their perpetual displeasure, neither to speak of him, entreat for him, nor any way sustain him.

EDMUND. Most savage and unnatural !

GLOUCESTER. Go to; say you nothing. There's a division betwixt the dukes; and a worse matter than that: I have received a letter this night; tis dangerous to be spoken. These injuries the king now bears will be revenged home; there's part of a power already footed: we must incline to the king. I will seek him, and privily relieve him. Go you and maintain talk with the duke, that my charity be not of him perceived. Though I die for it, as no less is threatened me, the king my old master must be relieved. There is some strange thing toward, Edmund; pray you, be careful.

EDMUND (*to himself*). This courtesy, forbid thee, shall the duke
Instantly know; and of that letter too:
This seems a fair deserving, and must draw me
That which my father loses; no less than all:
The younger rises when the old doth fall.

Scene 4—Lear before a Hovel on the Heath

KENT. Here is the place, my lord; good my lord, enter:
The tyranny of the open night's too rough
For nature to endure.

LEAR. Let me alone.

KENT. Good my lord, enter here.

LEAR. Wilt break my heart?

KENT. I had rather break mine own. Good my lord, enter.

LEAR. Thou think'st tis much that this contentious storm
Invades us to the skin: so tis to thee;
But where the greater malady is fixed
The lesser is scarce felt. Thou'dst shun a bear;
But if thy flight lay toward the raging sea,
Thou'dst meet the bear i' the mouth. When the mind's free
The body's delicate: the tempest in my mind
Doth from my senses take all feeling else
Save what beats there. Filial ingratitude!
Is it not as this mouth should tear this hand
For lifting food to 't? But I will punish home:
No, I will weep no more. In such a night
To shut me out! Pour on; I will endure.
In such a night as this! O Regan, Goneril!
Your old kind father, whose frank heart gave all—
O, that way madness lies; let me shun that;
No more of that.

KENT. Good my lord, enter here.

LEAR. Prithee, go in thyself; seek thine own ease:
This tempest will not give me leave to ponder
On things would hurt me more. But I'll go in.
In, boy; go first. You houseless poverty—
Nay, get thee in. I'll pray, and then I'll sleep.

Poor naked wretches, wheresoe'er you are,
That bide the pelting of this pitiless storm,
How shall your houseless heads and unfed sides,
Your looped and windowed raggedness, defend you
From seasons such as these ? O, I have ta'en
Too little care of this ! Take physic, pomp ;
Expose thyself to feel what wretches feel,
That thou mayst shake the superflux to them,
And show the heavens more just.

EDGAR (*within*). Fathom and half, fathom and half! Poor Tom!

FOOL (*running out from the hovel*). Come not in here, nuncle ; here's a spirit. Help me, help me !

KENT. Give me thy hand. Who's there ?

FOOL. A spirit, a spirit ; he says his name's poor Tom.

KENT. What art thou that dost grumble there i' the straw ? Come forth.

EDGAR (*appearing as a madman*). Away ! the foul fiend follows me !
Through the sharp hawthorn blows the cold wind.
Hum ! go to thy cold bed, and warm thee.

LEAR. Hast thou given all to thy two daughters,
And art thou come to this ?

EDGAR. Who gives anything to poor Tom, whom the foul fiend hath led through fire and through flame, and through ford and whirlpool, o'er bog and quagmire ; that hath laid knives under his pillow, and halters in his pew ; set ratsbane by his porridge ; made him proud of heart, to ride on a bay trotting-horse over four-inched bridges, to course his own shadow for a traitor ? Bless thy five wits ! Tom's a-cold.

LEAR. What, have his daughters brought him to this pass ?
Couldst thou save nothing ? Didst thou give them all ?

KENT. He hath no daughters, sir.

LEAR. Death, traitor ! nothing could have subdued nature
To such a lowness but his unkind daughters.

FOOL. This cold night will turn us all to fools and madmen.

EDGAR. Take heed of the foul fiend : obey thy parents ; keep thy word justly ; swear not. Tom's a-cold.

LEAR. What hast thou been ?

EDGAR. A serving-man, proud in heart and mind ; that curled my hair, wore gloves in my cap, swore as many oaths as I spake words, and broke them in the sweet face of heaven.

LEAR. Why, thou wert better in thy grave than to answer with thy uncovered body this extremity of the skies. Is man no more than this ? Consider him well. Thou owest the worm no silk, the beast no hide, the sheep no wool, the cat no perfume.

KENT. Who's there? What is't you seek?

GLOUCESTER (*approaching*). What are you there? Your names?

EDGAR. Poor Tom, that eats the swimming frog, the toad, the tadpole, drinks the green mantle of the standing pool; who is whipped from tithing to tithing, and stock-punished, and imprisoned; who hath had three suits to his back, six shirts to his body, horse to ride, and weapon to wear;

But mice and rats, and such small deer,
Have been Tom's food for seven long year.

GLOUCESTER (*seeing Lear*). What, hath your grace no better company?
Go in with me: my duty cannot suffer
To obey in all your daughters' hard commands:
Though their injunction be to bar my doors,
And let this tyrannous night take hold upon you,
Yet have I ventured to come seek you out,
And bring you where both fire and food are ready.

LEAR. First let me talk with this philosopher.
What is the cause of thunder?

KENT. Good my lord, take his offer; go into the house.

LEAR. I'll talk a word with this same learned Theban.

KENT. Importune him once more to go, my lord;
His wits begin to unsettle.

GLOUCESTER. Canst thou blame him?
His daughters seek his death: ah, that good Kent!
He said it would be thus, poor banished man!
Thou say'st the king grows mad; I'll tell thee, friend,
I am almost mad myself: I had a son,
Now outlawed from my blood; he sought my life,
But lately, very late; I loved him, friend;
No father his son dearer: truth to tell thee,
The grief hath crazed my wits. What a night's this!
I do beseech your grace—

LEAR. O, cry you mercy, sir.
Noble philosopher, your company.

EDGAR. Tom's a-cold.

GLOUCESTER. In, fellow, there, into the hovel: keep thee warm.

LEAR. Come, let's in all with him;
I will keep still with my philosopher.

KENT. Good my lord, soothe him; let him take the fellow.

GLOUCESTER. Take him you on.

KENT. Sirrah, come on; go along with us.

LEAR. Come, good Athenian.

GLOUCESTER. No words, no words: hush.

EDGAR. Child Rowland to the dark tower came,
His word was still,—Fie, foh, and fum,
I smell the blood of a British man.

Scene 5—A Room in the Castle

In this scene Cornwall is treacherously informed by Edmund of Gloucester's friendliness to the King, and swears to take revenge

Scene 6—A Chamber in a Farmhouse by the Castle

GLOUCESTER. Here is better than the open air; take it thankfully. I will piece out the comfort with what addition I can: I will not be long from you.

KENT. All the power of his wits has given way to his impatience: the gods reward your kindness!

LEAR. The little dogs and all,
Tray, Blanch, and Sweetheart, see, they bark at me.

EDGAR. Tom will throw his head at them.
Avaunt, you curs!
Be thy mouth or black or white,
Tooth that poisons if it bite;
Mastiff, greyhound, mongrel grim,
Hound or spaniel, brach or lym,
Or bobtail tike or trundle-tail,
Tom will make them weep and wail:
For, with throwing thus my head,
Dogs leap the hatch, and all are fled.

GLOUCESTER. Come hither, friend: where is the king my master?

KENT. Here, sir; but trouble him not, his wits are gone.

GLOUCESTER. Good friend, I prithee, take him in thy arms;
I have o'erheard a plot of death upon him.
There is a litter ready; lay him in 't,
And drive towards Dover, friend, where thou shalt meet
Both welcome and protection. Take up thy master:
If thou shouldst dally half an hour, his life,
With thine, and all that offer to defend him,
Stand in assurèd loss: take up, take up;
And follow me, that will to some provision
Give thee quick conduct.

KENT. Oppressèd nature sleeps:
This rest might yet have blamed thy broken senses,
Which, if convenience will not allow,
Stand in hard cure. (*To the Fool*) Come, help to bear thy master;
Thou must not stay behind.

Scene 7—Gloucester's Castle

Gloucester is seized. Regan plucks him by his beard, and, on his admitting he has sent the King away, Cornwall proceeds to destroy his eyes. At this cruelty, when one of the eyes has gone, an old servant of Cornwall interferes to prevent the loss of the other eye, and wounds his master.

Regan kills the servant and Cornwall dies, but not before he has destroyed the other eye of the old earl, who is now thrust forth into the night, blind, and grief-stricken because he has at last discovered Edmund's treachery.

ACT 4

Scene 1—The Heath

Gloucester, blind, is led by an old man.

EDGAR. My father, poorly led? World, world, O world!
But that thy strange mutations make us hate thee,
Life would not yield to age.

OLD MAN. O, my good lord, I have been your tenant, and your father's tenant, these fourscore years.

GLOUCESTER. Away, get thee away; good friend, be gone:
Thy comforts can do me no good at all;
Thee they may hurt.

OLD MAN. Alack, sir, you cannot see your way.

GLOUCESTER. I have no way, and therefore want no eyes;
I stumbled when I saw: full oft tis seen,
Our means secure us, and our mere defects
Prove our commodities. O dear son Edgar,
The food of thy abusèd father's wrath!
Might I but live to see thee in thy touch,
I'd say I had eyes again!

OLD MAN. How now! Who's there?

EDGAR (*aside*). O gods! Who is't can say *I am at the worst*?
I am worse than e'er I was.

OLD MAN. Tis poor mad Tom.

EDGAR (*aside*). And worse I may be yet: the worst is not
So long as we can say *This is the worst.*

OLD MAN. Fellow, where goest?

GLOUCESTER. Is it a beggarman?

OLD MAN. Madman and beggar too.

GLOUCESTER. He has some reason, else he could not beg.
I' the last night's storm I such a fellow saw
Which made me think a man a worm: my son
Came then into my mind; and yet my mind
Was then scarce friends with him; I have heard more since.
As flies to wanton boys are we to the gods;
They kill us for their sport.

EDGAR. Bless thee, master!

GLOUCESTER. Is that the naked fellow?

OLD MAN. Ay, my lord.

GLOUCESTER. Then, prithee, get thee gone
And bring some covering for this naked soul,
Whom I'll entreat to lead me.

OLD MAN. Alack, sir, he is mad.

GLOUCESTER. Tis the time's plague, when madmen lead the blind.
Do as I bid thee, or rather do thy pleasure.

OLD MAN. I'll bring him the best apparel that I have,
Come on't what will.

GLOUCESTER. Sirrah, naked fellow—

EDGAR. Poor Tom's a-cold.

GLOUCESTER. Here, take this purse. Dost thou know Dover?

EDGAR. Ay, master.

GLOUCESTER. There is a cliff, whose high and bending head
Looks fearfully in the confinèd deep:
Bring me but to the very brim of it,
And I'll repair the misery thou dost bear
With something rich about me; from that place
I shall no leading need.

EDGAR. Give me thy arm; poor Tom shall lead thee.

Scene 2—Before the Duke of Albany's Palace

GONERIL (*meeting Edmund*). Welcome, my lord: I marvel our mild husband
Not met us on the way.
(*To Oswald, entering*) Now, where's your master?

OSWALD. Madam, within; but never man so changed.
I told him of the army that was landed;
He smiled at it: I told him you were coming;
His answer was *The worse*: of Gloucester's treachery,
And of the loyal service of his son,
When I informed him, then he called me sot,
And told me I had turned the wrong side out:
What most he should dislike seems pleasant to him;
What like, offensive.

GONERIL. Then shall you go no further.
Back, Edmund, to my brother;
Hasten his musters and conduct his powers.
Wear this; spare speech;
Decline your head: this kiss, if it durst speak,
Would stretch thy spirits up into the air:
Conceive, and fare thee well.

EDMUND. Yours in the ranks of death.

GONERIL. My most dear Gloucester!

OSWALD. Madam, here comes my lord. (*Enter Albany*)

GONERIL. I have been worth the whistle.

ALBANY. O Goneril!
You are not worth the dust which the rude wind

Blows in your face. I fear your disposition.
What have you done?
Tigers, not daughters, what have you performed?
A father, and a gracious aged man,
Whose reverence even the head-lugged bear would lick,
Most barbarous, most degenerate! have you madded.
Could my good brother suffer you to do it?
A man, a prince, by him so benefited!
If that the heavens do not their visible spirits
Send quickly down to tame these vile offences,
It will come;
Humanity must perforce prey on itself,
Like monsters of the deep.

GONERIL. Milk-livered man!
That bear'st a cheek for blows, a head for wrongs:
Who hast not in thy brows an eye discerning
Thine honour from thy suffering; that not know'st
Fools do those villains pity who are punished
Ere they have done their mischief. Where's thy drum?
France spreads his banners in our noiseless land;
With plumèd helm thy slayer begins threats;
Whiles thou, a moral fool, sitt'st still, and criest
Alack, why does he so?

ALBANY. Thou changèd and self-covered thing, for shame,
Be-monster not thy feature. Were't my fitness
To let these hands obey my blood,
They are apt enough to dislocate and tear
Thy flesh and bones: howe'er thou art a fiend,
A woman's shape doth shield thee.

A MESSENGER. O, my good lord, the Duke of Cornwall's dead;
Slain by his servant, going to put out
The other eye of Gloucester.

ALBANY. Gloucester's eyes!

MESSENGER. A servant that he bred, thrilled with remorse,
Opposed against the act, bending his sword
To his great master; who, thereat enraged,
Flew on him, and amongst them felled him dead;
But not without that harmful stroke which since
Hath plucked him after.

ALBANY. This shows you are above,
You justicers, that these our nether crimes
So speedily can venge! But, O poor Gloucester!
Lost he his other eye?

MESSENGER. Both, both, my lord.

ALBANY. Where was his son, when they did take his eyes?

MESSENGER. Come with my lady hither.

ALBANY. He is not here.

MESSENGER. No, my good lord; I met him back again.

ALBANY. Knows he the wickedness?

MESSENGER. Ay, my good lord; twas he informed against him.

ALBANY. Gloucester, I live
To thank thee for the love thou show'dst the king,
And to revenge thine eyes. Come hither, friend:
Tell me what more thou know'st.

Scene 3—The French Camp near Dover

KENT (*to a Gentleman*). Why the King of France is so suddenly gone back know you the reason?

GENTLEMAN. Something he left imperfect in the State.

KENT. Did your letters pierce the queen to any demonstration of grief?

GENTLEMAN. Ay, sir; she took them, read them in my presence;
And now and then an ample tear trilled down
Her delicate cheek: it seemed she was a queen
Over her passion; who, most rebel-like,
Sought to be king o'er her.

KENT. O, then it moved her?

GENTLEMAN. Not to a rage: patience and sorrow strove
Who should express her goodliest. You have seen
Sunshine and rain at once: her smiles and tears
Were like a better way: those happy smilets,
That played on her ripe lip, seemed not to know
What guests were in her eyes; which parted thence,
As pearls from diamonds dropped. In brief,
Sorrow would be a rarity most beloved,
If all could so become it.

KENT. Made she no verbal question?

GENTLEMAN. Faith, once or twice she heaved the name of Father
Pantingly forth, as if it pressed her heart;
Cried *Sisters! sisters! Shame of ladies! sisters!*
Kent! father! sisters! What, i' the storm? i' the night?
Let pity not be believed! There she shook
The holy water from her heavenly eyes,
And clamour-moistened: then away she started
To deal with grief alone.

KENT. It is the stars,
The stars above us, govern our conditions;
Else one self mate and mate could not beget
Such different issues. You spoke not with her since?

GENTLEMAN. No.

KENT. Was this before the king returned?

GENTLEMAN. No, since.

KENT. Well, sir, the poor distressed Lear's i' the town;
Who sometime, in his better tune, remembers
What we are come about, and by no means
Will yield to see his daughter.

GENTLEMAN. Why, good sir?

KENT. A sovereign shame so elbows him: his own unkindness,
That stripped her from his benediction, turned her
To foreign casualties, gave her dear rights
To his dog-hearted daughters, these things sting
His mind so venomously that burning shame
Detains him from Cordelia.

GENTLEMAN. Alack, poor gentleman!

KENT. Of Albany's and Cornwall's powers you heard not?

GENTLEMAN. Tis so, they are afoot.

KENT. Well, sir, I'll bring you to our master Lear,
And leave you to attend him: some dear cause
Will in concealment wrap me up awhile;
When I am known aright you shall not grieve
Lending me this acquaintance. I pray you, go
Along with me.

Scene 4—A Tent in the Field

CORDELIA (*with doctor*). Alack, tis he: why, he was met even now
As mad as the vexed sea; singing aloud;
Crowned with rank fumiter and furrow-weeds,
With burdocks, hemlock, nettles, cuckoo-flowers,
Darnel, and all the idle weeds that grow
In our sustaining corn. A century send forth;
Search every acre in the high-grown field,
And bring him to our eye. What can man's wisdom
In the restoring his bereavèd sense?
He that helps him take all my outward worth.

DOCTOR. There is means, madam:
Our foster-nurse of nature is repose,
The which he lacks; that to provoke in him,
Are many simples operative, whose power
Will close the eye of anguish.

CORDELIA. All blest secrets,
All you unpublished virtues of the earth,
Spring with my tears! Be aidant and remediate
In the good man's distress! Seek, seek for him;
Lest his ungoverned rage dissolve the life
That wants the means to lead it.

A MESSENGER. News, madam;
The British powers are marching hitherward.

CORDELIA. Tis known before; our preparation stands
In expectation of them. O dear father,
It is thy business that I go about;
Therefore great France
My mourning and important tears hath pitied.
No blown ambition doth our arms incite,
But love, dear love, and our aged father's right:
Soon may I hear and see him!

Scene 5—In Gloucester's Castle

Regan, whose husband is now dead, resolves to marry Edmund, and is jealous of Goneril, whom she suspects of also regarding him with favour.

Scene 6—Fields near Dover; Edgar leading Gloucester

GLOUCESTER. When shall we come to the top of that same hill?

EDGAR. You do climb up it now: look, how we labour.

GLOUCESTER. Methinks the ground is even.

EDGAR. Horrible steep.
Hark, do you hear the sea?

GLOUCESTER. No, truly.

EDGAR. Why, then, your other senses grow imperfect
By your eyes' anguish.

GLOUCESTER. So may it be, indeed:
Methinks thy voice is altered; and thou speak'st
In better phrase and matter than thou didst.

EDGAR. You're much deceived: in nothing am I changed
But in my garments.

GLOUCESTER. Methinks you're better spoken.

EDGAR. Come on, sir; here's the place: stand still. How fearful
And dizzy tis to cast one's eyes so low!
The crows and choughs that wing the midway air
Show scarce so gross as beetles: half-way down
Hangs one that gathers samphire, dreadful trade!
Methinks he seems no bigger than his head:
The fishermen, that walk upon the beach,
Appear like mice; the murmuring surge,
That on the unnumbered idle pebbles chafes,
Cannot be heard so high. I'll look no more,
Lest my brain turn, and the deficient sight
Topple down headlong.

GLOUCESTER. Set me where you stand.

EDGAR. Give me your hand; you are now within a foot
Of the extreme verge: for all beneath the moon
Would I not leap upright.

GLOUCESTER. Let go my hand.
Here, friend, 's another purse; in it a jewel
Well worth a poor man's taking: fairies and gods
Prosper it with thee! Go thou farther off;
Bid me farewell, and let me hear thee going.

EDGAR. Now fare you well, good sir.

GLOUCESTER. With all my heart.

EDGAR. Why I do trifle thus with his despair
Is done to cure it.

GLOUCESTER (*kneeling*). O you mighty gods!
This world I do renounce, and, in your sights,
Shake patiently my great affliction off:
If I could bear it longer, and not fall
To quarrel with your great opposeless wills,
My snuff and loathèd part of nature should
Burn itself out. If Edgar live, O, bless him!
Now, fellow, fare thee well. (*He falls forward*)

EDGAR. Gone, sir: farewell.
And yet I know not how conceit may rob
The treasury of life when life itself
Yields to the theft: had he been where he thought,
By this had thought been past. Alive or dead?

Edgar here pretends to be a passer-by

Ho, you sir! friend! Hear you, sir! speak!
Thus might he pass indeed: yet he revives.
What are you, sir?

GLOUCESTER. Away, and let me die.

EDGAR. Hadst thou been aught but gossamer, feathers, air,
So many fathom down precipitating,
Thou'dst shivered like an egg: but thou dost breathe;
Hast heavy substance; bleed'st not; speak'st; art sound.
Ten masts at each make not the altitude
Which thou hast perpendicularly fell:
Thy life's a miracle. Speak yet again.

GLOUCESTER. But have I fallen, or no?

EDGAR. From the dread summit of this chalky bourn.
Look up a-height; the shrill-gorged lark so far
Cannot be seen or heard: do but look up.

GLOUCESTER. Alack, I have no eyes.
Is wretchedness deprived that benefit,
To end itself by death? Twas yet some comfort,
When misery could beguile the tyrant's rage,
And frustrate his proud will.

EDGAR. Give me your arm:
Up: so. How is't? Feel you your legs? You stand.

GLOUCESTER. Too well, too well.

EDGAR. This is above all strangeness.
But who comes here?

Enter Lear decked with wild flowers

EDGAR. O thou side-piercing sight!

GLOUCESTER. The trick of that voice I do well remember:
Is't not the king?

LEAR. Ay, every inch a king:
When I do stare, see how the subject quakes.

GLOUCESTER. O, let me kiss that hand!

LEAR. Let me wipe it first: it smells of mortality.

GLOUCESTER. A ruined piece of nature! This great world
Shall so wear out to nought. Dost thou know me?

LEAR. I remember thine eyes well enough.
Read thou this challenge; mark but the penning of it.

GLOUCESTER. Were all the letters suns I could not see one.

LEAR. O, ho! are you there with me? No eyes in your head, nor no money in your purse? Your eyes are in a heavy case, your purse in a light: yet you see how this world goes.

GLOUCESTER. I see it feelingly.

LEAR. What, art mad? A man may see how this world goes with no eyes. Look with thine ears: see how yond justice rails upon yond simple thief. Hark, in thine ear: change places; and, handy-dandy, which is the justice, which is the thief? Thou hast seen a farmer's dog bark at a beggar?

GLOUCESTER. Ay, sir.

LEAR. And the creature run from the cur? There thou mightst behold the great image of authority: a dog's obeyed in office.
Get thee glass eyes,
And, like a scurvy politician, seem
To see the things thou dost not. Now, now, now, now:
Pull off my boots: harder, harder: so.

EDGAR. O, matter and impertinency mixed!
Reason in madness!

LEAR. If thou wilt weep my fortunes, take my eyes.
I know thee well enough; thy name is Gloucester:
Thou must be patient; we came crying hither:
Thou know'st, the first time that we smell the air,
We wail and cry. I will preach to thee: mark.

GLOUCESTER. Alack, alack the day!

LEAR. When we are born, we cry that we are come
To this great stage of fools.

A GENTLEMAN. O, here he is: lay hand upon him. Sir,
Your most dear daughter—

LEAR. No rescue? What, a prisoner? I am even
The natural fool of fortune. Use me well;
You shall have ransom.

GENTLEMAN. Good sir—

LEAR. I will die bravely, like a bridegroom. What!
I will be jovial: come, come; I am a king,
My masters, know you that.

GENTLEMAN. You are a royal one, and we obey you.

LEAR. Then there's life in't. Nay, if you get it, you shall get it with running. (*He runs*)

GENTLEMAN. A sight most pitiful in the meanest wretch,
Past speaking of in a king! Thou hast one daughter,
Who redeems nature from the general curse
Which twain have brought her to.

EDGAR (*approaching with Gloucester*). Hail, gentle sir.

GENTLEMAN. Sir, speed you; what's your will?

EDGAR. Do you hear aught of a battle toward?

GENTLEMAN. Most sure and vulgar: everyone hears that which can distinguish sound.

EDGAR. But, by your favour,
How near's the other army?

GENTLEMAN. Near, and on speedy foot.

EDGAR. I thank you, sir: that's all.

GENTLEMAN. Though that the queen on special cause is here,
Her army is moved on.

GLOUCESTER. You ever-gentle gods, take my breath from me;
Let not my worser spirit tempt me again
To die before you please!

EDGAR. Well pray you, father.

GLOUCESTER. Now, good sir, what are you?

EDGAR. A most poor man, made tame to fortune's blows;
Who, by the art of known and feeling sorrows,
Am pregnant to good pity. Give me your hand,
I'll lead you to some biding.

GLOUCESTER. Hearty thanks:
The bounty and the benison of heaven.

OSWALD (*entering*). A proclaimèd prize! Most happy!
That eyeless head of thine was first framed flesh
To raise my fortunes. Thou old unhappy traitor,
Briefly thyself remember: the sword is out
That must destroy thee.

GLOUCESTER. Now let thy friendly hand
Put strength enough to't. (*Edgar interposes*)

OSWALD. Wherefore, bold peasant,
Darest thou support a published traitor? Hence;
Lest that the infection of his fortune take
Like hold on thee. Let go his arm.

Edgar strikes him and Oswald falls, dying

OSWALD. Slave, thou hast slain me: villain, take my purse:
If ever thou wilt thrive, bury my body;
And give the letters which thou find'st about me
To Edmund Earl of Gloucester; seek him out
Upon the British party: O, untimely death!

EDGAR. I know thee well: a serviceable villain.

GLOUCESTER. What, is he dead?

EDGAR. Sit you down, father; rest you.
Let's see these pockets: the letters that he speaks of
May be my friends. He's dead; I am only sorry
He had no other death's-man. Let us see:
Leave, gentle wax; and, manners, blame us not:
To know our enemies' minds we'd rip their hearts.

The letter disclosed a plot on the life of Albany, and when the scene closes Edgar is leading his father away to place him with a friend.

Scene 7—A Tent in the French Camp; Lear Sleeping

CORDELIA. O thou good Kent, how shall I live and work
To match thy goodness? My life will be too short,
And every measure fail me.

KENT. To be acknowledged, madam, is o'er-paid.
My boon I make it that you know me not
Till time and I think meet.

CORDELIA. Then be 't so, my good lord. (*To the doctor*) How does the king?

DOCTOR. Madam, sleeps still.
Please you, draw near. Louder the music there!

CORDELIA. O my dear father! Restoration hang
Thy medicine on my lips; and let this kiss
Repair those violent harms that my two sisters
Have in thy reverence made!

KENT. Kind and dear princess!

CORDELIA. Had you not been their father, these white flakes
Had challenged pity of them. Was this a face
To be opposed against the warring winds?
To stand against the deep dread-bolted thunder?
Mine enemy's dog,
Though he had bit me, should have stood that night
Against my fire; and wast thou fain, poor father,
To hovel thee with swine, and rogues forlorn,

In short and musty straw? Alack, alack!
Tis wonder that thy life and wits at once
Had not concluded all. He wakes; speak to him.

DOCTOR. Madam, do you; tis fittest.

CORDELIA. How does my royal lord? How fares your majesty?

LEAR. You do me wrong to take me out o' the grave:
Thou art a soul in bliss; but I am bound
Upon a wheel of fire, that mine own tears
Do scald like molten lead.

CORDELIA. Sir, do you know me?

LEAR. You are a spirit, I know: when did you die?

CORDELIA. Still, still, far wide!

DOCTOR. He's scarce awake: let him alone awhile.

LEAR. Where have I been? Where am I? Fair daylight?
I am mightily abused. I should e'en die with pity
To see another thus. I know not what to say.
I will not swear these are my hands: let's see;
I feel this pin prick. Would I were assured
Of my condition!

CORDELIA. O, look upon me, sir,
And hold your hands in benediction o'er me:
No, sir, you must not kneel.

LEAR. Pray, do not mock me:
I am a very foolish fond old man,
Fourscore and upward, not an hour more nor less;
And, to deal plainly,
I fear I am not in my perfect mind.
Methinks I should know you, and know this man,
Yet I am doubtful, for I am mainly ignorant
What place this is; and all the skill I have
Remembers not these garments; nor I know not
Where I did lodge last night. Do not laugh at me;
For, as I am a man, I think this lady
To be my child Cordelia.

CORDELIA. And so I am, I am.

LEAR. Be your tears wet? yes, faith. I pray, weep not:
If you have poison for me, I will drink it.
I know you do not love me; for your sisters
Have, as I do remember, done me wrong:
You have some cause, they have not.

CORDELIA. No cause, no cause.

LEAR. Am I in France?

KENT. In your own kingdom, sir.

LEAR. Do not abuse me.

DOCTOR. Be comforted, good madam: the great rage,
You see, is killed in him: and yet it is danger
To make him even o'er the time he has lost.
Desire him to go in; trouble him no more
Till further settling.

CORDELIA. Will't please your highness walk?

LEAR. You must bear with me:
Pray you now, forget and forgive: I am old and foolish.

ACT 5

Scene 1—The British Camp near Dover

Edmund commands the army of Regan, who is jealous of Goneril. Goneril and her husband Albany arrive with their force to combine against the troops with Cordelia. Edgar, still disguised, brings Albany a letter, asking that it shall be read before the battle, and that if Albany's army is victorious he will sound a trumpet to call forth a champion. Meanwhile Edmund is anticipating victory and the death of Albany, when he will marry either Regan or Goneril.

Scene 2—A Field between the Camps

EDGAR. Here, father, take the shadow of this tree
For your good host; pray that the right may thrive:
If ever I return to you again,
I'll bring you comfort.

GLOUCESTER. Grace go with you, sir!

EDGAR (*returning after battle*). Away, old man; give me thy hand; away!
King Lear hath lost, he and his daughter ta'en:
Give me thy hand; come on.

GLOUCESTER. No farther, sir; a man may rot even here.

EDGAR. What, in ill thoughts again? Men must endure
Their going hence, even as their coming hither:
Ripeness is all: come on.

GLOUCESTER. And that's true too.

Scene 3—A British Camp near Dover

Enter Edmund, with Lear and Cordelia as prisoners

EDMUND. Some officers take them away: good guard,
Until their greater pleasures first be known
That are to censure them.

CORDELIA. We are not the first
Who, with best meaning, have incurred the worst.
For thee, oppressèd king, am I cast down;
Myself could else out-frown false fortune's frown.
Shall we not see these daughters and these sisters?

LEAR. No, no, no, no! Come, let's away to prison:
We two alone will sing like birds i' the cage:
When thou dost ask me blessing I'll kneel down
And ask of thee forgiveness: so we'll live,
And pray, and sing, and tell old tales, and laugh
At gilded butterflies, and hear poor rogues
Talk of court news; and we'll talk with them too,
Who loses and who wins; who's in, who's out;
And take upon's the mystery of things,
As if we were God's spies: and we'll wear out,
In a walled prison, packs and sects of great ones,
That ebb and flow by the moon.

EDMUND. Take them away.

LEAR. Upon such sacrifices, my Cordelia,
The gods themselves throw incense. Have I caught thee?
He that parts us shall bring a brand from heaven,
And fire us hence like foxes. Wipe thine eyes;
The good years shall devour them, flesh and fell,
Ere they shall make us weep: we'll see 'em starve first.
Come. *(They are led away)*

EDMUND. Come hither, captain; hark.
Take thou this note; go follow them to prison:
One step I have advanced thee; if thou dost
As this instructs thee thou dost make thy way
To noble fortunes: know thou this, that men
Are as the time is: to be tender-minded
Does not become a sword: thy great employment
Will not bear question; either say thou'lt do't,
Or thrive by other means.

CAPTAIN. I cannot draw a cart, nor eat dried oats;
If it be man's work, I'll do't.

He goes, and Albany, Goneril, and Regan enter

ALBANY. Sir, you have shown today your valiant strain,
And fortune led you well: you have the captives
That were the opposites of this day's strife:
We do require them of you, so to use them
As we shall find their merits and our safety
May equally determine.

EDMUND. Sir, I thought it fit
To send the old and miserable king
To some retention and appointed guard;
With him I sent the queen; and they are ready
Tomorrow, or at further space, to appear
Where you shall hold your session. At this time
We sweat and bleed: the friend hath lost his friend:

And the best quarrels, in the heat, are cursed
By those that feel their sharpness :
The question of Cordelia and her father
Requires a fitter place.

ALBANY. Sir, by your patience,
I hold you but a subject of this war,
Not as a brother.

REGAN. That's as we list to grace him.
Methinks our pleasure might have been demanded,
Ere you had spoke so far.

At this point Albany asserts himself, and takes charge of the situation. Regan takes Edmund's side, declaring him her lord and master. Albany replies by charging Edmund with treason. He throws down his glove, and Edmund responds by throwing his own glove down. The trumpet is sounded and a man appears armed for the test of battle. It is Edgar.

EDGAR. What's he that speaks for Edmund Earl of Gloucester ?

EDMUND. Himself : what say'st thou to him ?

EDGAR. Draw thy sword,
That, if my speech offend a noble heart,
Thy arm may do thee justice : here is mine.
Despite thy victor sword and fire-new fortune,
Thy valour and thy heart, thou art a traitor ;
False to thy gods, thy brother, and thy father ;
Conspirant 'gainst this high-illustrious prince ;
And, from the extremest upward of thy head
To the descent and dust below thy foot,
A most toad-spotted traitor. Say thou *No*,
This sword, this arm, and my best spirits, are bent
To prove upon thy heart, whereto I speak,
Thou liest.

EDMUND. In wisdom I should ask thy name ;
But, since thy outside looks so fair and warlike,
And that thy tongue some say of breeding breathes,
What safe and nicely I might well delay
By rule of knighthood, I disdain and spurn :
Back do I toss these treasons to thy head ;
This sword of mine shall give them instant way,
Where they shall rest for ever. Trumpets, speak !

They fight, and Edmund falls

ALBANY. Save him, save him !

GONERIL. This is practice, Gloucester :
By the law of arms thou wast not bound to answer
An unknown opposite ; thou art not vanquished,
But cozened and beguiled.

ALBANY (*giving Edmund a letter*). Shut your mouth, dame,

Or with this paper shall I stop it. Hold, sir;
Thou worse than any name, read thine own evil:
No tearing, lady; I perceive you know it.

GONERIL. Say if I do, the laws are mine, not thine:
Who can arraign me for't?

ALBANY. Most monstrous! oh!
Know'st thou this paper?

GONERIL (*leaving*). Ask me not what I know.

ALBANY. Go after her: she's desperate; govern her.

EDMUND (*dying*). What you have charged me with, that have I done;
And more, much more; the time will bring it out:
Tis past, and so am I. But what art thou
That hast this fortune on me? If thou'rt noble,
I do forgive thee.

EDGAR. Let's exchange charity.
I am no less in blood than thou art, Edmund;
If more, the more thou hast wronged me.
My name is Edgar, and thy father's son.
The gods are just.

EDMUND. Thou hast spoken right, tis true;
The wheel is come full circle; I am here.

ALBANY. Methought thy very gait did prophesy
A royal nobleness: I must embrace thee:
Let sorrow split my heart, if ever I
Did hate thee or thy father!

EDGAR. Worthy prince, I know 't.

ALBANY. Where have you hid yourself?
How have you known the miseries of your father?

EDGAR. By nursing them, my lord. List a brief tale;
And when tis told, O, that my heart would burst!
The proclamation to escape,
That followed me so near, taught me to shift
Into a madman's rags: to assume a semblance
That very dogs disdained: and in this habit
Met I my father with his bleeding rings,
Their precious stones new lost; became his guide,
Led him, begged for him, saved him from despair;
Never (O fault!) revealed myself unto him,
Until some half-hour past, when I was armed.
Not sure, though hoping, of this good success,
I asked his blessing, and from first to last
Told him my pilgrimage: but his flawed heart,
Alack, too weak the conflict to support,
Twixt two extremes of passion, joy, and grief,
Burst smilingly.

EDMUND. This speech of yours hath moved me,
And shall perchance do good: but speak you on;
You look as you had something more to say.

ALBANY. If there be more, more woeful, hold it in;
For I am almost ready to dissolve,
Hearing of this.

EDGAR. Whilst I was big in clamour came there in a man,
Who, having seen me in my worst estate,
Shunned my abhorred society; but then, finding
Who 'twas that so endured, with his strong arms
He fastened on my neck, and bellowed out
As he'd burst heaven; threw him on my father;
Told the most piteous tale of Lear and him
That ever ear received; which in recounting
His grief grew puissant, and the strings of life
Began to crack. Twice then the trumpets sounded,
And there I left him tranced.

ALBANY. But who was this?

EDGAR. Kent, sir, the banished Kent, who in disguise
Followed his enemy king, and did him service
Improper for a slave.

Here a gentleman in Albany's service enters to say that Regan, who had been complaining of illness, is poisoned, and that Goneril has confessed the crime and has taken her own life also. Kent now enters.

KENT. I am come.
To bid my king and master aye Good-night:
Is he not here?

ALBANY. Great thing of us forgot!
Speak, Edmund, where's the king? and where's Cordelia?
See'st thou this object, Kent?

The bodies of Goneril and Regan are brought in

KENT. Alack, why thus?

EDMUND (*seeing the bodies*). Yet Edmund was beloved:
The one the other poisoned for my sake,
And after slew herself.

ALBANY. Even so. Cover their faces.

EDMUND. I pant for life: some good I mean to do,
Despite of mine own nature. Quickly send,
Be brief in it, to the castle; for my writ
Is on the life of Lear and on Cordelia:
Nay, send in time.

ALBANY. Run, run, O, run!

EDGAR. To whom, my lord? Who hath the office? Send
Thy token of reprieve.

EDMUND. Well thought on: take my sword,
Give it the captain.

ALBANY. Haste thee, for thy life.

EDMUND. He hath commission from thy wife and me
To hang Cordelia in the prison, and
To lay the blame upon her own despair,
That she fordid herself.

ALBANY. The gods defend her! Bear him hence awhile.

Edmund is borne off, and Lear enters with Cordelia dead in his arms

LEAR. Howl, howl, howl, howl! O, you are men of stones:
Had I your tongues and eyes, I'd use them so
That heaven's vault should crack. She's gone for ever!
I know when one is dead, and when one lives;
She's dead as earth. Lend me a looking-glass;
If that her breath will mist or stain the stone,
Why, then she lives.
This feather stirs; she lives! if it be so,
It is a chance which does redeem all sorrows
That ever I have felt.

KENT (*kneeling*). O my good master!

LEAR. Prithee, away.

EDGAR. Tis noble Kent, your friend.

LEAR. A plague upon you, murderers, traitors all!
I might have saved her; now she's gone for ever!
Cordelia, Cordelia! stay a little. Ha!
What is't thou say'st? Her voice was ever soft,
Gentle, and low, an excellent thing in woman.
I killed the slave that was a-hanging thee.

CAPTAIN. Tis true, my lords, he did.

LEAR. Did I not, fellow?
I have seen the day, with my good biting falchion
I would have made them skip: I am old now,
And these same crosses spoil me. Who are you?
Mine eyes are not o' the best: I'll tell you straight.

KENT. If fortune brag of two she loved and hated,
One of them we behold.

LEAR. This is a dull sight. Are you not Kent?

KENT. The same,
Your servant Kent. Where is your servant Caius?

LEAR. He's a good fellow, I can tell you that;
He'll strike, and quickly too: he's dead and rotten.

KENT. No, my good lord; I am the very man
That, from your first of difference and decay,
Have followed your sad steps.

LEAR. You are welcome hither.

KENT. Nor no man else: all's cheerless, dark, and deadly.
Your eldest daughters have fordone themselves,
And desperately are dead.

LEAR. Ay, so I think.

ALBANY. He knows not what he says; and vain it is
That we present us to him.

CAPTAIN (*entering*). Edmund is dead, my lord.

ALBANY. That's but a trifle here.
You lords and noble friends, know our intent.
What comfort to this great decay may come
Shall be applied: for us, we will resign,
During the life of this old majesty,
To him our absolute power: (*to Edgar and Kent*) you, to your rights;
With boot, and such addition as your honours
Have more than merited. All friends shall taste
The wages of their virtue, and all foes
The cup of their deservings. O, see, see!

LEAR. And my poor fool is hanged! No, no, no life!
Why should a dog, a horse, a rat, have life,
And thou no breath at all? Thou'lt come no more,
Never, never, never, never, never!
(Pray you, undo this button: thank you, sir.)
Do you see this? Look on her, look, her lips,
Look there, look there! (*He dies*)

EDGAR. He faints! My lord, my lord!

KENT. Break, heart; I prithee, break!

EDGAR. Look up, my lord.

KENT. Vex not his ghost: O, let him pass! He hates him
That would upon the rack of this tough world
Stretch him out longer.

EDGAR. He is gone, indeed.

KENT. The wonder is he hath endured so long:
He but usurped his life.

ALBANY. Bear them from hence. Our present business
Is general woe. Friends of my soul, you twain,
Rule in this realm, and the gored State sustain.

KENT. I have a journey, sir, shortly to go;
My master calls me; I must not say no.

EDGAR. The weight of this sad time we must obey;
Speak what we feel, not what we ought to say.
The oldest hath borne most: we that are young
Shall never see so much, nor live so long.

The Story of

The First Part of Henry the Fourth

HENRY THE FOURTH has got his crown, but it has brought him little peace. Here we see him settled on the throne from which he put down Richard. Though there is much interesting history in this play, we can hardly help feeling that Shakespeare is using his stage to prepare for the coming of his great king.

WE meet Prince Henry all through the cycle of plays of which this is one. He comes into Richard the Second for a moment; here he is entering on his career as Prince of Wales. But he has yet to find the dignity of his high place. He is keeping bad company; he is found in taverns. It is all a little hard to believe, and we feel that Shakespeare exaggerated the story to serve his dramatic purpose.

IT is not the only injustice (if we are to call it so) that Shakespeare allowed himself in this play. He took his material too hastily from a crude story called The Famous Victories of Henry the Fifth, and he did wrong to the memory of a worthy man. In drawing the picture of a swaggering knight, he gave him the name of Sir John Oldcastle. Men have laughed at this knight for three hundred years, and may laugh at him three hundred more, yet he is anything but a hero, and it was not fair to give him the name of an upright man. When somebody complained the poet changed the name to Falstaff, and there is a line in the Epilogue which has puzzled many people. It says: *Oldcastle died a martyr, and this is not the man.* That is Shakespeare's apology to an honest man's memory.

THOUGH Henry the Fourth gives his name to the play, he is nowhere of great importance. He is rather a figure of pathos. His conscience is uneasy, and he is honestly saddened by the life the young prince is leading. He wishes that some strange fate could change his son for Northumberland's, that he might leave behind as his successor a man like Hotspur.

IT is around the rebel Hotspur and the wayward Prince that the vivid historical scenes of the play are staged. The young Percy is daring and brave; he dare do all that doth become a man. But the pity is that he dare do more, for he is rash and impetuous and will not be held back. Prince Henry, with all his faults, is the better man.

THOSE who read Shakespeare in the order in which he wrote his plays cannot fail to notice that these four plays which take us from Richard the Second to Henry the Fifth, the longest chain of history that Shakespeare gives us, are written in a more masterly way than the rest of his English history. They were all written between 1593 and 1598, when Shakespeare was approaching the height of his powers. He was caught up by a flash of hero-worship for the hero king of Agincourt, and he wrote it all with a will.

THE PLAYERS

King Henry the Fourth, who, having been placed on the throne by English noblemen and popular feeling, has haughtily estranged his friends, some of whom rise in rebellion.

Henry, Prince of Wales. He has disappointed his father by his wild youth, seeking experience of low life, but rebellious war brings him back to a sense of duty.

John of Lancaster, a younger son of the king, without character.

Earl of Westmoreland, a nobleman loyal to the King.

Sir Walter Blunt, a fine soldier on the King's side.

Earl of Worcester, Thomas Percy, brother of Northumberland. Dismissed by Henry, he becomes an open enemy.

Earl of Northumberland, Henry Percy, the most influential but undecided of the King's enemies.

Hotspur (Henry Percy), son of Northumberland, a brave, honourable, but impetuous soldier, who leads the rebellion.

Edmund Mortimer (Earl of March), heir to the Crown by birth, and feared by the King as dangerous.

Richard Scroop, Archbishop of York, rebel against the King.

Archibald, Earl of Douglas, Scottish nobleman who, after invading England and being captured by Hotspur, assists his rebellion.

Owen Glendower, a Welsh patriot whose daughter is married to Mortimer; superstitious and impulsive.

Sir Richard Vernon, a cautious soldier on the rebels' side.

Sir John Falstaff, a fat convivial knight, loud in threats but backward in meeting danger. A boon companion of Prince Henry, who is amused by his wit and his hollow pretences.

Poins, companion of Prince Henry.

Peto and Bardolph, cronies of Falstaff and the Prince in wild and sometimes lawless doings.

Gadshill, who shares in Falstaff's escapades.

Lady Percy, wife of Hotspur and sister of Mortimer.

Lady Mortimer, the Welsh wife of Mortimer.

Mistress Quickly, landlady of a tavern in Eastcheap where Falstaff and his drinking companions meet.

Lords, sheriff, chamberlain, tapsters, carriers, travellers, servants.

SCENES—London, Rochester, Bangor, Shrewsbury, and near Coventry.

The First Part of Henry the Fourth

ACT 1

Scene 1—The King's Palace, with King and Lords

KING. So shaken as we are, so wan with care,
Find we a time for frighted peace to pant.
No more the thirsty entrance of this soil
Shall daub her lips with her own children's blood.
No more shall trenching war channel her fields,
Nor bruise her flowerets : those opposèd eyes,
Which, like the meteors of a troubled heaven,
All of one nature, of one substance bred,
Did lately meet in civil butchery,
Shall now, in mutual well-beseeming ranks,
March all one way, and be no more opposed
Against acquaintance, kindred, and allies :
The edge of war, like an ill-sheathèd knife,
No more shall cut his master. Therefore, friends,
As far as to the sepulchre of Christ,
Whose soldier now, under whose blessed cross
We are impressèd and engaged to fight,
Forthwith a power of English shall we levy,
To chase these pagans in those holy fields
Over whose acres walked those blessed feet
Which fourteen hundred years ago were nailed
For our advantage on the bitter cross.
But this our purpose is a twelvemonth old,
And bootless tis to tell you we will go :
Therefore we meet not now. Then let me hear
Of you, my gentle cousin Westmoreland,
What yesternight our council did decree
In forwarding this dear expedience.

WESTMORELAND. My liege, this haste was hot in question,
And many limits of the charge set down
But yesternight, when all athwart there came
A post from Wales loaden with heavy news,
Whose worst was that the noble Mortimer,
Leading the men of Herefordshire to fight
Against the irregular and wild Glendower,

Was by the rude hands of that Welshman taken,
A thousand of his people butchered.

KING. It seems then that the tidings of this broil
Brake off our business for the Holy Land.

WESTMORELAND. This matched with other did, my gracious lord;
For more uneven and unwelcome news
Came from the north, and thus it did import:
On Holy-rood day, the gallant Hotspur there,
Young Harry Percy and brave Archibald,
That ever-valiant and approvèd Scot,
At Holmedon met,
Where they did spend a sad and fearful hour;
As by discharge of their artillery,
And shape of likelihood, the news was told,
For he that brought them, in the very heat
And pride of their contention, did take horse,
Uncertain of the issue any way.

KING. Here is a dear, a true industrious friend,
Sir Walter Blunt, new lighted from his horse,
Stained with the variation of each soil
Betwixt that Holmedon and this seat of ours;
And he hath brought us smooth and welcome news.
The Earl of Douglas is discomfited;
Ten thousand bold Scots, two and twenty knights,
Balked in their own blood did Sir Walter see
On Holmedon's plains. Of prisoners Hotspur took
Mordake the Earl of Fife, and eldest son
To beaten Douglas; and the Earl of Athol,
Of Murray, Angus, and Menteith:
And is not this an honourable spoil?
A gallant prize? ha, cousin, is it not?

WESTMORELAND. In faith,
It is a conquest for a prince to boast of.

KING. Yea, there thou mak'st me sad and mak'st me sin
In envy that my Lord Northumberland
Should be the father to so blest a son,
A son who is the theme of honour's tongue;
Amongst a grove, the very straightest plant;
Who is sweet Fortune's minion and her pride:
Whilst I, by looking on the praise of him,
See riot and dishonour stain the brow
Of my young Harry. O that it could be proved
That some night-tripping fairy had exchanged
In cradle-clothes our children where they lay,
And called mine Percy, his Plantagenet!
Then would I have his Harry, and he mine.

But let him from my thoughts. What think you, coz,
Of this young Percy's pride? The prisoners,
Which he in this adventure hath surprised,
To his own use he keeps; and sends me word
I shall have none but Mordake Earl of Fife.

WESTMORELAND. This is his uncle's teaching; this is Worcester,
Malevolent to you in all aspects,
Which makes him prune himself, and bristle up
The crest of youth against your dignity.

KING. But I have sent for him to answer this,
And for this cause awhile we must neglect
Our holy purpose to Jerusalem.
Cousin, on Wednesday next our council we
Will hold at Windsor; so inform the lords:
But come yourself with speed to us again;
For more is to be said and to be done
Than out of anger can be utterèd.

WESTMORELAND. I will, my liege.

Scene 2—The Prince's Room in the Palace

FALSTAFF. Now, Hal, what time of day is it, lad?

PRINCE. Thou art so fat-witted, with drinking of old sack, and unbuttoning thee after supper and sleeping upon benches after noon, that thou hast forgotten to demand that truly which thou wouldst truly know. What hast thou to do with the time of the day? Unless hours were cups of sack and minutes capons, I see no reason why thou shouldst be so superfluous to demand the time of the day.

FALSTAFF. Indeed, you come near me now, Hal; for we that take purses go by the moon and the seven stars, and not by Phoebus, he, "that wandering knight so fair." And, I prithee, sweet wag, when thou art king, let not us that are squires of the night's body be called thieves of the day's beauty: let us be Diana's foresters, gentlemen of the shade, minions of the moon; and let men say we be men of good government, being governed, as the sea is, by our noble and chaste mistress the moon, under whose countenance we steal.

PRINCE. Thou sayest well, and it holds well too; for the fortune of us that are the moon's men doth ebb and flow like the sea, being governed, as the sea is, by the moon.

FALSTAFF. By the Lord, thou sayest true, lad. And is not my hostess of the tavern a most sweet wench?

PRINCE. As the honey of Hybla, my old lad of the castle. And is not a buff jerkin a most sweet robe of durance?

FALSTAFF. How now, how now, mad wag! What a plague have I to do with a buff jerkin?

PRINCE. Why, what have I to do with my hostess of the tavern?

FALSTAFF. Well, thou hast called her to a reckoning many a time and oft.

PRINCE. Did I ever call for thee to pay thy part?

FALSTAFF. No; I'll give thee thy due, thou hast paid all there.

PRINCE. Yea, and elsewhere, so far as my coin would stretch; and where it would not I have used my credit.

FALSTAFF. Yea, and so used it that, were it not here apparent that thou art heir apparent—But, I prithee, sweet wag, shall there be gallows standing in England when thou art king? Do not thou, when thou art king, hang a thief.

PRINCE. No; thou shalt.

FALSTAFF. Shall I? O rare! By the Lord, I'll be a brave judge.

PRINCE. Thou judgest false already: I mean, thou shalt have the hanging of the thieves and so become a rare hangman.

FALSTAFF. Well, Hal, well. Thou art indeed the most comparative, rascalliest, sweet young prince. But, Hal, I prithee, trouble me no more with vanity. I would to God thou and I knew where a commodity of good names were to be bought. An old lord of the council rated me the other day in the street about you, sir, but I marked him not; and yet he talked very wisely, but I regarded him not.

PRINCE. Thou didst well; for wisdom cries out in the streets, and no man regards it.

FALSTAFF. Thou hast done much harm upon me, Hal; God forgive thee for it! Before I knew thee, Hal, I knew nothing; and now am I, if a man should speak truly, little better than one of the wicked. I must give over this life, and I will give it over: by the Lord, an I do not, I am a villain.

PRINCE. Where shall we take a purse tomorrow, Jack?

FALSTAFF. Zounds, where thou wilt, lad; I'll make one; an I do not, call me villain and baffle me.

PRINCE. I see a good amendment of life in thee; from praying to purse-taking.

FALSTAFF. Why, Hal, tis my vocation, Hal; tis no sin for a man to labour in his vocation. Poins! Now shall we know if Gadshill have set a match.

PRINCE (*to Poins, entering*). Good-morrow, Ned.

POINS. Good-morrow, sweet Hal. My lads, my lads, tomorrow morning, by four o'clock, early at Gadshill! There are pilgrims going to Canterbury with rich offerings, and traders riding to London with fat purses: I have vizards for you all; you have horses for yourselves. Gadshill lies tonight in Rochester: I have bespoke supper tomorrow night in Eastcheap: we may do it as secure as sleep. If you will go, I will stuff your purses full of crowns; if you will not, tarry at home and be hanged.

FALSTAFF. Hal, wilt thou make one?

PRINCE. Who, I rob? I a thief? Not I, by my faith.

FALSTAFF. There's neither honesty, manhood, nor good fellowship in thee, nor thou camest not of the blood royal, if thou darest not stand for ten shillings.

PRINCE. Well then, once in my days I'll be a madcap.

FALSTAFF. Why, that's well said.

PRINCE. Well, come what will, I'll tarry at home.

FALSTAFF. I'll be a traitor then, when thou art king.

PRINCE. I care not.

POINS. Sir John, I prithee, leave the prince and me alone: I will lay him down such reasons for this adventure that he shall go.

FALSTAFF. Well, God give thee the spirit of persuasion and him the ears of profiting, that what thou speakest may move and what he hears may be believed, that the true prince may, for recreation sake, prove a false thief; for the poor abuses of the time want countenance. Farewell: you shall find me in Eastcheap.

PRINCE. Farewell, thou latter spring! farewell, All-hallown summer!

POINS. Now, my good sweet honey lord, ride with us tomorrow: I have a jest to execute that I cannot manage alone. Falstaff, Bardolph, Peto, and Gadshill shall rob those men that we have already waylaid; yourself and I will not be there; and when they have the booty, if you and I do not rob them cut this head off from my shoulders.

PRINCE. How shall we part with them in setting forth?

POINS. Why, we will set forth before or after them, and appoint them a place of meeting wherein it is at our pleasure to fail, and then will they adventure upon the exploit themselves, which they shall have no sooner achieved but we'll set upon them.

PRINCE. Yea, but I doubt they will be too hard for us.

POINS. Well, for two of them, I know them to be as true-bred cowards as ever turned back; and for the third, if he fight longer than he sees reason I'll forswear arms. The virtue of this jest will be the incomprehensible lies that this same fat rogue will tell us when we meet at supper: how thirty, at least, he fought with; what wards, what blows, what extremities he endured; and in the reproof of this lies the jest.

PRINCE. Well, I'll go with thee: provide us all things necessary and meet me tomorrow night in Eastcheap; there I'll sup. Farewell.

POINS. Farewell, my lord.

PRINCE. I know you all, and will awhile uphold
The unyoked humour of your idleness :
Yet herein will I imitate the sun,
Who doth permit the base contagious clouds
To smother up his beauty from the world,
That, when he please again to be himself,
Being wanted, he may be more wondered at,
By breaking through the foul and ugly mists
Of vapours that did seem to strangle him.
If all the year were playing holidays,
To sport would be as tedious as to work ;
But when they seldom come they wished-for come,
And nothing pleaseth but rare accidents.
So, when this loose behaviour I throw off
And, pay the debt I never promisèd,
By how much better than my word I am,
By so much shall I falsify men's hopes ;
And, like bright metal on a sullen ground,
My reformation, glittering o'er my fault,
Shall show more goodly and attract more eyes
Than that which hath no foil to set it off.
I'll so offend to make offence a skill,
Redeeming time when men think least I will.

Scene 3—The Palace ; King with Lords, Hotspur, and others

KING. My blood hath been too cold and temperate,
Unapt to stir at these indignities,
And you have found me so ; accordingly
You tread upon my patience : but be sure
I will from henceforth rather be myself,
Mighty and to be feared, than my condition,
Which hath been smooth as oil, soft as young down,
And therefore lost that title of respect
Which the proud soul ne'er pays but to the proud.

WORCESTER. Our house, my sovereign liege, little deserves
The scourge of greatness to be used on it ;
And that same greatness, too, which our own hands
Have helped to make so portly.

KING. Worcester, get thee gone ; for I do see
Danger and disobedience in thine eye :
O, sir, your presence is too bold and peremptory,
And majesty might never yet endure
The moody frontier of a servant brow.
You have good leave to leave us : when we need
Your use and counsel, we shall send for you.

NORTHUMBERLAND. Those prisoners in your highness' name demanded,

Which Harry Percy here at Holmedon took,
Were, as he says, not with such strength denied
As is delivered to your majesty :
Either envy, therefore, or misprision
Is guilty of this fault, and not my son.

HOTSPUR. My liege, I did deny no prisoners.
But I remember, when the fight was done,
When I was dry with rage and extreme toil,
Breathless and faint, leaning upon my sword,
Came there a certain lord, neat, and trimly dressed,
Fresh as a bridegroom ; and his chin new reaped
Showed like a stubble-land at harvest-home ;
He was perfumèd like a milliner ;
And 'twixt his finger and his thumb he held
A pouncet-box, which ever and anon
He gave his nose and took't away again ;
Who therewith angry, when it next came there,
Took it in snuff ; and still he smiled and talked,
And as the soldiers bore dead bodies by,
He called them untaught knaves, unmannerly,
To bring a slovenly unhandsome corse
Betwixt the wind and his nobility.
With many holiday and lady terms
He questioned me ; amongst the rest, demanded
My prisoners in your majesty's behalf.
I then, all smarting with my wounds being cold,
To be so pestered with a popinjay,
Out of my grief and my impatience,
Answered neglectingly I know not what,
He should, or he should not ; for he made me mad
To see him shine so brisk and smell so sweet
And talk so like a waiting-gentlewoman
Of guns and drums and wounds (God save the mark !) ;
And telling me the sovereign'st thing on earth
Was parmaceti for an inward bruise ;
And that it was great pity, so it was,
This villainous salt-petre should be digged
Out of the bowels of the harmless earth,
Which many a good tall fellow had destroyed
So cowardly ; and but for these vile guns
He would himself have been a soldier.
This bald unjointed chat of his, my lord,
I answered indirectly, as I said ;
And I beseech you, let not his report
Come current for an accusation
Betwixt my love and your high majesty.

BLUNT. The circumstance considered, good my lord,

Whate'er Lord Harry Percy then had said
To such a person and in such a place,
At such a time, with all the rest retold,
May reasonably die and never rise
To do him wrong or any way impeach
What then he said, so he unsay it now.

KING. Why, yet he doth deny his prisoners,
But with proviso and exception,
That we at our own charge shall ransom straight
His brother-in-law, the foolish Mortimer;
Who, on my soul, hath wilfully betrayed
The lives of those that he did lead to fight
Against that great magician, Owen Glendower,
Whose daughter, as we hear, the Earl of March
Hath lately married. Shall our coffers, then,
Be emptied to redeem a traitor home?
Shall we buy treason, and indent with fears,
When they have lost and forfeited themselves?
No, on the barren mountains let him starve;
For I shall never hold that man my friend
Whose tongue shall ask me for one penny cost
To ransom home revolted Mortimer.

HOTSPUR. Revolted Mortimer,
He never did fall off, my sovereign liege,
But by the chance of war: to prove that true
Needs no more but one tongue for all those wounds,
Those mouthèd wounds, which valiantly he took,
When on the gentle Severn's sedgy bank,
In single opposition, hand to hand,
He did confound the best part of an hour
In changing hardiment with great Glendower.
Three times they breathed and three times did they drink,
Upon agreement, of swift Severn's flood.
Never did base and rotten policy
Colour her working with such deadly wounds;
Nor never could the noble Mortimer
Receive so many, and all willingly:
Then let not him be slandered with revolt.

KING. Thou dost belie him, Percy, thou dost belie him;
He never did encounter with Glendower:
I tell thee,
He durst as well have met the devil alone
As Owen Glendower for an enemy.
Art thou not ashamed? But, sirrah, henceforth
Let me not hear you speak of Mortimer:
Send me your prisoners with the speediest means,

Or you shall hear in such a kind from me
As will displease you. My Lord Northumberland,
We license your departure with your son.
Send us your prisoners, or you will hear of it. (*King leaves*)

HOTSPUR. An if the devil come and roar for them,
I will not send them : I will after straight
And tell him so ; for I will ease my heart,
Albeit I make a hazard of my head.

NORTHUMBERLAND. What, drunk with choler ? Stay and pause awhile :
Here comes your uncle. (*Worcester returns*)

HOTSPUR. Speak of Mortimer !
Zounds, I will speak of him ; and let my soul
Want mercy if I do not join with him :
In his behalf I'll empty all these veins,
And shed my dear blood drop by drop i' the dust,
But I will lift the downtrod Mortimer
As high i' the air as this unthankful king,
As this ingrate and cankered Bolingbroke.

NORTHUMBERLAND. Brother, the king hath made your nephew mad.

WORCESTER. Who struck this heat up after I was gone ?

HOTSPUR. He will, forsooth, have all my prisoners ;
And when I urged the ransom once again
Of my wife's brother, then his cheek looked pale,
And on my face he turned an eye of death,
Trembling even at the name of Mortimer.

WORCESTER. I cannot blame him : was not he proclaimed
By Richard, that dead is, the next-of-blood ?

NORTHUMBERLAND. He was ; I heard the proclamation.

HOTSPUR. But, soft, I pray you ; did King Richard then
Proclaim my brother Edmund Mortimer
Heir to the crown ?

NORTHUMBERLAND. He did ; myself did hear it.

HOTSPUR. Nay, then I cannot blame his cousin king,
That wished him on the barren mountains starve.
But shall it be, that you, that set the crown
Upon the head of this forgetful man,
That you a world of curses undergo,
Being the agents, or base second means,
The cords, the ladder, or the hangman rather ?
O, pardon me that I descend so low,
To show the line and the predicament
Wherein you range under this subtle king ;
Shall it for shame be spoken in these days,

Or fill up chronicles in time to come,
That men of your nobility and power
Did gage them both in an unjust behalf,
As both of you (God pardon it !) have done,
To put down Richard, that sweet lovely rose,
And plant this thorn, this canker, Bolingbroke ?
And shall it in more shame be further spoken,
That you are fooled, discarded, and shook off
By him for whom these shames ye underwent ?
No ; yet time serves wherein you may redeem
Your banished honours, and restore yourselves
Into the good thoughts of the world again,
Revenge the jeering and disdained contempt
Of this proud king, who studies day and night
To answer all the debt he owes to you.

WORCESTER. Peace, cousin, say no more :
And now I will unclasp a secret book,
And read you matter deep and dangerous.

HOTSPUR. Send danger from the east unto the west,
So honour cross it from the north to south,
And let them grapple : O, the blood more stirs
To rouse a lion than to start a hare !
By heaven, methinks it were an easy leap
To pluck bright honour from the pale-faced moon,
Or dive into the bottom of the deep,
Where fathom-line could never touch the ground,
And pluck up drownèd honour by the locks :
So he that doth redeem her thence might wear
Without a rival all her dignities :
But out upon this half-faced fellowship !

WORCESTER. Good cousin, give me audience for a while.

HOTSPUR. I cry you mercy.

WORCESTER. Those same noble Scots
That are your prisoners—

HOTSPUR. I'll keep them all ;
He shall not have a Scot of them ;
No, if a Scot would save his soul he shall not :
I'll keep them, by this hand.

WORCESTER. You start away
And lend no ear unto my purposes.
Those prisoners you shall keep.

HOTSPUR. Nay, I will ; that's flat :
He said he would not ransom Mortimer ;
Forbade my tongue to speak of Mortimer ;
But I will find him when he lies asleep,
And in his ear I'll holla *Mortimer* !

I'll have a starling shall be taught to speak
Nothing but *Mortimer*, and give it him,
To keep his anger still in motion.

WORCESTER. Farewell, kinsman: I'll talk to you
When you are better tempered to attend.

NORTHUMBERLAND. Why, what a wasp-stung and impatient fool
Art thou to break into this woman's mood,
Tying thine ear to no tongue but thine own!

HOTSPUR. Why, look you, I am whipped and scourged with rods,
Nettled and stung with pismires, when I hear
Of this vile politician Bolingbroke.
In Richard's time—what do you call the place?—
A plague upon it, it is in Gloucestershire;
Twas where the madcap duke his uncle kept,
His uncle York; where I first bowed my knee
Unto this king of smiles, this Bolingbroke—
Why, what a candy deal of courtesy
This fawning greyhound then did proffer me!
O, the devil take such cozeners! God forgive me!
Good uncle, tell your tale; I have done.

WORCESTER. Nay, if you have not, to it again;
We will stay your leisure.

HOTSPUR. I have done, i' faith.

WORCESTER. Then once more to your Scottish prisoners.
Deliver them up without their ransoms straight,
And make the Douglas' son your only mean
For powers in Scotland; which, for divers reasons
Which I shall send you written, be assured,
Will easily be granted. You, my lord (*to Northumberland*),
Your son in Scotland being thus employed,
Shall secretly into the bosom creep
Of that same noble prelate, well beloved,
The archbishop.

HOTSPUR. Of York, is it not?

WORCESTER. True; who bears hard
His brother's death at Bristol, the Lord Scroop.

HOTSPUR. Why, it cannot choose but be a noble plot:
And then the power of Scotland and of York,
To join with Mortimer, ha!

WORCESTER. And so they shall.

HOTSPUR. In faith, it is exceedingly well aimed.

WORCESTER. And tis no little reason bids us speed,
For, bear ourselves as even as we can,
The king will always think him in our debt,
And think we think ourselves unsatisfied,

Till he hath found a time to pay us home:
And see already how he doth begin
To make us strangers to his looks of love.

HOTSPUR. He does, he does: we'll be revenged on him.

WORCESTER. Cousin, farewell: no further go in this
Than I by letters shall direct your course.
When time is ripe, which will be suddenly,
I'll steal to Glendower and Lord Mortimer;
Where you and Douglas and our powers at once,
As I will fashion it, shall happily meet,
To bear our fortunes in our own strong arms,
Which now we hold at much uncertainty.

NORTHUMBERLAND. Farewell, good brother: we shall thrive, I trust.

HOTSPUR. Uncle, adieu: O, let the hours be short
Till fields and blows and groans applaud our sport!

ACT 2

Scene 1—An Inn Yard in Rochester

FIRST CARRIER (*with a lantern*). Heigh-ho! an it be not four by the day, I'll be hanged: Charles' wain is over the new chimney, and yet our horse not packed. What, ostler!

OSTLER. Anon, anon.

SECOND CARRIER. This house is turned upside down since Robin Ostler died.

FIRST CARRIER. Poor fellow, never joyed since the price of oats rose; it was the death of him.

SECOND CARRIER. I think this be the most villainous house in all London road for fleas: I am stung like a tench. . . . I have a gammon of bacon and two razes of ginger to be delivered as far as Charing-cross.

GADSHILL (*entering*). Good-morrow, carriers. What's o'clock?

FIRST CARRIER. I think it be two o'clock.

GADSHILL. Sirrah, what time do you mean to come to London?

SECOND CARRIER. Time enough to go to bed with a candle, I warrant thee. Come, neighbour Mugs, we'll call up the gentlemen: they will along with company, for they have great charge.

GADSHILL. What, ho! chamberlain!

CHAMBERLAIN (*entering*). Good-morrow, Master Gadshill. It holds current that I told you yesternight: there's a franklin in the wild of Kent hath brought three hundred marks with him in gold. I heard him tell it to one of his company last night at supper, a kind of auditor, one that hath abundance of charge too, God knows what. They are up already, and call for eggs and butter: they will away presently.

GADSHILL. Sirrah, if they meet not with Saint Nicholas' clerks I'll give thee this neck.

CHAMBERLAIN. No, I'll none of it: I pray thee, keep that for the hangman.

GADSHILL. Give me thy hand: thou shalt have a share in our purchase, as I am a true man. Farewell, you muddy knave.

Scene 2—The Highway near Gadshill

POINS. Come, shelter, shelter: I have removed Falstaff's horse.

PRINCE. Stand close.

FALSTAFF (*approaching*). Poins! Poins, and be hanged! Poins!

PRINCE. Peace, ye fat-kidneyed rascal! What a brawling dost thou keep!

FALSTAFF. Where's Poins, Hal?

PRINCE. He is walked up to the top of the hill: I'll seek him.

FALSTAFF. I am accursed to rob in that thief's company: the rascal hath removed my horse, and tied him I know not where. If I travel but four foot further afoot I shall break my wind. Well, I doubt not but to die a fair death for all this, if I scape hanging for killing that rogue. I have forsworn his company hourly any time these two-and-twenty years, and yet I am bewitched with the rogue's company. If the rascal have not given me medicines to make me love him, I'll be hanged: it could not be else; I have drunk medicines. Poins! Hal! a plague upon you both! Bardolph! Peto! I'll starve ere I'll rob a foot further. An 'twere not as good a deed as drink to turn true man and to leave these rogues, I am the veriest varlet that ever chewed with a tooth. Eight yards of uneven ground is threescore and ten miles afoot with me; and the stony-hearted villains know it well enough: a plague upon it when thieves cannot be true one to another! A plague upon you all! Give me my horse, you rogues; give me my horse, and be hanged!

PRINCE. Peace, ye! lie down; lay thine ear close to the ground and list if thou canst hear the tread of travellers.

FALSTAFF. Have you any levers to lift me up again, being down? I'll not bear mine own flesh so far afoot again for all the coin in thy father's exchequer. I prithee, good Prince Hal, help me to my horse, good king's son.

PRINCE. Out, ye rogue! shall I be your ostler?

FALSTAFF. Go, hang thyself in thine own heir-apparent garters! If I be ta'en I'll peach for this. An I have not ballads made on you all and sung to filthy tunes, let a cup of sack be my poison.

Enter Gadshill, with Bardolph and Peto

GADSHILL. Stand.

FALSTAFF. So I do, against my will.

POINS. O, tis our setter: I know his voice. Bardolph, what news?

Bardolph. Case ye, case ye; on with your vizards. There's money of the king's coming down the hill; tis going to the king's exchequer.

Falstaff. You lie, ye rogue; tis going to the king's tavern.

Gadshill. There's enough to make us all.

Falstaff. To be hanged.

Prince. Sirs, you four shall front them in the narrow lane; Ned Poins and I will walk lower: if they scape from your encounter, then they light on us.

Peto. How many be there of them?

Gadshill. Some eight or ten.

Falstaff. Zounds, will they not rob us?

Prince. What, a coward, Sir John Paunch?

Falstaff. Indeed, I am not John of Gaunt, your grandfather; but yet no coward, Hal.

Prince. Well, we leave that to the proof.

Poins. Sirrah Jack, thy horse stands behind the hedge: when thou needest him, there thou shalt find him. Farewell, and stand fast.

Falstaff. Now cannot I strike him, if I should be hanged.

Prince. Ned, where are our disguises?

Poins. Here, hard by: stand close. (*The Prince and Poins leave*)

Falstaff. Now, my masters, every man to his business.

First Traveller (*descending from his horse*). Come, neighbour: the boy shall lead our horses down the hill; we'll walk afoot awhile, and ease our legs.

Thieves. Stand!

Travellers. Jesus bless us!

Falstaff. Strike; down with them; cut the villains' throats: ah! caterpillars! down with them: fleece them.

Travellers. O, we are undone, both we and ours for ever!

The thieves rob them, bind them, and carry them off;
and the Prince and Poins then approach, not recognised.

Prince. The thieves have bound the true men. Now could thou and I rob the thieves and go merrily to London, it would be argument for a week, laughter for a month, and a good jest for ever.

Poins. Stand close; I hear them coming.

Falstaff. Come, my masters, let us share, and then to horse before day. An the Prince and Poins be not two arrant cowards there's no equity stirring: there's no more valour in that Poins than in a wild duck.

Prince. Your money!

Poins. Villains!

The Prince and Poins set upon them, and the thieves all run away, leaving the booty behind.

PRINCE. Got with much ease. Now merrily to horse!
The thieves are scattered and possessed with fear
So strongly that they dare not meet each other;
Each takes his fellow for an officer.
Away, good Ned. Falstaff sweats to death,
And lards the lean earth as he walks along:
Were't not for laughing I should pity him.

POINS. How the rogue roared!

Scene 3—Warkworth Castle, Northumberland

Hotspur enters reading a letter, which suggests that the plot is dangerous. His wife, Lady Percy, enters as he reads.

HOTSPUR. How now, Kate! I must leave you within two hours.

LADY PERCY. O, my good lord, why are you thus alone?
Tell me, sweet lord, what is't that takes from thee
Thy stomach, pleasure, and thy golden sleep?
Why dost thou bend thine eyes upon the earth,
And start so often when thou sitt'st alone?
Why hast thou lost the fresh blood in thy cheeks,
And given my treasures and my rights of thee
To thick-eyed musing and cursed melancholy?
In thy faint slumbers I by thee have watched,
And heard thee murmur tales of iron wars;
Speak terms of manage to thy bounding steed;
Cry *Courage! to the field!* And thou hast talked
Of sallies and retires, of trenches, tents,
Of palisadoes, frontiers, parapets,
Of basilisks, of cannon, culverin,
Of prisoners' ransom and of soldiers slain,
And all the currents of a heady fight.
Thy spirit within thee hath been so at war,
And thus hath so bestirred thee in thy sleep,
That beads of sweat have stood upon thy brow,
Like bubbles in a late-disturbèd stream;
And in thy face strange motions have appeared,
Such as we see when men restrain their breath
On some great sudden hest. O, what portents are these?
Some heavy business hath my lord in hand,
And I must know it, else he loves me not.

HOTSPUR. What, ho! Is Gilliams with the packet gone?

SERVANT. He is, my lord, an hour ago.

HOTSPUR. Hath Butler brought those horses from the sheriff?

SERVANT. One horse, my lord, he brought even now.

HOTSPUR. What horse ? a roan, a crop-ear, is it not ?

SERVANT. It is, my lord.

HOTSPUR. That roan shall be my throne.
Well, I will back him straight : O *Esperance !*
Bid Butler lead him forth into the park.

LADY PERCY. But hear you, my lord.

HOTSPUR. What say'st thou, my lady ?

LADY PERCY. What is it carries you away ?

HOTSPUR. Why, my horse, my love, my horse.

LADY PERCY. Out, you mad-headed ape !
A weasel hath not such a deal of spleen
As you are tossed with. In faith,
I'll know your business, Harry, that I will.
I fear my brother Mortimer doth stir
About his title, and hath sent for you
To line his enterprise : but if you go—

HOTSPUR. So far afoot, I shall be weary, love.

LADY PERCY. Come, come, you paraquito, answer me.

HOTSPUR. Away, you trifler ! Love ! I love thee not,
I care not for thee, Kate : this is no world
To play with puppets and to tilt with lips.
What say'st thou, Kate ? What would'st thou have with me ?

LADY PERCY. Do you not love me ? Do you not, indeed ?
Nay, tell me if you speak in jest or no.

HOTSPUR. Come, wilt thou see me ride ?
And when I am o' horseback, I will swear
I love thee infinitely. But hark you, Kate ;
I must not have you henceforth question me
Whither I go, nor reason whereabout :
Whither I must, I must ; and, to conclude,
This evening must I leave you, gentle Kate.
I know you wise, but yet no farther wise
Than Harry Percy's wife : constant you are,
But yet a woman : and for secrecy,
No lady closer ; for I well believe
Thou wilt not utter what thou dost not know ;
And so far will I trust thee, gentle Kate.

LADY PERCY. How ! so far !

HOTSPUR. Not an inch further. But hark you, Kate :
Whither I go, thither shall you go too ;
Today will I set forth, tomorrow you.
Will this content you, Kate ?

LADY PERCY. It must of force.

Scene 4—The Boar's Head Tavern in Eastcheap

PRINCE. Ned, prithee, lend me thy hand to laugh a little.

POINS. Where hast been, Hal?

PRINCE. With three or four loggerheads amongst three or four score hogsheads. I have sounded the very base-string of humility. Sirrah, I am sworn brother to a leash of drawers; and can call them all by their christen names, as Tom, Dick, and Francis. They take it already upon their salvation that, though I be but Prince of Wales, yet I am the king of courtesy; and tell me flatly I am no proud Jack, like Falstaff, but a Corinthian, a lad of mettle, a good boy (by the Lord, so they call me), and when I am king of England I shall command all the good lads in Eastcheap.

VINTNER (*entering*). My lord, old Sir John, with half-a-dozen more, are at the door; shall I let them in?

PRINCE. Let them alone awhile, and then open the door. Poins! Falstaff and the rest of the thieves are at the door: shall we be merry?

POINS. As merry as crickets, my lad.

Enter Falstaff, Gadshill, Bardolph, and Peto

POINS. Welcome, Jack: where hast thou been?

FALSTAFF. A plague of all cowards, I say, and a vengeance too! marry, and amen! Give me a cup of sack, boy. Ere I lead this life long I'll sew nether socks and mend them and foot them too. A plague of all cowards! Give me a cup of sack, rogue. Is there no virtue extant? You rogue, here's lime in this sack too: there is nothing but roguery to be found in villainous man: yet a coward is worse than a cup of sack with lime in it. A villainous coward! Go thy ways, old Jack; die when thou wilt; if manhood, good manhood, be not forgot upon the face of the earth, then am I a shotten herring. There live not three good men unhanged in England, and one of them is fat and grows old: God help the while! a bad world, I say. I would I were a weaver; I could sing psalms or anything. A plague of all cowards, I say still.

PRINCE. How now, wool-sack! what mutter you?

FALSTAFF. A king's son! If I do not beat thee out of thy kingdom with a dagger of lath, and drive all thy subjects afore thee like a flock of wild-geese, I'll never wear hair on my face more. You Prince of Wales!

PRINCE. Why, what's the matter?

FALSTAFF. Are not you a coward? Answer me to that: and Poins there?

POINS. Zounds, ye fat paunch, an ye call me coward, by the Lord, I'll stab thee.

FALSTAFF. I call thee coward! I would give a thousand pound

I could run as fast as thou canst. You are straight enough in the shoulders, you care not who sees your back: call you that backing of your friends? A plague upon such backing! give me them that will face me. Give me a cup of sack; I am a rogue if I drunk today.

PRINCE. O villain! thy lips are scarce wiped since thou drunkest last.

FALSTAFF (*drinking*). All's one for that. A plague of all cowards, still say I.

PRINCE. What's the matter?

FALSTAFF. What's the matter! there be four of us here have ta'en a thousand pound this day morning.

PRINCE. Where is it, Jack? Where is it?

FALSTAFF. Where is it! taken from us it is: a hundred upon poor four of us.

PRINCE. What, a hundred, man?

FALSTAFF. I am a rogue if I were not at half-sword with a dozen of them two hours together. I have scaped by miracle. I am eight times thrust through the doublet, four through the hose; my buckler cut through and through; my sword hacked like a handsaw. I never dealt better since I was a man: all would not do. A plague of all cowards! Let them speak: if they speak more or less than truth they are villains and the sons of darkness.

PRINCE. Speak, sirs; how was it?

GADSHILL. We four set upon some dozen—

FALSTAFF. Sixteen at least, my lord.

GADSHILL. And bound them.

PETO. No, no, they were not bound.

FALSTAFF. You rogue, they were bound, every man of them; or I am a Jew else.

GADSHILL. As we were sharing, some six or seven fresh men set upon us—

FALSTAFF. And unbound the rest, and then come in the other.

PRINCE. What, fought you with them all?

FALSTAFF. All! I know not what you call all; but if I fought not with fifty of them I am a bunch of radish: if there were not two or three and fifty upon poor old Jack, then am I no two-legged creature.

PRINCE. Pray God you have not murdered some of them.

FALSTAFF. Nay, that's past praying for: I have peppered two of them; two I am sure I have paid, two rogues in buckram suits. I tell thee what, Hal, if I tell thee a lie spit in my face, call me horse. Thou knowest my old ward; here I lay, and thus I bore my point. Four rogues in buckram let drive at me—

PRINCE. What, four? thou saidst but two even now.

FALSTAFF. Four, Hal; I told thee four.

POINS. Ay, ay, he said four.

FALSTAFF. These four came all a-front, and mainly thrust at me. I made me no more ado but took all their seven points in my target, thus.

PRINCE. Seven? Why, there were but four even now.

FALSTAFF. Seven, by these hilts, or I am a villain else.

PRINCE. Prithee, let him alone; we shall have more anon.

FALSTAFF. Dost thou hear me, Hal?

PRINCE. Ay, and mark thee too, Jack.

FALSTAFF. Do so, for it is worth the listening to. These nine in buckram that I told thee of began to give me ground: but I followed me close, came in foot and hand; and with a thought seven of the eleven I paid.

PRINCE. O monstrous! Eleven buckram men grown out of two!

FALSTAFF. But, as the devil would have it, three misbegotten knaves in Kendal-green came at my back and let drive at me; for it was so dark, Hal, that thou couldst not see thy hand.

PRINCE. These lies are like their father that begets them; gross as a mountain, open, palpable. Why, thou knotty-pated fool, thou greasy tallow-catch—

FALSTAFF. What, art thou mad? Art thou mad? Is not the truth the truth?

PRINCE. Why, how couldst thou know these men in Kendal-green when it was so dark thou couldst not see thy hand? Come, tell us your reason: what sayest thou to this?

POINS. Come, your reason, Jack, your reason.

FALSTAFF. What, upon compulsion? Zounds, an I were at the strappado, or all the racks in the world, I would not tell you on compulsion. Give you a reason on compulsion! If reasons were as plentiful as blackberries I would give no man a reason upon compulsion, I.

PRINCE. I'll be no longer guilty of this sin; this sanguine coward, this huge hill of flesh—

FALSTAFF. You starveling, you elf-skin, you dried neat's tongue, you stock-fish! O for breath to utter what is like thee! you tailor's-yard—

PRINCE. Well, breathe awhile, and then to it again: and when thou hast tired thyself in base comparisons, hear me speak but this.

POINS. Mark, Jack.

PRINCE. We two saw you four set on four and bound them, and were masters of their wealth. Mark now how a plain tale shall put you down. Then did we two set on you four; and, with a word, out-faced you from your prize, and have it; yea, and can show it you here in the house: and, Falstaff, you carried yourself away as nimbly, with as quick dexterity, and roared for mercy and still run and roared, as ever I heard bull-calf. What a slave art thou, to hack thy sword as thou hast done, and then say it was in fight! What trick, what device, what starting-hole canst thou now find out to hide thee from this open and apparent shame?

POINS. Come, let's hear, Jack; what trick hast thou now?

FALSTAFF. By the Lord, I knew ye as well as he that made ye. Why, hear you, my masters: was it for me to kill the heir-apparent? Should I turn upon the true prince? Why, thou knowest I am as valiant as Hercules, but beware instinct: the lion will not touch the true prince. Instinct is a great matter; I was now a coward on instinct. I shall think the better of myself and thee during my life; I for a valiant lion, and thou for a true prince. But, by the Lord, lads, I am glad you have the money. Hostess, clap to the doors: watch tonight, pray tomorrow. Gallants, lads, boys, hearts of gold, all the titles of good fellowship come to you! What, shall we be merry? Shall we have a play extempore?

PRINCE. Content; and the argument shall be thy running away.

FALSTAFF. Ah, no more of that, Hal, an thou lovest me!

QUICKLY (*entering*). O, my lord the prince!

PRINCE. How now, my lady the hostess! What sayest thou to me?

QUICKLY. Marry, my lord, there is a nobleman of the court at door would speak with you: he says he comes from your father.

PRINCE. Give him as much as will make him a royal man, and send him back again to my mother.

FALSTAFF. What manner of man is he?

QUICKLY. An old man.

FALSTAFF. What doth gravity out of his bed at midnight? Shall I give him his answer?

PRINCE. Prithee, do, Jack.

FALSTAFF. Faith, and I'll send him packing. (*He goes*)

PRINCE. Now, sirs: by our lady, you fought fair; so did you, Peto; so did you, Bardolph: you are lions too, you ran away upon instinct, you will not touch the true prince; no, fie!

BARDOLPH. Faith, I ran when I saw others run.

PRINCE. Faith, tell me now in earnest, how came Falstaff's sword so hacked?

PETO. Why, he hacked it with his dagger, and said he would swear truth out of England but he would make you believe it was done in fight, and persuaded us to do the like.

BARDOLPH. Yea, and to tickle our noses with speargrass to make them bleed, and then to beslubber our garments with it and swear it was the blood of true men. I did that I did not this seven year before, I blushed to hear his monstrous devices.

PRINCE. Here comes lean Jack. How now, my sweet creature of bombast! How long is't ago, Jack, since thou sawest thine own knee?

FALSTAFF. My own knee! When I was about thy years, Hal, I was not an eagle's talon in the waist; I could have crept into any alderman's thumb-ring: a plague of sighing and grief! it blows a man up like a bladder. There's villainous news abroad. Here was Sir John Bracy from your father; you must to the court in the morning. That same mad fellow of the north, Percy, and he of Wales, what a plague call you him?

POINS. O, Glendower.

FALSTAFF. Owen, Owen, the same; and his son-in-law Mortimer, and old Northumberland, and that sprightly Scot of Scots, Douglas, that runs o' horseback up a hill perpendicular—well, he is there too, and one Mordake, and a thousand blue-caps more: Worcester is stolen away tonight; thy father's beard is turned white with the news: you may buy land now as cheap as stinking mackerel. Tell me, Hal, art not thou horribly afeard? Thou being heir-apparent, could the world pick thee out three such enemies again as that fiend Douglas, that spirit Percy, and that devil Glendower? Art thou not horribly afraid? Doth not thy blood thrill at it?

PRINCE. Not a whit, i' faith; I lack some of thy instinct.

FALSTAFF. Well, thou wilt be horribly chid tomorrow when thou comest to thy father: if thou love me, practise an answer.

PRINCE. Do thou stand for my father, and examine me upon the particulars of my life.

FALSTAFF. Shall I? Content: this chair shall be my state, this dagger my sceptre, and this cushion my crown.

PRINCE. Thy state is taken for a joint-stool, thy golden sceptre for a leaden dagger, and thy precious rich crown for a pitiful bald crown!

FALSTAFF. Well, an the fire of grace be not quite out of thee, now shalt thou be moved. Give me a cup of sack to make my eyes look red, that it may be thought I have wept; for I must speak in passion, and I will do it in King Cambyses' vein. . . . Stand aside, nobility. Harry, I do not only marvel where thou spendest thy time, but also how thou art accompanied; for though the camomile, the more it is trodden on the faster it grows, yet youth, the more it is wasted the sooner it wears. Why, being son to me, art thou so pointed at? Shall the son of England prove a thief and take purses? There is a thing, Harry, which thou hast often heard of, and it is known to many in our land by the name of pitch: this pitch, as ancient writers do report, doth defile; so doth the company thou keepest, for, Harry, now I do not speak to thee in drink but in tears, not in pleasure but in passion, not in words only, but in woes also: and yet there is a virtuous man whom I have often noted in thy company, but I know not his name.

PRINCE. What manner of man, an it like your majesty?

FALSTAFF. A goodly portly man, i' faith, and a corpulent; of a cheerful look, a pleasing eye, and a most noble carriage; and, as I think, his age some fifty, or, by'r lady, inclining to three-score; and, now I remember me, his name is Falstaff: if that man should be lewdly given he deceiveth me; for, Harry, I see virtue in his looks. If then the tree may be known by the fruit, as the fruit by the tree, then, peremptorily I speak it, there is virtue in that Falstaff: him keep with, the rest banish. And tell me now, thou naughty varlet, tell me, where hast thou been this month?

PRINCE. Dost thou speak like a king? Do thou stand for me, and I'll play my father.

FALSTAFF. Depose me? If thou dost it half so gravely, so majestically, both in word and matter, hang me up by the heels for a poulter's hare.

PRINCE. Well, here I am set.

FALSTAFF. And here I stand: judge, my masters.

PRINCE. Now, Harry, whence come you?

FALSTAFF. My noble lord, from Eastcheap.

PRINCE. The complaints I hear of thee are grievous.

FALSTAFF. My lord, they are false.

PRINCE. Thou art violently carried away from grace: there is a devil haunts thee in the likeness of an old fat man; a tun of man is thy companion. Why dost thou converse with that trunk of humours, that bolting-hutch of beastliness, that swollen parcel of dropsies, that huge bombard of sack, that reverend vice, that grey iniquity, that father ruffian, that vanity in years? Wherein is he good, but to taste sack and drink it? wherein neat and cleanly, but to carve a capon and eat it? wherein cunning, but in craft? wherein crafty, but in villainy? wherein villainous, but in all things; wherein worthy, but in nothing?

FALSTAFF. I would your grace would take me with you: whom means your grace?

PRINCE. That villainous abominable misleader of youth, Falstaff, that old white-bearded Satan.

FALSTAFF. My lord, the man I know.

PRINCE. I know thou dost.

FALSTAFF. But to say I know more harm in him than in myself were to say more than I know. That he is old, the more the pity; his white hairs do witness it If sack and sugar be a fault, God help the wicked! If to be old and merry be a sin, then many an old host that I know is doomed. If to be fat be to be hated, then

Pharaoh's lean kine are to be loved. No, my good lord; banish Peto, banish Bardolph, banish Poins; but for sweet Jack Falstaff, kind Jack Falstaff, true Jack Falstaff, valiant Jack Falstaff, banish not him thy Harry's company; banish plump Jack, and banish all the world.

PRINCE. I do, I will.

A knocking is heard, and Bardolph goes to the door

BARDOLPH (*returning*). O, my lord, my lord! the sheriff with a most monstrous watch is at the door.

QUICKLY. O my lord, my lord! They are come to search the house. Shall I let them in?

FALSTAFF. Dost thou hear, Hal?

PRINCE. Go, hide thee behind the arras: the rest walk up above. Now, my masters, for a true face and good conscience.

FALSTAFF. Both which I have had, but their date is out, and therefore I'll hide me.

PRINCE. Call in the sheriff.
Now, master sheriff, what is your will with me?

SHERIFF. First, pardon me, my lord. A hue and cry
Hath followed certain men unto this house.

PRINCE. What men?

SHERIFF. One of them is well known, my gracious lord,
A gross fat man.

CARRIER. As fat as butter.

PRINCE. The man, I do assure you, is not here,
For I myself at this time have employed him.
And, sheriff, I will engage my word to thee
That I will, by tomorrow dinner time,
Send him to answer thee, or any man,
For anything he shall be charged withal:
And so let me entreat you leave the house.

SHERIFF. I will, my lord. There are two gentlemen
Have in this robbery lost three hundred marks.

PRINCE. It may be so: if he have robbed these men
He shall be answerable: and so farewell.

SHERIFF. Good-night, my noble lord.

PRINCE. I think it is Good-morrow, is it not?

SHERIFF. Indeed, my lord, I think it be two o'clock.

PRINCE. This oily rascal is known as well as Paul's. Go, call him forth.

PETO. Falstaff! Fast asleep behind the arras, and snorting like a horse.

PRINCE. There let him sleep till day. I'll to the court in the morning. We must all to the wars, and thy place shall be honourable. I'll procure this fat rogue a charge of foot, and I know his death will be a march of twelve-score. The money shall be paid back again with advantage. Be with me betimes in the morning; and so, Good-morrow, Peto.

PETO. Good-morrow, good my lord.

ACT 3

Scene 1—The Archdeacon's House at Bangor

Enter Hotspur, Worcester, Mortimer, and Glendower

MORTIMER. These promises are fair, the parties sure,
And our induction full of prosperous hope.

HOTSPUR. Lord Mortimer, and cousin Glendower,
Will you sit down?
And uncle Worcester: a plague upon it!
I have forgot the map.

GLENDOWER. No, here it is.
Sit, cousin Percy; sit, good cousin Hotspur,
For by that name as oft as Lancaster
Doth speak of you his cheek looks pale, and with
A rising sigh he wisheth you in heaven.

HOTSPUR. And you in hell, as oft as he hears Owen Glendower spoke of.

GLENDOWER. I cannot blame him: at my nativity
The front of heaven was full of fiery shapes,
Of burning cressets; and at my birth
The frame and huge foundation of the earth
Shaked like a coward.

HOTSPUR. Why, so it would have done at the same season if your mother's cat had but kittened, though yourself had never been born.

GLENDOWER. I say the earth did shake when I was born.

HOTSPUR. And I say the earth was not of my mind
If you suppose as fearing you it shook.

GLENDOWER. The heavens were all on fire, the earth did tremble.

HOTSPUR. O, then the earth shook to see the heavens on fire,
And not in fear of your nativity.

GLENDOWER. Cousin, of many men
I do not bear these crossings. Give me leave
To tell you once again that at my birth
The front of heaven was full of fiery shapes,
The goats ran from the mountains, and the herds
Were strangely clamorous to the frighted fields.
These signs have marked me extraordinary;
And all the courses of my life do show
I am not in the roll of common men.

HOTSPUR. No man speaks better Welsh. I'll to dinner.

MORTIMER. Peace, cousin Percy; you will make him mad.

GLENDOWER. I can call spirits from the vasty deep.

HOTSPUR. Why, so can I, or so can any man;
But will they come when you do call for them?

GLENDOWER. Why, I can teach you, cousin, to command the devil.

HOTSPUR. And I can teach thee, coz, to shame the devil
By telling truth: tell truth and shame the devil.

MORTIMER. Come, come, no more of this unprofitable chat.

GLENDOWER. Three times hath Henry Bolingbroke made head
Against my power; thrice from the banks of Wye
And sandy-bottomed Severn have I sent him
Bootless home and weather-beaten back.

HOTSPUR. Home without boots, and in foul weather too!
How scapes he agues, in the devil's name?

GLENDOWER. Come, here's the map: shall we divide our right
According to our threefold order ta'en?

MORTIMER. The archdeacon hath divided it
Into three limits very equally.
England, from Trent and Severn hitherto,
By south and east is to my part assigned:
All westward, Wales beyond the Severn shore,
And all the fertile land within that bound,
To Owen Glendower: and, dear coz, to you
The remnant northward, lying off from Trent.

HOTSPUR. Methinks my moiety, north from Burton here,
In quantity equals not one of yours:
See how this river comes me cranking in,
And cuts me from the best of all my land
A huge half-moon, a monstrous cantle out.
I'll have the current in this place dammed up;
And here the smug and silver Trent shall run
In a new channel, fair and evenly;
It shall not wind with such a deep indent,
To rob me of so rich a bottom here.

GLENDOWER. Not wind? It shall, it must; you see it doth.
I'll not have it altered.

HOTSPUR. Will not you?

GLENDOWER. No, nor you shall not.

HOTSPUR. Who shall say me nay?

GLENDOWER. Why, that will I.

HOTSPUR. Let me not understand you, then; speak it in Welsh.

GLENDOWER. I can speak English, lord, as well as you,

For I was trained up in the English court;
Where, being but young, I framèd to the harp
Many an English ditty lovely well
And gave the tongue a helpful ornament,
A virtue that was never seen in you.
  HOTSPUR. And I am glad of it with all my heart:
I had rather be a kitten and cry mew
Than one of these same metre ballad-mongers;
I had rather hear a brazen canstick turned,
Or a dry wheel grate on the axle-tree:
And that would set my teeth nothing on edge,
Nothing so much as mincing poetry:
'Tis like the forced gait of a shuffling nag.
  GLENDOWER. Come, you shall have Trent turned.
  HOTSPUR. I do not care: I'll give thrice so much land
To any well-deserving friend;
But in the way of bargain, mark ye me,
I'll cavil on the ninth part of a hair.
Are the indentures drawn? Shall we be gone?
  GLENDOWER. The moon shines fair; you may away by night:
I'll haste the writer and withal
Break with your wives of your departure hence:
I am afraid my daughter will run mad,
So much she doteth on her Mortimer. (*He goes*)
  MORTIMER. Fie, cousin Percy! how you cross my father!
  HOTSPUR. I cannot choose: sometimes he angers me
With telling me of the moldwarp and the ant,
Of the dreamer Merlin and his prophecies,
And of a dragon and a finless fish,
A clip-winged griffin and a moulten raven,
A couching lion and a ramping cat,
And such a deal of skimble-skamble stuff
As puts me from my faith. I tell you what;
He held me last night at least nine hours
In reckoning up the several devils' names
That were his lackeys. O, he is as tedious
As a tired horse, a railing wife;
Worse than a smoky house: I had rather live
With cheese and garlic in a windmill, far,
Than feed on cates and have him talk to me
In any summer-house in Christendom.
  MORTIMER. In faith, he is a worthy gentleman,
Exceedingly well read, and profited
In strange concealments, valiant as a lion,
And wondrous affable and as bountiful
As mines of India. Shall I tell you, cousin?

He holds your temper in a high respect
And curbs himself even of his natural scope
When you come 'cross his humour; faith, he does:
I warrant you, that man is not alive
Might so have tempted him as you have done
Without the taste of danger and reproof:
But do not use it oft, let me entreat you.

WORCESTER. In faith, my lord, you are too wilful-blame;
And since your coming hither have done enough
To put him quite beside his patience.
You must needs learn, lord, to amend this fault:
Though sometimes it show greatness, courage, blood,
(And that's the dearest grace it renders you),
Yet oftentimes it doth present harsh rage,
Defect of manners, want of government,
Pride, haughtiness, opinion, and disdain:
The least of which haunting a nobleman
Loseth men's hearts and leaves behind a stain
Upon the beauty of all parts besides,
Beguiling them of commendation.

HOTSPUR. Well, I'm schooled: good manners be your speed!
Here come our wives, and let us take our leave.

MORTIMER. This is the deadly spite that angers me;
My wife can speak no English, I no Welsh.

GLENDOWER (*advancing*). My daughter weeps: she will not part with you;
She'll be a soldier too; she'll to the wars.

MORTIMER. Good father, tell her that she and my aunt Percy
Shall follow in your conduct speedily.

GLENDOWER. She is desperate here, one that no persuasion can do good upon. (*The lady speaks in Welsh*)

MORTIMER. I understand thy looks: that pretty Welsh
Which thou pour'st down from these swelling heavens
I am too perfect in; and, but for shame,
In such a parley should I answer thee.
I understand thy kisses, and thou mine,
And that's a feeling disputation:
But I will never be a truant, love,
Till I have learned thy language; for thy tongue
Makes Welsh as sweet as ditties highly penned,
Sung by a fair queen in a summer's bower.

The lady speaks again in Welsh

O, I am ignorance itself in this!

GLENDOWER. She bids you on the wanton rushes lay you down
And rest your gentle head upon her lap,

And she will sing the song that pleaseth you
And on your eyelids crown the god of sleep,
Charming your blood with pleasing heaviness,
Making such difference 'twixt wake and sleep
As is the difference betwixt day and night
The hour before the heavenly-harnessed team
Begins his golden progress in the east.

MORTIMER. With all my heart I'll sit and hear her sing:
By that time will our book, I think, be drawn.

GLENDOWER. Do so;
And those musicians that shall play to you
Hang in the air a thousand leagues from hence,
And straight they shall be here: sit, and attend.

HOTSPUR. Come, Kate, I'll have your song too.

LADY PERCY. Not mine, in good sooth.

HOTSPUR. Not yours, in good sooth! Heart! you swear like a comfit-maker's wife. Come sing.

LADY PERCY. I will not sing.

HOTSPUR. An the indentures be drawn, I'll away within these two hours; and so, come in when ye will.

GLENDOWER. Come, come, Lord Mortimer; you are as slow
As hot Lord Percy is on fire to go.
By this our book is drawn; we'll but seal,
And then to horse immediately.

MORTIMER. With all my heart.

Scene 2—The King and the Prince in the Palace

KING. I know not whether God will have it so,
For some displeasing service I have done,
That, in his secret doom, out of my blood
He'll breed revengement and a scourge for me;
But thou dost in thy passages of life
Make me believe that thou art only marked
For the hot vengeance and the rod of heaven
To punish my mistreadings. Tell me else,
Could such inordinate and low desires,
Such poor, such bare, such lewd, such mean attempts,
Such barren pleasures, rude society,
As thou art matched withal and grafted to,
Accompany the greatness of thy blood
And hold their level with thy princely heart?

PRINCE. So please your majesty, I would I could
Quit all offences with as clear excuse
As well as I am doubtless I can purge
Myself of many I am charged withal:
Yet such extenuation let me beg,

As, in reproof of many tales devised,
Which oft the ear of greatness needs must hear,
By smiling pick-thanks and base newsmongers,
I may, for some things true, wherein my youth
Hath faulty wandered and irregular,
Find pardon on my true submission.

KING. God pardon thee! yet let me wonder, Harry,
At thy affections, which do hold a wing
Quite from the flight of all thy ancestors.
Thy place in council thou hast rudely lost,
Which by thy younger brother is supplied,
And art almost an alien to the hearts
Of all the court and princes of my blood:
The hope and expectation of thy time
Is ruined, and the soul of every man
Prophetically doth forethink thy fall.
Had I so lavish of my presence been,
So common-hackneyed in the eyes of men,
So stale and cheap to vulgar company,
Opinion, that did help me to the crown,
Had still kept loyal to possession
And left me in reputeless banishment,
A fellow of no mark nor likelihood.
By being seldom seen, I could not stir
But like a comet I was wondered at;
That men would tell their children *This is he;*
Others would say *Where? Which is Bolingbroke?*
And then I stole all courtesy from heaven,
And dressed myself in such humility
That I did pluck allegiance from men's hearts,
Loud shouts and salutations from their mouths,
Even in the presence of the crownèd king.
Thus did I keep my person fresh and new;
My presence, like a robe pontifical,
Ne'er seen but wondered at: and so my state,
Seldom but sumptuous, showed like a feast
And won by rareness such solemnity.
The skipping king, he ambled up and down
With shallow jesters and rash bavin wits,
Soon kindled and soon burnt; carded his state,
Mingled his royalty with capering fools;
Had his great name profanèd with their scorns
And gave his countenance, against his name,
To laugh at gibing boys and stand the push
Of every beardless vain comparative;
Grew a companion to the common streets,
Enfeoffed himself to popularity;

So when he had occasion to be seen
He was but as the cuckoo is in June,
Heard, not regarded.
And in that very line, Harry, standest thou;
For thou hast lost thy princely privilege
With vile participation: not an eye
But is a-weary of thy common sight,
Save mine, which hath desired to see thee more;
Which now doth that I would not have it do,
Make blind itself with foolish tenderness.

PRINCE. I shall hereafter, my thrice gracious lord,
Be more myself.

KING. For all the world.
As thou art to this hour was Richard then
When I from France set foot at Ravenspurgh,
And even as I was then is Percy now.
Now, by my sceptre and my soul to boot,
He hath more worthy interest to the State
Than thou the shadow of succession;
For of no right, no colour like to right,
He doth fill fields with harness in the realm,
Turns head against the lion's armèd jaws,
And, being no more in debt to years than thou,
Leads ancient lords and reverend bishops on.
What never-dying honour hath he got
Against renownèd Douglas! whose high deeds,
Whose hot incursions and great name in arms,
Holds from all soldiers chief majority
And military title capital
Through all the kingdoms that acknowledge Christ!
Thrice hath this Hotspur, Mars in swaddling clothes,
This infant warrior, in his enterprises
Discomfited great Douglas, ta'en him once,
Enlargèd him and made a friend of him,
To fill the mouth of deep defiance up
And shake the peace and safety of our throne.
And what say you to this? Percy, Northumberland,
The Archbishop's grace of York, Douglas, Mortimer,
Capitulate against us and are up.
But wherefore do I tell these news to thee?
Why, Harry, do I tell thee of my foes,
Which art my near'st and dearest enemy?
Thou that art like enough, through vassal fear,
Base inclination and the start of spleen,
To fight against me under Percy's pay,
To dog his heels and curtsey at his frowns,
To show how much thou art degenerate.

PRINCE. Do not think so; you shall not find it so:
And God forgive them that so much have swayed
Your majesty's good thoughts away from me!
I will redeem all this on Percy's head
And in the closing of some glorious day
Be bold to tell you that I am your son;
For the time will come,
That I shall make this northern youth exchange
His glorious deeds for my indignities.
This, in the name of God, I promise here:
The which if He be pleased I shall perform,
I do beseech your majesty may salve
The long-grown wounds of my intemperance:
If not, the end of life cancels all bands,
And I will die a hundred thousand deaths
Ere break the smallest parcel of this vow.

KING. A hundred thousand rebels die in this:
Thou shalt have charge and sovereign trust herein.

BLUNT (*entering*). Lord Mortimer of Scotland hath sent word
That Douglas and the English rebels met
The eleventh of this month at Shrewsbury:
A mighty and a fearful head they are,
If promises be kept on every hand,
As ever offered foul play in a State.

KING. The Earl of Westmoreland set forth today;
With him my son Lord John of Lancaster;
For this advertisement is five days old:
On Wednesday next, Harry, you shall set forward;
On Thursday we ourselves will march: our meeting
Is Bridgenorth: and, Harry, you shall march
Through Gloucestershire; by which account,
Our business valued, some twelve days hence
Our general forces at Bridgenorth shall meet.
Our hands are full of business: let's away;
Advantage feeds him fat while men delay.

Scene 3—The Boar's Head Tavern in Eastcheap

FALSTAFF. Bardolph, am I not fallen away vilely since this last action? Do I not bate? Do I not dwindle? Why, my skin hangs about me like an old lady's loose gown; I am withered like an old apple-john. Well, I'll repent, and that suddenly, while I am in some liking; I shall be out of heart shortly, and then I shall have no strength to repent. An I have not forgotten what the inside of a church is made of I am a peppercorn, a brewer's horse. The inside of a church! Company, villainous company, hath been the spoil of me. I was as virtuously given as a gentleman need to be; and now I live out of all order, out of all compass.

BARDOLPH. Why, you are so fat, Sir John, that you must needs be out of all compass, out of all reasonable compass, Sir John.

FALSTAFF. Do thou amend thy face, and I'll amend my life: thou art our admiral, thou bearest the lantern in the poop, but tis in the nose of thee; thou art the Knight of the Burning Lamp.

BARDOLPH. Why, Sir John, my face does you no harm.

FALSTAFF. No, I'll be sworn; I make as good use of it as many a man doth of a Death's-head. If thou wert any way given to virtue, I would swear by thy face; but thou art altogether given over; and wert indeed, but for the light in thy face, the son of utter darkness. When thou rannest up Gadshill in the night to catch my horse, if I did not think thou hadst been a ball of wildfire there's no purchase in money. O, thou art a perpetual triumph, an everlasting bonfire-light! Thou hast saved me a thousand marks in links and torches, walking with thee in the night betwixt tavern and tavern; but the sack that thou hast drunk me would have bought me lights as good cheap at the dearest chandler's in Europe. I have maintained that salamander of yours with fire any time this two and thirty years; God reward me for it!

The Prince enters, followed by Quickly

QUICKLY. Good my lord, hear me.

FALSTAFF. Prithee, let her alone, and list to me.

PRINCE. What sayest thou, Jack?

FALSTAFF. The other night I fell asleep here behind the arras and had my pocket picked.

PRINCE. What didst thou lose, Jack?

FALSTAFF. Wilt thou believe me, Hal? three or four bonds of forty pound a-piece, and a seal-ring of my grandfather's.

PRINCE. A trifle, some eightpenny matter.

QUICKLY. So I told him, my lord; and I said I heard your grace say so: and, my lord, he speaks most vilely of you, like a foul-mouthed man as he is, and said he would cudgel you.

PRINCE. What! He did not?

QUICKLY. There's neither faith, truth, nor womanhood in me else.

FALSTAFF. There's no more faith in thee than in a stewed prune; nor no more truth in thee than in a drawn fox.

QUICKLY. I am an honest man's wife: and, setting thy knighthood aside, thou art a knave to call me so.

PRINCE. Thou sayest true, hostess, and he slanders thee most grossly.

QUICKLY. So he doth you, my lord; and said this other day you owe him a thousand pound.

PRINCE. Sirrah, do I owe you a thousand pound?

FALSTAFF. A thousand pound, Hal! a million; thy love is worth a million; thou owest me thy love.

Quickly. Nay, my lord, he called you Jack, and said he would cudgel you.

Falstaff. Did I, Bardolph ?

Bardolph. Indeed, Sir John, you said so.

Falstaff. Yea, if he said my ring was copper.

Prince. I say tis copper : darest thou be as good as thy word now ?

Falstaff. Why, Hal, thou knowest, as thou art but man, I dare : but as thou art prince I fear thee as I fear the roaring of the lion's whelp.

Prince. And why not as the lion ?

Falstaff. The king himself is to be feared as the lion : dost thou think I'll fear thee as I fear thy father ?

Prince. But, sirrah, there's no room for faith, truth, nor honesty in this bosom of thine. Charge an honest woman with picking thy pocket ! why, thou rascal, if there were anything in thy pocket but tavern-reckonings, and one poor pennyworth of sugar-candy to make thee long-winded—if thy pocket were enriched with any other injuries but these, I am a villain : and yet you will stand to it ; you will not pocket up wrong : art thou not ashamed ?

Falstaff. Dost thou hear, Hal ? Thou knowest in the state of innocency Adam fell ; and what should poor Jack Falstaff do in the days of villainy ? Thou seest I have more flesh than another man, and therefore more frailty. Hostess, I forgive thee : go, make ready breakfast ; love thy husband, look to thy servants, cherish thy guests : thou shalt find me tractable to any honest reason : thou seest I am pacified still. Nay, prithee, be gone. Now, Hal, to the news at court : for the robbery, lad, how is that answered ?

Prince. The money is paid back again.

Falstaff. O, I do not like that paying back ; tis a double labour.

Prince. I am good friends with my father and may do anything.

Falstaff. Rob me the exchequer the first thing thou doest.

Prince. I have procured thee, Jack, a charge of foot.

Falstaff. I would it had been of horse.

Prince. Bardolph, go bear this letter to Lord John of Lancaster, to my brother John ; this to my Lord of Westmoreland. Go, Peto, to horse, to horse ; for thou and I have thirty miles to ride yet ere dinner time. Jack, meet me tomorrow in the Temple-hall at two o'clock in the afternoon.
There shalt thou know thy charge ; and there receive
Money and order for their furniture.
The land is burning ; Percy stands on high ;
And either we or they must lower lie.

FALSTAFF. Rare words! Brave world! Hostess, my breakfast, come!
O, I could wish this tavern were my drum!

ACT 4

Scene 1—The Rebel Camp near Shrewsbury

HOTSPUR (*to Douglas*). Well said, my noble Scot: if speaking truth
In this fine age were not thought flattery,
Such attribution should the Douglas have,
As not a soldier of this season's stamp
Should go so general current through the world.
By God, I cannot flatter; do defy
The tongues of soothers; but a braver place
In my heart's love hath no man than yourself:
Nay, task me to my word; approve me, lord.

DOUGLAS. Thou art the king of honour:
No man so potent breathes upon the ground
But I will beard him.

HOTSPUR. Do so, and tis well.

MESSENGER (*entering*). These letters come from your father.

HOTSPUR. Letters from him! Why comes he not himself?

MESSENGER. He cannot come, my lord; he is grievous sick.

HOTSPUR. Zounds! how has he the leisure to be sick
In such a justling time? Who leads his power?
Under whose government come they along?

MESSENGER. His letters bear his mind, not I, my lord.

WORCESTER. I prithee, tell me, doth he keep his bed?

MESSENGER. He did, my lord, four days ere I set forth;
And at the time of my departure thence
He was much feared by his physicians.

WORCESTER. I would the state of time had first been whole
Ere he by sickness had been visited:
His health was never better worth than now.

HOTSPUR. Sick now! droop now! this sickness doth infect
The very life-blood of our enterprise;
Tis catching hither, even to our camp.
He writes me here, that inward sickness—
And that his friends by deputation could not
So soon be drawn, nor did he think it meet
To lay so dangerous and dear a trust
On any soul removed but on his own.
Yet doth he give us bold advertisement
That with our small conjunction we should on
To see how fortune is disposed to us;
For, as he writes, there is no quailing now,

Because the king is certainly possessed
Of all our purposes. What say you to it?

WORCESTER. I would your father had been here.
It will be thought
By some, that know not why he is away,
That wisdom, loyalty, and mere dislike
Of our proceedings kept the earl from hence:
And think how such an apprehension
May turn the tide of fearful faction
And breed a kind of question in our cause.
This absence of your father's draws a curtain
That shows the ignorant a kind of fear
Before not dreamt of.

HOTSPUR. You strain too far.
I rather of his absence make this use:
It lends a lustre and more great opinion,
A larger dare to our great enterprise,
Than if the earl were here; for men must think,
If we without his help can make a head
To push against a kingdom, with his help
We shall o'erturn it topsy-turvy down.
Yet all goes well, yet all our joints are whole.

DOUGLAS. As heart can think: there is not such a word
Spoke of in Scotland as this term of fear.

HOTSPUR. My cousin Vernon! welcome, by my soul.

VERNON (*entering*). Pray God my news be worth a welcome, lord.
The Earl of Westmoreland, seven thousand strong,
Is marching hitherwards; with him Prince John.

HOTSPUR. No harm: what more?

VERNON. And further, I have learned,
The king himself in person is set forth,
Or hitherwards intended speedily,
With strong and mighty preparation.

HOTSPUR. He shall be welcome too. Where is his son,
The nimble-footed madcap Prince of Wales,
And his comrades, that daffed the world aside,
And bid it pass?

VERNON. All furnished, all in arms,
As full of spirit as the month of May,
And gorgeous as the sun at midsummer;
Wanton as youthful goats, wild as young bulls.
I saw young Harry, with his beaver on,
His cuisses on his thighs, gallantly armed,
Rise from the ground like feathered Mercury,
And vaulted with such ease into his seat,
As if an angel dropped down from the clouds,

To turn and wind a fiery Pegasus
And witch the world with noble horsemanship.

HOTSPUR. No more, no more: worse than the sun in March,
This praise doth nourish agues. Let them come.
Come, let me taste my horse,
Who is to bear me like a thunderbolt
Against the bosom of the Prince of Wales:
Harry to Harry shall, hot horse to horse,
Meet and ne'er part till one drop down a corse.
O that Glendower were come!

VERNON. There is more news:
I learned in Worcester, as I rode along,
He cannot draw his power this fourteen days.

DOUGLAS. That's the worst tidings that I hear of yet.

WORCESTER. Ay, by my faith, that bears a frosty sound.

HOTSPUR. What may the king's whole battle reach unto?

VERNON. To thirty thousand.

HOTSPUR. Forty let it be:
My father and Glendower being both away,
The powers of us may serve so great a day.
Come, let us take a muster speedily:
Doomsday is near; die all, die merrily.

DOUGLAS. Talk not of dying: I am out of fear
Of death or death's hand for this one-half year.

Scene 2—A Public Road near Coventry

FALSTAFF. Bardolph, get thee before to Coventry; fill me a bottle of sack.

BARDOLPH. Will you give me money, captain?

FALSTAFF. Lay out, lay out. I'll answer the coinage. Bid my lieutenant Peto meet me at town's end.

BARDOLPH. I will, captain: farewell.

FALSTAFF. If I be not ashamed of my soldiers I am a soused gurnet. I have got, in exchange of a hundred and fifty soldiers, three hundred and odd pounds. I press me none but good householders, yeomen's sons; inquire me out contracted bachelors, such as had been asked twice on the banns. I pressed me none but such toasts-and-butter, with hearts no bigger than pins' heads, and they have bought out their services; and now my whole charge consists of ancients, corporals, lieutenants, gentlemen of companies, slaves as ragged as Lazarus, and such as indeed were never soldiers, but discarded unjust serving-men, younger sons to younger brothers, revolted tapsters and ostlers trade-fallen, the cankers of a calm world and a long peace, ten times more dishonourable ragged than an old faced ancient: and such have I, to fill up the rooms of them that have bought out their services, that you would think that I had a hundred and fifty tattered prodigals lately come from swine-keeping, from eating husks. A mad fellow met me on the way and told me I had unloaded all the gibbets and pressed the dead bodies. No eye hath seen such scarecrows. I'll not march through Coventry with them, that's flat: nay, and the villains march wide betwixt the legs, as if they had gyves on; for indeed I had the most of them out of prison. There's but a shirt and a half in all my company; and the half-shirt is two napkins tacked together and thrown over the shoulders like an herald's coat without sleeves; and the shirt, to say the truth, stolen from my host at Saint Alban's, or the red-nosed innkeeper of Daventry. But that's all one; they'll find linen enough on every hedge.

PRINCE (*entering with Westmoreland*). How now, blown Jack!

FALSTAFF. What, Hal! how now, mad wag! what dost thou in Warwickshire? My good Lord of Westmoreland, I cry you mercy: I thought your honour had already been at Shrewsbury.

WESTMORELAND. Faith, Sir John, tis more than time that I were there, and you too; but my powers are there already. The king, I can tell you, looks for us all: we must away all night.

FALSTAFF. Tut, never fear me: I am as vigilant as a cat to steal cream.

PRINCE. I think to steal cream indeed, for thy theft hath already made thee butter. But tell me, Jack, whose fellows are these that come after?

FALSTAFF. Mine, Hal, mine.

PRINCE. I did never see such pitiful rascals.

FALSTAFF. Tut, tut; good enough to toss; food for powder, food for powder; they'll fill a pit as well as better: tush, man, mortal men, mortal men.

WESTMORELAND. Ay, but, Sir John, methinks they are exceeding poor and bare, too beggarly.

FALSTAFF. Faith, for their poverty, I know not where they had that; and, for their bareness, I am sure they never learned that of me.

PRINCE. No, I'll be sworn. But, sirrah, make haste: Percy is already in the field.

FALSTAFF. What, is the king encamped?

WESTMORELAND. He is, Sir John: I fear we shall stay too long.

FALSTAFF. Well,
To the latter end of a fray and the beginning of a feast
Fits a dull fighter and a keen guest.

Scene 3—The Rebel Camp near Shrewsbury

HOTSPUR. We'll fight with him tonight.

WORCESTER. Good cousin, be advised; stir not tonight

VERNON. Do not, my lord.
DOUGLAS. You do not counsel well:
You speak it out of fear and cold heart.
VERNON. Do me no slander, Douglas: by my life,
And I dare well maintain it with my life,
If well-respected honour bid me on,
I hold as little counsel with weak fear
As you, my lord, or any Scot that this day lives:
Let it be seen tomorrow in the battle
Which of us fears.
HOTSPUR. Tonight, say I.
VERNON. Come, come, it may not be. I wonder much,
Being men of such great leading as you are,
That you foresee not what impediments
Drag back our expedition: certain horse
Of my cousin Vernon's are not yet come up:
Your uncle Worcester's horse came but today;
And now their pride and mettle is asleep,
Their courage with hard labour tame and dull,
That not a horse is half the half of himself.
HOTSPUR. So are the horses of the enemy
In general, journey-bated and brought low:
The better part of ours are full of rest.
WORCESTER. The number of the king exceedeth ours:
For God's sake, cousin, stay till all come in.
BLUNT (*entering*). I come with gracious offers from the king,
If you vouchsafe me hearing and respect.
HOTSPUR. Welcome, Sir Walter Blunt; and would to God
You were of our determination!
Some of us love you well; and even those some
Envy your great deservings and good name
Because you are not of our quality,
But stand against us like an enemy.
BLUNT. And God defend but still I should stand so,
So long as out of limit and true rule
You stand against anointed majesty.
But to my charge. The king hath sent to know
The nature of your griefs, and whereupon
You conjure from the breast of civil peace
Such bold hostility, teaching his duteous land
Audacious cruelty. If that the king
Have any way your good deserts forgot,
Which he confesseth to be manifold,
He bids you name your griefs; and with all speed
You shall have your desires with interest

And pardon absolute for yourself and these
Herein misled by your suggestion.

HOTSPUR. The king is kind; and well we know the king
Knows at what time to promise, when to pay.
My father and my uncle and myself
Did give him that same royalty he wears;
And when he was not six and twenty strong,
Sick in the world's regard, wretched and low,
A poor unminded outlaw sneaking home,
My father gave him welcome to the shore;
And when he heard him swear and vow to God
He came but to be Duke of Lancaster,
To sue his livery and beg his peace,
With tears of innocency and terms of zeal,
My father, in kind heart and pity moved,
Swore him assistance and performed it too.
Now when the lords and barons of the realm
Perceived Northumberland did lean to him,
The more and less came in with cap and knee;
Met him in boroughs, cities, villages,
Attended him on bridges, stood in lanes,
Laid gifts before him, proffered him their oaths,
Gave him their heirs, as pages followed him
Even at the heels in golden multitudes.
He presently, as greatness knows itself,
Steps me a little higher than his vow
Made to my father, while his blood was poor,
Upon the naked shore at Ravenspurgh;
And now, forsooth, takes on him to reform
Some certain edicts and some strait decrees
That lie too heavy on the Commonwealth,
Cries out upon abuses, seems to weep
Over his country's wrongs; and by this face,
This seeming brow of justice, did he win
The hearts of all that he did angle for.

BLUNT. Tut, I came not to hear this.

HOTSPUR. Then to the point.
In short time after, he deposed the king;
Soon after that deprivèd of his life;
And in the neck of that, tasked the whole State;
To make that worse, suffered his kinsman March,
Who is, if every owner were well placed,
Indeed his king, to be engaged in Wales,
There without ransom to lie forfeited;
Disgraced me in my happy victories,
Sought to entrap me by intelligence;

Rated mine uncle from the council-board;
In rage dismissed my father from the court;
Broke oath on oath, committed wrong on wrong.
And in conclusion drove us to seek out
This head of safety; and withal to pry
Into his title, the which we find
Too indirect for long continuance.

BLUNT. Shall I return this answer to the king?

HOTSPUR. Not so, Sir Walter: we'll withdraw awhile
Go to the king; and let there be impawned
Some surety for a safe return again,
And in the morning early shall my uncle
Bring him our purposes: and so farewell.

BLUNT. I would you would accept of grace and love.

HOTSPUR. And may be so we shall.

BLUNT. Pray God we do.

Scene 4—A Room in the Archbishop's Palace

The Archbishop of York is sending letters to friends who are committed to the rebellion. He has heard of the illness of Northumberland and the absence of Glendower and Mortimer, and fears that Hotspur will be defeated if he attacks the army advancing against him.

ACT 5

Scene 1—The King's Camp near Shrewsbury

Enter King, Worcester, Prince, and Falstaff.

KING. How now, my Lord of Worcester! tis not well
That you and I should meet upon such terms
As now we meet. You have deceived our trust,
And made us doff our easy robes of peace,
To crush our old limbs in ungentle steel:
This is not well, my lord, this is not well.
What say you to it? Will you again unknit
This churlish knot of all-abhorrèd war?
And more in that obedient orb again
Where you did give a fair and natural light,
And be no more an exhaled meteor,
A prodigy of fear and a portent
Of broachèd mischief to the unborn times?

WORCESTER. Hear me, my liege:
For mine own part, I could be well content
To entertain the lag-end of my life
With quiet hours; for I do protest,
I have not sought the day of this dislike.

KING. You have not sought it! How comes it, then?

FALSTAFF. Rebellion lay in his way, and he found it.

PRINCE. Peace, chewet, peace!

Worcester. It pleased your majesty to turn your looks
Of favour from myself and all our house;
And yet I must remember you, my lord,
We were the first and dearest of your friends.
For you my staff of office did I break
In Richard's time; and posted day and night
To meet you on the way, and kiss your hand,
When yet you were in place and in account
Nothing so strong and fortunate as I.
It was myself, my brother and his son,
That brought you home and boldly did outdare
The dangers of the time. You swore to us,
And you did swear that oath at Doncaster,
That you did nothing purpose 'gainst the State:
Nor claim no further than your new-fallen right,
The seat of Gaunt, dukedom of Lancaster:
To this we swore our aid. But in short space
It rained down fortune showering on your head;
And such a flood of greatness fell on you,
What with our help, what with the absent king,
What with the injuries of a wanton time,
The seeming sufferances that you had borne,
And the contrarious winds that held the king
So long in his unlucky Irish wars
That all in England did repute him dead:
And from this swarm of fair advantages
You took occasion to be quickly wooed
To gripe the general sway into your hand;
Forgot your oath to us at Doncaster;
And, being fed by us, you used us so
As that ungentle gull, the cuckoo's bird,
Useth the sparrow; did oppress our nest;
Grew by our feeding to so great a bulk
That even our love durst not come near your sight
For fear of swallowing; but with nimble wing
We were enforced, for safety sake, to fly
Out of your sight and raise this present head;
Whereby we stand opposèd by such means
As you yourself have forged against yourself
By unkind usage, dangerous countenance,
And violation of all faith and troth
Sworn to us in your younger enterprise.

King. These things indeed you have articulate,
Proclaimed at market-crosses, read in churches,
To face the garment of rebellion
With some fine colour that may please the eye
Of fickle changelings and poor discontents,

Which gape and rub the elbow at the news
Of hurly-burly innovation :
And never yet did insurrection want
Such water-colours to impaint his cause ;
Nor moody beggars, starving for a time
Of pellmell havoc and confusion.

PRINCE. In both your armies there is many a soul
Shall pay full dearly for this encounter,
If once they join in trial. Tell your nephew
The Prince of Wales doth join with all the world
In praise of Henry Percy.
I do not think a braver gentleman,
More active-valiant or more valiant-young,
More daring or more bold, is now alive
To grace this latter age with noble deeds.
For my part, I may speak it to my shame,
I have a truant been to chivalry ;
And so I hear he doth account me too ;
Yet this before my father's majesty :
I am content that he shall take the odds
Of his great name and estimation,
And will, to save the blood on either side,
Try fortune with him in a single fight.

KING. And, Prince of Wales, so dare we venture thee,
Albeit considerations infinite
Do make against it. No, good Worcester, no,
We love our people well ; even those we love
That are misled upon your cousin's part ;
And, will they take the offer of our grace,
Both he and they and you, yea, every man
Shall be my friend again and I'll be his :
So tell your cousin, and bring me word
What he will do : but if he will not yield
Rebuke and dread correction wait on us
And they shall do their office. So, be gone ;
We will not now be troubled with reply :
We offer fair ; take it advisedly.

PRINCE. It will not be accepted, on my life :
The Douglas and the Hotspur both together
Are confident against the world in arms.

KING. Hence, therefore, every leader to his charge ;
For, on their answer, will we set on them :
And God befriend us, as our cause is just !

All but the Prince of Wales and Falstaff leave

FALSTAFF. Hal, if thou see me down in the battle and bestride me, so ; tis a point of friendship.

PRINCE. Nothing but a colossus can do thee that friendship. Say thy prayers, and farewell.

FALSTAFF. I would 'twere bed-time, Hal, and all well.

PRINCE. Why, thou owest God a death.

FALSTAFF. Tis not due yet; I would be loth to pay him before his day. What need I be so forward with him that calls not on me? Well, tis no matter; honour pricks me on. Yea, but how if honour prick me off when I come on? How then? Can honour set to a leg? No. Or an arm? No. Or take away the grief of a wound? No. Honour hath no skill in surgery, then? No. What is honour? A word. What is in that word honour? What is that honour? Air. A trim reckoning! Who hath it? He that died o' Wednesday. Doth he feel it? No. Doth he hear it? No. Tis insensible, then. Yea, to the dead. But will it not live with the living? No. Why? Detraction will not suffer it. Therefore I'll none of it. Honour is a mere scutcheon; and so ends my catechism.

Scene 2—The Rebel Camp

WORCESTER (*to Vernon*). O, no, my nephew must not know
The liberal and kind offer of the king.

VERNON. Twere best he did.

WORCESTER. Then are we all undone.
It is not possible, it cannot be,
The king should keep his word in loving us;
He will suspect us still and find a time
To punish this offence in other faults:
Suspicion all our lives shall be stuck full of eyes;
For treason is but trusted like the fox,
Who, ne'er so tame, so cherished and locked up,
Will have a wild trick of his ancestors.
Look how we can, or sad or merrily,
Interpretation will misquote our looks,
And we shall feed like oxen at a stall,
The better cherished, still the nearer death.
My nephew's trespass may be well forgot;
It hath the excuse of youth and heat of blood,
And an adopted name of privilege,
A hare-brained Hotspur, governed by a spleen:
All his offences live upon my head
And on his father's; we did train him on,
And, his corruption being ta'en from us,
We, as the spring of all, shall pay for all.
Therefore, good cousin, let not Harry know,
In any case, the offer of the king.

VERNON. Deliver what you will; I'll say tis so.
Here comes your cousin.

HOTSPUR. Uncle, what news?

WORCESTER. There is no seeming mercy in the king.

HOTSPUR. Did you beg any? God forbid!

WORCESTER. I told him gently of our grievances,
Of his oath-breaking; which he mended thus,
By now forswearing that he is forsworn:
He calls us rebels, traitors; and will scourge
With haughty arms this hateful name in us.
The Prince of Wales stepped forth before the king,
And, nephew, challenged you to single fight.

HOTSPUR. O, would the quarrel lay upon our heads,
And that no man might draw short breath today
But I and Harry Monmouth! Tell me, tell me,
How showed his tasking? seemed it in contempt?

VERNON. No, by my soul; I never in my life
Did hear a challenge urged more modestly,
Unless a brother should a brother dare
To gentle exercise and proof of arms.
He gave you all the duties of a man;
Trimmed up your praises with a princely tongue,
Spoke your deservings like a chronicle,
Making you ever better than his praise,
And (which became him like a prince indeed)
He made a blushing cital of himself;
And chid his truant youth with such a grace
As if he mastered there a double spirit
Of teaching and of learning instantly.
There did he pause: but let me tell the world,
If he outlive the envy of this day,
England did never owe so sweet a hope,
So much mis*con*strued in his wantonness.

HOTSPUR. Cousin, I think thou art enamoured
On his follies: never did I hear
Of any prince so wild a libertine.
But be he as he will, yet once ere night
I will embrace him with a soldier's arm,
That he shall shrink under my courtesy.
Arm, arm with speed: and, fellows, soldiers, friends,
Better consider what you have to do
Than I, that have not well the gift of tongue,
Can lift your blood up with persuasion.

A MESSENGER. My lord, here are letters for you.

HOTSPUR. I cannot read them now.
O gentlemen, the time of life is short!
To spend that shortness basely were too long,
If life did ride upon a dial's point,

Still ending at the arrival of an hour.
An if we live, we live to tread on kings;
If die, brave death, when princes die with us!
Now, for our consciences, the arms are fair,
When the intent of bearing them is just.

MESSENGER (*running*). My lord, prepare; the king comes on apace.

HOTSPUR. I thank him that he cuts me from my tale,
For I profess not talking; only this:
Let each man do his best: and here draw I
A sword whose temper I intend to stain
With the best blood that I can meet withal
In the adventure of this perilous day.
Now, Esperance! Percy! and set on.
Sound all the lofty instruments of war,
And by that music let us all embrace;
For, heaven to earth, some of us never shall
A second time do such a courtesy.

Scene 3—A Plain between the Two Camps

Douglas and Sir Walter Blunt meet

BLUNT. What is thy name, that in the battle thus
Thou crossest me? What honour dost thou seek
Upon my head?

DOUGLAS. Know then, my name is Douglas;
And I do haunt thee in the battle thus
Because some tell me that thou art a king.

BLUNT (*deceiving him*). They tell thee true.

DOUGLAS. The Lord of Stafford dear today hath bought
Thy likeness, for instead of thee, King Harry,
This sword hath ended him: so shall it thee,
Unless thou yield thee as my prisoner.

BLUNT. I was not born a yielder, thou proud Scot;
And thou shalt find a king that will revenge
Lord Stafford's death. (*They fight, Blunt falls, and Hotspur appears*)

HOTSPUR. O Douglas, hadst thou fought at Holmedon thus,
I never had triumphed upon a Scot.

DOUGLAS. All's done, all's won; here breathless lies the king.

HOTSPUR. Where?

DOUGLAS. Here.

HOTSPUR. This, Douglas? no: I know this face full well:
A gallant knight he was, his name was Blunt;
Semblably furnished like the king himself.

DOUGLAS. A fool go with thy soul, whither it goes:
A borrowed title hast thou bought too dear:
Why didst thou tell me that thou wert a king?

HOTSPUR. The king hath many marching in his coats.

DOUGLAS. Now, by my sword, I will kill all his coats;
I'll murder all his wardrobe, piece by piece,
Until I meet the king.

HOTSPUR. Up, and away!
Our soldiers stand full fairly for the day.

FALSTAFF (*appearing alone*). Though I could scape shot-free at London, I fear the shot here; here's no scoring but upon the pate. I am as hot as molten lead, and as heavy too: God keep lead out of me! I need no more weight. I have led my ragamuffins where they are peppered: there's not three of my hundred and fifty left alive; and they are for the town's end, to beg during life. But who comes here?

PRINCE. What, stand'st thou idle here? lend me thy sword:
Many a nobleman lies stark and stiff
Under the hoofs of vaunting enemies,
Whose deaths are yet unrevenged: I prithee, lend me thy sword.

FALSTAFF. O Hal, I prithee, give me leave to breathe awhile. Turk Gregory never did such deeds in arms as I have done this day. I have paid Percy, I have made him sure.

PRINCE. He is, indeed; and living to kill thee. I prithee, lend me thy sword.

FALSTAFF. Nay, before God, Hal, if Percy be alive, thou gett'st not my sword; but take my pistol, if thou wilt.

PRINCE. Give it me: what, is it in the case?

FALSTAFF. Ay, Hal; tis hot, tis hot; there's that will sack a city. (*The Prince draws it out, and finds it to be a bottle of sack*)

PRINCE. What, is it a time to jest and dally now?

He throws the bottle at him and goes

Scene 4—The Field

KING. I prithee, Harry, withdraw thyself; thou bleed'st too much.
My Lord of Westmoreland, lead him to his tent.

WESTMORELAND. Come, my lord, I'll lead you to your tent.

PRINCE. Lead me, my lord? I do not need your help:
And God forbid a shallow scratch should drive
The Prince of Wales from such a field as this,
Where stained nobility lies trodden on,
And rebels' arms triumph in massacres!

LANCASTER. We breathe too long: come, cousin Westmoreland,
Our duty this way lies; for God's sake, come.

PRINCE (*watching Lancaster*). Thou hast deceived me, Lancaster;
I did not think thee lord of such a spirit:
Before, I loved thee as a brother, John;
But now, I do respect thee as my soul.

KING. I saw him hold Lord Percy at the point
With lustier maintenance than I did look for
Of such an ungrown warrior.

PRINCE. O, this boy
Lends mettle to us all! (*Douglas appears as the Prince goes*)

DOUGLAS. Another king! they grow like Hydra's heads;
I am the Douglas, fatal to all those
That wear those colours on them: what art thou,
That counterfeit'st the person of a king?

KING. The king himself; who, Douglas, grieves at heart
So many of his shadows thou hast met
And not the very king. I have two boys
Seek Percy and thyself about the field:
But, seeing thou fall'st on me so luckily,
I will assay thee: so, defend thyself.

DOUGLAS. I fear thou art another counterfeit;
And yet, in faith, thou bear'st thee like a king:
But mine I am sure thou art, whoe'er thou be,
And thus I win thee.

They fight, and the Prince returns to find the King in danger

PRINCE. Hold up thy head, vile Scot, or thou art like
Never to hold it up again! the spirits
Of valiant Shirley, Stafford, Blunt, are in my arms:
It is the Prince of Wales that threatens thee;
Who never promiseth but he means to pay.

They fight, and Douglas flies

KING (*to Prince*). Stay, and breathe awhile:
Thou hast redeemed thy lost opinion,
And showed thou mak'st some tender of my life,
In this fair rescue thou hast brought to me.

PRINCE. O God! they did me too much injury
That ever said I hearkened for your death.
If it were so, I might have let alone
The insulting hand of Douglas over you,
Which would have been as speedy in your end
As all the poisonous potions in the world
And saved the treacherous labour of your son.

The King goes and Hotspur appears

HOTSPUR. If I mistake not, thou art Harry Monmouth.

PRINCE. Thou speak'st as if I would deny my name.

HOTSPUR. My name is Harry Percy.

PRINCE. Why, then I see
A very valiant rebel of the name.
I am the Prince of Wales; and think not, Percy,
To share with me in glory any more:

Two stars keep not their motion in one sphere;
Nor can one England brook a double reign,
Of Harry Percy and the Prince of Wales.

HOTSPUR. Nor shall it, Harry; for the hour is come
To end the one of us; and would to God
Thy name in arms were now as great as mine!

PRINCE. I'll make it greater ere I part from thee;
And all the budding honours on thy crest
I'll crop, to make a garland for my head.

HOTSPUR. I can no longer brook thy vanities.

As they fight Falstaff enters, followed by Douglas. Douglas attacks Falstaff, who falls as dead. Hotspur is wounded, and falls also.

HOTSPUR (*dying*). O, Harry, thou hast robbed me of my youth!
I better brook the loss of brittle life
Than those proud titles thou hast won of me;
They wound my thoughts worse than thy sword my flesh;
But thought's the slave of life, and life time's fool;
And time, that takes survey of all the world,
Must have a stop. O, I could prophesy,
But that the earthy and cold hand of death
Lies on my tongue: no, Percy, thou art dust,
And food for— (*He dies*)

PRINCE. For worms, brave Percy: fare thee well, great heart!
Ill-weaved ambition, how much art thou shrunk!
When that this body did contain a spirit,
A kingdom for it was too small a bound;
But now two paces of the vilest earth
Is room enough: this earth that bears thee dead
Bears not alive so stout a gentleman.
If thou wert sensible of courtesy
I should not make so dear a show of zeal:
But let my favours hide thy mangled face,
And, even in thy behalf, I'll thank myself
For doing these fair rites of tenderness.
Adieu, and take thy praise with thee to heaven!
Thy ignominy sleep with thee in the grave,
But not remembered in thy epitaph!

The Prince sees Falstaff on the ground

What, old acquaintance! could not all this flesh
Keep in a little life? Poor Jack, farewell!
I could have better spared a better man:
O, I should have a heavy miss of thee,
If I were much in love with vanity!

The Prince having gone, Falstaff rises

FALSTAFF. The better part of valour is discretion; in the which better part I have saved my life. Zounds, I am afraid of this gunpowder Percy, though he be dead: how, if he should counterfeit too, and rise? by my faith, I am afraid he would prove the better counterfeit. Therefore I'll make him sure; yea, and I'll swear I killed him. Why may not he rise as well as I? Nothing confutes me but eyes, and nobody sees me. Therefore, sirrah (*stabbing him*), with a new wound in your thigh come you along with me.

He takes up Hotspur on his back, as the Prince and Lord John enter

PRINCE. Come, brother John; full bravely hast thou fleshed
Thy maiden sword.

LANCASTER. But, soft! whom have we here?
Did you not tell me this fat man was dead?

PRINCE. I did; I saw him dead,
Breathless and bleeding on the ground.
Art thou alive? or is it fantasy
That plays upon our eyesight? I prithee, speak;
We will not trust our eyes without our ears:
Thou art not what thou seem'st.

FALSTAFF. No, that's certain; I am not a double man: but if I be not Jack Falstaff then am I a Jack. There is Percy (*throwing the body down*); if your father will do me any honour, so; if not, let him kill the next Percy himself. I look to be either earl or duke, I can assure you.

PRINCE. Why, Percy I killed myself and saw thee dead.

FALSTAFF. Didst thou? Lord, Lord, how this world is given to lying! I grant you I was down and out of breath, and so was he: but we rose both at an instant and fought a long hour by Shrewsbury clock. If I may be believed, so; if not, let them that should reward valour bear the sin upon their own heads. I'll take it upon my death I gave him this wound in the thigh: if the man were alive and would deny it, zounds, I would make him eat a piece of my sword.

LANCASTER. This is the strangest tale that ever I heard.

PRINCE. This is the strangest fellow, brother John.
Come, bring your luggage nobly on your back:
For my part, if a lie may do thee grace,
I'll gild it with the happiest terms I have.
The trumpet sounds retreat; the day is ours.
Come, brother, let us to the highest of the field,
To see what friends are living, who are dead.

FALSTAFF. I'll follow, as they say, for reward. He that rewards me, God reward him! If I do grow great I'll grow less; for I'll purge, and leave sack, and live cleanly as a nobleman should do.

Scene 5—The Field

The trumpets sound. Enter King, Prince, Lancaster, and Westmoreland, with Worcester and Vernon as prisoners

KING. Thus ever did rebellion find rebuke.

Ill-spirited Worcester! did not we send grace,
Pardon, and terms of love to all of you?
And wouldst thou turn our offers contrary?
Misuse the tenour of thy kinsman's trust?
Three knights upon our party slain today,
A noble earl, and many a creature else
Had been alive this hour
If like a Christian thou hadst truly borne
Betwixt our armies true intelligence.

WORCESTER. What I have done my safety urged me to;
And I embrace this fortune patiently,
Since not to be avoided it falls on me.

KING. Bear Worcester to the death and Vernon too:
Other offenders we will pause upon. How goes the field?

PRINCE. The noble Scot Lord Douglas, when he saw
The fortune of the day quite turned from him,
The noble Percy slain, and all his men
Upon the foot of fear, fled with the rest;
And, falling from a hill, he was so bruised
That the pursuers took him. At my tent
The Douglas is; and I beseech your grace
I may dispose of him.

KING. With all my heart.

PRINCE. Then, brother John of Lancaster, to you
This honourable bounty shall belong:
Go to the Douglas, and deliver him
Up to his pleasure, ransomless and free:
His valour shown upon our crests today
Hath taught us how to cherish such high deeds
Even in the bosom of our adversaries.

LANCASTER. I thank your grace for this high courtesy,
Which I shall give away immediately.

KING. Then this remains, that we divide our power.
You, son John, and my cousin Westmoreland,
Towards York shall bend you with your dearest speed,
To meet Northumberland and the prelate Scroop,
Who, as we hear, are busily in arms:
Myself and you, son Harry, will towards Wales,
To fight with Glendower and the Earl of March.
Rebellion in this land shall lose his sway,
Meeting the check of such another day:
And since this bus*i*ness so fair is done,
Let us not leave till all our own be won.

The Story of

The Second Part of Henry the Fourth

We might almost call these two plays the Decline and Fall of Falstaff; or the Fall and Rise of the Prince of Wales.

This is a play of great humour and great pathos. We cannot help being moved by the thought of the dying king, passing out of the world uneasily, still remembering the way by which he reached the throne, still anxious for the son who is to wear his crown.

But it is Falstaff's play. Here is the supreme humorous creation of Shakespeare, perhaps the supreme comical figure in the literature of the world. We feel at times that we should not laugh at Falstaff, but we must. We have to forget that he is a thorough-paced rascal, a vainglorious old humbug, and allow ourselves to be carried away by his geniality and brazen cleverness.

The Falstaff scenes reach the topmost heights of the comedy based on human character. Look at that merry scene, in Part One, in which the old man and the young Prince play in turn the part of the reproachful king: who but Shakespeare could have written that? Look here at that scene in which Mr. Justice Shallow comes. Perhaps it is true that Shakespeare was pillorying Sir Thomas Lucy for punishing him for stealing a deer; if so he has made the lord of Charlecote the butt of the world's laughter for all time. How inimitable is the scene when Justice Shallow, trembling with age, calls on Falstaff to witness to his tales of a boisterous youth, while Falstaff listens half-wearily, yet delighted that here is a goose he will presently pluck.

It is a tribute to the wonderful power of Shakespeare that even while Falstaff is playing his meanest part, using his position as a recruiting officer solely for his own advantage, we are bound to laugh at him. His blustering is irresistible. He is the completest humbug ever seen on the stage. We see in him how Shakespeare got his effects. He brings his ideal king from an atmosphere like this; he leads us from the low life of Falstaff in his tavern to the very height of kingly pride.

And then he does a wonderful thing. The King is dead: long live the King! Ancient Pistol hurries down to Gloucestershire. Falstaff sees himself the greatest man in England, the power behind the throne. Shakespeare sets him down, in one of his tensest scenes, at the gate of Westminster Abbey when the King comes by. We may have forgiven Falstaff or we may not. We may think this corrupter of youth deserved no pity or we may think he had some virtue left to save him. We may think a rogue deserves whatever punishment he gets, but that Falstaff did not deserve it from Henry the Fifth. We may think what we will, but as long as we have a heart to feel we cannot read without emotion the scene outside Westminster when Henry the Fifth was crowned.

THE PLAYERS

King Henry the Fourth, in ill-health and anticipating death.

Henry, Prince of Wales. He reforms and becomes king.

Thomas, Duke of Clarence, son of Henry the Fourth.

John, Duke of Lancaster, son of Henry the Fourth.

Humphrey, Duke of Gloucester, son of Henry the Fourth.

Earl of Warwick, a courtier in attendance on the King.

Earl of Westmoreland, on active service with Lancaster, and with him seizes the rebel leaders by an act of treachery.

Gower, Harcourt, and Blunt, officers bringing news.

Earl of Northumberland, old and powerful; he starts the rebellion and then flees to Scotland, but is overpowered.

Archbishop of York (Scroop), rebel leader.

Lord Mowbray, one of the rebel leaders.

Lords Bardolph and Hastings, lords against the King.

Sir John Colevile, a rebel who surrenders to Falstaff.

Lord Chief Justice, who imprisoned Prince Henry for contempt.

Travers and Morton, bringing messages to Northumberland.

Sir John Falstaff, the Prince's graceless crony in a military rôle.

Pistol, a swaggering bully and braggart, but a coward.

Bardolph and Peto, associates of Falstaff.

Poins, companion of the Prince of Wales.

Shallow, a country justice, old and muddle-headed, an easy prey for Falstaff.

Silence, another country justice, an echo of Shallow.

Davy, Shallow's useful all-round servant.

Mouldy, Shadow, Wart, Feeble, Bullcalf, countrymen examined as recruits by Falstaff at Shallow's house.

Fang and Snare, sheriff's officers.

Lady Northumberland, opposed to the rebellion.

Lady Percy, wife of Northumberland's dead son Hotspur.

Mistress Quickly, landlady of the Eastcheap tavern.

Doll Tearsheet, a friend of Dame Quickly.

Lords, servants, a page, a porter, drawers, beadles.

SCENES--London, Northumberland, Gloucestershire, and Yorkshire.

Second Part of Henry the Fourth

ACT 1

Scene 1—Before Northumberland's Castle at Warkworth

After a prologue in which Rumour (personified) speaks of wild stories spread throughout England of the defeat of Henry by his northern enemies, Scene One shows Northumberland anxiously awaiting news of his son Henry Hotspur's encounter with the King and his sons at Shrewsbury. First Lord Bardolph reports victory, but close at his heels comes tidings that Hotspur is slain and Douglas captured, and that Worcester, the leader of the rebellion, is also a prisoner. Old Northumberland, braced by disaster, agrees to continue resistance.

Scene 2—A Street in London

Here we meet Falstaff in a state of prosperity, accompanied by a page given to him by Prince Henry, bearing his sword and buckler.

FALSTAFF. Men of all sorts take a pride to gird at me. The brain of this foolish-compounded clay, Man, is not able to invent anything that tends to laughter more than I invent or is invented on me. I am not only witty in myself, but the cause that wit is in other men. I do here walk before thee like a sow that hath overwhelmed all her litter but one. If the prince put thee into my service for any other reason than to set me off, why then I have no judgment. Thou mandrake, thou art fitter to be worn in my cap than to wait at my heels. What said Master Dombledon about the satin for my short cloak and my slops ?

PAGE. He said, sir, you should procure him better assurance than Bardolph : he would not take his bond and yours ; he liked not the security.

FALSTAFF. A rascally knave, to bear a gentleman in hand and then stand upon security ! Where's Bardolph ?

PAGE. He's gone into Smithfield to buy your worship a horse. Sir, here comes the nobleman that committed the prince for striking him about Bardolph.

FALSTAFF. Wait close ; I will not see him. (*Enter Lord Chief Justice*)

LORD CHIEF JUSTICE. What's he that goes there ?

SERVANT. Falstaff, an't please your lordship.

LORD CHIEF JUSTICE. He that was in question for the robbery ?

SERVANT. He, my lord : but he hath since done good service at

Shrewsbury; and, as I hear, is now going with some charge to the Lord John of Lancaster.

LORD CHIEF JUSTICE. What, to York? Call him back again.

SERVANT. Sir John Falstaff!

FALSTAFF. Boy, tell him I am deaf.

PAGE. You must speak louder; my master is deaf.

LORD CHIEF JUSTICE. I am sure he is, to the hearing of anything good. Go, pluck him by the elbow; I must speak with him.

SERVANT. Sir John!

FALSTAFF. What! a young knave, and begging! Is there not wars? Is there not employment? Doth not the king lack subjects? Do not the rebels need soldiers? Though it be a shame to be on any side but one, it is worse shame to beg than to be on the worst side, were it worse than the name of rebellion can tell how to make it.

SERVANT. You mistake me, sir. My lord would speak with you.

LORD CHIEF JUSTICE. Sir John Falstaff, a word with you.

FALSTAFF. My good lord! God give your lordship good time of day. I am glad to see your lordship abroad: I heard say your lordship was sick: I hope your lordship goes abroad by advice. I most humbly beseech your lordship to have a reverent care of your health.

LORD CHIEF JUSTICE. Sir John, I sent for you before your expedition to Shrewsbury.

FALSTAFF. An't please your lordship, I hear his majesty is returned with some discomfort from Wales.

LORD CHIEF JUSTICE. I talk not of his majesty: you would not come when I sent for you. There were matters against you for your life, to come speak with me.

FALSTAFF. As I was then advised, I did not come.

LORD CHIEF JUSTICE. Well, the truth is, Sir John, you live in great infamy.

FALSTAFF. He that buckles him in my belt cannot live in less.

LORD CHIEF JUSTICE. Your means are very slender, and your waste is great.

FALSTAFF. I would it were otherwise; I would my means were greater and my waist slenderer.

LORD CHIEF JUSTICE. You have misled the youthful prince.

FALSTAFF. The young prince hath misled me.

LORD CHIEF JUSTICE. Well, I am loth to gall a new-healed wound: your day's service at Shrewsbury hath a little gilded over your night's exploit on Gadshill: you may thank the unquiet time for your quiet o'er-posting that action. But, since all is well, keep it so: wake not a sleeping wolf. There is not a white hair on your face but should have his effect of gravity. You follow the young prince up and down, like his ill angel.

FALSTAFF. Not so, my lord. Virtue is of so little regard in these costermonger times that true valour is turned bear-herd. You that are old consider not the capacities of us that are young.

LORD CHIEF JUSTICE. Do you set down your name in the scroll of youth, that are written down old with all the characters of age? Have you not a moist eye? a dry hand? a yellow cheek? a white beard? Is not your voice broken? your wind short? your chin double? your wit single? and every part about you blasted with antiquity? And will you yet call yourself young? Fie, fie, fie, Sir John!

FALSTAFF. To approve my youth further, I will not: the truth is, I am only old in judgment and understanding. For the box of the ear that the prince gave you, he gave it like a rude prince, and you took it like a sensible lord. I have checked him for it, and the young lion repents; marry, not in ashes and sackcloth, but in new silk and old sack.

LORD CHIEF JUSTICE. Well, God send the prince a better companion!

FALSTAFF. God send the companion a better prince! I cannot rid my hands of him.

LORD CHIEF JUSTICE. Well, the king hath severed you and Prince Harry: I hear you are going with Lord John of Lancaster against the Archbishop and the Earl of Northumberland.

FALSTAFF. But look you pray, all you that kiss my lady Peace at home, that our armies join not in a hot day, for I take but two shirts out with me, and I mean not to sweat extraordinary. There is not a dangerous action can peep out his head but I am thrust upon it. Well, I cannot last ever: but it was always yet the trick of our English nation, if they have a good thing, to make it too common. If ye will needs say I am an old man, you should give me rest. I would to God my name were not so terrible to the enemy as it is; I were better to be eaten to death with a rust than to be scoured to nothing with perpetual motion.

LORD CHIEF JUSTICE. Well, be honest, be honest; and God bless your expedition!

FALSTAFF. Will your lordship lend me a thousand pound to furnish me forth?

LORD CHIEF JUSTICE. Not a penny, not a penny; you are too impatient to bear crosses. Fare you well: commend me to my cousin Westmoreland.

Scene 3—The Archbishop's Palace

The Archbishop of York is now in consultation with certain lords. Lord Bardolph holds that they should not advance without Northumberland's active support. Hastings thinks they are strong enough to succeed, and the Archbishop agrees, so the rebel forces prepare for battle.

ACT 2

Scene 1—A London Street

Here Falstaff is on the point of being arrested in the street for debt, on behalf of Hostess Quickly, of the Eastcheap tavern he frequents. The Lord Chief Justice, passing by, advises Falstaff to pay, but Falstaff talks the angry landlady round and induces her to lend him more money.

Scene 2—A London Street

Scene Two gives a conversation in a London street between Prince Henry and his favourite attendant in his wanderings, Ned Poins. The Prince is tired of the life he is leading. He feels it is unseemly that he should be in questionable company while his father is ill; and Poins tells him he wonders that he should be so engrossed with Falstaff. Yet they agree to go to the Eastcheap tavern disguised as drawers, or tapmen, and see Falstaff enjoying himself there when he thinks he is alone.

Scene 3—Before Northumberland's Castle

Lady Northumberland and Lady Percy (Hotspur's widow) discuss the prospects of the rebel rising. Northumberland thinks his honour is pledged and that he must go forward. Lady Percy reminds him that he broke his word in not supporting her husband, and asks why he should hold his honour more dearly for others than for his own son. His wife urges him to flee to Scotland, and this advice he decides to take.

Scene 4—Hostess Quickly's Tavern in Eastcheap

Falstaff and his cronies are supping, with much drink and noise, when the Prince and Poins enter disguised, and hear Falstaff talking of them to one of his queer guests, Doll Tearsheet.

DOLL. Sirrah, what humour is the Prince of?

FALSTAFF. A good shallow young fellow. A' would have made a good pantler, a' would have chipped bread well.

DOLL. They say Poins has a good wit.

FALSTAFF. He a good wit! hang him, baboon! His wit is as thick as Tewkesbury mustard.

DOLL. Why does the Prince love him so then?

FALSTAFF. Because their legs are both of a bigness, and a' plays at quoits well, swears with a good grace, and has such other gambol faculties as show a weak mind and an able body, for the which the prince admits him. For the prince himself is such another—the weight of a hair will turn the scales between their avoirdupois.

Under this provocation the Prince, who is still unrecognised, replies

PRINCE. Why, thou globe of sinful continents, what a life dost thou lead!

FALSTAFF. A better than thou; I am a gentleman; thou art a drawer.

PRINCE. Very true, sir; and I come to draw you out by the ears.

QUICKLY (*recognising the Prince*). O, the Lord preserve thy good grace! welcome to London. Now the Lord bless that sweet face of thine! Are you come from Wales?

PRINCE (*to Falstaff*). You candle-mine, you, how vilely did you speak of me even now!

FALSTAFF. Didst thou hear me?

PRINCE. Yea, and you knew me, as you did when you ran away by Gadshill. You knew I was at your back, and spoke it on purpose to try my patience.

FALSTAFF. No, no, no; not so; I did not think thou wast within hearing.

PRINCE. I shall drive you then to confess the wilful abuse; and then I know how to handle you.

FALSTAFF. No abuse, Hal.

POINS. No abuse?

FALSTAFF. No abuse, Ned, i' the world; honest Ned, none. No abuse, Hal; none; no, faith, boys, none. (*Knocking heard without*)

QUICKLY. Who knocks so loud? Look to the door there, Francis.

PRINCE (*to Peto, entering*). How now? What news?

PETO. The king, your father, is at Westminster;
And there are twenty weak and wearied posts
Come from the north: and, as I came along,
I met and overtook a dozen captains,
Bare-headed, sweating, knocking at the taverns,
And asking every one for Sir John Falstaff.

PRINCE. By heaven, Poins, I feel me much to blame,
So idly to profane the precious time,
When tempest of commotion, like the south,
Borne with black vapour, doth begin to melt
And drop upon our bare unarmèd heads.
Give me my sword and cloak. Falstaff, Good-night.

ACT 3

Scene 1—Night in the Palace at Westminster

KING. Go call the Earls of Surrey and of Warwick;
But, ere they come, bid them o'er-read these letters,
And well consider of them: make good speed.
How many thousand of my poorest subjects
Are at this hour asleep! O sleep, O gentle sleep,
Nature's soft nurse, how have I frighted thee,
That thou no more wilt weigh my eyelids down
And steep my senses in forgetfulness?
Why rather, sleep, liest thou in smoky cribs,
Upon uneasy pallets stretching thee,
And hushed with buzzing night-flies to thy slumber,
Than in the perfumed chambers of the great,

Under the canopies of costly state,
And lulled with sound of sweetest melody?
O thou dull god, why liest thou with the vile
In loathsome beds, and leavest the kingly couch
A watch-case or a common 'larum-bell?
Wilt thou upon the high and giddy mast
Seal up the ship-boy's eyes, and rock his brains
In cradle of the rude imperious surge,
And in the visitation of the winds,
Who take the ruffian billows by the top,
Curling their monstrous heads and hanging them
With deafening clamour in the slippery clouds,
That, with the hurly, death itself awakes?
Canst thou, O partial sleep, give thy repose
To the wet sea-boy in an hour so rude,
And in the calmest and most stillest night,
With all appliances and means to boot,
Deny it to a king? Then happy low, lie down!
Uneasy lies the head that wears a crown.

WARWICK (*entering*). Many Good-morrows to your majesty!

KING. Good-morrow to you all, my lords.
Have you read o'er the letters that I sent you?

WARWICK. We have, my liege.

KING. Then you perceive the body of our kingdom,
How foul it is; what rank diseases grow,
And with what danger, near the heart of it.

WARWICK. It is but as a body yet distempered,
Which to his former strength may be restored
With good advice and little medicine:
My Lord Northumberland will soon be cooled.

KING. O God! that one might read the book of fate,
And see the revolution of the times
Make mountains level, and the continent,
Weary of solid firmness, melt itself
Into the sea! O, if this were seen,
The happiest youth, viewing his progress through,
What perils past, what crosses to ensue,
Would shut the book, and sit him down and die.
Tis not ten years gone
Since Richard and Northumberland, great friends,
Did feast together, and in two years after
Were they at wars: it is but eight years since
This Percy was the man nearest my soul,
Who like a brother toiled in my affairs,
And laid his love and life under my foot,
Yea, for my sake, even to the eyes of Richard

Gave him defiance. But which of you was by
When Richard, with his eye brimful of tears,
Then checked and rated by Northumberland,
Did speak these words, now proved a prophecy?
Northumberland, thou ladder by the which
My cousin Bolingbroke ascends my throne;
Though then, God knows, I had no such intent,
But that necessity so bowed the State
That I and greatness were compelled to kiss:
The time shall come (thus did he follow it)
The time will come that foul sin, gathering head,
Shall break into corruption: so went on,
Foretelling this same time's condition
And the division of our amity.

WARWICK. There is a history in all men's lives,
Figuring the nature of the times deceased;
The which observed, a man may prophesy,
With a near aim, of the main chance of things
As yet not come to life.

KING. They say the bishop and Northumberland
Are fifty thousand strong.

WARWICK. It cannot be, my lord;
Rumour doth double, like the voice and echo,
The numbers of the feared. Please it your grace
To go to bed. Upon my soul, my lord,
The powers that you already have sent forth
Shall bring this prize in very easily.
To comfort you the more, I have received
A certain instance that Glendower is dead.
Your majesty hath been this fortnight ill,
And these unseasoned hours perforce must add
Unto your sickness.

KING. I will take your counsel:
And were these inward wars once out of hand,
We would, dear lords, unto the Holy Land.

Scene 2—Justice Shallow's House in Gloucestershire

SHALLOW. Come on, come on, come on, sir; give me your hand, sir, give me your hand, sir: an early stirrer, by the rood! And how doth my good cousin Silence?

SILENCE. Good-morrow, good cousin Shallow.

SHALLOW. I dare say my cousin William is become a good scholar: he is at Oxford still, is he not?

SILENCE. Indeed, sir, to my cost.

SHALLOW. A' must, then, to the Inns o' Court shortly. I was once of Clement's Inn, where I think they will talk of mad Shallow yet.

SILENCE. You were called *Lusty Shallow* then, cousin.

SHALLOW. By the mass, I was called anything; and I would have done anything indeed too, and roundly too. There was I, and little John Doit of Staffordshire, and black George Barnes, and Francis Pickbone, and Will Squele, a Cotswold man; you had not four such swinge-bucklers in all the Inns o' Court again. Then was Jack Falstaff, now Sir John, a boy, and page to Thomas Mowbray, Duke of Norfolk.

SILENCE. This Sir John, cousin, that comes hither anon about soldiers?

SHALLOW. The same Sir John, the very same. I saw him break Skogan's head at the court-gate, when a' was a crack not thus high; and the very same day did I fight with one Sampson Stockfish, a fruiterer, behind Gray's Inn. The mad days that I have spent! and to see how many of my old acquaintance are dead!

SILENCE. We shall all follow, cousin.

SHALLOW. Certain, tis certain; very sure, very sure: death, as the Psalmist saith, is certain to all; all shall die. How a good yoke of bullocks at Stamford fair?

SILENCE. By my troth, I was not there.

SHALLOW. Death is certain. Is old Double of your town living yet?

SILENCE. Dead, sir.

SHALLOW. Dead! a' drew a good bow; and dead! a' shot a fine shoot: John a Gaunt loved him well, and betted much money on his head. Dead! a' would have clapped i' the clout at twelve score. How a score of ewes now?

SILENCE. Thereafter as they be: a score of good ewes may be worth ten pounds.

SHALLOW. And is old Double dead?

SILENCE. Here come two of Sir John Falstaff's men, as I think.

BARDOLPH. Good-morrow, honest gentlemen: I beseech you, which is Justice Shallow?

SHALLOW. I am Robert Shallow, sir; a poor esquire of this county, and one of the king's justices of the peace: what is your good pleasure with me?

BARDOLPH. My captain, sir, commends him to you; my captain, Sir John Falstaff, a tall gentleman, by heaven, and a most gallant leader.

SHALLOW. He greets me well, sir. I knew him a good backsword man. How doth the good knight? Look, here comes good Sir John. Give me your worship's good hand: by my troth, you like well, and bear your years very well: welcome, good Sir John.

FALSTAFF. I am glad to see you well, good Master Robert Shallow: Master Surecard, as I think?

SHALLOW. No, Sir John; it is my cousin Silence, in commission with me.

FALSTAFF. Good Master Silence, it well befits you should be of the peace. Fie! this is hot weather, gentlemen. Have you provided me here half a dozen sufficient men?

SHALLOW. Marry, have we, sir. Will you sit?

FALSTAFF. Let me see them, I beseech you.

SHALLOW. Where's the roll? where's the roll? Let me see, let me see. So, so, so, so: yea, marry, sir: Ralph Mouldy! Let them appear as I call; let them do so. Let me see; where is Mouldy?

MOULDY. Here, an't please you.

SHALLOW. What think you, Sir John? a good-limbed fellow; young, strong, and of good friends.

FALSTAFF. Is thy name Mouldy?

MOULDY. Yea, an't please you.

FALSTAFF. Tis the more time thou wert used.

SHALLOW. Ha, ha, ha! most excellent, i' faith! things that are mouldy lack use: well said, Sir John, very well said.

FALSTAFF. Prick him.

MOULDY. My old dame will be undone now for one to do her husbandry and her drudgery: you need not to have pricked me; there are other men fitter to go out than I.

SHALLOW. Peace, fellow, peace; stand aside: know you where you are? For the other, Sir John: let me see: Simon Shadow!

FALSTAFF. Yea, marry, let me have him to sit under: he's like to be a cold soldier. Prick him, for we have a number of shadows to fill up the muster-book.

SHALLOW. Francis Feeble!

FALSTAFF. What trade art thou, Feeble?

FEEBLE. A woman's tailor, sir.

SHALLOW. Shall I prick him, sir?

FALSTAFF. You may. Wilt thou make as many holes in an enemy's battle as thou hast done in a woman's petticoat?

FEEBLE. I will do my good will, sir: you can have no more.

FALSTAFF. Well said, good woman's tailor! well said, courageous Feeble! thou wilt be as valiant as the wrathful dove or most magnanimous mouse. Prick the woman's tailor. Who is next?

SHALLOW. Peter Bullcalf o' the green!

FALSTAFF. 'Fore God, a likely fellow. Come, prick me Bullcalf till he roar again.

BULLCALF. O Lord, sir! I am a diseased man.

FALSTAFF. What disease hast thou?

BULLCALF. A cold, sir, a cough, sir, which I caught with ringing in the king's affairs upon his coronation-day, sir.

FALSTAFF. Come, thou shalt go to the wars in a gown. Is here all?

SHALLOW. Here is two more called than your number; you must have but four here, sir: and so, I pray you, go in with me to dinner.

FALSTAFF. Come, I will go drink with you, but I cannot tarry dinner. I am glad to see you, sir, by my troth, Master Shallow.

SHALLOW. O, Sir John, do you remember since we lay all night in the windmill in Saint George's field?

FALSTAFF. No more of that, good Master Shallow, no more of that.

SHALLOW. Ha! 'twas a merry night.

SILENCE. That's fifty-five year ago.

SHALLOW. Ha, cousin Silence, that thou hadst seen that this knight and I have seen! Ha, Sir John, said I well?

FALSTAFF. We have heard the chimes at midnight, Master Shallow.

SHALLOW. That we have, that we have, that we have; in faith, Sir John, we have. Come, let's to dinner; come, let's to dinner. The days that we have seen! Come, come.

BULLCALF. Good Master Corporate Bardolph, stand my friend; and here's four Harry ten shillings in French crowns for you.

BARDOLPH. Go to; stand aside.

MOULDY. And, good master corporal captain, for my old dame's sake, stand my friend: she has nobody to do anything about her when I am gone; and she is old, and cannot help herself: you shall have forty, sir.

BARDOLPH. Go to; stand aside.

FEEBLE. By my troth, I care not; a man can die but once. We owe God a death. I'll ne'er bear a base mind; an't be my destiny, so; an't be not, so; no man is too good to serve his prince; and, let it go which way it will, he that dies this year is quit for the next.

BARDOLPH. Well said; thou'rt a good fellow.

FEEBLE. Faith, I'll bear no base mind.

FALSTAFF (*returning*). Come, sir, which men shall I have?

SHALLOW. Four of which you please.

BARDOLPH. Sir, a word with you: I have three pound to free Mouldy and Bullcalf.

FALSTAFF. Go to; well.

SHALLOW. Come, Sir John, which four will you have?

FALSTAFF. Do you choose for me.

SHALLOW. Marry, then, Mouldy, Bullcalf, Feeble, and Shadow.

FALSTAFF. Mouldy and Bullcalf, I will none of you.

SHALLOW. Sir John, Sir John, do not yourself wrong: they are your likeliest men, and I would have you served with the best.

FALSTAFF. Will you tell me, Master Shallow, how to choose a man? Care I for the limb, the thewes, the stature, bulk, and big assemblance of a man! Give me the spirit, Master Shallow. This same half-faced fellow, Shadow, give me this man: he presents no mark to the enemy; the foeman may with as great aim level at the edge of a penknife. And, for a retreat, how swiftly will this Feeble the woman's tailor run off! O, give me the spare men and spare me the great ones. These fellows will do well, Master Shallow. God keep you, Master Silence: I will not use many words with you. Fare you well, gentlemen both: I thank you: I must a dozen mile tonight. Bardolph, give the soldiers coats.

SHALLOW. Sir John, the Lord bless you! God prosper your affairs! God send us peace! At your return visit our house; let our old acquaintance be renewed: peradventure I will with ye to the court.

FALSTAFF. 'Fore God, I would you would, Master Shallow. Fare you well, gentle gentlemen. On, Bardolph; lead the men away. As I return I will fetch off these justices. I do see the bottom of Justice Shallow. Lord, Lord, how subject we old men are to this vice of lying! This same starved justice hath done nothing but prate to me of the wildness of his youth, and the feats he hath done about Turnbull Street; and every third word a lie. I do remember him at Clement's Inn like a man made after supper of a cheese-paring: when a' was naked he was, for all the world, like a forked radish. He came ever in the rearward of the fashion, and sung those tunes that he heard the carmen whistle, and sware they were his fancies or his Good-nights. And now is this vice's dagger become a squire, and talks as familiarly of John a Gaunt as if he had been sworn brother to him; and I'll be sworn a' ne'er saw him but once in the Tilt-yard; and then he burst his head for crowding among the marshal's men. And now has he land and beeves. Well, I'll be acquainted with him if I return; and I see no reason in the law of nature but I may snap at him.

ACT 4

Scene 1—Gaultree Forest in Yorkshire

The Fourth Act opens with a meeting of rebel leaders in Gaultree Forest, Yorkshire. They have just heard that Northumberland is lukewarm, and has retired to Scotland, and that the King's army is near and numerous, when Westmoreland arrives in their midst as an envoy from the King's commander. His hope is that peace will be made. The Archbishop presents a list of grievances to be remedied, and is willing to make peace if a favourable answer is given. A parley is arranged.

Scene 2—In Gaultree Forest

The parley is reported, with John of Lancaster and Westmoreland for the King, and the Archbishop, Mowbray, and Hastings for the rebels.

Lancaster promises that the grievances shall be redressed, both sides pledge themselves to friendship, and the rebel army is immediately disbanded. Then, by an act of base treachery, the rebel leaders are instantly seized for execution, the excuse being that the grievances will be faithfully redressed, but those who rebel against the King must be punished.

Scene 3—In the Forest

In another part of the forest, while a pursuit is being made of the disbanded and deluded rebels, Falstaff meets a famous knight, Coleville of the Dale, who, recognising Falstaff, and believing his reputation for bravery, surrenders. Falstaff escorts him proudly to the commander-in-chief, but Lancaster is not deceived by Falstaff's professions of courage; he knows it has been a free surrender. Yet this treacherous prince sends Coleville to execution. Of Falstaff he promises to speak better than he deserves, and Sir John arranges to return to London by way of Mr. Justice Shallow's hospitable house in Gloucestershire.

Scene 4—The Jerusalem Chamber at Westminster

KING. Now, lords, if God doth give successful end
To this debate that bleedeth at our doors,
We will our youth lead on to higher fields
And draw no swords but what are sanctified.
Our navy is addressed, our power collected,
Our substitutes in absence well invested,
And everything lies level to our wish:
Only we want a little personal strength,
And pause us till these rebels now afoot
Come underneath the yoke of government.

WARWICK. Both which we doubt not but your majesty
Shall soon enjoy.

KING. Humphrey, my son of Gloucester,
Where is the prince your brother?

GLOUCESTER. I think he's gone to hunt, my lord, at Windsor.

KING. Is not his brother, Thomas of Clarence, with him?

GLOUCESTER. No, my good lord; he is in presence here.

CLARENCE. What would my lord and father?

KING. Nothing but well to thee, Thomas of Clarence.
How chance thou art not with the prince thy brother?
He loves thee, and thou dost neglect him, Thomas;
Thou hast a better place in his affection
Than all thy brothers: cherish it, my boy,
And noble offices thou mayest effect
Of mediation, after I am dead,
Between his greatness and thy other brethren:
Therefore omit him not; blunt not his love,
Nor lose the good advantage of his grace
By seeming cold or careless of his will;

For he is gracious, if he be observed:
He hath a tear for pity and a hand
Open as day for melting charity:
Yet notwithstanding, being incensed, he's flint,
As humorous as winter and as sudden
As flaws congealèd in the spring of day.
His temper, therefore, must be well observed:
Chide him for faults, and do it reverently,
When you perceive his blood inclined to mirth;
But, being moody, give him line and scope,
And thou shalt prove a shelter to thy friends,
A hoop of gold to bind thy brothers in.

CLARENCE. I shall observe him with all care and love.

KING. Why art thou not at Windsor with him, Thomas?

CLARENCE. He is not there today; he dines in London.

KING. And how accompanied? canst thou tell that?

CLARENCE. With Poins, and other his continual followers.

KING. Most subject is the fattest soil to weeds;
And he, the noble image of my youth,
Is overspread with them: therefore my grief
Stretches itself beyond the hour of death:
The blood weeps from my heart when I do shape
In forms imaginary the unguided days
And rotten times that you shall look upon
When I am sleeping with my ancestors.

WARWICK. My gracious lord, you look beyond him quite:
The prince but studies his companions
Like a strange tongue, wherein, to gain the language,
Tis needful that the most immodest word
Be looked upon and learned; which once attained,
Your highness knows, comes to no further use
But to be known and hated. So, like gross terms,
The prince will in the perfectness of time
Cast off his followers; and their memory
Shall as a pattern or a measure live,
By which his grace must mete the lives of others,
Turning past evils to advantages.

KING. Tis seldom when the bee doth leave her comb
In the dead carrion. Who's there? Westmoreland?

WESTMORELAND. Health to my sovereign, and new happiness
Added to that that I am to deliver!
Prince John your son doth kiss your grace's hand:
Mowbray, the Bishop Scroop, Hastings, and all
Are brought to the correction of your law;
There is not now a rebel's sword unsheathed,
But Peace puts forth her olive everywhere.

King. O Westmoreland, thou art a summer bird,
Which ever in the haunch of winter sings
The lifting up of day. Look, here's more news.

Harcourt (*appearing*). From enemies heaven keep your majesty;
And, when they stand against you, may they fall
As those that I am come to tell you of!
The Earl of Northumberland and the Lord Bardolph,
With a great power of English and of Scots,
Are by the sheriff of Yorkshire overthrown:
The manner and true order of the fight
This packet, please it you, contains at large.

King. And wherefore should these good news make me sick?
Will Fortune never come with both hands full,
But write her fair words still in foulest letters?
I should rejoice now at this happy news,
And now my sight fails, and my brain is giddy.
O me! come near me; now I am much ill.
I pray you, take me up, and bear me hence
Into some other chamber: softly, pray.

Scene 5—A Chamber in the Palace

King (*in bed*). Let there be no noise made, my gentle friends;
Unless some dull and favourable hand
Will whisper music to my weary spirit.

Worcester. Call for the music in the other room.

King. Set me the crown upon my pillow here.

Prince Henry (*entering*). Who saw the Duke of Clarence?

Clarence. I am here, brother, full of heaviness.

Prince. How now! Rain within doors, and none abroad!
How doth the king?

Gloucester. Exceeding ill.

Prince. Heard he the good news yet?
Tell it him.

Gloucester. He altered much upon the hearing it.

Prince. If he be sick with joy, he'll recover without physic.

Warwick. Not so much noise, my lords: sweet prince, speak low;
The king your father is disposed to sleep.

Clarence. Let us withdraw into the other room.

Warwick. Will't please your grace to go along with us?

Prince. No; I will sit and watch here by the king.

The Prince is left alone with the King

Why doth the crown lie there upon his pillow,
Being so troublesome a bedfellow?
O polished perturbation, golden care,

That keep'st the ports of slumber open wide
To many a watchful night, sleep with it now!
Yet not so sound and half so deeply sweet
As he whose brow with homely biggen bound
Snores out the watch of night. O majesty!
When thou dost pinch thy bearer, thou dost sit
Like a rich armour worn in heat of day,
That scalds with safety. By his gates of breath
There lies a downy feather which stirs not:
Did he suspire, that light and weightless down
Perforce must move. My gracious lord! my father!
This sleep is sound indeed; this is a sleep
That from this golden rigol hath divorced
So many English kings. Thy due from me
Is tears and heavy sorrows of the blood,
Which nature, love, and filial tenderness,
Shall, O dear father, pay thee plenteously:
My due from thee is this imperial crown,
Which, as immediate from thy place and blood,
Derives itself to me. Lo, here it sits (*putting on the crown*),
Which heaven shall guard: and put the world's whole strength
Into one giant arm, it shall not force
This lineal honour from me: this from thee
Will I to mine leave, as tis left to me.

The Prince leaves, with the Crown

KING (*waking*). Warwick! Gloucester! Clarence!

CLARENCE. Doth the king call?

WARWICK. What would your majesty? How fares your grace?

KING. Why did you leave me here alone, my lords?

CLARENCE. We left the prince my brother here, my liege,
Who undertook to sit and watch by you.

KING. The Prince of Wales! Where is he? Let me see him:
He is not here.

WARWICK. This door is open; he is gone this way.

GLOUCESTER. He came not through the chamber where we stayed.

KING. Where is the crown? Who took it from my pillow?

WARWICK. When we withdrew, my liege, we left it here.

KING. The prince hath ta'en it hence: go, seek him out.
Is he so hasty that he doth suppose
My sleep my death?
Find him, my Lord of Warwick; chide him hither.
This part of his conjoins with my disease,
And helps to end me. See, sons, what things you are!
How quickly nature falls into revolt
When gold becomes her object!

For this the foolish over-careful fathers
Have broke their sleep with thoughts, their brains with care,
Their bones with industry;
For this they have engrossèd and piled up
The cankered heaps of strange-achievèd gold;
For this they have been thoughtful to invest
Their sons with arts and martial exercises:
When, like the bee, culling from every flower
The virtuous sweets,
Our thighs packed with wax, our mouths with honey,
We bring it to the hive, and, like the bees,
Are murdered for our pains.
Now, where is he that will not stay so long
Till his friend sickness hath determined me?

WARWICK. My lord, I found the prince in the next room,
Washing with kindly tears his gentle cheeks.

KING. But wherefore did he take away the crown?
Lo, where he comes! Come hither to me, Harry.
Depart the chamber, leave us here alone.

PRINCE. I never thought to hear you speak again.

KING. Thy wish was father, Harry, to that thought:
I stay too long by thee; I weary thee.
Dost thou so hunger for mine empty chair
That thou wilt needs invest thee with my honours
Before thy hour be ripe? O foolish youth!
Thou seek'st the greatness that will overwhelm thee.
Stay but a little; for my cloud of dignity
Is held from falling with so weak a wind
That it will quickly drop: my day is dim.
Thou hast stolen that which after some few hours
Were thine without offence; and at my death
Thou hast sealed up my expectation.
Thy life did manifest thou lovedst me not,
And thou wilt have me die assured of it.
Thou hidest a thousand daggers in thy thoughts,
Which thou hast whetted on thy stony heart
To stab at half an hour of my life.
What! canst thou not forbear me half an hour?
Then get thee gone and dig my grave thyself,
And bid the merry bells ring to thine ear
That thou art crownèd, not that I am dead.
Let all the tears that should bedew my hearse
Be drops of balm to sanctify thy head.
Only compound me with forgotten dust;
Give that which gave thee life unto the worms.
Pluck down my officers, break my decrees;

For now a time is come to mock at form :
Harry the Fifth is crowned : up, vanity !
Down, royal state ! all you sage counsellors, hence !
And to the English court assemble now,
From every region, apes of idleness !
Now, neighbour confines, purge you of your scum :
Have you a ruffian that will swear, drink, dance,
Revel the night, rob, murder, and commit
The oldest sins the newest kind of ways ?
Be happy, he will trouble you no more ;
England shall double gild his treble guilt,
England shall give him office, honour, might ;
For the fifth Harry from curbed license plucks
The muzzle of restraint, and the wild dog
Shall flesh his tooth on every innocent.
O my poor kingdom, sick with civil blows !
When that my care could not withhold thy riots,
What wilt thou do when riot is thy care ?
O, thou wilt be a wilderness again,
Peopled with wolves, thy old inhabitants !

PRINCE. O, pardon me, my liege ! but for my tears,
The moist impediments unto my speech,
I had forestalled this dear and deep rebuke
Ere you with grief had spoke and I had heard
The course of it so far. There is your crown ;
And He that wears the crown immortally
Long guard it yours ! If I affect it more
Than as your honour and as your renown,
Let me no more from this obedience rise,
Which my most inward true and duteous spirit
Teacheth, this prostrate and exterior bending.
God witness with me, when I here came in,
And found no course of breath within your majesty,
How cold it struck my heart ! If I do feign,
O, let me in my present wildness die
And never live to show the incredulous world
The noble change that I have purposèd !
Coming to look on you, thinking you dead,
(And dead almost, my liege, to think you were),
I spake unto this crown as having sense,
And thus upbraided it : *The care on thee depending*
Hath fed upon the body of my father ;
Therefore, thou best of gold art worst of gold :
Other, less fine in carat, is more precious,
Preserving life in medicine potable ;
But thou, most fine, most honoured, most renowned,
Hast eat thy bearer up. Thus, my most royal liege

Accusing it, I put it on my head,
To try with it, as with an enemy
That had before my face murdered my father,
The quarrel of a true inheritor.
But if it did infect my blood with joy,
Or swell my thoughts to any strain of pride;
If any rebel or vain spirit of mine
Did with the least affection of a welcome
Give entertainment to the might of it,
Let God for ever keep it from my head
And make me as the poorest vassal is
That doth with awe and terror kneel to it!

KING. O my son,
God put it in thy mind to take it hence,
That thou mightst win the more thy father's love,
Pleading so wisely in excuse of it!
Come hither, Harry, sit thou by my bed;
And hear, I think, the very latest counsel
That ever I shall breathe. God knows, my son,
By what by-paths and indirect crook'd ways
I met this crown; and I myself know well
How troublesome it sat upon my head.
To thee it shall descend with better quiet,
Better opinion, better confirmation,
For all the soil of the achievement goes
With me into the earth. It seemed in me
But as an honour snatched with boisterous hand,
And I had many living to upbraid
My gain of it by their assistances;
Which daily grew to quarrel and to bloodshed,
Wounding supposèd peace. And now my death
Changes the mode; for what in me was purchased
Falls upon thee in a more fairer sort;
So thou the garland wear'st successively.
Yet, though thou stand'st more sure than I could do,
Thou art not firm enough, since griefs are green,
And all my friends, which thou must make thy friends,
Have but their stings and teeth newly ta'en out;
By whose fell working I was first advanced
And by whose power I well might lodge a fear
To be again displaced: which to avoid,
I cut them off; and had a purpose now
To lead out many to the Holy Land,
Lest rest and lying still might make them look
Too near unto my state. Therefore, my Harry,
Be it thy course to busy giddy minds
With foreign quarrels; that action, hence borne out,

May waste the memory of the former days.
More would I, but my lungs are wasted so
That strength of speech is utterly denied me.
How I came by the crown, O God forgive;
And grant it may with thee in true peace live!

PRINCE. My gracious liege,
You won it, wore it, kept it, gave it me;
Then plain and right must my possession be:
Which I with more than with a common pain
Gainst all the world will rightfully maintain.

KING. Look, look, here comes my John of Lancaster.

LANCASTER. Health, peace, and happiness to my royal father!

KING. Thou bring'st me happiness and peace, son John;
But health, alack, with youthful wings is flown
From this bare withered trunk; upon thy sight
My worldly business makes a period.
Where is my Lord of Warwick? (*Warwick enters*)

KING. Doth any name particular belong
Unto the lodging where I first did swoon?

WARWICK. Tis called Jerusalem, my noble lord.

KING. Laud be to God! even there my life must end.
It hath been prophesied to me many years,
I should not die but in Jerusalem,
Which vainly I supposed the Holy Land:
But bear me to that chamber: there I'll lie;
In that Jerusalem shall Harry die.

ACT 5

Scene 1—Falstaff at Justice Shallow's House

SHALLOW. Sir, you shall not away tonight. What, Davy, I say!

FALSTAFF. You must excuse me, Master Robert Shallow.

SHALLOW. I will not excuse you; you shall not be excused; excuses shall not be admitted. Why, Davy! Davy, Davy, let me see, Davy; let me see: yea, marry, William cook, bid him come hither. Sir John, you shall not be excused.

DAVY. Marry, sir, thus; those precepts cannot be served: and, again, sir, shall we sow the headland with wheat?

SHALLOW. With red wheat, Davy. But for William cook: are there no young pigeons?

DAVY. Yes, sir. Here is now the smith's note for shoeing and plough-irons.

SHALLOW. Let it be cast and paid. Sir John, you shall not be excused.

DAVY. Now, sir, a new link to the bucket must needs be had:

and, sir, do you mean to stop any of William's wages, about the sack he lost the other day at Hinckley fair ?

SHALLOW. A' shall answer it. Some pigeons, Davy, a couple of short-legged hens, a joint of mutton, and any pretty little tiny kickshaws, tell William cook.

DAVY. Doth the man of war stay all night, sir ?

SHALLOW. Yea, Davy. I will use him well : a friend i' the court is better than a penny in purse. Use his men well, Davy. About thy business, Davy. Where are you, Sir John ? Come, come, come, off with your boots. Give me your hand, Master Bardolph.

BARDOLPH. I am glad to see your worship.

SHALLOW. I thank thee with all my heart, kind Master Bardolph. Come, Sir John.

FALSTAFF. I'll follow you, good Master Robert Shallow. Bardolph, look to our horses. If I were sawed into quantities, I should make four dozen of such bearded hermit's staves as Master Shallow. It is a wonderful thing to see the semblable coherence of his men's spirits and his ; they, by observing of him, do bear themselves like foolish justices ; he, by conversing with them, is turned into a justice-like serving-man. I will devise matter enough out of this Shallow to keep Prince Henry in continual laughter the wearing out of six fashions.

SHALLOW. Sir John !

FALSTAFF. I come, Master Shallow ; I come, Master Shallow.

Scene 2—The Palace of Westminster

Warwick and the Lord Chief Justice meet

WARWICK. How now, my Lord Chief Justice ! whither away ?

LORD CHIEF JUSTICE. How doth the king ?

WARWICK. Exceeding well ; his cares are now all ended.

LORD CHIEF JUSTICE. I hope not dead.

WARWICK. He's walked the way of nature,
And to our purposes he lives no more.

LORD CHIEF JUSTICE. I would his majesty had called me with him :
The service that I truly did his life
Hath left me open to all injuries.

WARWICK. Indeed I think the young king loves you not.

LORD CHIEF JUSTICE. I know he doth not, and do arm myself
To welcome the condition of the time.

Lancaster, Clarence, and Gloucester approach with Westmoreland

WARWICK. Here come the heavy issue of dead Harry :
O that the living Harry had the temper
Of him, the worst of these three gentlemen !

How many nobles then should hold their places
That must strike sail to spirits of vile sort!

LORD CHIEF JUSTICE. O God, I fear all will be overturned!

GLOUCESTER. O, good my lord, you have lost a friend indeed;
And I dare swear you borrow not that face
Of seeming sorrow; it is sure your own.

LANCASTER. Though no man be assured what grace to find,
You stand in coldest expectation:
I am the sorrier; would 'twere otherwise.

CLARENCE. Well, you must now speak Sir John Falstaff fair;
Which swims against your stream of quality.

LORD CHIEF JUSTICE. Sweet princes, what I did, I did in honour,
Led by the impartial conduct of my soul:
And never shall you see that I will beg
A ragged and forestalled remission.
If truth and upright innocency fail me,
I'll to the king my master that is dead,
And tell him who hath sent me after him.

WARWICK. Here comes the prince.

Enter King Henry the Fifth

LORD CHIEF JUSTICE. Good-morrow; and God save your majesty!

KING. This new and gorgeous garment, majesty,
Sits not so easy on me as you think.
Brothers, you mix your sadness with some fear:
This is the English, not the Turkish court;
Not Amurath an Amurath succeeds,
But Harry Harry. Yet be sad, good brothers,
For, by my faith, it very well becomes you:
Sorrow so royally in you appears
That I will deeply put the fashion on
And wear it in my heart: why then, be sad;
But entertain no more of it, good brothers,
Than a joint burden laid upon us all.
For me, by heaven, I bid you be assured,
I'll be your father and your brother too;
Let me but bear your love, I'll bear your cares.
Yet weep that Harry's dead; and so will I;
But Harry lives, that shall convert those tears
By number into hours of happiness.

PRINCES. We hope no other from your majesty.

KING. You all look strangely on me: and you most;
You are, I think, assured I love you not.

LORD CHIEF JUSTICE. I am assured, if I be measured rightly,
Your majesty hath no just cause to hate me.

KING. No!

How might a prince of my great hopes forget
So great indignities you laid upon me ?
What ! rate, rebuke, and roughly send to prison
The immediate heir of England ! Was this easy ?
May this be washed in Lethe, and forgotten ?

CHIEF JUSTICE. I then did use the person of your father ;
The image of his power lay then in me :
And, in the administration of his law,
Whiles I was busy for the commonwealth,
Your highness pleasèd to forget my place,
The majesty and power of law and justice,
The image of the king whom I presented,
And struck me in my very seat of judgment ;
Whereon, as an offender to your father,
I gave bold way to my authority
And did commit you. If the deed were ill,
Be you contented, wearing now the garland,
To have a son set your decrees at nought,
To pluck down justice from your awful bench,
To trip the course of law and blunt the sword
That guards the peace and safety of your person ;
Nay, more, to spurn at your most royal image
And mock your workings in a second body.
Question your royal thoughts, make the case yours ;
Be now the father and propose a son,
Hear your own dignity so much profaned,
See your most dreadful laws so loosely slighted,
Behold yourself so by a son disdained ;
And then imagine me taking your part
And in your power soft silencing your son :
After this cold considerance, sentence me ;
And, as you are a king, speak in your state
What I have done that misbecame my place,
My person, or my liege's sovereignty.

KING. You are right, Justice, and you weigh this well ;
Therefore still bear the balance and the sword :
And I do wish your honours may increase,
Till you do live to see a son of mine
Offend you and obey you, as I did.
So shall I live to speak my father's words :
Happy am I, that have a man so bold,
That dares do justice on my proper son ;
And not less happy, having such a son,
That would deliver up his greatness so
Into the hands of justice. You did commit me,
For which I do commit into your hand
The unstained sword that you have used to bear ;

With this remembrance, that you use the same
With the like bold, just, and impartial spirit
As you have done 'gainst me. There is my hand.
You shall be as a father to my youth :
My voice shall sound as you do prompt mine ear.
And, princes all, believe me, I beseech you ;
My father is gone wild into his grave,
For in his tomb lie my affections ;
And with his spirit sadly I survive,
To mock the expectation of the world,
To frustrate prophecies and to raze out
Rotten opinion, who hath writ me down
After my seeming. The tide of blood in me
Hath proudly flowed in vanity till now :
Now doth it turn and ebb back to the sea,
Where it shall mingle with the state of floods
And flow henceforth in formal majesty.
Now call we our High Court of Parliament :
And let us choose such limbs of noble counsel
That the great body of our State may go
In equal rank with the best governed nation.
And, God consigning to my good intents,
No prince nor peer shall have just cause to say,
God shorten Harry's happy life one day!

Scene 3—Justice Shallow's Orchard

SHALLOW. Nay, you shall see my orchard, where, in an arbour, we will eat a last year's pippin of my own graffing, with a dish of caraways, and so forth : come, cousin Silence : and then to bed.

FALSTAFF. 'Fore God, you have here a goodly dwelling and a rich.

SHALLOW. Barren, barren, barren ; beggars all, beggars all, Sir John; marry, good air. Spread, Davy; spread, Davy: well said, Davy.

FALSTAFF. This Davy serves you for good uses ; he is your serving-man and your husband.

SHALLOW. A good varlet, a good varlet, a very good varlet, Sir John. Now sit down, now sit down : come, cousin.

SILENCE. Ah, sirrah ! quoth-a, we shall

> Do nothing but eat, and make good cheer,
> And praise God for the merry year.

FALSTAFF. There's a merry heart ! Good Master Silence, I'll give you a health for that anon.

SHALLOW. Give Master Bardolph some wine, Davy.

DAVY. Sweet sir, sit ; I'll be with you anon ; most sweet sir, sit.

SHALLOW. Be merry, Master Bardolph.

SILENCE. Be merry, be merry, my wife has all;
For women are shrews, both short and tall:
Tis merry in hall when beards wag all,
And welcome merry Shrove-tide.
Be merry, be merry.

FALSTAFF. Health and long life to you, Master Silence.

SILENCE. Fill the cup, and let it come;
I'll pledge you a mile to the bottom.

SHALLOW. Honest Bardolph, welcome: if thou wantest anything, and wilt not call, beshrew thy heart. I'll drink to Master Bardolph, and to all the cavaleros about London. Look who's at door there; ho! who knocks?

DAVY. An't please your worship, there's one Pistol come from the court with news.

FALSTAFF. From the court! Let him come in. How now, Pistol!

PISTOL. Sir John, God save you!

FALSTAFF. What wind blew you hither, Pistol?

PISTOL. Not the ill wind which blows no man to good. Sweet knight, thou art now one of the greatest men in this realm.

SHALLOW. Give me pardon, sir: if, sir, you come with news from the court, I take it there's but two ways, either to utter them or to conceal them. I am, sir, under the king, in some authority.

PISTOL. Harry the Fourth or Fifth?

SHALLOW. Harry the Fourth.

PISTOL. Sir John, thy tender lambkin now is king;
Harry the Fifth's the man. I speak the truth.

FALSTAFF. What, is the old king dead?

PISTOL. As nail in door: the things I speak are just.

FALSTAFF. Away, Bardolph! saddle my horse. Master Robert Shallow, choose what office thou wilt in the land, tis thine. Pistol, I will double-charge thee with dignities.

BARDOLPH. O joyful day!
I would not take a knighthood for my fortune.

PISTOL. What! I do bring good news.

FALSTAFF. Carry Master Silence to bed. Master Shallow, my Lord Shallow, be what thou wilt; I am Fortune's steward—get on thy boots: we'll ride all night. O sweet Pistol! Away, Bardolph! Come, Pistol, utter more to me; and withal devise something to do thyself good. Boot, boot, Master Shallow: I know the young king is sick for me. Let us take any man's horses; the laws of England are at my commandment. Blessed are they that have been my friends; and woe to my Lord Chief Justice!

Scene 4—A London Street

Hostess Quickly and Doll Tearsheet, Falstaff's women associates, are being dragged away in the custody of beadles, protesting loudly.

Scene 5—A Public Place near Westminster Abbey

FALSTAFF. Stand here by me, Master Robert Shallow; I will make the king do you grace: I will leer upon him as a' comes by; and do but mark the countenance that he will give me.

PISTOL. God bless thy lungs, good knight.

FALSTAFF. Come here, Pistol; stand behind me. O, if I had had time to have made new liveries, I would have bestowed the thousand pound I borrowed of you. But tis no matter; this poor show doth better: this doth infer the zeal I had to see him.

SHALLOW. It doth so.

FALSTAFF. It shows my earnestness of affection—

SHALLOW. It doth so.

FALSTAFF. My devotion—

SHALLOW. It doth, it doth, it doth.

FALSTAFF. As it were, to ride day and night; and not to deliberate, not to remember, not to have patience to shift me—

SHALLOW. It is best, certain.

FALSTAFF. But to stand stained with travel, and sweating with desire to see him; thinking of nothing else, putting all affairs else in oblivion, as if there were nothing else to be done but to see him.

Enter the King and his train, trumpets sounding

FALSTAFF. God save thy grace, King Hal! my royal Hal! God save thee, my sweet boy!

KING. My Lord Chief Justice, speak to that vain man.

LORD CHIEF JUSTICE. Have you your wits? know you what tis you speak?

FALSTAFF. My king! my Jove! I speak to thee, my heart!

KING. I know thee not, old man: fall to thy prayers;
How ill white hairs become a fool and jester!
I have long dreamed of such a kind of man,
So surfeit-swelled, so old and so profane;
But, being awaked, I do despise my dream.
Make less thy body hence, and more thy grace;
Leave gormandising; know the grave doth gape
For thee thrice wider than for other men.
Reply not to me with a fool-born jest:
Presume not that I am the thing I was,
For God doth know, so shall the world perceive,
That I have turned away my former self;
So will I those that kept me company.
When thou dost hear I am as I have been,
Approach me, and thou shalt be as thou wast,

The tutor and the feeder of my riots:
Till then, I banish thee, on pain of death,
As I have done the rest of my misleaders,
Not to come near our person by ten mile.
For competence of life I will allow you,
That lack of means enforce you not to evil;
And, as we hear you do reform yourselves,
We will, according to your strengths and qualities,
Give you advancement. Be it your charge, my lord,
To see performed the tenour of our word.
Set on.

FALSTAFF. Master Shallow, I owe you a thousand pound.

SHALLOW. Yea, marry, Sir John; which I beseech you to let me have home with me.

FALSTAFF. That can hardly be, Master Shallow. Do not you grieve at this; I shall be sent for in private to him: look you, he must seem thus to the world. Fear not your advancements; I will be the man yet that shall make you great.

SHALLOW. I cannot well perceive how, unless you should give me your doublet and stuff me out with straw. I beseech you, good Sir John, let me have five hundred of my thousand.

FALSTAFF. Sir, I will be as good as my word: this that you heard was but a colour.

SHALLOW. A colour that I fear you will die in, Sir John.

FALSTAFF. Fear no colours: go with me to dinner: come, Lieutenant Pistol; come, Bardolph: I shall be sent for soon at night.

Enter Prince John, Lord Chief Justice, and Officers

LORD CHIEF JUSTICE. Go, carry Sir John Falstaff to the Fleet:
Take all his company along with him.

FALSTAFF. My lord, my lord—

LORD CHIEF JUSTICE. I cannot now speak: I will hear you soon.
Take them away.

LANCASTER. I like this fair proceeding of the king's:
He hath intent his wonted followers
Shall all be very well provided for;
But all are banished till their conversations
Appear more wise and modest to the world.

LORD CHIEF JUSTICE. And so they are.

LANCASTER. The king hath called his parliament, my lord.

LORD CHIEF JUSTICE. He hath.

LANCASTER. I will lay odds that, ere this year expire,
We bear our civil swords and native fire
As far as France: I heard a bird so sing,
Whose music, to my thinking, pleased the king.
Come, will you hence?

The Story of Henry the Fifth

HENRY THE FIFTH was Shakespeare's patriot king, and he made this play like a trumpet blast from the battlefield of Agincourt.

IT is the last of his English historical plays, for Henry the Eighth is only Shakespeare's in a small degree, and the other histories were written before this. It is good, as we have seen, to read together Richard the Second, the two plays of Henry the Fourth, and then Henry the Fifth, for they form a continuous piece of history. It is believed that the play was written in 1598, and it shares with Richard the Third a greater popularity than any other of the plays dealing with English history.

IN Henry the Fourth Shakespeare shows us Prince Henry sowing his wild oats, as we say, mixing with bad companions and sharing the life of low people ; but here the poet pays abundant compensation for any injustice he may have done the prince. He holds him up to the admiration of the world, and makes him a heroic figure.

HE is English to the core, and the play is entirely English in its spirit. There is a sound basis of democracy in that scene where the English soldiers talk bluntly and plainly to all who come, great and small. They grumble and fight with equal zest ; they say what they think without fear ; they will die for their country if they must, but let the King beware on Judgment Day ! It is all very English.

WHO does not thrill as he reads Saint Crispin's Day ? It will go resounding down the ages as one of the noblest speeches ever spoken by a king. We feel that Henry really felt himself a brother with his soldiers. He has raised himself to a great height of power, from which he has never since fallen in the hearts of our people. If we judge him by the verdict of history we must admit that Henry should not have gone to France in search of a crown, and that the ultimate effects of his war were bad for France and England too ; but we must judge Shakespeare's Henry by Shakespeare's play. He stands here as the popular king of the English people.

THERE is one beautiful thing which creeps into this play, rather like the little bird that flew into the council hall of a king and his ministers in the Long Ago : it is the whisper of the death of Falstaff. We know what Shakespeare made of him ; how his swaggering humour has made men laugh for centuries, and still will. Here, for the first and only time, we shed a tear for this bluff and pompous boaster, for Falstaff he is dead, and he died babbling of green fields.

THE PLAYERS

English

King Henry the Fifth, before, at, and after Agincourt.

Duke of Bedford, brother of the King.

Duke of Gloucester, brother of the King.

Duke of Exeter, the King's uncle.

Earls of Salisbury and Westmoreland.

Archbishop of Canterbury, representing the Church.

Bishop of Ely, supporting the Archbishop.

Earl of Cambridge, a traitor in the pay of France.

Lord Scroop and Sir Thomas Grey, traitors.

Sir Thomas Erpingham, a veteran soldier.

Gower, an English captain, brave and sensible.

Macmorris, an Irish engineer officer, quick in quarrel.

Jamy, a Scottish captain, respected as a soldier.

Fluellen, a Welsh captain, forward, garrulous, hot-tempered; insisting on discipline, a brave and sound soldier.

Bates, Williams, and Court, honest private soldiers.

Pistol, a braggart, coward, and thief, married to Hostess Quickly.

Nym, a corporal, a sham soldier associated with Pistol.

Bardolph, a lieutenant and cowardly swaggerer.

Mistress Quickly, who reports the death of Falstaff at her house.

A Boy and a Herald.

French

King Charles the Sixth, preserving his dignity under defeat.

Lewis, the Dauphin, a royal braggart.

Burgundy, Orleans, and Bourbon, French dukes.

Constable of France, the one man to read Henry aright.

Rambures, a French lord.

Montjoy, a Herald who delivers scornful messages with courtesy.

Governor of Harfleur.

Isabel, Queen of France, and mother of Katharine.

Katharine, the bright French princess whom Henry marries.

Alice, lady-in-waiting to Katharine, whom she coaches in English.

Ambassadors, messengers, lords and ladies, soldiers, and citizens.

Scene—England and France

Henry the Fifth

ACT 1

CHORUS. O for a Muse of fire, that would ascend
The brightest heaven of invention;
A kingdom for a stage, princes to act,
And monarchs to behold the swelling scene!
Then should the warlike Harry, like himself,
Assume the port of Mars; and at his heels,
Leashed in like hounds, should famine, sword, and fire
Crouch for employment. But pardon, gentles all,
The flat unraisèd spirits that have dared
On this unworthy scaffold to bring forth
So great an object. Can this cockpit hold
The vasty fields of France? Or may we cram
Within this wooden O the very casques
That did affright the air at Agincourt?
O, pardon!
Suppose within the girdle of these walls
Are now confined two mighty monarchies,
Whose high upreārèd and abutting fronts
The perilous narrow ocean parts asunder:
Piece out our imperfections with your thoughts;
Into a thousand parts divide one man,
And make imaginary puissance:
Think, when we talk of horses, that you see them
Printing their proud hoofs i' the receiving earth;
For tis your thoughts that now must deck our kings,
Carry them here and there; jumping o'er times,
Turning the accomplishment of many years
Into an hour-glass: for the which supply,
Admit me Chorus to this history;
Who prologue-like your humble patience pray,
Gently to hear, kindly to judge, our play.

Scene 1—A Room in the Palace

In the first scene of Act One the Archbishop of Canterbury and the Bishop of Ely discuss, in an ante-chamber in the King's palace, a Bill which would strip the Church of half its possessions. They hope the new king will show himself a lover of the Church, and they rejoice over the change that has been seen in him. In place of his early wild behaviour he is now showing a statesmanlike mind. The Archbishop mentions that, to win the king's goodwill, the Church has already offered him a greater sum than had ever been offered to an English king before, and he was about to explain to him his right to the French crown when the conversation was interrupted by the French ambassador asking for an audience.

Scene 2—The Presence Chamber, with King, Lords, and Bishops following

KING. Where is my gracious Lord of Canterbury?

EXETER. Not here in presence.

KING. Send for him, good uncle.

WESTMORELAND. Shall we call in the ambassador, my liege?

KING. Not yet, my cousin: we would be resolved,
Before we hear him, of some things of weight
That task our thoughts concerning us and France.

CANTERBURY. God and his angels guard your sacred throne
And make you long become it!

KING. Sure, we thank you.
My learned lord, we pray you to proceed
And justly and religiously unfold
Why the law Salique that they have in France
Or should or should not bar us in our claim;
And God forbid, my dear and faithful lord,
That you should fashion, wrest, or bow your reading,
Or nicely charge your understanding soul
With opening titles miscreate, whose right
Suits not in native colours with the truth;
For God doth know how many now in health
Shall drop their blood in approbation
Of what your reverence shall incite us to.
Therefore take heed how you impawn our person,
How you awake our sleeping sword of war:
We charge you, in the name of God, take heed,
For never two such kingdoms did contend
Without much fall of blood, whose guiltless drops
Are every one a woe, a sore complaint
Gainst him whose wrong gives edge unto the swords
That make such waste in brief mortality.

CANTERBURY. Then hear me, gracious sovereign, and you peers,
That owe yourselves, your lives and services,
To this imperial throne. There is no bar
To make against your highness' claim to France
But this, which they produce from Pharamond:
No woman shall succeed in Salique land,
Which Salique land the French unjustly gloze
To be the realm of France, and Pharamond

The founder of this law and female bar.
Yet their own authors faithfully affirm
That the land Salique is in Germany,
Between the floods of Sala and of Elbe.
Then doth it well appear the Salique law
Was not devisèd for the realm of France.
Howbeit they would hold up this Salique law
To bar your highness.

KING. May I with right and conscience make this claim?

CANTERBURY. The sin upon my head, dread sovereign!
For in the Book of Numbers is it writ:
When the man dies let the inheritance
Descend unto the daughter. Gracious lord,
Stand for your own; unwind your royal flag;
Look back into your mighty ancestors:
Go, my dread lord, to your great-grandsire's tomb,
From whom you claim; invoke his warlike spirit.
O noble English! that could entertain
With half their forces the full pride of France
And let another half stand laughing by,
All out of work and cold for action!

ELY. Awake remembrance of these valiant dead
And with your puissant arm renew their feats;
You are their heir; you sit upon their throne;
The blood and courage that renownèd them
Runs in your veins.

EXETER. Your brother kings and monarchs of the earth
Do all expect that you should rouse yourself,
As did the former lions of your blood.

WESTMORELAND. They know your grace hath cause and means and might;
So hath your highness; never king of England
Had nobles richer and more loyal subjects,
Whose hearts have left their bodies here in England
And lie pavilioned in the fields of France.

CANTERBURY. O, let their bodies follow, my dear liege,
With blood and sword and fire to win your right;
In aid whereof we of the spiritualty
Will raise your highness such a mighty sum
As never did the clergy at one time
Bring in to any of your ancestors.

KING. We must not only arm to invade the French,
But lay down our proportions to defend
Against the Scot, who will make road upon us
With all advantages;
For you shall read that my great-grandfather

Never went with his forces into France
But that the Scot on his unfurnished kingdom
Came pouring like the tide into a breach,
Girding with grievous siege castles and towns;
That England, being empty of defence,
Hath shook and trembled.

CANTERBURY. She hath been then more feared than harmed, my liege,
For hear her but exampled by herself:
When all her chivalry hath been in France,
And she a mourning widow of her nobles,
She hath herself not only well defended
But taken and impounded as a stray
The King of Scots; whom she did send to France,
To fill King Edward's fame with prisoner kings
And make her chronicle as rich with praise
As is the ooze and bottom of the sea
With sunken wreck and sumless treasuries.

WESTMORELAND. But there's a saying very old and true:

If that you will France win,
Then with Scotland first begin.

For once the eagle England being in prey,
To her unguarded nest the weasel Scot
Comes sneaking, and so sucks her princely eggs,
Playing the mouse in absence of the cat,
To tear and havoc more than she can eat.

EXETER. It follows then the cat must stay at home:
Yet that is but a crushed necessity,
Since we have locks to safeguard necessaries,
And pretty traps to catch the petty thieves.
While that the armèd hand doth fight abroad,
The advisèd head defends itself at home.

CANTERBURY. Therefore doth heaven divide
The state of man in divers functions.
So work the honey-bees,
Creatures that by a rule in nature teach
The act of order to a peopled kingdom.
They have a king and officers of sorts;
Where some, like magistrates, correct at home,
Others, like merchants, venture trade abroad,
Others, like soldiers, armèd in their stings,
Make boot upon the summer's velvet buds,
Which pillage they with merry march bring home
To the tent-royal of their emperor,
Who, busied in his majesty, surveys
The singing masons building roofs of gold,

The civil citizens kneading up the honey,
The poor mechanic porters crowding in
Their heavy burdens at his narrow gate,
The sad-eyed justice, with his surly hum,
Delivering o'er to executors pale
The lazy yawning drone. I this infer:
That many things, having full reference
To one consent, may work contrariously:
As many arrows, loosèd several ways,
Come to one mark; as many ways meet in one town;
As many fresh streams meet in one salt sea;
As many lines close in the dial's centre;
So may a thousand actions, once afoot,
End ni one purpose, and be all well borne
Without defeat. Therefore to France, my liege.
Divide your happy England into four;
Whereof take you one quarter into France,
And you withal shall make all Gallia shake.
If we, with thrice such powers left at home,
Cannot defend our own doors from the dog,
Let us be worried and our nation lose
The name of hardiness and policy.

King. Call in the messengers sent from the Dauphin.
Now are we well resolved; and, by God's help,
And yours, the noble sinews of our power,
France being ours, we'll bend it to our awe,
Or break it all to pieces. (*Enter Ambassadors of France*)
Now are we well prepared to know the pleasure
Of our fair cousin Dauphin; for we hear
Your greeting is from him, not from the king.

First Ambassador. May 't please your majesty to give us leave
Freely to render what we have in charge,
Or shall we sparingly show you far off
The Dauphin's meaning and our embassy?

King. We are no tyrant, but a Christian king,
Unto whose grace our passion is as subject
As are our wretches fettered in our prisons:
Therefore with frank and with uncurbèd plainness
Tell us the Dauphin's mind.

First Ambassador. Thus, then, in few.
Your highness, lately sending into France,
Did claim some certain dukedom, in the right
Of your great predecessor, King Edward the Third.
In answer of which claim the prince our master
Says that you savour too much of your youth,
And bids you be advised there 's nought in France

That can be with a nimble galliard won;
You cannot revel into dukedoms there.
He therefore sends you, meeter for your spirit,
This tun of treasure; and, in lieu of this,
Desires you let the dukedoms that you claim
Hear no more of you. This the Dauphin speaks.

KING. What treasure, uncle?

EXETER. Tennis-balls, my liege.

KING. We are glad the Dauphin is so pleasant with us
His present and your pains we thank you for:
When we have matched our rackets to these balls
We will in France, by God's grace, play a set
Shall strike his father's crown into the hazard.
Tell him he hath made a match with such a wrangler
That all the courts of France will be disturbed
With chaces. And we understand him well,
How he comes o'er us with our wilder days,
Not measuring what use we made of them.
We never valued this poor seat of England;
And therefore, living hence, did give ourself
To barbarous license; as tis ever common
That men are merriest when they are from home.
But tell the Dauphin I will keep my state,
Be like a king and show my sail of greatness,
When I do rouse me in my throne of France:
For that I have laid by my majesty
And plodded like a man for working-days,
But I will rise there with so full a glory
That I will dazzle all the eyes of France,
Yea, strike the Dauphin blind to look on us.
And tell the pleasant prince this mock of his
Hath turned his balls to gun-stones; and his soul
Shall stand sore chargèd for the wasteful vengeance
That shall fly with them: for many a thousand widows
Shall this his mock mock out of their dear husbands;
Mock mothers from their sons, mock castles down;
And some are yet ungotten and unborn
That shall have cause to curse the Dauphin's scorn.
But this lies all within the will of God,
To whom I do appeal; and in whose name
Tell you the Dauphin I am coming on,
To venge me as I may, and to put forth
My rightful hand in a well-hallowed cause.
So get you hence in peace; and tell the Dauphin
His jest will savour but of shallow wit,
When thousands weep more than did laugh at it.

Convey them with safe conduct. Fare you well.

EXETER. This was a merry message.

KING. We hope to make the sender blush at it.
Therefore, my lords, omit no happy hour
That may give furtherance to our expedition ;
For we have now no thought in us but France,
Save those to God, that run before our business.
Therefore let our proportions for these wars
Be soon collected, and all things thought upon
That may with reasonable swiftness add
More feathers to our wings ; for, God before,
We'll chide this Dauphin at his father's door.

ACT 2

CHORUS. Now all the youth of England are on fire,
And silken dalliance in the wardrobe lies :
Now thrive the armourers, and honour's thought
Reigns solely in the breast of every man :
They sell the pasture now to buy the horse.
For now sits Expectation in the air,
And hides a sword from hilts unto the point
With crowns imperial, crowns and coronets,
Promised to Harry and his followers.
The French, advised by good intelligence
Of this most dreadful preparation,
Shake in their fear, and with pale policy
Seek to divert the English purposes.
O England ! model to thy inward greatness,
Like little body with a mighty heart,
What mightst thou do, that honour would thee do,
Were all thy children kind and natural !
But see thy fault ! France hath in thee found out
A nest of hollow bosoms, which he fills
With treacherous crowns ; and three corrupted men
Have, for the gilt of France (O guilt indeed !)
Confirmed conspiracy with fearful France ;
And by their hands this grace of kings must die
Ere he take ship for France.
The sum is paid ; the traitors are agreed ;
The king is set from London ; and the scene
Is now transported, gentles, to Southampton.

Scene 1—A Street in London

BARDOLPH. Well met, Corporal Nym.

NYM. Good-morrow, Lieutenant Bardolph.

BARDOLPH. What, are Ancient Pistol and you friends yet ?

NYM. For my part I care not: I say little; but when time shall serve there shall be smiles; but that shall be as it may.

BARDOLPH. I will bestow a breakfast to make you friends, and we'll be all three sworn brothers to France; let it be so, good Corporal Nym.

NYM. Faith, I will live so long as I may, that's the certain of it; and when I cannot live any longer I will do as I may.

BARDOLPH. It is certain, corporal, that he is married to Nell Quickly: and certainly she did you wrong; for you were troth-plight to her.

NYM. I cannot tell; things must be as they may.

BARDOLPH. Here comes Ancient Pistol and his wife. Good corporal, be patient here.

NYM. Pish!

PISTOL. Pish for thee, Iceland dog!

NYM. I have a humour to knock you indifferently well. If you grow foul with me, Pistol, I will scour you with my rapier, and that's the humour of it.

PISTOL. O braggart vile and cursèd furious wight!
The grave doth gape, and doting death is near.

BARDOLPH. Hear me, hear me what I say: he that strikes the first stroke I'll run him up to the hilts, as I am a soldier.

PISTOL. An oath of mickle might; and fury shall abate.

NYM. I will cut thy throat, one time or other, in fair terms: that is the humour of it.

PISTOL. That is the word. I thee defy again.
O hound of Crete, think'st thou my spouse to get?

BOY (*entering*). Mine host Pistol, you must come to my master, and you, hostess: he is very sick, and would to bed. Good Bardolph, put thy face between his sheets, and do the office of a warming-pan. Faith, he's very ill.

BARDOLPH. Away, you rogue!

HOSTESS (*leaving*). The king has killed his heart. Good husband, come home presently.

BARDOLPH. Come, shall I make you two friends? We must to France together; why should we keep knives to cut one another's throats?

NYM. You'll pay me the eight shillings I won of you at betting?

PISTOL. Base is the slave that pays.

NYM. That now I will have; that's the humour of it.

PISTOL. As manhood shall compound: push home. (*They draw*)

BARDOLPH. By this sword, he that makes the first thrust, I'll kill him; by this sword, I will.

PISTOL. Sword is an oath, and oaths must have their course.

BARDOLPH. Corporal Nym, an thou wilt be friends, be friends: an thou wilt not, why, then, be enemies with me too. Prithee, put up.

NYM. I shall have my eight shillings I won of you at betting?

PISTOL. A noble shalt thou have, and present pay;
And friendship shall combine, and brotherhood:
Give me thy hand.

NYM. I shall have my noble?

PISTOL. In cash most justly paid.

NYM. Well, then, that's the humour of't.

HOSTESS (*returning*). As ever you came of women, come in quickly to Sir John Falstaff. Ah, poor heart! he is so shaked that it is most lamentable to behold. Sweet men, come to him.

Scene 2—A Council Chamber at Southampton

BEDFORD. 'Fore God, his grace is bold to trust these traitors.

EXETER. They shall be apprehended by and by.

WESTMORELAND. How smooth and even they do bear themselves!
As if allegiance in their bosoms sat,
Crownèd with faith and constant loyalty.

BEDFORD. The king hath note of all that they intend,
By interception which they dream not of.

EXETER. Nay, but the man that was his bedfellow,
Whom he hath dulled and cloyed with gracious favours,
That he should, for a foreign purse, so sell
His sovereign's life to death and treachery!

Trumpets sound. Enter King, Scroop, Cambridge, and Grey

KING. Now sits the wind fair, and we will aboard.
My Lord of Cambridge, and my kind Lord of Masham,
And you, my gentle knight, give me your thoughts:
Think you not that the powers we bear with us
Will cut their passage through the force of France,
Doing the execution and the act
For which we have in head assembled them?

SCROOP. No doubt, my liege, if each man do his best.

KING. I doubt not that, since we are well persuaded
We carry not a heart with us from hence
That grows not in a fair consent with ours,
Nor leave not one behind that doth not wish
Success and conquest to attend on us.

CAMBRIDGE. Never was monarch better feared and loved
Than is your majesty: there's not, I think, a subject
That sits in heart-grief and uneasiness
Under the sweet shade of your government.

GREY. True: those that were your father's enemies
Have steeped their galls in honey and do serve you
With hearts create of duty and of zeal.

KING. We therefore have great cause of thankfulness;
And shall forget the office of our hand,
Sooner than quittance of desert and merit
According to the weight and worthiness.
We judge no less. Uncle of Exeter,
Enlarge the man committed yesterday,
That railed against our person; we consider
It was excess of wine that set him on,
And on his more advice we pardon him.

SCROOP. That's mercy, but too much security:
Let him be punished, sovereign, lest example
Breed, by his sufferance, more of such a kind.

KING. O, let us yet be merciful.

CAMBRIDGE. So may your highness, and yet punish too.

GREY. You show great mercy, if you give him life,
After the taste of much correction.

KING. Alas, your too much love and care of me
Are heavy orisons 'gainst this poor wretch!
We'll yet enlarge that man,
Though Cambridge, Scroop and Grey, in their dear care
And tender preservation of our person,
Would have him punished. And now to our French causes:
Who are the late commissioners?

CAMBRIDGE. I one, my lord:
Your highness bade me ask for it today.

SCROOP. So did you me, my liege.

GREY. And I, my royal sovereign.

KING. Then, Richard Earl of Cambridge, there is yours;
There yours, Lord Scroop of Masham; and, sir knight,
Grey of Northumberland, this same is yours:
Read them; and know, I know your worthiness.
My Lord of Westmoreland, and uncle Exeter,
We will aboard tonight. Why, how now, gentlemen!
What see you in those papers that you lose
So much complexion? Look ye, how they change!
Their cheeks are paper. Why, what read you there,
That hath so cowarded and chased your blood
Out of appearance?

CAMBRIDGE. I do confess my fault;
And do submit me to your highness' mercy.

GREY. SCROOP. To which we all appeal.

KING. The mercy that was quick in us but late,

By your own counsel is suppressed and killed :
You must not dare, for shame, to talk of mercy ;
For your own reasons turn into your bosoms,
As dogs upon their masters, worrying you.
See you, my princes and my noble peers,
These English monsters ! My Lord of Cambridge here,
You know how apt our love was to accord
To furnish him with all appertinents
Belonging to his honour ; and this man
Hath, for a few light crowns, lightly conspired,
And sworn unto the practices of France
To kill us here in Hampton : to the which
This knight, no less for bounty bound to us
Than Cambridge is, hath likewise sworn. But, O,
What shall I say to thee, Lord Scroop ? thou cruel,
Ingrateful, savage, and inhuman creature !
Thou that didst bear the key of all my counsels,
That knew'st the very bottom of my soul,
That almost mightst have coined me into gold
Wouldst thou have practised on me for thy use !
May it be possible that foreign hire
Could out of thee extract one spark of evil
That might annoy my finger ? Tis so strange
That, though the truth of it stands off as gross
As black and white, my eye will scarcely see it.
O, how hast thou with jealousy infected
The sweetness of affiance ! Show men dutiful ?
Why, so didst thou : seem they grave and learned ?
Why, so didst thou : come they of noble family ?
Why, so didst thou : seem they religious ?
Why, so didst thou : or are they spare in diet,
Free from gross passion or of mirth or anger,
Constant in spirit ?
Such and so finely bolted didst thou seem :
And thus thy fall hath left a kind of blot. . . .
I will weep for thee ;
For this revolt of thine, methinks, is like
Another fall of man. Their faults are open :
Arrest them to the answer of the law,
And God acquit them of their practices !

SCROOP. Our purposes God justly hath discovered ;
And I repent my fault more than my death,
Which I beseech your highness to forgive,
Although my body pay the price of it.

CAMBRIDGE. For me the gold of France did not seduce ;
Although I did admit it as a motive
The sooner to effect what I intended :

But God be thankèd for prevention,
Which I in sufferance heartily will rejoice,
Beseeching God and you to pardon me.

GREY. Never did faithful subject more rejoice
At the discovery of most dangerous treason
Than I do at this hour.
My fault, but not my body, pardon, sovereign.

KING. God quit you in his mercy! Hear your sentence.
You have conspired against our royal person,
Joined with an enemy proclaimed, and from his coffers
Received the golden earnest of our death,
Wherein you would have sold your king to slaughter,
His princes and his peers to servitude,
His subjects to oppression and contempt,
And his whole kingdom into desolation.
Touching our person seek we no revenge;
But we our kingdom's safety must so tender,
Whose ruin you have sought, that to her laws
We do deliver you. Get you therefore hence,
Poor miserable wretches, to your death:
The taste whereof, God of his mercy give
You patience to endure, and true repentance
Of all your dear offences! Bear them hence.
Now, lords, for France; the enterprise whereof
Shall be to you, as us, like glorious.
We doubt not of a fair and lucky war,
Since God so graciously hath brought to light
This dangerous treason lurking in our way
To hinder our beginnings. We doubt not now
But every rub is smoothèd on our way.
Then forth, dear countrymen: let us deliver
Our puissance into the hand of God,
Putting it straight in expedition.
Cheerly to sea; the signs of war advance:
No king of England if not king of France.

Scene 3—Before a Tavern in London

PISTOL. Bardolph, be blithe: Nym, rouse thy vaunting veins:
Boy, bristle thy courage up; for Falstaff he is dead,
And we must yearn therefore.

BARDOLPH. Would I were with him wheresome'er he is, either in heaven or in hell!

HOSTESS. Nay, sure, he's not in hell: he's in Arthur's bosom, if ever man went to Arthur's bosom. A' made a finer end and went away an it had been any christom child. A' parted even just between twelve and one, even at the turning o' the tide; for after I saw him fumble with the sheets, and play with flowers, and smile upon his fingers' ends, I knew there was but one way; for his nose was as sharp as a pen, and a' babbled of green fields. *How now, Sir John!* quoth I: *what, man! be o' good cheer.* So a' cried out *God, God, God!* three or four times. Now I, to comfort him, bid him a' should not think of God; I hoped there was no need to trouble himself with any such thoughts yet. So a' bade me lay more clothes on his feet: I put my hand into the bed and felt them, and they were as cold as any stone; then I felt to his knees, and they were as cold as any stone, and so upward and upward, and all was as cold as any stone.

PISTOL. Come, let's away. My love, give me thy lips.
Look to my chattels and my movables:
Let senses rule; the word is *Pitch and Pay*:
Trust none;
For oaths are straws, men's faiths are wafer-cakes,
And hold-fast is the only dog, my duck:
Therefore, *Caveto* be thy counsellor.
Go, clear thy crystals. Yoke-fellows in arms,
Let us to France.

HOSTESS. Farewell; adieu.

Scene 4—The French King's Palace, with King, Dauphin, and Lords

CHARLES. Thus come the English with full power upon us;
And more than carefully it us concerns
To answer royally in our defences.
Therefore the Dukes of Berri and of Bretagne,
Of Brabant and of Orleans, shall make forth,
And you, Prince Dauphin, with all swift dispatch,
To line and new repair our towns of war
With men of courage and with means defendant.

DAUPHIN. My most redoubted father,
It is most meet we arm us 'gainst the foe;
For peace itself should not so dull a kingdom,
Though war nor no known quarrel were in question,
But that defences, musters, preparations,
Should be maintained, assembled, and collected,
As were a war in expectation.
Therefore, I say tis meet we all go forth
To view the sick and feeble parts of France:
And let us do it with no show of fear;
No, with no more than if we heard that England
Were busied with a Whitsun morris-dance:
For, my good liege, she is so idly kinged,
Her sceptre so fantastically borne
By a vain, giddy, shallow, humorous youth,
That fear attends her not.

CONSTABLE. O peace, Prince Dauphin!
You are too much mistaken in this king:
Question your grace the late ambassadors,
With what great state he heard their embassy,
How well supplied with noble counsellors,
How modest in exception, and withal
How terrible in constant resolution,
And you shall find his vanities forespent
Were but the outside of the Roman Brutus,
Covering discretion with a coat of folly.

DAUPHIN. Well, tis not so, my Lord High Constable;
But though we think it so it is no matter:
In cases of defence tis best to weigh
The enemy more mighty than he seems.

CHARLES. Think we King Harry strong;
And, princes, look you strongly arm to meet him.

MESSENGER. Ambassadors from Harry King of England
Do crave admittance to your majesty.

CHARLES. We'll give them present audience. (*Enter Lords*)
From our brother England?

EXETER. From him; and thus he greets your majesty:
He wills you, in the name of God Almighty,
That you divest yourself, and lay apart
The borrowed glories that by gift of heaven,
By law of nature and of nations, belong
To him and to his heirs; namely, the crown
And all wide-stretchèd honours that pertain
By custom and the ordinance of times
Unto the crown of France.

CHARLES. Or else what follows?

EXETER. Constraint of war; for if you hide the crown
Even in your hearts, there will he rake for it:
Therefore in fierce tempest is he coming,
In thunder and in earthquake, like a Jove,
That, if requiring fail, he will compel.
This is his claim, his threatening, and my message;
Unless the Dauphin be in presence here,
To whom expressly I bring greeting too.

DAUPHIN. For the Dauphin,
I stand here for him: what to him from England?

EXETER. Scorn and defiance; slight regard, contempt,
And anything that may not misbecome
The mighty sender, doth he prize you at.
Thus says my king; an if your father's highness
Do not, in grant of all demands at large,
Sweeten the bitter mock you sent his majesty,

He'll call you to so hot an answer of it
That caves and womby vaultages of France
Shall chide your trespass and return your mock
In second accent of his ordnance.

DAUPHIN. Say, if my father render fair return,
It is against my will; for I desire
Nothing but odds with England: to that end,
As matching to his youth and vanity,
I did present him with the Paris balls.

EXETER. He'll make your Paris Louvre shake for it,
Were it the mistress-court of mighty Europe:
And, be assured, you'll find a difference,
As we his subjects have in wonder found,
Between the promise of his greener days
And these he masters now: now he weighs time
Even to the utmost grain: that you shall read
In your own losses, if he stay in France.

CHARLES. Tomorrow shall you know our mind at full.

ACT 3

CHORUS. Suppose that you have seen
The well-appointed king at Hampton pier
Embark his royalty.
Play with your fancies, and in them behold
Upon the hempen tackle ship-boys climbing;
Hear the shrill whistle which doth order give
To sounds confused; behold the threaden sails,
Borne with the invisible and creeping wind,
Draw the huge bottoms through the furrowed sea,
Breasting the lofty surge: O, do but think
You stand upon the rivage and behold
A city on the inconstant billows dancing;
For so appears this fleet majestical,
Holding due course to Harfleur. Follow, follow:
And leave your England, as dead midnight still,
Guarded with grandsires, babies, and old women.
Work, work your thoughts, and therein see a siege;
Behold the ordnance on their carriages,
With fatal mouths gaping on girded Harfleur.

Scene 1—King Henry, with Lords and Soldiers, before Harfleur

KING. Once more unto the breach, dear friends, once more;
Or close the wall up with our English dead.
In peace there's nothing so becomes a man
As modest stillness and humility;
But when the blast of war blows in our ears,

Then imitate the action of the tiger;
Stiffen the sinews, summon up the blood,
Disguise fair nature with hard-favoured rage;
Then lend the eye a terrible aspect.
Now set the teeth and stretch the nostril wide,
Hold hard the breath and bend up every spirit
To his full height. On, on, you noblest English,
Whose blood is fet from fathers of war-proof!
Fathers that, like so many Alexanders,
Have in these parts from morn till even fought
And sheathed their swords for lack of argument:
Dishonour not your mothers.
And you, good yeomen,
Whose limbs were made in England, show us here
The mettle of your pasture; let us swear
That you are worth your breeding, which I doubt not;
For there is none of you so mean and base,
That hath not noble lustre in your eyes.
I see you stand like greyhounds in the slips,
Straining upon the start. The game's afoot:
Follow your spirit, and upon this charge
Cry *God for Harry, England, and Saint George!*

Scene 2—Before Harfleur; Nym, Bardolph, Pistol, and Boy

Bardolph. On, on, on, on, on! to the breach, to the breach!

Nym. Pray thee, corporal, stay: the knocks are too hot; the humour of it is too hot, that is the very plain song of it.

Boy. Would I were in an alehouse in London! I would give all my fame for a pot of ale and safety.

Pistol. And I:

If wishes would prevail with me,
My purpose should not fail with me,
But thither would I hie.

Fluellen (*entering*). Up to the breach, you dogs!

Pistol. Be merciful, great duke, to men of mould.
Abate thy rage, abate thy manly rage. (*Fluellen drives them out*)

Boy (*alone*). As young as I am, I have observed these three swashers. I am boy to them all three, but all three could not be man to me; for indeed three such antics do not amount to a man. For Bardolph, he is white-livered and red-faced; by the means whereof a' faces it out, but fights not. For Pistol, he hath a killing tongue and a quiet sword; by the means whereof a' breaks words, and keeps whole weapons. For Nym, he hath heard that men of few words are the best men, and therefore he scorns to say his prayers, lest a' should be thought a coward: but his few bad words are matched with as few good deeds; for a' never broke any man's head but his own, and that was against a post when he was drunk. They will steal anything and call it purchase. Bardolph stole a lute-case, bore it twelve leagues, and sold it for three-halfpence. Nym and Bardolph are sworn brothers in filching, and in Calais they stole a fire-shovel. They would have me as familiar with men's pockets as their gloves or their handkerchers, which makes much against my manhood. I must leave them, and seek some better service: their villainy goes against my weak stomach.

Fluellen returns, with Gower following

GOWER. Captain Fluellen, you must come presently to the mines; the Duke of Gloucester would speak with you.

FLUELLEN. To the mines! Tell you the duke it is not so good to come to the mines, for, look you, the mines is not according to the disciplines of the war; the concavities of it is not sufficient.

GOWER. The Duke of Gloucester, to whom the order of the siege is given, is altogether directed by an Irishman, a very valiant gentleman, i' faith.

FLUELLEN. It is Captain Macmorris, is it not?

GOWER. I think it be.

FLUELLEN. He is an ass. I will verify as much in his beard: he has no more directions in the true disciplines of the wars, look you, of the Roman disciplines, than is a puppy-dog.

GOWER. Here a' comes; and the Scots captain, Captain Jamy, with him.

FLUELLEN. Captain Jamy is a marvellous falorous gentleman, that is certain; and of great expedition and knowledge in th' aunchient wars; he will maintain his argument as well as any military man in the world, in the disciplines of the pristine wars of the Romans.

JAMY. I say Gud-day, Captain Fluellen.

FLUELLEN. God-den to your worship, good Captain James.

GOWER. How now, Captain Macmorris! have you quit the mines? have the pioneers given o'er?

MACMORRIS. The work ish give over, the trumpet sound the retreat.

FLUELLEN. Captain Macmorris, I beseech you now, will you voutsafe me, look you, a few disputations with you, as partly touching or concerning the disciplines of the war, the Roman wars; partly to satisfy my opinion, and partly for the satisfaction, look you, of my mind, as touching the direction of the military discipline.

MACMORRIS. It is no time to discourse: the day is hot, and the weather, and the wars, and the king, and the dukes: it is no time to discourse. The town is beseeched, and the trumpet calls us to the breach; and we talk, and do nothing: tis shame for us all: and there is throats to be cut, and works to be done.

FLUELLEN. Captain Macmorris, I think, look you, under your correction, there is not many of your nation—

MACMORRIS. Of my nation! What ish my nation? Ish a villain, and a knave, and a rascal. What ish my nation? Who talks of my nation?

FLUELLEN. Look you, if you take the matter otherwise than is meant, Captain Macmorris, peradventure I shall think you do not use me with that affability as in discretion you ought to use me, look you; being as good a man as yourself, both in the disciplines of war, and in the derivation of my birth, and in other particularities.

MACMORRIS. I do not know you so good a man as myself: I will cut off your head.

GOWER. The town sounds a parley.

FLUELLEN. Captain Macmorris, when there is more better opportunity to be required, look you, I will be so bold as to tell you I know the disciplines of war.

Scene 3—The Gates of Harfleur

Governor and Citizens on the walls; the English below

KING. How yet resolves the Governor of the town?
This is the latest parle we will admit:
Therefore to our best mercy give yourselves;
Or like to men proud of destruction
Defy us to our worst, for, as I am a soldier,
A name that in my thoughts becomes me best,
If I begin the battery once again,
I will not leave the half-achieved Harfleur
Till in her ashes she lie burièd.
The gates of mercy shall be all shut up.
Therefore, you men of Harfleur,
Take pity of your town and of your people,
Whiles yet my soldiers are in my command.

GOVERNOR. Our expectation hath this day an end:
The Dauphin, whom of succours we entreated,
Returns us that his powers are yet not ready
To raise so great a siege. Therefore, great king,
We yield our town and lives to thy soft mercy.
Enter our gates; dispose of us and ours;
For we no longer are defensible.

KING. Open your gates. Come, uncle Exeter,
Go you and enter Harfleur: there remain,
And fortify it strongly 'gainst the French:
Use mercy to them all. For us, dear uncle,
The winter coming on, and sickness growing

Upon our soldiers, we will retire to Calais.
Tonight in Harfleur we will be your guest;
Tomorrow for the march are we addrest.

Scene 4—The French King's Palace

KATHARINE. *Alice, tu as été en Angleterre, et tu parles bien le langage.*

ALICE. *Un peu, madame.*

KATHARINE. *Je te prie, m'enseignez; il faut que j'apprenne à parler. Comment appelez-vous la main en Anglois?*

ALICE. *La main? elle est appelée* de hand.

KATHARINE. De hand. *Et les doigts?*

ALICE. *Les doigts? ma foi, j'oublie les doigts; mais je me souviendrai. Les doigts? je pense qu'ils sont appelés* de fingres; *oui,* de fingres.

KATHARINE. *La main,* de hand; *les doigts,* de fingres. *Je pense que je suis le bon écolier; j'ai gagné deux mots d'Anglois vitement. Comment appelez-vous les ongles?*

ALICE. *Les ongles? nous les appelons* de nails.

KATHARINE. De nails. *Écoutez; dites-moi, si je parle bien:* de hand, de fingres, et de nails.

ALICE. *C'est bien dit, madame; il est fort bon Anglois.*

KATHARINE. *Dites-moi l'Anglois pour le bras.*

ALICE. De arm, *madame.*

KATHARINE. *Et le coude?*

ALICE. De elbow.

KATHARINE. De elbow. *Je m'en fais la répétition de tous les mots que vous m'avez appris dès à présent.*

ALICE. *Il est trop difficile, madame, comme je pense.*

KATHARINE. *Excusez-moi, Alice; écoutez:* de hand, de fingres, de nails, de arma, de bilbow.

ALICE. De elbow, *madame.*

KATHARINE. *O Seigneur Dieu, je m'en oublie!* de elbow. *Comment appelez-vous le col?*

ALICE. De neck, *madame.*

KATHARINE. De nick. *Et le menton?*

ALICE. De chin.

KATHARINE. De sin. *Le col,* de nick; *le menton,* de sin.

ALICE. *Oui. Sauf votre honneur, en vérité, vous prononcez les mots aussi droit que les natifs d'Angleterre.*

KATHARINE. *Je ne doute point d'apprendre, par la grâce de Dieu, et en peu de temps.*

ALICE. *N'avez-vous pas déjà oublié ce que je vous ai enseigné?*

KATHARINE. *Non, je réciterai à vous promptement:* de hand, de fingres, de mails—

ALICE. De nails, *madame*.

KATHARINE. De nails, de arm, de ilbow.

ALICE. *Sauf votre honneur*, de elbow.

Scene 5—The French King's Palace

CHARLES. Tis certain he hath passed the river Somme.

CONSTABLE. And if he be not fought withal, my lord,
Let us not live in France ; let us quit all
And give our vineyards to a barbarous people.

BOURBON. *Mort de ma vie !* if they march along
Unfought withal, but I will sell my dukedom,
To buy a slobbery and a dirty farm
In that nook-shotten isle of Albion.

CONSTABLE. *Dieu des batailles !* Where have they this mettle ?
Is not their climate foggy, raw, and dull,
On whom, as in despite, the sun looks pale,
Killing their fruit with frowns ?

DAUPHIN. By faith and honour,
Our madams mock at us, and plainly say
Our mettle is bred out.

BOURBON. They bid us to the English dancing-schools,
Saying our grace is only in our heels,
And that we are most lofty runaways.

CHARLES. Where is Montjoy the herald ? Speed him hence :
Let him greet England with our sharp defiance.
Up, princes ! and, with spirit of honour edged
More sharper than your swords, hie to the field :
Bar Harry England, that sweeps through our land
With pennons painted in the blood of Harfleur :
Rush on his host as doth the melted snow
Upon the valleys.
Go down upon him, you have power enough,
And in a captive chariot into Rouen
Bring him our prisoner.

CONSTABLE. This becomes the great.
Sorry am I his numbers are so few,
His soldiers sick and famished in their march,
For I am sure, when he shall see our army,
He'll drop his heart into the sink of fear
And for achievement offer us his ransom.

CHARLES. Therefore, lord constable, haste on Montjoy,
And let him say to England that we send
To know what willing ransom he will give.
Prince Dauphin, you shall stay with us in Rouen.

DAUPHIN. Not so, I do beseech your majesty.

CHARLES. Be patient, for you shall remain with us.
Now forth, lord constable and princes all,
And quickly bring us word of England's fall.

Scene 6—The English Camp in Picardy

GOWER. How now, Captain Fluellen! come you from the bridge?

FLUELLEN. I assure you there is very excellent services committed at the bridge.

GOWER. Is the Duke of Exeter safe?

FLUELLEN. The Duke of Exeter is as magnanimous as Agamemnon; and a man that I love and honour with my soul, and my heart, and my duty, and my life, and my living, and my uttermost power: he is not—God be praised and blessed!—any hurt in the world; but keeps the bridge most valiantly, with excellent discipline. There is an aunchient lieutenant there at the pridge, I think in my very conscience he is as valiant a man as Mark Antony; and he is a man of no estimation in the world; but I did see him do as gallant service.

GOWER. What do you call him?

FLUELLEN. He is called Aunchient Pistol.

GOWER. I know him not.

FLUELLEN. Here is the man.

PISTOL (*approaching*). Captain, I thee beseech to do me favours:
The Duke of Exeter doth love thee well.

FLUELLEN. Ay, I praise God; and I have merited some love at his hands.

PISTOL. Bardolph, a soldier, firm and sound of heart,
And of buxom valour, hath, by cruel fate,
And giddy Fortune's furious fickle wheel,
That goddess blind,
That stands upon the rolling restless stone—

FLUELLEN. By your patience, Aunchient Pistol. Fortune is painted blind, with a muffler afore her eyes, to signify to you that Fortune is blind; and she is painted also with a wheel, to signify to you that she is turning, and inconstant, and mutability, and variation: and her foot is fixed upon a spherical stone, which rolls, and rolls, and rolls; in good truth, the poet makes a most excellent description of it: Fortune is an excellent moral.

PISTOL. Fortune is Bardolph's foe, and frowns on him;
For he hath stolen a pyx, and hangèd must a' be:
Therefore, go speak: the duke will hear thy voice;
And let not Bardolph's vital thread be cut
With edge of penny cord and vile reproach:
Speak, captain, for his life, and I will thee requite.

FLUELLEN. Aunchient Pistol, I do partly understand your meaning.

PISTOL. Why then, rejoice therefore.

FLUELLEN. Certainly, aunchient, it is not a thing to rejoice at: for if, look you, he were my brother, I would desire the duke to use his good pleasure, and put him to execution; for discipline ought to be used.

PISTOL. Die, and *figo* for thy friendship!

FLUELLEN. It is well. (*Pistol goes*)

GOWER. Why, this is an arrant counterfeit rascal; I remember him now; a cutpurse.

FLUELLEN. I'll assure you, a' uttered as brave words at the pridge as you shall see in a summer's day.

GOWER. Why, tis a gull, a fool, a rogue, that now and then goes to the wars to grace himself at his return into London under the form of a soldier. And such fellows are perfect in the great commanders' names: and they will learn you by rote where services were done; at such and such a breach, at such a convoy; who came off bravely, who was shot, who disgraced; and this they con perfectly in the phrase of war, which they trick up with new-tuned oaths. But you must learn to know such slanders of the age, or else you may be marvellously mistook.

FLUELLEN. I tell you what, Captain Gower; I do perceive he is not the man that he would gladly make show to the world he is: if I find a hole in his coat, I will tell him my mind. Hark you, the king is coming, and I must speak with him from the pridge.

KING (*entering*). How now, Fluellen! camest thou from the bridge?

FLUELLEN. Ay, so please your majesty. The Duke of Exeter has very gallantly maintained the pridge. I can tell your majesty, the duke is a prave man.

KING. What men have you lost, Fluellen?

FLUELLEN. The perdition of th' athversary hath been very great: marry, for my part, I think the duke hath lost never a man, but one that is like to be executed for robbing a church, one Bardolph, if your majesty know the man: his face is all bubukles, and whelks, and knobs, and flames o' fire.

KING. We would have all such offenders so cut off, and we give express charge that in our marches through the country there be nothing compelled from the villages, nothing taken but paid for, none of the French upbraided or abused in disdainful language; for when lenity and cruelty play for a kingdom, the gentler gamester is the soonest winner.

MONTJOY (*entering*). You know me by my habit.

KING. Well then I know thee: what shall I know of thee?

MONTJOY. My master's mind.

KING. Unfold it.

MONTJOY. Thus says my king: *Say thou to Harry of England:* Though we seemed dead, we did but sleep: advantage is a better soldier than rashness. Tell him we could have rebuked him at Harfleur, but that we thought not good to bruise an injury till it were full ripe: now we speak upon our cue, and our voice is imperial: England shall repent his folly, see his weakness, and admire our sufferance. Bid him therefore consider of his ransom. For our losses, his exchequer is too poor; for the effusion of our blood, the muster of his kingdom too faint a number; and for our disgrace, his own person, kneeling at our feet, but a weak and worthless satisfaction. To this add defiance.

KING. Thou dost thy office fairly. Turn thee back,
And tell thy king I do not seek him now;
But could be willing to march on to Calais
Without impeachment: for, to say the sooth,
Though tis no wisdom to confess so much
Unto an enemy of craft and vantage,
My people are with sickness much enfeebled,
My numbers lessened, and those few I have
Almost no better than so many French;
Who, when they were in health, I tell thee, herald,
I thought upon one pair of English legs
Did march three Frenchmen. Yet, forgive me, God,
That I do brag thus! This your air of France
Hath blown that vice in me; I must repent.
Go therefore, tell thy master here I am;
My ransom is this frail and worthless trunk,
My army but a weak and sickly guard;
Yet, God before, tell him we will come on,
Though France himself and such another neighbour
Stand in our way. There's for thy labour, Montjoy.
Go, bid thy master well advise himself:
If we may pass, we will; if we be hindered
We shall your tawny ground with your red blood
Discolour; and so, Montjoy, fare you well.
The sum of all our answer is but this:
We would not seek a battle, as we are;
Nor, as we are, we say we will not shun it:
So tell your master.

MONTJOY. I shall deliver so. Thanks to your highness.

Scene 7—Night in the French Camp near Agincourt

CONSTABLE (*to Dauphin and Lords*). Tut! I have the best armour of the world. Would it were day!

ORLEANS. You have an excellent armour, but let my horse have his due.

CONSTABLE. It is the best horse of Europe.

ORLEANS. Will it never be morning?

DAUPHIN. My Lord of Orleans, and my Lord High Constable, you talk of horse and armour ?

ORLEANS. You are as well provided of both as any prince in the world.

DAUPHIN. What a long night is this ! I will not change my horse with any that treads on four pasterns. When I bestride him I soar, I am a hawk : he trots the air ; the earth sings when he touches it ; the basest horn of his hoof is more musical than the pipe of Hermes. It is a beast for Perseus : he is pure air and fire ; and the dull elements of earth and water never appear in him, but only in patient stillness while his rider mounts him. He is indeed a horse ; and all other jades you may call beasts.

CONSTABLE. Indeed, my lord, it is a most absolute and excellent horse.

DAUPHIN. It is the prince of palfreys ; his neigh is like the bidding of a monarch, and his countenance enforces homage.

ORLEANS. No more, cousin.

DAUPHIN. Nay, the man hath no wit that cannot, from the rising of the lark to the lodging of the lamb, vary deserved praise on my palfrey. It is a theme as fluent as the sea : turn the sands into eloquent tongues and my horse is argument for them all : tis a subject for a sovereign to reason on, and for a sovereign's sovereign to ride on. Would I were able to load him with his desert ! Will it never be day ? I will trot tomorrow a mile, and my way shall be paved with English faces.

CONSTABLE. I will not say so, for fear I should be faced out of my way ; but I would it were morning, for I would fain be about the ears of the English.

DAUPHIN. Tis midnight ; I'll go arm myself.

Enter a Messenger

MESSENGER. My Lord High Constable, the English lie within fifteen hundred paces of your tents.

CONSTABLE. Would it were day ! Alas, poor Harry of England ! he longs not for the dawning as we do. If the English had any apprehension they would run away.

ORLEANS. That they lack ; for if their heads had any intellectual armour they could never wear such heavy head-pieces.

RAMBURES. That island of England breeds very valiant creatures ; their mastiffs are of unmatchable courage.

CONSTABLE. Just, just ; and the men do sympathise with the mastiffs in robustious and rough coming on, leaving their wits with their wives : and then give them great meals of beef and iron and steel, they will eat like wolves and fight like devils. Now is it time to arm : come, shall we about it ?

ORLEANS. It is now two o'clock: but, let me see, by ten
We shall have each a hundred Englishmen.

ACT 4

CHORUS. Now entertain conjecture of a time
When creeping murmur and the poring dark
Fills the wide vessel of the universe.
From camp to camp through the foul womb of night
The hum of either army stilly sounds,
That the fixed sentinels almost receive
The secret whispers of each other's watch:
Fire answers fire, and through their paly flames
Each battle sees the other's umbered face;
Steed threatens steed, in high and boastful neighs
Piercing the night's dull ear, and from the tents
The armourers, accomplishing the knights,
With busy hammers closing rivets up,
Give dreadful note of preparation.
The country cocks do crow, the clocks do toll,
And the third hour of drowsy morning name.
Proud of their numbers and secure in soul,
The confident and over-lusty French
Do the low-rated English play at dice;
And chide the cripple tardy-gaited night
Who, like a foul and ugly witch, doth limp
So tediously away. The poor condemnèd English,
Like sacrifices, by their watchful fires
Sit patiently. . . . O now, who will behold
The royal captain of this ruined band
Walking from watch to watch, from tent to tent,
Let him cry *Praise and glory on his head!*
For forth he goes and visits all his host,
Bids them Good-morrow with a modest smile,
And calls them brothers, friends, and countrymen.

Scene 1—The English Camp at Agincourt

KING. Gloucester, tis true that we are in great danger;
The greater therefore should our courage be.
Good-morrow, brother Bedford. God Almighty!
There is some soul of goodness in things evil,
Would men observingly distil it out,
For our bad neighbour makes us early stirrers,
Which is both healthful and good husbandry.
Good-morrow, old Sir Thomas Erpingham:
A good soft pillow for that good white head
Were better than a churlish turf of France.

ERPINGHAM. Not so, my liege: this lodging likes me better,
Since I may say *Now lie I like a king.*

KING. Tis good for men to love their present pains
Upon example; so the spirit is eased.
Lend me thy cloak, Sir Thomas. Brothers both,
Commend me to the princes in our camp;
Do my Good-morrow to them, and anon
Desire them all to my pavilion.

ERPINGHAM. The lord in heaven bless thee, noble Harry!

KING. God-a-mercy, old heart! thou speak'st cheerfully.

The King is left alone, and Pistol enters

PISTOL. *Qui va là?*

KING. A friend.

PISTOL. Discuss unto me; art thou officer?
Or art thou base, common, and popular?

KING. I am a gentleman of a company. What are you?

PISTOL. As good a gentleman as the emperor.

KING. Then you are a better than the king.

PISTOL. The king's a bawcock, and a heart of gold,
A lad of life, an imp of fame;
Of parents good, of fist most valiant:
I kiss his dirty shoe, and from heart-string
I love the lovely bully. What is thy name?

KING. Harry le Roy.

PISTOL. Le Roy! a Cornish name: art thou of Cornish crew?

KING. No, I am a Welshman.

PISTOL. Know'st thou Fluellen?

KING. Yes.

PISTOL. Tell him I'll knock his leek about his pate
Upon Saint Davy's day.

KING. Do not you wear your dagger in your cap that day, lest he knock that about yours.

PISTOL. Art thou his friend?

KING. And his kinsman too.

PISTOL. The *figo* for thee, then!

KING. I thank you: God be with you!

PISTOL (*leaving*). My name is Pistol called.

KING. It sorts well with your fierceness. (*King withdraws*)

GOWER (*entering with others*). Captain Fluellen!

FLUELLEN. So! in the name of Jesu Christ, speak lower. If you would take the pains but to examine the wars of Pompey the Great you shall find, I warrant you, that there is no tiddle-taddle nor pibble-pabble in Pompey's camp.

Gower. Why, the enemy is loud; you hear him all night.

Fluellen. If the enemy is an ass and a fool and a prating coxcomb, is it meet, think you, that we should also, look you, be an ass and a fool and a prating coxcomb? in your own conscience, now?

Gower. I will speak lower.

Fluellen. I pray you and beseech you that you will. (*They leave*)

King (*re-appearing*). Though it appear a little out of fashion,
There is much care and valour in this Welshman.

Enter John Bates, Alexander Court, Michael Williams, and soldiers

Court. Brother John Bates, is not that the morning which breaks yonder?

Bates. I think it be: but we have no great cause to desire the approach of day.

Williams. We see yonder the beginning of the day, but I think we shall never see the end of it. Who goes there?

King. A friend.

Williams. Under what captain serve you?

King. Under Sir Thomas Erpingham.

Williams. A good old commander and a most kind gentleman: I pray you, what thinks he of our estate?

King. Even as men wrecked upon a sand, that look to be washed off the next tide.

Bates. He hath not told his thought to the king?

King. No; nor it is not meet he should. For, though I speak it to you, I think the king is but a man, as I am: the violet smells to him as it doth to me; the element shows to him as it doth to me; all his senses have but human conditions: his ceremonies laid by, in his nakedness he appears but a man. Therefore when he sees reason of fears, as we do, his fears, out of doubt, be of the same relish as ours are: yet, in reason, no man should possess him with any appearance of fear, lest he, by showing it, should dishearten his army.

Bates. He may show what outward courage he will; but I believe, as cold a night as tis, he could wish himself in Thames up to the neck; and so I would he were, and I by him, so we were quit here.

King. By my troth, I will speak my conscience of the king: I think he would not wish himself anywhere but where he is.

Bates. Then I would he were here alone; so should he be sure to be ransomed, and a many poor men's lives saved.

King. I dare say you love him not so ill to wish him here alone, howsoever you speak this to feel other men's minds: methinks I could not die anywhere so contented as in the king's company, his cause being just and his quarrel honourable.

Williams. That's more than we know.

BATES. Ay, or more than we should seek after; for we know enough if we know we are the king's subjects: if his cause be wrong, our obedience to the king wipes the crime of it out of us.

WILLIAMS. But if the cause be not good the king himself hath a heavy reckoning to make, when all those legs and arms and heads, chopped off in a battle, shall join together at the latter day and cry all *We died at such a place*; some swearing, some crying for a surgeon, some upon their wives left poor behind them, some upon the debts they owe, some upon their children rawly left. I am afeard there are few die well that die in a battle; for how can they charitably dispose of anything when blood is their argument? Now, if these men do not die well, it will be a black matter for the king that led them to it, whom to disobey were against all proportion of subjection.

KING. So, if a son that is by his father sent about merchandise do sinfully miscarry upon the sea, the imputation of his wickedness, by your rule, should be imposed upon his father that sent him: but this is not so. The king is not bound to answer the particular endings of his soldiers, the father of his son, for they purpose not their death when they purpose their services. Besides, there is no king, be his cause never so spotless, if it come to the arbitrement of swords, can try it out with all unspotted soldiers. Every subject's duty is the king's; but every subject's soul is his own. Therefore should every soldier in the wars do as every sick man in his bed, wash every mote out of his conscience: and, dying so, death is to him advantage; or, not dying, the time was blessedly lost wherein such preparation was gained: and in him that escapes, it were not sin to think that, making God so free an offer, He let him outlive that day to see His greatness and to teach others how they should prepare.

WILLIAMS. Tis certain every man that dies ill, the ill upon his own head, the king is not to answer it.

BATES. I do not desire he should answer for me; and yet I determine to fight lustily for him.

KING. I myself heard the king say he would not be ransomed.

WILLIAMS. Ay, he said so, to make us fight cheerfully; but when our throats are cut he may be ransomed and we ne'er the wiser.

KING. If I live to see it I will never trust his word after.

WILLIAMS. *You'll* never trust his word after! Come, tis a foolish saying.

KING. Your reproof is something too round: I should be angry with you if the time were convenient.

WILLIAMS. Let it be a quarrel between us, if you live.

KING. I embrace it.

WILLIAMS. How shall I know thee again?

KING. Give me any gage of thine, and I will wear it in my bonnet: then, if ever thou darest acknowledge it, I will make it my quarrel.

WILLIAMS. Here's my glove: give me another of thine.

KING. There.

WILLIAMS. This will I also wear in my cap: if ever thou come to me and say, after tomorrow, *This is my glove*, by this hand I will take thee a box on the ear.

KING. Well, I will do it, though I take thee in the king's company.

WILLIAMS. Keep thy word: fare thee well.

BATES. Be friends, you English fools, be friends: we have French quarrels enow, if you could tell how to reckon.

They go, leaving the King alone with the night

KING. Upon the king! let us our lives, our souls,
Our debts, our careful wives,
Our children and our sins, lay on the king!
We must bear all. O hard condition,
Twin-born with greatness, subject to the breath
Of every fool, whose sense no more can feel
But his own wringing! What infinite heart's-ease
Must kings neglect that private men enjoy!
And what have kings that privates have not too,
Save ceremony, save general ceremony?
And what art thou, thou idol ceremony?
What kind of god art thou, that suffer'st more
Of mortal griefs than do thy worshippers?
What are thy rents? What are thy comings-in?
O ceremony, show me but thy worth!
What is thy soul of adoration?
Art thou aught else but place, degree, and form,
Creating awe and fear in other men?
Wherein thou art less happy being feared
Than they in fearing.
What drink'st thou oft, instead of homage sweet,
But poisoned flattery? O, be sick, great greatness,
And bid thy ceremony give thee cure!
Think'st thou the fiery fever will go out
With titles blown from adulation?
Will it give place to flexure and low bending?
Canst thou, when thou command'st the beggar's knee,
Command the health of it? No, thou proud dream,
That play'st so subtly with a king's repose,
I am a king that find thee, and I know
Tis not the balm, the sceptre, and the ball,
The sword, the mace, the crown imperial,
The intertissued robe of gold and pearl,
The farcèd title running 'fore the king,
The throne he sits on, nor the tide of pomp

That beats upon the high shore of this world,
No, not all these, thrice-gorgeous ceremony,
Not all these, laid in bed majestical,
Can sleep so soundly as the wretched slave,
Who with a body filled and vacant mind
Gets him to rest, crammed with distressful bread;
Never sees horrid night, the child of hell,
But, like a lackey, from the rise to set
Sweats in the eye of Phoebus, and all night
Sleeps in Elysium; next day after dawn,
Doth rise and help Hyperion to his horse,
And follows so the ever-running year
With profitable labour, to his grave:
And, but for ceremony, such a wretch,
Winding up days with toil and nights with sleep,
Had the fore-hand and vantage of a king.
The slave, a member of the country's peace,
Enjoys it; but in gross brain little wots
What watch the king keeps to maintain the peace,
Whose hours the peasant best advantages.

Sir Thomas Erpingham (*entering*). My lord, your nobles, jealous of your absence,
Seek through your camp to find you.

King. Good old knight,
Collect them all together at my tent:
I'll be before thee.

Erpingham. I shall do't, my lord.

King. O God of battles! steel my soldiers' hearts;
Possess them not with fear; take from them now
The sense of reckoning, if the opposèd numbers
Pluck their hearts from them. Not today, O Lord,
O, not today, think not upon the fault
My father made in compassing the crown!
I Richard's body have interred anew;
And on it have bestowed more contrite tears
Than from it issued forcèd drops of blood:
Five hundred poor I have in yearly pay,
Who twice a day their withered hands hold up
Toward heaven, to pardon blood; and I have built
Two chantries, where the sad and solemn priests
Sing still for Richard's soul. More will I do;
Though all that I can do is nothing worth,
Since that my penitence comes after all,
Imploring pardon.

Gloucester (*entering*). My liege!

King. My brother Gloucester's voice? Ay;

I know thy errand, I will go with thee:
The day, my friends, and all things stay for me.

Scene 2—The French Camp

MESSENGER. The English are embattled, you French peers.

CONSTABLE. To horse, you gallant princes! straight to horse!
Do but behold yon poor and starvèd band,
And your fair show shall suck away their souls,
Leaving them but the shales and husks of men.
There is not work enough for all our hands;
Scarce blood enough in all their sickly veins
To give each naked curtle-axe a stain,
That our French gallants shall today draw out,
And sheathe for lack of sport: let us but blow on them,
The vapour of our valour will o'erturn them.
A very little little let us do,
And all is done. Then let the trumpets sound,
For our approach shall so much dare the field
That England shall couch down in fear and yield.

Scene 3—The English Camp

GLOUCESTER. Where is the king?

BEDFORD. The king himself is rode to view their battle.

WESTMORELAND. Of fighting men they have full three score thousand.

EXETER. There's five to one; besides, they all are fresh.

SALISBURY. God's arm strike with us! tis a fearful odds.
God be wi' you, princes all; I'll to my charge:
If we no more meet till we meet in heaven,
Then, joyfully, my noble Lord of Bedford,
My dear Lord Gloucester, and my good Lord Exeter,
And my kind kinsman, warriors all, adieu!

BEDFORD. Farewell, good Salisbury; and good luck go with thee!

EXETER. Farewell, kind lord; fight valiantly today:
And yet I do thee wrong to mind thee of it,
For thou art framed of the firm truth of valour.

BEDFORD. He is as full of valour as of kindness; princely in both.

WESTMORELAND. O that we now had here
But one ten thousand of those men in England
That do no work today!

KING. What's he that wishes so?
My cousin Westmoreland? No, my fair cousin:
If we are marked to die, we are enow
To do our country loss; and if to live,
The fewer men the greater share of honour.

God's will ! I pray thee, wish not one man more.
By Jove, I am not covetous for gold,
Nor care I who doth feed upon my cost ;
It yearns me not if men my garments wear ;
Such outward things dwell not in my desires :
But if it be a sin to covet honour
I am the most offending soul alive.
No, faith, my coz, wish not a man from England :
God's peace ! I would not lose so great an honour
As one man more, methinks, would share from me
For the best hope I have. O, do not wish one more !
Rather proclaim it, Westmoreland, through my host,
That he which hath no stomach to this fight,
Let him depart ; his passport shall be made
And crowns for convoy put into his purse :
We would not die in that man's company
That fears his fellowship to die with us.
This day is called the feast of Crispian :
He that outlives this day, and comes safe home,
Will stand a tip-toe when this day is named,
And rouse him at the name of Crispian.
He that shall live this day, and see old age,
Will yearly on the vigil feast his neighbours,
And say *Tomorrow is Saint Crispian :*
Then will he strip his sleeve and show his scars,
And say *These wounds I had on Crispin's day.*
Old men forget ; yet all shall be forgot,
But he'll remember with advantages
What feats he did that day : then shall our names,
Familiar in his mouth as household words,
Harry the king, Bedford and Exeter,
Warwick and Talbot, Salisbury and Gloucester,
Be in their flowing cups freshly remembered.
This story shall the good man teach his son,
And Crispin Crispian shall ne'er go by,
From this day to the ending of the world,
But we in it shall be rememberèd ;
We few, we happy few, we band of brothers ;
For he today that sheds his blood with me
Shall be my brother ; be he ne'er so vile,
This day shall gentle his condition ;
And gentlemen in England now a-bed
Shall think themselves accursed they were not here,
And hold their manhoods cheap whiles any speaks
That fought with us upon Saint Crispin's day.

LORD SALISBURY (*entering*). My sovereign lord, bestow yourself with speed :

The French are bravely in their battles set,
And will with all expedience charge on us.

KING. All things are ready, if our minds be so.

WESTMORELAND. Perish the man whose mind is backward now!

KING. Thou dost not wish more help from England, coz?

WESTMORELAND. God's will! my liege, would you and I alone,
Without more help, could fight this royal battle!

KING. Why, now thou hast unwished five thousand men;
Which likes me better than to wish us one.
You know your places: God be with you all! (*Enter Montjoy*)

MONTJOY. Once more I come to know of thee, King Harry,
If for thy ransom thou wilt now compound,
Before thy most assurèd overthrow.

KING. Who hath sent thee now?

MONTJOY. The Constable of France.

KING. I pray thee, bear my former answer back:
Bid them achieve me and then sell my bones.
Good God! why should they mock poor fellows thus?
The man that once did sell the lion's skin
While the beast lived was killed with hunting him.
Let me speak proudly: tell the constable
We are but warriors for the working day;
Our gayness and our gilt are all besmirched
With rainy marching in the painful field;
There's not a piece of feather in our host
(Good argument, I hope, we will not fly)
And time hath worn us into slovenry;
But, by the mass, our hearts are in the trim;
And my poor soldiers tell me yet ere night
They'll be in fresher robes or they will pluck
The gay new coats o'er the French soldiers' heads,
And turn them out of service.
Come thou no more for ransom, gentle herald:
They shall have none, I swear, but these my joints;
Which if they have as I will leave 'em them,
Shall yield them little, tell the constable.

MONTJOY. I shall, King Harry. And so fare thee well:
Thou never shalt hear herald any more.

KING. Now, soldiers, march away:
And how thou pleasest, God, dispose the day!

Scene 4—On the Battlefield

Pistol is ranging the field to gather ransom from prisoners by swagger and threats

PISTOL. Come hither, boy: ask me this slave in French
What is his name.

BOY. *Écoutez : comment êtes-vous appelé ?*

FRENCH SOLDIER. *Monsieur le Fer.*

BOY. He says his name is Master Fer.

PISTOL. Master Fer ! I'll fer him, and firk him, and ferret him : discuss the same in French unto him.

BOY. I do not know the French for fer, and ferret, and firk.

PISTOL. Bid him prepare ; for I will cut his throat.
Peasant, unless thou give me crowns, brave crowns ;
Or mangled shalt thou be by this my sword.

FRENCH SOLDIER. *O, je vous supplie, pour l'amour de Dieu, me pardonner ! Je suis gentilhomme de bonne maison : gardez ma vie, et je vous donnerai deux cents écus.*

PISTOL. What are his words ?

BOY. He prays you to save his life : he is a gentleman of a good house ; and for his ransom he will give you two hundred crowns.

PISTOL. Tell him my fury shall abate, and I
The crowns will take.

BOY. He gives you, upon his knees, a thousand thanks ; and he esteems himself happy that he hath fallen into the hands of one, as he thinks, the most brave, valorous, and thrice-worthy signieur of England.

PISTOL. As I suck blood, I will some mercy show. Follow me !

Scene 5—With the French on the Field

CONSTABLE. *O diable !*

ORLEANS. *O seigneur ! le jour est perdu, tout est perdu !*

DAUPHIN. *Mort de ma vie !* all is confounded, all !
Reproach and everlasting shame
Sits mocking in our plumes.

CONSTABLE. Why, all our ranks are broke.

DAUPHIN. O perdurable shame ! let's stab ourselves.
Be these the wretches that we played at dice for ?

ORLEANS. Is this the king we sent to for his ransom ?

BOURBON. Shame and eternal shame, nothing but shame !
Let us die in honour : once more back again.
Let life be short, else shame will be too long.

Scene 6—The Field of Battle

KING. Well have we done, thrice valiant countrymen :
But all's not done ; yet keep the French the field.

EXETER. The Duke of York commends him to your majesty.

KING. Lives he, good uncle ? Thrice within this hour
I saw him down ; thrice up again, and fighting ;
From helmet to the spur all blood he was.

EXETER. In which array, brave soldier, doth he lie,
Larding the plain; and by his wounded side,
The noble Earl of Suffolk also lies.
Suffolk first died: and York, all haggled over,
Comes to him where in gore he lay insteeped,
And takes him by the beard; kisses his face;
And cries aloud *Tarry, dear cousin Suffolk!*
My soul shall thine keep company to heaven;
Tarry, sweet soul, for mine, then fly abreast,
As in this glorious and well-foughten field
We kept together in our chivalry!
Upon these words I came and cheered him up:
He smiled me in the face, raught me his hand,
And, with a feeble grip, says *Dear my lord,*
Commend my service to my sovereign.
So did he turn, and over Suffolk's neck
He threw his wounded arm, and kissed his lips;
And, so espoused to death, with blood he sealed
A testament of noble-ending love.
The pretty and sweet manner of it forced
Those waters from me which I would have stopped;
But I had not so much of man in me,
And all my mother came into mine eyes
And gave me up to tears.
KING. I blame you not;
For, hearing this, I must perforce compound
With mistful eyes, or they will issue too.
But hark! what new alarum is this same?
The French have reinforced their scattered men:
Then every soldier kill his prisoners;
Give the word through.

Scene 7—Another Part of the Field

FLUELLEN. Kill the poys and the luggage! tis expressly against the law of arms: tis as arrant a piece of knavery, mark you now, as can be offer't; in your conscience, now, is it not?

GOWER. Tis certain there's not a boy left alive; and the cowardly rascals that ran from the battle ha' done this slaughter. Besides, they have burned and carried away all that was in the king's tent; wherefore the king, most worthily, hath caused every soldier to cut his prisoner's throat. O, tis a gallant king!

FLUELLEN. Ay, he was porn at Monmouth, Captain Gower. What call you the town's name where Alexander the Pig was born?

GOWER. Alexander the Great.

FLUELLEN. Why, I pray you, is not pig great? The pig, or the great, or the mighty, or the huge, or the magnanimous, are all one reckonings, save the phrase is a little variations.

GOWER. I think Alexander the Great was born in Macedon.

FLUELLEN. I think it is in Macedon where Alexander is porn. I tell you, captain, if you look in the maps of the world I warrant you sall find, in the comparisons between Macedon and Monmouth, that the situations, look you, is both alike. There is a river in Macedon; and there is also moreover a river at Monmouth: it is called Wye at Monmouth; but it is out of my prains what is the name of the other river; and there is salmons in both. If you mark Alexander's life well, Harry of Monmouth's life is come after it indifferent well. I'll tell you there is good men porn at Monmouth.

GOWER. Here comes his majesty.

KING. I was not angry since I came to France
Until this instant. Take a trumpet, herald;
Ride thou unto the horsemen on yon hill:
If they will fight with us bid them come down,
Or void the field; they do offend our sight:
If they'll do neither, we will come to them,
And make them skirr away, as swift as stones
Enforcèd from the old Assyrian slings:
Besides, we'll cut the throats of those we have,
And not a man of them that we shall take
Shall taste our mercy. Go and tell them so.

EXETER. Here comes the herald of the French, my liege.

GLOUCESTER. His eyes are humbler than they used to be.

KING. How now! What means this, herald? Know'st thou not
That I have fined these bones of mine for ransom?
Com'st thou again for ransom?

MONTJOY. No, great king:
I come to thee for charitable licence,
That we may wander o'er this sodden field
To look our dead, and then to bury them;
To sort our nobles from our common men.
For many of our princes (woe the while!)
Lie drowned and soakèd in mercenary blood;
So do our vulgar drench their peasant limbs
In blood of princes; and their wounded steeds
Fret fetlock deep in gore and with wild rage
Yerk out their armèd heels at their dead masters,
Killing them twice. O, give us leave, great king,
To view the field in safety and dispose
Of their dead bodies!

KING. I tell thee truly, herald,
I know not if the day be ours or no;
For yet a many of your horsemen peer
And gallop o'er the field.

MONTJOY. The day is yours.

KING. Praisêd be God, and not our strength, for it!
What is this castle called that stands hard by?

MONTJOY. They call it Agincourt.

KING. Then call we this the Field of Agincourt,
Fought on the day of Crispin Crispianus.

FLUELLEN. Your grandfather of famous memory, an't please your majesty, and your great-uncle Edward the Plack Prince of Wales, as I have read in the chronicles, fought a most prave battle here in France.

KING. They did, Fluellen.

FLUELLEN. Your majesty says very true: if your majesties is remembered of it, the Welshmen did good service in a garden where leeks did grow, wearing leeks in their Monmouth caps—which, your majesty know, to this hour is an honourable badge of the service; and I do believe your majesty takes no scorn to wear the leek upon Saint Tavy's day.

KING. I wear it for a memorable honour;
For I am Welsh, you know, good countryman.

FLUELLEN. All the water in Wye cannot wash your majesty's Welsh plood out of your pody, I can tell you that: God pless it and preserve it, as long as it pleases his grace, and his majesty too!

KING. Thanks, good my countryman.

FLUELLEN. I am your majesty's countryman, I care not who know it; I will confess it to all the world: I need not to be ashamed of your majesty, praised be God, so long as your majesty is an honest man.

KING. God keep me so! Our heralds go with him:
Bring me just notice of the numbers dead
On both our parts. Call yonder fellow hither.

EXETER. Soldier, you must come to the king.

KING. Soldier, why wearest thou that glove in thy cap?

WILLIAMS. An't please your majesty, tis the gage of one that I should fight withal, if he be alive.

KING. An Englishman?

WILLIAMS. An't please your majesty, a rascal that swaggered with me last night; who, if alive and ever dare to challenge this glove, I have sworn to take him a box o' the ear: or if I can see my glove in his cap (which he swore, as he was a soldier, he would wear if alive), I will strike it out soundly.

KING. What think you, Captain Fluellen? Is it fit this soldier keep his oath?

FLUELLEN. He is a craven and a villain else, an't please your majesty, in my conscience.

KING. It may be his enemy is a gentleman of great sort, quite from the answer of his degree.

FLUELLEN. Though he be as good a gentleman as the devil is, it is necessary that he keep his vow and his oath.

KING. Then keep thy vow, sirrah, when thou meetest the fellow.

WILLIAMS. So I will, my liege, as I live.

KING. Whom servest thou under ?

WILLIAMS. Under Captain Gower, my liege.

FLUELLEN. Gower is a good captain, and is good knowledge and literatured in the wars.

KING. Call him hither to me, soldier.

WILLIAMS. I will, my liege.

KING. Here, Fluellen ; wear thou this favour for me and stick it in thy cap : when Alençon and myself were down together, I plucked this glove from his helm : if any man challenge this, he is a friend to Alençon, and an enemy to our person ; if thou encounter any such, apprehend him, an thou dost me love.

FLUELLEN. Your grace does me as great honours as can be desired in the hearts of his subjects : I would fain see the man that has but two legs that shall find himself aggriefed at this glove ; that is all ; please God of his grace that I might see.

KING. Knowest thou Gower ?

FLUELLEN. He is my dear friend, an please you.

KING. Pray thee, go seek him, and bring him to my tent.

FLUELLEN. I will fetch him.

KING. My Lord of Warwick, and my brother Gloucester,
Follow Fluellen closely at the heels :
The glove which I have given him for a favour
May haply purchase him a box o' the ear ;
It is the soldier's ; I by bargain should
Wear it myself. Follow, good cousin Warwick :
If that the soldier strike him, as I judge
By his blunt bearing he will keep his word,
Some sudden mischief may arise of it ;
For I do know Fluellen valiant
And, touched with choler, hot as gunpowder,
And quickly will return an injury :
Follow, and see there be no harm between them.

Scene 8—Before King Henry's Pavilion

FLUELLEN (*to Gower*). God's will and his pleasure, captain, I beseech you now come apace to the king ; there is more good toward you peradventure than is in your knowledge to dream of.

WILLIAMS. Sir, know you this glove ?

FLUELLEN. Know the glove ! I know the glove is a glove.

WILLIAMS. I know this ; and thus I challenge it. (*Strikes him*)

Fluellen. An arrant traitor as any is in the universal world, or in France, or in England!

Gower (*to Williams*). How now, sir! you villain!

Williams. Do you think I'll be forsworn?

Fluellen. Stand away, Captain Gower; I will give treason his payment into plows, I warrant you.

Williams. I am no traitor.

Fluellen. That's a lie in thy throat. I charge you in his majesty's name, apprehend him: he's a friend of the Duke Alençon.

Warwick (*entering*). How now, how now! what's the matter?

Fluellen. My Lord of Warwick, here is—praised be God for it!—a most contagious treason come to light, look you, as you shall desire in a summer's day. Here is his majesty.

King (*entering*). How now! what's the matter?

Fluellen. My liege, here is a villain and a traitor, that, look your grace, has struck the glove which your majesty is take out of the helmet of Alençon.

Williams. My liege, this was my glove; here is the fellow of it; and he that I gave it to in change promised to wear it in his cap: I promised to strike him if he did: I met this man with my glove in his cap, and I have been as good as my word.

Fluellen. Your majesty hear now, saving your majesty's manhood, what an arrant, rascally, beggarly, lousy knave it is: I hope your majesty is pear me testimony and witness that this is the glove of Alençon, that your majesty is give me; in your conscience, now?

King. Give me thy glove, soldier: look, here is the fellow of it.
'Twas I, indeed, thou promised'st to strike;
And thou hast given me most bitter terms.

Fluellen. An please your majesty, let his neck answer for it, if there is any martial law in the world.

King. How canst thou make me satisfaction?

Williams. All offences, my lord, come from the heart: never came any from mine that might offend your majesty.

King. It was ourself thou didst abuse.

Williams. Your majesty came not like yourself: you appeared to me but as a common man; witness the night, your garments, your lowliness; and what your highness suffered under that shape I beseech you take it for your own fault and not mine, for had you been as I took you for I made no offence; therefore, I beseech your highness, pardon me.

King. Here, uncle Exeter, fill this glove with crowns,
And give it to this fellow. Keep it, fellow;
And wear it for an honour in thy cap

Till I do challenge it. Give him the crowns:
And, captain, you must needs be friends with him.

FLUELLEN. By this day and this light, the fellow has mettle enough. Hold, there is twelve pence for you; and I pray you to serve Got, and keep you out of prawls, and prabbles, and quarrels, and dissensions.

WILLIAMS. I will none of your money.

FLUELLEN. It is with a good will; I can tell you, it will serve you to mend your shoes: come, wherefore should you be so pashful? Your shoes is not so good; tis a good shilling, I warrant you, or I will change it.

Enter an English Herald

KING. Now, herald, are the dead numbered?

HERALD. Here is the number of the slaughtered French.

KING. This note doth tell me of ten thousand French
That in the field lie slain: of princes, in this number,
And nobles bearing banners, there lie dead
One hundred twenty-six: added to these,
Of knights, esquires, and gallant gentlemen,
Eight thousand and four hundred; of the which,
Five hundred were but yesterday dubbed knights:
So that, in these ten thousand they have lost,
There are but sixteen hundred mercenaries;
The rest are princes, barons, lords, knights, squires,
And gentlemen of blood and quality.
Here was a royal fellowship of death!
Where is the number of our English dead?

The Herald shows him another paper

Edward the Duke of York, the Earl of Suffolk,
Sir Richard Ketly, Davy Gam, esquire:
None else of name; and of all other men
But five and twenty. O God, thy arm was here;
And not to us, but to thy arm alone,
Ascribe we all!
Come, go we in procession to the village:
And be it death proclaimèd through our host
To boast of this or take that praise from God
Which is his only.

FLUELLEN. Is it not lawful, an please your majesty, to tell how many is killed?

KING. Yes, captain; but with this acknowledgment,
That God fought for us.

FLUELLEN. Yes, my conscience; he did us great good.

KING. Do we all holy rites:
We'll then to Calais; and to England then,
Where ne'er from France arrived more happy men.

ACT 5

CHORUS. Now we bear the king
Toward Calais: grant him there; there seen,
Heave him away upon your wingêd thoughts
Athwart the sea. Behold the English beach
Pales in the flood with men, with wives and boys,
Whose shouts and claps out-voice the deep-mouthed sea.
Now behold,
In the quick forge and working-house of thought,
How London doth pour out her citizens!
The mayor and all his brethren in best sort,
With the plebeians swarming at their heels,
Go forth and fetch their conquering Caesar in.

Scene 1—The English Camp in France

GOWER. Nay, that's right; but why wear you your leek today? Saint Davy's day is past.

FLUELLEN. There is occasions and causes why and wherefore in all things: I will tell you, asse my friend, Captain Gower: the rascally, scald, beggarly, lousy, pragging knave, Pistol, which you and yourself and all the world know to be no better than a fellow, look you now, of no merits, he is come to me and prings me pread and salt yesterday, look you, and bid me eat my leek: it was in a place where I could not breed no contention with him; but I will be so bold as to wear it in my cap till I see him once again, and then I will tell him a little piece of my desires. (*Here Pistol comes*)

GOWER. Why, here he comes, swelling like a turkey-cock.

FLUELLEN. Tis no matter for his swellings nor his turkey-cocks. God pless you, Aunchient Pistol! you scurvy, lousy knave, God pless you!

PISTOL. Ha! art thou bedlam? dost thou thirst, base Trojan? Hence! I am qualmish at the smell of leek.

FLUELLEN. I peseech you heartily, scurvy, lousy knave, at my desires, and my requests, and my petitions, to eat this leek.

PISTOL. Not for Cadwallader and all his goats.

FLUELLEN. There is one goat for you (*striking him*). Will you be so good, scald knave, as eat it?

PISTOL. Base Trojan, thou shalt die.

FLUELLEN. You say very true, scald knave, when God's will is: I will desire you to live in the meantime, and eat your victuals: come, there is sauce for it (*striking him*). You called me yesterday mountain-squire; but I will make you today a squire of low degree. I pray you, fall to: if you can mock a leek you can eat a leek.

GOWER. Enough, captain: you have astonished him.

FLUELLEN. I say I will make him eat some part of my leek, or I will peat his pate four days. Bite, I pray you.

PISTOL. Must I bite?

FLUELLEN. Yes, certainly, and out of doubt and out of question too, and ambiguities.

PISTOL. By this leek, I will most horribly revenge; I eat and eat, I swear—

FLUELLEN. Eat, I pray you: will you have some more sauce to your leek? There is not enough leek to swear by.

PISTOL. Quiet thy cudgel; thou dost see I eat.

FLUELLEN. Nay, pray you, throw none away; the skin is good for your broken coxcomb. When you take occasions to see leeks hereafter, I pray you, mock at 'em; that is all.

PISTOL. Good.

FLUELLEN. Ay, leeks is good: hold you, there is a groat to heal your pate.

PISTOL. Me a groat!

FLUELLEN. Yes, verily and in truth, you shall take it; or I have another leek in my pocket, which you shall eat.

PISTOL. I take thy groat in earnest of revenge.

FLUELLEN. If I owe you anything I will pay you in cudgels: you shall be a woodmonger, and buy nothing of me but cudgels. God be wi' you, and keep you, and heal your pate. (*He leaves*)

PISTOL. All hell shall stir for this.

GOWER. Go, go; you are a counterfeit cowardly knave. Will you mock at an ancient tradition, and dare not avouch in your deeds any of your words? I have seen you gleeking and galling at this gentleman twice or thrice. You thought, because he could not speak English in the native garb, he could not therefore handle an English cudgel: you find it otherwise; and henceforth let a Welsh correction teach you a good English condition. Fare ye well.

PISTOL. Doth Fortune play the huswife with me now!
News have I that my Nell is dead.
To England will I steal, and there I'll steal:
And patches will I get unto these cudgelled scars,
And swear I got them in the Gallia wars.

Scene 2—A Royal Palace in France

Enter King Henry and lords; French King and ladies

KING HENRY. Peace to this meeting, wherefore we are met!
Unto our brother France, and to our sister,
Health and fair time of day; joy and good wishes
To our most fair and princely cousin Katharine;
And, princes French, and peers, health to you all!

CHARLES. Right joyous are we to behold your face,

Most worthy brother England; fairly met:
So are you, princes English, every one.

ISABEL. So happy be the issue, brother England,
Of this good day and of this gracious meeting,
As we are now glad to behold your eyes.
You English princes all, I do salute you.

BURGUNDY. My duty to you both, on equal love,
Great Kings of France and England! Let it not disgrace me
If I demand, before this royal view,
What rub or what impediment there is,
Why that the naked, poor, and mangled Peace,
Dear nurse of arts, plenties, and joyful births,
Should not in this best garden of the world
Our fertile France, put up her lovely visage?
Alas, she hath from France too long been chased,
And all her husbandry doth lie on heaps,
Corrupting in its own fertility.
Her vine, the merry cheerer of the heart,
Unprunèd dies; her hedges even-pleached,
Like prisoners wildly overgrown with hair
Put forth disordered twigs; her fallow leas
The darnel, hemlock, and rank fumitory
Doth root upon . . . and nothing teems
But hateful docks, rough thistles, kecksies, burs,
Losing both beauty and utility.
And as our vineyards, fallows, meads, and hedges,
Defective in their natures, grow to wildness,
Even so our houses and ourselves and children
Have lost, or do not learn for want of time,
The sciences that should become our country;
But grow like savages. . . My speech entreats
That I may know why gentle Peace
Should not expel these inconveniences
And bless us with her former qualities.

KING. If, Duke of Burgundy, you would the peace,
Whose want gives growth to the imperfections
Which you have cited, you must buy that peace
With full accord to all our just demands;
Whose tenours and particular effects
You have enscheduled briefly in your hands.

BURGUNDY. The king hath heard them; to the which as yet
There is no answer made.

CHARLES. I have but with a cursorary eye
O'erglanced the articles: pleaseth your grace
To appoint some of your council presently
To sit with us once more.

KING. Brother, we shall. Go, uncle Exeter,
And brother Clarence, and you, brother Gloucester,
Warwick and Huntingdon, go with the King;
And take with you free power to ratify,
Augment, or alter, as your wisdoms best
Shall see advantageable for our dignity,
Anything in or out of our demands.

ISABEL. Our gracious brother, I will go with them:
Haply a woman's voice may do some good,
When articles too nicely urged be stood on.

KING. Yet leave our cousin Katharine here with us:
She is our capital demand, comprised
Within the fore-rank of our articles. (*They leave*)
Fair Katharine, and most fair,
Will you vouchsafe to teach a soldier terms
Such as will enter at a lady's ear
And plead his love-suit to her gentle heart?

KATHARINE. Your majesty shall mock at me; I cannot speak your England.

KING. O fair Katharine, if you will love me soundly with your French heart I will be glad to hear you confess it brokenly with your English tongue. Do you like me, Kate?

KATHARINE. *Pardonnez-moi,* I cannot tell vat is *like me.*

KING. An angel is like you, Kate, and you are like an angel.

KATHARINE. *Que dit-il? que je suis semblable à les anges?*

KING. I said so, dear Katharine; and I must not blush to affirm it. I' faith, Kate, my wooing is fit for thy understanding. I am glad thou canst speak no better English; for, if thou couldst, thou wouldst find me such a plain king that thou wouldst think I had sold my farm to buy my crown. I know no ways to mince it in love, but directly to say *I love you*: then if you urge me further than to say *Do you in faith?* I wear out my suit. Give me your answer; i' faith, do; and so clap hands and a bargain. How say you, lady?

KATHARINE. *Sauf votre honneur,* me understand vell.

KING. Marry, if you would put me to verses or to dance for your sake, Kate, why, you undid me. If I could win a lady at leap-frog, or by vaulting into my saddle with my armour on my back (under the correction of bragging be it spoken) I should quickly leap into a wife. Or if I might buffet for my love, or bound my horse for her favours, I could lay on like a butcher and sit like a jackanapes, never off. But, before God, Kate, I cannot look greenly nor gasp out my eloquence, nor I have no cunning in protestation; only downright oaths, which I never use till urged, nor never break for urging. If thou canst love a fellow of this temper, Kate, whose face is not worth sunburning, that never looks in his glass for love of anything he sees there, let thine eye be thy cook. I speak to thee plain soldier: if thou canst love me for this, take me; if not, to say to thee that I shall die is true; but for thy love, by the Lord, no: yet I love thee too. And while thou livest, dear Kate, take a fellow of plain and uncoined constancy; for he perforce must do thee right, because he hath not the gift to woo in other places: for these fellows of infinite tongue, that can rhyme themselves into ladies' favours, they do always reason themselves out again. What! a speaker is but a prater; a rhyme is but a ballad. A good leg will fall; a straight back will stoop; a black beard will turn white; a curled pate will grow bald; a fair face will wither; a full eye will wax hollow: but a good heart, Kate, is the sun and the moon, or rather the sun and not the moon, for it shines bright and never changes, but keeps his course truly. If thou would have such a one, take me; and take me, take a soldier; take a soldier, take a king. And what sayest thou then to my love? Speak, my fair, and fairly, I pray thee.

KATHARINE. Is it possible dat I sould love de enemy of France?

KING. No; it is not possible you should love the enemy of France, Kate: but, in loving me, you should love the friend of France; for I love France so well that I will not part with a village of it: I will have it all mine; and, Kate, when France is mine and I am yours, then yours is France and you are mine.

KATHARINE. I cannot tell vat is dat.

KING. No, Kate? I will tell thee in French; which I am sure will hang upon my tongue like a new-married wife about her husband's neck, hardly to be shook off. *Je quand sur le possession de France, et quand vous avez le possession de moi*—let me see, what then? Saint Denis be my speed!—*donc votre est France et vous êtes mienne.* It is as easy for me, Kate, to conquer the kingdom as to speak so much more French. But, Kate, dost thou understand thus much English, canst thou love me?

KATHARINE. I cannot tell.

KING. Can any of your neighbours tell, Kate? By mine honour, in true English, I love thee, Kate: by which honour I dare not swear thou lovest me; yet my blood begins to flatter me that thou dost, and therefore tell me, most fair Katharine, will you have me? Put off your maiden blushes; avouch the thoughts of your heart with the looks of an empress; take me by the hand, and say *Harry of England, I am thine*: which word thou shalt no sooner bless mine ear withal, but I will tell thee aloud *England is thine, Ireland is thine, France is thine, and Henry Plantagenet is thine*; who, though I speak it before his face, if he be not fellow with the best king, thou shalt find the best king of good fellows. Come, your answer in broken music; for thy voice is music and thy English broken; therefore, queen of all, Katharine, break thy mind to me in broken English; wilt thou have me?

KATHARINE. Dat is as it sall please *de roi mon père.*

KING. Nay, it will please him well, Kate; it *shall* please him, Kate.

KATHARINE. Den it sall also content me.

KING. Upon that I kiss your hand, and I call you my queen.

KATHARINE. *Laissez, mon seigneur, laissez, laissez: ma foi, je ne veux point que vous abaissiez votre grandeur en baisant la main d'une de votre seigneurie indigne serviteur; excusez-moi, je vous supplie, mon très-puissant seigneur.*

KING. Then I will kiss your lips, Kate.

KATHARINE. *Les dames et demoiselles pour être baisées devant leur noces, il n'est pas la coutume de France.*

KING. It is not a fashion for the maids in France to kiss before they are married, would she say?

ALICE. *Oui, vraiment.*

KING. O Kate, nice customs curtsey to great kings. Dear Kate, you and I cannot be confined within the weak list of a country's fashion. We are the makers of manners, Kate; and the liberty that follows our places stops the mouth of all find-faults; as I will do yours, for upholding the nice fashion of your country in denying me a kiss: therefore, patiently and yielding. You have witchcraft in your lips, Kate: there is more eloquence in a sugar touch of them than in the tongues of the French Council; and they should sooner persuade Harry of England than a general petition of monarchs. Here comes your father.

CHARLES. We have consented to all terms of reason.

KING. Is't so, my lords of England?

WESTMORELAND. The king hath granted every article:
His daughter first.

CHARLES. Take her, fair son, and from her blood raise up
Issue to me; that the contending kingdoms
Of France and England, whose very shores look pale
With envy of each other's happiness,
May cease their hatred, and this dear conjunction
Plant neighbourhood and Christian-like accord
In their sweet bosoms, that never war advance
His bleeding sword 'twixt England and fair France.

ALL. Amen!

KING. Now, welcome, Kate: and bear me witness all,
That here I kiss her as my sovereign queen.

ISABEL. God, the best maker of all marriages,
Combine your hearts in one, your realms in one!

ALL. Amen.

KING. Prepare we for our marriage: on which day,
My Lord of Burgundy, we'll take your oath,
And all the peers', for surety of our leagues.
Then shall I swear to Kate, and you to me;
And may our oaths well kept and prosperous be!

The Story of Twelfth Night

TWELFTH NIGHT is one of the lightest and brightest of Shakespeare's plays. It is probably the latest comedy of his brightest period, when he had become successful and was brimming with high spirits, before he reached his tragic mood.

IT was written in 1600 or 1601, and was played for the first time within a stone's throw of Fleet Street, in the beautiful Hall of the Middle Temple, about the beginning of 1602. Queen Elizabeth is said to have been there, and we may be sure that Shakespeare was.

FOR the main plot of the play Shakespeare went once more to the Italian stage, where the idea of Twelfth Night had been used in several comedies; but he improved the characters of the old stories beyond all recognition. The play makes use of the old stage device of confusing two people who are very much alike, an idea which Shakespeare uses in two other plays. Depending on this confusion of identity, Twelfth Night gains much by being seen rather than read. Its poetical beauties are rich and abundant, but its lighter parts appeal to us more strongly when we see them played.

WE see in Twelfth Night the fine influence of the life of a bright and natural girl; perhaps it may make us think of the girl who passes in and out among little groups of Italian people in one of Robert Browning's poems and sings the famous song which ends: *God's in His Heaven, All's right with the World.*

IN this play are several people living artificial lives, their minds unbalanced by being self-centred and self-conscious. There is an unhealthy atmosphere about the life of two rich houses. Olivia is moping with an unreal sentimentality for her lost brother. The Duke Orsino imagines himself to be in love with Olivia, but is rather dotingly in love with love, and not with anybody in particular. Into the midst of these two comes Viola, a girl of great beauty and charm, modest, true, and unselfish; and her coming is a blessing to all concerned. She bursts into this little world of artificial life and brings it back to Nature.

SHAKESPEARE is here laughing with us at some of the follies and fantastic fancies of mankind. He is in the best of humours, but is showing up some of Life's little realities. He is being rather like a caricaturist in the newspaper, who shows things off by exaggeration, and holds up folly to ridicule. We see this especially in the famous and pompous character of Malvolio, who is made ridiculous by his artificial manner and the mighty airs he gives himself. The coarser characters of the play have coarser follies, and almost all the players have parts more or less artificial. So it is that we love the one truly natural figure in the play, the incomparable Viola, one of the rarest and brightest of all the women who live and move in Shakespeare.

THE PLAYERS

Olivia, a rich young lady of Illyria, whom several suitors wish to marry, but who lives retired in grief for her dead brother.

Orsino, Duke of Illyria, a fanciful and romantic suitor imagining himself in love with Olivia.

Viola, a young Italian lady of great charm, wrecked on the coast of Illyria. Dressed as a youth, she becomes the Duke's page and his messenger to Olivia.

Sebastian, twin brother of Viola, and her exact likeness. He, too, is wrecked, and each fears that the other is drowned.

A Sea Captain, who rescues Viola and finds her a disguise.

Antonio, a sea captain who rescues Sebastian and accompanies him to the Duke's city, though he is in danger there.

Sir Toby Belch, a boisterous, tipsy uncle of Olivia, attached to her household but not wanted there.

Sir Andrew Aguecheek, a wealthy, foolish, countryfied suitor of Olivia, who is encouraged by Sir Toby for the sake of his money.

Malvolio, Olivia's steward, busy keeping order, pompous and self-satisfied, with no sense of humour, and under the delusion that his mistress is in love with him ; a ready butt for sharper people.

Maria, Olivia's maid, a keen-witted woman full of fun.

Valentine and Curio, attendants on the Duke.

Fabian, a servant of Olivia.

Clown, an excellent fool, singing quaint and melancholy songs.

Other attendants and officers.

SCENES—A city of Illyria, and the sea-coast close by.

Twelfth Night

ACT 1

Scene 1—The Duke's Palace

DUKE. If music be the food of love, play on;
Give me excess of it, that, surfeiting
The appetite may sicken, and so die.
That strain again! it had a dying fall:
O, it came o'er my ear like the sweet sound
That breathes upon a bank of violets,
Stealing and giving odour! Enough; no more:
Tis not so sweet now as it was before.

CURIO. Will you go hunt, my lord?

DUKE. What, Curio?

CURIO. The hart.

DUKE. Why, so I do, the noblest that I have:
O, when mine eyes did see Olivia first,
Methought she purged the air of pestilence!
That instant was I turned into a hart;
And my desires, like fell and cruel hounds,
E'er since pursue me.
(*To Valentine, entering*) How now! what news from her?

VALENTINE. So please my lord, I might not be admitted;
But from her handmaid do return this answer:
The element itself, till seven years' heat,
Shall not behold her face at ample view;
But, like a cloistress, she will veilèd walk
And water once a day her chamber round
With eye-offending brine: all this to season
A brother's dead love, which she would keep fresh
And lasting in her sad remembrance.

DUKE. O, she that hath a heart of that fine frame
To pay this debt of love but to a brother,
How will she love, when the rich golden shaft
Hath killed the flock of all affections else
That live in her; when liver, brain, and heart,
These sovereign thrones, are all supplied, and filled
Her sweet perfections with one self king!

Away before me to sweet beds of flowers:
Love-thoughts lie rich when canopied with bowers.

Scene 2—The Sea-Coast

VIOLA. What country, friends, is this?

CAPTAIN. This is Illyria, lady.

VIOLA. And what should I do in Illyria?
My brother he is in Elysium.
Perchance he is not drowned: what think you, sailors?

CAPTAIN. It is perchance that you yourself were saved.

VIOLA. O my poor brother! and so perchance may he be.

CAPTAIN. True, madam: and, to comfort you with chance,
Assure yourself, after our ship did split,
When you and those poor number saved with you
Hung on our driving boat, I saw your brother,
Most provident in peril, bind himself,
Courage and hope both teaching him the practice,
To a strong mast that lived upon the sea;
Where, like Arion on the dolphin's back,
I saw him hold acquaintance with the waves
So long as I could see.

VIOLA. For saying so, there's gold. Know'st thou this country?

CAPTAIN. Ay, madam, well; for I was bred and born
Not three hours' travel from this very place.

VIOLA. Who governs here?

CAPTAIN. A noble duke, in nature as in name.

VIOLA. What is his name?

CAPTAIN. Orsino.

VIOLA. Orsino! I have heard my father name him:
He was a bachelor then.

CAPTAIN. And so is now, or was so very late;
For but a month ago I went from hence,
And then 'twas fresh in murmur (as you know,
What great ones do the less will prattle of)
That he did seek the love of fair Olivia.

VIOLA. What's she?

CAPTAIN. A virtuous maid, the daughter of a count
That died some twelvemonth since, then leaving her
In the protection of his son, her brother,
Who shortly also died; for whose dear love,
They say, she hath abjured the company
And sight of men.

VIOLA. O that I served that lady,
And might not be delivered to the world

Till I had made mine own occasion mellow,
What my estate is!

CAPTAIN. That were hard to compass;
Because she will admit no kind of suit,
No, not the duke's.

VIOLA. There is a fair behaviour in thee, captain;
And though that nature with a beauteous wall
Doth oft close in pollution, yet of thee
I will believe thou hast a mind that suits
With this thy fair and outward character.
I prithee (and I'll pay thee bounteously)
Conceal me what I am. I'll serve this duke:
Thou shalt present me as a page to him:
It may be worth thy pains, for I can sing
And speak to him in many sorts of music
That will allow me very worth his service.
What else may hap to time I will commit;
Only shape thou thy silence to my wit.

CAPTAIN. Be you his page, then, and your mute I'll be:
When my tongue blabs, then let mine eyes not see.

VIOLA. I thank thee: lead me on.

Scene 3—Olivia's House

SIR TOBY BELCH. What a plague means my niece, to take the death of her brother thus? I am sure care's an enemy to life.

MARIA. By my troth, Sir Toby, you must come in earlier o' nights; your cousin, my lady, takes great exceptions to your ill hours. That quaffing and drinking will undo you. I heard my lady talk of it yesterday; and of a foolish knight that you brought in one night here to be her wooer.

SIR TOBY. Who, Sir Andrew Aguecheek?

MARIA. Ay, he.

SIR TOBY. He's as tall a man as any in Illyria.

MARIA. What's that to the purpose?

SIR TOBY. Why, he has three thousand ducats a year.

MARIA. Ay, but he'll have but a year in all these ducats; he's a very fool and a prodigal.

SIR TOBY. Fie, that you'll say so! He plays o' the viol-de-gamboys, and speaks three or four languages word for word without book, and hath all the good gifts of nature.

MARIA. He hath indeed, almost natural; for, besides that he's a fool, he's a great quarreller. Moreover, he's drunk nightly in your company.

SIR TOBY. With drinking healths to my niece: I'll drink to her as long as there is a passage in my throat and drink in Illyria.

He's a coward and a coystrill that will not drink to my niece till his brains turn like a parish-top. Here comes Sir Andrew Agueface.

Sir Andrew. Sir Toby Belch! how now, Sir Toby Belch

Sir Toby. Sweet Sir Andrew!

Sir Andrew. Faith, I'll home tomorrow, Sir Toby: your niece will not be seen; or, if she be, it's four to one she'll none of me. The count himself here hard by woos her.

Sir Toby. She'll none o' the count: she'll not match above her degree, neither in estate, years, nor wit; I have heard her swear't. Tut, there's life in't, man.

Sir Andrew. I'll stay a month longer. I am a fellow o' the strangest mind i' the world; I delight in masques and revels.

Scene 4—The Duke's Palace

Valentine. If the duke continue these favours towards you, Cesario, you are like to be much advanced: he hath known you but three days, and already you are no stranger.

Viola (*as a boy*). You either fear his humour or my negligence, that you call in question the continuance of his love: is he inconstant, sir, in his favours?

Valentine. No, believe me.

Viola. I thank you. Here comes the count.

Duke. Who saw Cesario, ho?

Viola. On your attendance, my lord; here.

Duke. Stand you a while aloof. Cesario,
Thou know'st no less but all; I have unclasped
To thee the book even of my secret soul:
Therefore, good youth, address thy gait unto her;
Be not denied access, stand at her doors,
And tell them there thy fixèd foot shall grow
Till thou have audience.

Viola. Sure, my noble lord,
If she be so abandoned to her sorrow
As it is spoke, she never will admit me.

Duke. Be clamorous and leap all civil bounds
Rather than make unprofited return.

Viola. Say I do speak with her, my lord, what then?

Duke. O, then unfold the passion of my love,
Surprise her with discourse of my dear faith:
It shall become thee well to act my woes;
She will attend it better in thy youth
Than in a nuncio's of more grave aspect.

Viola. I think not so, my lord.

Duke. Dear lad, believe it;

I know thy constellation is right apt
For this affair. Some four or five attend him;
All, if you will; for I myself am best
When least in company. Prosper well in this,
And thou shalt live as freely as thy lord,
To call his fortunes thine.

VIOLA. I'll do my best
To woo your lady: (*aside*) yet, a barful strife!
Whoe'er I woo, myself would be his wife.

Scene 5—Olivia's House

MARIA (*to Clown*). Nay, either tell me where thou hast been, or I will not open my lips so wide as a bristle may enter in way of thy excuse; my lady will hang thee for thy absence. Here comes my lady: make your excuse wisely; you were best.

CLOWN. God bless thee, lady!

OLIVIA. Take the fool away.

CLOWN. Do you not hear, fellows? Take away the lady.

OLIVIA. Sir, I bade them take away you.

CLOWN. Good madonna, give me leave to prove you a fool.

OLIVIA. Can you do it?

CLOWN. Dexteriously, good madonna.

OLIVIA. Make your proof.

CLOWN. I must catechise you for it, madonna.

OLIVIA. Well, sir, for want of other idleness, I'll bide your proof.

CLOWN. Good madonna, why mournest thou?

OLIVIA. Good fool, for my brother's death.

CLOWN. I think his soul is in hell, madonna.

OLIVIA. I know his soul is in heaven, fool.

CLOWN. The more fool, madonna, to mourn for your brother's soul being in heaven. Take away the fool, gentlemen.

OLIVIA. What think you of this fool, Malvolio? Doth he not mend?

MALVOLIO. Yes, and shall do till the pangs of death shake him. Infirmity, that decays the wise, doth ever make the better fool.

CLOWN. God send you, sir, a speedy infirmity, for the better increasing your folly! Sir Toby will be sworn that I am no fox; but he will not pass his word for twopence that you are no fool.

OLIVIA. How say you to that, Malvolio?

MALVOLIO. I marvel your ladyship takes delight in such a barren rascal. I saw him put down the other day with an ordinary fool that has no more brain than a stone. Look you now, he's out of his guard already; unless you laugh and minister occasion to him he is gagged. I protest, I take these wise men, that crow so at these set kind of fools, no better than the fools' zanies.

OLIVIA. O, you are sick of self-love, Malvolio, and taste with a distempered appetite. To be generous, guiltless, and of free disposition, is to take those things for bird-bolts that you deem cannon-bullets: there is no slander in an allowed fool, though he do nothing but rail; nor no railing in a known discreet man, though he do nothing but reprove.

MARIA (*entering*). Madam, there is at the gate a young gentleman much desires to speak with you.

OLIVIA. From the Count Orsino, is it?

MARIA. I know not, madam: tis a fair young man, and well attended.

OLIVIA. Who of my people hold him in delay?

MARIA. Sir Toby, madam, your kinsman.

OLIVIA. Fetch him off, I pray you; he speaks nothing but madman: fie on him! Go you, Malvolio: if it be a suit from the count, I am sick, or not at home; what you will, to dismiss it. Now (*to Clown*) you see, sir, how your fooling grows old, and people dislike it.

CLOWN. Thou hast spoke for us, madonna, as if thy eldest son should be a fool.

MALVOLIO (*returning*). Madam, yond young fellow swears he will speak with you. I told him you were sick; he takes on him to understand so much, and therefore comes to speak with you. I told him you were asleep; he seems to have a foreknowledge of that too, and therefore comes to speak with you. What is to be said to him, lady? he's fortified against any denial.

OLIVIA. Tell him he shall not speak with me.

MALVOLIO. Has been told so; and he says he'll stand at your door like a sheriff's post, and be the supporter to a bench, but he'll speak with you.

OLIVIA. What kind o' man is he?

MALVOLIO. Why, of mankind.

OLIVIA. What manner of man?

MALVOLIO. Of very ill manner; he'll speak with you, will you or no.

OLIVIA. Of what personage and years is he?

MALVOLIO. Not yet old enough for a man, nor young enough for a boy; as a squash is before tis a peascod, or a codling when tis almost an apple: tis with him between boy and man. He is very well-favoured and he speaks very shrewishly.

OLIVIA. Let him approach: call in my gentlewoman.
(*To Maria*) Give me my veil: come, throw it o'er my face.
We'll once more hear Orsino's embassy.

VIOLA (*entering*). The honourable lady of the house, which is she?

OLIVIA. Speak to me; I shall answer for her. Your will?

VIOLA. Most radiant, exquisite, and unmatchable beauty. I pray you, tell me if this be the lady of the house, for I never saw her: I would be loth to cast away my speech, for, besides that it is excellently well penned, I have taken great pains to con it. Good beauties, let me sustain no scorn.

OLIVIA. Whence came you, sir?

VIOLA. I can say little more than I have studied, and that question's out of my part. Good gentle one, give me modest assurance if you be the lady of the house, that I may proceed.

OLIVIA. Are you a comedian?

VIOLA. No, my profound heart: and yet, by the very fangs of malice I swear, I am not that I play. Are you the lady of the house?

OLIVIA. If I do not usurp myself, I am.

VIOLA. Most certain, if you are she, you do usurp yourself; for what is yours to bestow is not yours to reserve. But this is from my commission: I will on with my speech in your praise, and then show you the heart of my message.

OLIVIA. Come to what is important in't: I forgive you the praise.

VIOLA. Alas, I took great pains to study it, and tis poetical.

OLIVIA. It is the more like to be feigned: I pray you, keep it in. I heard you were saucy at my gates, and allowed your approach rather to wonder at you than to hear you. Speak your office.

VIOLA. It alone concerns your ear. I bring no overture of war, no taxation of homage: I hold the olive in my hand; my words are as full of peace as matter.

OLIVIA. Yet you began rudely. What are you? What would you?

VIOLA. The rudeness that hath appeared in me have I learned from my entertainment. What I am, and what I would, are to your ears divinity, to any other's profanation.

OLIVIA. Give us the place alone: we will hear this divinity. Now, sir, what is your text?

VIOLA. Most sweet lady—

OLIVIA. A comfortable doctrine, and much may be said of it. Where lies your text?

VIOLA. In Orsino's bosom.

OLIVIA. In his bosom! In what chapter of his bosom?

VIOLA. To answer by the method, in the first of his heart.

OLIVIA. O, I have read it: it is heresy. Have you no more to say?

VIOLA. Good madam, let me see your face.

OLIVIA. Have you any commission from your lord to negotiate with my face? You are now out of your text, but we will draw the curtain and show you the picture. Look you, sir (*unveiling*) such a one I was this present: is't not well done?

VIOLA. Excellently done, if God did all.

OLIVIA. Tis in grain, sir; 'twill endure wind and weather.

VIOLA. Tis beauty truly blent, whose red and white
Nature's own sweet and cunning hand laid on:
Lady, you are the cruellest she alive
If you will lead these graces to the grave
And leave the world no copy.

OLIVIA. O, sir, I will not be so hard-hearted; I will give out divers schedules of my beauty. It shall be inventoried, and every particle and utensil labelled to my will: as, *item*, two lips, indifferent red; *item*, two grey eyes, with lids to them; *item*, one neck, one chin, and so forth. Were you sent hither to praise me?

VIOLA. I see you what you are, you are too proud;
But, if you were the devil, you are fair.
My lord and master loves you: O, such love
Could be but recompensed, though you were crowned
The nonpareil of beauty!

OLIVIA. How does he love me?

VIOLA. With adorations, fertile tears,
With groans that thunder love, with sighs of fire.

OLIVIA. Your lord does know my mind; I cannot love him:
Yet I suppose him virtuous, know him noble,
Of great estate, of fresh and stainless youth;
In voices well divulged, free, learned, and valiant;
And in dimension and the shape of nature
A gracious person: but yet I cannot love him;
He might have took his answer long ago.

VIOLA. If I did love you in my master's flame,
With such a suffering, such a deadly life,
In your denial I would find no sense;
I would not understand it.

OLIVIA. Why, what would you?

VIOLA. Make me a willow cabin at your gate
And call upon my soul within the house;
Write loyal cantons of contemnèd love
And sing them loud even in the dead of night;
Halloo your name to the reverberate hills
And make the babbling gossip of the air
Cry out *Olivia!* O, you should not rest
Between the elements of air and earth
But you should pity me!

OLIVIA. You might do much. What is your parentage?

VIOLA. Above my fortunes, yet my state is well:
I am a gentleman.

OLIVIA. Get you to your lord;
I cannot love him: let him send no more;
Unless, perchance, you come to me again,
To tell me how he takes it. Fare you well:
I thank you for your pains; spend this for me.

VIOLA. I am no fee'd post, lady; keep your purse:
My master, not myself, lacks recompense.
Love make his heart of flint that you shall love;
And let your fervour, like my master's, be
Placed in contempt! Farewell, fair cruelty.

OLIVIA (*alone*). *What is your parentage?*
" Above my fortunes, yet my state is well:
I am a gentleman." I'll be sworn thou art;
Thy tongue, thy face, thy limbs, actions, and spirit,
Do give thee five-fold blazon: (not too fast: soft, soft!)
Unless the master were the man! How now?
Even so quickly may one catch the plague?
Methinks I feel this youth's perfections
With an invisible and subtle stealth
To creep in at mine eyes. Well, let it be.
What ho, Malvolio!

MALVOLIO. Here, madam, at your service.

OLIVIA. Run after that same peevish messenger,
The county's man: he left this ring behind him,
Would I or not: tell him I'll none of it.
Desire him not to flatter with his lord,
Nor hold him up with hopes; I am not for him:
If that the youth will come this way tomorrow,
I'll give him reasons for't: hie thee, Malvolio.

MALVOLIO. Madam, I will.

OLIVIA. I do I know not what, and fear to find
Mine eye too great a flatterer for my mind.
Fate, show thy force: ourselves we do not owe;
What is decreed must be, and be this so.

ACT 2

Scene 1—The Sea-Coast

ANTONIO. Will you stay no longer? nor will you not that I go with you?

SEBASTIAN. By your patience, no. My stars shine darkly over me; therefore I shall crave of you your leave that I may bear my evils alone. It were a bad recompense for your love to lay any of them on you.

ANTONIO. Let me yet know whither you are bound.

SEBASTIAN. No, sooth, sir: my voyage is mere extravagancy. But I perceive in you so excellent a touch of modesty that you will not extort from me what I am willing to keep in; therefore it charges me in manners the rather to express myself. You must know of me then, Antonio, my name is Sebastian. My father was that Sebastian of Messaline whom I know you have heard of. He left behind him myself and a sister, both born in an hour: if the heavens had been pleased, would we had so ended! but you, sir, altered that, for some hour before you took me from the sea was my sister drowned.

ANTONIO. Alas the day!

SEBASTIAN. A lady, sir, though it was said she much resembled me, was yet of many accounted beautiful; but, though I could not with such estimable wonder overfar believe that, yet thus far I will boldly publish her; she bore a mind that envy could not but call fair.

ANTONIO. Pardon me, sir, your bad entertainment.

SEBASTIAN. O good Antonio, forgive me your trouble.

ANTONIO. If you will not murder me for my love, let me be your servant.

SEBASTIAN. If you will not undo what you have done, that is, kill him whom you have recovered, desire it not. Fare ye well at once: my bosom is full of kindness, and I am yet so near the manners of my mother that upon the least occasion more mine eyes will tell tales. I am bound to the Count Orsino's court: farewell.

ANTONIO. The gentleness of all the gods go with thee!
(*Aside*) I have many enemies in Orsino's court,
Else would I very shortly see thee there.
But, come what may, I do adore thee so
That danger shall seem sport, and I will go.

Scene 2—Malvolio Overtakes Viola in the Street

MALVOLIO. Were not you even now with the Countess Olivia?

VIOLA. Even now, sir; on a moderate pace I have since arrived but hither.

MALVOLIO. She returns this ring to you, sir: you might have save me my pains, to have taken it away yourself. She adds, moreover, that you should put your lord into a desperate assurance she will none of him: and one thing more, that you be never so hardy to come again in his affairs, unless it be to report your lord's taking of this. Receive it so.

VIOLA (*hiding her surprise*). She took the ring of me: I'll none of it.

MALVOLIO. Come, sir, you peevishly threw it to her; and her will is it should be so returned. If it be worth stooping for, there it lies in your eye; if not, be it his that finds it. (*Malvolio goes*)

VIOLA. I left no ring with her: what means this lady?
Fortune forbid my outside have not charmed her!
She made good view of me; indeed, so much
That sure methought her eyes had lost her tongue,
For she did speak in starts distractedly.
She loves me, sure; the cunning of her passion
Invites me in this churlish messenger.
None of my lord's ring! why, he sent her none.
I am the man! If it be so, as tis,
Poor lady, she were better love a dream.
How will this fadge? My master loves her dearly;
And I, poor monster, fond as much on him;
And she, mistaken, seems to dote on me!
What will become of this? As I am man,
My state is desperate for my master's love;
As I am woman (now alas the day!)
What thriftless sighs shall poor Olivia breathe!
O Time! thou must untangle this, not I;
It is too hard a knot for me to untie!

Scene 3—Olivia's House

SIR ANDREW. Now, a song.

SIR TOBY. Come on; there is sixpence for you: let's have a song.

SIR ANDREW. There's a testril of me, too.

CLOWN. Would you have a love-song, or a song of good life?

SIR TOBY. A love-song, a love-song.

SIR ANDREW. Ay, ay: I care not for good life.

The Clown's Song

O mistress mine, where are you roaming?
O, stay and hear; your true love's coming,
  That can sing both high and low:
Trip no further, pretty sweeting;
Journeys end in lovers meeting,
  Every wise man's son doth know.

What is love? Tis not hereafter;
Present mirth hath present laughter;
  What's to come is still unsure:
In delay there lies no plenty;
Then come kiss me, sweet and twenty,
  Youth's a stuff will not endure.

A little merrymaking follows, the noise of which alarms Maria

MARIA. What a caterwauling do you keep here! If my lady have not called up her steward Malvolio and bid him turn you out of doors never trust me. For the love o' God, peace!

Malvolio enters in a storm of indignation

MALVOLIO. My masters, are you mad, or what are you? Have you no wit, manners, nor honesty, but to gabble like tinkers at this time of night? Do ye make an alehouse of my lady's house? Is there no respect of place, persons, nor time in you?

SIR TOBY. We did keep time, sir, in our catches. Sneck up!

MALVOLIO. Sir Toby, I must be round with you. My lady bade me tell you that, though she harbours you as her kinsman, she's nothing allied to your disorders. If you can separate yourself and your misdemeanours you are welcome to the house; if not, an it would please you to take leave of her, she is very willing to bid you farewell. Mistress Mary, if you prized my lady's favour at anything more than contempt you would not give means for this uncivil rule; she shall know of it, by this hand. (*Exit Malvolio*)

MARIA. Go, shake your ears. A time-pleaser; an affectioned ass, the best persuaded of himself, so crammed, as he thinks, with excellencies that it is his ground of faith that all that look on him love him; and on that vice in him will my revenge find notable cause to work.

SIR TOBY. What wilt thou do?

MARIA. I will drop in his way some obscure epistles of love, wherein by the colour of his beard, the shape of his leg, the manner of his gait, the expressure of his eyes, forehead, and complexion, he shall find himself most feelingly personated. I can write very like my lady your niece; on a forgotten matter we can hardly make distinction of our hands.

SIR TOBY. Excellent! He shall think, by the letters thou wilt drop, that they come from my niece, and that she's in love with him.

MARIA. My purpose is, indeed, a horse of that colour.

SIR TOBY. Come, come, I'll go burn some sack; tis too late to go to bed now. Come, knight; come, knight.

Scene 4—The Duke's Palace

DUKE. Give me some music. Now, Good-morrow, friends.
Now, good Cesario, but that piece of song,
That old and antique song we heard last night.

CURIO. He is not here, so please your lordship, that should sing it.

DUKE. Who was it?

CURIO. Feste, the jester, my lord; a fool that the Lady Olivia's father took much delight in. He is about the house.

DUKE. Seek him out, and play the tune the while.
Come hither, boy: if ever thou shalt love,
In the sweet pangs of it remember me;
For such as I am all true lovers are,
Unstaid and skittish in all motions else,

Save in the constant image of the creature
That is beloved. How dost thou like this tune?

VIOLA. It gives a very echo to the seat
Where Love is throned.

DUKE. Thou dost speak masterly:
My life upon't, young though thou art, thine eye
Hath stayed upon some favour that it loves:
Hath it not, boy?

VIOLA. A little, by your favour.

DUKE. What kind of woman is't?

VIOLA. Of your complexion.

DUKE. She is not worth thee, then. What years, i' faith?

VIOLA. About your years, my lord.

DUKE. Too old, by heaven; let still the woman take
An elder than herself: so wears she to him,
So sways she level in her husband's heart:
For, boy, however we do praise ourselves,
Our fancies are more giddy and unfirm,
More longing, wavering, sooner lost and worn,
Than women's are.

VIOLA. I think it well, my lord.

DUKE. Then let thy love be younger than thyself,
Or thy affection cannot hold the bent;
For women are as roses, whose fair flower
Being once displayed, doth fall that very hour.

VIOLA. And so they are: alas, that they are so;
To die, even when they to perfection grow!

DUKE. O, fellow, come, the song we had last night.
Mark it, Cesario, it is old and plain;
The spinsters and the knitters in the sun,
And the free maids that weave their thread with bones,
Do use to chant it: it is silly sooth,
And dallies with the innocence of love,
Like the old age.

CLOWN. Are you ready, sir?

DUKE. Ay; prithee, sing.

The Clown's Song

Come away, come away, death,
And in sad cypress let me be laid;
Fly away, fly away, breath;
I am slain by a fair cruel maid.

My shroud of white, stuck all with yew,
O, prepare it!
My part of death, no one so true
Did share it.

Not a flower, not a flower sweet,
On my black coffin let there be strown ;
Not a friend, not a friend greet
My poor corpse, where my bones shall be thrown :

A thousand thousand sighs to save,
Lay me, O, where
Sad true lover never find my grave,
To weep there !

DUKE. There's for thy pains.

CLOWN. No pains, sir ; I take pleasure in singing, sir.

DUKE. I'll pay thy pleasure then.

CLOWN. Truly, sir, and pleasure will be paid, one time or another.

DUKE. Let all the rest give place. Once more, Cesario,
Get thee to yond same sovereign cruelty :
Tell her, my love, more noble than the world,
Prizes not quantity of dirty lands ;
The parts that fortune hath bestowed upon her,
Tell her, I hold as giddily as fortune ;
But tis that miracle and queen of gems
That nature pranks her in attracts my soul.

VIOLA. But if she cannot love you, sir ?

DUKE. I cannot be so answered.

VIOLA. Sooth, but you must.
Say that some lady, as perhaps there is,
Hath for your love as great a pang of heart
As you have for Olivia : you cannot love her ;
You tell her so ; must she not then be answered ?

DUKE. There is no woman's sides
Can bide the beating of so strong a passion
As love doth give my heart ; no woman's heart
So big, to hold so much ; make no compare
Between that love a woman can bear me
And that I owe Olivia.

VIOLA. Ay, but I know—

DUKE. What dost thou know ?

VIOLA. Too well what love women to men may owe :
In faith, they are as true of heart as we.
My father had a daughter loved a man,
As it might be, perhaps, were I a woman,
I should your lordship.

DUKE. And what 's her history ?

VIOLA. A blank, my lord. She never told her love,
But let concealment, like a worm i' the bud,
Feed on her damask cheek : she pined in thought,
And with a green and yellow melancholy

She sat like patience on a monument,
Smiling at grief. Was not this love indeed ?
We men may say more, swear more : but indeed
Our shows are more than will ; for still we prove
Much in our vows, but little in our love.

DUKE. But died thy sister of her love, my boy ?

VIOLA. I am all the daughters of my father's house,
And all the brothers too ; and yet I know not.
Sir, shall I to this lady ?

DUKE. Ay, that's the theme.
To her in haste ; give her this jewel ; say
My love can give no place, bide no denay.

Scene 5—Olivia's Garden

Sir Toby, Sir Andrew Aguecheek, and Fabian, gather secretly to watch Maria scatter her letters in Malvolio's path. Malvolio enters and talks to himself in their hearing about Olivia, to whom he fancies himself married. He pompously imagines aloud how he will then treat Sir Toby and the rest, who are listening unseen. Then he finds the letter Maria has left.

MALVOLIO. By my life, this is my lady's hand : these be her very C's, her U's, and her T's ; and thus makes she her great P's. *To the unknown beloved, this, and my good wishes.* Her very phrases ! By your leave, wax. (*He reads*)

If this fall into thy hand, revolve. In my stars I am above thee, but be not afraid of greatness : some are born great, some achieve greatness, and some have greatness thrust upon them. Thy Fates open their hands ; let thy blood and spirit embrace them ; and, to inure thyself to what thou art like to be, cast thy humble slough and appear fresh. Be opposite with a kinsman, surly with servants ; let thy tongue tang arguments of state ; put thyself into the trick of singularity : she thus advises thee that sighs for thee. Remember who commended thy yellow stockings, and wished to see thee ever cross-gartered. Go to, thou art made, if thou desirest to be so ; if not, let me see thee a steward still, the fellow of servants, and not worthy to touch Fortune's fingers. Farewell. She that would alter services with thee, THE FORTUNATE-UNHAPPY

Daylight and champain discovers not more : this is open. I will be proud ; I will read politic authors ; I will baffle Sir Toby ; I will wash off gross acquaintance. I do not now fool myself, to let imagination jade me, for every reason excites to this, that my lady loves me. She did commend my yellow stockings of late ; she did praise my leg being cross-gartered ; and in this she manifests herself to my love, and with a kind of injunction drives me to these habits of her liking. I thank my stars I am happy. Jove and my stars be praised ! Here is yet a postscript :

Thou canst not choose but know who I am. If thou entertainest my love, let it appear in thy smiling. Thy smiles become thee well ; therefore in my presence still smile, dear my sweet, I prithee.

Jove, I thank thee: I will smile: I will do everything that thou wilt have me. (*Malvolio leaves, smiling*)

MARIA. If you will then see the fruits of the sport, mark his first approach before my lady. He will come to her in yellow stockings, and tis a colour she abhors; and cross-gartered, a fashion she detests; and he will smile upon her, which will now be so unsuitable to her disposition that it cannot but turn him into a notable contempt. If you will see it, follow me.

ACT 3

Scene 1—Olivia's Garden

VIOLA (*meeting Clown*). Save thee, friend, and thy music: dost thou live by thy tabor?

CLOWN. No, sir, I live by the church.

VIOLA. Art thou a churchman?

CLOWN. No such matter, sir: I do live by the church; for I do live at my house, and my house doth stand by the church.

VIOLA. So thou mayst say the king lies by a beggar if a beggar dwell near him; or, the church stands by thy tabor if thy tabor stand by the church. Art not thou the Lady Olivia's fool?

CLOWN. No, indeed, sir; the Lady Olivia has no folly: she will keep no fool, sir, till she be married.

VIOLA. I saw thee late at the Count Orsino's.

CLOWN. Foolery, sir, does walk about the orb like the sun; it shines everywhere. I think I saw your wisdom there.

VIOLA. Nay, an thou pass upon me I'll no more with thee. Hold, there's expenses for thee. Is thy lady within?

CLOWN. My lady is within, sir. I will construe to them whence you come. (*Olivia appears*)

VIOLA. My duty, madam, and most humble service.

OLIVIA. What is your name?

VIOLA. Cesario is your servant's name, fair princess.

OLIVIA. My servant, sir!
You're servant to the Count Orsino, youth.

VIOLA. And he is yours, and his must needs be yours:
Your servant's servant is your servant, madam.

OLIVIA. For him, I think not on him; for his thoughts,
Would they were blanks, rather than filled with me!

VIOLA. Madam, I come to whet your gentle thoughts
On his behalf.

OLIVIA. O, by your leave, I pray you,
I bade you never speak again of him:
But, would you undertake another suit.

I had rather hear you to solicit that
Than music from the spheres.

VIOLA. Dear lady—

OLIVIA. Give me leave, beseech you. I did send,
After the last enchantment you did here,
A ring in chase of you : so did I abuse
Myself, my servant, and, I fear me, you.
Under your hard construction must I sit,
To force that on you, in a shameful cunning,
Which you knew none of yours. What might you think ?
Have you not set mine honour at the stake ?

VIOLA. I pity you.

OLIVIA. That's a degree to love.

VIOLA. No ; very oft we pity enemies.

OLIVIA. Why, then, methinks tis time to smile again.
Be not afraid, good youth, I will not have you :
And yet, when wit and youth is come to harvest,
Your wife is like to reap a proper man.

VIOLA. You'll nothing, madam, to my lord by me

OLIVIA. Stay :
I prithee, tell me what thou think'st of me.

VIOLA. That you do think you are not what you are.

OLIVIA. If I think so, I think the same of you.

VIOLA. Then think you right : I am not what I am.

OLIVIA. I would you were as I would have you be !

VIOLA. Would it be better, madam, than I am ?
I wish it might, for now I am your fool.

OLIVIA. O, what a deal of scorn looks beautiful
In the contempt and anger of his lip !
Cesario, by the roses of the spring,
By maidhood, honour, truth, and everything,
I love thee so, that, maugre all thy pride,
Nor wit nor reason can my passion hide.
Do not extort thy reasons from this clause,
For that I woo, thou therefore hast no cause ;
But rather reason thus with reason fetter,
Love sought is good, but given unsought is better.

VIOLA. By innocence I swear, and by my youth,
I have one heart, one bosom, and one truth,
And that no woman has ; nor never none
Shall mistress be of it, save I alone.
And so adieu, good madam : never more
Will I my master's tears to you deplore.

OLIVIA. Yet come again ; for thou perhaps mayst move
That heart, which now abhors, to like his love.

Scene 2—Olivia's House

Sir Andrew announces his intention of not staying a moment longer, as he has seen Olivia treat the Duke's page with much greater favour than ever she had treated him. Toby and Fabian, anticipating some amusement, urge him to challenge the page to fight. Sir Andrew withdraws to write the letter. Sir Toby is sure neither will have enough courage to fight. Then Maria enters, and warns them of the approach of Malvolio, extraordinarily dressed, in the expectation of winning the favour of his mistress.

MARIA. If you will laugh yourselves into stitches, follow me. Yond gull Malvolio is turned heathen, a very renegado ; for there is no Christian, that means to be saved by believing rightly, can ever believe such impossible passages of grossness. He's in yellow stockings.

SIR TOBY. And cross-gartered ?

MARIA. Most villainously ; like a pedant that keeps a school i' the church. He does obey every point of the letter that I dropped to betray him : he does smile his face into more lines than is in the new map of the Indies. You have not seen such a thing as tis ; I can hardly forbear hurling things at him. I know my lady will strike him : if she do, he'll smile and take it for a great favour.

SIR TOBY. Come, bring us, bring us where he is.

Scene 3—A Street

Sebastian and Antonio appear in a street in the city, Antonio having refused to leave him in a strange country. Sebastian wishes to see the city, but Antonio thinks it wiser that he should himself retire to lodgings, and gives his address to Sebastian. His reason is that he had once been in a sea-fight with the galleys of the city, and was known as an old-time enemy. Antonio therefore leaves Sebastian, to whom he gives his purse, and Sebastian proceeds to view the sights of the city.

Scene 4—Olivia's Garden

OLIVIA. I have sent after him : he says he'll come ;
How shall I feast him ? what bestow of him ?
For youth is bought more oft than begged or borrowed.
I speak too loud.
Where is Malvolio ? He is sad and civil,
And suits well for a servant with my fortunes :
(*To Maria*) Where is Malvolio ?

MARIA. He's coming, madam ; but in very strange manner. He is sure possessed, madam.

OLIVIA. Why, what's the matter ? Does he rave ?

MARIA. No, madam, he does nothing but smile ; your ladyship were best to have some guard about you if he come, for sure the man is tainted in his wits.

OLIVIA. Go call him hither. I am as mad as he

If sad and merry madness equal be.
How now, Malvolio!

MALVOLIO. Sweet lady, ho, ho.

OLIVIA. Smilest thou? I sent for thee upon a sad occasion.

MALVOLIO. Sad, lady? I could be sad: this does make some obstruction in the blood, this cross-gartering; but what of that? If it please the eye of one, it is with me as the very true sonnet is, *Please one, please all.*

OLIVIA. Why, how dost thou, man? What is the matter with thee?

MARIA. Why appear you with this ridiculous boldness before my lady?

MALVOLIO. *Be not afraid of greatness:* 'twas well writ.

OLIVIA. What meanest thou by that, Malvolio?

MALVOLIO. *Some are born great*—

OLIVIA. Ha!

MALVOLIO. *Some achieve greatness*—

OLIVIA. What sayest thou?

MALVOLIO. *And some have greatness thrust upon them.*

OLIVIA. Heaven restore thee!

MALVOLIO. *Remember who commended thy yellow stockings*—

OLIVIA. Why, this is very midsummer madness.

SERVANT (*entering*). Madam, the young gentleman of the Count Orsino is returned. I could hardly entreat him back; he attends your ladyship's pleasure.

OLIVIA. I'll come to him. Good Maria, let this fellow be looked to. Where's my cousin Toby? Let some of my people have a special care of him: I would not have him miscarry for the half of my dowry.

MALVOLIO (*alone*). O, ho! No worse man than Sir Toby to look to me! This concurs directly with the letter: she sends him on purpose, that I may appear stubborn to him; for she incites me to that in the letter. "Cast thy humble slough," says she; "be opposite with a kinsman, surly with servants; let thy tongue tang with arguments of state; put thyself into the trick of singularity." It is Jove's doing, and Jove make me thankful!

Sir Toby enters, and Malvolio speaks in a way that makes Sir Toby doubt his sanity. Maria asks Toby to get Malvolio to say his prayers.

MARIA. Get him to say his prayers, good Sir Toby.

MALVOLIO. My prayers, minx!

MARIA. No, I warrant you, he will not hear of godliness.

MALVOLIO. Go, hang yourselves all! you are idle shallow things: I am not of your element: you shall know more hereafter.

Sir Toby is now convinced that Malvolio has become really mad, and makes plans to place him bound in a dark room. Sir Andrew now enters with his challenge to fight the page, a confused and ridiculous letter. Sir Toby dare not deliver the letter to Viola, as it would show the writer to be a clodpole of whom no one need be afraid ; so he determines to give a challenge by word of mouth. Then Olivia and Viola enter.

OLIVIA. I have said too much unto a heart of stone
And laid mine honour too unchary out :
There's something in me that reproves my fault,
But such a headstrong potent fault it is
That it but mocks reproof.
Here, wear this jewel for me, tis my picture ;
Refuse it not ; it hath no tongue to vex you ;
And I beseech you come again tomorrow.
What shall you ask of me that I'll deny,
That honour saved may upon asking give ?

VIOLA. Nothing but this : your true love for my master.

OLIVIA. How with mine honour may I give him that
Which I have given to you ?

VIOLA. I will acquit you.

OLIVIA. Well, come again tomorrow : fare thee well :
A fiend like thee might bear my soul to hell.

When Olivia has retired Sir Toby addresses Viola and gives a fearsome picture of the challenger waiting at the orchard-end. Viola denies that she has given anyone offence, and declares she is no fighter. While Fabian continues to frighten Viola by accounts of Sir Andrew's fighting skill, Sir Toby has left to bring Sir Andrew, and on the way tells him equally terrible tales, so that both become thoroughly unnerved. Sir Andrew is ready to give Viola his grey horse Capilet to make up the dispute, and Viola is almost on the point of admitting that she is a woman. However, they are urged on until at last they draw their swords, when Antonio enters and joins in the dispute, imagining Viola to be Sebastian.

ANTONIO. Put up your sword. If this young gentleman
Have done offence, I take the fault on me :
If you offend him, I for him defy you.

SIR TOBY. You, sir ! why, what are you ?

ANTONIO. One, sir, that for his love dares yet do more
Than you have heard him brag to you he will.

SIR TOBY. Nay, if you be an undertaker, I am for you.

They fight, and Officers of the Law enter

OFFICER. Antonio, I arrest thee at the suit of Count Orsino.

ANTONIO. You do mistake me, sir.

OFFICER. No, sir, no jot ; I know your favour well,
Though now you have no sea-cap on your head.
Take him away : he knows I know him well.

ANTONIO. I must obey. (*To Viola*) This comes with seeking you:
But there's no remedy; I shall answer it.
What will you do, now my necessity
Makes me to ask you for my purse? It grieves me
Much more for what I cannot do for you
Than what befalls myself. You stand amazed,
But be of comfort.

OFFICER. Come, sir, away.

ANTONIO. I must entreat of you some of that money.

VIOLA. What money, sir?
For the fair kindness you have showed me here,
And, part, being prompted by your present trouble,
Out of my lean and low ability
I'll lend you something: my having is not much;
I'll make division of my present with you.
Hold, there's half my coffer.

ANTONIO. Will you deny me now?
Is't possible that my deserts to you
Can lack persuasion? Do not tempt my misery,
Lest that it make me so unsound a man
As to upbraid you with those kindnesses
That I have done for you.

VIOLA. I know of none;
Nor know I you by voice or any feature:
I hate ingratitude more in a man
Than lying, vainness, babbling, drunkenness,
Or any taint of vice whose strong corruption
Inhabits our frail blood.

ANTONIO. O heavens themselves!

OFFICER. Come, sir, I pray you, go.

ANTONIO. Let me speak a little. This youth that you see here
I snatched one half out of the jaws of death,
Relieved him with such sanctity of love,
And to his image, which methought did promise
Most venerable worth, did I devotion.
But O how vile an idol proves this god!
Thou hast, Sebastian, done good feature shame.
In nature there's no blemish but the mind;
None can be called deformed but the unkind.

OFFICER. The man grows mad: away with him! Come, come, sir.

ANTONIO. Lead me on.

VIOLA. Methinks his words do from such passion fly
That he believes himself: so do not I.
Prove true, imagination, O, prove true,
That I, dear brother, be now ta'en for you!

He named Sebastian : I my brother know
Yet living in my glass ; even such and so
In favour was my brother, and he went
Still in this fashion, colour, ornament,
For him I imitate : O, if it prove,
Tempests are kind and salt waves fresh in love. (*Viola goes*)

SIR TOBY. A very dishonest paltry boy, and more a coward than a hare : his dishonesty appears in leaving his friend here in necessity and denying him ; and for his cowardship, ask Fabian.

FABIAN. A coward, a most devout coward, religious in it.

SIR ANDREW. I'll after him again and beat him.

ACT 4

Scene 1—Before Olivia's House

CLOWN. Will you make me believe that I am not sent for you ?

SEBASTIAN. Go to, go to, thou art a foolish fellow :
Let me be clear of thee.

CLOWN. Well held out, i' faith ! No, I do not know you ; nor I am not sent to you by my lady, to bid you come speak with her ; nor your name is not Master Cesario ; nor this is not my nose neither. Nothing that is so is so.

SEBASTIAN. I prithee, vent thy folly somewhere else : thou know'st not me.

CLOWN. Vent my folly ! He has heard that word of some great man and now applies it to a fool. Vent my folly ! I prithee now ungird thy strangeness and tell me what I shall vent to my lady : shall I vent to her that thou art coming ?

SEBASTIAN. I prithee, foolish Greek, depart from me :
There's money for thee : if you tarry longer
I shall give worse payment.

CLOWN. By my troth, thou hast an open hand. These wise men that give fools money get themselves a good report—after fourteen years' purchase.

Sir Toby and Sir Andrew enter, mistaking Sebastian for Viola

SIR ANDREW. Now, sir, have I met you again ? there's for you.

SEBASTIAN. Why, there's for thee, and there, and there. Are all the people mad ?

SIR TOBY. Hold, sir, or I'll throw your dagger o'er the house.

CLOWN. This will I tell my lady straight : I would not be in some of your coats for twopence. (*Here Olivia enters*)

OLIVIA. Hold, Toby ; on thy life I charge thee, hold !

SIR TOBY. Madam !

OLIVIA. Will it be ever thus ? Ungracious wretch,
Fit for the mountains and the barbarous caves,

Where manners ne'er were preached ! Out of my sight !
Be not offended, dear Cesario. I prithee, gentle friend,
Let thy fair wisdom, not thy passion, sway
In this uncivil and unjust extent
Against thy peace. Go with me to my house,
And hear thou there how many fruitless pranks
This ruffian hath botched up, that thou thereby
Mayst smile at this : thou shalt not choose but go :
Do not deny.

SEBASTIAN. What relish is in this ? How runs the stream ?
Or I am mad, or else this is a dream :
Let fancy still my sense in Lethe steep ;
If it be thus to dream, still let me sleep !

OLIVIA. Nay, come, I prithee ; would thou'dst be ruled by me !

SEBASTIAN. Madam, I will.

OLIVIA. O say so, and so be.

Scene 2—In Olivia's House

Malvolio having been confined in a dark and uncomfortable chamber, Sir Toby, Maria, and the Clown visit him with a mock priest, calling outside his prison, pretending he is mad, while he declares himself sane and begs their aid. At last, however, even Toby becomes tired of all this.

Scene 3—Olivia's Garden

SEBASTIAN. This is the air ; that is the glorious sun ;
This pearl she gave me, I do feel 't and see 't ;
And though tis wonder that enwraps me thus,
Yet tis not madness. Where's Antonio, then ?
I could not find him at the Elephant,
Yet there he was ; and there I found this credit,
That he did range the town to seek me out.
His counsel now might do me golden service ;
For I am ready to distrust mine eyes
And wrangle with my reason that persuades me
To any other trust but that I am mad
Or else the lady's mad ; yet, if 'twere so,
She could not sway her house, command her followers,
Take and give back affairs and their dispatch
With such a smooth, discreet, and stable bearing
As I perceive she does : there's something in't
That is deceivable. But here the lady comes.

Olivia comes with a Priest

OLIVIA. Blame not this haste of mine. If you mean well
Now go with me and with this holy man
Into the chantry by : there, before him,
And underneath that consecrated roof,
Plight me the full assurance of your faith,

That my most jealous and too doubtful soul
May live at peace. He shall conceal it
Whiles you are willing it shall come to note,
What time we will our celebration keep
According to my birth. What do you say ?

SEBASTIAN. I'll follow this good man, and go with you ;
And, having sworn truth, ever will be true.

OLIVIA. Then lead the way, good father ; and heavens so shine,
That they may fairly note this act of mine !

ACT 5

Scene 1—Before Olivia's House

As the Duke and Viola enter, Officers appear with Antonio

VIOLA. Here comes the man, sir, that did rescue me.
He did me kindness, sir, drew on my side ;
But in conclusion put strange speech upon me :
I know not what 'twas but distraction.

DUKE. Notable pirate ! thou salt-water thief !
What foolish boldness brought thee to their mercies,
Whom thou hast made thine enemies ?

ANTONIO. Orsino, noble sir,
Be pleased that I shake off these names you give me :
Antonio never yet was thief or pirate,
Though I confess, on base and ground enough,
Orsino's enemy. A witchcraft drew me hither :
That most ingrateful boy there by your side
From the rude sea's enraged and foamy mouth
Did I redeem ; a wreck past hope he was :
His life I gave him, and did thereto add
My love, without retention or restraint,
All his in dedication ; for his sake
Did I expose myself, pure for his love,
Into the danger of this adverse town ;
Drew to defend him when he was beset :
Where being apprehended, his false cunning,
Not meaning to partake with me in danger,
Taught him to face me out of his acquaintance,
And grew a twenty-years-removèd thing
While one would wink ; denied me mine own purse,
Which I had recommended to his use
Not half an hour before.

VIOLA. How can this be ?

DUKE. When came he to this town ?

ANTONIO. Today, my lord ; and for three months before,
No interim, not a minute's vacancy,
Both day and night did we keep company.

DUKE. Here comes the countess ; now heaven walks on earth :
But for thee, fellow ; fellow, thy words are madness :
Three months this youth hath tended upon me ;
But more of that anon. Take him aside.
OLIVIA. What would my lord, but that he may not have,
Wherein Olivia may seem serviceable ?
Cesario, you do not keep promise with me.
VIOLA. Madam !
DUKE. Gracious Olivia—
OLIVIA. What do you say, Cesario ? Good my lord—
VIOLA. My lord would speak ; my duty hushes me.
OLIVIA. If it be aught to the old tune, my lord,
It is as fat and fulsome to mine ear
As howling after music.
DUKE. Still so cruel ?
OLIVIA. Still so constant, lord.
DUKE. What, to perverseness ? you uncivil lady,
To whose ingrate and unauspicious altars
My soul the faithfull'st offerings hath breathed out
That e'er devotion tendered ! What shall I do ?
OLIVIA. Even what it please my lord, that shall become him.
DUKE. Why should I not, had I the heart to do it,
Like to the Egyptian thief at point of death,
Kill what I love ?—a savage jealousy
That sometime savours nobly. But hear me this :
Since you to non-regardance cast my faith,
And that I partly know the instrument
That screws me from my true place in your favour,
Live you the marble-breasted tyrant still ;
But this your minion, whom I know you love,
And whom, by heaven I swear, I tender dearly,
Him will I tear out of that cruel eye,
Where he sits crownèd in his master's spite.
Come, boy, with me ; my thoughts are ripe in mischief :
I 'll sacrifice the lamb that I do love,
To spite a raven's heart within a dove.
VIOLA. And I, most jocund, apt and willingly,
To do you rest, a thousand deaths would die.
OLIVIA. Where goes Cesario ?
VIOLA. After him I love
More than I love these eyes, more than my life.
OLIVIA. Ay me, detested ! How am I beguiled !
VIOLA. Who does beguile you ? Who does do you wrong ?
OLIVIA. Hast thou forgot thyself ? Is it so long ?
Call forth the holy father.

DUKE. Come, away!

OLIVIA. Whither, my lord? Cesario, husband, stay!

DUKE. Husband!

OLIVIA. Ay, husband: can he that deny?

DUKE. Her husband, sirrah!

VIOLA. No, my lord, not I.

OLIVIA. Alas, it is the baseness of thy fear
That makes thee strangle thy propriety:
Fear not, Cesario; take thy fortunes up;
Be that thou know'st thou art, and then thou art
As great as that thou fear'st.

Here the Priest enters

Father, I charge thee, by thy reverence,
Here to unfold what thou dost know
Hath newly passed between this youth and me.

PRIEST. A contract of eternal bond of love,
Sealed in my function, by my testimony:
Since when, my watch hath told me, toward my grave
I have travelled but two hours.

DUKE. O thou dissembling cub! What wilt thou be
When time hath sowed a grizzle on thy case?
Or will not else thy craft so quickly grow
That thine own trip shall be thine overthrow?
Farewell, and take her; but direct thy feet
Where thou and I henceforth may never meet.

VIOLA. My lord, I do protest—

OLIVIA. O, do not swear!
Hold little faith, though thou hast too much fear.

Enter Sir Andrew in great excitement

SIR ANDREW. For the love of God, a surgeon! Send one presently to Sir Toby.

OLIVIA. What's the matter?

SIR ANDREW. He has broke my head across and has given Sir Toby a broken coxcomb too; for the love of God, your help! I had rather than forty pound I were at home.

OLIVIA. Who has done this, Sir Andrew?

SIR ANDREW. The count's gentleman, one Cesario.

DUKE. My gentleman, Cesario?

SIR ANDREW. Here he is! You broke my head for nothing; and that that I did I was set on to do't by Sir Toby.

VIOLA. Why do you speak to me? I never hurt you:
You drew your sword upon me without cause;
But I bespake you fair, and hurt you not.

SIR ANDREW. If a broken coxcomb be a hurt, you have hurt me. Here comes Sir Toby halting; you shall hear more.

DUKE. How now, gentleman! how is't with you?

SIR TOBY. He has hurt me, and there's the end on't.

OLIVIA. Away with him! Who hath made this havoc with them? Get him to bed, and let his hurt be looked to.

Enter Sebastian

SEBASTIAN. I am sorry, madam, I have hurt your kinsman;
But, had it been the brother of my blood,
I must have done no less with wit and safety.
You throw a strange regard upon me, and by that
I do perceive it hath offended you:
Pardon me, sweet one, even for the vows
We made each other but so late ago.

DUKE. One face, one voice, one habit, and two persons,
A natural perspective, that is and is not!

SEBASTIAN. Antonio, O my dear Antonio!
How have the hours racked and tortured me,
Since I have lost thee!

ANTONIO. Sebastian are you?

SEBASTIAN. Fear'st thou that, Antonio?

ANTONIO. How have you made division of yourself?
An apple cleft in two is not more twin
Than these two creatures. Which is Sebastian?

OLIVIA. Most wonderful!

SEBASTIAN. Do I stand there? I never had a brother;
Nor can there be that deity in my nature,
Of here and everywhere. I had a sister,
Whom the blind waves and surges have devoured.
Of charity, what kin are you to me?
What countryman? What name? What parentage?

VIOLA. Of Messaline: Sebastian was my father;
Such a Sebastian was my brother too,
So went he suited to his watery tomb:
If spirits can assume both form and suit
You come to fright us.

SEBASTIAN. A spirit I am indeed;
Were you a woman, as the rest goes even,
I should my tears let fall upon your cheek,
And say *Thrice-welcome, drownèd Viola!*

VIOLA. My father had a mole upon his brow.

SEBASTIAN. And so had mine.

VIOLA. And died that day when Viola from her birth
Had numbered thirteen years.

SEBASTIAN. O, that record is lively in my soul!

VIOLA. If nothing lets to make us happy both
But this my masculine usurped attire,
Do not embrace me till each circumstance
Of place, time, fortune, do cohere and jump
That I am Viola: which to confirm,
I'll bring you to a captain in this town,
Where lie my maiden weeds; by whose gentle help
I was preserved to serve this noble count.
All the occurrence of my fortune since
Hath been between this lady and this lord.

SEBASTIAN (*to Olivia*). So comes it, lady, you have been mistook:
But nature to her bias drew in that.
You would have been contracted to a maid;
Nor are you therein, by my life, deceived,
You are betrothed both to a maid and man.

DUKE. Be not amazed; right noble is his blood.
If this be so, as yet the glass seems true,
I shall have share in this most happy wreck.
Boy, thou hast said to me a thousand times
Thou never shouldst love woman like to me.

VIOLA. And all those sayings will I over-swear;
And all those swearings keep as true in soul
As doth that orbèd continent the fire
That severs day from night.

DUKE. Give me thy hand;
And let me see thee in thy woman's weeds.

VIOLA. The captain that did bring me first on shore
Hath my maid's garments: he upon some action
Is now in durance, at Malvolio's suit,
A gentleman and follower of my lady's.

OLIVIA. He shall enlarge him: fetch Malvolio hither:
And yet, alas, now I remember me,
They say, poor gentleman, he's much distract.
How does he, sirrah?

CLOWN. Truly, madam, he holds Belzebub at the staves's end as well as a man in his case may do: he has here writ a letter to you.

OLIVIA. Read it you, sirrah.

FABIAN (*reading*). By the Lord, madam, you wrong me, and the world shall know it. Though you have put me into darkness and given your drunken cousin rule over me, yet have I the benefit of my senses. I have your own letter that induced me to the semblance I put on; with the which I doubt not but to do myself much right, or you much shame. Think of me as you please. I leave my duty a little unthought of, and speak out of my injury. THE MADLY-USED MALVOLIO

OLIVIA. Did he write this?

CLOWN. Ay, madam.

DUKE. This savours not much of distraction.

OLIVIA. See him delivered, Fabian; bring him hither.
My lord, so please you, these things further thought on,
To think me as well a sister as a wife,
One day shall crown the alliance on't, so please you,
Here at my house and at my proper cost.

DUKE. Madam, I am most apt to embrace your offer.
(*To Viola*) Your master quits you; and for your service done him,
So much against the mettle of your sex,
So far beneath your soft and tender breeding,
And since you called me master for so long,
Here is my hand: you shall from this time be
Your master's mistress.

Fabian enters, bringing with him Malvolio

OLIVIA. How now, Malvolio!

MALVOLIO. Madam, you have done me wrong, notorious wrong.

OLIVIA. Have I, Malvolio? no.

MALVOLIO. Lady, you have. Pray you, peruse that letter.
You must not now deny it is your hand:
Or say tis not your seal, nor your invention:
You can say none of this: well, grant it then,
And tell me, in the modesty of honour,
Why you have given me such clear lights of favour,
Bade me come smiling and cross-gartered to you,
To put on yellow stockings and to frown
Upon Sir Toby and the lighter people;
And, acting this in an obedient hope,
Why have you suffered me to be imprisoned,
Kept in a dark house, visited by the priest,
And made the most notorious geck and gull
That e'er invention played on? Tell me why.

OLIVIA. Alas, Malvolio, this is not my writing,
Though, I confess, much like the character:
But out of question tis Maria's hand.
And now I do bethink me, it was she
First told me thou wast mad. Thou cam'st in smiling,
And in such forms which here were presupposed
Upon thee in the letter. Prithee, be content:
This practice hath most shrewdly passed upon thee;
But when we know the grounds and authors of it,
Thou shalt be both the plaintiff and the judge
Of thine own cause.

FABIAN. Good madam, hear me speak,
And let no quarrel nor no brawl to come
Taint the condition of this present hour,
Which I have wondered at. In hope it shall not,
Most freely I confess myself and Toby
Set this device against Malvolio here,
Upon some stubborn and uncourteous parts
We had conceived against him. Maria writ
The letter at Sir Toby's great importance;
In recompense whereof he hath married her.
How with a sportful malice it was followed
May rather pluck on laughter than revenge;
If that the injuries be justly weighed
That have on both sides passed.

OLIVIA. Alas, poor fool, how have they baffled thee!

CLOWN. And thus the whirligig of time brings in his revenges.

MALVOLIO. I'll be revenged on the whole pack of you. (*He goes*)

OLIVIA. He hath been most notoriously abused.

DUKE. Pursue him, and entreat him to a peace:
He hath not told us of the captain yet.
When that is known and golden time convents,
A solemn combination shall be made
Of our dear souls. Meantime, sweet sister,
We will not part from hence. Cesario, come
For so you shall be, while you are a man;
But when in other habits you are seen,
Orsino's mistress, and his fancy's queen.

The Clown's Song

When that I was and a little tiny boy,
  With hey, ho, the wind and the rain,
A foolish thing was but a toy,
  For the rain it raineth every day.

But when I came to man's estate,
  With hey, ho, the wind and the rain,
Gainst knaves and thieves men shut their gate,
  For the rain it raineth every day.

But when I came, alas! to wive,
  With hey, ho, the wind and the rain,
By swaggering could I never thrive,
  For the rain it raineth every day.

A great while ago the world began,
  With hey, ho, the wind and the rain,
But that's all one, our play is done,
  And we'll strive to please you every day.

The Story of Macbeth

MACBETH is one of the supremely great plays, a masterpiece of imagination. It is a terrible lesson of what ambition may lead to when it takes to evil ways.

IT is a page from the history of Scotland, far back in the days before the Conqueror came to England. Shakespeare found in Holinshed's Chronicle the story of Macbeth's murder of King Duncan and his seizing of the throne, and, mixing his dramatic materials as suited his purpose, he freely changed the destinies and developed the characters of the people. He wrote the play when he was forty-two.

THERE is some reason for believing that the play was meant to please King James the First. James, though he was called the wisest fool in Christendom, firmly believed in witchcraft, and witchcraft is the basis of this play. It takes us back to prophecies by witches that Banquo's sons should sit in Macbeth's seat and reign as kings of Scotland. Tradition tells us that one son of Banquo did escape the fury of Macbeth, and lived to found the Stuart line of kings.

WE must remember that, though kings and poets believed in witchcraft then, there was no such thing existing, and the prophecies which changed the mind and ruined the character of Macbeth were probably invented by Shakespeare to accomplish his purpose. He wished to show us a man willing to pay any price for a throne, and he used witchcraft as an influence in changing a good man to a bad man.

WE see in Macbeth a man who had made an honourable start in life. A man of thought and imagination, he believed (as Shakespeare himself believed) in mysterious powers governing and controlling the world. Proud and ambitious in a high degree, he was ready to listen to malicious spirits of the air, and, urged on by an ambitious wife with a heart of stone, he was swept off his feet. His belief in a dazzling destiny carried away his mind, until, after plunging deeper and deeper in crime, he lost success, honour, love, respect, and life itself.

THE play contains one of the most wonderful scenes in Shakespeare, the sleep-walking of Lady Macbeth. It is an intensely powerful drama of an uneasy conscience, and of the relentless and remorseless forces pursuing those who follow evil ways. Lady Macbeth knows no rest, and Macbeth hears voices crying *Macbeth doth murder sleep.*

A PLAY of swift and unceasing action, it is one of the most stirring and poetical plays in the world's drama ; and it shows us what history shows us many, many times—that, though the mills of God grind slowly, yet they grind exceeding small.

THE PLAYERS

Duncan, King of Scotland, well beloved.

Macbeth, a victorious General of King Duncan, amply rewarded by him, but drawn from loyalty by ambition, encouraged by malicious prophecies of witches and by a strong-minded wife.

Banquo, a fellow General with Macbeth, armed against superstition by common sense.

Malcolm and Donalbain, sons of Duncan. They flee into exile, but Malcolm returns.

Macduff, Lennox, and Ross, Scottish noblemen.

Menteith, Angus, and Caithness, Scottish noblemen.

Fleance, a young son of Banquo, who escapes from the murderers sent by Macbeth to slay him.

Siward, an English earl who helps to put Malcolm on the Scottish throne.

Young Siward, Earl Siward's son.

Seyton, one of Macbeth's officers.

Lady Macbeth, a proud and cruel woman, the dominating personality of the play, whose overpowering ambition urges Macbeth on at all hazards.

Lady Macduff, wife of Macduff.

Witches, a doctor, a porter, murderers, courtiers, and soldiers.

SCENE—Scotland and England

Macbeth

ACT 1

Scene 1—Three Witches at a Lonely Place in a Storm

FIRST WITCH. When shall we three meet again
In thunder, lightning, or in rain?
SECOND WITCH. When the hurly-burly's done,
When the battle's lost and won.
THIRD WITCH. That will be ere the set of sun.
FIRST WITCH. Where the place?
SECOND WITCH. Upon the heath.
THIRD WITCH. There to meet with Macbeth.
ALL. Fair is foul, and foul is fair:
Hover through the fog and filthy air.

Scene 2—A Camp near Forres

DUNCAN. What bloodstained man is that? He can report,
As seemeth by his plight, of the revolt.
MALCOLM. This is the sergeant
Who like a good and hardy soldier fought
Gainst my captivity. Hail, brave friend!
Say to the king the knowledge of the broil
As thou didst leave it.
SERGEANT. Doubtful it stood;
As two spent swimmers, that do cling together
And choke their art. The merciless Macdonwald, from the western isles
Of kerns and gallow-glasses is supplied;
And fortune, on his quarrel smiling,
Showed like a rebel: but all's too weak:
For brave Macbeth (well he deserves that name)
Disdaining fortune, with his brandished steel,
Like valour's minion carvèd out his passage
Till he faced the slave;
And fixed his head upon our battlements.
DUNCAN. O valiant cousin! worthy gentleman!
SERGEANT. Mark, king of Scotland, mark:
No sooner justice had, with valour armed,

Compelled these skipping kerns to trust their heels,
But the Norweyan lord, surveying vantage,
Began a fresh assault.

DUNCAN. Dismayed not this
Our captains, Macbeth and Banquo ?

SERGEANT. Yes ;
As sparrows eagles, or the hare the lion.
If I say sooth, I must report they were
As cannons overcharged with double cracks, so they
Doubly redoubled strokes upon the foe :
But I am faint ; my gashes cry for help.

DUNCAN. So well thy words become thee as thy wounds ;
They smack of honour both. Go get him surgeons.
Who comes here ?

MALCOLM. The worthy thane of Ross.

LENNOX. What a haste looks through his eyes ! So should he look
That seems to speak things strange.

ROSS. God save the king !

DUNCAN. Whence cam'st thou, worthy thane ?

ROSS. From Fife, great king ;
Where the Norweyan banners flout the sky
And fan our people cold. Norway himself,
Assisted by that most disloyal traitor
The thane of Cawdor, began a dismal conflict,
Till, to conclude, the victory fell on us.

DUNCAN. Great happiness !
No more that thane of Cawdor shall deceive
Our bosom interest : go pronounce his present death,
And with his former title greet Macbeth.

Scene 3—A Heath near Forres

Enter the Witches, followed later by Macbeth with Banquo

FIRST WITCH. Where hast thou been, sister ?

SECOND WITCH. Killing swine.

THIRD WITCH. Sister, where thou ?

FIRST WITCH. A sailor's wife had chestnuts in her lap,
And munched, and munched, and munched. Give me, quoth I :
Aroint thee, witch, the ronyon cries.
Her husband's to Aleppo gone, master o' the Tiger :
But in a sieve I'll thither sail,
And, like a rat without a tail,
I'll do, I'll do, and I'll do.

SECOND WITCH. I'll give thee a wind.

THIRD WITCH. And I another.

FIRST WITCH. I myself have all the other,

And the very ports they blow,
All the quarters that they know
I' the shipman's card.
I will drain him dry as hay :
Sleep shall neither night nor day
Hang upon his pent-house lid ;
He shall live a man forbid :
Weary se'nnights nine times nine
Shall he dwindle, peak and pine :
Though his bark cannot be lost,
Yet it shall be tempest-tossed.
Look what I have.

SECOND WITCH. Show me, show me.

FIRST WITCH. Here I have a pilot's thumb,
Wrecked as homeward he did come.

THIRD WITCH. A drum, a drum ! Macbeth doth come.

ALL. The weird sisters, hand in hand,
Posters of the sea and land,
Thus do go about, about :
Thrice to thine and thrice to mine,
And thrice again, to make up nine.
Peace ! the charm's wound up.

MACBETH. So foul and fair a day I have not seen.

BANQUO. How far is't called to Forres ? What are these
So withered and so wild in their attire,
That look not like the inhabitants o' the earth,
And yet are on't ? Live you, or are you aught
That man may question ?

MACBETH. Speak, if you can : what are you ?

FIRST WITCH. All hail, Macbeth ! hail to thee, thane of Glamis !

SECOND WITCH. All hail, Macbeth ! hail to thee, thane of Cawdor !

THIRD WITCH. All hail, Macbeth, that shalt be king hereafter !

BANQUO. Good sir, why do you start ; and seem to fear
Things that do sound so fair ? I' the name of truth,
Are ye fantastical, or that indeed
Which outwardly ye show ? (*To witches*) My noble partner
You greet with present grace and great prediction
Of noble having and of royal hope,
That he seems rapt withal : to me you speak not.
If you can look into the seeds of time,
And say which grain will grow and which will not,
Speak then to me who neither beg nor fear
Your favours nor your hate.

WITCHES. Hail !

FIRST WITCH. Lesser than Macbeth, and greater.

SECOND WITCH. Not so happy, yet much happier.

THIRD WITCH. Thou shalt get kings, though thou be none.

MACBETH. Stay, you imperfect speakers, tell me more:
By Sinel's death I know I am thane of Glamis;
But how of Cawdor? Say from whence
You owe this strange intelligence? or why
Upon this blasted heath you stop our way
With such prophetic greeting? Speak, I charge you.

The Witches suddenly vanish from sight

BANQUO. The earth hath bubbles, as the water has,
And these are of them. Whither are they vanished?

MACBETH. Into the air, and what seemed corporal melted
As breath into the wind. Would they had stayed!

BANQUO. Were such things here as we do speak about?
Or have we eaten on the insane root
That takes the reason prisoner?

MACBETH. Your children shall be kings.

BANQUO. You shall be king.

MACBETH. And thane of Cawdor too: went it not so?

BANQUO. To the selfsame tune and words. Who's here?

ROSS (*entering*). The king hath happily received, Macbeth,
The news of thy success; and when he reads
Thy personal venture in the rebels' fight
His wonders and his praises do contend
Which should be thine or his. As thick as hail
Came post with post; and every one did bear
Thy praises in his kingdom's great defence,
And poured them down before him.

ANGUS (*with Ross*). We are sent
To give thee from our royal master thanks.

ROSS. And, for an earnest of a greater honour,
He bade me, from him, call thee thane of Cawdor.

MACBETH. The thane of Cawdor lives: why do you dress me
In borrowed robes?

ANGUS. Who was the thane lives yet,
But treasons capital, confessed and proved,
Have overthrown him.

MACBETH (*aside*). Glamis, and thane of Cawdor!
Thanks for your pains.
Do you (*to Banquo*) not hope your children shall be kings,
When those that gave the thane of Cawdor to me
Promised no less to them?

BANQUO. That trusted home
Might yet enkindle you unto the crown,

Besides the thane of Cawdor. But tis strange :
And oftentimes, to win us to our harm,
The instruments of darkness tell us truths,
Win us with honest trifles, to betray us
In deepest consequence. Cousins, a word, I pray you.

MACBETH. I thank you, gentlemen.
(*Aside*) This supernatural soliciting
Cannot be ill, cannot be good : if ill,
Why hath it given me earnest of success,
Commencing in a truth ? I am thane of Cawdor :
If good, why do I yield to that suggestion
Whose horrid image doth unfix my hair
And make my seated heart knock at my ribs,
Against the use of nature ? Present fears
Are less than horrible imaginings :
My thought, whose murder yet is but fantastical,
Shakes so my single state of man that function
Is smothered in surmise, and nothing is
But what is not.
If chance will have me king, why, chance may crown me
Without my stir. Come what come may,
Time and the hour runs through the roughest day.

BANQUO. Worthy Macbeth, we stay upon your leisure.

MACBETH. Give me your favour : my dull brain was wrought
With things forgotten. Kind gentlemen, your pains
Are registered where every day I turn
The leaf to read them. Let us toward the king.
(*To Banquo*) Think upon what hath chanced, and, at more time,
The interim having weighed it, let us speak
Our free hearts each to other.

Scene 4—The Palace at Forres

DUNCAN (*to Malcolm*). Is execution done on Cawdor ? Are not
Those in commission yet returned ?

MALCOLM. My liege,
They are not yet come back. But I have spoke
With one that saw him die : who did report
That very frankly he confessed his treasons,
Implored your highness' pardon, and set forth
A deep repentance : nothing in his life
Became him like the leaving it ; he died
As one that had been studied in his death
To throw away the dearest thing he owed,
As 'twere a careless trifle.

DUNCAN. There's no art
To find the mind's construction in the face :

He was a gentleman on whom I built
An absolute trust. (*To Macbeth, entering*) O worthiest cousin!
The sin of my ingratitude even now
Was heavy on me: thou art so far before
That swiftest wing of recompense is slow
To overtake thee. Would thou hadst less deserved,
That the proportion both of thanks and payment
Might have been mine! Only I have left to say,
More is thy due than more than all can pay.
I have begun to plant thee, and will labour
To make thee full of growing. Noble Banquo,
That hast no less deserved, let me infold thee
And hold thee to my heart.

BANQUO. There if I grow, the harvest is your own.

DUNCAN. My plenteous joys,
Wanton in fulness, seek to hide themselves
In drops of sorrow. Sons, kinsmen, thanes,
And you whose places are the nearest, know
We will establish our estate upon
Our eldest, Malcolm, whom we name hereafter
The Prince of Cumberland; which honour must
Not unaccompanied invest him only,
But signs of nobleness, like stars, shall shine
On all deservers. From hence to Inverness,
And bind us further to you.

MACBETH. The rest is labour, which is not used for you:
I'll be myself the harbinger and make joyful
The hearing of my wife with your approach;
So humbly take my leave.

DUNCAN. My worthy Cawdor!

MACBETH (*aside*). The Prince of Cumberland! that is a step
On which I must fall down, or else o'erleap,
For in my way it lies. Stars, hide your fires;
Let not light see my black and deep desires;
The eye wink at the hand; yet let that be
Which the eye fears, when it is done, to see. (*Macbeth leaves*)

DUNCAN. True, worthy Banquo; he is full so valiant,
And in his commendations I am fed;
It is a banquet to me. Let's after him,
Whose care is gone before to bid us welcome:
It is a peerless kinsman.

Scene 5—Macbeth's Castle

Lady Macbeth enters reading this letter from her husband

They met me in the day of success; and I have learned by the perfectest report they have more in them than mortal knowledge.

When I burned in desire to question them further they made themselves air, into which they vanished. Whiles I stood rapt in the wonder of it came missives from the king, who all-hailed me *Thane of Cawdor*, by which title, before, these weird sisters saluted me, and referred me to the coming on of time, with *Hail, king that shalt be!* This have I thought good to deliver thee, my dearest partner of greatness, that thou mightst not lose rejoicing by being ignorant of what greatness is promised thee. Lay it to thy heart, and farewell.

LADY MACBETH. Glamis thou art, and Cawdor; and shalt be
What thou art promised: yet do I fear thy nature;
It is too full o' the milk of human kindness
To catch the nearest way: thou wouldst be great;
Art not without ambition, but without
The illness should attend it: what thou wouldst highly,
That wouldst thou holily; wouldst not play false,
And yet wouldst wrongly win. Hie thee hither,
That I may pour my spirits in thine ear;
And chastise with the valour of my tongue
All that impedes thee from the golden round.

MESSENGER (*entering*). The king comes here tonight.

LADY MACBETH. Thou'rt mad to say it:
Is not thy master with him, who, were't so,
Would have informed for preparation?

MESSENGER. So please you, it is true: our thane is coming:
One of my fellows had the speed of him,
Who, almost dead for breath, had scarcely more
Than would make up his message.

LADY MACBETH. Give him tending; he brings great news.
The raven himself is hoarse
That croaks the fatal entrance of Duncan
Under my battlements. Come, you spirits
That tend on mortal thoughts, unsex me here,
And fill me from the crown to the toe top-full
Of direst cruelty! Make thick my blood;
Stop up the access and passage to remorse,
That no compunctious visitings of nature
Shake my fell purpose, nor keep peace between
The effect and it! (*Here Macbeth appears*)
Great Glamis! worthy Cawdor!
Greater than both, by the all-hail hereafter!
Thy letters have transported me beyond
This ignorant present, and I feel now
The future in the instant.

MACBETH. My dearest love, Duncan comes here tonight.

LADY MACBETH. And when goes hence?

MACBETH. Tomorrow, as he purposes.

LADY MACBETH. O, never shall sun that morrow see!
Your face, my thane, is as a book where men
May read strange matters. To beguile the time,
Look like the time; bear welcome in your eye,
Your hand, your tongue: look like the innocent flower,
But be the serpent under it. He that's coming
Must be provided for: and you shall put
This night's great business into my dispatch,
Which shall to all our nights and days to come
Give solely sovereign sway and masterdom.
MACBETH. We will speak further.

Scene 6—Duncan before Macbeth's Castle

DUNCAN. This castle hath a pleasant seat; the air
Nimbly and sweetly recommends itself
Unto our gentle senses.
BANQUO. This guest of summer,
The temple-haunting martlet, does approve,
By his loved mansionry, that the heaven's breath
Smells wooingly here: no jutty, frieze,
Buttress, nor coign of vantage, but this bird
Hath made his pendent bed and procreant cradle:
Where they most breed and haunt, I have observed,
The air is delicate. See, see, our honoured hostess!
LADY MACBETH (*approaching*). All our service
In every point twice done and then done double
Were poor and single business to contend
Against those honours deep and broad wherewith
Your majesty loads our house: for those of old,
And the late dignities heaped up to them,
We rest your hermits.
DUNCAN. Where's the thane of Cawdor?
We coursed him at the heels, and had a purpose
To be his purveyor: but he rides well;
And his great love, sharp as his spur, hath helped him
To his home before us. Fair and noble hostess,
We are your guests tonight. Give me your hand;
Conduct me to mine host: we love him highly,
And shall continue our graces towards him.
By your leave, hostess.

Scene 7—Macbeth's Castle at Inverness

MACBETH. If it were done when tis done, then 'twere well
It were done quickly. He's here in double trust;
First, as I am his kinsman and his subject,
Strong both against the deed; then, as his host,

Who should against his murderer shut the door,
Not bear the knife myself. Besides, this Duncan
Hath borne his faculties so meek, hath been
So clear in his great office, that his virtues
Will plead like angels, trumpet-tongued,
And pity, like a naked new-born babe,
Striding the blast, or heaven's cherubim, horsed
Upon the sightless couriers of the air,
Shall blow the horrid deed in every eye,
That tears shall drown the wind. I have no spur
To prick the sides of my intent, but only
Vaulting ambition, which o'erleaps itself
And falls on the other. How now! what news?

LADY MACBETH (*entering*). He has almost supped: why have you left the chamber?

MACBETH. Hath he asked for me?

LADY MACBETH. Know you not he has?

MACBETH. We will proceed no further in this business:
He hath honoured me of late; and I have bought
Golden opinions from all sorts of people,
Which would be worn now in their newest gloss,
Not cast aside so soon.

LADY MACBETH. Was the hope drunk
Wherein you dressed yourself? Hath it slept since?
And wakes it now, to look so green and pale
At what it did so freely? From this time
Such I account thy love. Art thou afeard
To be the same in thine own act and valour
As thou art in desire? Wouldst thou have that
Which thou esteem'st the ornament of life,
And live a coward in thine own esteem,
Letting *I dare not* wait upon *I would?*

MACBETH. Prithee, peace:
I dare do all that may become a man;
Who dares do more is none.

LADY MACBETH. What beast was't, then,
That made you break this enterprise to me?
When you durst do it, then you were a man;
And, to be more than what you were, you would
Be so much more the man. Nor time nor place
Did then adhere, and yet you would make both:
They have made themselves, and that their fitness now
Does unmake you.

MACBETH. If we should fail?

LADY MACBETH. We fail!
But screw your courage to the sticking-place,

And we'll not fail. When Duncan is asleep
(Whereto the rather shall his day's hard journey
Soundly invite him) his two chamberlains
Will I with wine and wassail so convince
That memory, the warder of the brain,
Shall be a fume; and when in swinish sleep
Their drenchèd nature lies as in a death,
What cannot you and I perform upon
The unguarded Duncan? what not put upon
His spongy officers, who shall bear the guilt?

MACBETH. Will it not be received,
When we have marked with blood those sleepy two
Of his own chamber and used their very daggers,
That they have done 't?

LADY MACBETH. Who dares receive it other,
As we shall make our griefs and clamour roar
Upon his death?

MACBETH. I am settled, and bend up
Each corporal agent to this terrible feat.
Away, and mock the time with fairest show:
False face must hide what the false heart doth know

ACT 2

Scene 1—The Court of Macbeth's Castle

BANQUO. How goes the night, boy?

FLEANCE. The moon is down; I have not heard the clock.

BANQUO. Hold, take my sword. There's husbandry in heaven
Their candles are all out. Take thee that too.
A heavy summons lies like lead upon me,
And yet I would not sleep: merciful powers,
Restrain in me the cursèd thoughts that nature
Gives way to in repose! Give me my sword. (*Here Macbeth comes*)

BANQUO. What, sir, not yet at rest? The king's a-bed:
He hath been in unusual pleasure, and
Sent forth great largess to your offices.
This diamond he greets your wife withal,
By the name of most kind hostess. All's well.
I dreamt last night of the three weird sisters:
To you they have showed some truth.

MACBETH. I think not of them:
Yet, when we can entreat an hour to serve,
We would spend it in some words upon that business,
If you would grant the time.

BANQUO. At your kindest leisure.

MACBETH. If you shall cleave to my consent, when tis,
It shall make honour for you.

BANQUO. So I lose none
In seeking to augment it, but still keep
My bosom franchised and allegiance clear,
I shall be counselled.

MACBETH. Good repose the while!

BANQUO. Thanks, sir: the like to you!

MACBETH (*to servant*). Go bid thy mistress, when my drink is ready,
She strike upon the bell. Get thee to bed.
(Alone) Is this a dagger which I see before me,
The handle toward my hand? Come, let me clutch thee.
I have thee not, and yet I see thee still.
Art thou not, fatal vision, sensible
To feeling as to sight? Or art thou but
A dagger of the mind, a false creation,
Proceeding from the heat-oppressèd brain?
I see thee yet, in form as palpable
As this which now I draw.
Now o'er the one half-world
Nature seems dead, and wicked dreams abuse
The curtained sleep; witchcraft celebrates
Pale Hecate's offerings, and withered murder
Moves like a ghost. Thou sure and firm-set earth,
Hear not my steps, which way they walk, for fear
Thy very stones prate of my whereabout,
And take the present horror from the time,
Which now suits with it. Whiles I threat, he lives:
Words to the heat of deeds too cold breath gives. (*A bell rings*)
I go, and it is done; the bell invites me.
Hear it not, Duncan; for it is a knell
That summons thee to heaven or to hell.

Scene 2—The Court of Macbeth's Castle

LADY M. That which hath made them drunk hath made me bold;
What hath quenched them hath given me fire. Hark! Peace!
It was the owl that shrieked, the fatal bellman,
Which gives the stern'st Good-night. He is about it:
The doors are open; and the surfeited grooms
Do mock their charge with snores: I have drugged their possets,
That death and nature do contend about them,
Whether they live or die.

MACBETH (*within*). Who's there? what, ho!

LADY MACBETH. Alack, I am afraid they have awaked
And tis not done. The attempt and not the deed
Confound us. Hark! I laid their daggers ready;

He could not miss 'em. Had he not resembled
My father as he slept, I had done 't. (*Macbeth enters*)

MACBETH. I have done the deed. Didst thou not hear a noise?

LADY MACBETH. I heard the owl scream and the crickets cry.

MACBETH. There's one did laugh in's sleep, and one cried *Murder!*
That they did wake each other: I stood and heard them:
But they did say their prayers, and addressed them
Again to sleep.

LADY MACBETH. There are two lodged together.

MACBETH. One cried *God bless us!* and *Amen* the other;
As they had seen me with these hangman's hands.
Listening their fear, I could not say *Amen*
When they did say *God bless us!*

LADY MACBETH. Consider it not so deeply.

MACBETH. But wherefore could not I pronounce *Amen?*
I had most need of blessing, and *Amen*
Stuck in my throat.

LADY MACBETH. These deeds must not be thought
After these ways; so, it will make us mad.

MACBETH. Methought I heard a voice cry *Sleep no more!*
Macbeth does murder sleep, the innocent sleep,
Sleep that knits up the ravelled sleave of care,
The death of each day's life, sore labour's bath,
Balm of hurt minds, great nature's second course,
Chief nourisher in life's feast—

LADY MACBETH. What do you mean?

MACBETH. Still it cried, *Sleep no more!* to all the house:
Glamis hath murdered sleep, and therefore Cawdor
Shall sleep no more; Macbeth shall sleep no more.

LADY M. Who was it that thus cried? Why, worthy thane,
You do unbend your noble strength, to think
So brain-sickly of things. Go get some water,
And wash this filthy witness from your hand.
Why did you bring these daggers from the place?
They must lie there: go carry them; and smear
The sleepy grooms with blood.

MACBETH. I'll go no more:
I am afraid to think what I have done;
Look on't again I dare not.

LADY MACBETH. Infirm of purpose!
Give me the daggers: the sleeping and the dead
Are but as pictures: tis the eye of childhood
That fears a painted devil. (*She leaves*)

MACBETH. Whence is that knocking?
How is't with me, when every noise appals me?

What hands are here ? ha ! they pluck out mine eyes.
Will all great Neptune's ocean wash this blood
Clean from my hand ?

LADY MACBETH (*returning*). My hands are of your colour ; but I shame
To wear a heart so white. I hear a knocking
At the south entry : retire we to our chamber :
A little water clears us of this deed :
How easy is it, then ! Hark ! more knocking.

MACBETH. Wake Duncan with thy knocking ! I would thou couldst !

Scene 3—In Macbeth's Castle

MACDUFF (*to Lennox*). Is thy master stirring ?
Our knocking has awaked him ; here he comes.

LENNOX. Good-morrow, noble sir.

MACBETH. Good-morrow, both.

MACDUFF. Is the king stirring, worthy thane ?

MACBETH. Not yet.

MACDUFF. He did command me to call timely on him.
I have almost slipped the hour.

MACBETH. I'll bring you to him. This is the door.

MACDUFF. I'll make so bold to call.

LENNOX. Goes the king hence today ?

MACBETH. He does : he did appoint so.

LENNOX. The night has been unruly : where we lay,
Our chimneys were blown down ; and, as they say,
Lamentings heard i' the air ; strange screams of death,
And prophesying with accents terrible
Of dire combustion and confused events
New hatched to the woeful time : the obscure bird
Clamoured the livelong night : some say the earth
Was feverous and did shake.

MACBETH. Twas a rough night.

LENNOX. My young remembrance cannot parallel a fellow to it.

MACDUFF (*returning*). O horror, horror, horror ! Tongue nor heart
Cannot conceive nor name thee !
Confusion now hath made his masterpiece !
Most sacrilegious murder hath broke ope
The Lord's anointed temple, and stole thence
The life o' the building !

MACBETH. What is't you say ? the life ?

LENNOX. Mean you his majesty ?

MACDUFF. Do not bid me speak ;
See, and then speak yourselves. (*They go.*) Awake, awake !

Ring the alarum-bell. Murder and treason !
Banquo and Donalbain ! Malcolm ! awake !
Shake off this downy sleep, death's counterfeit,
And look on death itself ! Up, up, and see
The Great Doom's image ! Malcolm ! Banquo !
As from your graves rise up, and walk like sprites,
To countenance this horror ! Ring the bell.

LADY MACBETH (*entering*). What's the business
That such a hideous trumpet calls to parley
The sleepers of the house ? Speak, speak !

MACDUFF. O gentle lady,
Tis not for you to hear what I can speak :
The repetition in a woman's ear
Would murder as it fell. (*Enter Banquo*)
O Banquo, Banquo, our royal master's murdered !

LADY MACBETH. Woe, alas ! What, in our house ?

BANQUO. Dear Duff, I prithee, contradict thyself,
And say it is not so.

MACBETH (*returning*). Had I but died an hour before this chance,
I had lived a blessed time ; for, from this instant,
There's nothing serious in mortality :
All is but toys : renown and grace is dead ;
The wine of life is drawn, and the mere lees
Is left this vault to brag of.

DONALBAIN (*entering*). What is amiss ?

MACBETH. You are, and do not know't :
The spring, the head, the fountain of your blood
Is stopped ; the very source of it is stopped.

MACDUFF. Your royal father's murdered.

MALCOLM. O, by whom ?

LENNOX. Those of his chamber, as it seemed, had done't :
Their hands and faces were all badged with blood ;
So were their daggers, which unwiped we found
Upon their pillows :
They stared, and were distracted ; no man's life
Was to be trusted with them.

MACBETH. O, yet I do repent me of my fury,
That I did kill them.

MACDUFF. Wherefore did you so ?

MACBETH. Who can be wise, amazed, temperate and furious,
Loyal and neutral, in a moment ? Here lay Duncan,
His silver skin laced with his golden blood ;
There, the murderers, steeped in the colours of their trade :
Who could refrain,
That had a heart to love, and in that heart

Courage to make's love known ?

LADY MACBETH. Help me hence, ho ! (*She is carried out*)

BANQUO. Look to the lady :
And when we have our naked frailties hid,
That suffer in exposure, let us meet,
And question this most cruel piece of work,
To know it further. Fears and scruples shake us :
In the great hand of God I stand ; and thence
Against the undivulged pretence I fight
Of treasonous malice.

MACDUFF. And so do I.

ALL. So all. (*All but Malcolm and Donalbain go*)

MALCOLM. What will you do ? Let's not consort with them :
To show an unfelt sorrow is an office
Which the false man does easy. I'll to England.

DONALBAIN. To Ireland, I ; our separated fortune
Shall keep us both the safer : where we are
There's daggers in men's smiles.

Scene 4—Outside Macbeth's Castle

Ross and an aged man tell of signs and omens which affright the country-side, and Macduff, entering, announces the rumour that Duncan's two sons inspired the murder, and have fled to escape the consequences. Macbeth has gone to Scone to be crowned King of Scotland. Macduff says he will not attend the coronation, but goes to Fife.

ROSS. Here comes the good Macduff.
How goes the world, sir, now ?

MACDUFF. Why, see you not ?

ROSS. Is't known who did this more than cruel deed ?

MACDUFF. Those that Macbeth hath slain.

ROSS. Alas, the day ! What good could they pretend ?

MACDUFF. They were suborned :
Malcolm and Donalbain, the king's two sons,
Are stolen away and fled ; which puts upon them
Suspicion of the deed.

ROSS. Gainst nature still !
Thriftless ambition, that wilt ravin up
Thine own life's means ! Then tis most like
The sovereignty will fall upon Macbeth.

MACDUFF. He is already named, and gone to Scone
To be invested.

ROSS. Where is Duncan's body ?

MACDUFF. Carried to Colmekill,
The sacred storehouse of his predecessors,
And guardian of their bones.

Ross. Will you to Scone ?

Macduff. No, cousin, I'll to Fife.

Ross. Well, I will thither.

Macduff. Well, may you see things well done there : adieu !
Lest our old robes sit easier than our new.

Ross. Farewell, father.

Old Man. God's benison go with you ; and with those
That would make good of bad, and friends of foes !

ACT 3

Scene 1—The Palace at Forres

Banquo (*alone*). Thou hast it now : King, Cawdor, Glamis, all,
As the weird women promised, and, I fear,
Thou play'dst most foully for't : yet it was said
It should not stand in thy posterity,
But that myself should be the root and father
Of many kings. If there come truth from them,
Why, by the verities on thee made good,
May they not be my oracles as well,
And set me up in hope ? But hush ! no more.

Macbeth enters as King, with his Queen and attendants

Macbeth. Here's our chief guest.

Lady Macbeth. If he had been forgotten,
It had been as a gap in our great feast,
And all-thing unbecoming.

Macbeth. Tonight we hold a solemn supper, sir,
And I'll request your presence.

Banquo. Let your highness command upon me.

Macbeth. Ride you this afternoon ?

Banquo. Ay, my good lord.

Macbeth. We should have else desired your good advice,
Which still hath been both grave and prosperous,
In this day's council ; but we'll take tomorrow.
Is't far you ride ?

Banquo. As far, my lord, as will fill up the time
Twixt this and supper : go not my horse the better,
I must become a borrower of the night
For a dark hour or twain.

Macbeth. Fail not our feast.

Banquo. My lord, I will not.

Macbeth. We hear our fearful cousins are bestowed
In England and in Ireland, not confessing
Their cruel parricide, filling their hearers
With strange invention : but of that tomorrow,

When therewithal we shall have cause of State
Craving us jointly. Hie you to horse : adieu
Till you return at night. Goes Fleance with you ?

BANQUO. Ay, my good lord : our time does call upon us.

MACBETH. I wish your horses swift and sure of foot ;
And so I do commend you to their backs. *(Banquo leaves)*
Farewell.
Let every man be master of his time
Till seven at night : to make society
The sweeter welcome we will keep ourself
Till supper-time alone : while then, God be with you !
Sirrah, a word with you : attend those men our pleasure ?

SERVANT. They are, my lord, without the palace gate.

MACBETH. Bring them before us . . . To be thus is nothing ;
But to be safely thus. Our fears in Banquo
Stick deep ; and in his royalty of nature
Reigns that which would be feared : tis much he dares ;
And, to that dauntless temper of his mind,
He hath a wisdom that doth guide his valour
To act in safety. There is none but he
Whose being I do fear : and, under him,
My genius is rebuked ; as, it is said,
Mark Antony's was by Caesar. He chid the sisters
When first they put the name of king upon me,
And bade them speak to him : then prophet-like
They hailed him father to a line of kings :
Upon my head they placed a fruitless crown,
And put a barren sceptre in my grip,
Thence to be wrenched with an unlineal hand,
No son of mine succeeding. If't be so,
For Banquo's issue have I filed my mind ;
For them the gracious Duncan have I murdered ;
Put rancours in the vessel of my peace
Only for them ; and mine eternal jewel
Given to the common enemy of man,
To make them kings, the seed of Banquo kings
Rather than so, come Fate into the list,
And champion me ! Who's there ?

Servant returns with murderers, whom he leaves with Macbeth

MACBETH. Was it not yesterday we spoke together ?

FIRST MURDERER. It was, so please your highness.

MACBETH. Have you considered of my speeches ? Know
That it was he in the times past which held you
So under fortune, which you thought had been
Our innocent self.

FIRST MURDERER. You made it known to us.

MACBETH. I did so, and went further, which is now
Our point of second meeting. Do you find
Your patience so predominant in your nature
That you can let this go? Are you so gospelled
To pray for this good man and for his issue,
Whose heavy hand hath bowed you to the grave
And beggared yours for ever?

FIRST MURDERER. We are men, my liege.

MACBETH. Ay, in the catalogue ye go for men;
As hounds and greyhounds, mongrels, spaniels, curs,
Shoughs, water-rugs, and demi-wolves, are clept
All by the name of dogs: the valued file
Distinguishes the swift, the slow, the subtle,
The housekeeper, the hunter, every one
According to the gift which bounteous nature
Hath in him closed; whereby he does receive
Particular addition, from the bill
That writes them all alike: and so of men.
Now, if you have a station in the file,
Not i' the worst rank of manhood, say't,
And I will put that business in your bosoms,
Whose execution takes your enemy off,
Grapples you to the heart and love of us,
Who wear our health but sickly in his life,
Which in his death were perfect.

SECOND MURDERER. I am one, my liege,
Whom the vile blows and buffets of the world
Have so incensed that I am reckless what
I do to spite the world.

FIRST MURDERER. And I another
So weary with disasters, tugged with fortune,
That I would set my life on any chance,
To mend it or be rid on't.

MACBETH. Both of you
Know Banquo was your enemy.
So is he mine; and in such distance,
That every minute of his being thrusts
Against my near'st of life: and though I could
With barefaced power sweep him from my sight
And bid my will avouch it, yet I must not,
For certain friends that are both his and mine,
Whose loves I may not drop, but wail his fall
Whom I myself struck down; and thence it is,
That I to your assistance do make love,
Masking the business from the common eye
For sundry weighty reasons.

SECOND MURDERER. We shall, my lord,
Perform what you command us.

MACBETH. Your spirits shine through you. Within this hour at most
I will advise you where to plant yourselves,
Acquaint you with the perfect spy o' the time,
The moment on't; for't must be done tonight,
And something from the palace; and with him
Fleance his son, that keeps him company,
Whose absence is no less material to me
Than is his father's, must embrace the fate
Of that dark hour. Resolve yourselves apart;
I'll come to you anon.

MURDERERS. We are resolved, my lord.

MACBETH. I'll call upon you straight: abide within.
It is concluded. Banquo, thy soul's flight,
If it find heaven, must find it out tonight.

Scene 2—The Palace

LADY MACBETH. Is Banquo gone from court?

SERVANT. Ay, madam, but returns again tonight.

LADY MACBETH. Say to the king I would attend his leisure
For a few words.

SERVANT. Madam, I will.

LADY MACBETH. Nought's had, all's spent,
Where our desire is got without content:
Tis safer to be that which we destroy
Than by destruction dwell in doubtful joy.
How now, my lord! (*to Macbeth*) why do you keep alone,
Of sorriest fancies your companions making,
Using those thoughts which should indeed have died
With them they think on? Things without all remedy
Should be without regard: what's done is done.

MACBETH. We have scotched the snake, not killed it:
She'll close and be herself, whilst our poor malice
Remains in danger of her former tooth.
But let the frame of things disjoint, both the worlds suffer
Ere we will eat our meal in fear, and sleep
In the affliction of these terrible dreams
That shake us nightly. Better be with the dead,
Whom we, to gain our peace, have sent to peace,
Than on the torture of the mind to lie
In restless ecstasy. Duncan is in his grave;
After life's fitful fever he sleeps well;
Treason has done his worst: nor steel, nor poison,
Malice domestic, foreign levy, nothing,
Can touch him further.

LADY MACBETH. Come on,
Gentle my lord, sleek o'er your rugged looks ;
Be bright and jovial among your guests tonight.

MACBETH. So shall I, love ; and so, I pray, be you :
Let your remembrance apply to Banquo ;
Present him eminence, both with eye and tongue :
Unsafe the while, that we
Must lave our honours in these flattering streams,
And make our faces vizards to our hearts,
Disguising what they are.

LADY MACBETH. You must leave this.

MACBETH. O, full of scorpions is my mind, dear wife !
Thou know'st that Banquo and his Fleance live.

LADY MACBETH. But in them nature's copy's not eterne.

MACBETH. There's comfort yet ; they are assailable ;
Then be thou jocund ; ere the bat hath flown
His cloistered flight, ere to black Hecate's summons
The shard-borne beetle with his drowsy hums
Hath rung night's yawning peal, there shall be done
A deed of dreadful note.

LADY MACBETH. What's to be done ?

MACBETH. Be innocent of the knowledge, dearest chuck,
Till thou applaud the deed. Come, seeling night,
Scarf up the tender eye of pitiful day ;
Cancel and tear to pieces that great bond
Which keeps me pale ! Light thickens ; and the crow
Makes wing to the rooky wood :
Good things of day begin to droop and drowse ;
Whiles night's black agents to their preys do rouse.
Thou marvell'st at my words, but hold thee still :
Things bad begun make strong themselves by ill.
So, prithee, go with me.

Scene 3—Murderers in Wait near the Palace

FIRST MURDERER. But who did bid thee join us ?

THIRD MURDERER. Macbeth.

FIRST MURDERER. Then stand with us.
The west yet glimmers with some streaks of day :
Now spurs the lated traveller apace
To gain the timely inn ; and near approaches
The subject of our watch.

THIRD MURDERER. Hark ! I hear horses.

SECOND MURDERER. Then tis he ! A light, a light !

THIRD MURDERER. Tis he.

FIRST MURDERER. Stand to't.

BANQUO (*approaching, talking to Fleance*). It will be rain tonight.

FIRST MURDERER. Let it come down. (*They set upon Banquo*)

BANQUO. O, treachery ! Fly, good Fleance, fly, fly, fly !
Thou mayst revenge. O slave ! (*He dies, and Fleance escapes*)

THIRD MURDERER. There's but one down ; the son is fled.

SECOND MURDERER. We have lost best half of our affair.

FIRST MURDERER. Well, let's away, and say how much is done.

Scene 4—Banquet Hall in the Palace

MACBETH. You know your own degrees ; sit down : at first
And last the hearty welcome.

LORDS. Thanks to your majesty.

MACBETH. Ourself will mingle with society,
And play the humble host.
Our hostess keeps her state, but in best time
We will require her welcome.

LADY MACBETH. Pronounce it for me, sir, to all our friends ;
For my heart speaks they are welcome.

The First Murderer appears at the door

MACBETH. See, they encounter thee with their hearts' thanks.
Both sides are even : here I'll sit i' the midst :
Be large in mirth ; anon we'll drink a measure
The table round. (*Nearing the door*) There's blood upon thy face.

MURDERER. Tis Banquo's then.

MACBETH. Tis better thee without than he within.
Is he dispatched ?

MURDERER. My lord, his throat is cut ; that I did for him.

MACBETH. Thou art the best o' the cut-throats : yet he's good
That did the like for Fleance : if thou didst it,
Thou art the nonpareil.

MURDERER. Most royal sir,
Fleance is scaped.

MACBETH. Then comes my fit again : I had else been perfect,
Whole as the marble, founded as the rock,
As broad and general as the casing air ;
But now I am cabined, cribbed, confined, bound in
To saucy doubts and fears. But Banquo's safe ?

MURDERER. Ay, my good lord : safe in a ditch he bides.

MACBETH. Thanks for that :
There the grown serpent lies ; the worm that's fled
Hath nature that in time will venom breed,
No teeth for the present. Get thee gone : tomorrow
We'll hear, ourselves, again.

LADY MACBETH. My royal lord,
You do not give the cheer : the feast is sold

That is not often vouched, while tis a-making
Tis given with welcome : to feed were best at home ;
From thence the sauce to meat is ceremony ;
Meeting were bare without it.

MACBETH. Sweet remembrancer !
Now, good digestion wait on appetite,
And health on both !

LENNOX. May it please your highness sit.

The Ghost of Banquo sits in Macbeth's place

MACBETH. Here had we now our country's honour roofed,
Were the graced person of our Banquo present,
Whom may I rather challenge for unkindness
Than pity for mischance !

ROSS. His absence, sir,
Lays blame upon his promise. Please 't your highness
To grace us with your royal company.

MACBETH. The table's full.

LENNOX. Here is a place reserved, sir.

MACBETH. Where ?

LENNOX. Here, my good lord. What is't that moves your highness ?

MACBETH. Which of you have done this ?

LORDS. What, my good lord ?

MACBETH. Thou canst not say I did it : never shake
Thy gory locks at me.

ROSS. Gentlemen, rise : his highness is not well.

LADY MACBETH. Sit, worthy friends : my lord is often thus,
And hath been from his youth : pray you, keep seat ;
The fit is momentary ; upon a thought
He will again be well : if much you note him,
You shall offend him and extend his passion :
Feed, and regard him not.

As the banquet goes on Lady Macbeth reproves her husband, and a low conversation aside takes place between them.

LADY MACBETH. Are you a man ?

MACBETH. Ay, and a bold one, that dare look on that
Which might appal the devil.

LADY MACBETH. O proper stuff !
This is the very painting of your fear :
This is the air-drawn dagger which, you said,
Led you to Duncan. O, these flaws and starts,
Impostors to true fear, would well become
A woman's story at a winter's fire,
Authorised by her grandam. Shame itself !
Why do you make such faces ? When all's done
You look but on a stool.

MACBETH. Prithee, see there! behold! look! lo! how say you?
Why, what care I? If thou canst nod, speak too.

The Ghost now vanishes

LADY MACBETH. What, quite unmanned in folly?

MACBETH. If I stand here, I saw him.

LADY MACBETH. Fie, for shame!

MACBETH. Blood hath been shed ere now, i' the olden time,
Ere human statute purged the gentle weal;
Ay, and since too, murders have been performed
Too terrible for the ear: the times have been
That when the brains were out the man would die,
And there an end; but now they rise again,
With twenty mortal murders on their crowns,
And push us from our stools: this is more strange
Than such a murder is.

LADY MACBETH. My worthy lord, your noble friends do lack you.

MACBETH. I do forget.
Do not muse at me, my most worthy friends;
I have a strange infirmity, which is nothing
To those that know me. Come, love and health to all;
Then I'll sit down. Give me some wine; fill full.
I drink to the general joy o' the whole table,
And to our dear friend Banquo, whom we miss;
Would he were here! To all, and him, we thirst,
And all to all. (*As they drink the Ghost returns*)

MACBETH. Avaunt! and quit my sight! let the earth hide thee!
Thy bones are marrowless, thy blood is cold;
Thou hast no speculation in those eyes
Which thou dost glare with!

LADY MACBETH. Think of this, good peers,
But as a thing of custom: tis no other;
Only it spoils the pleasure of the time.

MACBETH. What man dare, I dare:
Approach thou like the rugged Russian bear,
The armed rhinoceros, or the Hyrcan tiger;
Take any shape but that, and my firm nerves
Shall never tremble: or be alive again,
And dare me to the desert with thy sword;
If trembling I inhabit then, protest me
The baby of a girl. Hence, horrible shadow!
Unreal mockery, hence! (*Ghost vanishes*) Why, so: being gone,
I am a man again. Pray you, sit still.

LADY M. You have displaced the mirth, broke the good meeting.

MACBETH. Can such things be,
And overcome us like a summer's cloud,

Without our special wonder? You make me strange
Even to the disposition that I owe,
When now I think you can behold such sights,
And keep the natural ruby of your cheeks,
When mine is blanched with fear.

Ross. What sights, my lord?

Lady M. I pray you, speak not; he grows worse and worse;
Question enrages him. At once, Good-night:
Stand not upon the order of your going,
But go at once. A kind Good-night to all!

Macbeth. It will have blood; they say blood will have blood:
Stones have been known to move and trees to speak;
Augurs and understood relations have
By maggot-pies and choughs and rooks brought forth
The secretest man of blood. What is the night?

Lady Macbeth. Almost at odds with morning, which is which.

Macbeth. How say'st thou, that Macduff denies his person
At our great bidding?

Lady Macbeth. Did you send to him, sir?

Macbeth. I hear it by the way; but I will send:
There's not a one of them but in his house
I keep a servant fee'd. I will tomorrow,
And betimes I will, to the weird sisters:
More shall they speak; for now I am bent to know,
By the worst means, the worst. For mine own good,
All causes shall give way: I am in blood
Stepped in so far that, should I wade no more,
Returning were as tedious as go o'er:
Strange things I have in head, that will to hand;
Which must be acted ere they may be scanned.

Lady Macbeth. You lack the season of all natures, sleep.

Macbeth. Come, we'll to sleep. My strange and self-abuse
Is the initiate fear that wants hard use:
We are yet but young in deed.

Scene 5—The Heath

The three witches meet Hecate, to whose will they are subject. She reproves them for having given information to Macbeth, and commands that when next he sees them they shall mislead him to disaster.

Scene 6—The Forest

The scene changes to the forest, where Lennox explains the plot which enabled Macbeth to throw suspicion on Fleance, who has fled to England.

ACT 4

Scene 1—The Cavern of the Witches

First Witch. Thrice the brinded cat hath mewed.

Second Witch. Thrice and once the hedge-pig whined.

THIRD WITCH. Harpier cries *Tis time, tis time.*

FIRST WITCH. Round about the cauldron go;
In the poisoned entrails throw.
Toad, that under cold stone
Days and nights has thirty-one
Sweltered venom sleeping got,
Boil thou first i' the charmèd pot.

ALL. Double, double, toil and trouble;
Fire burn and cauldron bubble.

SECOND WITCH. Fillet of a fenny snake,
In the cauldron boil and bake;
Eye of newt and toe of frog,
Wool of bat and tongue of dog,
Adder's fork and blind-worm's sting,
Lizard's leg and owlet's wing,
For a charm of powerful trouble,
Like a hell-broth boil and bubble.

ALL. Double, double, toil and trouble;
Fire burn and cauldron bubble.

THIRD WITCH. Scale of dragon, tooth of wolf,
Witch's mummy, maw and gulf
Of the ravined salt-sea shark,
Root of hemlock digged i' the dark,
Liver of blaspheming Jew,
Gall of goat, and slips of yew
Slivered in the moon's eclipse,
Nose of Turk and Tartar's lips;
Add thereto a tiger's chaudron,
For the ingredients of our cauldron.

ALL. Double, double, toil and trouble;
Fire burn and cauldron bubble.

SECOND WITCH. Cool it with a baboon's blood,
Then the charm is firm and good.

SECOND WITCH. By the pricking of my thumbs,
Something wicked this way comes.
Open, locks, whoever knocks!

MACBETH. How now, you secret, black, and midnight hags!
What is't you do?

ALL. A deed without a name.

MACBETH. I conjure you, by that which you profess,
Howe'er you come to know it, answer me:
Though you untie the winds and let them fight
Against the churches; though the yesty waves
Confound and swallow navigation up;

Though bladed corn be lodged and trees blown down;
Though castles topple on their warders' heads;
Though palaces and pyramids do slope
Their heads to their foundations,
Even till destruction sicken; answer me
To what I ask you.

FIRST WITCH. Speak.

SECOND WITCH. Demand.

THIRD WITCH. We'll answer.

FIRST WITCH. Say if thou'dst rather hear it from our mouths,
Or from our masters?

MACBETH. Call 'em; let me see 'em.

WITCH. Pour in sow's blood, that hath eaten
Her nine farrow; grease that's sweaten
From the murderer's gibbet throw
Into the flame.

ALL. Come, high or low;
Thyself and office deftly show!

The first Apparition, an armed head, appears

MACBETH. Tell me, thou unknown power—

WITCH. He knows thy thought:
Hear his speech, but say thou nought.

APPARITION. Macbeth! Macbeth! Macbeth! beware Macduff;
Beware the thane of Fife. Dismiss me. Enough.

MACBETH. Whate'er thou art, for thy good caution, thanks;
Thou hast harped my fear aright: but one word more—

WITCH. He will not be commanded: here's another,
More potent than the first.

The second Apparition, a bloodstained child, appears

APPARITION. Macbeth! Macbeth! Macbeth!

MACBETH. Had I three ears I'd hear thee.

APPARITION. Be fearless, bold, and resolute; laugh to scorn
The power of man, for none of woman born
Shall harm Macbeth.

MACBETH. Then live, Macduff; what need I fear of thee?
But yet I'll make assurance double sure,
And take a bond of fate: thou shalt not live;
That I may tell pale-hearted fear it lies,
And sleep in spite of thunder.

The third Apparition appears, a child crowned, with a tree in his hand

What is this that rises like the issue of a king,
And wears upon his baby-brow the round
And top of sovereignty?

ALL. Listen, but speak not to 't.

Apparition. Be lion-mettled, proud ; and take no care
Who chafes, who frets, or where conspirers are :
Macbeth shall never vanquished be until
Great Birnam wood to high Dunsinane hill
Shall come against him.

Macbeth. That will never be :
Who can impress the forest, bid the tree
Unfix his earth-bound root ? Sweet bodements ! good !
Rebellion's head, rise never till the wood
Of Birnam rise, and our high-placed Macbeth
Shall live the lease of nature, pay his breath
To time and mortal custom. Yet my heart
Throbs to know one thing : tell me, if your art
Can tell so much : shall Banquo's issue ever
Reign in this kingdom ?

All. Seek to know no more.

Macbeth. I will be satisfied : deny me this,
And an eternal curse fall on you ! Let me know.
Why sinks that cauldron ? and what noise is this ?

All. Show his eyes, and grieve his heart ;
Come like shadows, so depart !

A show of Eight Kings passes before the vision of Macbeth, the last with a glass in his hand, Banquo's Ghost following. Macbeth stares at the procession in terrified amazement, crying out at last: What, will the line stretch out to the Crack of Doom? The Witches then vanish.

Macbeth. Where are they ? Gone ? Let this pernicious hour
Stand aye accursèd in the calendar !
Come in, without there !

Lennox (*entering*). What's your grace's will ?

Macbeth. Saw you the weird sisters ?

Lennox. No, my lord.

Macbeth. Came they not by you ?

Lennox. No, indeed, my lord.

Macbeth. Infected be the air whereon they ride ;
And cursed all those that trust them ! I did hear
The galloping of horse : who was't came by ?

Lennox. Tis two or three, my lord, that bring you word
Macduff is fled to England.

Macbeth. Fled to England !

Lennox. Ay, my good lord.

Macbeth. Time, thou anticipat'st my dread exploits :
The flighty purpose never is o'ertook
Unless the deed go with it : from this moment
The very firstlings of my heart shall be
The firstlings of my hand. And even now,

To crown my thoughts with acts, be it thought and done:
The castle of Macduff I will surprise;
Seize upon Fife; give to the edge o' the sword
His wife, his babes, and all unfortunate souls
That trace him in his line. No boasting like a fool;
This deed I'll do before this purpose cool.
But no more sights! Where are these gentlemen?
Come, bring me where they are.

Scene 2—Macduff's Castle in Fife

Enter Lady Macduff, her Son, and Ross

Lady Macduff. What had he done, to make him fly the land?
Ross. You must have patience, madam.
Lady Macduff. He had none:
His flight was madness: when our actions do not,
Our fears do make us traitors.
Ross. You know not
Whether it was his wisdom or his fear.
Lady Macduff. Wisdom! To leave his wife, to leave his babes,
His mansion and his titles in a place
From whence himself does fly? He loves us not:
He wants the natural touch: for the poor wren,
The most diminutive of birds, will fight,
Her young ones in her nest, against the owl.
All is the fear and nothing is the love;
As little is the wisdom, where the flight
So runs against all reason.
Ross. My dearest coz,
I pray you, school yourself: but for your husband,
He is noble, wise, judicious, and best knows
The fits o' the season. I dare not speak much further;
But cruel are the times, when we are traitors
And do not know ourselves, when we hold rumour
From what we fear, yet know not what we fear,
But float upon a wild and violent sea
Each way and move. I take my leave of you:
Shall not be long but I'll be here again:
Things at the worst will cease, or else climb upward
To what they were before. My pretty cousin,
Blessing upon you! (*Embracing Macduff's little son*)
Lady Macduff. Fathered he is, and yet he's fatherless.
Sirrah, your father's dead:
And what will you do now? How will you live?
Son. As birds do, mother.
Messenger. Bless you, fair dame! I am not to you known,

Though in your state of honour I am perfect.
I doubt some danger does approach you nearly :
If you will take a homely man's advice,
Be not found here ; hence, with your little ones.
To fright you thus, methinks, I am too savage ;
To do worse to you were fell cruelty,
Which is too nigh your person. Heaven preserve you!
I dare abide no longer.

LADY MACDUFF. Whither should I fly ?
I have done no harm.

The conversation is interrupted by a hasty messenger with warning of danger, followed by the murderers, who kill the mother and her children.

Scene 3—England, before the King's Palace

Macduff has reached England, where Malcolm at first suspects his friend of treacherous intent. Macduff, in grief and indignation, denounces him, and is about to leave him when Malcolm, convinced of the brave man's sincerity, reveals himself in his true nature as a gallant prince, ready to avenge the wrongs that have been done. A doctor enters, and describes the King as engaged in the old superstition of touching sick people to heal them, and at that moment Ross appears from the North, with sorrowful and very tragic news.

MACDUFF. See, who comes here ?

MALCOLM. My countryman ; but yet I know him not.

MACDUFF. My ever-gentle cousin, welcome hither.

MALCOLM. I know him now. Good God, betimes remove
The means that makes us strangers!

ROSS. Sir, amen.

MACDUFF. Stands Scotland where it did ?

ROSS. Alas, poor country!
Almost afraid to know itself. It cannot
Be called our mother, but our grave, where nothing
(But who knows nothing) is once seen to smile :
Where sighs and groans and shrieks that rend the air
Are made, not marked ; where violent sorrow seems
A modern ecstasy : the dead man's knell
Is there scarce asked for whom ; and good men's lives
Expire before the flowers in their caps,
Dying or ere they sicken.

MACDUFF. O, relation too nice, and yet too true!

MALCOLM. What's the newest grief ?

ROSS. That of an hour's age doth hiss the speaker :
Each minute teems a new one.

MACDUFF. How does my wife ?

ROSS. Why, well.

MACDUFF. And all my children?

ROSS. Well, too.

MACDUFF. The tyrant has not battered at their peace?

ROSS. No; they were well at peace when I did leave 'em.

MACDUFF. Be not a niggard of your speech: how goes 't?

ROSS. When I came hither to transport the tidings,
Which I have heavily borne, there ran a rumour
Of many worthy fellows that were out;
Now is the time of help; your eye in Scotland
Would create soldiers, make our women fight,
To doff their dire distresses.

MALCOLM. Be 't their comfort
We are coming thither: gracious England hath
Lent us good Siward and ten thousand men;
An older and a better soldier none
That Christendom gives out.

ROSS. Would I could answer
This comfort with the like! But I have words
That would be howled out in the desert air,
Where hearing should not latch them.

MACDUFF. What concern they?
The general cause? or is it a fee-grief
Due to some single breast?

ROSS. No mind that's honest
But in it shares some woe, though the main part
Pertains to you alone.

MACDUFF. If it be mine,
Keep it not from me, quickly let me have it.

ROSS. Let not your ears despise my tongue for ever,
Which shall possess them with the heaviest sound
That ever yet they heard.

MACDUFF. Hum! I guess at it.

ROSS. Your castle is surprised; your wife and babes
Savagely slaughtered.

MALCOLM. Merciful heaven!
What, man! ne'er pull your hat upon your brows;
Give sorrow words: the grief that does not speak
Whispers the o'er-fraught heart and bids it break.

MACDUFF. My children too?

ROSS. Wife, children, servants, all that could be found.

MACDUFF. And I must be from thence! My wife killed too?

ROSS. I have said.

MALCOLM. Be comforted:
Let's make us medicines of our great revenge,

To cure this deadly grief.

MACDUFF. He has no children. All my pretty ones?
Did you say all? O hell-kite! All?
What, all my pretty chickens and their dam
At one fell swoop?

MALCOLM. Dispute it like a man.

MACDUFF. I shall do so;
But I must also feel it as a man:
I cannot but remember such things were,
That were most precious to me. Did heaven look on
And would not take their part? Sinful Macduff,
They were all struck for thee! Naught that I am,
Not for their own demerits, but for mine,
Fell slaughter on their souls. Heaven rest them now.
O, I could play the woman with mine eyes
And braggart with my tongue! But, gentle heavens,
Cut short all intermission; front to front
Bring thou this fiend of Scotland and myself;
Within my sword's length set him; if he scape,
Heaven forgive him too!

MALCOLM. This tune goes manly.
Come, go we to the king; our power is ready;
Our lack is nothing but our leave: Macbeth
Is ripe for shaking, and the powers above
Put on their instruments. Receive what cheer you may:
The night is long that never finds the day.

ACT 5

Scene 1—A Night Watch in the Castle at Dunsinane

DOCTOR. I have two nights watched with you, but can perceive no truth in your report. When was it she last walked?

GENTLEWOMAN. Since his majesty went into the field I have seen her rise from her bed, throw her nightgown upon her, unlock her closet, take forth paper, fold it, write upon't, read it, afterwards seal it, and again return to bed; yet all this while in a most fast sleep.

DOCTOR. A great perturbation in nature, to receive at once the benefit of sleep and do the effects of watching! In this slumbery agitation, besides her walking and other actual performances, what, at any time, have you heard her say?

GENTLEWOMAN. That, sir, which I will not report after her.

DOCTOR. You may to me; and tis most meet you should.

GENTLEWOMAN. Neither to you nor any one, having no witness to confirm my speech.

Enter Lady Macbeth, with a lighted candle

Lo you, here she comes! This is her very guise; and, upon my life, fast asleep. Observe her; stand close.

DOCTOR. How came she by that light?

GENTLEWOMAN. Why, it stood by her: she has light by her continually; tis her command.

DOCTOR. You see, her eyes are open.

GENTLEWOMAN. Ay, but their sense is shut.

DOCTOR. What is it she does now? Look, how she rubs her hands.

GENTLEWOMAN. It is an accustomed action with her to seem thus washing her hands: I have known her continue in this a quarter of an hour.

LADY MACBETH. Yet here's a spot.

DOCTOR. Hark! she speaks: I will set down what comes from her, to satisfy my remembrance the more strongly.

LADY MACBETH. Out, damnèd spot! out, I say! One: two: why, then tis time to do't. Fie, my lord, fie! a soldier, and afeard? What need we fear who knows it, when none can call our power to account? Yet who would have thought the old man to have had so much blood in him.

DOCTOR. Do you mark that?

LADY MACBETH. The thane of Fife had a wife: where is she now? (What, will these hands ne'er be clean?) No more o' that, my lord, no more o' that: you mar all with this starting.

DOCTOR. Go to, go to; you have known what you should not.

GENTLEWOMAN. She has spoke what she should not, I am sure of that: heaven knows what she has known.

LADY MACBETH. Here's the smell of the blood still: all the perfumes of Arabia will not sweeten this little hand. Oh, oh, oh!

DOCTOR. What a sigh is there. The heart is sorely charged.

GENTLEWOMAN. I would not have such a heart in my bosom for the dignity of the whole body.

DOCTOR. Well, well, well!

GENTLEWOMAN. Pray God it be, sir.

DOCTOR. This disease is beyond my practice; yet I have known those which have walked in their sleep who have died holily in their beds.

LADY MACBETH. Wash your hands, put on your nightgown; look not so pale. I tell you yet again, Banquo's buried; he cannot come out on 's grave. To bed, to bed! There's knocking at the gate: come, come, come, come, give me your hand. What's done cannot be undone. To bed, to bed, to bed! (*She walks away*)

DOCTOR. Will she go now to bed?

GENTLEWOMAN. Directly.

DOCTOR. Foul whisperings are abroad: unnatural deeds
Do breed unnatural troubles: infected minds
To their deaf pillows will discharge their secrets:
More needs she the divine than the physician.
God, God forgive us all! Look after her;
Remove from her the means of all annoyance,
And still keep eyes upon her. So, Good-night.
I think, but dare not speak.

GENTLEWOMAN. Good-night, good doctor.

Scene 2—The Country near Dunsinane

MENTEITH. The English power is near, led on by Malcolm,
His uncle Siward, and the good Macduff.

ANGUS. Near Birnam wood
Shall we well meet them; that way are they coming.

CAITHNESS. Who knows if Donalbain be with his brother?

LENNOX. For certain, sir, he is not: I have a file
Of all the gentry: there is Siward's son,
And many unrough youths that even now
Protest their first of manhood.

MENTEITH. What does the tyrant?

CAITHNESS. Great Dunsinane he strongly fortifies:
Some say he's mad; others that lesser hate him
Do call it valiant fury.

ANGUS. Now does he feel
His secret murders sticking on his hands;
Those he commands move only in command,
Nothing in love: now does he feel his title
Hang loose about him, like a giant's robe
Upon a dwarfish thief.

MENTEITH. Who then shall blame
His pestered senses to recoil and start,
When all that is within him does condemn
Itself for being there?

CAITHNESS. Well, march we on.

LENNOX. Make we our march towards Birnam.

Scene 3—A Room in the Castle at Dunsinane

MACBETH. Bring me no more reports; let them fly all:
Till Birnam wood remove to Dunsinane,
I cannot taint with fear. What's the boy Malcolm?
Was he not born of woman? The spirits that know
All mortal consequences have pronounced me thus:
Fear not, Macbeth; no man that's born of woman

Shall e'er have power upon thee. Then fly, false thanes,
And mingle with the English epicures :
The mind I sway by and the heart I bear
Shall never sag with doubt nor shake with fear.

SERVANT (*entering*). There is ten thousand—

MACBETH. Geese, villain ?

ERVANT. Soldiers, sir.

MACBETH. Go prick thy face, and over-red thy fear,
Thou lily-livered boy. What soldiers, patch ?
Death of thy soul ! those linen cheeks of thine
Are counsellors to fear. What soldiers, whey-face ?

SERVANT. The English force, so please you.

MACBETH. Take thy face hence. I am sick at heart.
This push will cheer me or dis-seat me now.
I have lived long enough : my way of life
Is fallen into the sear, the yellow leaf ;
And that which should accompany old age,
As honour, love, obedience, troops of friends,
I must not look to have ; but, in their stead,
Curses, not loud but deep, mouth-honour, breath,
Which the poor heart would fain deny, and dare not.
Seyton !

SEYTON (*entering*). What is your gracious pleasure ?

MACBETH. What news more ?

SEYTON. All is confirmed, my lord, which was reported.

MACBETH. I'll fight till from my bones my flesh be hacked.
Give me my armour.

SEYTON. Tis not needed yet.

MACBETH. I'll put it on.
Send out more horses ; skirr the country round ;
Hang those that talk of fear. Give me mine armour.
How does your patient, doctor ?

DOCTOR. Not so sick, my lord,
As she is troubled with thick-coming fancies,
That keep her from her rest.

MACBETH. Cure her of that.
Canst thou not minister to a mind diseased,
Pluck from the memory a rooted sorrow,
Raze out the written troubles of the brain
And with some sweet oblivious antidote
Cleanse the stuffed bosom of that perilous stuff
Which weighs upon the heart ?

DOCTOR. Therein the patient must minister to himself.

MACBETH. Throw physic to the dogs ; I'll none of it.

Come, put mine armour on ; give me my staff.
I will not be afraid of death and bane,
Till Birnam forest come to Dunsinane.

Scene 4—Soldiers Marching near Birnam Wood

MALCOLM. Cousins, I hope the days are near at hand
That chambers will be safe.

MENTEITH. We doubt it nothing.

SIWARD. What wood is this before us ?

MENTEITH. The wood of Birnam.

MALCOLM. Let every soldier hew him down a bough
And bear't before him : thereby shall we shadow
The numbers of our host and make discovery
Err in report of us.

SOLDIERS. It shall be done.

Scene 5—Macbeth in His Castle

MACBETH. Hang out our banners on the outward walls ;
The cry is still *They come* : our castle's strength
Will laugh a siege to scorn : here let them lie
Till famine and the ague eat them up :
Were they not forced with those that should be ours
We might have met them dareful, beard to beard,
And beat them backward home. What is that noise ?

SEYTON. It is the cry of women, my good lord.

MACBETH. I have almost forgot the taste of fears :
The time has been my senses would have cooled
To hear a night-shriek. I have supped full with horrors
Direness, familiar to my slaughterous thoughts,
Cannot once start me. Wherefore was that cry ?

SEYTON. The queen, my lord, is dead.

MACBETH. She should have died hereafter ;
There would have been a time for such a word.
Tomorrow, and tomorrow, and tomorrow,
Creeps in this petty pace from day to day
To the last syllable of recorded time,
And all our yesterdays have lighted fools
The way to dusty death. Out, out, brief candle !
Life's but a walking shadow, a poor player
That struts and frets his hour upon the stage
And then is heard no more : it is a tale
Told by an idiot, full of sound and fury,
Signifying nothing.

MESSENGER (*approaching*). Gracious my lord,
I should report that which I say I saw,
But know not how to do it.

MACBETH. Well, say, sir.

MESSENGER. As I did stand my watch upon the hill,
I looked toward Birnam, and anon, methought,
The wood began to move.

MACBETH. Liar and slave!

MESSENGER. Let me endure your wrath, if 't be not so.
Within this three mile may you see it coming.

MACBETH. If thou speak'st false,
Upon the next tree shalt thou hang alive,
Till famine cling thee: if thy speech be sooth,
I care not if thou dost for me as much.
Fear not till Birnam wood
Do come to Dunsinane: and now a wood
Comes toward Dunsinane. Arm, arm, and out!
If this which he avouches does appear,
There is nor flying hence nor tarrying here.
I 'gin to be aweary of the sun,
And wish the estate o' the world were now undone.
Ring the alarum-bell! Blow, wind! come, wrack!
At least we'll die with harness on our back.

Scene 6—Malcolm's Army Approaching the Castle with Boughs

MALCOLM. Now near enough: your leafy screens throw down,
And show like those you are. You, worthy uncle.
Shall, with my cousin, your right-noble son,
Lead our first battle: worthy Macduff and we
Shall take upon's what else remains to do,
According to our order.

SIWARD. Fare you well.
Do we but find the tyrant's power tonight,
Let us be beaten, if we cannot fight.

MACDUFF. Make all our trumpets speak; give them all breath,
Those clamorous harbingers of blood and death.

Scene 7—The Field

MACBETH. They have tied me to a stake; I cannot fly,
But, bear-like, I must fight the course. What's he
That was not born of woman? Such a one
Am I to fear, or none.

YOUNG SIWARD (*entering*). What is thy name?

MACBETH. Thou'lt be afraid to hear it.

YOUNG SIWARD. No; though thou call'st thyself a hotter name
Than any is in hell.

MACBETH. My name's Macbeth.

YOUNG SIWARD. The devil himself could not pronounce a title
More hateful to mine ear.

MACBETH. No, nor more fearful.

YOUNG SIWARD. Thou liest, abhorrèd tyrant ; with my sword
I'll prove the lie thou speak'st. (*They fight, and Siward dies*)

MACBETH. Thou wast born of woman,
But swords I smile at, weapons laugh to scorn,
Brandished by man that's of a woman born. (*Macbeth goes*)

MACDUFF (*entering*). That way the noise is. Tyrant, show thy face !
If thou be'st slain, and with no stroke of mine,
My wife and children's ghosts will haunt me still.
I cannot strike at wretched kerns whose arms
Are hired to bear their staves : either thou, Macbeth,
Or else my sword with an unbattered edge
I sheathe again undeeded.
Let me find him, fortune ! And more I beg not.

He goes to seek Macbeth, who reappears

MACBETH. Why should I play the Roman fool, and die
On mine own sword ?

MACDUFF (*entering*). Turn, hell-hound, turn !

MACBETH. Of all men else I have avoided thee :
But get thee back ; my soul is too much charged
With blood of thine already.

MACDUFF. I have no words : my voice is in my sword. (*They fight*)

MACBETH. Thou losest labour :
As easy mayst thou the intrenchant air
With thy keen sword impress as make me bleed :
Let fall thy blade on vulnerable crests ;
I bear a charmèd life, which must not yield
To one of woman born. I'll not fight with thee.

MACDUFF. Then yield thee, coward,
And live to be the show and gaze o' the time :
We'll have thee, as our rarer monsters are,
Painted upon a pole, and underwrit :
Here may you see the tyrant.

MACBETH. I will not yield,
To kiss the ground before young Malcolm's feet,
And to be baited with the rabble's curse.
Though Birnam wood be come to Dunsinane,
Yet I will try the last. Lay on, Macduff,
And cursed be him that first cries *Hold, enough !*

They go out fighting, and lords and soldiers enter

MALCOLM. I would the friends we miss were safe arrived.

SIWARD. Some must go off : and yet, by these I see,
So great a day as this is cheaply bought.

MALCOLM. Macduff is missing, and your noble son.

ROSS. Your son, my lord, has paid a soldier's debt:
He only lived but till he was a man;
The which no sooner had his prowess confirmed
In the unshrinking station where he fought,
But like a man he died.

SIWARD. Then he is dead?

ROSS. Ay, and brought off the field: your cause of sorrow
Must not be measured by his worth, for then
It hath no end.

SIWARD. Had he his hurts before?

ROSS. Ay, on the front.

SIWARD. Why then, God's soldier be he!
Had I as many sons as I have hairs,
I would not wish them to a fairer death:
And so his knell is knolled.

MALCOLM. He's worth more sorrow,
And that I'll spend for him.

SIWARD. He's worth no more:
They say he parted well, and paid his score:
And so, God be with him! Here comes newer comfort.

Macduff approaches, bearing Macbeth's head

MACDUFF. Hail, king! for so thou art: behold where stands
The usurper's cursèd head! The time is free:
I see thee compassed with thy kingdom's pearl,
That speak my salutation in their minds;
Whose voices I desire aloud with mine:
Hail, King of Scotland!

ALL. Hail, King of Scotland!

MALCOLM. We shall not spend a large expense of time
Before we reckon with your several loves,
And make us even with you. My thanes and kinsmen,
Henceforth be earls, the first that ever Scotland
In such an honour named. What's more to do,
Which would be planted newly with the time,
As calling home our exiled friends abroad
That fled the snares of watchful tyranny;
Producing forth the cruel ministers
Of this dead butcher and his fiend-like queen,
Who, as tis thought, by self and violent hands
Took off her life; this, and what needful else
That calls upon us, by the grace of Grace,
We will perform in measure, time, and place:
So, thanks to all at once and to each one,
Whom we invite to see us crowned at Scone.

The Story of the Tempest

It is almost certain that The Tempest is the last of Shakespeare's plays, the poet's farewell to the stage.

We like to think it is so, for there is something in The Tempest that is not entirely of this world. We see Shakespeare with his magic at its highest, taking three little hours of life on an island far away and giving it a touch of immortality. He makes us feel, as he makes Prospero say, that we are such stuff as dreams are made on.

Shakespeare found the idea of the play in old books of many lands, but it suited him well that a new island had just come into history. A shipload of the early founders of the British Empire, on their way to Sir Walter Raleigh's much-loved colony of Virginia, had been shipwrecked on what Shakespeare calls the vexed Bermoothes, and it is odd that, in the magic hands of Shakespeare, this first known event in the history of Bermuda should give the island an imperishable place in literature.

There was wide public interest in the story of the wreck, the fertility of the island, the alluring climate, and the mysterious noises that were said to have been heard. Shakespeare took the island for the scene of his play, transporting it from the Atlantic into the Mediterranean so that it would serve for the shipwreck of a royal party storm-driven while returning home to Naples from a marriage in Tunis. It was probably at a wedding festivity that the play was first produced, in February 1613.

In this beautiful play it is impossible not to notice how perfectly Shakespeare blends his mixed materials into a charming story. Human beings, airy sprites, and visions from nowhere hold the stage, and the poet's imagination so captures us that we accept it as a true romance. Through it all runs a delicate fancy deepened by an undertone of profound thought, and breathing a spirit of gracious forgiveness for all wrongs.

But the impressiveness of The Tempest lies not only in the thought that runs through the play, but in the conviction, growing upon us as we read, that Shakespeare is saying farewell and laying down his pen. We feel that Prospero laying down his cloak is Shakespeare laying aside his magic. Prospero breaking his wand and drowning his book is Shakespeare saying farewell to the magic by which he could create a play like this.

In the Epilogue Prospero stands before the world with his magic powers voluntarily laid down, and so, we believe, does Shakespeare, the master magician of the human mind, the greatest writer since the world began.

THE PLAYERS

Prospero, a wise and popular Duke of Milan, a master of magic, secretly turned adrift at sea by his treacherous brother Antonio, helped by Alonso, King of Naples.

Miranda, Prospero's daughter, who shares her father's exile. She has been brought up by him on a remote island, the only other inhabitants being Caliban and certain spirits, whom Prospero controls by his magic.

Ariel, a clever and winsome sprite, a great lover of liberty, imprisoned by the foul witch Sycorax, but rescued by the magic art of Prospero, whom he serves loyally and well.

Caliban, a monstrous half-human son of Sycorax, gross and debased, resentfully doing rough work under Prospero's orders.

Ferdinand, son and heir of the King of Naples, the first man, except her father, whom Miranda sees after she grows up.

Alonso, the King of Naples, who joined in deporting Prospero.

Antonio, Prospero's brother, wrongfully made Duke of Milan.

Sebastian, King Alonso's brother, and a scoundrel, like Antonio.

Gonzalo, a wise old counsellor of Naples, who fitted out Prospero's crazy boat so as to make it possible for him to survive. Honest, thoughtful, and talkative.

Adrian, an attendant lord of Naples, talkative like Gonzalo.

Francisco, another lord of Naples, less talkative than the others.

Trinculo, a jester from the Court of Naples.

Stephano, a drunken butler of the King.

Ship's officers and seamen, and spirits controlled by Prospero.

SCENE—An Island in the Mediterranean

The Tempest

ACT 1

Scene 1—At Sea in a Storm

MASTER. Boatswain!

BOATSWAIN. Here, master: what cheer?

MASTER. Good, speak to the mariners: fall to it, or we run ourselves aground: bestir, bestir.

BOATSWAIN. Heigh, my hearts! cheerly, cheerly, my hearts! Take in the topsail. Tend to the master's whistle. Blow, till thou burst thy wind, if room enough!

ALONSO (*appearing on deck*). Good boatswain, have care. Where's the master? Play the men.

BOATSWAIN. I pray now, keep below.

ANTONIO. Where is the master, boatswain?

BOATSWAIN. Do you not hear him? You mar our labour: keep your cabins: you do assist the storm.

GONZALO. Nay, good, be patient.

BOATSWAIN. When the sea is. Hence! What care these roarers for the name of king? To cabin: silence! trouble us not.

GONZALO. Good, yet remember whom thou hast aboard.

BOATSWAIN. None that I more love than myself. You are a counsellor; if you can command these elements to silence, and work the peace of the present, we will not hand a rope more; use your authority. If you cannot, give thanks you have lived so long, and make yourself ready in your cabin for the mischance of the hour, if it so hap. Cheerly, good hearts! Out of our way, I say.

The storm increases in violence, and soon the interfering passengers reappear from below with more protests, only to be told that all is lost, and to hear the sailors raise the cry, To prayers! To prayers!

ANTONIO. Let's all sink with the king.

SEBASTIAN. Let's take leave of him.

GONZALO. Now would I give a thousand furlongs of sea for an acre of barren ground, long heath, brown furze, anything. The wills above be done, but I would fain die a dry death.

Scene 2—Before Prospero's Cell

MIRANDA. If by your art, my dearest father, you have
Put the wild waters in this roar, allay them.

O, I have suffered
With those that I saw suffer : a brave vessel,
Who had, no doubt, some noble creature in her,
Dashed all to pieces. O, the cry did knock
Against my very heart. Poor souls, they perished.
Had I been any god of power, I would
Have sunk the sea within the earth or ere
It should the good ship so have swallowed.

PROSPERO. Be collected :
No more amazement : tell your piteous heart
There's no harm done.

MIRANDA. O, woe the day !

PROSPERO. I have done nothing but in care of thee,
Of thee, my dear one, thee, my daughter, who
Art ignorant of what thou art, nought knowing
Of whence I am, nor that I am more better
Than Prospero, master of a full poor cell,
And thy no greater father.

MIRANDA. More to know
Did never meddle with my thoughts.

PROSPERO. Tis time
I should inform thee further. Lend thy hand,
And pluck my magic garment from me. So.
Lie there, my art. Wipe thou thine eyes ; have comfort.
The direful spectacle of the wreck, which touched
The very virtue of compassion in thee,
I have with such provision in mine art
So safely ordered that there's no soul lost
(No, not so much perdition as a hair
Betid to any creature) in the vessel
Which thou heard'st cry, which thou saw'st sink. Sit down ;
For thou must now know further. Canst thou remember
A time before we came unto this cell ?
I do not think thou canst, for then thou wast not
Out three years old.

MIRANDA. Certainly, sir, I can. Had I not
Four or five women once that tended me ?

PROSPERO. Thou hadst, and more, Miranda. But how is it
That this lives in thy mind ? What seest thou else
In the dark backward and abysm of time ?
If thou remember'st aught ere thou cam'st here,
How thou cam'st here thou mayst.

MIRANDA. But that I do not.

PROSPERO. Twelve year since, Miranda, twelve year since,
Thy father was the Duke of Milan and
A prince of power.

MIRANDA. O the heavens !
What foul play had we that we came from thence ?
Or blessèd was't we did ?

PROSPERO. Both, both, my girl :
By foul play, as thou say'st, were we heaved thence,
But blessedly helped hither.

Prospero now tells Miranda how, deeply absorbed in his books, he had handed over the government of his dukedom to his much-loved brother Antonio, who abused his trust, gave way to ambition, and sought to overthrow him. Antonio offered to pay tribute to Prospero's bitter enemy, the King of Naples, in return for his support, and the King agreed. The King secretly brought an army to Milan. At dead of night the gates were opened by Antonio, and Prospero and Miranda were hurried away.

MIRANDA. Wherefore did they not that hour destroy us ?

PROSPERO. Well demanded, wench ;
My tale provokes that question. Dear, they durst not,
So dear the love my people bore me.
They hurried us aboard a bark,
Bore us some leagues to sea, where they prepared
A rotten carcass of a boat, not rigged,
Nor tackle, sail, nor mast ; the very rats
Instinctively had quit it. There they hoist us,
To cry to the sea that roared to us, to sigh
To the winds whose pity, sighing back again,
Did us but loving wrong.

MIRANDA. Alack, what trouble was I then to you !

PROSPERO. O, a cherubin
Thou wast that did preserve me. Thou didst smile,
Infusèd with a fortitude from heaven,
When I have decked the sea with drops full salt.

MIRANDA. How came we ashore ?

PROSPERO. By Providence divine.
Some food we had, and some fresh water that
A noble Neapolitan, Gonzalo,
Out of his charity (being then appointed
Master of this design) did give us, with
Rich garments, linens, stuffs, and necessaries,
Which since have steaded much ; so, of his gentleness,
Knowing I loved my books, he furnished me
From mine own library with volumes that
I prize above my dukedom.

MIRANDA. Would I might
But ever see that man !

PROSPERO (*putting on his mantle*). Now I arise :
Sit still, and hear the last of our sea-sorrow.

Here in this island we arrived ; and here
Have I, thy schoolmaster, made thee more profit
Than other princes can that have more time
For vainer hours and tutors not so careful.

MIRANDA. Heavens thank you for 't ! And now, I pray you, sir,
(For still tis beating in my mind) your reason
For raising this sea-storm ?

PROSPERO. Know thus far forth.
By accident most strange, bountiful Fortune,
Now my dear lady, hath mine enemies
Brought to this shore. . . . Here cease more questions :
Thou art inclined to sleep ; tis a good dulness,
And give it way : I know thou canst not choose. (*She sleeps*)
Approach, my Ariel, come.

ARIEL. All hail, great master ! grave sir, hail ! I come
To answer thy best pleasure ; be 't to fly,
To swim, to dive into the fire, to ride
On the curled clouds, to thy strong bidding task
Ariel and all his quality.

PROSPERO. Hast thou, spirit,
Performed to point the tempest that I bade thee ?

ARIEL. To every article.
I boarded the king's ship ; now on the beak,
Now in the waist, the deck, in every cabin
I flamed amazement : sometime I'd divide
And burn in many places ; on the topmast,
The yards and bowsprit, would flame distinctly.
Jove's lightnings, the precursors
O the dreadful thunder-claps, more momentary
And sight-outrunning were not : the fire and cracks
Of sulphurous roaring the most mighty Neptune
Seemed to besiege, and make his bold waves tremble :
Yea, his dread trident shake.

PROSPERO. My brave spirit ! But are they, Ariel, safe ?

ARIEL. Not a hair perished ;
On their sustaining garments not a blemish,
But fresher than before : and, as thou badèst me,
In troops I have dispersed them 'bout the isle.
The king's son have I landed by himself ;
Whom I left cooling of the air with sighs
In an odd angle of the isle, and sitting,
His arms in this sad knot. . . . Safely in harbour
Is the king's ship ; in the deep nook, where once
Thou call'dst me up at midnight to fetch dew
From the still-vexed Bermoothes, there she's hid,

The mariners all under hatches stowed,
Who, with a charm joined to their suffered labour,
I have left asleep : and for the rest o' the fleet
Which I dispersed, they all have met again
And are upon the Mediterranean flote,
Bound sadly home for Naples,
Supposing that they saw the king's ship wrecked
And his great person perish.

PROSPERO. Ariel, thy charge
Exactly is performed : but there's more work.
What is the time o' the day ?

ARIEL. Past the mid season.

PROSPERO. At least two glasses. The time 'twixt six and now
Must by us both be spent most preciously.

ARIEL. Is there more toil ? Since thou dost give me pains,
Let me remember thee what thou hast promised,
Which is not yet performed me.

PROSPERO. How now ? moody ?
What is't thou canst demand ?

ARIEL. My liberty.

PROSPERO. Before the time be out ? No more !

ARIEL. I prithee,
Remember I have done thee worthy service ;
Told thee no lies, made thee no mistakings, served
Without or grudge or grumblings : thou didst promise
To bate me a full year.

PROSPERO. Dost thou forget
From what a torment I did free thee ?

ARIEL. No.

PROSPERO. Thou dost, and think'st it much to tread the ooze
Of the salt deep,
To run upon the sharp wind of the north,
To do me business in the veins o' the earth
When it is baked with frost.

ARIEL. I do not, sir,

PROSPERO. Thou liest, malignant thing ! Hast thou forgot
The foul witch Sycorax, who with age and envy
Was grown into a hoop ? Hast thou forgot her ?

ARIEL. No, sir.

PROSPERO. This blue-eyed hag was hither brought,
And here was left by the sailors. Thou, my slave,
As thou report'st thyself, wast then her servant ;
And (for thou wast a spirit too delicate
To act her earthy and abhorred commands,

Refusing her grand hests) she did confine thee,
By help of her more potent ministers,
And in her most unmitigable rage,
Into a cloven pine ; within which rift
Imprisoned thou didst painfully remain
A dozen years ; within which space she died
And left thee there, where thou didst vent thy groans
As fast as mill-wheels strike. Then was this island,
(Save for the son that she did litter here,
A freckled whelp hag-born), not honoured with
A human shape.

ARIEL. Yes, Caliban her son.

PROSPERO. Dull thing, I say so ; he, that Caliban
Whom now I keep in service. Thou best know'st
What torment I did find thee in ; thy groans
Did make wolves howl and penetrate the breasts
Of ever-angry bears : it was mine art,
When I arrived and heard thee, that made gape
The pine and let thee out.

ARIEL. I thank thee, master.

PROSPERO. If thou more murmur'st, I will rend an oak
And peg thee in his knotty entrails till
Thou hast howled away twelve winters.

ARIEL. Pardon, master ;
I will be correspondent to command,
And do my spiriting gently.

PROSPERO. Do so, and after two days
I will discharge thee.

ARIEL. That's my noble master !
What shall I do ? say what ; what shall I do ?

PROSPERO. Go make thyself like a nymph o' the sea : be subject
To no sight but thine and mine, invisible
To every eyeball else. Go take this shape
And hither come in't : go, hence with diligence !
(*To Miranda*) Awake, dear heart, awake ! thou hast slept well.

MIRANDA (*waking*). The strangeness of your story put
Heaviness in me.

PROSPERO. Shake it off. Come on ;
We'll visit Caliban my slave, who never
Yields us kind answer.

MIRANDA. Tis a villain, sir,
I do not love to look on.

PROSPERO. But, as tis,
We cannot miss him : he does make our fire,
Fetch in our wood ; and serves in offices

That profit us. What, ho! slave! Caliban!
Thou earth, thou! speak.

CALIBAN (*calling*). There's wood enough within.

PROSPERO. Come forth, I say! there's other business for thee:
Come, thou tortoise! when?

CALIBAN (*appearing*). As wicked dew as e'er my mother brushed
With raven's feather from unwholesome fen
Drop on you both! a south-west blow on ye
And blister you all o'er!

PROSPERO. For this, be sure, tonight thou shalt have cramps,
Side-stitches that shall pen thy breath up; urchins
Shall exercise on thee; thou shalt be pinched
As thick as honeycomb, each pinch more stinging
Than bees that made 'em.

CALIBAN. I must eat my dinner.
This island's mine, by Sycorax my mother,
Which thou tak'st from me. When thou camèst first,
Thou strok'dst me and mad'st much of me, wouldst give me
Water with berries in't, and teach me how
To name the bigger light and how the less
That burn by day and night: and then I loved thee
And showed thee all the qualities o' the isle,
The fresh springs, brine-pits, barren place and fertile:
Cursèd be I that did so! All the charms
Of Sycorax, toads, beetles, bats, light on you!
For I am all the subjects that you have,
Which first was mine own king: and here you sty me
In this hard rock, whiles you do keep from me
The rest o' the island.

PROSPERO. Thou most lying slave,
Whom stripes may move, not kindness! I have used thee,
Filth as thou art, with human care, and lodged thee
In mine own cell. I pitied thee,
Took pains to make thee speak, taught thee each hour
One thing or other: when thou didst not, savage,
Know thine own meaning, but wouldst gabble like
A thing most brutish, I endowed thy purposes
With words that made them known. But thy vile race,
Though thou didst learn, had that in't which good natures
Could not abide to be with; therefore wast thou
Deservedly confined into this rock,
Who hadst deserved more than a prison.

CALIBAN. You taught me language; and my profit on't
Is, I know how to curse. The red plague rid you
For learning me your language!

PROSPERO. Hag-seed, hence!
Fetch us in fuel; and be quick (thou'rt best)
To answer other business. Shrug'st thou, malice?
If thou neglect'st or dost unwillingly
What I command, I'll rack thee with old cramps,
Fill all thy bones with aches, make thee roar
That beasts shall tremble at thy din.

CALIBAN. No, pray thee!
(*Aside*) I must obey: his art is of such power. . . .

PROSPERO. So, slave; hence!

Ferdinand comes, followed by Ariel invisible, playing and singing

Come unto these yellow sands,
And then take hands:
Courtsied when you have and kissed
The wild waves whist,
Foot it featly here and there;
And, sweet sprites, the burthen bear.

Hark, hark! (*Bow-wow*)
The watch-dogs bark! (*Bow-wow*)
Hark, hark! I hear
The strain of strutting Chanticleer (*Cock-a-diddle-dow*).

FERDINAND. Where should this music be?
I' the air or the earth?
It sounds no more: and, sure, it waits upon
Some god o' the island. Sitting on a bank,
Weeping again the king my father's wreck,
This music crept by me upon the waters,
Allaying both their fury and my passion
With its sweet air: thence I have followed it,
Or it hath drawn me, rather. But tis gone.
No, it begins again.

Full fathom five thy father lies;
Of his bones are coral made;
Those are pearls that were his eyes;
Nothing of him that doth fade
But doth suffer a sea-change
Into something rich and strange.
Sea-nymphs hourly ring his knell:
Hark! now I hear them, Ding, dong, bell.

FERDINAND. The ditty does remember my drowned father.
This is no mortal business, nor no sound
That the earth owes. I hear it now above me.

PROSPERO (*to Miranda*). The fringèd curtains of thine eye advance
And say what thou seest yond.

MIRANDA. What is't? a spirit?

Lord, how it looks about! Believe me, sir,
It carries a brave form. But tis a spirit.

PROSPERO. No, wench; it eats and sleeps and hath such senses
As we have, such. This gallant which thou seest
Was in the wreck; and, but he's something stained
With grief (that's beauty's canker), thou mightst call him
A goodly person: he hath lost his fellows
And strays about to find 'em.

MIRANDA. I might call him
A thing divine, for nothing natural
I ever saw so noble.

PROSPERO (*to himself*). It goes on, I see,
As my soul prompts it. Spirit, fine spirit! I'll free thee
Within two days for this.

FERDINAND (*seeing Miranda*). Most sure, the goddess
On whom these airs attend! Vouchsafe my prayer
May know if you remain upon this island;
And that you will some good instruction give
How I may bear me here: my prime request,
Which I do last pronounce, is, O you wonder!
If you be maid or no?

MIRANDA. No wonder, sir;
But certainly a maid.

FERDINAND. My language! heavens!
I am the best of them that speak this speech
Were I but where tis spoken.

PROSPERO. How? the best?
What wert thou if the King of Naples heard thee?

FERDINAND. A single thing, as I am now, that wonders
To hear thee speak of Naples. He does hear me,
And that he does I weep: myself am Naples,
Who with mine eyes, never since at ebb, beheld
The king my father wrecked.

MIRANDA. Alack, for mercy!

FERDINAND. Yes, faith, and all his lords, the Duke of Milan
And his brave son being twain.

PROSPERO (*aside*). The Duke of Milan
And his more braver daughter could control thee,
If now 'twere fit to do 't. At the first sight
They have changed eyes. Delicate Ariel,
I'll set thee free for this. (*To Ferdinand*) A word, good sir;
I fear you have done yourself some wrong: a word.

MIRANDA. Why speaks my father so ungently? This
Is the third man that e'er I saw, the first

That e'er I sighed for: pity move my father
To be inclined my way!

FERDINAND. O, if a virgin,
And your affection not gone forth, I 'll make you
The Queen of Naples.

PROSPERO. Soft, sir! one word more.
(*Aside.* They are both in either's powers; but this swift business
I must uneasy make, lest too light winning
Make the prize light.) One word more; I charge thee
That thou attend me: thou dost here usurp
The name thou ownest not; and hast put thyself
Upon this island as a spy, to win it.

FERDINAND. No, as I am a man.

MIRANDA. There's nothing ill can dwell in such a temple:
If the ill spirit have so fair a house
Good things will strive to dwell with 't.

PROSPERO. Follow me.
Speak not you for him; he's a traitor. Come;
I'll manacle thy neck and feet together:
Sea-water shalt thou drink; thy food shall be
The fresh-brook muscles, withered roots, and husks
Wherein the acorn cradled. Follow.

FERDINAND. No;
I will resist such entertainment till
Mine enemy has more power.

He draws his sword, but is charmed from moving

MIRANDA. O dear father,
Make not too rash a trial of him, for
He's gentle and not fearful.

PROSPERO. Put thy sword up, traitor,
Who makest a show but darest not strike, thy conscience
Is so possessed with guilt. Come from thy ward,
For I can here disarm thee with this stick
And make thy weapon drop.

MIRANDA. Beseech you, father.

PROSPERO. Hence! hang not on my garments.

MIRANDA. Sir, have pity; I'll be his surety.

PROSPERO. Silence! one word more
Shall make me chide thee, if not hate thee. What!
An advocate for an impostor! hush!
Thou think'st there are no more such shapes as he,
Having seen but him and Caliban. Foolish wench!
To the most of men this is a Caliban
And they to him are angels.

MIRANDA. My affections
Are then most humble ; I have no ambition
To see a goodlier man.

PROSPERO. Come on ; obey.

FERDINAND. My spirits, as in a dream, are all bound up.
My father's loss, the weakness which I feel,
The wreck of all my friends, nor this man's threats
To whom I am subdued, are but light to me
Might I but through my prison once a day
Behold this maid : all corners else o' the earth
Let liberty make use of ; space enough
Have I in such a prison.

PROSPERO (*aside*). It works ; thou hast done well, fine Ariel !

MIRANDA (*to Ferdinand*). Be of comfort ;
My father's of a better nature, sir,
Than he appears by speech : this is unwonted
Which now came from him.

PROSPERO (*aside to Ariel*). Thou shalt be as free
As mountain winds : but then exactly do
All points of my command.

ARIEL. To the syllable.

PROSPERO. Come, follow. Speak not for him.

ACT 2

Scene 1—Another Part of the Island

GONZALO (*to Alonso*). Beseech, you, sir, be merry ; you have cause,
So have we all, of joy ; for our escape
Is much beyond our loss. Our hint of woe
Is common ; every day some sailor's wife,
The masters of some merchant, and the merchant,
Have just our theme of woe ; but for the miracle
(I mean our preservation) few in millions
Can speak like us : then wisely, good sir, weigh
Our sorrow with our comfort.

ALONSO. Prithee, peace.

Gonzalo's comfort is not readily accepted. The King rebukes him ; Sebastian and Antonio chaff him. But they do not silence the most sensible man in the party. The King grieves for Ferdinand, and will not believe he may have reached shore. Sebastian rails against the King for having come to sea, while Gonzalo protests that such complaints lack gentleness, and points out that the island might be made a paradise.

GONZALO. Had I plantation of this isle, my lord,
And were the king on 't, what would I do ?
I' the commonwealth I would by contraries
Execute all things ; for no kind of traffic

Would I admit; no name of magistrate;
Letters should not be known; riches, poverty
And use of service, none; contract, succession,
Bourn, bound of land, tilth, vineyard, none;
No use of metal, corn, or wine or oil;
No occupation; all men idle, all;
And women too, but innocent and pure.
All things in common nature should produce
Without sweat or endeavour: treason, felony,
Sword, pike, knife, gun, or need of any engine,
Would I not have; but nature should bring forth,
Of its own kind, all foison, all abundance,
To feed my innocent people.
I would with such perfection govern, sir,
To excel the golden age.

SEBASTIAN. God save his majesty!

ANTONIO. Long live Gonzalo!

GONZALO. And,—do you mark me, sir?

ALONSO. Prithee, no more: thou dost talk nothing to me.

GONZALO. I do well believe your highness; and did it to minister occasion to these gentlemen, who are of such sensible and nimble lungs that they always use to laugh at nothing.

Ariel enters invisible, playing solemn music, and all fall suddenly asleep save Alonso, Sebastian, and Antonio.

ALONSO. What, all so soon asleep! I wish mine eyes
Would with themselves shut up my thoughts: I find
They are inclined to do so.

SEBASTIAN. Please you, sir,
Do not omit the heavy offer of it:
It seldom visits sorrow; when it doth,
It is a comforter.

ANTONIO. We two, my lord,
Will guard your person while you take your rest,
And watch your safety.

ALONSO. Thank you. Wondrous heavy. (*Alonso sleeps*)

SEBASTIAN. What a strange drowsiness possesses them!

ANTONIO. It is the quality o' the climate.

SEBASTIAN. Why
Doth it not then our eyelids sink? I find not
Myself disposed to sleep.

ANTONIO. Nor I; my spirits are nimble.
They fell together all, as by consent;
They dropped as by a thunder-stroke. What might,
Worthy Sebastian? O, what might?—No more:

And yet methinks I see it in thy face,
What thou shouldst be: the occasion speaks thee, and
My strong imagination sees a crown
Dropping upon thy head. Say this were death
That now hath seized them—why, they were no worse
Than now they are. There be that can rule Naples
As well as he that sleeps. O that you bore
The mind that I do, what a sleep were this
For your advancement! Do you understand me?

SEBASTIAN. Me thinks I do. I remember
You did supplant your brother Prospero.

ANTONIO. True;
And look how well my garments sit upon me:
Much feater than before. My brother's servants
Were then my fellows: now they are my men.

SEBASTIAN. Thy case, dear friend,
Shall be my precedent; as thou gott'st Milan
I'll come by Naples. Draw thy sword: one stroke
Shall force thee from the tribute which thou payest,
And I the king shall love thee.

ANTONIO. Draw together;
And when I rear my hand, do you the like,
To fall it on Gonzalo.

SEBASTIAN. O, but one word.

As they talk apart Ariel enters invisible, singing in Gonzalo's ear:

While you here do snoring lie,
Open-eyed conspiracy
His time doth take.
If of life you keep a care,
Shake off slumber, and beware:
Awake, awake!

ANTONIO. Then let us both be sudden.

GONZALO (*waking*). Now, good angels, preserve the King.

ALONSO (*waking*). Why, how now? ho, awake! Why are you drawn?
Wherefore this ghastly looking?

GONZALO. What's the matter?

SEBASTIAN. Whiles we stood here securing your repose,
Even now, we heard a hollow burst of bellowing
Like bulls, or rather lions: did 't not wake you?
It struck mine ear most terribly.

ALONSO. I heard nothing.

ANTONIO. O, 'twas a din to fright a monster's ear,
To make an earthquake! sure, it was the roar
Of a whole herd of lions.

ALONSO. Heard you this, Gonzalo ?

GONZALO. Upon mine honour, sir, I heard a humming,
And that a strange one too, which did awake me.
Tis best we stand upon our guard.

ALONSO. Lead off this ground ; and let's make further search
For my poor son.

GONZALO. Heavens keep him from these beasts !
For he is, sure, i' the island.

ALONSO. Lead away.

ARIEL. Prospero my lord shall know what I have done :
So, king, go safely on to seek thy son.

Scene 2—Another Part of the Island

CALIBAN. All the infections that the sun sucks up
From bogs, fens, flats, on Prosper fall, and make him
By inch-meal a disease ! His spirits hear me
And yet I needs must curse. But they 'll nor pinch,
Fright me with urchin-shows, pitch me i' the mire,
Nor lead me, like a firebrand, in the dark
Out of my way, unless he bid 'em ; but
For every trifle are they set upon me ;
Sometime like apes that mow and chatter at me
And after bite me, then like hedgehogs which
Lie tumbling in my barefoot way and mount
Their pricks at my footfall ; sometime am I
All wound with adders who with cloven tongues
Do hiss me into madness. (*Enter Trinculo*) Lo, now, lo !
Here comes a spirit of his, and to torment me
For bringing wood in slowly. I'll fall flat ;
Perchance he will not mind me.

TRINCULO. Here's neither bush nor shrub to bear off any weather at all, and another storm brewing ; I hear it sing i' the wind. If it should thunder as it did before I know not where to hide my head : yond cloud cannot choose but fall by pailfuls. What have we here ? a man or a fish ? dead or alive ? A fish ! He smells like a fish ; a very ancient and fish-like smell. A strange fish ! Were I in England now, as once I was, and had but this fish painted, not a holiday fool there but would give a piece of silver. There would this monster make a man ; any strange beast there makes a man ; when they will not give a doit to relieve a lame beggar they will lay out ten to see a dead Indian. Warm, o' my troth ! This is no fish, but an islander, that hath lately suffered by a thunderbolt. Alas, the storm is come again ! my best way is to creep under his gaberdine ; there is no other shelter : misery acquaints a man with strange bedfellows. I will here shroud till the dregs of the storm be past.

As Caliban and Trinculo lie there Stephano comes along, tipsy and singing, with a bottle. Caliban, thinking him a spirit, calls for mercy, and Stephano puts the wine bottle in his mouth. Trinculo recognises Stephano's voice, and is pulled from under the gaberdine. Each is amazed to see the other. Caliban at once accepts Stephano as his new master.

CALIBAN. I'll swear upon that bottle to be thy true subject, for the liquor is not earthly. I'll show thee every fertile inch o' the island, and I will kiss thy foot. I prithee, be my god.

TRINCULO. A most perfidious and drunken monster! When his god's asleep he'll rob his bottle.

CALIBAN. I'll kiss thy foot; I'll swear myself thy subject.

STEPHANO. Come on then; down, and swear.

TRINCULO. I shall laugh myself to death at this puppy-headed monster. A most scurvy monster! I could find in my heart to beat him.

CALIBAN. I'll show thee the best springs; I'll pluck thee berries;
I'll fish for thee and get thee wood enough.
A plague upon the tyrant that I serve!
I'll bear him no more sticks, but follow thee,
Thou wondrous man.

TRINCULO. A most ridiculous monster, to make a wonder of a poor drunkard!

CALIBAN. I prithee, let me bring thee where crabs grow;
And I with my long nails will dig thee pig-nuts;
Show thee a jay's nest and instruct thee how
To snare the nimble marmoset; I'll bring thee
To clustering filberts, and sometimes I'll get thee
Young scamels from the rock. Wilt thou go with me?

STEPHANO. I prithee now, lead the way without any more talking.

CALIBAN. Farewell, master; farewell, farewell!

ACT 3

Scene 1—Before Prospero's Cell

FERDINAND. There be some sports are painful, and their labour
Delight in them sets off. This my mean task
Would be as heavy to me as odious, but
The mistress which I serve quickens what's dead
And makes my labours pleasures: O, she is
Ten times more gentle than her father's crabbed,
And he's composed of harshness. I must remove
Some thousands of these logs and pile them up,
Upon a sore injunction: my sweet mistress
Weeps when she sees me work,
But these sweet thoughts do even refresh my labours.

Enter Miranda, Prospero following unseen

MIRANDA (*seeing Ferdinand bearing a log*). Alas, now, pray you,
Work not so hard: I would the lightning had
Burnt up those logs that you are enjoined to pile:
Pray, set it down and rest you: when this burns,
Twill weep for having wearied you. My father
Is hard at study; pray now, rest yourself;
He's safe for these three hours.

FERDINAND. O most dear mistress,
The sun will set before I shall discharge
What I must strive to do.

MIRANDA. If you'll sit down,
I'll bear your logs the while: pray, give me that;
I'll carry it to the pile.

FERDINAND. No, precious creature;
I had rather crack my sinews, break my back,
Than you should such dishonour undergo,
While I sit lazy by.

MIRANDA. You look wearily.

FERDINAND. No, noble mistress; tis fresh morning with me
When you are by at night. I do beseech you
(Chiefly that I might set it in my prayers)
What is your name?

MIRANDA. Miranda. O my father,
I have broke your hest to say so!

FERDINAND. Admired Miranda!
Indeed the top of admiration! worth
What's dearest to the world! Full many a lady
I have eyed with best regard, and many a time
The harmony of their tongues hath into bondage
Brought my too diligent ear: for several virtues
Have I liked several women; never any
With so full soul but some defect in her
Did quarrel with the noblest grace she owed
And put it to the foil: but you, O you,
So perfect and so peerless, are created
Of every creature's best!

MIRANDA. I do not know
One of my sex; no woman's face remember,
Save, from my glass, mine own; nor have I seen
More that I may call men than you, good friend,
And my dear father: how features are abroad
I am skilless of; but, by my modesty,
The jewel in my dower, I would not wish
Any companion in the world but you,
Nor can imagination form a shape,

Besides yourself, to like of. But I prattle
Something too wildly, and my father's precepts
I therein do forget.

FERDINAND. I am in my condition
A prince, Miranda; I do think, a king.
The very instant that I saw you did
My heart fly to your service; there resides,
To make me slave to it; and for your sake
Am I this patient log-man.

MIRANDA. Do you love me?

FERDINAND. O heaven, O earth, bear witness to this sound
And crown what I profess with kind event
If I speak true! I
Beyond all limit of what else i' the world
Do love, prize, honour you.

MIRANDA (*weeping*). I am a fool
To weep at what I am glad of.

PROSPERO (*unseen*). Fair encounter
Of two most rare affections! Heavens rain grace
On that which breeds between 'em!

FERDINAND. Wherefore weep you?

MIRANDA. At mine unworthiness that dare not offer
What I desire to give, and much less take
What I shall die to want. But this is trifling;
And all the more it seeks to hide itself
The bigger bulk it shows. Hence, bashful cunning!
And prompt me, plain and holy innocence!
I am your wife if you will marry me;
If not I'll die your maid.

FERDINAND. My mistress, dearest; and I thus humble ever.

MIRANDA. My husband, then?

FERDINAND. Ay, with a heart as willing
As bondage e'er of freedom: here's my hand.

MIRANDA. And mine, with my heart in't; and now farewell
Till half an hour hence.

FERDINAND. A thousand thousand!

PROSPERO. So glad of this as they I cannot be,
Who are surprised withal; but my rejoicing
At nothing can be more. I'll to my book,
For yet ere supper-time must I perform
Much business appertaining.

Scene 2—Another Part of the Island

STEPHANO. Tell not me; when the butt is out we will drink water; not a drop before: therefore bear up. Servant-monster, drink to me.

TRINCULO. Servant-monster, the folly of this island! They say there's but five upon this isle: we are three of them; if th' other two be brained like us the State totters.

STEPHANO. Trinculo, keep a good tongue in your head: if you prove a mutineer,—the next tree! The poor monster's my subject, and he shall not suffer indignity.

CALIBAN. I thank my noble lord. Wilt thou be pleased to hearken?

STEPHANO. Marry, will I: kneel. I will stand, and so shall Trinculo.

CALIBAN. As I told thee before, I am subject to a tyrant, a sorcerer, that by his cunning hath cheated me of the island.

ARIEL (*entering invisible*). Thou liest.

CALIBAN (*to Trinculo*). Thou liest, thou jesting monkey, thou: I would my valiant master would destroy thee! I do not lie.

STEPHANO. Trinculo, if you trouble him any more in 's tale, by this hand I will supplant some of your teeth.

TRINCULO. Why, I said nothing.

STEPHANO. Mum, then, and no more. Proceed.

CALIBAN. I say, by sorcery he got this isle;
From me he got it. If thy greatness will,
Revenge it on him, for I know thou darest,
But this thing dare not.

STEPHANO. That's most certain.

CALIBAN. Thou shalt be lord of it and I'll serve thee.

STEPHANO. How now shall this be compassed? Canst thou bring me to the party?

CALIBAN. Yea, yea, my lord: I'll yield him thee asleep,
Where thou mayst knock a nail into his head.

ARIEL. Thou liest; thou canst not.

CALIBAN. What a pied ninny's this! Thou scurvy patch!
I do beseech thy greatness, give him blows
And take his bottle from him: when that's gone
He shall drink nought but brine, for I'll not show him
Where the quick freshes are.

STEPHANO. Trinculo, run into no further danger: interrupt the monster one word further, and, by this hand, I'll turn my mercy out o' doors and make a stock-fish of thee.

TRINCULO. Why, what did I? I did nothing. I'll go farther off.

STEPHANO. Didst thou not say he lied?

ARIEL. Thou liest.

STEPHANO. Do I so? Take thou that (*beating Trinculo*).

CALIBAN. Beat him enough; after a little time
I'll beat him too.

STEPHANO. Stand farther. Come, proceed.

CALIBAN. Why, as I told thee, tis a custom with him,
In th' afternoon to sleep : there thou mayst brain him,
Having first seized his books, or with a log
Batter his skull, or paunch him with a stake,
Or cut his weasand with thy knife. Remember
First to possess his books, for without them
He's but a sot, as I am, nor hath not
One spirit to command : they all do hate him
As rootedly as I. Burn but his books.
He has brave utensils (for so he calls them),
Which, when he has a house, he'll deck withal.
And that most deeply to consider is
The beauty of his daughter.

STEPHANO. Monster, I will kill this man : his daughter and I will be king and queen, and Trinculo and thyself shall be viceroys. Dost thou like the plot, Trinculo ?

TRINCULO. Excellent.

STEPHANO. Give me thy hand : I am sorry I beat thee ; but, while thou livest, keep a good tongue in thy head.

CALIBAN. Within this half hour will he be asleep :
Wilt thou destroy him then ?

STEPHANO. Ay, on mine honour.

ARIEL. This will I tell my master.

CALIBAN. Thou makest me merry ; I am full of pleasure.
Be not afeard ; the isle is full of noises,
Sounds and sweet airs, that give delight and hurt not.
Sometimes a thousand twangling instruments
Will hum about mine ears, and sometime voices
That, if I then had waked after long sleep,
Will make me sleep again : and then, in dreaming,
The clouds methought would open and show riches
Ready to drop upon me, that, when I waked,
I cried to dream again.

STEPHANO. This will prove a brave kingdom to me, where I shall have my music for nothing.

CALIBAN. When Prospero is destroyed.

STEPHANO. That shall be by and by : I remember the story.

Scene 3—Another Part of the Island

Alonso and Gonzalo are wandering in hopeless search for Ferdinand. Sebastian and Antonio have not given up their scheme of murdering the King, but have planned the plot for the night. Suddenly strange spirits appear, accompanied by Prospero invisible, with music. A mysterious banquet is spread before the King ; then the spirits vanish.

While the astonished travellers discuss whether it is well to eat, Ariel enters and the banquet vanishes. The courtiers, more bewildered than ever, draw their swords, but they have become too heavy to be lifted, and Ariel warns them that he and his fellow-ministers are invulnerable.

At the feast of Belshazzar it was the writing on the wall that accused the king; here it is the voice in the wind that stirs the guilty conscience. The voice of Ariel interprets to them the meaning of their plight, explaining that the shipwreck is a punishment for their treatment of Prospero.

The vision vanishes and the conspirators are left distracted by the voices:

GONZALO. I' the name of something holy, sir, why stand you
In this strange stare?

ALONSO. O, it is monstrous, monstrous!
Methought the billows spoke and told me of it;
The winds did sing it to me, and the thunder,
That deep and dreadful organ-pipe, pronounced
The name of Prosper: it did bass my trespass.
Therefore my son i' the ooze is bedded, and
I'll seek him deeper than e'er plummet sounded
And with him there lie mudded.

ACT 4

Scene 1—Before Prospero's Cell

Prospero appears to Ferdinand and Miranda

PROSPERO. If I have too austerely punished you,
Your compensation makes amends, for I
Have given you here a thread of mine own life,
Or that for which I live; who once again
I tender to thy hand. All thy vexations
Were but my trials of thy love, and thou
Hast strangely stood the test: here, afore Heaven,
I ratify this my rich gift. O Ferdinand,
Do not smile at me that I boast her off,
For thou shalt find she will outstrip all praise
And make it halt behind her.

FERDINAND. I do believe it
Against an oracle.

PROSPERO. Sit then and talk with her; she is thine own.
What, Ariel! my industrious servant, Ariel!

ARIEL. What would my potent master? here I am.

PROSPERO. Thou and thy meaner fellows your last service
Did worthily perform; and I must use you
In such another trick. Go bring the rabble,
O'er whom I give thee power, here to this place:
Incite them to quick motion; for I must
Bestow upon the eyes of this young couple

Some vanity of mine art: it is my promise,
And they expect it from me.

ARIEL. Presently?

PROSPERO. Ay, with a twink.

ARIEL. Before you can say *Come* and *Go*,
And breathe twice and cry, *So, so*,
Each one, tripping on his toe,
Will be here with mop and mow.
Do you love me, master! No?

PROSPERO. Dearly, my delicate Ariel. Do not approach
Till thou dost hear me call.

Prospero now summons up, for the delight of Ferdinand and Miranda, a classical spirit-show. Iris appears as Juno's messenger and summons Ceres, the goddess of Earth's fruitfulness. Then Juno herself comes, and joins Ceres in bestowing a blessing on the lovers.

FERDINAND. This is a most majestic vision, and
Harmonious charmingly. May I be bold
To think these spirits?

PROSPERO. Spirits, which by mine art
I have from their confines called to enact
My present fancies.

FERDINAND. Let me live here ever;
So rare a wondered father and a wise
Makes this place Paradise.

Nymphs and visionary harvestmen join in a country dance, when suddenly Prospero starts, speaks, and with a confused noise the scene fades.

PROSPERO (*aside*). I had forgot that foul conspiracy
Of the beast Caliban and his confederates
Against my life: the minute of their plot
Is almost come.

FERDINAND. This is strange: your father's in some passion
That works him strongly.

MIRANDA. Never till this day
Saw I him touched with anger so distempered.

PROSPERO. You do look, my son, in a moved sort,
As if you were dismayed: be cheerful, sir.
Our revels now are ended. These our actors,
As I foretold you, were all spirits, and
Are melted into air, into thin air:
And, like the baseless fabric of this vision,
The cloud-capped towers, the gorgeous palaces,
The solemn temples, the great globe itself,
Yea, all which it inherit, shall dissolve

And, like this insubstantial pageant faded,
Leave not a rack behind. We are such stuff
As dreams are made on, and our little life
Is rounded with a sleep. Sir, I am vexed ;
Bear with my weakness ; my old brain is troubled.
Be not disturbed with my infirmity :
If you be pleased, retire into my cell
And there repose : a turn or two I'll walk
To still my beating mind.

FERDINAND AND MIRANDA. We wish your peace.

PROSPERO. Come with a thought. I thank thee ; Ariel, come.

ARIEL. Thy thoughts I cleave to. What's thy pleasure ?

PROSPERO. Spirit,
We must prepare to meet with Caliban.

ARIEL. I thought to have told thee of it, but I feared
Lest I might anger thee.

PROSPERO. Say again, where didst thou leave these varlets ?

ARIEL. I told you, sir, they were red-hot with drinking ;
So full of valour that they smote the air
For breathing in their faces ; beat the ground
For kissing of their feet ; yet always bending
Towards their project. Then I beat my tabor ;
At which, like unbacked colts, they pricked their ears,
Advanced their eyelids, lifted up their noses
As they smelt music : so I charmed their ears
That calf-like they my lowing followed through
Toothed briers, sharp furzes, pricking goss, and thorns,
Which entered their frail shins : at last I left them
I' the filthy-mantled pool beyond your cell.

PROSPERO. This was well done, my bird.
Thy shape invisible retain thou still :
The trumpery in my house, go bring it hither,
For stale to catch these thieves.

ARIEL. I go, I go.

PROSPERO. A devil, a born devil, on whose nature
Nurture can never stick ; on whom my pains,
Humanely taken, all, all lost, quite lost ;
And as with age his body uglier grows,
So his mind cankers. I will plague them all,
Even to roaring.

Ariel enters with glistening apparel, which he hangs on the line. He and Prospero remain invisible while Caliban, Stephano, and Trinculo enter.

CALIBAN. Pray you, tread softly, that the blind mole may not
Hear a foot fall : we now are near his cell.

STEPHANO. Monster, your fairy, which you say is a harmless fairy, has done little better than played the Jack with us.

CALIBAN. Good my lord, give me thy favour still.
Speak softly; all's hushed as midnight yet.
Prithee, my king, be quiet. See'st thou here,
This is the mouth o' the cell: no noise, and enter.
Do that good mischief which may make this island
Thine own for ever, and I, thy Caliban,
For aye thy foot-licker.

TRINCULO. O King Stephano! O peer! O worthy Stephano! look what a wardrobe here is for thee!

CALIBAN. Let it alone, thou fool; it is but trash.

TRINCULO. O, ho, monster! we know what belongs to a frippery. O King Stephano!

STEPHANO. Put off that gown, Trinculo; by this hand, I'll have that gown.

TRINCULO. Thy grace shall have it.

CALIBAN. The dropsy drown this fool! What do you mean
To dote thus on such luggage? Let's alone
And do the murder first: if he awake,
From toe to crown he'll fill our skins with pinches,
Make us strange stuff.

STEPHANO. Be you quiet, monster. Mistress line, is not this my jerkin?

CALIBAN. I will have none on't: we shall lose our time
And all be turned to barnacles, or to apes
With foreheads villainous low.

STEPHANO. Monster, lay-to your fingers: help to bear this away, or I'll turn you out of my kingdom: go to, carry this.

TRINCULO. And this.

STEPHANO. Ay, and this.

A noise of hunters is heard. Spirits, in shape of dogs and hounds, hunt them about, Prospero and Ariel setting them on.

ARIEL. Hark, they roar!

PROSPERO. Let them be hunted soundly. At this hour
Lie at my mercy all mine enemies:
Shortly shall all my labours end, and thou
Shalt have the air at freedom: for a little
Follow, and do me service.

ACT 5

Scene 1—Before Prospero's Cell

PROSPERO. Now does my project gather to a head:
My charms crack not; my spirits obey; and Time

Goes upright with his carriage. How's the day ?

ARIEL. On the sixth hour ; at which time, my lord,
You said our work should cease.

PROSPERO. I did say so,
When first I raised the tempest. Say, my spirit,
How fares the king and's followers ?

ARIEL. Confined together
In the same fashion as you gave in charge,
Just as you left them ; all prisoners, sir,
In the lime-grove which weather-fends your cell ;
They cannot budge till your release. The king,
His brother and yours, abide all three distracted,
And the remainder mourning over them,
Brimful of sorrow and dismay ; but chiefly
Him that you termed, sir, *The good old lord, Gonzalo* ;
His tears run down his beard, like winter's drops
From eaves of reeds. Your charm so strongly works them
That if you now beheld them your affections
Would become tender.

PROSPERO. Dost thou think so, spirit ?

ARIEL. Mine would, sir, were I human.

PROSPERO. And mine shall.
Hast thou, which art but air, a touch, a feeling
Of their afflictions, and shall not myself,
One of their kind, that relish all as sharply
Passion as they, be kindlier moved than thou art ?
Though with their high wrongs I am struck to the quick,
Yet with my nobler reason 'gainst my fury
Do I take part : the rarer action is
In virtue than in vengeance : they being penitent,
The sole drift of my purpose doth extend
Not a frown further. Go release them, Ariel :
My charms I'll break, their senses I'll restore,
And they shall be themselves.

ARIEL. I'll fetch them, sir.

PROSPERO. Ye elves of hills, brooks, standing lakes, and groves,
And ye that on the sands with printless foot
Do chase the ebbing Neptune and do fly him
When he comes back ; you demi-puppets that
By moonshine do the green sour ringlets make
Whereof the ewe not bites, and you whose pastime
Is to make midnight mushrooms ; that rejoice
To hear the solemn curfew ; by whose aid,
Weak masters though ye be, I have bedimmed
The noontide sun, called forth the mutinous winds,

And 'twixt the green sea and the azured vault
Set roaring war: to the dread rattling thunder
Have I given fire, and rifted Jove's stout oak
With his own bolt; the strong-based promontory
Have I made shake, and by the spurs plucked up
The pine and cedar: graves at my command
Have waked their sleepers, oped, and let them forth
By my so potent art. But this rough magic
I here abjure, and, when I have required
Some heavenly music (which even now I do),
To work mine end upon their senses that
This airy charm is for, I'll break my staff,
Bury it certain fathoms in the earth,
And deeper than did ever plummet sound
I'll drown my book.

Ariel enters to solemn music; then Alonso attended by Gonzalo, with Sebastian and Antonio attended by Adrian and Francisco. All enter the circle Prospero has made, and there stand charmed.

PROSPERO (*to himself*). A solemn air and the best comforter
To an unsettled fancy cure thy brains,
Now useless, boiled within thy skull! There stand,
For you are spell-stopped.
Holy Gonzalo, honourable man,
Mine eyes, even sociable to the show of thine,
Fall fellowly drops. The charm dissolves apace,
And as the morning steals upon the night,
Melting the darkness, so their rising senses
Begin to chase the ignorant fumes that mantle
Their clearer reason. O good Gonzalo,
My true preserver, and a loyal sir
To him thou follow'st, I will pay thy graces
Home both in word and deed. Most cruelly
Didst thou, Alonso, use me and my daughter:
Thy brother was a furtherer in the act.
Thou'rt pinched for't now, Sebastian. Flesh and blood,
You, brother mine, that entertained ambition,
Expelled remorse and nature, who with Sebastian
Would here have killed your king, I do forgive thee,
Unnatural though thou art. Their understanding
Begins to swell, and the approaching tide
Will shortly fill the reasonable shore
That now lies foul and muddy. Not one of them
That yet looks on me, or would know me. Ariel,
Fetch me the hat and rapier in my cell:
I will discase me, and myself present
As I was sometime Milan: quickly, spirit;
Thou shalt ere long be free.

Ariel sings

Where the bee sucks, there suck I:
In a cowslip's bell I lie;
There I couch when owls do cry.
On the bat's back I do fly
After summer merrily.
  Merrily, merrily shall I live now
  Under the blossom that hangs on the bough.

PROSPERO. Why, that's my dainty Ariel! I shall miss thee,
But yet thou shalt have freedom: so, so, so.
To the king's ship, invisible as thou art:
There shalt thou find the mariners asleep
Under the hatches; the master and the boatswain
Being awake, enforce them to this place,
And presently, I prithee.

ARIEL. I drink the air before me, and return
Or ere your pulse twice beat.

GONZALO. All torment, trouble, wonder, and amazement
Inhabits here: some heavenly power guide us
Out of this fearful country!

PROSPERO (*appearing to them*). Behold, sir king,
The wrongèd Duke of Milan, Prospero:
For more assurance that a living prince
Does now speak to thee, I embrace thy body;
And to thee and thy company I bid
A hearty welcome.

ALONSO. Whether thou be'st he or no,
Or some enchanted trifle to abuse me,
As late I have been, I not know: thy pulse
Beats as of flesh and blood; and, since I saw thee,
The affliction of my mind amends, with which,
I fear, a madness held me: this must crave,
An if this be at all, a most strange story.
Thy dukedom I resign and do entreat
Thou pardon me my wrongs. But how should Prospero
Be living and be here?

PROSPERO (*to Gonzalo*). First, noble friend,
Let me embrace thine age, whose honour cannot
Be measured or confined.

GONZALO. Whether this be
Or be not, I'll not swear.

PROSPERO. You do yet taste
Some subtleties o' the isle, that will not let you
Believe things certain. Welcome, my friends all!
For you, most wicked sir, whom to call brother
Would even infect my mouth, I do forgive

Thy rankest fault; all of them; and require
My dukedom of thee, which perforce, I know,
Thou must restore.

ALONSO. If thou be'st Prospero,
Give us particulars of thy preservation;
How thou hast met us here, who three hours since
Were wrecked upon this shore; where I have lost
(How sharp the point of this remembrance is!)
My dear son Ferdinand.

PROSPERO. I am woe for't, sir.

ALONSO. Irreparable is the loss, and patience
Says it is past her cure.

PROSPERO. I rather think
You have not sought her help, of whose soft grace
For the like loss I have her sovereign aid,
And rest myself content.

ALONSO. You the like loss!

PROSPERO. As great to me as late; and, supportable
To make the dear loss, have I means much weaker
Than you may call to comfort you, for I
Have lost my daughter.

ALONSO. A daughter?
O heavens, that they were living both in Naples,
The king and queen there! that they were, I wish
Myself were mudded in that oozy bed
Where my son lies. When did you lose your daughter?

PROSPERO. In this last tempest. I perceive these lords
At this encounter do so much admire
That they devour their reason, and scarce think
Their eyes do offices of truth, their words
Are natural breath: but, howsoe'er you have
Been justled from your senses, know for certain
That I am Prospero, and that very duke
Which was thrust forth of Milan, who most strangely
Upon this shore, where you were wrecked, was landed,
To be the lord on't. No more yet of this;
For tis a chronicle of day by day,
Not a relation for a breakfast, nor
Befitting this first meeting. Welcome, sir;
This cell's my court: here have I few attendants,
And subjects none abroad: pray you, look in.
My dukedom since you have given me again,
I will requite you with as good a thing;
At least bring forth a wonder, to content ye
As much as me my dukedom.

Here Prospero reveals Ferdinand and Miranda playing chess

MIRANDA. Sweet lord, you play me false.
FERDINAND. No, my dear'st love,
I would not for the world.
MIRANDA. Yes, for a score of kingdoms you should wrangle,
And I would call it fair play.
ALONSO. If this prove
A vision of the island, one dear son
Shall I twice lose.
SEBASTIAN. A most high miracle!
FERDINAND (*looking up*). Though the seas threaten, they are merciful;
I have cursed them without cause.
ALONSO. Now all the blessings
Of a glad father compass thee about!
Arise, and say how thou cam'st here.
MIRANDA. O, wonder!
How many goodly creatures are there here!
How beauteous mankind is! O brave new world,
That has such people in't!
ALONSO. What is this maid with whom thou wast at play?
Your eldest acquaintance cannot be three hours:
Is she the goddess that hath severed us,
And brought us thus together?
FERDINAND. Sir, she is mortal,
But by immortal Providence she's mine:
I chose her when I could not ask my father
For his advice, nor thought I had one. She
Is daughter to this famous Duke of Milan,
Of whom so often I have heard renown
But never saw before; of whom I have
Received a second life; and second father
This lady makes him to me.
ALONSO. I am hers:
But, O, how oddly will it sound that I
Must ask my child forgiveness!
PROSPERO. There, sir, stop:
Let us not burden our remembrance with
A heaviness that's gone.
GONZALO. I have inly wept,
Or should have spoke ere this. Look down, you gods,
And on this couple drop a blessèd crown!
For it is you that have chalked forth the way
Which brought us hither.
ALONSO. I say, Amen, Gonzalo!
GONZALO. Was Milan thrust from Milan, that his issue

Should become kings of Naples ? O, rejoice
Beyond a common joy, and set it down
With gold on lasting pillars : *In one voyage*
Did Claribel her husband find at Tunis ;
And Ferdinand her brother found a wife
Where he himself was lost ; Prospero his dukedom
In a poor isle ; and all of us ourselves
When no man was his own.

ALONSO (*to Ferdinand and Miranda*). Give me your hands :
Let grief and sorrow still embrace his heart
That doth not wish you joy !

Enter Ariel, Master and Boatswain following amazed

GONZALO. O, look, sir, look, sir ! here is more of us :
What is the news ?

BOATSWAIN. The best news is that we have safely found
Our king and company ; the next, our ship
Is tight and yare and bravely rigged as when
We first put out to sea.

ARIEL (*aside to Prospero*). Sir, all this service
Have I done since I went.

PROSPERO (*aside to Ariel*). My tricksy spirit !

ALONSO. These are not natural events ; they strengthen
From strange to stranger. Say, how came you hither ?

BOATSWAIN. If I did think, sir, I were well awake,
I 'd strive to tell you. We were dead of sleep,
And (how we know not) all clapped under hatches ;
Where but even now with strange and several noises
Of roaring, shrieking, howling, jingling chains,
And more diversity of sounds, all horrible,
We were awaked ; straightway, at liberty ;
Where we, in all her trim, freshly beheld
Our royal, good, and gallant ship, our master
Capering to eye her : on a trice, so please you,
Even in a dream, were we divided from them
And were brought moping hither.

ARIEL (*aside to Prospero*). Was't well done ?

PROSPERO. Bravely, my diligence. Thou shalt be free.
Come hither, spirit :
Set Caliban and his companions free ;
Untie the spell.

Ariel now re-enters, driving Caliban, Stephano, and Trinculo in their stolen apparel. Prospero includes them in his forgiveness, and sends them away to put back their plunder and tidy up his cell, an order which Caliban receives with deep relief.

CALIBAN. Ay, that I will ; and I'll be wise hereafter
And seek for grace. What a thrice-double ass

Was I, to take this drunkard for a god
And worship this dull fool!

PROSPERO. Sir, I invite your highness and your train
To my poor cell, where you shall take your rest
For this one night; which, part of it, I'll waste
With such discourse as, I not doubt, shall make it
Go quick away; the story of my life
And the particular accidents gone by
Since I came to this isle: and in the morn
I'll bring you to your ship, and so to Naples,
Where I have hope to see the nuptial
Of these our dear-belovèd solemnized;
And thence retire me to my Milan, where
Every third thought shall be my grave.

ALONSO. I long
To hear the story of your life, which must
Take the ear strangely.

PROSPERO. I'll deliver all;
And promise you calm seas, auspicious gales,
And sail so expeditious that shall catch
Your royal fleet far off. My Ariel, chick,
That is thy charge: then to the elements
Be free, and fare thou well! Please you, draw near.

Prospero's Farewell

Now my charms are all o'erthrown,
And what strength I have's mine own,
Which is most faint: now, tis true,
I must be here confined by you,
Or sent to Naples. Let me not,
Since I have my dukedom got
And pardoned the deceiver, dwell
In this bare island by your spell;
But release me from my bands
With the help of your good hands:
Gentle breath of yours my sails
Must fill, or else my project fails,
Which was to please. Now I want
Spirits to enforce, art to enchant,
And my ending is despair,
Unless I be relieved by prayer,
Which pierces so that it assaults
Mercy itself and frees all faults.
As you from crimes would pardoned be,
Let your indulgence set me free.

The Story of A Midsummer Night's Dream

FOR pure mirth and originality the dainty drama of A Midsummer Night's Dream is second to none among all Shakespeare's plays. From its first night on the stage it has been popular.

SHAKESPEARE wrote it in the full flush of his youthful poetical powers, feeling free to write whatever pleased his fancy. It pleased him to place in ancient Greece a play as English as anything he ever wrote. It is a lovely tale, with stories all mixed up and blended with imagination. Interwoven with the traditional belief in fairies, and suffused with the spirit of poetry, the stories are presented in a surprising dramatic combination. By this play Shakespeare gave fairy lore a lasting place in English literature.

IN a number of his early plays the poet has used the idea of confusion between lovers to create dramatic situations. In the Dream this confusion is brought about by fairies, through misplaced enchantment. There is a delicious mix-up of the lofty and the humble, of mortals and of spirits, but in good time the entanglements are smoothly straightened out.

THE play is frankly a piece of sheer imagination. It is not for minds that have no imaginative delights. For those who live in the world we see and touch, and know nothing of that realm in which the mind can roam as it will, when it will, where it will, there is no enjoyment here. But for those who can follow fancy nothing doubting, those who can happily get away from worldly cares when they like, it lives as one of the exquisite triumphs of our literature.

IT has been said that the Dream cannot be staged to satisfy the spectator, but that its delicacy allows it only to be read. That is probably not a general feeling among lovers of Shakespeare. He wrote it to be acted when the resources of the stage were far scantier than now, and his audiences had imagination enough to appreciate it keenly.

LIGHT, free, and rippling with mirth, the Dream gives us no strong character. It is meant to do our hearts good by giving us a merry laugh. It is all charmingly typical of the poet's mind at a time when he revelled in fancy and loved to dally with quaint and fantastic things. We are quite sure that Shakespeare tremendously enjoyed this play within a play—above all, the delightful character of Puck, who put a girdle round the Earth in forty minutes (sixteen thousand times slower than wireless does it !) and shares immortal fame with Ariel. Shakespeare was not half through his life when the Dream came to him, and his mind had not taken that deeper and somewhat sombre tone which came from searching fateful experiences. He was still in his happy world of comedy and fantasy, and the Dream is concerned with it all, with love and youth, with laughter and rare imaginings, and with the music of sweet poetry.

THE PLAYERS

Mortals

Theseus, Duke of Athens, betrothed to Hippolyta.

Egeus, a tyrannical Athenian, father of Hermia.

Lysander, in love with Hermia but rejected by her father.

Demetrius, in love with Hermia and favoured by her father.

Philostrate, master of the revels at the Duke's wedding.

Quince, a carpenter, arranging a play to be acted by craftsmen at the wedding feast.

Bottom, a weaver, supposed to be the best craftsman-actor; a hustler who takes the lead whenever he has an opportunity.

Snug, a joiner and member of the company.

Flute, a bellows-mender, acting in the company.

Snout, a tinker, and one of the actors.

Starveling, a tailor, and one of the actors.

Hippolyta, a queen, betrothed to Theseus.

Hermia, daughter of Egeus, in love with Lysander.

Helena, once engaged to Demetrius, and still in love with him.

Fairies

Oberon, King of the Fairies, but estranged from their Queen.

Titania, Queen of the Fairies, but in disagreement with Oberon.

Puck, or **Robin Goodfellow,** a sprite obeying Oberon, but greatly delighting in mischief.

Peaseblossom and Cobweb, fairies attending Titania.

Moth and Mustardseed, fairies attending Titania.

Scene—At first in Athens, then in the wood of the fairies, and afterwards in Athens again.

A Midsummer-Night's Dream

ACT 1

Scene 1—The Duke's Palace in Athens

Enter Theseus, Hippolyta, Philostrate, and Attendants

THESEUS. Now, fair Hippolyta, our nuptial hour
Draws on apace ; four happy days bring in
Another moon : but, O, methinks, how slow
This old moon wanes !

HIPPOLYTA. Four days will quickly steep themselves in night
Four nights will quickly dream away the time ;
And then the moon, like to a silver bow
New-bent in heaven, shall behold the night
Of our solemnities.

THESEUS. Go, Philostrate,
Stir up the Athenian youth to merriments ;
Awake the pert and nimble spirit of mirth :
Turn melancholy forth to funerals ;
The pale companion is not for our pomp.
Hippolyta, I wooed thee with my sword,
But I will wed thee in another key,
With pomp, with triumph, and with revelling.

Enter Egeus, Hermia, Lysander, and Demetrius

EGEUS. Happy be Theseus, our renownèd duke !

THESEUS. Thanks, good Egeus : what's the news with thee ?

EGEUS. Full of vexation come I, with complaint
Against my child, my daughter Hermia.
Stand forth, Demetrius. My noble lord,
This man hath my consent to marry her.
Stand forth, Lysander : and, my gracious duke,
This man hath bewitched the bosom of my child :
Thou, thou, Lysander, thou hast given her rhymes
And interchanged love-tokens with my child :
Thou hast by moonlight at her window sung
With feigning voice verses of feigning love,
And stolen the impression of her fantasy

With bracelets of thy hair, rings, gawds, conceits,
Knacks, trifles, nosegays, sweetmeats, messengers
Of strong prevailment in unhardened youth :
Be it so she will not here before your grace
Consent to marry with Demetrius,
I beg the ancient privilege of Athens,
As she is mine, I may dispose of her :
Which shall be either to this gentleman
Or to her death, according to our law
Immediately provided in that case.

THESEUS. What say you, Hermia ? Be advised, fair maid :
To you your father should be as a god ;
Demetrius is a worthy gentleman.

HERMIA. So is Lysander.

THESEUS. In himself he is ;
But in this kind, wanting your father's voice,
The other must be held the worthier.

HERMIA. I would my father looked but with my eyes.

THESEUS. Rather your eyes must with his judgment look.

HERMIA. I do entreat your grace to pardon me.
I know not by what power I am made bold,
Nor how it may concern my modesty,
In such a presence here to plead my thoughts ;
But I beseech your grace that I may know
The worst that may befall me in this case,
If I refuse to wed Demetrius.

THESEUS. Either to die the death or to abjure
For ever the society of men.
Therefore, fair Hermia, question your desires ;
Know of your youth, examine well your blood,
Whether, if you yield not to your father's choice,
You can endure the livery of a nun,
For aye to be in shady cloister mewed.
Thrice-blessèd they that master so their blood,
To undergo such maiden pilgrimage ;
But earthlier happy is the rose distilled,
Than that which withering on the virgin thorn
Grows, lives, and dies in single blessedness.

HERMIA. So will I grow, so live, so die, my lord,
Ere I will yield my virgin patent up
Unto his lordship, whose unwished yoke
My soul consents not to give sovereignty.

THESEUS. Take time to pause ; and, by the next new moon
(The sealing-day betwixt my love and me,
For everlasting bond of fellowship)

Upon that day either prepare to die
For disobedience to your father's will,
Or else to wed Demetrius, as he would ;
Or on Diana's altar to protest
For aye austerity and single life.

DEMETRIUS. Relent, sweet Hermia : and, Lysander, yield
Thy crazèd title to my certain right.

LYSANDER. You have her father's love, Demetrius ;
Let me have Hermia's : do you marry him.

EGEUS. Scornful Lysander ! True, he hath my love,
And what is mine my love shall render him.
And she is mine, and all my right of her
I do estate unto Demetrius.

LYSANDER. I am, my lord, as well derived as he,
As well possessed ; my love is more than his ;
My fortunes every way as fairly ranked,
If not with vantage, as Demetrius' ;
And, which is more than all these boasts can be,
I am beloved of beauteous Hermia :
Why should not I then prosecute my right ?
Demetrius, I'll avouch it to his head,
Made love to Nedar's daughter, Helena,
And won her soul ; and she, sweet lady, dotes,
Devoutly dotes, dotes in idolatry,
Upon this spotted and inconstant man.

THESEUS. I must confess that I have heard so much,
And with Demetrius thought to have spoke thereof ;
But, being over-full of self-affairs,
My mind did lose it. But, Demetrius, come ;
And come, Egeus ; you shall go with me,
I have some private schooling for you both.
For you, fair Hermia, look you arm yourself
To fit your fancies to your father's will ;
Or else the law of Athens yields you up
(Which by no means we may extenuate)
To death, or to a vow of single life.
Come, my Hippolyta : what cheer, my love ?
Demetrius and Egeus, go along :
I must employ you in some business
Against our nuptial, and confer with you
Of something nearly that concerns yourselves.

EGEUS. With duty and desire we follow you.

All but Lysander and Hermia leave

LYSANDER. How now, my love ! why is your cheek so pale ?
How chance the roses there do fade so fast ?

HERMIA. Belike for want of rain, which I could well
Beteem them from the tempest of my eyes.

LYSANDER. Ay me! for aught that I could ever read,
Could ever hear by tale or history,
The course of true love never did run smooth;
But, either it was different in blood,
Or else misgraffèd in respect of years,
Or else it stood upon the choice of friends,
Or, if there were a sympathy in choice,
War, death, or sickness did lay siege to it,
Making it momentary as a sound,
Swift as a shadow, short as any dream;
Brief as the lightning in the collied night,
That, in a spleen, unfolds both heaven and earth,
And ere a man hath power to say *Behold!*
The jaws of darkness do devour it up:
So quick bright things come to confusion.

HERMIA. Then let us teach our trial patience,
Because it is a customary cross,
As due to love as thoughts and dreams and sighs,
Wishes and tears, poor fancy's followers.

LYSANDER. A good persuasion: therefore, hear me, Hermia.
I have a widow aunt, a dowager
Of great re*ven*ue, and she hath no child:
From Athens is her house remote seven leagues;
And she respects me as her only son.
There, gentle Hermia, may I marry thee;
And to that place the sharp Athenian law
Cannot pursue us. If thou lovest me then,
Steal forth thy father's house tomorrow night;
And in the wood, a league without the town,
There will I stay for thee.

HERMIA. My good Lysander!
By all the vows that ever men have broke,
In number more than ever women spoke,
In that same place thou hast appointed me,
Tomorrow truly will I meet with thee.

LYSANDER. Keep promise, love. Look, here comes Helena.

HERMIA. God speed fair Helena! whither away?

HELENA. Call you me fair? that fair again unsay.
Demetrius loves your fair: O happy fair!
Your eyes are lode-stars; and your tongue's sweet air
More tunable than lark to shepherd's ear,
When wheat is green, when hawthorn buds appear.
Sickness is catching: O, were favour so,

Yours would I catch, fair Hermia, ere I go;
My ear should catch your voice, my eye your eye,
My tongue should catch your tongue's sweet melody.
O, teach me how you look, and with what art
You sway the motion of Demetrius' heart.

HERMIA. I frown upon him, yet he loves me still.

HELENA. O that your frowns would teach my smiles such skill!

HERMIA. I give him curses, yet he gives me love.

HELENA. O that my prayers could such affection move!

HERMIA. The more I hate, the more he follows me.

HELENA. The more I love, the more he hateth me.

HERMIA. His folly, Helena, is no fault of mine.

HELENA. None, but your beauty: would that fault were mine!

HERMIA. Take comfort: he no more shall see my face;
Lysander and myself will fly this place.

LYSANDER. Helen, to you our minds we will unfold:
Tomorrow night, when Phoebe doth behold
Her silver visage in the watery glass,
Decking with liquid pearl the bladed grass,
A time that lovers' flights doth still conceal,
Through Athens' gates have we devised to steal.

HERMIA. And in the wood where often you and I
Upon faint primrose-beds were wont to lie,
Emptying our bosoms of their counsel sweet,
There my Lysander and myself shall meet;
And thence from Athens turn away our eyes,
To seek new friends and stranger companies.
Farewell, sweet playfellow: pray thou for us;
And good luck grant thee thy Demetrius!
Keep word, Lysander: we must starve our sight
From lovers' food till morrow deep midnight.

LYSANDER. I will, my Hermia. Helena, adieu:
As you on him, Demetrius dote on you!

HELENA *(alone)*. How happy some o'er other some can be!
Through Athens I am thought as fair as she.
But what of that? Demetrius thinks not so;
He will not know what all but he do know:
And as he errs, doting on Hermia's eyes,
So I, admiring of his qualities:
Things base and vile, holding no quantity,
Love can transpose to form and dignity:
Love looks not with the eyes, but with the mind;
And therefore is winged Cupid painted blind:

Nor hath Love's mind of any judgment taste ;
Wings and no eyes figure unheedy haste :
And therefore is Love said to be a child,
Because in choice he is so oft beguiled.
For ere Demetrius looked on Hermia's eyne,
He hailed down oaths that he was only mine ;
I will go tell him of fair Hermia's flight :
Then to the wood will he tomorrow night
Pursue her ; and for this intelligence
If I have thanks, it is a dear expense :
But herein mean I to enrich my pain,
To have his sight thither and back again.

Scene 2—Quince's House in Athens

Enter Quince, Snug, Bottom, Flute, Snout, and Starveling

QUINCE. Is all our company here ?

BOTTOM. You were best to call them generally, man by man, according to the scrip.

QUINCE. Here is the scroll of every man's name, which is thought fit, through all Athens, to play in our interlude before the duke and the duchess, on his wedding-day at night.

BOTTOM. First, good Peter Quince, say what the play treats on, then read the names of the actors, and so grow to a point.

QUINCE. Marry, our play is, *The most lamentable comedy and most cruel death of Pyramus and Thisby.*

BOTTOM. A very good piece of work, I assure you, and a merry. Now, good Peter Quince, call forth your actors by the scroll. Masters, spread yourselves.

QUINCE. Answer as I call you. Nick Bottom, the weaver. You, Nick Bottom, are set down for Pyramus.

BOTTOM. What is Pyramus ? a lover, or a tyrant ?

QUINCE. A lover, that kills himself most gallant for love.

BOTTOM. That will ask some tears in the true performing of it : if I do it, let the audience look to their eyes ; I will move storms. Yet my chief humour is for a tyrant : I could play Hercules rarely.

The raging rocks
And shivering shocks
Shall break the locks
    Of prison gates ;
And Phibbus' car
Shall shine from far
And make and mar
    The foolish Fates.

This was lofty! Now name the rest of the players. This is a tyrant's vein; a lover is more condoling.

QUINCE. Francis Flute, the bellows-mender, you must take Thisby on you. It is the lady that Pyramus must love.

FLUTE. Nay, faith, let not me play a woman; I have a beard coming.

QUINCE. That's all one: you shall play it in a mask, and you may speak as small as you will. Robin Starveling, the tailor; you must play Thisby's mother. Tom Snout, the tinker, you, Pyramus' father: myself, Thisby's father. Snug, the joiner; you, the lion's part: and, I hope, here is a play fitted.

SNUG. Have you the lion's part written? pray you, if it be, give it me, for I am slow of study.

QUINCE. You may do it extempore, for it is nothing but roaring.

BOTTOM. Let me play the lion too: I will roar, that I will do any man's heart good to hear me; I will roar, that I will make the duke say 'Let him roar again, let him roar again.'

QUINCE. An you should do it too terribly you would fright the duchess and the ladies, that they would shriek; and that were enough to hang us all.

ALL. That would hang us, every mother's son.

BOTTOM. I grant you, friends, if that you should fright the ladies out of their wits, they would have no more discretion but to hang us; but I will aggravate my voice so that I will roar you as gently as any sucking dove; I will roar you an 'twere any nightingale.

QUINCE. You can play no part but Pyramus; for Pyramus is a sweet-faced man; a proper man as one shall see in a summer's day; a most lovely gentleman-like man: therefore you must needs play Pyramus.

BOTTOM. Well, I will undertake it. What beard were I best to play it in?

QUINCE. Why, what you will. Some of your French crowns have no hair at all, and then you will play barefaced. But, masters, here are your parts; and I am to entreat you to con them by tomorrow night; and meet me in the palace wood, a mile without the town, by moonlight. There will we rehearse, for if we meet in the city we shall be dogged with company, and our devices known. In the meantime I will draw a bill of properties, such as our play wants. I pray you, fail me not.

BOTTOM. We will meet; and there we may rehearse most courageously. Take pains; be perfect: adieu.

QUINCE. At the duke's oak we meet.

ACT 2

Scene 1—A Wood near Athens

PUCK. How now, spirit! whither wander you?

FAIRY. Over hill, over dale,
Through bush, through brier,
Over park, over pale,
Through flood, through fire,
I do wander everywhere,
Swifter than the moonë's sphere;
And I serve the fairy queen,
To dew her orbs upon the green.
The cowslips tall her pensioners be:
In their gold coats spots you see;
Those be rubies, fairy favours,
In those freckles live their savours:
I must go seek some dewdrops here
And hang a pearl in every cowslip's ear.
Farewell, thou lob of spirits; I'll be gone:
Our queen and all our elves come here anon.

PUCK. The king doth keep his revels here tonight:
Take heed the queen come not within his sight;
For Oberon is passing fell and wrath,
Because that she as her attendant hath
A lovely boy, stolen from an Indian king;
She never had so sweet a changeling;
And jealous Oberon would have the child
Knight of his train, to trace the forests wild;
But she perforce withholds the lovèd boy,
Crowns him with flowers and makes him all her joy:
And now they never meet in grove or green,
By fountain clear, or spangled starlight sheen,
But they do square, that all their elves for fear
Creep into acorn-cups and hide them there.

FAIRY. Either I mistake your shape and making quite,
Or else you are that shrewd and knavish sprite
Called Robin Goodfellow. Are not you he
That frights the maidens of the villagery;
Skim milk, and sometimes labour in the quern
And bootless make the breathless housewife churn;
And sometime make the drink to bear no barm;
Mislead night-wanderers, laughing at their harm?
Those that Hobgoblin call you and sweet Puck,
You do their work, and they shall have good luck:
Are not you he?

PUCK. Thou speak'st aright;
I am that merry wanderer of the night.
I jest to Oberon and make him smile
When I a fat and bean-fed horse beguile,
Neighing in likeness of a filly foal:
And sometime lurk I in a gossip's bowl,
And on her withered dewlap pour the ale.
And then the whole quire hold their hips and laugh,
And waxen in their mirth and neeze and swear
A merrier hour was never wasted there.
But, room, fairy! here comes Oberon.
FAIRY. And here my mistress. Would that he were gone!

Enter Oberon with his train, and Titania with hers

OBERON. Ill met by moonlight, proud Titania.
TITANIA. What, jealous Oberon! Fairies, skip hence:
I have forsworn his company.
OBERON. Tarry, rash wanton: am not I thy lord?
TITANIA. Then I must be thy lady: Why art thou here,
Come from the farthest steppe of India?
But that, forsooth, the bouncing Amazon,
Your buskined mistress and your warrior love,
To Theseus must be wedded, and you come
To give their bond joy and prosperity.
OBERON. How canst thou thus for shame, Titania,
Glance at my credit with Hippolyta,
Knowing I know thy love to Theseus?
TITANIA. These are the forgeries of jealousy:
And never, since the middle summer's spring,
Met we on hill, in dale, forest, or mead,
By pavèd fountain or by rushy brook,
Or in the beachèd margent of the sea,
To dance our ringlets to the whistling wind,
But with thy brawls thou hast disturbed our sport.
Therefore the winds, piping to us in vain,
As in revenge, have sucked up from the sea
Contagious fogs; which falling in the land
Have every pelting river made so proud
That they have overborne their continents:
The ox hath therefore stretched his yoke in vain,
The ploughman lost his sweat, and the green corn
Hath rotted ere his youth attained a beard;
The fold stands empty in the drownèd field,
And crows are fatted with the murrion flock;
The Nine Men's Morris is filled up with mud,
And the quaint mazes in the wanton green
For lack of tread are undistinguishable:

The human mortals want their winter here ;
No night is now with hymn or carol blest ;
Therefore the moon, the governess of floods,
Pale in her anger, washes all the air,
That *rheu*matic diseases do abound.
The seasons alter : the spring, the summer,
The childing autumn, angry winter, change
Their wonted liveries, and the mazed world,
By their increase, now knows not which is which :
And this same progeny of evils comes
From our debate, from our dissension ;
We are their parents and original.

OBERON. Do you amend it then ; it lies in you :
Why should Titania cross her Oberon ?
I do but beg a little changeling boy,
To be my henchman.

TITANIA. Set your heart at rest :
The fairy land buys not the child of me.

OBERON. How long within this wood intend you stay ?

TITANIA. Perchance till after Theseus' wedding-day.
If you will patiently dance in our round
And see our moonlight revels, go with us ;
If not, shun me, and I will spare your haunts.

OBERON. Give me that boy, and I will go with thee.

TITANIA. Not for thy fairy kingdom. Fairies, away !
We shall chide downright if I longer stay.

Titania leaves with her train

OBERON. Well, go thy way : thou shalt not from this grove
Till I torment thee for this injury.
My gentle Puck, come hither. Thou rememberest
Since once I sat upon a promontory,
And heard a mermaid on a dolphin's back
Uttering such dulcet and harmonious breath
That the rude sea grew civil at her song
And certain stars shot madly from their spheres
To hear the sea-maid's music ?

PUCK. I remember.

OBERON. That very time I saw, but thou couldst not,
Flying between the cold moon and the earth,
Cupid all armed : a certain aim he took
At a fair vestal thronèd by the west,
And loosed his love-shaft smartly from his bow,
As it should pierce a hundred thousand hearts ;
But I might see young Cupid's fiery shaft
Quenched in the chaste beams of the watery moon,

And the imperial votaress passed on,
In maiden meditation, fancy-free.
Yet marked I where the bolt of Cupid fell:
It fell upon a little western flower,
Before milk-white, now purple with love's wound,
And maidens call it love-in-idleness.
Fetch me that flower; the herb I showed thee once:
The juice of it on sleeping eyelids laid
Will make or man or woman madly dote
Upon the next live creature that it sees.
Fetch me this herb; and be thou here again
Ere the leviathan can swim a league.

PUCK. I'll put a girdle round about the earth
In forty minutes.

OBERON. Having once this juice,
I'll watch Titania when she is asleep,
And drop the liquor of it in her eyes.
The next thing then she waking looks upon,
Be it on lion, bear, or wolf, or bull,
On meddling monkey, or on busy ape,
She shall pursue it with the soul of love:
And ere I take this charm from off her sight,
As I can take it with another herb,
I'll make her render up her page to me.
But who comes here? I am invisible;
And I will overhear their conference.

Enter Demetrius, Helena following him

DEMETRIUS. I love thee not, therefore pursue me not.
Where is Lysander and fair Hermia?
The one I'll slay, the other slayeth me.
Thou told'st me they were stolen unto this wood.
Hence, get thee gone, and follow me no more.

HELENA. You draw me, you hard-hearted adamant;
But yet you draw not iron, for my heart
Is true as steel: leave you your power to draw,
And I shall have no power to follow you.

DEMETRIUS. Do I entice you? Do I speak you fair?
Or, rather, do I not in plainest truth
Tell you I do not, nor I cannot, love you?

HELENA. And even for that do I love you the more.
I am your spaniel; and, Demetrius,
The more you beat me, I will fawn on you.

DEMETRIUS. You do impeach your modesty too much,
To leave the city and commit yourself
Into the hands of one that loves you not.

I'll run from thee and hide me in the brakes,
And leave thee to the mercy of wild beasts.

HELENA. The wildest hath not such a heart as you.

DEMETRIUS. I will not stay thy questions ; let me go :
Or, if thou follow me, do not believe
But I shall do thee mischief in the wood.

HELENA. Ay, in the temple, in the town, the field,
You do me mischief. Fie, Demetrius !
Your wrongs do set a scandal on my sex :
We cannot fight for love, as men may do ;
We should be wooed and were not made to woo.
I'll follow thee and make a heaven of hell,
To die upon the hand I love so well. *(They leave)*

OBERON. Fare thee well, nymph : ere he do leave this grove,
Thou shalt fly him and he shall seek thy love. *(Puck returns)*
Hast thou the flower there ? Welcome, wanderer.

PUCK. Ay, there it is.

OBERON. I pray thee, give it me.
I know a bank where the wild thyme blows,
Where oxlips and the nodding violet grows,
Quite over-canopied with luscious woodbine,
With sweet musk-roses and with eglantine :
There sleeps Titania sometime of the night,
Lulled in these flowers with dances and delight ;
And there the snake throws her enamelled skin,
Weed wide enough to wrap a fairy in :
And with the juice of this I'll streak her eyes,
And make her full of hateful fantasies.
Take thou some of it, and seek through this grove :
A sweet Athenian lady is in love
With a disdainful youth : anoint his eyes ;
But do it when the next thing he espies
May be the lady : thou shalt know the man
By the Athenian garments he hath on.
Effect it with some care that he may prove
More fond on her than she upon her love :
And look thou meet me ere the first cock crow.

PUCK. Fear not, my lord, your servant shall do so.

Scene 2—The Wood outside Athens

TITANIA. Come, now a roundel and a fairy song ;
Then, for the third part of a minute, hence ;
Some to kill cankers in the musk-rose buds,
Some war with rere-mice for their leathern wings,
To make my small elves coats, and some keep back

The clamorous owl that nightly hoots and wonders
At our quaint spirits. Sing me now asleep;
Then to your offices and let me rest.

SONG OF THE FAIRIES

You spotted snakes with double tongue,
Thorny hedgehogs, be not seen;
Newts and blind-worms, do no wrong,
Come not near our fairy queen.
Philomel, with melody
Sing in our sweet lullaby;
Never harm,
Nor spell nor charm,
Come our lovely lady nigh;
So, Good-night, with lullaby.
Weaving spiders, come not here;
Hence, you long-legged spinners, hence!
Beetles black, approach not near;
Worm nor snail, do no offence.
Philomel, with melody,
Sing in our sweet melody.

A FAIRY. Hence, away! now all is well:
One aloof stand sentinel.

Fairies go and Titania sleeps. Enter Oberon, who squeezes the flower on Titania's eyelids.

OBERON. What thou seest when thou dost wake,
Do it for thy true-love take,
Love and languish for his sake:
Be it ounce, or cat, or bear,
Pard, or boar with bristled hair,
In thy eye that shall appear
When thou wak'st, it is thy dear:
Wake when some vile thing is near.

Enter Lysander and Hermia

LYSANDER. Fair love, you faint with wandering in the wood;
And to speak troth, I have forgot our way:
We'll rest us, Hermia, if you think it good,
And tarry for the comfort of the day.

HERMIA. Be it so, Lysander: find you out a bed;
For I upon this bank will rest my head.

LYSANDER. One turf shall serve as pillow for us both;
One heart, one bed, two bosoms, and one troth.

HERMIA. Nay, good Lysander; for my sake, my dear,
Lie further off yet, do not lie so near.

LYSANDER. O, take the sense, sweet, of my innocence!

HERMIA. But, gentle friend, for love and courtesy
Lie further off: in human modesty,

Such separation as may well be said
Becomes a virtuous bachelor and a maid,
So far be distant ; and, Good-night, sweet friend :
Thy love ne'er alter till thy sweet life end !

LYSANDER. Amen, amen, to that fair prayer, say I ;
And then end life when I end loyalty !

Puck enters and finds them sleeping

PUCK. Through the forest have I gone,
But Athenian found I none,
On whose eyes I might approve
This flower's force in stirring love.
Night and silence. Who is here ?
Weeds of Athens he doth wear :
This is he, my master said,
Despised the Athenian maid ;
And here the maiden, sleeping sound,
On the dank and dirty ground.
Pretty soul ! she durst not lie
Near this lack-love, this kill-courtesy.
Churl, upon thy eyes I throw
All the power this charm doth owe.
When thou wakest let love forbid
Sleep his seat on thy eyelid :
So awake when I am gone ;
For I must now to Oberon.

Demetrius and Helena come running

HELENA. Stay, though thou kill me, sweet Demetrius.

DEMETRIUS. I charge thee, hence, and do not haunt me thus.

HELENA. O, wilt thou darkling leave me ? Do not so.

DEMETRIUS. Stay, on thy peril : I alone will go. *(He goes)*

HELENA. O, I am out of breath in this fond chase !
The more my prayer, the lesser is my grace.
Happy is Hermia, wheresoe'er she lies ;
For she hath blessèd and attractive eyes.
How came her eyes so bright ? Not with salt tears :
If so, my eyes are oftener washed than hers.
But who is here ? Lysander ! on the ground !
Dead ? or asleep ? I see no blood, no wound.
Lysander, if you live, good sir, awake.

LYSANDER. And run through fire I will for thy sweet sake.
Transparent Helena ! Nature shows art,
That through thy bosom makes me see thy heart.
Where is Demetrius ? O, how fit a word
Is that vile name to perish on my sword !

HELENA. Do not say so, Lysander; say not so.
What though he love your Hermia? Lord, what though?
Yet Hermia still loves you: then be content.

LYSANDER. Content with Hermia! No; I do repent
The tedious minutes I with her have spent.
Not Hermia but Helena I love:
Who will not change a raven for a dove?
The will of man is by his reason swayed
And reason says you are the worthier maid.

HELENA. Wherefore was I to this keen mockery born?
When at your hands did I deserve this scorn?
Is't not enough, is't not enough, young man,
That I did never, no, nor never can,
Deserve a sweet look from Demetrius' eye,
But you must flout my insufficiency?
Good troth, you do me wrong, good sooth, you do,
In such disdainful manner me to woo.
But fare you well: perforce I must confess
I thought you lord of more true gentleness.
O, that a lady, of one man refused,
Should of another therefore be abused! *(She goes)*

LYSANDER. She sees not Hermia. Hermia, sleep thou there:
And never mayst thou come Lysander near!
And, all my powers, address your love and might
To honour Helen and to be her knight! *(He follows her)*

HERMIA *(waking)*. Help me, Lysander, help me! do thy best
To pluck this crawling serpent from my breast!
Ay me, for pity! what a dream was here!
Lysander, look how I do quake with fear:
Methought a serpent ate my heart away,
And you sat smiling at his cruel prey.
Lysander! what, removed? Lysander! lord!
What, out of hearing? Gone? No sound, no word?
Alack, where are you? Speak, an if you hear;
Speak, of all loves! I swoon almost with fear.
No? Then I well perceive you are not nigh:
Either death or you I'll find immediately.

ACT 3

Scene 1—Titania Lying Asleep in the Wood

Enter Quince, Snug, Bottom, Flute, Snout, and Starveling

BOTTOM. Are we all met?

QUINCE. Pat, pat; and here 's a marvellous convenient place for our rehearsal. This green plot shall be our stage, this hawthorn-brake our tiring-house; and we will do it in action as we will do it before the duke.

BOTTOM. Peter Quince——

QUINCE. What sayest thou, Bully Bottom?

BOTTOM. There are things in this comedy of Pyramus and Thisby that will never please. First, Pyramus must draw a sword to kill himself, which the ladies cannot abide. How answer you that?

STARVELING. I believe we must leave the killing out.

BOTTOM. Not a whit: I have a device to make all well. Write me a prologue; and let the prologue seem to say we will do no harm with our swords and that Pyramus is not killed indeed; and, for the more better assurance, tell them that I Pyramus am not Pyramus, but Bottom the weaver: this will put them out of fear.

QUINCE. Well, we will have such a prologue.

SNOUT. Will not the ladies be afeard of the lion?

STARVELING. I fear it, I promise you.

BOTTOM. Masters, you ought to consider with yourselves: to bring in (God shield us!) a lion among ladies, is a most dreadful thing; for there is not a more fearful wild-fowl than your lion living; and we ought to look to it.

SNOUT. Therefore another prologue must tell he is not a lion.

BOTTOM. Nay, you must name his name, and half his face must be seen through the lion's neck: and he himself must speak through, saying: *Ladies*, or *Fair ladies, I would wish you*, or *I would request you*, or *I would entreat you*—not to fear, not to tremble. If you think I come hither as a lion, it were pity of my life: no, I am no such thing; I am a man as other men are; and there indeed let him name his name, and tell them plainly he is Snug the joiner.

QUINCE. Well, it shall be so. But there are two hard things; that is, to bring the moonlight into a chamber; for, you know, Pyramus and Thisby meet by moonlight.

SNOUT. Doth the moon shine that night we play our play?

BOTTOM. A calendar, a calendar! look in the almanac.

QUINCE. Yes, it doth shine that night.

BOTTOM. Why, then may you leave a casement of the great chamber-window open, and the moon may shine in at the casement.

QUINCE. Ay; or else one must come in with a bush of thorns and a lanthorn, and say he comes to present the person of Moonshine. Then there is another thing: we must have a wall in the great chamber; for Pyramus and Thisby, says the story, did talk through the chink of a wall.

SNOUT. You can never bring in a wall. What say you, Bottom?

BOTTOM. Some man or other must present Wall: and let him have some plaster, or some loam, or some rough-cast about him, to signify Wall; and let him hold his fingers thus, and through that cranny shall Pyramus and Thisby whisper.

QUINCE. If that may be, then all is well. Come, sit down, every mother's son, and rehearse your parts. Pyramus, you begin: when you have spoken your speech, enter into that brake: and so every one according to his cue. *(Enter Puck behind)*

PUCK. What hempen home-spuns have we swaggering here,
So near the cradle of the fairy queen?
What, a play toward! I'll be an auditor;
An actor too, perhaps, if I see cause.

QUINCE. Speak, Pyramus. Thisby, stand forth.

BOTTOM. Thisby, the flowers of odious savours sweet—

QUINCE. Odours, odours.

BOTTOM. . . . odours savours sweet:
So hath thy breath, my dearest Thisby dear.
But hark, a voice! stay thou but here awhile,
And by and by I will to thee appear. *(He leaves)*

FLUTE. Must I speak now?

QUINCE. Ay, marry, must you: for you must understand he goes but to see a noise that he heard, and is to come again.

FLUTE. Most radiant Pyramus, most lily-white of hue,
Of colour like the red rose on triumphant brier,
Most brisky juvenal and eke most lovely Jew,
As true as truest horse that yet would never tire,
I'll meet thee, Pyramus, at Ninny's tomb.

QUINCE. Ninus' tomb, man: why, you must not speak that yet; that you answer to Pyramus: you speak all your part at once, cues and all. Pyramus enter: your cue is past; it is, *never tire.*

FLUTE. O, as true as truest horse, that yet would never tire.

Bottom returns with an ass's head

BOTTOM. If I were fair, Thisby, I were only thine.

QUINCE. O monstrous! O strange! We are haunted. Pray, masters! Fly, masters! Help! *(They run)*

PUCK. I'll follow you, I'll lead you about a round,
Through bog, through bush, through brake, through brier:
Sometime a horse I'll be, sometime a hound,
A hog, a headless bear, sometime a fire;
And neigh, and bark, and grunt, and roar, and burn
Like horse, hound, hog, bear, fire, at every turn.

BOTTOM. Why do they run away? This is a knavery of them to make me afeard.

SNOUT *(returning)*. O Bottom, thou art changed! what do I see on thee?

BOTTOM. What do you see? You see an ass-head of your own, do you? *(Snout goes)*

QUINCE *(returning)*. Bless thee, Bottom! bless thee! thou art translated. *(He goes)*

BOTTOM. I see their knavery: this is to make an ass of me; to fright me, if they could. But I will not stir from this place, do what they can: I will walk up and down here, and I will sing, that they shall hear I am not afraid. *(He sings)*

The ousel cock so black of hue,
  With orange-tawny bill,
The throstle with his note so true,
  The wren with little quill.

TITANIA *(waking)*. What angel wakes me from my flowery bed?

BOTTOM *(singing)*. The finch, the sparrow, and the lark,
The plain-song cuckoo gray.

TITANIA. I pray thee, gentle mortal, sing again:
Mine ear is much enamoured of thy note;
So is mine eye enthrallèd to thy shape;
And thy fair virtue's force perforce doth move me
On the first view to say, to swear, I love thee.

BOTTOM. Methinks, mistress, you should have little reason for that; and yet, to say the truth, reason and love keep little company together nowadays: the more the pity that some honest neighbours will not make them friends.

TITANIA. Thou art as wise as thou art beautiful.

BOTTOM. Not so, neither: but if I had wit enough to get out of this wood I have enough to serve mine own turn.

TITANIA. Out of this wood do not desire to go:
Thou shalt remain here, whether thou wilt or no.
I am a spirit of no common rate:
The summer still doth tend upon my state;
And I do love thee: therefore, go with me;
I'll give thee fairies to attend on thee,
And they shall fetch thee jewels from the deep,
And sing while thou on pressèd flowers dost sleep:
And I will purge thy mortal grossness so
That thou shalt like an airy spirit go.
Peaseblossom! Cobweb! Moth! and Mustardseed!

ALL. Where shall we go?

TITANIA. Be kind and courteous to this gentleman;
Hop in his walks and gambol in his eyes;
Feed him with apricocks and dewberries,

With purple grapes, green figs, and mulberries ;
The honey-bags steal from the humble-bees,
And for night-tapers crop their waxen thighs
And light them at the fiery glow-worm's eyes,
To have my love to bed and to arise ;
And pluck the wings from painted butterflies
To fan the moonbeams from his sleeping eyes :
Nod to him, elves, and do him courtesies.

ALL. Hail !

BOTTOM. I cry your worships mercy, heartily. I beseech your worship's name.

COBWEB. Cobweb.

BOTTOM. I shall desire you of more acquaintance, good Master Cobweb : if I cut my finger I shall make bold with you. Your name, honest gentleman ?

PEASEBLOSSOM. Peaseblossom.

BOTTOM. I pray you, commend me to Mistress Squash, your mother, and to Master Peascod, your father. Good Master Peaseblossom, I shall desire you of more acquaintance too. Your name, I beseech you, sir ?

MUSTARDSEED. Mustardseed.

BOTTOM. Good Master Mustardseed, I know your patience well : that same cowardly, giant-like ox-beef hath devoured many a gentleman of your house. I desire your more acquaintance, good Master Mustardseed.

TITANIA. Come, wait upon him ; lead him to my bower.
The moon methinks looks with a watery eye ;
And when she weeps, weeps every little flower.

Scene 2—The Wood

OBERON. I wonder if Titania be awaked ;
Then, what it was that next came in her eye,
Which she must dote on in extremity.
Here comes my messenger. How now, mad spirit !
What night-rule now about this haunted grove ?

PUCK *(approaching)*. My mistress with a monster is in love.
Near to her close and consecrated bower,
While she was in her dull and sleeping hour,
A crew of patches, rude mechanicals,
That work for bread upon Athenian stalls,
Were met together to rehearse a play
Intended for great Theseus' nuptial-day.
The shallowest thick-skin of that barren sort,

Who Pyramus presented, in their sport
Forsook his scene and entered in a brake:
When I did him at this advantage take,
An ass's nole I fixèd on his head:
Anon his Thisbe must be answerèd,
And forth my mimic comes. When they him spy,
As wild geese that the creeping fowler eye,
Or russet-pated choughs, many in sort,
Rising and cawing at the gun's report,
Sever themselves and madly sweep the sky,
So, at his sight, away his fellows fly;
And, at our stamp, here o'er and o'er one falls;
He murder cries and help from Athens calls.
I led them on in this distracted fear,
And left sweet Pyramus translated there:
When in that moment, so it came to pass,
Titania waked and straightway loved an ass.

OBERON. This falls out better than I could devise.
But hast thou yet latched the Athenian's eyes
With the love-juice, as I did bid thee do?

PUCK. I took him sleeping—that is finished too—
And the Athenian woman by his side;
That, when he waked, of force she must be eyed.

Enter Hermia and Demetrius

OBERON. Stand close: this is the same Athenian.

PUCK. This is the woman, but not this the man.

DEMETRIUS. O, why rebuke you him that loves you so?
Lay breath so bitter on your bitter foe.

HERMIA. Now I but chide; but I should use thee worse,
For thou, I fear, hast given me cause to curse.
If thou hast slain Lysander in his sleep,
Being o'er shoes in blood, plunge in the deep,
And kill me too.
The sun was not so true unto the day
As he to me: would he have stolen away
From sleeping Hermia?
It cannot be but thou hast murdered him;
So should a murderer look, so dead, so grim.

DEMETRIUS. So should the murdered look, and so should I,
Pierced through the heart with your stern cruelty:
Yet you, the murderer, look as bright, as clear,
As yonder Venus in her glimmering sphere.

HERMIA. What's this to my Lysander? Where is he?
Ah, good Demetrius, wilt thou give him me?

DEMETRIUS. I had rather give his carcase to my hounds.

HERMIA. Out, dog! out, cur! thou drivest me past the bounds
Of maiden's patience. Hast thou slain him then?
Henceforth be never numbered among men!
O, once tell true, tell true, even for my sake!
Durst thou have looked upon him being awake,
And hast thou killed him sleeping? O brave touch!
Could not a worm, an adder, do so much?
An adder did it; for with doubler tongue
Than thine, thou serpent, never adder stung.

DEMETRIUS. You spend your passion on a misprised mood:
I am not guilty of Lysander's blood;
Nor is he dead, for aught that I can tell.

HERMIA. I pray thee, tell me then that he is well.

DEMETRIUS. An if I could, what should I get therefore?

HERMIA. A privilege never to see me more.
And from thy hated presence part I so:
See me no more, whether he be dead or no.

DEMETRIUS. There is no following her in this fierce vein:
Here therefore for a while I will remain. *(He lies down and sleeps)*

OBERON. What hast thou done? Thou hast mistaken quite
And laid the love-juice on some true-love's sight:
Of thy misprision must perforce ensue
Some true love turned and not a false turned true.
About the wood go swifter than the wind
And Helena of Athens look thou find:
All fancy-sick she is and pale of cheer,
With sighs of love, that costs the fresh blood dear:
By some illusion see thou bring her here:
I'll charm his eyes against she do appear.

PUCK. I go, I go; look how I go,
Swifter than arrow from the Tartar's bow.

OBERON. Flower of this purple dye,
Hit with Cupid's archery,
Sink in apple of his eye.
When his love he doth espy,
Let her shine as gloriously
As the Venus of the sky.
When thou wak'st, if she be by,
Beg of her for remedy.

PUCK *returning* Captain of our fairy band,
Helena is here at hand;
And the youth, mistook by me,
Pleading for a lover's fee.
Shall we their fond pageant see?
Lord, what fools these mortals be!

OBERON. Stand aside: the noise they make
Will cause Demetrius to awake.

PUCK. Then will two at once woo one;
That must needs be sport alone;
And those things do best please me
That befal preposterously.

Enter Lysander and Helena

LYSANDER. Why should you think that I should woo in scorn?
Scorn and derision never come in tears:
Look, when I vow, I weep; and vows so born,
In their nativity all truth appears.

HELENA. You do advance your cunning more and more.
These vows are Hermia's: will you give her o'er?

LYSANDER. I had no judgment when to her I swore.

HELENA. Nor none, in my mind, now you give her o'er.

LYSANDER. Demetrius loves her, and he loves not you.

DEMETRIUS *(waking)*. O Helen, goddess, nymph, perfect, divine!
To what, my love, shall I compare thine eyne?
Crystal is muddy. O, how ripe in show
Thy lips, those kissing cherries, tempting grow!

HELENA. O spite! I see you all are bent
To set against me for your merriment:
If you were civil and knew courtesy,
You would not do me thus much injury.
Can you not hate me, as I know you do,
But you must join in souls to mock me too?
If you were men, as men you are in show,
You would not use a gentle lady so;
To vow, and swear, and superpraise my parts,
When I am sure you hate me with your hearts.
You both are rivals, and love Hermia;
And now both rivals, to mock Helena:
A trim exploit, a manly enterprise,
To conjure tears up in a poor maid's eyes!

LYSANDER. You are unkind, Demetrius; be not so,
For you love Hermia; this you know I know:
And here, with all goodwill, with all my heart,
In Hermia's love I yield you up my part;
And yours of Helena to me bequeath,
Whom I do love and will do till my death.

HELENA. Never did mockers waste more idle breath.

DEMETRIUS. Lysander, keep thy Hermia; I will none:
If e'er I loved her, all that love is gone.

HERMIA *(entering)*. Dark night, that from the eye his function takes,
The ear more quick of apprehension makes ;
Thou art not by mine eye, Lysander, found ;
Mine ear, I thank it, brought me to thy sound.
But why unkindly didst thou leave me so ?

LYSANDER. Why should he stay, whom love doth press to go ?

HERMIA. What love could press Lysander from my side ?

LYSANDER. Lysander's love, that would not let him bide,
Fair Helena, who more engilds the night
Than all yon fiery oes and eyes of light.
Why seek'st thou me ? Could not this make thee know,
The hate I bear thee made me leave thee so ?

HERMIA. You speak not as you think : it cannot be.

HELENA. Lo, she is one of this confederacy !
Now I perceive they have conjoined all three
To fashion this false sport, in spite of me.
Injurious Hermia ! most ungrateful maid !
Have you conspired, have you with these contrived
To bait me with this foul derision ?
Is all the counsel that we two have shared,
The sisters' vows, the hours that we have spent,
When we have chid the hasty-footed time
For parting us—O, is it all forgot ?
All schooldays' friendship, childhood innocence ?
And will you rent our ancient love asunder,
To join with men in scorning your poor friend ?
It is not friendly, tis not maidenly :
Our sex, as well as I, may chide you for it,
Though I alone do feel the injury.

HERMIA. I am amazèd at your passionate words.
I scorn you not : it seems that you scorn me.

HELENA. Have you not set Lysander, as in scorn,
To follow me and praise my eyes and face ?
And made your other love, Demetrius,
Who even but now did spurn me with his foot,
To call me goddess, nymph, divine, and rare,
Precious, celestial ? Wherefore speaks he this
To her he hates ? And wherefore doth Lysander
Deny your love, so rich within his soul,
And tender me, forsooth, affection,
But by your setting on, by your consent ?
What though I be not so in grace as you,
So hung upon with love, so fortunate,
But miserable most, to love unloved ?
This you should pity rather than despise.

HERMIA. I understand not what you mean by this.

HELENA. If you have any pity, grace, or manners,
You would not make me such an argument.
But fare ye well : tis partly my own fault ;
Which death or absence soon shall remedy.

LYSANDER. Stay, gentle Helena ; hear my excuse :
My love, my life, my soul, fair Helena !

HELENA. O excellent !

HERMIA. Sweet, do not scorn her so.

DEMETRIUS. If she cannot entreat, I can compel.

LYSANDER. Thou canst compel no more than she entreat :
Thy threats have no more strength than her weak prayers.
Helen, I love thee ; by my life, I do ;
I swear by that which I will lose for thee,
To prove him false that says I love thee not.

DEMETRIUS. I say I love thee more than he can do.

LYSANDER. If thou say so, withdraw, and prove it too.

DEMETRIUS. Quick, come !

HERMIA. Lysander, whereto tends all this ?

LYSANDER. Away, you Ethiope !
Hang off, thou cat, thou burr ! vile thing, let loose,
Or I will shake thee from me like a serpent !

HERMIA. Why are you grown so rude ? What change is this ?
Sweet love——

LYSANDER. Thy love ! out, tawny Tartar, out !

HERMIA. Do you not jest ?

HELENA. Yes, sooth ; and so do you.

LYSANDER. Demetrius, I will keep my word with thee.

DEMETRIUS. I would I had your bond, for I perceive
A weak bond holds you : I'll not trust your word.

LYSANDER. What, should I hurt her, strike her, kill her dead ?
Although I hate her, I'll not harm her so.

HERMIA. What, can you do me greater harm than hate ?
Hate me ! wherefore ? O me ! what news, my love !
Am not I Hermia ? Are not you Lysander ?
I am as fair now as I was erewhile.
Since night you loved me ; yet since night you left me :
Why, then you left me (O, the gods forbid !)
In earnest, shall I say ?

LYSANDER. Ay, by my life ;
And never did desire to see thee more.
Therefore be out of hope, of question, of doubt ;
Be certain, nothing truer ; tis no jest
That I do hate thee and love Helena.

HERMIA. O me ! you juggler ! you canker-blossom !
You thief of love ! what, have you come by night
And stolen my love's heart from him ?

HELENA. Fine, i' faith !
Have you no modesty, no maiden shame,
No touch of bashfulness ? What, will you tear
Impatient answers from my gentle tongue ?
Fie, fie ! you counterfeit, you puppet, you !

HERMIA. Puppet ? why so ? ay, that way goes the game.
Now I perceive that she hath made compare
Between our statures ; she hath urged her height ;
And with her personage, her tall personage,
Her height, forsooth, she hath prevailed with him.
And are you grown so high in his esteem,
Because I am so dwarfish and so low ?
How low am I, thou painted maypole ? speak ;
How low am I ? I am not yet so low
But that my nails can reach unto thine eyes.

HELENA. I pray you, though you mock me, gentlemen,
Let her not hurt me : I was never curst ;
I have no gift at all in shrewishness ;
I am a right maid for my cowardice :
Let her not strike me. You perhaps may think,
Because she is something lower than myself,
That I can match her.

HERMIA. Lower ! hark, again.

HELENA. Good Hermia, do not be so bitter with me.
I evermore did love you, Hermia,
Did ever keep your counsels, never wronged you ;
Save that, in love unto Demetrius,
I told him of your stealth unto this wood.
He followed you ; for love I followed him ;
But he hath chid me hence and threatened me
To strike me, spurn me, nay, to kill me too :
And now, so you will let me quiet go,
To Athens will I bear my folly back
And follow you no further : let me go :
You see how simple and how fond I am.

HERMIA. Why, get you gone : who is't that hinders you ?

HELENA. A foolish heart, that I leave here behind.

HERMIA. What, with Lysander ?

HELENA. With Demetrius.

LYSANDER. Be not afraid : she shall not harm thee, Helena.

DEMETRIUS. No, sir, she shall not, though you take her part.
Let her alone : speak not of Helena.

LYSANDER. Now follow, if thou darest, to try whose right,
Of thine or mine, is most in Helena.

DEMETRIUS. Follow! nay, I'll go with thee, cheek by jole.

Lysander and Demetrius go

HERMIA. You, mistress, all this coil is 'long of you:
Nay, go not back.

HELENA. I will not trust you, I,
Nor longer stay in your curst company.
Your hands than mine are quicker for a fray,
My legs are longer though, to run away.

HERMIA. I am amazed, and know not what to say. *(Both go)*

OBERON. This is thy negligence: still thou mistakest,
Or else committ'st thy knaveries wilfully.

PUCK. Believe me, king of shadows, I mistook.
Did not you tell me I should know the man
By the Athenian garment he had on?
And so far blameless proves my enterprise,
That I have 'nointed an Athenian's eyes;
And so far am I glad it so did sort
As this their jangling I esteem a sport.

OBERON. Thou see'st these lovers seek a place to fight:
Hie therefore, Robin, overcast the night;
The starry welkin cover thou anon
With drooping fog as black as Acheron,
And lead these testy rivals so astray
As one come not within another's way.
Like to Lysander sometime frame thy tongue,
Then stir Demetrius up with bitter wrong;
And sometime rail thou like Demetrius;
And from each other look thou lead them thus,
Till o'er their brows death-counterfeiting sleep
With leaden legs and batty wings doth creep:
Then crush this herb into Lysander's eye;
Whose liquor hath this virtuous property,
To take from thence all error with his might,
And make his eyeballs roll with wonted sight.
When they next wake, all this derision
Shall seem a dream and fruitless vision,
And back to Athens shall the lovers wend,
With league whose date till death shall never end.
Whiles I in this affair do thee employ,
I'll to my queen and beg her Indian boy;
And then I will her charmèd eye release
From monster's view, and all things shall be peace.

PUCK. My fairy lord, this must be done with haste,
For night's swift dragons cut the clouds full fast.

OBERON. I with the morning's love have oft made sport,
And, like a forester, the groves may tread,
Even till the eastern gate, all fiery-red,
Opening on Neptune with fair blessèd beams,
Turns into yellow gold his salt green streams.
But, notwithstanding, haste; make no delay:
We may effect this business yet ere day.

PUCK. Up and down, up and down,
I will lead them up and down:
I am feared in field and town:
Goblin, lead them up and down.

Puck, invisible, leads them on: Lysander enters

LYSANDER. Where art thou, proud Demetrius? speak thou now.

PUCK. Here, villain; drawn and ready. Where art thou?

LYSANDER. I will be with thee straight.

PUCK. Follow me, then, to plainer ground.

Lysander follows the voice

DEMETRIUS. Lysander! speak again:
Thou runaway, thou coward, art thou fled?
Speak! In some bush? Where dost thou hide thy head?

PUCK. Thou coward, art thou bragging to the stars,
Telling the bushes that thou look'st for wars,
And wilt not come? Come, recreant; come, thou child;
I'll whip thee with a rod: he is defiled
That draws a sword on thee.

DEMETRIUS. Yea, art thou there?

PUCK. Follow my voice: we'll try no manhood here.

LYSANDER. He goes before me and still dares me on;
When I come where he calls, then he is gone.
Come, thou gentle day!
For if but once thou show me thy grey light,
I'll find Demetrius and revenge this spite. (*He sleeps*)

PUCK. Ho! ho! ho! Coward, why comest thou not?

DEMETRIUS. Abide me, if thou darest; for well I wot
Thou runn'st before me, shifting every place,
And darest not stand, nor look me in the face.
Where art thou now?

PUCK. Come hither: I am here.

DEMETRIUS. Nay, then, thou mock'st me. Thou shalt buy this dear
If ever I thy face by daylight see:
Now, go thy way. Faintness constraineth me

To measure out my length on this cold bed.
By day's approach look to be visited. *(He lies down and sleeps)*

HELENA *(arriving)*. O weary night, O long and tedious night,
Abate thy hours! Shine comforts from the east,
That I may back to Athens by daylight,
From these that my poor company detest:
And sleep, that sometimes shuts up sorrow's eye,
Steal me awhile from mine own company. *(She sleeps)*

PUCK. Yet but three? Come one more;
Two of both kinds makes up four.
Here she comes, curst and sad:
Cupid is a knavish lad,
Thus to make poor females mad.

HERMIA *(entering)*. Never so weary, never so in woe,
Bedabbled with the dew and torn with briers,
I can no further crawl, no further go;
My legs can keep no pace with my desires.
Here will I rest me till the break of day.
Heavens shield Lysander, if they mean a fray! *(She sleeps)*

PUCK. On the ground sleep sound:
I'll apply to your eye,
Gentle lover, remedy.
When thou wak'st thou tak'st
True delight in the sight
Of thy former lady's eye:
And the country proverb known,
That every man should take his own,
In your waking shall be shown:
Jack shall have Jill, nought shall go ill;
The man shall have his mare again, and all shall be well.

ACT 4

Scene 1—In the Wood

Lysander, Demetrius, Helena, and Hermia sleep. Enter Titania and Bottom, with fairies and Oberon behind unseen.

TITANIA. Come, sit thee down upon this flowery bed,
While I thy amiable cheeks do coy,
And stick musk-roses in thy sleek smooth head,
And kiss thy fair large ears, my gentle joy.
Wilt thou hear some music, my sweet love?

BOTTOM. I have a reasonable good ear in music. Let's have the tongs and the bones.

TITANIA. Or say, sweet love, what thou desirest to eat.

BOTTOM. Truly, a peck of provender: I could munch your good

dry oats. Methinks I have a great desire to a bottle of hay: good hay, sweet hay, hath no fellow.

TITANIA. I have a venturous fairy that shall seek
The squirrel's hoard, and fetch thee new nuts.

BOTTOM. I had rather have a handful or two of dried peas. But, I pray you, let none of your people stir me: I have an exposition of sleep come upon me.

TITANIA. Sleep thou, and I will wind thee in my arms.
Fairies, be gone, and be all ways away.
So doth the woodbine the sweet honeysuckle
Gently entwist; the female ivy so
Enrings the barky fingers of the elm.
O, how I love thee! how I dote on thee! *(They sleep)*

Enter Puck

OBERON. Welcome, good Robin. See'st thou this sweet sight?
Her dotage now I do begin to pity:
For, meeting her of late behind the wood,
Seeking sweet favours for this hateful fool,
I did upbraid her and fall out with her;
For she his hairy temples then had rounded
With coronet of fresh and fragrant flowers;
And that same dew, which sometime on the buds
Was wont to swell like round and orient pearls,
Stood now within the pretty flowerets' eyes
Like tears that did their own disgrace bewail.
When I had at my pleasure taunted her
And she in mild terms begged my patience,
I then did ask of her her changeling child;
Which straight she gave me, and her fairy sent
To bear him to my bower in fairy land.
And now I have the boy, I will undo
This hateful imperfection of her eyes:
And, gentle Puck, take this transformèd scalp
From off the head of this Athenian swain;
That, he awaking when the other do,
May all to Athens back again repair
And think no more of this night's accidents
But as the fierce vexation of a dream.
But first I will release the fairy queen.

Be as thou wast wont to be;
See as thou wast wont to see:
Dian's bud o'er Cupid's flower
Hath such force and blessed power.

Now, my Titania; wake you, my sweet queen.

TITANIA. My Oberon! what visions have I seen!
Methought I was enamoured of an ass.

OBERON. There lies your love.

TITANIA. How came these things to pass?
O, how mine eyes do loathe his visage now!

OBERON. Sound, music! Come, my queen, take hands with me,
And rock the ground whereon these sleepers be.
Now thou and I are new in amity
And will tomorrow midnight solemnly
Dance in Duke Theseus' house triumphantly
And bless it to all fair prosperity:
There shall the pairs of faithful lovers be
Wedded, with Theseus, all in jollity.

PUCK. Fairy king, attend, and mark:
I do hear the morning lark.

OBERON. Then, my queen, in silence sad,
Trip we after the night's shade:
We the globe can compass soon,
Swifter than the wandering moon.

TITANIA. Come, my lord, and in our flight
Tell me how it came this night
That I sleeping here was found
With these mortals on the ground.

Enter Theseus, Hippolyta, Egeus, and train

THESEUS. Go, one of you, find out the forester;
For now our observation is performed;
And since we have the vaward of the day,
My love shall hear the music of my hounds.
But, soft! what nymphs are these?

EGEUS. My lord, this is my daughter here asleep;
And this, Lysander; this Demetrius is;
This Helena, old Nedar's Helena:
I wonder of their being here together.

THESEUS. No doubt they rose up early to observe
The rite of May, and, hearing our intent,
Came here in grace of our solemnity.
But speak, Egeus; is not this the day
That Hermia should give answer of her choice?

EGEUS. It is, my lord.

THESEUS. Go, bid the huntsmen wake them with their horns.

They all awake

Good-morrow, friends. Saint Valentine is past.

LYSANDER. Pardon, my lord.

THESEUS. I pray you all, stand up.
I know you two are rival enemies:
How comes this gentle concord in the world,
That hatred is so far from jealousy,
To sleep by hate, and fear no enmity?

LYSANDER. My lord, I shall reply amazedly,
Half sleep, half waking: but as yet, I swear,
I cannot truly say how I came here;
But, as I think (for truly would I speak,
And now do I bethink me, so it is),
I came with Hermia hither: our intent
Was to be gone from Athens, where we might,
Without the peril of the Athenian law—

EGEUS. Enough, enough, my lord; you have enough:
I beg the law, the law, upon his head.
They would have stolen away; they would, Demetrius,
Thereby to have defeated you and me,
You of your wife and me of my consent,
Of my consent that she should be your wife.

DEMETRIUS. My lord, fair Helen told me of their stealth,
Of this their purpose hither to this wood;
And I in fury hither followed them,
Fair Helena in fancy following me.
But, my good lord, I wot not by what power
(But by some power it is), my love to Hermia,
Melted as the snow, seems to me now
As the remembrance of an idle gaud
Which in my childhood I did dote upon;
And all the faith, the virtue of my heart,
The object and the pleasure of mine eye,
Is only Helena. To her, my lord,
Was I betrothed ere I saw Hermia:
But, like in sickness, did I loathe this food;
But, as in health, come to my natural taste,
Now I do wish it, love it, long for it,
And will for evermore be true to it.

THESEUS. Fair lovers, you are fortunately met:
Of this discourse we more will hear anon.
Egeus, I will overbear your will;
For in the temple, by and by, with us
These couples shall eternally be knit:
And (for the morning now is something worn)
Our purposed hunting shall be set aside.
Away with us to Athens; three and three,
We'll hold a feast in great solemnity.

The Duke and his train leave

DEMETRIUS. These things seem small and undistinguishable,
Like far-off mountains turnèd into clouds.

HERMIA. Methinks I see these things with parted eye,
When everything seems double.

HELENA. So methinks:
And I have found Demetrius like a jewel,
Mine own, and not mine own.

DEMETRIUS. Are you sure
That we are awake? It seems to me
That yet we sleep, we dream. Do not you think
The duke was here, and bid us follow him?

HERMIA. Yea; and my father.

HELENA. And Hippolyta.

LYSANDER. And he did bid us follow to the temple.

DEMETRIUS. Why, then, we are awake: let's follow him;
And by the way let us recount our dreams.

BOTTOM *(awaking)*. When my cue comes, call me, and I will answer. I have had a most rare vision. I have had a dream, past the wit of man to say what dream it was: man is but an ass if he go about to expound this dream. Methought I was—there is no man can tell what. Methought I was, and methought I had—but man is but a patched fool if he will offer to say what methought I had. The eye of man hath not heard, the ear of man hath not seen, man's hand is not able to taste, his tongue to conceive, nor his heart to report, what my dream was. I will get Peter Quince to write a ballad of this dream: it shall be called Bottom's Dream.

Scene 2—Quince's House in Athens

Enter Quince, Flute, Snout, and Starveling

QUINCE. Have you sent to Bottom's house? Is he come home?

STARVELING. He cannot be heard of. Out of doubt he is transported.

FLUTE. If he come not, then the play is marred: it goes not forward, doth it?

QUINCE. It is not possible: you have not a man in all Athens able to discharge Pyramus but he.

FLUTE. No, he hath simply the best wit of any handicraft man in Athens.

SNUG *(entering)*. Masters, the duke is coming from the temple, and there is two or three lords and ladies more married: if our sport had gone forward, we had all been made men.

FLUTE. O sweet bully Bottom! Thus hath he lost sixpence a day during his life; an the duke had not given him sixpence a day for playing Pyramus, I'll be hanged; he would have deserved it: sixpence a day in Pyramus, or nothing.

BOTTOM *(entering)*. Where are these lads? where are these hearts?

QUINCE. Bottom! O most courageous day! O most happy hour!

BOTTOM. Masters, I am to discourse wonders, but ask me not what; for if I tell you I am no true Athenian. I will tell you everything, right as it fell out.

QUINCE. Let us hear, sweet Bottom.

BOTTOM. Not a word of me. All that I will tell you is that the duke hath dined. Get your apparel together, good strings to your beards, new ribbons to your pumps; meet presently at the palace; every man look o'er his part; for the short and the long is, our play is preferred. In any case, let Thisby have clean linen; and let not him that plays the lion pare his nails, for they shall hang out for the lion's claws. No more words: away! go, away!

ACT 5

Scene 1—The Palace of Theseus

Enter Theseus, Hippolyta, Philostrate, and Attendants

HIPPOLYTA. Tis strange, my Theseus, that these lovers speak of.

THESEUS. More strange than true: I never may believe
These antique fables, nor these fairy toys.
Lovers and madmen have such seething brains,
Such shaping fantasies, that apprehend
More than cool reason ever comprehends.
The lunatic, the lover, and the poet
Are of imagination all compact:
The poet's eye, in a fine frenzy rolling,
Doth glance from heaven to earth, from earth to heaven;
And as imagination bodies forth
The forms of things unknown, the poet's pen
Turns them to shapes and gives to airy nothing
A local habitation and a name.
Such tricks hath strong imagination.

HIPPOLYTA. But all the story of the night told over,
And all their minds transfigured so together,
More witnesseth than fancy's images,
And grows to something of great constancy,
But, howsoever, strange and admirable.

THESEUS. Here come the lovers, full of joy and mirth.

Joy, gentle friends! joy and fresh days of love
Accompany your hearts!

LYSANDER. More than to us wait in your royal walks.

THESEUS. Come now; what masques, what dances shall we have,
To wear away this long age of three hours
Between our after-supper and bedtime?
Where is our usual manager of mirth?
What revels are in hand? Is there no play
To ease the anguish of a torturing hour?
What masque? what music? How shall we beguile
The lazy time, if not with some delight?

Philostrate gives him a list of entertainments

THESEUS *(reading). A tedious brief scene of young Pyramus
And his love Thisbe; very tragical mirth.*
Merry and tragical! tedious and brief!
That is, hot ice and wondrous strange snow.
How shall we find the concord of this discord?

PHILOSTRATE. A play there is, my lord, some ten words long,
Which is as brief as I have known a play;
But by ten words, my lord, it is too long,
Which makes it tedious; for in all the play
There is not one word apt, one player fitted:
And tragical, my noble lord, it is;
For Pyramus therein doth kill himself.
Which, when I saw rehearsed, I must confess,
Made mine eyes water; but more merry tears
The passion of loud laughter never shed.

THESEUS. What are they that do play it?

PHILOSTRATE. Hard-handed men that work in Athens here,
Which never laboured in their minds till now.

THESEUS. We will hear it.

PHILOSTRATE. No, my noble lord;
It is not for you: I have heard it over,
And it is nothing, nothing in the world,
Unless you can find sport in their intents.

THESEUS. I will hear that play;
For never anything can be amiss,
When simpleness and duty tender it.
Go, bring them in: and take your places, ladies.

HIPPOLYTA. I love not to see wretchedness o'ercharged
And duty in his service perishing.

THESEUS. Why, gentle sweet, you shall see no such thing.

HIPPOLYTA. He says they can do nothing in this kind.

THESEUS. The kinder we, to give them thanks for nothing.
Our sport shall be to take what they mistake.
Where I have come, great clerks have purposèd
To greet me with premeditated welcomes;
Where I have seen them shiver and look pale,
Make periods in the midst of sentences,
Throttle their practised accent in their fears,
And in conclusion dumbly have broke off,
Not paying me a welcome. Trust me, sweet,
Out of this silence yet I picked a welcome;
And in the modesty of fearful duty
I read as much as from the rattling tongue
Of saucy and audacious eloquence.
Love, therefore, and tongue-tied simplicity
In least speak most, to my capacity.

PHILOSTRATE. So please your grace, the Prologue is addressed.

THESEUS. Let him approach.

Enter Quince for the Prologue

PROLOGUE. If we offend, it is with our goodwill.
That you should think we come not to offend,
But with goodwill. To show our simple skill,
That is the true beginning of our end.
The actors are at hand, and by their show
You shall know all that you are like to know.

Enter Pyramus and Thisbe, Wall, Moonshine, and Lion

PROLOGUE. Gentles, perchance you wonder at this show;
But wonder on, till truth make all things plain.
This man is Pyramus, if you would know;
This beauteous lady Thisby is certain.
This man, with lime and rough-cast, doth present
Wall, that vile Wall which did these lovers sunder;
And through Wall's chink, poor souls, they are content
To whisper. At the which let no man wonder.
This man, with lanthorn, dog, and bush of thorn,
Presenteth Moonshine; for, if you will know,
By moonshine did these lovers think no scorn
To meet at Ninus' tomb, there, there to woo.
This grisly beast, which Lion is by name,
The trusty Thisby, coming first by night,
Did scare away, or rather did affright;
And, as she fled, her mantle she did fall,
Which Lion vile with bleeding mouth did stain.
Anon comes Pyramus, sweet youth and tall,
And finds his trusty Thisby's mantle slain:

His dagger drew, and died. For all the rest
Let Lion, Moonshine, Wall, and lovers twain
At large discourse, while here they do remain.

All but Wall go

THESEUS. I wonder if the lion be to speak.

DEMETRIUS. No wonder, my lord: one lion may, when many asses do.

WALL. In this same interlude it doth befall
That I, one Snout by name, present a wall;
And such a wall, as I would have you think,
That had in it a crannied hole or chink,
Through which the lovers, Pyramus and Thisby,
Did whisper often very secretly.
This loam, this rough-cast, and this stone doth show
That I am that same wall; the truth is so;
And this the cranny is, right and sinister,
Through which the fearful lovers are to whisper.

THESEUS. Would you desire lime and hair to speak better?

DEMETRIUS. It is the wittiest partition that ever I heard discourse, my lord.

THESEUS. Pyramus draws near the wall: silence!

PYRAMUS. O grim-looked night! O night with hue so black!
O night, which ever art when day is not!
O night, O night! alack, alack, alack,
I fear my Thisby's promise is forgot!
And thou, O wall, O sweet, O lovely wall,
That stand'st between her father's ground and mine!
Thou wall, O wall, O sweet and lovely wall,
Show me thy chink, to blink through with mine eyne!

Wall holds up his fingers

Thanks, courteous wall: Jove shield thee well for this!
But what see I? No Thisby do I see.
O wicked wall, through whom I see no bliss!
Cursed be thy stones for thus deceiving me!

THESEUS. The wall, methinks, being sensible, should curse again.

PYRAMUS. No, in truth, sir, he should not. *Deceiving me* is Thisby's cue: she is to enter now, and I am to spy her through the wall. You shall see; it will fall pat as I told you. Yonder she comes.

THISBE. O wall, full often hast thou heard my moans,
For parting my fair Pyramus and me!
My cherry lips have often kissed thy stones,
Thy stones with lime and hair knit up in thee.

PYRAMUS. I see a voice: now will I to the chink,
To spy an I can hear my Thisby's face. Thisby!

THISBE. My love thou art, my love I think.

PYRAMUS. Think what thou wilt, I am thy lover's grace;
And, like Limander, am I trusty still.

THISBE. And I like Helen, till the Fates me kill.

PYRAMUS. Not Shafalus to Procrus was so true.

THISBE. As Shafalus to Procrus, I to you.

PYRAMUS. O, kiss me through the hole of this vile wall!

THISBE. I kiss the wall's hole, not your lips at all.

PYRAMUS. Wilt thou at Ninny's tomb meet me straightway?

THISBE. 'Tide life, 'tide death, I come without delay. *(They leave)*

WALL. Thus have I, Wall, my part dischargèd so;
And, being done, thus Wall away doth go.

HIPPOLYTA. This is the silliest stuff that ever I heard.

THESEUS. If we imagine no worse of them than they of themselves, they may pass for excellent men. Here come two noble beasts in, a man and a lion.

LION. You, ladies, you, whose gentle hearts do fear
The smallest monstrous mouse that creeps on floor,
May now perchance both quake and tremble here,
When lion rough in wildest rage doth roar.
Then know that I, one Snug the joiner, am.

THESEUS. A very gentle beast, and of a good conscience.

DEMETRIUS. The very best at a beast, my lord, that e'er I saw.

LYSANDER. This lion is a very fox for his valour.

THESEUS. True; and a goose for his discretion.

MOONSHINE. This lanthorn doth the hornèd moon present;
Myself the man i' the moon do seem to be.

THESEUS. This is the greatest error of all the rest: the man should be put into the lanthorn. How is it else the man i' the moon?

HIPPOLYTA. I am a weary of this moon: would he would change!

THESEUS. It appears, by his small light of discretion, that he is in the wane; but yet, in courtesy, we must stay the time.

LYSANDER. Proceed, Moon.

MOONSHINE. All that I have to say is to tell you that the lanthorn is the moon; I, the man in the moon; this thorn-bush my thorn-bush; and this dog my dog.

DEMETRIUS. Why, all these should be in the lanthorn; for all these are in the moon. But, silence! here comes Thisbe.

THISBE. This is old Ninny's tomb. Where is my love?

LION *(roaring)*. Oh—— *(Thisbe runs)*

DEMETRIUS. Well roared, Lion.

THESEUS. Well run, Thisbe.

HIPPOLYTA. Well shone, Moon. Truly, the moon shines with a good grace. *(The Lion shakes Thisbe's mantle, and goes)*

THESEUS. Well moused, Lion.

LYSANDER. And so the lion vanished.

DEMETRIUS. And then came Pyramus.

PYRAMUS. Sweet Moon, I thank thee for thy sunny beams;
I thank thee, Moon, for shining now so bright;
For, by thy gracious, golden, glittering gleams,
I trust to take of truest Thisby sight.
But stay, O spite!
But mark, poor knight,
What dreadful dole is here!
Eyes, do you see?
How can it be?
O dainty duck! O dear!
Thy mantle good,
What, stained with blood!
Approach, ye Furies fell!
O Fates, come, come,
Cut thread and thrum;
Quail, crush, conclude, and quell!

THESEUS. This passion, and the death of a dear friend, would go near to make a man look sad.

HIPPOLYTA. Beshrew my heart, but I pity the man.

PYRAMUS. O wherefore, Nature, didst thou lions frame?
Since lion vile hath here deflowered my dear:
Which is—no, no—which was the fairest dame
That lived, that loved, that liked, that looked with cheer.
Come, tears, confound;
Out, sword, and wound.
Thus die I, thus, thus, thus.
Now am I dead,
Now am I fled;
My soul is in the sky:
Tongue, lose thy light;
Moon, take thy flight:
Now die, die, die, die, die.

HIPPOLYTA. How chance Moonshine is gone before Thisbe comes back and finds her lover?

THESEUS. She will find him by starlight. Here she comes; and her passion ends the play. *(Thisbe returns)*

HIPPOLYTA. Methinks she should not use a long one for such a Pyramus: I hope she will be brief.

DEMETRIUS. A mote will turn the balance, which Pyramus, which

Thisbe, is the better; he for a man, God warrant us; she for a woman, God bless us.

LYSANDER. She hath spied him already with those sweet eyes.

THISBE. Asleep, my love?
What, dead, my dove?
O Pyramus, arise!
Speak, speak. Quite dumb?
Dead, dead? A tomb
Must cover thy sweet eyes.
These lily lips,
This cherry nose,
These yellow cowslip cheeks,
Are gone, are gone:
Lovers, make moan:
His eyes were green as leeks.
O Sisters Three,
Come, come to me,
With hands as pale as milk,
Lay them in gore,
Since you have shore
With shears his thread of silk.
Tongue, not a word:
Come, trusty sword:
Come, blade, my breast imbrue:
And, farewell, friends;
Thus Thisby ends:
Adieu, adieu, adieu.

THESEUS. Moonshine and Lion are left to bury the dead.

DEMETRIUS. Ay, and Wall too.

BOTTOM *(starting up)*. No, I assure you; the wall is down that parted their fathers. Will it please you to see the epilogue, or to hear a Bergomask dance between two of our company?

THESEUS. No epilogue, I pray you; for your play needs no excuse.
But, come, your Bergomask: let your epilogue alone.
The iron tongue of midnight hath told twelve:
Lovers, to bed; tis almost fairy time.
I fear we shall out-sleep the coming morn
As much as we this night have overwatched.
This palpable-gross play hath well beguiled
The heavy gait of night. Sweet friends, to bed.
A fortnight hold we this solemnity,
In nightly revels and new jollity.

PUCK *entering* Now the hungry lion roars,
And the wolf behowls the moon;
Whilst the heavy ploughman snores,
All with weary task fordone.
Now the wasted brands do glow,
Whilst the screech-owl, screeching loud,

Puts the wretch that lies in woe
   In remembrance of a shroud.
Now it is the time of night
   That the graves all gaping wide,
Every one lets forth his sprite,
   In the church-way paths to glide:
And we fairies, that do run
   By the triple Hecate's team,
From the presence of the sun,
   Following darkness like a dream,
Now are frolic: not a mouse
Shall disturb this hallowed house:
I am sent with broom before,
To sweep the dust behind the door.

Oberon and Titania come with their train

OBERON. Through the house give glimmering light,
   By the dead and drowsy fire:
Every elf and fairy sprite
   Hop as light as bird from brier;
And this ditty, after me,
Sing, and dance it trippingly.

TITANIA. First rehearse your song by rote,
To each word a warbling note:
Hand in hand, with fairy grace,
Will we sing, and bless this place.

OBERON. Now, until the break of day,
Through this house each fairy stray.
So shall all the couples three
Ever true in loving be.
With this field-dew consecrate,
Every fairy take his gait;
And each several chamber bless,
Through this palace, with sweet peace;
And the owner of it blest
Ever shall in safety rest.
Trip away; make no stay;
Meet me all by break of day.

PUCK. If we shadows have offended,
Think but this, and all is mended,
That you have but slumbered here
While these visions did appear.
And this weak and idle theme,
No more yielding but a dream,
Gentles, do not reprehend:
If you pardon, we will mend:
And, as I'm an honest Puck,
If we have unearnèd luck
Now to scape the serpent's tongue,
We will make amends ere long.

The Story of King John

IT may always bring a little regret to us that Shakespeare put a few of his finest words on England into this picture of her most unworthy sovereign; yet the noble words of Philip Faulconbridge close well this play, in which our country is seen to be passing through some of its darkest days.

SHAKESPEARE took this piece of English history from an unknown play he saw in his youth. It is not one of the greatest of his plays, but it is a precious piece of our nation's life, for it shows us what things were really like about seven hundred years ago.

THEN a man like John could come to the throne of England, could seize the throne from his young nephew, and seek to put out his nephew's eyes. Strange it is that so exquisite a figure as this little prince should come into so terrible a play. It was Shakespeare's way to make it so; heroes and villains mix on his stage as on the highway of the world.

MANY things will be forgotten in Shakespeare as the centuries roll on, but the picture of Arthur and Hubert will never cease to bring tears to the eye. We know that Hubert de Burgh was one of the few great men of his time. From that June day in 1215 when John signed Magna Carta in a rage, the Hubert of this play was one of the virtual rulers of the realm. But it is in literature and not in history that he lives. He lives as the gaoler of Arthur in Brittany.

SHAKESPEARE has given us no more moving scene than that in which this gentle lad, the true heir to the throne, pleads with Hubert for his eyes, "These eyes that never did nor never shall so much as frown on you." As tender a scene it is as Shakespeare himself could paint with all his power of words, and it thrills us to see the heart of Hubert moved from the dark deed to which his King had set his hand.

ONE more fine Englishman dominates this stage. Fearing nobody and speaking his mind about all that happens, he expressed the instinctive feeling of an honest plain man. He is Philip Faulconbridge. We feel all the time that he and Hubert have the spirit of England in their keeping, whatever the wretched John may do.

THEY make us feel, in spite of all the plots and treacheries and crimes of that foul reign, that there was something worth preserving yet in this England that

never did nor never shall
Lie at the proud foot of a conqueror,
But when it first did help to wound itself.

The play ends on those famous words, "Naught shall make us rue, if England to itself do rest but true." All these years England was not true to itself, but we see that her spirit was alive and was bound to live, and she has famously and greatly endured.

THE PLAYERS

John, King of England. Clever, dishonourable, never prospering.

Prince Henry, John's son, succeeding his father in the last scene.

Arthur, Duke of Bretagne. John's young nephew, heir to the throne as son of John's brother. The best character in the play.

Pembroke and Salisbury, two English earls, who distrust and desert the King, and then rejoin him.

Lord Bigot, an English nobleman, who acts with Pembroke and Salisbury.

Hubert de Burgh, John's Chamberlain. A fine character, too honourable to do the bidding of the infamous John.

Philip Faulconbridge, knighted as Sir Richard Plantagenet; enters the service of Queen Elinor, and becomes the most successful English leader.

Peter of Pomfret, a man pretending to foretell the future.

Philip, King of France. A man devoted to his own interests.

Lewis the Dauphin, heir to the throne of France. A young man of some vigour and spirit.

Lymoges, Archduke of Austria. A man false to his word, and a special enemy of Philip Faulconbridge.

Cardinal Pandulf, representative of the Pope, bending all other men's wills to his.

Melun, a lord of France, honourable, exposing treachery.

Chatillon, a plain-speaking French ambassador.

Queen Elinor, John's mother, sudden and quick in quarrel.

Constance, Arthur's mother, passionately defending his rights.

Blanch of Spain, John's niece, married to the Dauphin as part of a bargain.

Lords, citizens, heralds, officers, soldiers, messengers.

SCENES—Partly in England and partly in France

King John

ACT 1

Scene 1—King John's Palace

King John with Queen Elinor receives the French Ambassador

JOHN. Now, say, Chatillon, what would France with us ?

CHATILLON. Thus, after greeting, speaks the King of France
In my behaviour to the majesty,
The borrowed majesty, of England here.

ELINOR. A strange beginning—*borrowed majesty :*

JOHN. Silence, good mother ; hear the embassy.

CHATILLON. Philip of France, in right and true behalf
Of thy deceasèd brother Geffrey's son,
Arthur Plantagenet, lays most lawful claim
To this fair island and the territories,
To Ireland, Poictiers, Anjou, Touraine, Maine,
Desiring thee to lay aside the sword
Which sways usurpingly these several titles,
And put the same into young Arthur's hand,
Thy nephew and right royal sovereign.

JOHN. What follows if we disallow of this ?

CHATILLON. The proud control of war,
To enforce these rights so forcibly withheld.

JOHN. Here have we war for war and blood for blood,
Controlment for controlment : so answer France.

CHATILLON. Then take my king's defiance from my mouth,
The farthest limit of my embassy.

JOHN. Bear mine to him, and so depart in peace.
Be thou as lightning in the eyes of France,
For ere thou canst report I will be there ;
The thunder of my cannon shall be heard. *(The Ambassador leaves)*

ELINOR. What now, my son ! Have I not ever said
How that ambitious Constance would not cease
Till she had kindled France and all the world,
Upon the right and party of her son ?
This might have been prevented and made whole
With very easy arguments of love.

JOHN. Our strong possession and our right for us.

ELINOR. Your strong possession much more than your right,
Or else it must go wrong with you and me:
So much my conscience whispers in your ear,
Which none but heaven and you and I shall hear.

A Sheriff now introduces Philip Faulconbridge and his brother Robert, who crave the King's judgment as to an estate which both claim. It is discovered that Plantagenet blood runs in Philip's veins, and the King and his mother trace in his bold demeanour something of the audacious courage of Richard Coeur de Lion. So, although the King decides in favour of Philip, the Queen's heart yearns towards him because he recalls to her the form and bearing of the dead Richard. "I like thee well," she tells him, and asks him if he will give his land to his brother and follow her. "I am a soldier, and now bound to France," she adds. Philip chooses instantly. "Madam, I'll follow you unto the death," he says, and the King knights him Sir Richard Plantagenet. So the fearless and adventurous suitor becomes knight, courtier, soldier, and counsellor.

ACT 2

Scene 1—At the Gate of Angiers

The King of France enters with Austria, Lewis, Arthur, and Constance

LEWIS. Before Angiers well met, brave Austria.
Arthur, that great forerunner of thy blood,
Richard, that robbed the lion of his heart
And fought the holy wars in Palestine,
By this brave duke came early to his grave:
And for amends to his posterity,
At our importance hither is he come,
To spread his colours, boy, in thy behalf
And to rebuke the usurpation
Of thy unnatural uncle, English John:
Embrace him, love him, give him welcome hither.

ARTHUR. God shall forgive you Coeur de Lion's death
The rather that you give his offspring life,
Shadowing their right under your wings of war:
I give you welcome with a powerless hand,
But with a heart full of unstainèd love:
Welcome before the gates of Angiers, duke.

LEWIS. A noble boy! Who would not do thee right?

AUSTRIA. Upon thy cheek lay I this zealous kiss,
As seal to this indenture of my love,
That to my home I will no more return,
Till Angiers and the right thou hast in France,
Together with that pale, that white-faced shore,
Whose foot spurns back the ocean's roaring tides
Salute thee for her king: till then, fair boy,
Will I not think of home, but follow arms.

Constance. O, take his mother's thanks, a widow's thanks,
Till your strong hand shall help to give him strength
To make a more requital to your love!

Austria. The peace of heaven is theirs that lift their swords
In such a just and charitable war.

Philip. Well then, to work: our cannon shall be bent
Against the brows of this resisting town.
We'll lay before this town our royal bones,
Wade to the marketplace in Frenchmen's blood,
But we will make it subject to this boy.

Constance. Stay for an answer to your embassy,
Lest unadvised you stain your swords with blood.
My Lord Chatillon may from England bring
That right in peace which here we urge in war,
And then we shall repent each drop of blood
That hot rash haste so indirectly shed. *(Chatillon enters)*

Philip. A wonder, lady! lo, upon thy wish,
Our messenger Chatillon is arrived!
What England says, say briefly, gentle lord.

The Ambassador reports that the English forces are arriving immediately, and the drums beat as he speaks, signalling the entry of John and his Queen, with Faulconbridge and their power. The French King offers peace if John will resign the throne in favour of Arthur, his brother Geffrey's son, to whom it rightly belongs.

John. From whom hast thou this great commission, France?

Philip. From that supernal judge that stirs good thoughts
In any breast of strong authority,
To look into the blots and stains of right:
That judge hath made me guardian to this boy:
Under whose warrant I impeach thy wrong
And by whose help I mean to chastise it.

John. Alack, thou dost usurp authority.

Philip. Excuse; it is to beat usurping down.

Elinor. Who is it thou dost call usurper, France?

Constance. Let me make answer: *thy usurping son.*

Austria. Peace!

Faulconbridge. Hear the crier.

Blanch. O, well did he become that lion's robe
That did disrobe the lion of that robe!

Faulconbridge. It lies as sightly on the back of him
As great Alcides' shows upon an ass:
But, ass, I'll take that burthen from your back,
Or lay on that shall make your shoulders crack.

AUSTRIA. What cracker is this same that deafs our ears
With this abundance of superfluous breath?

PHILIP. Lewis, determine what we shall do straight.

LEWIS. Women and fools, break off your conference.
King John, this is the very sum of all;
England and Ireland, Anjou, Touraine, Maine,
In right of Arthur do I claim of thee:
Wilt thou resign them and lay down thy arms?

JOHN. My life as soon: I do defy thee, France.
Arthur of Bretagne, yield thee to my hand,
And out of my dear love I'll give thee more
Than e'er the coward hand of France can win:
Submit thee, boy.

ELINOR. Come to thy grandam, child.

CONSTANCE. Do, child, go to grandam, child;
Give grandam kingdom, and grandam will
Give it a plum, a cherry, and a fig:
There's a good grandam.

ARTHUR. Good my mother, peace!
I would that I were low laid in my grave:
I am not worth this coil that's made for me.

ELINOR. His mother shames him so, poor boy, he weeps.

CONSTANCE. Now shame upon you, whether she does or no!
His grandam's wrongs, and not his mother's shames,
Draws those heaven-moving pearls from his poor eyes,
Which heaven shall take in nature of a fee;
Ay, with these crystal beads heaven shall be bribed
To do him justice and revenge on you.

ELINOR. Thou monstrous slanderer of heaven and earth!

CONSTANCE. Thou monstrous injurer of heaven and earth!
Call not me slanderer; thou and thine usurp
The dominations, royalties, and rights
Of this oppressèd boy: this is thy son's son,
Unfortunate in nothing but in thee.

JOHN. Beldam, have done.

ELINOR. Thou unadvisèd scold, I can produce
A will that bars the title of thy son.

CONSTANCE. Ay, who doubts that? a will! a wicked will;
A woman's will; a cankered grandam's will.

PHILIP. Peace, lady! pause, or be more temperate:
Some trumpet summon hither to the walls
These men of Angiers: let us hear them speak
Whose title they admit, Arthur's or John's.

A trumpet sounds, and citizens appear upon the walls

CITIZEN. Who is it that hath warned us to the walls?
PHILIP. Tis France, for England.
JOHN. England, for itself.
You men of Angiers, and my loving subjects—
PHILIP. You loving men of Angiers, Arthur's subjects,
Our trumpet called you to this gentle parle—
JOHN. For our advantage; therefore hear us first.
These flags of France, that are advancèd here
Before the eye and prospect of your town,
Have hither marched to your endamagement.
The cannons have their bowels full of wrath,
And ready mounted are they to spit forth
Their iron indignation 'gainst your walls;
And but for our approach those sleeping stones
By this time from their fixèd beds of lime
Had been dishabited, and wide havoc made
For power to rush upon your peace.
But on the sight of us, your lawful king,
Who painfully with much expedient march
Have brought a countercheck before your gates,
To save unscratched your city's threatened cheeks,
Behold, the French, amazed, vouchsafe a parle;
And now, instead of bullets wrapped in fire,
To make a shaking fever in your walls,
They shoot but calm words folded up in smoke,
To make a faithless error in your ears:
Which trust accordingly, kind citizens,
And let us in, your king.
PHILIP. When I have said, make answer to us both.
Lo, in this right hand, whose protection
Is most divinely vowed upon the right
Of him it holds, stands young Plantagenet,
Son to the elder brother of this man,
And king o'er him and all that he enjoys:
For this down-trodden equity we tread
In warlike march these greens before your town,
Being no farther enemy to you
Than the constraint of hospitable zeal
In the relief of this oppressèd child
Religiously provokes. Be pleasèd then
To pay that duty which you truly owe
To him that owns it, namely this young prince.
Or shall we give the signal to our rage
And stalk in blood to our possession?
CITIZEN. In brief, we are the king of England's subjects;
For him, and in his right, we hold this town.

JOHN. Acknowledge then the king, and let me in.

CITIZEN. That can we not; but he that proves the king,
To him will we prove loyal: till that time
Have we rammed up our gates against the world.

JOHN. Doth not the crown of England prove the king?
And if not that, I bring you witnesses,
Twice fifteen thousand hearts of England's breed,
To verify our title with their lives.

PHILIP. As many and as well-born bloods as those
Stand in his face to contradict his claim.

CITIZEN. Till you compound whose right is worthiest,
We for the worthiest hold the right from both.

JOHN. Then God forgive the sin of all those souls
That to their everlasting residence,
Before the dew of evening fall, shall fleet,
In dreadful trial of our kingdom's king!

After inconclusive fighting, first a French herald and then an English herald appear before the walls. Each claims victory for his side. Next come the kings, with equal pretensions, demanding the city and its allegiance as before. The Citizens, having watched the battle from the walls and witnessed the mutual withdrawal, still refuse to open the gates to a king of England until they know by victory who the King of England is. This brings a wrathful outburst from Faulconbridge, who begins: "By heaven, these scroyles of Angiers flout you, kings," and he proposes that the two kings join forces to overcome the city and then fight each other for its possession. The kings "like it well" and are about to begin when the citizens make a new proposal.

CITIZEN. Hear us, great kings: vouchsafe awhile to stay,
And I shall show you peace and fair-faced league;
Win you this city without stroke or wound;
Rescue those breathing lives to die in beds
That here come sacrifices for the field:
Persevèr not, but hear me, mighty kings.

JOHN. Speak on with favour; we are bent to hear.

CITIZEN. That daughter there of Spain, the Lady Blanch,
Is niece to England: look upon the years
Of Lewis the Dauphin and that lovely maid:
If lusty love should go in quest of beauty,
Where should he find it fairer than in Blanch?
If zealous love should go in search of virtue,
Where should he find it purer than in Blanch?
If love ambitious sought a match of birth,
Whose veins bound richer blood than Lady Blanch?
Such as she is, in beauty, virtue, birth,
Is the young Dauphin every way complete.

This union shall do more than battery can
To our fast-closèd gates; but without this match,
The sea enragèd is not half so deaf,
Lions more confident, mountains and rocks
More free from motion, no, not Death himself
In mortal fury half so peremptory,
As we to keep this city.

ELINOR. Son, list to this conjunction, make this match;
Give with our niece a dowry large enough:
For by this knot thou shalt so surely tie
Thy now unsured assurance to the crown,
That yon green boy shall have no sun to ripe
The bloom that promiseth a mighty fruit.
I see a yielding in the looks of France;
Mark, how they whisper: urge them while their souls
Are capable of this ambition,
Lest zeal, now melted by the windy breath
Of soft petitions, pity, and remorse,
Cool and congeal again to what it was.

CITIZEN. Why answer not the double majesties
This friendly treaty of our threatened town?

PHILIP. Speak England first, that hath been forward first
To speak unto this city; what say you?

JOHN. If that the Dauphin there, thy princely son,
Can in this book of beauty read *I love,*
Her dowry shall weigh equal with a queen:
For Anjou and fair Touraine, Maine, Poictiers,
And all that we upon this side the sea,
Except this city now by us besieged,
Find liable to our crown and dignity,
Shall make her rich
In titles, honours, and promotions,
As she in beauty, education, blood,
Holds hand with any princess of the world.

PHILIP. What say'st thou, boy? look in the lady's face.

LEWIS. I do, my lord; and in her eye I find
A wonder, or a wondrous miracle,
The shadow of myself formed in her eye;
I do protest I never loved myself
Till now infixèd I beheld myself
Drawn in the flattering table of her eye.

BLANCH *(to Lewis)*. My uncle's will in this respect is mine:
If he see aught in you that makes him like,
I will enforce it easily to my love.
Farther I will not flatter you, my lord,

That all I see in you is worthy love,
Than this: that nothing do I see in you
That I can find should merit any hate.

JOHN. What say these young ones? What say you, my niece?

BLANCH. That she is bound in honour still to do
What you in wisdom still vouchsafe to say.

JOHN. Speak then, prince Dauphin; can you love this lady?

LEWIS. Nay, ask me if I can refrain from love;
For I do love her most unfeignedly.

JOHN. Then do I give Volquessen, Touraine, Maine,
Poictiers and Anjou, these five provinces,
With her to thee, and this addition more,
Full thirty thousand marks of English coin.
Philip of France, if thou be pleased withal,
Command thy son and daughter to join hands.

PHILIP. It likes us well; young princes, close your hands.
Now, citizens of Angiers, ope your gates,
Let in that amity which you have made,
For at Saint Mary's chapel presently
The rites of marriage shall be solemnised.
Is not the Lady Constance in this troop?
I know she is not, for this match made up
Her presence would have interrupted much:
Where is she and her son? tell me, who knows.

LEWIS. She is sad and passionate at your highness' tent.

PHILIP. And, by my faith, this league that we have made
Will give her sadness very little cure.
Brother of England, how may we content
This widow lady? In her right we came;
Which we, God knows, have turned another way,
To our own vantage.

JOHN. We will heal up all;
For we'll create young Arthur Duke of Bretagne
And Earl of Richmond; and this rich fair town
We make him lord of. Call the Lady Constance;
Some speedy messenger bid her repair
To our solemnity: I trust we shall,
If not fill up the measure of her will,
Yet in some measure satisfy her so
That we shall stop her exclamation.
Go we, as well as haste will suffer us,
To this unlooked for, unpreparèd pomp.

All leave except Faulconbridge

FAULCONBRIDGE. Mad world! mad kings! mad composition!
John, to stop Arthur's title in the whole,

Hath willingly departed with a part,
And France, whose armour conscience buckled on,
Whom zeal and charity brought to the field
As God's own soldier, rounded in the ear
With that same purpose-changer, that sly devil,
That daily break-vow, he that wins of all,
Of kings, of beggars, old men, young men, maids,
That smooth-faced gentleman, tickling Commodity,
This sway of motion, this Commodity,
Hath drawn him from his own determined aid,
From a resolved and honourable war,
To a most base and vile-concluded peace.
And why rail I on this Commodity?
But for because he hath not wooed me yet:
Not that I have the power to clutch my hand,
When his fair angels would salute my palm;
But for my hand, as unattempted yet,
Like a poor beggar, raileth on the rich.
Well, whiles I am a beggar, I will rail
And say there is no sin but to be rich;
And being rich, my virtue then shall be
To say there is no vice but beggary.
Since kings break faith upon commodity,
Gain, be my lord, for I will worship thee.

ACT 3

Scene 1—The Pavilion of the French King

Enter Constance and Arthur, to whom Salisbury has brought news

CONSTANCE. Gone to be married! gone to swear a peace!
False blood to false blood joined! gone to be friends!
Shall Lewis have Blanch, and Blanch those provinces?
It is not so; thou hast misspoke, misheard;
Be well advised, tell o'er thy tale again:
It cannot be; thou dost but say tis so:
I trust I may not trust thee; for thy word
Is but the vain breath of a common man:
Believe me, I do not believe thee, man;
I have a king's oath to the contrary.
Thou shalt be punished for thus frighting me,
For I am sick and capable of fears,
Oppressed with wrongs and therefore full of fears,
A widow, husbandless, subject to fears,
A woman, naturally born to fears;
And, though thou now confess thou didst but jest,
With my vexed spirits I cannot take a truce,
But they will quake and tremble all this day.

Then speak again; not all thy former tale,
But this one word, whether thy tale be true.

SALISBURY. As true as I believe you think them false.
That give you cause to prove my saying true.

CONSTANCE. O, if thou teach me to believe this sorrow,
Teach thou this sorrow how to make me die.
Lewis marry Blanch! O boy, then where art thou?
France friend with England, what becomes of me?
Fellow, be gone: I cannot brook thy sight:
This news hath made thee a most ugly man.

ARTHUR. I do beseech you, madam, be content.

CONSTANCE. If thou, that bid'st me be content, wert grim,
Full of unpleasing blots and sightless stains,
I would not care, I then would be content,
For then I should not love thee, no, nor thou
Become thy great birth nor deserve a crown.
But thou art fair, and at thy birth, dear boy,
Nature and Fortune joined to make thee great:
Of Nature's gifts thou mayst with lilies boast
And with the half-blown rose.
Tell me, thou fellow, is not France forsworn?
Envenom him with words, or get thee gone.

SALISBURY. Pardon me, madam,
I may not go without you to the kings.

CONSTANCE. Thou mayst, thou shalt; I will not go with thee:
I will instruct my sorrows to be proud;
For grief is proud and makes his owner stoop.
To me and to the state of my great grief
Let kings assemble; for my grief's so great
That no supporter but the huge firm earth
Can hold it up. Here I and sorrows sit;
Here is my throne, bid kings come bow to it.

She seats herself on the ground. Enter King John, King Philip, Lewis, Blanch, Elinor, Faulconbridge, Austria, and Attendants.

PHILIP. Tis true, fair daughter; and this blessèd day
Ever in France shall be kept festival:
To solemnise this day the glorious sun
Stays in his course and plays the alchemist,
Turning with splendour of his precious eye
The meagre cloddy earth to glittering gold;
The yearly course that brings this day about
Shall never see it but a holiday.

CONSTANCE. A wicked day, and not a holy day!
What hath this day deserved? what hath it done,
That it in golden letters should be set

Among the high tides in the calendar?
Nay, rather turn this day out of the week,
This day of shame, oppression, perjury.
This day all things begun come to ill end,
Yea, faith itself to hollow falsehood change!

PHILIP. By heaven, lady, you shall have no cause
To curse the fair proceedings of this day:
Have I not pawned to you my majesty?

CONSTANCE. You have beguiled me with a counterfeit
Resembling majesty, which, being touched and tried,
Proves valueless: you are forsworn, forsworn;
You came in arms to spill mine enemies' blood
But now in arms you strengthen it with yours:
The grappling vigour and rough frown of war
Is cold in amity and painted peace,
And our oppression hath made up this league.
Arm, arm, you heavens, against these perjured kings!
A widow cries; be husband to me, heavens!
Let not the hours of this ungodly day
Wear out the day in peace; but, ere sunset,
Set armèd discord 'twixt these perjured kings!

AUSTRIA. Lady Constance, peace!

CONSTANCE. War! war! no peace! O Austria! thou dost shame
That spoil: thou slave, thou wretch, thou coward!
Thou little valiant, great in villainy!
Thou ever strong upon the stronger side!
Thou Fortune's champion that dost never fight
But when her humorous ladyship is by
To teach thee safety! thou art perjured too,
And sooth'st up greatness. Thou cold-blooded slave,
Hast thou not spoke like thunder on my side,
Been sworn my soldier, bidding me depend
Upon thy stars, thy fortune, and thy strength,
And dost thou now fall over to my foes?
Thou wear a lion's hide! doff it for shame,
And hang a calf's-skin on those recreant limbs.

AUSTRIA. O, that a man should speak those words to me!

FAULCONBRIDGE. And hang a calf's-skin on those recreant limbs.

AUSTRIA. Thou darest not say so, villain, for thy life.

FAULCONBRIDGE. And hang a calf's-skin on those recreant limbs.

JOHN. We like not this; thou dost forget thyself.

PHILIP. Here comes the holy legate of the pope.

PANDULF *(entering)*. Hail, you anointed deputies of heaven!
To thee, King John, my holy errand is.

I Pandulf, of fair Milan cardinal,
And from Pope Innocent the legate here,
Do in his name religiously demand
Why thou against the church, our holy mother,
So wilfully dost spurn; and force perforce
Keep Stephen Langton, chosen archbishop
Of Canterbury, from that holy see?

JOHN. What earthly name to interrogatories
Can task the free breath of a sacred king?
Thou canst not, cardinal, devise a name
So slight, unworthy, and ridiculous,
To charge me to an answer, as the pope.
Tell him this tale, and from the mouth of England
Add thus much more—that no Italian priest
Shall tithe or toll in our dominions;
But as we, under heaven, are supreme head,
So under Him that great supremacy,
Where we do reign, we will alone uphold,
Without the assistance of a mortal hand:
So tell the pope, all reverence set apart
To him and his usurped authority.

PHILIP. Brother of England, you blaspheme in this.

JOHN. Though you and all the kings of Christendom
Are led so grossly by this meddling priest,
Dreading the curse that money may buy out;
And by the merit of vile gold, dross, dust,
Purchase corrupted pardon of a man,
Who in that sale sells pardon from himself:
Though you and all the rest so grossly led
This juggling witchcraft with revènue cherish,
Yet I alone, alone do me oppose
Against the pope, and count his friends my foes.

PANDULF. Then, by the lawful power that I have,
Thou shalt stand cursed and excommunicate:
And blessèd shall he be that doth revolt
From his allegiance to a heretic;
And meritorious shall that hand be called,
Canonised and worshipped as a saint,
That takes away by any secret course
Thy hateful life.

CONSTANCE. O, lawful let it be
That I have room with Rome to curse awhile!
Good father cardinal, cry thou amen
To my keen curses; for without my wrong
There is no tongue hath power to curse him right.

PANDULF. There's law and warrant, lady, for my curse.

CONSTANCE. And for mine too : when law can do no right
Let it be lawful that law bar no wrong :
Law cannot give my child his kingdom here,
For he that holds his kingdom holds the law ;
Therefore, since law itself is perfect wrong,
How can the law forbid my tongue to curse ?

PANDULF. Philip of France, on peril of a curse,
Let go the hand of that arch-heretic ;
And raise the power of France upon his head,
Unless he do submit himself to Rome.

ELINOR. Look'st thou pale, France ? Do not let go thy hand.

AUSTRIA. King Philip, listen to the cardinal.

JOHN. Philip, what say'st thou to the cardinal ?

PHILIP. I am perplexed, and know not what to say.
Good reverend father, make my person yours,
And tell me how you would bestow yourself.
This royal hand and mine are newly knit,
And the conjunction of our inward souls
Married in league, coupled and linked together
With all religious strength of sacred vows ;
The latest breath that gave the sound of words
Was deep-sworn faith, peace, amity, true love
Between our kingdoms and our royal selves,
And shall these hands, so lately purged of blood,
So newly joined in love, so strong in both,
Unyoke this seizure and this kind regreet ?
Play fast and loose with faith ? so jest with heaven,
Make such unconstant children of ourselves,
As now again to snatch our palm from palm,
And make a riot on the gentle brow
Of true sincerity ? O, holy sir,
My reverend father, let it not be so !
Out of your grace devise, ordain, impose
Some gentle order ; and then we shall be blest
To do your pleasure and continue friends.

PANDULF. All form is formless, order orderless,
Save what is opposite to England's love.
Therefore to arms ! be champion of our church,
Or let the church, our mother, breathe her curse,
A mother's curse, on her revolting son.
France, thou mayst hold a serpent by the tongue,
A chafèd lion by the mortal paw,
A fasting tiger safer by the tooth,
Than keep in peace that hand which thou dost hold.
It is religion that doth make vows kept.

LEWIS. Father, to arms!

BLANCH. Upon thy wedding-day?
Against the blood that thou hast married?
What, shall our feast be kept with slaughtered men?
Shall braying trumpets and loud churlish drums,
Clamours of hell, be measures to our pomp?
O husband, hear me! ay, alack, how new
Is husband in my mouth! even for that name,
Which till this time my tongue did ne'er pronounce,
Upon my knee I beg, go not to arms
Against mine uncle.

CONSTANCE. O, upon my knee,
Made hard with kneeling, I do pray to thee,
Thou virtuous Dauphin, alter not the doom
Forethought by heaven!

BLANCH. Now shall I see thy love: what motive may
Be stronger with thee than the name of wife?

CONSTANCE. That which upholdeth him that thee upholds,
His honour: O, thine honour, Lewis, thine honour!

LEWIS. I muse your majesty doth seem so cold,
When such profound respects do pull you on.

PANDULF. I will denounce a curse upon his head.

PHILIP. Thou shalt not need. England, I will fall from thee.

CONSTANCE. O fair return of banished majesty!

ELINOR. O foul revolt of French inconstancy!

JOHN. France, thou shalt rue this hour within this hour.

BLANCH. The sun's o'ercast with blood: fair day, adieu!
Which is the side that I must go withal?
I am with both: each army hath a hand;
And in their rage, I having hold of both,
They whirl asunder and dismember me.
Husband, I cannot pray that thou mayst win;
Uncle, I needs must pray that thou mayst lose;
Father, I may not wish the fortune thine;
Grandam, I will not wish thy wishes thrive:
Whoever wins, on that side shall I lose;
Assurèd loss before the match be played.

LEWIS. Lady, with me, with me thy fortune lies.

BLANCH. There where my fortune lives, there my life dies.

JOHN. France, I am burned up with inflaming wrath;
A rage whose heat hath this condition,
That nothing can allay, nothing but blood,
The blood, and dearest-valued blood, of France.

PHILIP. Thy rage shall burn thee up, and thou shalt turn
To ashes, ere our blood shall quench that fire :
Look to thyself, thou art in jeopardy.

JOHN. No more than he that threats. To arms let's hie !

Scene 2—Plains around Angiers

Faulconbridge enters from the battlefield, having slain the Duke of Austria. John, Arthur, and Hubert approach.

JOHN. Hubert, keep this boy. Philip, make up :
My mother is assailèd in our tent,
And ta'en, I fear.

FAULCONBRIDGE. My lord, I rescued her ;
Her highness is in safety, fear you not :
But on, my liege ; for very little pains
Will bring this labour to an happy end.

Scene 3—The Battlefield

Enter John, Elinor, Arthur, Faulconbridge, and Hubert

JOHN *(to Elinor)*. So shall it be ; your grace shall stay behind
So strongly guarded. *(To Arthur)* Cousin, look not sad :
Thy grandam loves thee ; and thy uncle will
As dear be to thee as thy father was.

ARTHUR. O, this will make my mother die with grief !

JOHN *(to Faulconbridge)*. Cousin, away for England ! haste before,
And, ere our coming, see thou shake the bags
Of hoarding abbots ; imprisoned angels
Set at liberty : the fat ribs of peace
Must by the hungry now be fed upon :
Use our commission in his utmost force.

FAULCONBRIDGE. Bell, book, and candle shall not drive me back,
When gold and silver becks me to come on.
I leave your highness. Grandam, I will pray,
If ever I remember to be holy,
For your fair safety ; so, I kiss your hand.

ELINOR. Farewell, gentle cousin.

JOHN. Coz, farewell. *(Faulconbridge leaves)*

ELINOR. Come hither, little kinsman ; hark, a word.

JOHN. Come hither, Hubert. O my gentle Hubert,
We owe thee much ! within this wall of flesh
There is a soul counts thee her creditor
And with advantage means to pay thy love :
And, my good friend, thy voluntary oath
Lives in this bosom, dearly cherishèd.
Give me thy hand. I had a thing to say,

But I will fit it with some better time.
By heaven, Hubert, I am almost ashamed
To say what good respect I have of thee.

HUBERT. I am much bounden to your majesty.

JOHN. Good friend, thou hast no cause to say so yet,
But thou shalt have; and, creep time ne'er so slow,
Yet it shall come for me to do thee good.
I had a thing to say, but let it go:
I would into thy bosom pour my thoughts,
But, ah, I will not! yet I love thee well;
And, by my troth, I think thou lovest me well.

HUBERT. So well that what you bid me undertake,
Though that my death were adjunct to my act,
By heaven, I would do it.

JOHN. Do not I know thou wouldst?
Good Hubert, Hubert, Hubert, throw thine eye
On yon young boy: I'll tell thee what, my friend,
He is a very serpent in my way,
And wheresoe'er this foot of mine doth tread
He lies before me: dost thou understand me?
Thou art his keeper.

HUBERT. And I'll keep him so,
That he shall not offend your majesty.

JOHN. Death.

HUBERT. My lord?

JOHN. A grave.

HUBERT. He shall not live.

JOHN. Enough.
I could be merry now. Hubert, I love thee;
Well, I'll not say what I intend for thee:
Remember. Madam, fare you well:
I'll send those powers o'er to your majesty.

ELINOR. My blessing go with thee!

JOHN. For England, cousin, go:
Hubert shall be your man, attend on you
With all true duty. On toward Calais, ho!

Scene 4—The French King's Pavilion

Enter King Philip, Lewis the Dauphin, and Cardinal Pandulf

PHILIP. So, by a roaring tempest on the flood,
A whole armado of convicted sail
Is scattered and disjoined from fellowship.

PANDULF. Courage and comfort! all shall yet go well.

PHILIP. What can go well, when we have run so ill?
Are we not beaten? Is not Angiers lost?
Arthur ta'en prisoner? divers dear friends slain?

LEWIS. Who hath read or heard
Of any kindred action like to this?

PHILIP. Look, who comes here! a grave unto a soul,
Holding the eternal spirit, against her will,
In the vile prison of afflicted breath.
I prithee, lady, go away with me.

CONSTANCE. Lo, now! now see the issue of your peace.

PHILIP. Patience, good lady! comfort, gentle Constance!

CONSTANCE. No, I defy all counsel, all redress,
But that which ends all counsel, true redress,
Death, death; O amiable lovely death,
O, come to me!

PHILIP. O fair affliction, peace!

CONSTANCE. No, no, I will not, having breath to cry:
O, that my tongue were in the thunder's mouth!
Then with a passion would I shake the world.

PANDULF. Lady, you utter madness, and not sorrow.

CONSTANCE. Thou art not holy to belie me so;
I am not mad: this hair I tear is mine;
My name is Constance; I was Geffrey's wife;
Young Arthur is my son, and he is lost:
I am not mad: I would to heaven I were,
For then, tis like I should forget myself:
O, if I could, what grief should I forget!

PHILIP. Bind up your hairs.

CONSTANCE. Yes, that I will; and wherefore will I do it?
I tore them from their bonds and cried aloud,
O that these hands could so redeem my son,
As they have given these hairs their liberty!
But now I envy at their liberty,
And will again commit them to their bonds,
Because my poor child is a prisoner.
And, father cardinal, I have heard you say
That we shall see and know our friends in heaven:
If that be true I shall see my boy again,
For since the birth of Cain, the first male child,
There was not such a gracious creature born.
But now will canker-sorrow eat my bud
And chase the native beauty from his cheek
And he will look as hollow as a ghost,

As dim and meagre as an ague's fit,
And so he'll die ; and, rising so again,
When I shall meet him in the court of heaven
I shall not know him : therefore never, never
Must I behold my pretty Arthur more.

PANDULF. You hold too heinous a respect of grief.

CONSTANCE. He talks to me that never had a son.

PHILIP. You are as fond of grief as of your child.

CONSTANCE. Grief fills the room up of my absent child,
Lies in his bed, walks up and down with me,
Puts on his pretty looks, repeats his words,
Remembers me of all his gracious parts,
Stuffs out his vacant garments with his form ;
Then, have I reason to be fond of grief ?
Fare you well : had you such a loss as I
I could give better comfort than you do.
O Lord ! my boy, my Arthur, my fair son !
My life, my joy, my food, my all the world !
My widow-comfort, and my sorrow's cure ! *(She leaves)*

PHILIP. I fear some outrage, and I'll follow her. *(He leaves)*

LEWIS. There's nothing in this world can make me joy :
Life is as tedious as a twice-told tale
Vexing the dull ear of a drowsy man ;
And bitter shame hath spoiled the sweet world's taste,
That it yields nought but shame and bitterness.

PANDULF. Before the curing of a strong disease,
Even in the instant of repair and health,
The fit is strongest ; evils that take leave,
On their departure most of all show evil :
What have you lost by losing of this day ?

LEWIS. All days of glory, joy, and happiness.

PANDULF. If you had won it, certainly you had.
No, no, when Fortune means to men most good,
She looks upon them with a threatening eye.
Tis strange to think how much King John hath lost
In this which he accounts so clearly won.

Pressed for his meaning, Pandulf cynically shows that, as John must feel unsafe while Arthur lives, the boy is doomed to die. The crime will alienate the English from the royal murderer, and make them welcome the advent of a French army in England to avenge the wrong and transfer the crown to Lewis, to whom the murdered prince's rights will pass. The fickle Dauphin complacently accepts the position.

LEWIS. Strong reasons make strong actions : let us go :
If you say *Ay*, the king will not say *No*.

ACT 4

Scene 1—A Room in the Castle: Hubert, Arthur, and Executioners

HUBERT. Heat me these irons hot; and look thou stand
Within the arras: when I strike my foot
Upon the bosom of the ground, rush forth,
And bind the boy which you shall find with me
Fast to the chair: be heedful: hence, and watch.

EXECUTIONER. I hope your warrant will bear out the deed.

HUBERT. Uncleanly scruples! fear not you: look to't.
Young lad, come forth; I have to say with you.

ARTHUR *(entering)*. Good-morrow, Hubert.

HUBERT. Good-morrow, little prince.

ARTHUR. As little prince, having so great a title
To be more prince, as may be. You are sad.

HUBERT. Indeed, I have been merrier.

ARTHUR. Mercy on me!
Methinks nobody should be sad but I:
Yet I remember, when I was in France,
Young gentlemen would be as sad as night,
Only for wantonness. By my christendom,
So I were out of prison and kept sheep,
I should be as merry as the day is long;
And so I would be here, but that I doubt
My uncle practises more harm to me:
He is afraid of me and I of him:
Is it my fault that I was Geffrey's son?
No, indeed, is't not; and I would to heaven
I were your son, so you would love me, Hubert.

HUBERT *(aside)*. If I talk to him, with his innocent prate
He will awake my mercy which lies dead:
Therefore I will be sudden and dispatch.

ARTHUR. Are you sick, Hubert? you look pale today:
In sooth, I would you were a little sick,
That I might sit all night and watch with you:
I warrant I love you more than you do me.

HUBERT *(aside)*. His words do take possession of my bosom.
Read here, young Arthur *(showing a paper)*.
I must be brief, lest resolution drop
Out at mine eyes in tender womanish tears.
Can you not read it? Is it not fair writ?

ARTHUR *(reading)*. Too fairly, Hubert, for so foul effect:
Must you with hot irons burn out both mine eyes?

HUBERT. Young boy, I must.

ARTHUR. And will you?

HUBERT. And I will.

ARTHUR. Have you the heart? When your head did but ache,
I knit my handkerchief about your brows,
The best I had—a princess wrought it me,
And I did never ask it you again;
And with my hand at midnight held your head,
And, like the watchful minutes to the hour,
Still and anon cheered up the heavy time,
Saying, *What lack you?* and *Where lies your grief?*
Or *What good love may I perform for you?*
Many a poor man's son would have lien still
And ne'er have spoke a loving word to you;
But you at your sick service had a prince.
Nay, you may think my love was crafty love
And call it cunning: do, an if you will:
If heaven be pleased that you must use me ill,
Why then you must. Will you put out mine eyes,
These eyes that never did nor never shall
So much as frown on you?

HUBERT. I have sworn to do it;
And with hot irons must I burn them out.

ARTHUR. Ah, none but in this iron age would do it!
The iron of itself, though heat red-hot,
Approaching near these eyes, would drink my tears
And quench his fiery indignation
Even in the matter of mine innocence;
Nay, after that, consume away in rust,
But for containing fire to harm mine eye.
Are you more stubborn-hard than hammered iron?
An if an angel should have come to me
And told me Hubert should put out mine eyes
I would not have believed him,—no tongue but Hubert's.

HUBERT *(calling outside)*. Come forth. Do as I bid you do.

The executioners enter with cords and irons

ARTHUR. O, save me, Hubert, save me! my eyes are out
Even with the fierce looks of these fearful men.

HUBERT. Give me the iron, I say, and bind him here.

ARTHUR. Alas, what need you be so boisterous-rough?
I will not struggle, I will stand stone-still.
For heaven sake, Hubert, let me not be bound!
Nay, hear me, Hubert, drive these men away,
And I will sit as quiet as a lamb;
I will not stir, nor wince, nor speak a word,
Nor look upon the iron angerly:
Thrust but these men away, and I'll forgive you,
Whatever torment you do put me to.

HUBERT. Go, stand within; let me alone with him.

EXECUTIONER *(going)*. I am best pleased to be from such a deed.

ARTHUR. Alas, I then have chid away my friend!
He hath a stern look, but a gentle heart:
Let him come back, that his compassion may
Give life to yours.

HUBERT. Come, boy, prepare yourself.

ARTHUR. Is there no remedy?

HUBERT. None, but to lose your eyes.

ARTHUR. O heaven, that there were but a mote in yours,
A grain, a dust, a gnat, a wandering hair,
Any annoyance in that precious sense!
Then feeling what small things are boisterous there,
Your vile intent must needs seem horrible.

HUBERT. Is this your promise? go to, hold your tongue.

ARTHUR. Hubert, the utterance of a brace of tongues
Must needs want pleading for a pair of eyes:
Let me not hold my tongue, let me not, Hubert;
Or, Hubert, if you will, cut out my tongue,
So I may keep mine eyes: O, spare mine eyes,
Though to no use but still to look on you!
Lo, by my troth, the instrument is cold
And would not harm me.

HUBERT. I can heat it, boy.

ARTHUR. No, in good sooth; the fire is dead with grief,
Being create for comfort, to be used
In undeserved extremes: see else yourself;
There is no malice in this burning coal;
The breath of heaven has blown his spirit out
And strewed repentant ashes on his head.

HUBERT. But with my breath I can revive it, boy.

ARTHUR. An if you do, you will but make it blush
And glow with shame of your proceedings, Hubert:
Nay, it perchance will sparkle in your eyes;
And like a dog that is compelled to fight,
Snatch at his master that doth tarre him on.
All things that you should use to do me wrong
Deny their office; only you do lack
That mercy which fierce fire and iron extends,
Creatures of note for mercy-lacking uses.

HUBERT. Well, see to live; I will not touch thine eyes
For all the treasure that thine uncle owes:
Yet am I sworn and I did purpose, boy,
With this same very iron to burn them out.

ARTHUR. O, now you look like Hubert! all this while
You were disguised.

HUBERT. Peace; no more. Adieu.
Your uncle must not know but you are dead;
I'll fill these doggèd spies with false reports:
And, pretty child, sleep doubtless and secure,
That Hubert, for the wealth of all the world,
Will not offend thee.

ARTHUR. O heaven! I thank you, Hubert.

HUBERT. Silence; no more: go closely in with me:
Much danger do I undergo for thee.

Scene 2—King John's Palace

Enter King, Pembroke, and Salisbury

JOHN. Here once again we sit, once again crowned,
And looked upon, I hope, with cheerful eyes.

PEMBROKE. This *once again*, but that your highness pleased,
Was once superfluous: you were crowned before,
And that high royalty was ne'er plucked off,
The faiths of men ne'er stainèd with revolt;
Fresh expectation troubled not the land
With any longed-for change or better state.

SALISBURY. Therefore, to be possessed with double pomp,
To guard a title that was rich before,
To gild refinèd gold, to paint the lily,
To throw a perfume on the violet,
To smooth the ice, or add another hue
Unto the rainbow, or with taper-light
To seek the beauteous eye of heaven to garnish,
Is wasteful and ridiculous excess.

JOHN. Some reasons of this double coronation
I have possessed you with and think them strong;
And more, more strong, then lesser is my fear,
I shall indue you with: meantime but ask
What you would have reformed that is not well,
And well shall you perceive how willingly
I will both hear and grant you your requests.

PEMBROKE. Then I, as one that am the tongue of these
To sound the purposes of all their hearts,
Both for myself and them, but, chief of all,
Your safety (for the which myself and them
Bend their best studies), heartily request
The enfranchisement of Arthur, whose restraint
Doth move the murmuring lips of discontent.
That the time's enemies may not have this

To grace occasions, let it be our suit
That you have bid us ask his liberty.

Hubert enters

JOHN. Let it be so: I do commit his youth
To your direction. Hubert, what news with you?

The King and Hubert speak apart

PEMBROKE *(aside)*. This is the man should do the monstrous deed;
He showed his warrant to a friend of mine,
And I do fearfully believe tis done
What we so feared he had a charge to do.

SALISBURY. The colour of the king doth come and go
Between his purpose and his conscience,
Like heralds 'twixt two dreadful battles set;
His passion is so ripe, it needs must break.

PEMBROKE. And when it breaks I fear will issue thence
The foul corruption of a sweet child's death.

JOHN. We cannot hold mortality's strong hand:
Good lords, although my will to give is living,
The suit which you demand is gone and dead:
He tells us Arthur is deceased tonight.

SALISBURY. Indeed we feared his sickness was past cure.

PEMBROKE. Indeed we heard how near his death he was
Before the child himself felt he was sick:
This must be answered either here or hence.

JOHN. Why do you bend such solemn brows on me?
Think you I bear the shears of destiny?
Have I commandment on the pulse of life?

SALISBURY. It is apparent foul play; and tis shame
That greatness should so grossly offer it:
So thrive it in your game! and so, farewell.

PEMBROKE. Stay yet, Lord Salisbury; I'll go with thee,
And find the inheritance of this poor child,
His little kingdom of a forcèd grave.
That blood which owed the breadth of all this isle,
Three foot of it doth hold: bad world the while!
This must not be thus borne: this will break out
To all our sorrows, and ere long I doubt. *(They go)*

JOHN. They burn in indignation. I repent:
There is no sure foundation set on blood,
No certain life achieved by others' death.

Enter a Messenger

A fearful eye thou hast: where is that blood
That I have seen inhabit in those cheeks?
So foul a sky clears not without a storm:
Pour down thy weather: how goes all in France?

MESSENGER. From France to England. Never such a power
For any foreign preparation
Was levied in the body of a land.
The tidings comes that they are all arrived.

JOHN. O, where hath our intelligence been drunk?
Where hath it slept? Where is my mother's care,
That such an army could be drawn in France,
And she not hear of it?

MESSENGER. My liege, her ear
Is stopped with dust; the first of April died
Your noble mother; and, as I hear, my lord,
The Lady Constance in a frenzy died
Three days before: but this from rumour's tongue
I idly heard; if true or false I know not.

JOHN. Withhold thy speed, dreadful occasion!
O, make a league with me, till I have pleased
My discontented peers! What! mother dead!
How wildly then walks my estate in France!
Under whose conduct came those powers of France
That thou for truth givest out are landed here?

MESSENGER. Under the Dauphin.

JOHN. Thou hast made me giddy
With these ill tidings. *(Enter Faulconbridge and Peter of Pomfret)*
Now, what says the world
To your proceedings? do not seek to stuff
My head with more ill news, for it is full.

FAULCONBRIDGE. But if you be afeard to hear the worst,
Then let the worst unheard fall on your head.

JOHN. Bear with me, cousin; for I was amazed
Under the tide: but now I breathe again
Aloft the flood, and can give audience
To any tongue, speak it of what it will.

FAULCONBRIDGE. How I have sped among the clergymen,
The sums I have collected shall express.
But as I travelled hither through the land,
I find the people strangely fantasied;
Possessed with rumours, full of idle dreams,
Not knowing what they fear, but full of fear:
And here's a prophet, that I brought with me
From forth the streets of Pomfret, whom I found
With many hundreds treading on his heels;
To whom he sung, in rude harsh-sounding rhymes,
That, ere the next Ascension-day at noon,
Your highness should deliver up your crown.

JOHN. Thou idle dreamer, wherefore didst thou so?

PETER. Foreknowing that the truth will fall out so.

JOHN. Hubert, away with him; imprison him;
And on that day at noon, whereon he says
I shall yield up my crown, let him be hanged.
Deliver him to safety; and return,
For I must use thee. *(To Faulconbridge)* O my gentle cousin,
Hear'st thou the news abroad? Who are arrived?

FAULCONBRIDGE. The French, my lord; men's mouths are full of it:
Besides, I met Lord Bigot and Lord Salisbury,
With eyes as red as new-enkindled fire,
And others more, going to seek the grave
Of Arthur, who they say is killed tonight
On your suggestion.

JOHN. Gentle kinsman, go,
And thrust thyself into their companies:
I have a way to win their loves again;
Bring them before me.
Be Mercury, set feathers to thy heels,
And fly like thought from them to me again.

FAULCONBRIDGE. The spirit of the time shall teach me speed.

JOHN *(alone)*. My mother dead!

HUBERT *(entering)*. My lord, they say five moons were seen tonight;
Four fixèd, and the fifth did whirl about
The other four in wondrous motion.

JOHN. Five moons!

HUBERT. Old men and beldams in the streets
Do prophesy upon it dangerously:
Young Arthur's death is common in their mouths:
And when they talk of him they shake their heads
And whisper one another in the ear;
And he that speaks doth grip the hearer's wrist
Whilst he that hears makes fearful action,
With wrinkled brows, with nods, with rolling eyes.
I saw a smith stand with his hammer, thus,
The whilst his iron did on the anvil cool,
With open mouth swallowing a tailor's news,
Who, with his shears and measure in his hand,
Standing on slippers, which his nimble haste
Had falsely thrust upon contrary feet,
Told of a many thousand warlike French
That were embattailèd and ranked in Kent:
Another lean unwashed artificer
Cuts off his tale and talks of Arthur's death.

JOHN. Why seek'st thou to possess me with these fears?
Why urgest thou so oft young Arthur's death?

Thy hand hath murdered him : I had a mighty cause
To wish him dead, but thou hadst none to kill him.

HUBERT. No had, my lord ! why, did you not provoke me ?

JOHN. It is the curse of kings to be attended
By slaves that take their humours for a warrant
To break within the house of life,
And on the winking of authority
To understand a law, to know the meaning
Of dangerous majesty, when perchance it frowns
More upon humour than advised respect.

HUBERT. Here is your hand and seal for what I did.

JOHN. O, when the last account 'twixt heaven and earth
Is to be made, then shall this hand and seal
Witness against us to damnation !
How oft the sight of means to do ill deeds
Make deeds ill done ! Hadst not thou been by,
A fellow by the hand of nature marked,
Quoted and signed to do a deed of shame,
This murder had not come into my mind :
But taking note of thy abhorred aspect,
Finding thee fit for villainy,
Apt, liable to be employed in danger,
I faintly broke with thee of Arthur's death ;
And thou, to be endearèd to a king,
Made it no conscience to destroy a prince.

HUBERT. My lord . . .

JOHN. Hadst thou but shook thy head or made a pause
When I spake darkly what I purposèd,
Or turned an eye of doubt upon my face,
As bid me tell my tale in express words,
Deep shame had struck me dumb, made me break off,
And those thy fears might have wrought fears in me :
But thou didst understand me by my signs
And didst in signs again parley with sin ;
Yea, without stop, didst let thy heart consent,
And consequently thy rude hand to act
The deed, which both our tongues held vile to name.
Out of my sight, and never see me more !
My nobles leave me ; and my State is braved,
Even at my gates, with ranks of foreign powers :
Nay, in the body of this fleshly land,
This kingdom, this confine of blood and breath,
Hostility and civil tumult reigns
Between my conscience and my cousin's death.

HUBERT. Arm you against your other enemies,
I'll make a peace between your soul and you.
Young Arthur is alive: this hand of mine
Is yet a maiden and an innocent hand,
Not painted with the crimson spots of blood.
Within this bosom never entered yet
The dreadful motion of a murderous thought;
And you have slandered nature in my form,
Which, howsoever rude exteriorly,
Is yet the cover of a fairer mind
Than to be butcher of an innocent child.

JOHN. Doth Arthur live? O, haste thee to the peers,
Throw this report on their incensèd rage,
And make them tame to their obedience!
Forgive the comment that my passion made
Upon thy feature; for my rage was blind,
And foul imaginary eyes of blood
Presented thee more hideous than thou art.
O, answer not, but to my closet bring
The angry lords with all expedient haste.
I conjure thee but slowly; run more fast.

Scene 3—Arthur on the Castle Walls

ARTHUR. The wall is high, and yet will I leap down;
Good ground, be pitiful and hurt me not!
There's few or none do know me: if they did,
This ship-boy's semblance hath disguised me quite.
I am afraid; and yet I'll venture it.
If I get down, and do not break my limbs,
I'll find a thousand shifts to get away:
As good to die and go, as die and stay. *(He leaps down)*
O me! my uncle's spirit is in these stones:
Heaven take my soul, and England keep my bones! *(He dies)*

Enter Pembroke, Salisbury, and Bigot

SALISBURY. Lords, I will meet him at Saint Edmundsbury:
It is our safety, and we must embrace
This gentle offer of the perilous time.

PEMBROKE. Who brought that letter from the cardinal?

SALISBURY. The Count Melun, a noble lord of France;
Whose private with me of the Dauphin's love
Is much more general than these lines import.

BIGOT. Tomorrow morning let us meet him then.

SALISBURY. Or rather then set forward; for 'twill be
Two long days' journey, lords, or ere we meet.

FAULCONBRIDGE *(entering).* Once more today well met, distempered lords!
The king by me requests your presence straight.

SALISBURY. The king hath dispossessed himself of us:
We will not line his thin bestainèd cloak
With our pure honours, nor attend the foot
That leaves the print of blood where'er it walks.
Return and tell him so: we know the worst.

FAULCONBRIDGE. Whate'er you think, good words, I think, were best.

SALISBURY. Our griefs, and not our manners, reason now.

FAULCONBRIDGE. But there is little reason in your grief;
Therefore 'twere reason you had manners now.

PEMBROKE. Sir, sir, impatience hath his privilege.

FAULCONBRIDGE. Tis true, to hurt his master, no man else.

SALISBURY. This is the prison. What is he lies here?

They discover Arthur's body

PEMBROKE. O death, made proud with pure and princely beauty!
The earth had not a hole to hide this deed.

SALISBURY. Murder, as hating what himself hath done,
Doth lay it open to urge on revenge.

BIGOT. Or, when he doomed this beauty to a grave,
Found it too precious-princely for a grave.

SALISBURY. Sir Richard, what think you? have you beheld,
Or have you read or heard? or could you think?
Or do you almost think, although you see,
That you do see? could thought, without this object,
Form such another? This is the very top,
The height, the crest, or crest unto the crest,
Of murder's arms: this is the foulest shame,
The wildest savagery, the vilest stroke,
That ever wall-eyed wrath or staring rage
Presented to the tears of soft remorse.

PEMBROKE. All murders past do stand excused in this:
And this, so sole and so unmatchable,
Shall give a holiness, a purity,
To the yet unbegotten sin of times;
And prove a deadly bloodshed but a jest,
Exampled by this heinous spectacle.

FAULCONBRIDGE. It is a damnèd and a fearful work;
The graceless action of a heavy hand,
If that it be the work of any hand.

SALISBURY. If that it be the work of any hand!
We had a kind of light what would ensue:

It is the shameful work of Hubert's hand;
The practice and the purpose of the king:
From whose obedience I forbid my soul,
Kneeling before this ruin of sweet life,
And breathing to his breathless excellence
The incense of a vow, a holy vow,
Never to taste the pleasures of the world,
Never to be infected with delight,
Nor conversant with ease and idleness,
Till I have set a glory to this hand,
By giving it the worship of revenge.

PEMBROKE AND BIGOT. Our souls religiously confirm thy words.

HUBERT *(entering)*. Lords, I am hot with haste in seeking you:
Arthur doth live; the king hath sent for you.

SALISBURY. O, he is bold and blushes not at death.
Avaunt, thou hateful villain, get thee gone!

HUBERT. I am no villain.

SALISBURY *(drawing his sword)*. Must I rob the law?

FAULCONBRIDGE. Your sword is bright, sir; put it up again.

SALISBURY. Not till I sheathe it in a murderer's skin.

HUBERT. Stand back, Lord Salisbury, stand back, I say;
By heaven, I think my sword's as sharp as yours:
I would not have you, lord, forget yourself,
Nor tempt the danger of my true defence;
Lest I, by marking of your rage, forget
Your worth, your greatness, and nobility.

BIGOT. Out, dunghill! darest thou brave a nobleman?

HUBERT. Not for my life: but yet I dare defend
My innocent life against an emperor.

SALISBURY. Thou art a murderer.

HUBERT. Do not prove me so;
Yet I am none: whose tongue soe'er speaks false,
Not truly speaks; who speaks not truly, lies.

BIGOT. Who killed this prince?

HUBERT *(seeing Arthur)*. Tis not an hour since I left him well:
I honoured him, I loved him, and will weep
My date of life out for his sweet life's loss.

SALISBURY. Trust not those cunning waters of his eyes,
For villainy is not without such rheum;
And he, long traded in it, makes it seem
Like rivers of remorse and innocency.
Away with me, all you whose souls abhor
The uncleanly savours of a slaughter-house;
For I am stifled with this smell of sin.

BIGOT. Away toward Bury, to the Dauphin there!

PEMBROKE. There tell the king he may inquire us out.

FAULCONBRIDGE. Here's a good world! Knew you of this fair work?
Beyond the infinite and boundless reach
Of mercy, if thou didst this deed of death,
Art thou damned, Hubert.

HUBERT. Do but hear me, sir.

FAULCONBRIDGE. Ha! I'll tell thee what;
There is not yet so ugly a fiend of hell
As thou shalt be if thou didst kill this child.

HUBERT. Upon my soul—

FAULCONBRIDGE. If thou didst but consent
To this most cruel act, do but despair;
And if thou want'st a cord, the smallest thread
That ever spider twisted from her womb
Will serve to strangle thee; a rush will be a beam
To hang thee on; or wouldst thou drown thyself,
Put but a little water in a spoon
And it shall be as all the ocean,
Enough to stifle such a villain up.
I do suspect thee very grievously.

HUBERT. If I in act, consent, or sin of thought,
Be guilty of the stealing that sweet breath
Which was embounded in this beauteous clay,
Let hell want pains enough to torture me.
I left him well.

FAULCONBRIDGE. Go, bear him in thine arms.
I am amazed, methinks, and lose my way
Among the thorns and dangers of this world.
How easy dost thou take all England up!
From forth this morsel of dead royalty
The life, the rights, and truth of all this realm
Is fled to heaven.
Now for the bare-picked bone of majesty
Doth doggèd war bristle his angry crest
And snarleth in the gentle eyes of peace:
Now powers from home and discontents at home
Meet in one line; and vast confusion waits,
As doth a raven on a sick-fallen beast.
Bear away that child
And follow me with speed: I'll to the king:
A thousand businesses are brief in hand,
And heaven itself doth frown upon the land.

ACT 5

Scene 1—King John's Palace: the King receiving the Cardinal

JOHN. Thus have I yielded up into your hand
The circle of my glory. *(Passing crown to Cardinal)*

PANDULF. Take again
From this my hand, as holding of the pope
Your sovereign greatness and authority.

JOHN. Now keep your holy word: go meet the French,
And from his holiness use all your power
To stop their marches 'fore we are inflamed.
Our discontented counties do revolt;
Our people quarrel with obedience.
Then pause not; for the present time's so sick,
That present medicine must be ministered,
Or overthrow incurable ensues.

PANDULF. It was my breath that blew this tempest up,
Upon your stubborn usage of the pope;
But since you are a gentle convertite,
My tongue shall hush again this storm of war
And make fair weather in your blustering land.
On this Ascension-day, remember well,
Upon your oath of service to the pope,
Go I to make the French lay down their arms.

JOHN. Is this Ascension-day? Did not the prophet
Say that before Ascension-day at noon
My crown I should give off?

Enter Faulconbridge

FAULCONBRIDGE. All Kent hath yielded; nothing there holds out
But Dover castle: London hath received,
Like a kind host, the Dauphin and his powers:
Your nobles will not hear you, but are gone
To offer service to your enemy,
And wild amazement hurries up and down
The little number of your doubtful friends.

JOHN. Would not my lords return to me again,
After they heard young Arthur was alive?

FAULCONBRIDGE. They found him dead and cast into the streets.

JOHN. That villain Hubert told me he did live.

FAULCONBRIDGE. So, on my soul, he did, for aught he knew.
But wherefore do you droop? why look you sad?
Be great in act, as you have been in thought;
Let not the world see fear and sad distrust
Govern the motion of a kingly eye:
Be stirring as the time; be fire with fire;
Threaten the threatener and outface the brow

Of bragging horror: so shall inferior eyes,
That borrow their behaviours from the great,
Grow great by your example and put on
The dauntless spirit of resolution.
Away, and glister like the god of war,
When he intendeth to become the field:
Show boldness and aspiring confidence.
What, shall they seek the lion in his den,
And fright him there? and make him tremble there?
O, let it not be said: forage, and run
To meet displeasure farther from the doors,
And grapple with him ere he comes so nigh.

JOHN. The legate of the pope hath been with me,
And I have made a happy peace with him;
And he hath promised to dismiss the powers
Led by the Dauphin.

FAULCONBRIDGE *(amazed)*. O inglorious league!
Shall we, upon the footing of our land,
Send fair-play orders and make compromise,
Insinuation, parley, and base truce
To arms invasive? Shall a beardless boy,
A cockered silken wanton, brave our fields,
And flesh his spirit in a warlike soil,
Mocking the air with colours idly spread,
And find no check? Let us, my liege, to arms:
Perchance the cardinal cannot make your peace;
Or if he do, let it at least be said
They saw we had a purpose of defence.

JOHN. Have thou the ordering of this present time.

FAULCONBRIDGE. Away, then, with good courage! yet, I know,
Our party may well meet a prouder foe.

Scene 2—The Dauphin's Camp at St. Edmundsbury

LEWIS. My Lord Melun, let this be copied out,
And keep it safe for our remembrance:
Return the precedent to these lords again;
That, having our fair order written down,
Both they and we, perusing o'er these notes,
May know wherefore we took the sacrament
And keep our faiths firm and inviolable.

SALISBURY. Upon our sides it never shall be broken.
And, noble Dauphin, albeit we swear
A voluntary zeal and an unurged faith
To your proceedings; yet O, it grieves my soul
That I must draw this metal from my side
To be a widow-maker!

And is't not pity, O my grievèd friends,
That we, the sons and children of this isle,
Were born to see so sad an hour as this?

LEWIS. A noble temper dost thou show in this;
And great affections wrestling in thy bosom
Doth make an earthquake of nobility.
O, what a noble combat hast thou fought
Between compulsion and a brave respect!
Let me wipe off this honourable dew,
That silverly doth progress on thy cheeks.
Lift up thy brow, renownèd Salisbury,
And with a great heart heave away the storm.
Come, come; for thou shalt thrust thy hand as deep
Into the purse of rich prosperity
As Lewis himself: so, nobles, shall you all,
That knit your sinews to the strength of mine.
And even there, methinks, an angel spake.

Cardinal Pandulf enters

Look, where the holy legate comes apace,
To give us warrant from the hand of heaven,
And in our actions set the name of right
With holy breath.

PANDULF. Hail, noble prince of France!
The next is this, King John hath reconciled
Himself to Rome; his spirit is come in,
That so stood out against the holy church,
The great metropolis and see of Rome:
Therefore thy threatening colours now wind up;
And tame the savage spirit of wild war,
That, like a lion fostered up at hand,
It may lie gently at the foot of peace,
And be no further harmful than in show.

LEWIS. Your grace shall pardon me, I will not back;
I am too high-born to be propertied,
To be a secondary at control,
Or useful serving-man and instrument,
To any sovereign State throughout the world.
Your breath first kindled the dead coal of wars
Between this chastised kingdom and myself,
And brought in matter that should feed this fire;
And now tis far too huge to be blown out
With that same weak wind which enkindled it.
You taught me how to know the face of right,
Acquainted me with interest to this land,
Yea, thrust this enterprise into my heart;
And come ye now to tell me John hath made

His peace with Rome? What is that peace to me?
I, after Arthur, claim this land for mine;
And, now it is half-conquered, must I back
Because that John hath made his peace with Rome?
Am I Rome's slave? What penny hath Rome borne,
What men provided, what munition sent,
To underprop this action? Is't not I
That undergo this charge? who else but I,
And such as to my claim are liable,
Sweat in this business and maintain this war?
Have I not heard these islanders shout out
Vive le roi! as I have banked their towns?
Have I not here the best cards for the game,
To win this easy match played for a crown?
And shall I now give o'er the yielded set?
No, no, on my soul, it never shall be said.

PANDULF. You look but on the outside of this work.

LEWIS. Outside or inside, I will not return
Till my attempt so much be glorified
As to my ample hope was promisèd
Before I drew this gallant head of war,
And culled these fiery spirits from the world,
To outlook conquest and to win renown
Even in the jaws of danger and of death. *(Trumpet sounds)*
What lusty trumpet thus doth summon us?

Enter Faulconbridge

FAULCONBRIDGE. According to the fair play of the world,
Let me have audience: I am sent to speak:
My holy lord of Milan, from the king
I come, to learn how you have dealt for him;
And, as you answer, I do know the scope
And warrant limited unto my tongue.

PANDULF. The Dauphin is too wilful-opposite,
And will not temporise with my entreaties;
He flatly says he'll not lay down his arms.

FAULCONBRIDGE. By all the blood that ever fury breathed,
The youth says well. Now hear our English king;
For thus his royalty doth speak in me.
He is prepared, and reason too he should:
This apish and unmannerly approach,
This harnessed masque and unadvisèd revel,
This unhaired sauciness and boyish troops,
The king doth smile at; and is well prepared
To whip this dwarfish war, these pigmy arms,
From out the circle of his territories.
That hand which had the strength, even at your door,

To cudgel you and make you take the hatch,
To dive like buckets in concealèd wells,
To crouch in litter of your stable planks,
To lie like pawns locked up in chests and trunks,
To hug with swine, to seek sweet safety out
In vaults and prisons, and to thrill and shake
Even at the crying of your nation's crow,
Thinking his voice an armèd Englishman;
Shall that victorious hand be feebled here,
That in your chambers gave you chastisement?
No: know the gallant monarch is in arms
And like an eagle o'er his aery towers,
To souse annoyance that comes near his nest.

LEWIS. There end thy brave, and turn thy face in peace;
We grant thou canst outscold us: fare thee well;
We hold our time too precious to be spent
With such a brabbler.
Strike up the drums; and let the tongue of war
Plead for our interest and our being here.
Strike up our drums, to find this danger out.

FAULCONBRIDGE. And thou shalt find it, Dauphin, do not doubt.

Scene 3—The Battlefield

JOHN *(to Hubert)*. How goes the day with us? O, tell me, Hubert.

HUBERT. Badly, I fear. How fares your majesty?

JOHN. This fever, that hath troubled me so long,
Lies heavy on me; O, my heart is sick!

A MESSENGER. My lord, your valiant kinsman, Faulconbridge,
Desires your majesty to leave the field
And send him word by me which way you go.

JOHN. Tell him, toward Swinstead, to the abbey there.

MESSENGER. Be of good comfort; for the great supply
That was expected by the Dauphin here,
Are wrecked three nights ago on Goodwin Sands.
This news was brought to Richard but even now:
The French fight coldly, and retire themselves.

JOHN. Ay me! this tyrant fever burns me up,
And will not let me welcome this good news.
Set on toward Swinstead: to my litter straight;
Weakness possesseth me, and I am faint.

Scene 4—Another part of the Battlefield

SALISBURY. I did not think the king so stored with friends.

PEMBROKE. Up once again; put spirit in the French:
If they miscarry, we miscarry too.

Salisbury. Faulconbridge,
In spite of spite, alone upholds the day.

Pembroke. They say King John sore sick hath left the field.

Melun *(entering wounded)*. Fly, noble English, you are bought and sold;
Unthread the rude eye of rebellion
And welcome home again discarded faith.
Seek out King John and fall before his feet,
For if the French be lords of this loud day
He means to recompense the pains you take
By cutting off your heads: thus hath he sworn.

Salisbury. May this be possible? may this be true?

Melun. Have I not hideous death within my view,
Retaining but a quantity of life,
Which bleeds away, even as a form of wax
Resolveth from his figure 'gainst the fire?
What in the world should make me now deceive,
Since I must lose the use of all deceit?
Why should I then be false, since it is true
That I must die here and live hence by truth?
I say again, if Lewis do win the day,
He is forsworn, if e'er those eyes of yours
Behold another day break in the east:
But even this night, whose black contagious breath
Already smokes about the burning crest
Of the old, feeble, and day-wearied sun,
Even this ill night your breathing shall expire,
Paying the fine of rated treachery
Even with a treacherous fine of all your lives,
If Lewis by your assistance win the day.
Commend me to one Hubert with your king:
The love of him, and this respect besides,
For that my grandsire was an Englishman,
Awakes my conscience to confess all this.
In lieu whereof, I pray you, bear me hence
From forth the noise and rumour of the field,
Where I may think the remnant of my thoughts
In peace, and part this body and my soul
With contemplation and devout desires.

Salisbury. We do believe thee: and beshrew my soul
But I do love the favour and the form
Of this most fair occasion, by the which
We will untread the steps of flight,
And like a bated and retirèd flood,
Leaving our rankness and irregular course,
Stoop low within those bounds we have o'erlooked

And calmly run on in obedience
Even to our ocean, to our great King John.
My arm shall give thee help to bear thee hence;
For I do see the cruel pangs of death
Right in thine eye. Away, my friends! New flight;
And happy newness, that intends old right.

Scene 5—In the French Camp

Enter Lewis the Dauphin, and his train

LEWIS. The sun of heaven methought was loth to set,
But stayed and made the western welkin blush,
When English measure backward their own ground
In faint retire. O, bravely came we off,
When with a volley of our needless shot,
After such toil, we bid Goodnight:
And wound our tattering colours clearly up,
Last in the field, and almost lords of it!

MESSENGER. Where is my prince, the Dauphin?

LEWIS. Here: what news?

MESSENGER. The Count Melun is slain; the English lords
By his persuasion are again fallen off,
And your supply, which you have wished so long,
Are cast away and sunk on Goodwin Sands.

LEWIS. Ah, foul shrewd news! beshrew thy very heart!
I did not think to be so sad tonight
As this hath made me. Who was he that said
King John did fly an hour or two before
The stumbling night did part our weary powers?

MESSENGER. Whoever spoke it, it is true, my lord.

LEWIS. Well; keep good quarter and good care tonight:
The day shall not be up so soon as I,
To try the fair adventure of tomorrow.

Scene 6—Night in the neighbourhood of Swinstead Abbey

FAULCONBRIDGE *(meeting Hubert)*. What news abroad?

HUBERT. Why, here walk I in the black brow of night,
To find you out.

FAULCONBRIDGE. Brief, then; and what's the news?

HUBERT. O, my sweet sir, news fitting to the night,
Black, fearful, comfortless, and horrible.
The king, I fear, is poisoned by a monk;
I left him almost speechless; and broke out
To acquaint you with this evil, that you might
The better arm you to the sudden time
Than if you had at leisure known of this.

FAULCONBRIDGE. Whom didst thou leave to tend his majesty?

HUBERT. Why, know you not? the lords are all come back,
And brought Prince Henry in their company;
At whose request the king hath pardoned them,
And they are all about his majesty.

FAULCONBRIDGE. Withhold thine indignation, mighty heaven,
And tempt us not to bear above our power!
I'll tell thee, Hubert, half my power this night,
Passing these flats, are taken by the tide;
These Lincoln Washes have devoured them;
Myself, well mounted, hardly have escaped.
Away before: conduct me to the king;
I doubt he will be dead or ere I come.

Scene 7—The Orchard at Swinstead Abbey

Enter Prince Henry, Salisbury, and Bigot

HENRY. It is too late: the life of all his blood
Is touched corruptibly, and his pure brain,
Which some suppose the soul's frail dwelling-house,
Doth by the idle comments that it makes
Foretell the ending of mortality.

PEMBROKE *(entering)*. His highness yet doth speak, and holds belief
That, being brought into the open air,
It would allay the burning quality
Of that fell poison which assaileth him.

HENRY. Let him be brought into the orchard here.
Doth he still rage?

PEMBROKE. He is more patient
Than when you left him; even now he sung.

HENRY. O vanity of sickness! fierce extremes
In their continuance will not feel themselves.
Death, having preyed upon the outward parts,
Leaves them invisible, and his siege is now
Against the mind, the which he pricks and wounds
With many legions of strange fantasies.
Tis strange that death should sing.
I am the cygnet to this pale faint swan,
Who chants a doleful hymn to his own death,
And from the organ-pipe of frailty sings
His soul and body to their lasting rest.

SALISBURY. Be of good comfort, prince; for you are born
To set a form upon that indigest
Which he hath left so shapeless and so rude.

Enter Attendants, carrying John in a chair

JOHN. Ay, marry, now my soul hath elbow-room;
It would not out at windows nor at doors.
There is so hot a summer in my bosom,

That all my bowels crumble up to dust :
I am a scribbled form, drawn with a pen
Upon a parchment, and against this fire
Do I shrink up.

HENRY. How fares your majesty ?

JOHN. Poisoned,—ill fare—dead, forsook, cast off :
And none of you will bid the winter come
To thrust his icy fingers in my maw,
Nor let my kingdom's rivers take their course
Through my burned bosom, nor entreat the north
To make his bleak winds kiss my parchèd lips
And comfort me with cold. I do not ask you much,
I beg cold comfort ; and you are so strait
And so ingrateful, you deny me that.

HENRY. O that there were some virtue in my tears,
That might relieve you !

JOHN. The salt in them is hot.
Within me is a hell ; and there the poison
Is as a fiend confined to tyrannise
On unreprievable condemnèd blood.

Enter Faulconbridge running

JOHN. O cousin, thou art come to set mine eye
The tackle of my heart is cracked and burned,
And all the shrouds wherewith my life should sail
Are turnèd to one thread, one little hair :
My heart hath one poor string to stay it by,
Which holds but till thy news be utterèd ;
And then all this thou seest is but a clod
And module of confounded royalty.

FAULCONBRIDGE. The Dauphin is preparing hitherward,
Where heaven He knows how we shall answer him ;
For in a night the best part of my power,
As I upon advantage did remove,
Were in the Washes all unwarily
Devourèd by the unexpected flood. *(The King dies)*

SALISBURY. You breathe these dead news in as dead an ear.
My liege ! my lord ! but now a king, now thus.

HENRY. Even so must I run on, and even so stop.
What surety of the world, what hope, what stay,
When this was now a king, and now is clay ?

FAULCONBRIDGE. Art thou gone so ? I do but stay behind
To do the office for thee of revenge,
And then my soul shall wait on thee to heaven,
As it on earth hath been thy servant still.
Now, now, you stars that move in your right spheres,

Where be your powers ? show now your mended faiths,
And instantly return with me again,
To push destruction and perpetual shame
Out of the weak door of our fainting land.
Straight let us seek, or straight we shall be sought;
The Dauphin rages at our very heels.

SALISBURY. It seems you know not, then, so much as we:
The Cardinal Pandulf is within at rest,
Who half an hour since came from the Dauphin,
And brings from him such offers of our peace
As we with honour and respect may take,
With purpose presently to leave this war.

FAULCONBRIDGE. He will the rather do it when he sees
Ourselves well sinewèd to our defence.

SALISBURY. Nay, it is in a manner done already;
For many carriages he hath dispatched
To the seaside, and put his cause and quarrel
To the disposing of the cardinal,
With whom yourself, myself, and other lords,
If you think meet, this afternoon will post
To consummate this business happily.

FAULCONBRIDGE. Let it be so: and you, my noble prince,
With other princes that may best be spared,
Shall wait upon your father's funeral.

HENRY. At Worcester must his body be interred;
For so he willed it.

FAULCONBRIDGE. Thither shall it then:
And happily may your sweet self put on
The lineal state and glory of the land!
To whom, with all submission, on my knee
I do bequeath my faithful services
And true subjection everlastingly.

SALISBURY. And the like tender of our love we make,
To rest without a spot for evermore.

HENRY. I have a kind soul that would give you thanks
And knows not how to do it but with tears.

FAULCONBRIDGE. O, let us pay the time but needful woe,
Since it hath been beforehand with our griefs.
This England never did, nor never shall,
Lie at the proud foot of a conqueror,
But when it first did help to wound itself.
Now these her princes are come home again,
Come the three corners of the world in arms,
And we shall shock them. Nought shall make us rue,
If England to itself do rest but true.

The Story of Antony and Cleopatra

We are in the presence of one of the most moving tragedies in all the written annals of mankind. We see as with our own eyes the fall of one of the world's great men.

He was Julius Caesar's friend Mark Antony, he who, when Caesar fell, swayed the crowd and changed the face of Rome. Live a thousand years he would not find himself so apt to die, no place to please him so, as there by Caesar. He lived another fourteen years, and it were better for his fame had he died with Caesar.

Many dramatists have been drawn to the theme of this play, the demoralisation of a generous-minded man by a subtle, alluring, and dominating woman; but it is Shakespeare who knows what to do when he sees a heart bowed down and a great mind gone. That is the spectacle of this poignant drama. It has a mighty stage. It covers the years when the Roman State was emerging as an Empire under a single Caesar. The rule of the Triumvirate was falling. Octavius Caesar, Mark Antony, and Lepidus were drawing to the end of their united power. The younger Pompey was looming in the shadows, threatening and uncertain; Octavius was emerging as the central figure, Augustus.

That is the time; that is the state of Rome; those are the men. Now comes Cleopatra on the scene. She is the last Queen of Egypt, the glory of the Pharaohs is about her, and the spell of Egypt, with its long long time, draws the Roman to her. He falls to pieces at her touch. He is perhaps the most colossal failure in history of a man who had in him elements of greatness, but succumbed to the temptations of a pleasure-loving woman.

He sees his danger; he struggles to escape and gives himself the opportunity; but the spell of Egypt draws him back. More than all the Roman Empire to him is a tear in Cleopatra's eye. He threw away his manhood and his power, his mind and his will; he left himself without even the dignity to die in the old Roman way.

Cleopatra at least preserves her dignity. She stages her death as she stages her journeys down the Nile. She will not grace a triumph in the streets of Rome. A word to her attendant, and Cleopatra of Egypt has a death that all the world will look at. It is one of her women who sums up, in that great hour, in a few of the simplest words in literature, the pagan approach to a hopeless end:

> Finish, good lady; the bright day is done,
> And we are for the dark.

As a pageant of history the play may cover too long a time and too wide a space, but it is a great human play, and the interest of its more poignant scenes is intense. It will remain one of the undying pieces of literature on the everlasting theme of a woman and a man.

THE PLAYERS

Mark Antony, ruler of a third of the Roman Empire, a strong man demoralised by the fascination of Cleopatra.

Octavius Caesar, ruler of the country round Rome.

Lepidus, third member of the triumvirate, a much inferior man.

Demetrius, Dercetas, Eros, friends of Antony.

Enobarbus, Ventidius, Scarus, friends of Antony.

Mecaenas, Dolabella, Thyreus, friends of Octavius Caesar.

Agrippa, Gallus, Proculeius, friends of Caesar.

Pompey (Sextus Pompeius), a rebel at heart against the rulers.

Menas, Menecrates, Varrius, all friends of Pompey.

Taurus, lieutenant-general to Caesar.

Canidius, lieutenant-general to Mark Antony.

Euphronius, an ambassador from Mark Antony to Caesar.

Silius, an officer in the army of Ventidius.

Alexas, Mardian, Seleucus, Diomedes, attending Cleopatra.

Cleopatra, the beautiful Queen of Egypt.

Octavia, sister of Caesar, who marries Antony.

Charmian, lady-in-waiting to Cleopatra.

Iras, lady-in-waiting to Cleopatra.

A soothsayer and a clown.

Officers, soldiers, messengers, attendants.

SCENES—Italy and Egypt. TIME—Between about 40 B.C. and 30 B.C.

Antony and Cleopatra

ACT 1

Scene 1—Palace in Alexandria : Cleopatra and Antony approaching

PHILO *(to Demetrius).* Nay, but this dotage of our general's
O'erflows the measure : those his goodly eyes,
That o'er the files and musters of the war
Have glowed like plated Mars, now bend, now turn
The office and devotion of their view
Upon a tawny front. Look, where they come :
Take but good note, and you shall see in him
The triple pillar of the world transformed
Into a woman's fool : behold and see.

CLEOPATRA. If it be love indeed, tell me how much.

ANTONY. There's beggary in the love that can be reckoned.

CLEOPATRA. I'll set a bourn how far to be beloved.

ANTONY. Then must thou needs find out new heaven, new earth.

ATTENDANT. News, my good lord, from Rome.

CLEOPATRA. Hear them, Antony :
Fulvia perchance is angry ; or, who knows
If the scarce-bearded Caesar have not sent
His powerful mandate to you, *Do this, or this ;*
Take in that kingdom, and enfranchise that.
Perchance ! nay, and most like :
You must not stay here longer, your dismission
Is come from Caesar ; therefore hear it, Antony.
Call in the messengers. As I am Egypt's queen,
Thou blushest, Antony ; and that blood of thine
Is Caesar's homager : else so thy cheek pays shame
When shrill-tongued Fulvia scolds. The messengers !

ANTONY. Let Rome in Tiber melt, and the wide arch
Of the ranged empire fall ! Here is my space.
Kingdoms are clay : our dungy earth alike
Feeds beast as man : the nobleness of life
Is to do thus *(embracing her)*, when such a mutual pair
And such a twain can do 't, in which I bind,
On pain of punishment, the world to know
We stand up peerless.

CLEOPATRA. Excellent falsehood!
Why did he marry Fulvia, and not love her?
I'll seem the fool I am not; Antony
Will be himself.

ANTONY. But stirred by Cleopatra.
Now, for the love of Love and her soft hours,
Let's not confound the time with conference harsh:
There's not a minute of our lives should stretch
Without some pleasure now. What sport tonight?

CLEOPATRA. Hear the ambassadors.

ANTONY. Fie, wrangling queen!
Whom everything becomes, to chide, to laugh,
To weep; whose every passion fully strives
To make itself, in thee, fair and admired!
No messenger, but thine; and all alone
Tonight we'll wander through the streets and note
The qualities of people. Come, my queen;
Last night you did desire it: speak not to us.

Scene 2—Cleopatra's Palace

CHARMIAN. Lord Alexas, sweet Alexas, most anything Alexas, almost most absolute Alexas, where's the soothsayer that you praised so to the queen?

ALEXAS. Soothsayer!

SOOTHSAYER. Your will?

CHARMIAN. Good sir, give me good fortune.

He predicts that she will outlive her mistress, but experience worse fortune than she has so far enjoyed. Enobarbus enters and orders supper.

ENOBARBUS. Hush! here comes Antony.

CHARMIAN. Not he; the queen.

CLEOPATRA. Saw you my lord?

ENOBARBUS. No, lady.

CLEOPATRA. Was he not here?

CHARMIAN. No, madam.

CLEOPATRA. He was disposed to mirth; but on the sudden
A Roman thought hath struck him. Enobarbus!

ENOBARBUS. Madam?

CLEOPATRA. Seek him, and bring him hither. Where's Alexas?

ALEXAS. Here, at your service. My lord approaches.

CLEOPATRA. We will not look upon him: go with us.

Enter Antony with a Messenger and Attendants

MESSENGER. Fulvia thy wife first came into the field.

ANTONY. Against my brother Lucius?

MESSENGER. Ay:
But soon that war had end, and the time's state
Made friends of them, jointing their force 'gainst Caesar,
Whose better issue in the war, from Italy,
Upon the first encounter, drave them.

ANTONY. Well, what worst?

MESSENGER. The nature of bad news infects the teller.

ANTONY. When it concerns the fool or coward. On:
Things that are past are done with me. Tis thus:
Who tells me true, though in his tale lie death,
I hear him as he flattered.

MESSENGER. Labienus
(This is stiff news) hath, with his Parthian force,
Extended Asia from Euphrates;
His conquering banner shook from Syria
To Lydia and to Ionia; whilst—

ANTONY. Antony, thou wouldst say—

MESSENGER. O, my lord!

ANTONY. Speak to me home, mince not the general tongue:
Name Cleopatra as she is called in Rome;
Rail thou in Fulvia's phrase; and taunt my faults
With such full license as both truth and malice
Have power to utter. O, then we bring forth weeds
When our quick minds lie still; and our ills told us
Is as our earing. Fare thee well awhile.

MESSENGER. At your noble pleasure. *(He leaves)*

ANTONY. From Sicyon, ho, the news! Speak there!

FIRST ATTENDANT. The man from Sicyon—is there such a one?

SECOND ATTENDANT. He stays upon your will.

ANTONY. Let him appear.
These strong Egyptian fetters I must break,
Or lose myself in dotage. *(To another messenger)* What are you?

MESSENGER. Fulvia thy wife is dead.

ANTONY. Where died she?

MESSENGER. In Sicyon:
Her length of sickness, with what else more serious
Importeth thee to know, this bears. *(Gives him a letter)*

ANTONY. There's a great spirit gone! Thus did I desire it:
What our contempt doth often hurl from us,
We wish it ours again. She's good, being gone;
I must from this enchanting queen break off:
Ten thousand harms, more than the ills I know,
My idleness doth hatch. How now! Enobarbus!

ENOBARBUS *(entering)*. What's your pleasure, sir?

ANTONY. I must with haste from hence.

ENOBARBUS. Why, then, we kill all our women: we see how mortal an unkindness is to them; if they suffer our departure, death's the word.

ANTONY. I must be gone.

ENOBARBUS. Under a compelling occasion, let women die: it were pity to cast them away for nothing, though between them and a great cause they should be esteemed nothing. Cleopatra, catching but the least noise of this, dies instantly; I have seen her die twenty times upon far poorer moment. I do think there is mettle in death, which commits some loving act upon her, she hath such a celerity in dying.

ANTONY. She is cunning past man's thoughts.

ENOBARBUS. Alack, sir, no; her passions are made of nothing but the finest part of pure love. We cannot call her winds and waters sighs and tears; they are greater storms and tempests than almanacs can report: this cannot be cunning in her; if it be, she makes a shower of rain as well as Jove.

ANTONY. Would I had never seen her!

ENOBARBUS. O, sir, you had then left unseen a wonderful piece of work, which not to have been blest withal would have discredited your travel.

ANTONY. Fulvia is dead.

ENOBARBUS. Sir?

ANTONY. Fulvia is dead.

ENOBARBUS. Fulvia!

ANTONY. Dead.

ENOBARBUS. Why, sir, give the gods a thankful sacrifice. If there were no more women but Fulvia, then had you indeed a case to be lamented. This grief is crowned with consolation, and indeed the tears live in an onion that should water this sorrow.

ANTONY. The business she hath broached in the State
Cannot endure my absence.

ENOBARBUS. And the business you have broached here cannot be without you; especially Cleopatra's, which wholly depends on your abode.

ANTONY. No more light answers. Let our officers
Have notice what we purpose. I shall break
The cause of our expedience to the queen,
And get her leave to part. For not alone
The death of Fulvia, with more urgent touches,
Do strongly speak to us, but the letters too
Of many our contriving friends in Rome
Petition us at home: Sextus Pompeius

Hath given the dare to Caesar, and commands
The empire of the sea : our slippery people,
Whose love is never linked to the deserver
Till his deserts are past, begin to throw
Pompey the Great and all his dignities
Upon his son ; who, high in name and power,
Higher than both in blood and life, stands up
For the main soldier ; whose quality, going on,
The sides of the world may danger : much is breeding.
Say our pleasure requires our quick remove from hence.

ENOBARBUS. I shall do 't.

Scene 3—Cleopatra's Palace

Cleopatra, learning from Antony that he must go to Rome, seeks by all her arts to retain him, but the news of the serious situation at home steels his resolution, and he resists her. In the end she bids him go, saying :

Your honour calls you hence ;
Therefore be deaf to my unpitied folly,
And all the gods go with you.

Scene 4—Caesar's House in Rome

Caesar reading a letter, Lepidus following

CAESAR. You may see, Lepidus, and henceforth know,
It is not Caesar's natural vice to hate
Our great competitor : from Alexandria
This is the news : he fishes, drinks, and wastes
The lamps of night in revel ; is not more manlike
Than Cleopatra ; nor the queen of Ptolemy
More womanly than he ; hardly gave audience, or
Vouchsafed to think he had partners : you shall find there
A man who is the abstract of all faults
That all men follow.

LEPIDUS. I must not think there are
Evils enow to darken all his goodness :
His faults in him seem as the spots of heaven,
More fiery by night's blackness ; hereditary,
Rather than purchased ; what he cannot change,
Than what he chooses.

CAESAR. You are too indulgent. Let us grant it is not
Amiss to give a kingdom for a mirth ; to sit
And keep the turn of tippling with a slave ;
To reel the streets at noon, and stand the buffet
With knaves that smell of sweat : say this becomes him
(As his composure must be rare indeed
Whom these things cannot blemish), yet must Antony
No way excuse his soils, when we do bear
So great weight in his lightness.

LEPIDUS *(observing a messenger)*. Here's more news.

MESSENGER. Thy biddings have been done; and every hour,
Most noble Caesar, shalt thou have report
How tis abroad. Pompey is strong at sea;
And it appears he is beloved of those
That only have feared Caesar: to the ports
The discontents repair, and men's reports
Give him much wronged. Menecrates and Menas, famous pirates,
Make the sea serve them, which they ear and wound
With keels of every kind: many hot inroads
They make in Italy; the borders maritime
Lack blood to think on 't, and flush youth revolt:
No vessel can peep forth, but tis as soon
Taken as seen; for Pompey's name strikes more
Than could his war resisted.

CAESAR. Antony, leave thy wassails! When thou once
Wast beaten from Modena, where thou slew'st
Hirtius and Pansa, consuls, at thy heel
Did famine follow, whom thou fought'st against,
Though daintily brought up, with patience more
Than savages could suffer: thy palate then did deign
The roughest berry on the rudest hedge;
Yea, like the stag, when snow the pasture sheets,
The barks of trees thou browsed'st; on the Alps
It is reported thou didst eat strange flesh,
Which some did die to look on: and all this
(It wounds thine honour that I speak it now)
Was borne so like a soldier that thy cheek
So much as lanked not.

LEPIDUS. Tis pity of him.

CAESAR. Let his shames quickly
Drive him to Rome: tis time we twain
Did show ourselves i' the field; and to that end
Assemble we immediate council: Pompey
Thrives in our idleness.

LEPIDUS. Tomorrow, Caesar,
I shall be furnished to inform you rightly
Both what by sea and land I can be able
To front this present time.

CAESAR. Till which encounter,
It is my business too. Farewell.

Scene 5—Cleopatra in her Palace

CLEOPATRA. O Charmian,
Where think'st thou he is now? Stands he, or sits he?
Or does he walk? Or is he on his horse?

O happy horse, to bear the weight of Antony!
Do bravely, horse! for wot'st thou whom thou movest?
The demi-Atlas of this earth, the arm
And burgonet of men. He's speaking now,
Or murmuring *Where's my serpent of old Nile?*
For so he calls me.

ALEXAS *(entering)*. Sovereign of Egypt, hail!

CLEOPATRA. How goes it with my brave Mark Antony?

ALEXAS. Last thing he did, dear queen,
He kissed (the last of many doubled kisses)
This orient pearl. His speech sticks in my heart.

CLEOPATRA. Mine ear must pluck it thence.

ALEXAS. *Good friend* (quoth he),
Say, the firm Roman to great Egypt sends
This treasure of an oyster; at whose foot,
To mend the petty present, I will piece
Her opulent throne with kingdoms; all the east,
Say thou, shall call her mistress. So he nodded,
And soberly did mount an arm-gaunt steed,
Who neighed so high that what I would have spoke
Was beastly dumbed by him.

CLEOPATRA. What, was he sad or merry?

ALEXAS. Like to the time o' the year between the extremes
Of hot and cold, he was nor sad nor merry.

CLEOPATRA. O well-divided disposition! Note him,
Note him, good Charmian, tis the man, but note him:
He was not sad, for he would shine on those
That make their looks by his; he was not merry,
Which seemed to tell them his remembrance lay
In Egypt with his joy; but between both:
O heavenly mingle! Be'st thou sad or merry,
The violence of either thee becomes,
So does it no man else. Met'st thou my posts?

ALEXAS. Ay, madam, twenty several messengers.

CLEOPATRA. Who's born that day
When I forget to send to Antony
Shall die a beggar. Ink and paper, Charmian.
Welcome, my good Alexas. Did I, Charmian,
Ever love Caesar so?

CHARMIAN. O that brave Caesar!

CLEOPATRA. Be choked with such another emphasis!
Say, *the brave Antony*. Get me ink and paper:
He shall have every day a several greeting,
Or I'll unpeople Egypt.

ACT 2

Scene 1—Pompey's House in Messina

Pompey discusses with Menecrates the prospects of his campaign, and hopefully counts upon the love of the people for him, their coldness towards Caesar and his exactions, the instability of Lepidus, and the sloth of the absent Antony. He learns from Varrius, however, that Caesar and Lepidus are in the field, and hourly expecting Antony in Rome, a surprise which draws from Pompey the comment on Antony that "his soldiership is twice the other twain." But, with their profound causes for disagreement, will the three agree? Pompey sums up.

POMPEY. But how the fear of us
May cement their divisions and bind up
The petty difference, we yet not know.
Be 't as our gods will have 't! It only stands
Our lives upon to use our strongest hands.

Scene 2—The House of Lepidus in Rome: Lepidus and Enobarbus

LEPIDUS. Good Enobarbus, tis a worthy deed,
And shall become you well, to entreat your captain
To soft and gentle speech.
ENOBARBUS. I shall entreat him
To answer like himself: if Caesar move him,
Let Antony look over Caesar's head
And speak as loud as Mars.
LEPIDUS. Tis not a time for private stomaching.
ENOBARBUS. Every time
Serves for the matter that is then born in 't.
LEPIDUS. But small to greater matters must give way.
ENOBARBUS. Not if the small come first.
LEPIDUS. Your speech is passion:
But, pray you, stir no embers up. Here comes
The noble Antony.
ENOBARBUS. And yonder, Caesar.

Enter Antony with Ventidius, and Caesar with Mecaenas and Agrippa

ANTONY. If we compose well here, to Parthia:
Hark, Ventidius.
CAESAR. I do not know,
Mecaenas; ask Agrippa.
LEPIDUS. Noble friends,
That which combined us was most great, and let not
A leaner action rend us. What's amiss,
May it be gently heard: when we debate
Our trivial difference loud, we do commit
Murder in healing wounds: then, noble partners,
The rather, for I earnestly beseech,
Touch you the sourest points with sweetest terms.

ANTONY. Tis spoken well.
Were we before our armies, and to fight,
I should do thus.

CAESAR. Welcome to Rome.

ANTONY. Thank you.
I learn you take things ill which are not so.
My being in Egypt, Caesar, what was't to you ?

CAESAR. No more than my residing here at Rome
Might be to you in Egypt : yet, if you there
Did practise on my state, your being in Egypt
Might be my question.

ANTONY. How intend you, practised ?

CAESAR. You may be pleased to catch at mine intent
By what did here befal me. Your wife and brother
Made wars upon me ; and their contestation
Was theme for you—you were the word of war.

ANTONY. You do mistake your business ; my brother never
Did urge me in his act : I did inquire it,
And have my learning from some true reports,
That drew their swords with you. If you patch a quarrel
It must not be with this.

CAESAR. You praise yourself
By laying defects of judgment to me ; but
You patched up your excuses. I wrote to you
When rioting in Alexandria ; you
Did pocket up my letters, and with taunts
Did gibe my missive out of audience.

ANTONY. Sir, he fell upon me ere admitted : then
Three kings I had newly feasted, and did want
Of what I was i' the morning : but next day
I told him of myself ; which was as much
As to have asked him pardon. Let this fellow
Be nothing of our strife ; if we contend,
Out of our question wipe him.

CAESAR. You have broken
The article of your oath ; which you shall never
Have tongue to charge me with.

LEPIDUS. Soft, Caesar !

ANTONY. No, Lepidus, let him speak :
The honour is sacred which he talks on now,
Supposing that I lacked it. But, on, Caesar ;
The article of my oath.

CAESAR. To lend me arms and aid when I required them ;
The which you both denied.

ANTONY. Neglected, rather;
And then when poisoned hours had bound me up
From mine own knowledge. As nearly as I may
I'll play the penitent to you, but mine honesty
Shall not make poor my greatness, nor my power
Work without it. Truth is that Fulvia,
To have me out of Egypt, made wars here;
For which myself, the ignorant motive, do
So far ask pardon as befits mine honour
To stoop in such a case.

LEPIDUS. Tis noble spoken.

MECAENAS. If it might please you, to enforce no further
The griefs between ye: to forget them quite
Were to remember that the present need
Speaks to atone you.

LEPIDUS. Worthily spoken, Mecaenas.

ENOBARBUS. Or, if you borrow one another's love for the instant, you may, when you hear no more words of Pompey, return it again: you shall have time to wrangle in when you have nothing else to do.

ANTONY. Thou art a soldier only: speak no more.

ENOBARBUS. That truth should be silent I had almost forgot.

ANTONY. You wrong this presence; therefore speak no more.

CAESAR. I do not much dislike the matter, but
The manner of his speech; for 't cannot be
We shall remain in friendship, our conditions
So differing in their acts. Yet, if I knew
What hoop should hold us stanch, from edge to edge
O' the world I would pursue it.

AGRIPPA. Give me leave, Caesar.
Thou hast a sister by the mother's side,
Admired Octavia: great Mark Antony
Is now a widower.

CAESAR. Say not so, Agrippa:
If Cleopatra heard you, your reproof
Were well deserved of rashness.

ANTONY. I am not married, Caesar: let me hear
Agrippa further speak.

AGRIPPA. To hold you in perpetual amity,
To make you brothers, and to knit your hearts
With an unslipping knot, take Antony
Octavia to his wife; whose beauty claims
No worse a husband than the best of men;
Whose virtue and whose general graces speak
That which none else can utter. By this marriage,
All little jealousies, which now seem great,

And all great fears, which now import their dangers,
Would then be nothing.

ANTONY. Will Caesar speak?

CAESAR. Not till he hears how Antony is touched
With what is spoke already.

ANTONY. What power is in Agrippa,
If I would say, *Agrippa, be it so,*
To make this good?

CAESAR. The power of Caesar, and
His power unto Octavia.

ANTONY. May I never
To this good purpose, that so fairly shows,
Dream of impediment! Let me have thy hand:
Further this act of grace, and from this hour
The heart of brothers govern in our loves
And sway our great designs!

CAESAR. There is my hand.
A sister I bequeath you, whom no brother
Did ever love so dearly: let her live
To join our kingdoms and our hearts; and never
Fly off our loves again!

LEPIDUS. Happily, amen!

ANTONY. I did not think to draw my sword 'gainst Pompey;
For he hath laid strange courtesies and great
Of late upon me: I must thank him only,
Lest my remembrance suffer ill report;
At heel of that, defy him.

LEPIDUS. Time calls upon us:
Of us must Pompey presently be sought,
Or else he seeks out us.

ANTONY. Where lies he?

CAESAR. About the mount Misenum.

ANTONY. What is his strength by land?

CAESAR. Great and increasing; but by sea
He is an absolute master.

ANTONY. So is the fame.
Would we had spoke together! Haste we for it:
Yet, ere we put ourselves in arms, dispatch we
The business we have talked of.

CAESAR. With most gladness;
And do invite you to my sister's view,
Whither straight I'll lead you.

ANTONY. Let us, Lepidus, not lack your company.

LEPIDUS. Noble Antony, not sickness should detain me.

Caesar, Antony, and Lepidus leave

MECAENAS *(to Enobarbus)*. Welcome from Egypt, sir.

ENOBARBUS. Half the heart of Caesar, worthy Mecaenas! My honourable friend, Agrippa!

AGRIPPA. Good Enobarbus!

MECAENAS. We have cause to be glad that matters are so well digested. You stayed well by 't in Egypt.

ENOBARBUS. Ay, sir; we did sleep day out of countenance, and made the night light with drinking.

MECAENAS. Eight wild-boars roasted whole at a breakfast, and but twelve persons there; is this true?

ENOBARBUS. This was but as a fly by an eagle: we had much more monstrous matter of feast, which worthily deserved noting.

MECAENAS. A most triumphant lady, if report be square to her.

ENOBARBUS. When she first met Mark Antony she pursed up his heart, upon the river of Cydnus.
The barge she sat in, like a burnished throne,
Burned on the water: the poop was beaten gold;
Purple the sails, and so perfumèd that
The winds were love-sick with them; the oars were silver
Which to the tune of flutes kept stroke, and made
The water which they beat to follow faster,
As amorous of their strokes. For her own person
It beggared all description: she did lie
In her pavilion, cloth-of-gold of tissue,
O'er-picturing that Venus where we see
The fancy outwork nature: on each side her
Stood pretty dimpled boys, like smiling Cupids,
With divers-coloured fans, whose wind did seem
To glow the delicate cheeks which they did cool,
And what they undid did.

AGRIPPA. O, rare for Antony!

ENOBARBUS. Her gentlewomen, like the Nereides,
So many mermaids, tended her i' the eyes,
And made their bends adornings: at the helm
A seeming mermaid steers: the silken tackle
Swell with the touches of those flower-soft hands,
That yarely frame the office. From the barge
A strange invisible perfume hits the sense
Of the adjacent wharfs. The city cast
Her people out upon her; and Antony,
Enthroned i' the market-place, did sit alone,
Whistling to the air—which, but for vacancy,

Had gone to gaze on Cleopatra too
And made a gap in nature.

AGRIPPA. Rare Egyptian!

ENOBARBUS. Upon her landing, Antony sent to her,
Invited her to supper: she replied,
It should be better he became her guest;
Which she entreated: our courteous Antony,
Whom ne'er the word of *No* woman heard speak,
Being barbered ten times o'er, goes to the feast,
And for his ordinary pays his heart
For what his eyes eat only.
I saw her once
Hop forty paces through the public street;
And, having lost her breath, she spoke, and panted,
That she did make defect perfection,
And, breathless, power breathe forth.

MECAENAS. Now Antony must leave her utterly.

ENOBARBUS. Never; he will not:
Age cannot wither her, nor custom stale
Her infinite variety: other women cloy
The appetites they feed, but she makes hungry
Where most she satisfies.

MECAENAS. If beauty, wisdom, modesty, can settle
The heart of Antony, Octavia is
A blessed lottery to him.

AGRIPPA. Let us go.
Good Enobarbus, make yourself my guest
Whilst you abide here.

ENOBARBUS. Humbly, sir, I thank you.

Scene 3—Caesar's House; Caesar and Antony with Octavia

ANTONY. The world and my great office will sometimes
Divide me from your bosom.

OCTAVIA. All which time
Before the gods my knee shall bow my prayers
To them for you.

ANTONY. Good-night, sir. My Octavia,
Read not my blemishes in the world's report:
I have not kept my square; but that to come
Shall all be done by the rule. Good-night, dear lady.
Good-night, sir.

Antony is alone, when a Soothsayer enters

ANTONY. Now, sirrah; you do wish yourself in Egypt?

SOOTHSAYER. Would I had never come from thence, nor you thither!
But yet hie you to Egypt again.

ANTONY. Say to me,
Whose fortunes shall rise higher, Caesar's or mine ?

SOOTHSAYER. Caesar's.
Therefore, O Antony, stay not by his side :
Thy demon, that's thy spirit which keeps thee, is
Noble, courageous, high, unmatchable,
Where Caesar's is not ; but, near him, thy angel
Becomes a fear, as being o'erpowered : therefore
Make space enough between you.

ANTONY. Speak this no more.

SOOTHSAYER. To none but thee ; no more but when to thee.
If thou dost play with him at any game,
Thou art sure to lose ; and, of that natural luck,
He beats thee 'gainst the odds : thy lustre thickens
When he shines by : I say again, thy spirit
Is all afraid to govern thee near him ;
But, he away, tis noble.

ANTONY *(as Soothsayer goes)*. Get thee gone :
Say to Ventidius I would speak with him.
He shall to Parthia. Be it art or hap,
He hath spoken true : the very dice obey him ;
And in our sports my better cunning faints
Under his chance : if we draw lots, he speeds ;
His cocks do win the battle still of mine
When it is all to nought ; and his quails ever
Beat mine, inhooped, at odds. I will to Egypt
And though I make this marriage for my peace,
I' the east my pleasure lies.

Scene 4—A Street in Rome

In this scene the soldiers are departing to the Parthian wars

Scene 5—Cleopatra's Palace

CLEOPATRA. Give me some music ; music, moody food
Of us that trade in love.

ATTENDANT. The music, ho !

CLEOPATRA. Let it alone ; let's to billiards : come, Charmian.

CHARMIAN. My arm is sore ; best play with Mardian.

CLEOPATRA. Give me mine angle ; we'll to the river : there,
My music playing far off, I will betray
Tawny-finned fishes ; my bended hook shall pierce
Their slimy jaws ; and, as I draw them up,
I'll think them every one an Antony,
And say *Ah, ha ! you're caught.*

CHARMIAN. Twas merry when
You wagered on your angling; when your diver
Did hang a salt-fish on his hook, which he
With fervency drew up.

As Cleopatra recalls memories of Antony, a messenger brings her word that he has married Octavia. In rage she beats the man and threatens him with horrible death; in anguish she offers him gold and a province to say the story is false. All the emotions of a proud and jealous queen are stirred in turn, until curiosity masters her and she bids Alexas seek out the terrified messenger, who has fled.

CLEOPATRA. Go to the fellow, good Alexas; bid him
Report the feature of Octavia, her years,
Her inclination, let him not leave out
The colour of her hair: bring me word quickly.
Let him for ever go:—let him not, Charmian,
Though he be painted one way like a Gorgon,
The other way's a Mars. *(To Mardian)* Bid you Alexas
Bring me word how tall she is. Pity me, Charmian,
But do not speak to me. Lead me to my chamber.

Scene 6—Near Misenum

Enter Pompey and Menas, with drum and trumpet on one side: Caesar, Antony, Lepidus, and followers on the other side.

POMPEY. Your hostages I have, so have you mine;
And we shall talk before we fight.

CAESAR. Most meet
That first we come to words; and therefore have we
Our written purposes before us sent;
Which, if thou hast considered, let us know
If 'twill tie up thy discontented sword,
And carry back to Sicily much tall youth
That else must perish here.

POMPEY. To you all three,
The senators alone of this great world,
Chief factors for the gods, I do not know
Wherefore my father should revengers want,
Having a son and friends; since Julius Caesar,
Who at Philippi the good Brutus ghosted,
There saw you labouring for him. What was't
That moved pale Cassius to conspire; and what
Made the all-honoured, honest Roman, Brutus,
With the armed rest, courtiers of beauteous freedom,
To drench the Capitol, but that they would
Have one man but a man? And that is it
Hath made me rig my navy; at whose burthen
The angered ocean foams; with which I meant

To scourge the ingratitude that despiteful Rome
Cast on my noble father.

CAESAR. Take your time.

ANTONY. Thou canst not fear us, Pompey, with thy sails;
We'll speak with thee at sea: at land, thou know'st
How much we do o'er-count thee.

POMPEY. At land, indeed,
Thou dost o'er-count me of my father's house:
But, since the cuckoo builds not for himself,
Remain in't as thou mayst.

LEPIDUS. Be pleased to tell us
(For this is from the present) how you take
The offers we have sent you.

POMPEY. You have made me offer
Of Sicily, Sardinia; and I must
Rid all the sea of pirates; then, to send
Measures of wheat to Rome.
I came before you here a man prepared
To take this offer: but Mark Antony
Put me to some impatience: though I lose
The praise of it by telling, you must know,
When Caesar and your brother were at blows,
Your mother came to Sicily and did find
Her welcome friendly.

ANTONY. I have heard it, Pompey;
And am well studied for a liberal thanks
Which I do owe you.

POMPEY. Let me have your hand:
I did not think, sir, to have met you here.

ANTONY. The beds i' the east are soft; and thanks to you.
That called me timelier than my purpose hither,
For I have gained by 't.

CAESAR. Since I saw you last,
There is a change upon you.

POMPEY. Well, I know not
What counts harsh fortune casts upon my face;
But in my bosom shall she never come,
To make my heart her vassal.

LEPIDUS. Well met here.

POMPEY. I hope so, Lepidus. Thus we are agreed:
I crave our composition may be written,
And sealed between us.

CAESAR. That's the next to do.

POMPEY. Aboard my galley I invite you all:
Will you lead, lords?

As they file out Menas whispers to Pompey, "Thy father would ne'er have made this treaty." Menas then turns to Enobarbus, from whom he learns of Antony's marriage. Enobarbus protests that, as Octavia is "of a holy, cold, and still conversation," Antony will leave her for Cleopatra and so bring on strife with Caesar.

Scene 7—On Pompey's Galley off Misenum

ANTONY *(to Caesar)*. Thus do they, sir: they take the flow o' the Nile
By certain scales i' the pyramid; they know,
By the height, the lowness, or the mean, if dearth
Or foison follow: the higher Nilus swells,
The more it promises: as it ebbs, the seedsman
Upon the slime and ooze scatters his grain,
And shortly comes to harvest.

LEPIDUS. You've strange serpents there.

ANTONY. Ay, Lepidus.

LEPIDUS. Your serpent of Egypt is bred now of your mud by the operation of your sun: so is your crocodile.

ANTONY. They are so.

Menas now proposes that Pompey should slip the cable of the galley, carry off Caesar, Antony, and Lepidus, kill them, and so become master of the world; but he received this answer:

POMPEY. Ah, this thou shouldst have done,
And not have spoke on't! In me tis villainy;
In thee 't had been good service. Thou must know,
Tis not my profit that does lead mine honour;
Mine honour, it. Repent that e'er thy tongue
Hath so betrayed thine act: being done unknown,
I should have found it afterwards well done,
But must condemn it now. Desist, and drink.

MENAS. For this
I'll never follow thy palled fortunes more.
Who seeks, and will not take when once tis offered,
Shall never find it more.

POMPEY *(returning to the feast)*. This health to Lepidus!

ANTONY. Bear him ashore. I'll pledge it for him, Pompey.

ENOBARBUS. Here's to thee, Menas!

MENAS. Enobarbus, welcome!

POMPEY. Fill till the cup be hid.

ANTONY. Here is to Caesar!

CAESAR. I could well forbear 't.
It's monstrous labour, when I wash my brain,
And it grows fouler.

ANTONY. Be a child o' the time.

CAESAR. But I had rather fast from all four days
Than drink so much in one.
What would you more? Pompey, Good-night. Good brother,
Let me request you off: our graver business
Frowns at this levity. Gentle lords, let's part;
You see we have burnt our cheeks: strong Enobarb
Is weaker than the wine; and mine own tongue
Splits what it speaks: the wild disguise hath almost
Anticked us all. What needs more words? Good-night.
Good Antony, your hand.

ACT 3

Scene 1—A Plain in Syria

This scene shows Ventidius bearing in triumph the body of a fallen king, having won the Parthian war for Mark Antony.

Scene 2—A Room in Caesar's House

Enter Agrippa at one door, Enobarbus at another

AGRIPPA. What, are the brothers parted?

ENOBARBUS. They have dispatched with Pompey, he is gone;

AGRIPPA. Tis a noble Lepidus.

ENOBARBUS. A very fine one: O, how he loves Caesar!

AGRIPPA. Nay, but how dearly he adores Mark Antony!

ENOBARBUS. Caesar? Why, he's the Jupiter of men.

AGRIPPA. What's Antony? The god of Jupiter.

ENOBARBUS. Spake you of Caesar? How! the nonpareil!

AGRIPPA. O Antony! O thou Arabian bird!

ENOBARBUS. But he loves Caesar best; yet he loves Antony:
Ho! hearts, tongues, figures, scribes, bards, poets, cannot
Think, speak, cast, write, sing, number, ho!
His love to Antony. But as for Caesar,
Kneel down, kneel down, and wonder.

AGRIPPA. Both he loves.

ENOBARBUS. They are his shards, and he their beetle.

Enter Caesar, Antony, Lepidus, and Octavia, trumpets sounding

ANTONY. No further, sir.

CAESAR. You take from me a great part of myself;
Use me well in 't. Sister, prove such a wife
As my thoughts make thee, and as my farthest band
Shall pass on thy approof. Most noble Antony,

Let not the piece of virtue, which is set
Betwixt us as the *ce*ment of our love,
To keep it builded, be the ram to batter
The fortress of it; for better might we
Have loved without this mean, if on both parts
This be not cherished.

ANTONY. You shall not find,
Though you be therein curious, the least cause
For what you seem to fear: so, the gods keep you,
And make the hearts of Romans serve your ends!
We will here part.

CAESAR. Farewell, my dearest sister, fare thee well:
The elements be kind to thee, and make
Thy spirits all of comfort! fare thee well.

OCTAVIA. My noble brother!

ANTONY. The April's in her eyes: it is love's spring,
And these the showers to bring it on. Be cheerful.

OCTAVIA. Sir, look well to my husband's house; and—

CAESAR. What, Octavia?

OCTAVIA. I'll tell you in your ear.

ANTONY. Her tongue will not obey her heart, nor can
Her heart obey her tongue; the swan's down-feather,
That stands upon the swell at full of tide,
And neither way inclines.

CAESAR. No, sweet Octavia,
You shall hear from me still; the time shall not
Out-go my thinking on you.

ANTONY. Come, sir, come;
I'll wrestle with you in my strength of love:
Look, here I have you; thus I let you go,
And give you to the gods.

CAESAR. Adieu; be happy!

LEPIDUS. Let all the number of the stars give light
To thy fair way!

CAESAR *(kissing Octavia)*. Farewell, farewell!

ANTONY. Farewell!

Scene 3—Cleopatra's Palace

CLEOPATRA. Where is the fellow?

ALEXAS. Half afeard to come.

CLEOPATRA. Go to, go to. Come hither, sir.

ALEXAS. Good majesty,
Herod of Jewry dare not look upon you
But when you are well pleased.

CLEOPATRA. That Herod's head
I'll have : but how, when Antony is gone
Through whom I might command it ? Come thou near.

MESSENGER *(approaching)*. Most gracious majesty—

CLEOPATRA. Didst thou behold Octavia ?

MESSENGER. Ay, dread queen.

CLEOPATRA. Where ?

MESSENGER. Madam, in Rome ;
I looked her in the face, and saw her led
Between her brother and Mark Antony.

CLEOPATRA. Is she as tall as me ?

MESSENGER. She is not, madam.

CLEOPATRA. Didst hear her speak ? is she shrill-tongued or low ?

MESSENGER. Madam, I heard her speak ; she is low-voiced.

CLEOPATRA. That's not so good : he cannot like her long.

CHARMIAN. Like her ! O Isis ! tis impossible.

CLEOPATRA. I think so, Charmian : dull of tongue, and dwarfish !
What majesty is in her gait ? Remember,
If e'er thou look'dst on majesty.

MESSENGER. She creeps :
Her motion and her station are as one :
She shows a body rather than a life,
A statue than a breather.

CLEOPATRA. Is this certain ?

MESSENGER. Or I have no observance.

CHARMIAN. Three in Egypt cannot make better note.

CLEOPATRA. He's very knowing ;
I do perceive 't : there's nothing in her yet :
The fellow has good judgment.

CHARMIAN. Excellent.

CLEOPATRA. Guess at her years, I prithee.

MESSENGER. Madam, she was a widow.

CLEOPATRA. Widow ! Charmian, hark.

MESSENGER. And I do think she's thirty.

CLEOPATRA. Bear'st thou her face in mind ? is't long or round ?

MESSENGER. Round even to faultiness.

CLEOPATRA. For the most part, too, they are foolish that are so.
Her hair, what colour ?

MESSENGER. Brown, madam : and her forehead
As low as she would wish it.

CLEOPATRA. There's gold for thee.
Thou must not take my former sharpness ill :
I will employ thee back again ; I find thee

Most fit for business: go make thee ready;
Our letters are prepared.

CHARMIAN. A proper man.

CLEOPATRA. Indeed, he is so: I repent me much
That so I harried him. Why, methinks, by him,
This creature's no such thing.
The man hath seen some majesty, and should know.

CHARMIAN. Hath he seen majesty? Isis else defend,
And serving you so long!

CLEOPATRA. I have one thing more to ask him yet, good Charmian:
But tis no matter; thou shalt bring him to me
Where I will write. All may be well enough.

CHARMIAN. I warrant you, madam.

Scene 4—Antony's House in Athens: Octavia and Antony

ANTONY. Nay, nay, Octavia, not only that
(That were excusable, that, and thousands more
Of semblable import), but he hath waged
New wars 'gainst Pompey; made his will, and read it
To public ear:
Spoke scantly of me: when perforce he could not
But pay me terms of honour, cold and sickly
He vented them; most narrow measure lent me:
When the best hint was given him, he not took 't,
Or did it from his teeth.

OCTAVIA. O my good lord,
Believe not all; or, if you must believe,
Stomach not all. A more unhappy lady,
If this division chance, ne'er stood between,
Praying for both parts:
The good gods will mock me presently,
When I shall pray, *O, bless my lord and husband!*
Undo that prayer, by crying out as loud,
O, bless my brother!

ANTONY. Gentle Octavia, if I lose mine honour,
I lose myself: better I were not yours
Than yours so branchless. But, as you requested,
Yourself shall go between 's: the meantime, lady,
I'll raise the preparation of a war
Shall stain your brother; make your soonest haste;
So your desires are yours.

OCTAVIA. Thanks to my lord.
The Jove of power make me most weak, most weak,
Your reconciler! Wars 'twixt you twain would be
As if the world should cleave, and that slain men
Should solder up the rift.

ANTONY. When it appears to you where this begins,
Turn your displeasure that way ; for our faults
Can never be so equal that your love
Can equally move with them. Provide your going ;
Choose your own company, and command what cost
Your heart has mind to.

Scene 5—Antony's House in Athens

Eros and Enobarbus are discussing the war Caesar has declared on Pompey. Caesar has seized and imprisoned Lepidus, and they both agree that this is the beginning of trouble with Antony.

Scene 6—Caesar's House in Rome : Caesar, Agrippa, and Mecaenas

CAESAR. Contemning Rome, he has done all this, and more,
In Alexandria : here's the manner of 't :
I' the market-place, on a tribunal silvered,
Cleopatra and himself in chairs of gold
Were publicly enthroned. Unto her
He gave the stablishment of Egypt ; made her
Of lower Syria, Cyprus, Lydia, absolute queen.

MECAENAS. This in the public eye ?

CAESAR. I' the common show-place, where they exercise.
His sons he there proclaimed the kings of kings :
Great Media, Parthia, and Armenia,
He gave to Alexander ; to Ptolemy he assigned
Syria, Cilicia, and Phoenicia : she
In the habiliments of the goddess Isis
That day appeared, and oft before gave audience,
As tis reported, so.

MECAENAS. Let Rome be thus informed.

AGRIPPA. Who, queasy with his insolence
Already, will their good thoughts call from him.

CAESAR. The people know it ; and have now received
His accusations.

AGRIPPA. Whom does he accuse ?

CAESAR. Caesar : and that, having in Sicily
Sextus Pompeius spoiled, we had not rated him
His part o' the isle : then does he say he lent me
Some shipping unrestored : lastly, he frets
That Lepidus of the triumvirate
Should be deposed ; and, being, that we detain
All his revenue.

AGRIPPA. Sir, this should be answered.

CAESAR. Tis done already, and the messenger gone.
I have told him Lepidus was grown too cruel;
That he his high authority abused,
And did deserve his change: for what I have conquered,
I grant him part; but then, in his Armenia,
And other of his conquered kingdoms, I
Demand the like.

MECAENAS. He'll never yield to that.

CAESAR. Nor must not then be yielded to in this.

Enter Octavia with her train

OCTAVIA. Hail, Caesar, and my lord! Hail, most dear Caesar!

CAESAR. That ever I should call thee castaway!

OCTAVIA. You have not called me so, nor have you cause.

CAESAR. Why have you stolen upon us thus? You come not
Like Caesar's sister: the wife of Antony
Should have an army for an usher, and
The neighs of horse to tell of her approach
Long ere she did appear; the trees by the way
Should have borne men; and expectation fainted,
Longing for what it had not; nay, the dust
Should have ascended to the roof of heaven,
Raised by your populous troops. But you are come
A market-maid to Rome; and have prevented
The ostentation of our love, which, left unshown,
Is often left unloved: we should have met you
By sea and land; supplying every stage
With an augmented greeting.

OCTAVIA. Good my lord,
To come thus was I not constrained, but did
On my free will. My lord, Mark Antony,
Hearing that you prepared for war, acquainted
My grieved ear withal; whereon I begged
His pardon for return.

CAESAR. I have eyes upon him,
And his affairs come to me on the wind.
Where is he now?

OCTAVIA. My lord, in Athens.

CAESAR. No, my most wronged sister; Cleopatra
Hath nodded him to her. He hath given his empire,
Levying the kings o' the earth for war.

OCTAVIA. Ay me, most wretched,
That have my heart parted betwixt two friends
That do afflict each other!

CAESAR. Welcome hither:
Your letters did withhold our breaking forth,
Till we perceived, both how you were wrong led
And we in negligent danger. Cheer your heart:
Be you not troubled with the time, which drives
O'er your content these strong necessities;
But let determined things to destiny
Hold unbewailed their way. Welcome to Rome;
Nothing more dear to me. You are abused
Beyond the mark of thought: and the high gods,
To do you justice, make them ministers
Of us and those that love you. Best of comfort;
And ever welcome to us.

MECAENAS. Welcome, dear madam.
Each heart in Rome does love and pity you.

OCTAVIA. Is it so, sir?

CAESAR. Most certain. Sister, welcome: pray you,
Be ever known to patience: my dear'st sister!

Scene 7—At Actium

Cleopatra is rebuked by Enobarbus for hampering Antony by her presence in his camp. "Tis said in Rome that Photinus and your maids manage this war," he tells her. Cleopatra insists that her place is with Antony, who now enters, to learn that Caesar has crossed the sea and taken Toryne. Antony declares that he will fight at sea, though reminded that Caesar's men are practised warriors of the sea, whereas Antony's sea forces are ill-drilled levies, and his ships slow and inferior. Nevertheless, Antony will have his sea battle, and, if that fails, then a second battle, and victory on land. His decision is received with apprehension by his advisers, but the determined Roman goes his way.

Scene 8—The Plain near Actium

Canidius marching his soldiers one way; Taurus, Caesar's lieutenant, marching the other way. The noise of a sea fight is heard.

ENOBARBUS. Naught, naught, all naught! I can behold no longer:
The Antoniad, the Egyptian admiral,
With all their sixty, fly and turn the rudder.

SCARUS *(entering)*. Gods and goddesses,
All the whole synod of them!
The greater cantle of the world is lost
With very ignorance; we have kissed away
Kingdoms and provinces.

ENOBARBUS. How appears the fight?

SCARUS. On our side like the tokened pestilence,
Where death is sure. Yon nag of Egypt
(Whom leprosy o'ertake!) i' the midst o' the fight
Hoists sails and flies.

ENOBARBUS. That I beheld:
Mine eyes did sicken at the sight, and could not
Endure a further view.

SCARUS. She once being loofed,
The noble ruin of her magic, Antony,
Claps on his sea-wing, and, like a doting mallard,
Leaving the fight in height, flies after her:
I never saw an action of such shame;
Experience, manhood, honour, ne'er before
Did violate so itself.

ENOBARBUS. Alack, alack!

CANIDIUS *(entering)*. Our fortune on the sea is out of breath,
And sinks most lamentably. Had our general
Been what he knew himself, it had gone well:
O, he has given example for our flight,
Most grossly, by his own!

ENOBARBUS. Ay, are you thereabouts?
Why, then, Good-night indeed.

CANIDIUS. Toward Peloponnesus are they fled.

SCARUS. Tis easy to 't; and there I will attend
What further comes.

CANIDIUS. To Caesar will I render
My legions and my horse: six kings already
Show me the way of yielding.

ENOBARBUS. I'll yet follow
The wounded chance of Antony, though my reason
Sits in the wind against me.

Scene 9—Cleopatra's Palace in Alexandria : Antony with attendants

ANTONY. Hark! the land bids me tread no more upon 't;
It is ashamed to bear me! Friends, come hither:
I am so lated in the world, that I
Have lost my way for ever: I have a ship
Laden with gold; take that, divide it; fly,
And make your peace with Caesar.

ALL. Fly! not we.

ANTONY. I have fled myself; and have instructed cowards
To run and show their shoulders. Friends, be gone;
I have myself resolved upon a course
Which has no need of you; be gone:
My treasure's in the harbour, take it. O,
I followed that I blush to look upon:
My very hairs do mutiny.
Friends, be gone: you shall

Have letters from me to some friends that will
Sweep your way for you. Pray you, look not sad,
Nor make replies of lothness: take the hint
Which my despair proclaims; let that be left
Which leaves itself: to the seaside straightway:
I will possess you of that ship and treasure.
Leave me, I pray, a little: pray you now:
Nay, do so; for, indeed, I have lost command,
Therefore I pray you: I'll see you by and by.

As Antony sits down Cleopatra comes with her ladies

EROS. Nay, gentle madam, to him, comfort him.

IRAS. Do, most dear queen.

CHARMIAN. Do! why: what else?

CLEOPATRA. Let me sit down. O Juno!

ANTONY. No, no, no, no, no.

EROS. See you here, sir?

ANTONY. O fie, fie, fie!

CHARMIAN. Madam!

IRAS. Madam, O good empress!

EROS. Sir, sir—

ANTONY. Yes, my lord, yes; he at Philippi kept
His sword e'en like a dancer; while I struck
The lean and wrinkled Cassius; and 'twas I
That the mad Brutus ended: he alone
Dealt on lieutenantry, and no practice had
In the brave squares of war: yet now—No matter.

CLEOPATRA. Ah, stand by.

EROS. The queen, my lord, the queen.

IRAS. Go to him, madam, speak to him:
He is unqualitied with very shame.

CLEOPATRA. Well then, sustain me: O!

EROS. Most noble sir, arise; the queen approaches:
Her head's declined, and death will seize her, but
Your comfort makes the rescue.

ANTONY. I have offended reputation,
A most unnoble swerving.

EROS. Sir, the queen!

ANTONY. O, whither hast thou led me, Egypt?

CLEOPATRA. O my lord, my lord,
Forgive my fearful sails! I little thought
You would have followed.

ANTONY. Egypt, thou knew'st too well
My heart was to thy rudder tied by the strings,
And thou shouldst tow me after: o'er my spirit
Thy full supremacy thou knew'st, and that
Thy beck might from the bidding of the gods
Command me.

CLEOPATRA. O, my pardon!

ANTONY. Now I must
To the young man send humble treaties, dodge
And palter in the shifts of lowness; who
With half the bulk o' the world played as I pleased,
Making and marring fortunes. You did know
How much you were my conqueror; and that
My sword, made weak by my affection, would
Obey it on all cause.

CLEOPATRA. Pardon, pardon!

ANTONY. Fall not a tear, I say; one of them rates
All that is won and lost: give me a kiss;
Even this repays me. We sent our schoolmaster;
Is he come back? Love, I am full of lead.
Some wine, within there, and our viands! Fortune knows
We scorn her most when most she offers blows.

Scene 10—Caesar's Camp in Egypt

Euphronius, Antony's aged schoolmaster, comes to Caesar as Antony's ambassador to sue for peace, for the right of Antony to live in Egypt or Athens as a free man. Cleopatra craves the right to retain Egypt by Caesar's consent. Caesar refuses Antony's appeal. Cleopatra may hope for Caesar's favour if she casts off or kills Antony, and is secretly to be urged by Thyreus, Caesar's ambassador, to follow one of these courses.

Scene 11—Cleopatra's Palace

CLEOPATRA. What shall we do, Enobarbus?

ENOBARBUS. Think, and die.

CLEOPATRA. Is Antony or we in fault for this?

ENOBARBUS. Antony only, that would make his will
Lord of his reason. What though you fled
From that great face of war, whose several ranges
Frighted each other? why should he follow?
The itch of his affection should not then
Have nicked his captainship; at such a point,
When half to half the world opposed, he being
The single question: 'twas a shame no less
Than was his loss, to course your flying flags,
And leave his navy gazing.

CLEOPATRA. Prithee, peace.

Enter Antony with Euphronius, the Ambassador

ANTONY. Is that his answer?

EUPHRONIUS. Ay, my lord.

ANTONY. The queen shall then have courtesy, so she
Will yield us up. Let her know 't.
To the boy Caesar send this grizzled head,
And he will fill thy wishes to the brim
With principalities.

CLEOPATRA. That head, my lord?

ANTONY. To him again: tell him he wears the rose
Of youth upon him, from which the world should note
Something particular: his coin, ships, legions,
May be a coward's, whose ministers would prevail
Under the service of a child as soon
As i' the command of Caesar: I dare him therefore
To lay his gay comparisons apart,
And answer me declined, sword against sword,
Ourselves alone. I'll write it: follow me. *(They go)*

ENOBARBUS *(aside)*. Yes, like enough, high-battled Caesar will
Unstate his happiness, and be staged to the show
Against a sworder! I see men's judgments are
A parcel of their fortunes; and things outward
Do draw the inward quality after them,
To suffer all alike. That he should dream,
Knowing all measures, the full Caesar will
Answer his emptiness! Caesar, thou hast subdued
His judgment too.

ATTENDANT *(entering)*. A messenger from Caesar.

CLEOPATRA. Admit him, sir.

THYREUS *(entering)*. Thou most renownèd: Caesar entreats,
Not to consider in what case thou stand'st
Further than he is Caesar.

CLEOPATRA. Go on: right royal.

THYREUS. He knows that you embrace not Antony
As you did love but as you feared him.

CLEOPATRA. O!

THYREUS. The scars upon your honour, therefore, he
Does pity, as constrainèd blemishes,
Not as deserved.

CLEOPATRA. He is a god, and knows
What is most right: mine honour was not yielded,
But conquered merely.

THYREUS. Shall I say to Caesar
What you require of him? for he partly begs
To be desired to give. It much would please him

That of his fortunes you should make a staff
To lean upon : but it would warm his spirits,
To hear from me you had left Antony,
And put yourself under his shroud,
The universal landlord.

CLEOPATRA. Most kind messenger,
Say to great Caesar this : in deputation
I kiss his conquering hand : tell him, I am prompt
To lay my crown at 's feet, and there to kneel :
Tell him, from his all-obeying breath I hear
The doom of Egypt.

THYREUS. Tis your noblest course. Give me grace to lay
My duty on your hand.

CLEOPATRA. Your Caesar's father oft,
When he hath mused of taking kingdoms in,
Bestowed his lips on that unworthy place,
As it rained kisses.

ANTONY *(entering with Enobarbus)*. Favours, by Jove that thunders!
What art thou, fellow ?

THYREUS. One that but performs
The bidding of the fullest man, and worthiest
To have command obeyed.

ENOBARBUS *(aside)*. You will be whipped.

ANTONY. Approach, there ! Ah, you kite ! Now, gods and devils !
Authority melts from me : of late, when I cried *Ho !*
Kings would start forth and cry *Your will ?*
Have you no ears ? I am Antony yet.
(To attendants entering) Take hence this Jack, and whip him.
Moon and stars !
Whip him. Were't twenty of the greatest tributaries
That do acknowledge Caesar, should I find them
So saucy with the hand of she here—what's her name,
Since she was Cleopatra ? Whip him, fellows,
Till, like a boy, you see him cringe his face
And whine aloud for mercy : take him hence.

THYREUS. Mark Antony !

ANTONY. Tug him away : being whipped,
Bring him again : this Jack of Caesar's shall
Bear us an errand to him. . . . Is he whipped ?

FIRST ATTENDANT. Soundly, my lord.

ANTONY. Cried he ? and begged a' pardon ?

FIRST ATTENDANT. He did ask favour.

ANTONY. Get thee back to Caesar,
Tell him thy entertainment : look, thou say
He makes me angry with him ; for he seems

Proud and disdainful, harping on what I am,
Not what he knew I was : he makes me angry ;
And at this time most easy tis to do 't,
When my good stars, that were my former guides,
Have empty left their orbs, and shot their fires
Into the abysm of hell. If he mislike
My speech and what is done, tell him he has
Hipparchus, my enfranchèd bondman, whom
He may at pleasure whip, or hang, or torture,
As he shall like, to quit me : urge it thou :
Hence with thy stripes, begone ! *(Thyreus goes)*

CLEOPATRA. Have you done yet ?

ANTONY. Alack, our moon
Is now eclipsed ; and it portends alone
The fall of Antony !

CLEOPATRA. I must stay his time.

ANTONY. To flatter Caesar, would you mingle eyes
With one that ties his points ?

CLEOPATRA. Not know me yet ?

ANTONY. Cold-hearted toward me ?

CLEOPATRA. Ah, dear, if I be so
From my cold heart let heaven engender hail,
And poison it in the source ; and the first stone
Drop in my neck : as it determines, so
Dissolve my life ! The next Caesarion smite !
Till by degrees the memory of my brave Egyptians all
Lie graveless, till the flies and gnats of Nile
Have buried them for prey !

" I am satisfied ! " says Antony ; then, fired by fury, he declares that he will give battle on land to Caesar, who is quartered in Alexandria. He boasts that he will return victorious, he and his sword " having earned our chronicles." But first he and Cleopatra and his officers will have one more midnight festival of mirth and feasting. Wise Enobarbus sees in the new Antony fury frightening out fear, and imagines the worst.

ACT 4

Scene 1—Caesar's Camp in Alexandria

Caesar reading a letter from Antony

CAESAR. He calls me boy ; and chides, as he had power
To beat me out of Egypt ; my messenger
He hath whipped with rods ; dares me to personal combat,
Caesar to Antony. Let the old ruffian know
I have many other ways to die ; meantime
Laugh at his challenge.

MECAENAS. Caesar must think,
When one so great begins to rage, he's hunted
Even to falling. Give him no breath, but now
Make boot of his distraction: never anger
Made good guard for itself.

CAESAR. Let our best heads
Know that tomorrow the last of many battles
We mean to fight: within our files there are,
Of those that served Mark Antony but late,
Enough to fetch him in. See it done:
And feast the army; we have store to do 't,
And they have earned the waste. Poor Antony!

Scene 2—Cleopatra's Palace

Antony, hearing that Caesar declines the challenge to single-handed combat, bids the officials and servants of the palace to serve him well this night at the entertainment. His tone and terms are so wild and mournful that the men are moved to tears.

Scene 3—Soldiers on guard at the Palace

Soldiers on guard hear strange music in the air, and superstitiously interpret it as the god Hercules, whom Antony loved, now leaving him.

Scene 4—Cleopatra's Palace

Antony goes forth with his captains and soldiers, bidding farewell to Cleopatra, who says as the scene closes:

He goes forth gallantly. That he and Caesar might
Determine this great war in single fight!

Scene 5—Antony's Camp at Alexandria

Enter Antony and Eros, a Soldier meeting them

SOLDIER. The gods make this a happy day to Antony!

ANTONY. Would thou and those thy scars had once prevailed
To make me fight at land!

SOLDIER. Hadst thou done so
The kings that have revolted, and the soldier
That has this morning left thee, would have still
Followed thy heels.

ANTONY. Who's gone this morning?

SOLDIER. Who!
One ever near thee: call for Enobarbus,
He shall not hear thee; or from Caesar's camp
Say *I am none of thine.*

ANTONY. What say'st thou ?

SOLDIER. Sir, he is with Caesar.

EROS. Sir, his chests and treasure he has not with him.

ANTONY. Is he gone ?

SOLDIER. Most certain.

ANTONY. Go, Eros, send his treasure after ; do it ;
Detain no jot, I charge thee : write to him—
I will subscribe—gentle adieus and greetings ;
Say that I wish he never find more cause
To change a master. O, my fortunes have
Corrupted honest men ! Dispatch. Enobarbus !

Scene 6—Caesar's Camp in Alexandria

Enter Caesar with Agrippa, Enobarbus, and others

CAESAR. Go forth, Agrippa, and begin the fight :
Our will is Antony be took alive ;
Make it so known.

AGRIPPA. Caesar, I shall.

CAESAR. The time of universal peace is near :
Prove this a prosperous day, the three-nooked world
Shall bear the olive freely.

MESSENGER *(advancing)*. Antony
Is come into the field.

CAESAR. Go charge Agrippa
Plant those that have revolted in the van,
That Antony may seem to spend his fury
Upon himself. *(All but Enobarbus go)*

ENOBARBUS *(alone)*. Alexas did revolt ; and went to Jewry on
Affairs of Antony ; there did persuade
Great Herod to incline himself to Caesar,
And leave his master Antony : for this pains
Caesar hath hanged him. Canidius and the rest
That fell away have entertainment, but
No honourable trust. I have done ill ;
Of which I do accuse myself so sorely,
That I will joy no more.

SOLDIER *(entering)*. Enobarbus, Antony
Hath after thee sent all thy treasure, with
His bounty overplus : the messenger
Came on my guard ; and at thy tent is now
Unloading of his mules.

ENOBARBUS. I give it you.

SOLDIER. Mock not, Enobarbus.
I tell you true: best you shield the bringer
Out of the host; I must attend mine office,
Or would have done 't myself. Your emperor
Continues still a Jove.

ENOBARBUS. I am alone the villain of the earth,
And feel I am so most. O Antony,
Thou mine of bounty, how wouldst thou have paid
My better service, when my turpitude
Thou dost so crown with gold! This blows my heart:
If swift thought break it not, a swifter mean
Shall outstrike thought: but thought will do 't, I feel.
I fight against thee? No: I will go seek
Some ditch wherein to die; the foul'st best fits
My latter part of life.

Scene 7—Field of Battle between the Camps

Agrippa is in retreat, Caesar is pressed, Antony prospers. He enters with a proud sense of triumph, exchanging congratulations with Scarus, who is wounded. A pursuit is now ordered.

Scene 8—Under the Walls of Alexandria: Antony marching

ANTONY. We have beat him to his camp: run one before,
And let the queen know of our deeds. Tomorrow,
Before the sun shall see 's, we'll spill the blood
That has today escaped. I thank you all;
For doughty-handed are you, and have fought
Not as you served the cause, but as 't had been
Each man's like mine; you have shown all Hectors.

Enter Cleopatra

To this great fairy I'll commend thy acts,
Make her thanks bless thee. O thou day o' the world,
Chain mine armed neck; leap thou, attire and all,
Through proof of harness to my heart.

CLEOPATRA. Lord of lords!
O infinite virtue, comest thou smiling from
The world's great snare uncaught?

ANTONY. My nightingale,
We have beat them to their beds. What, girl! though grey
Do something mingle with our younger brown, yet ha' we
A brain that nourishes our nerves, and can
Get goal for goal of youth. Behold this man *(Scarus)*;
Commend unto his lips thy favouring hand:
Kiss it, my warrior: he hath fought today
As if a god, in hate of mankind, had
Destroyed in such a shape.

CLEOPATRA. I'll give thee, friend,
An armour all of gold; it was a king's.

ANTONY. He has deserved it. Give me thy hand:
Through Alexandria make a jolly march.
Trumpeters, with brazen din blast you the city's ear;
Make mingle with our rattling tabourines;
That heaven and earth may strike their sounds together,
Applauding our approach.

Scene 9—Sentinels at their post in Caesar's Camp

Sentinels discuss the prospects of further fighting, which is to begin at two in the morning. They perceive a strange figure and listen. It is Enobarbus, stricken to the heart with grief, moaning out his contrition and sadness as he dies before them.

Scenes 10 and 11—The Battlefield between the Camps

The armies are assembled for battle, Antony now pushing his power forward by sea and Caesar on land.

Scene 12—On the Battlefield: Antony with Scarus

ANTONY. Yet they are not joined: where yond pine does stand,
I shall discover all: I'll bring thee word
Straight, how tis like to go. *(He goes)*

SCARUS *(alone)*. Swallows have built
In Cleopatra's sails their nests: the augurers
Say they know not, they cannot tell; look grimly,
And dare not speak their knowledge. Antony
Is valiant, and dejected; and, by starts,
His fretted fortunes give him hope, and fear,
Of what he has, and has not.

ANTONY *(returning)*. All is lost;
This foul Egyptian hath betrayed me:
My fleet hath yielded to the foe; and yonder
They cast their caps up and carouse together
Like friends long lost. Bid them all fly;
For when I am revenged upon my charm,
I have done all. Bid them all fly; begone. *(Scarus goes)*
O Sun, thy uprise shall I see no more:
Fortune and Antony part here; even here
Do we shake hands. All come to this? The hearts
That spanielled me at heels, to whom I gave
Their wishes, do discandy, melt their sweets
On blossoming Caesar; and this pine is barked,
That overtopped them all. Betrayed I am:

O this false soul of Egypt! this grave charm
(Whose eye becked forth my wars, and called them home;
Whose bosom was my crownet, my chief end)
Like a right gipsy hath at fast and loose
Beguiled me to the very heart of loss. *(Cleopatra enters)*
Ah, thou spell! Avaunt!

CLEOPATRA. Why is my lord enraged against his love?

ANTONY. Vanish, or I shall give thee thy deserving,
And blemish Caesar's triumph. Let him take thee,
And hoist thee up to the shouting plebeians:
Follow his chariot, like the greatest spot
Of all thy sex. *(She goes.)* Tis well thou'rt gone,
If it be well to live; but better 'twere
Thou fell'st into my fury, for one death
Might have prevented many. Eros, ho!
The shirt of Nessus is upon me: teach me,
Alcides, thou mine ancestor, thy rage.
The witch shall die:
To the young Roman boy she hath sold me, and I fall
Under this plot; she dies for 't. Eros, ho!

Scene 13—Cleopatra's Palace

CLEOPATRA. Help me, my women! O, he is more mad
Than Telamon for his shield; the boar of Thessaly
Was never so embossed.

CHARMIAN. To the monument!
There lock yourself, and send him word you are dead.
The soul and body rive not more in parting
Than greatness going off.

CLEOPATRA. To the monument!
Mardian, go tell him I have slain myself;
Say that the last I spoke was *Antony*,
And word it, prithee, piteously: hence, Mardian,
And bring me how he takes my death. To the monument!

Scene 14—A Room in Cleopatra's Palace

ANTONY. Eros, thou yet behold'st me?

EROS. Ay, noble lord.

ANTONY. Sometime we see a cloud that's dragonish;
A vapour sometime like a bear or lion,
A towered citadel, a pendent rock,
A forkèd mountain, or blue promontory
With trees upon 't, that nod unto the world,
And mock our eyes with air: thou hast seen these signs;
They are black vesper's pageants.

EROS. Ay, my lord.

ANTONY. That which is now a horse, even with a thought
The rack dislimns, and makes it indistinct,
As water is in water.

EROS. It does, my lord.

ANTONY. My good knave Eros, now thy captain is
Even such a body : here I am Antony ;
Yet cannot hold this visible shape, my knave.
I made these wars for Egypt ; and the queen
(Whose heart I thought I had, for she had mine ;
Which whilst it was mine had annexed unto 't
A million more, now lost), she, Eros, has
Packed cards with Caesar, and false-played my glory
Unto an enemy's triumph.
Nay, weep not, gentle Eros ; there is left us
Ourselves to end ourselves. *(Here enters Mardian)*
O, thy vile lady ! She has robbed me of my sword.

MARDIAN. No, Antony ;
My mistress loved thee, and her fortunes mingled
With thine entirely.

ANTONY. Hence, peace !
She hath betrayed me and shall die the death.

MARDIAN. Death of one person can be paid but once,
And that she has discharged : what thou wouldst do
Is done unto thy hand : the last she spake
Was *Antony ! most noble Antony !*
Then in the midst a tearing groan did break
The name of Antony ; it was divided
Between her heart and lips : she rendered life,
Thy name so buried in her.

ANTONY. Dead, then ?

MARDIAN. Dead.

ANTONY. Unarm, Eros ; the long day's task is done,
And we must sleep. Off, pluck off :
The seven-fold shield of Ajax cannot keep
The battery from my heart. O, cleave, my sides !
Heart, once be stronger than thy continent,
Crack thy frail case ! Apace, Eros, apace.
No more a soldier : bruisèd pieces, go ;
You have been nobly borne. From me awhile. *(Eros goes)*
I will o'ertake thee, Cleopatra, and
Weep for my pardon. So it must be, for now
All length is torture : since the torch is out,
Lie down, and stray no farther : now all labour

Mars what it does ; yea, very force entangles
Itself with strength : seal then, and all is done.
Eros !—I come, my queen.—Eros !—Stay for me :
Where souls do couch on flowers, we'll hand in hand,
And with our sprightly port make the ghosts gaze :
Dido and her Aeneas shall want troops,
And all the haunt be ours. Come, Eros, Eros !

EROS. What would my lord ?

ANTONY. Since Cleopatra died,
I have lived in such dishonour, that the gods
Detest my baseness. I, that with my sword
Quartered the world, and o'er green Neptune's back
With ships made cities, condemn myself to lack
The courage of a woman ; less noble mind
Than she which by her death our Caesar tells,
I am conqueror of myself. Thou art sworn, Eros,
That, when the exigent should come, which now
Is come indeed, when I should see behind me
The inevitable prosecution of
Disgrace and horror, that, on my command,
Thou then wouldst kill me : do 't ; the time is come :
Thou strikest not me, tis Caesar thou defeat'st.
Put colour in thy cheek.

EROS. The gods withhold me !
Shall I do that which all the Parthian darts,
Though enemy, lost aim, and could not ?

ANTONY. Eros,
Wouldst thou be windowed in great Rome and see
Thy master thus with pleached arms, bending down
His corrigible neck, his face subdued
To penetrative shame, whilst the wheeled seat
Of fortunate Caesar, drawn before him, branded
His baseness that ensued ?

EROS. I would not see 't.

ANTONY. Come, then ; for with a wound I must be cured.
Draw that thy honest sword, which thou hast worn
Most useful for thy country.

EROS. O, sir, pardon me !

ANTONY. When I did make thee free, sworest thou not then
To do this when I bade thee ? Do it at once,
Or thy precedent services are all
But accidents unpurposed. Draw, and come.

EROS. Turn from me, then, that noble countenance,
Wherein the worship of the whole world lies.

ANTONY. Lo thee !

EROS. My sword is drawn *(turning away)*.

ANTONY. Then let it do at once
The thing why thou hast drawn it.

EROS. My dear master,
My captain, and my emperor, let me say,
Before I strike this stroke, Farewell.

ANTONY. Tis said, man ; and Farewell.

EROS. Farewell, great chief. Shall I strike now ?

ANTONY. Now, Eros.

EROS. Why, there then : thus I do escape the sorrow
Of Antony's death. *(He kills himself)*

ANTONY. Thrice-nobler than myself !
Thou teachest me, O valiant Eros, what
I should, and thou couldst not. My queen and Eros
Have by their brave instruction got upon me
A nobleness in record : but I will be
A bridegroom in my death, and run into 't
As to a bed. Come, then ; and, Eros,
Thy master dies thy scholar : to do thus
I learned of thee *(falling on his sword)*. How ! not dead ? not dead ?
The guard, ho ! O, dispatch me ! *(Enter Guards)*

FIRST GUARD. What's the noise ?

ANTONY. I have done my work ill, friends : O, make an end
Of what I have begun.

SECOND GUARD. The star is fallen.

FIRST GUARD. And time is at his period.

ALL. Alas, and woe !

ANTONY. Let him that loves me strike me dead.

FIRST GUARD. Not I.

SECOND GUARD. Nor I.

THIRD GUARD. Nor any one. *(All the Guards leave)*

DERCETAS. Thy death and fortunes bid thy followers fly.
This sword but shown to Caesar, with this tidings,
Shall enter me with him.

DIOMEDES *(approaching)*. Where's Antony ?

ANTONY. Art thou there, Diomed ? Draw thy sword, and give me
Sufficing strokes for death.

DIOMEDES. Most absolute lord,
My mistress Cleopatra sent me to thee.

ANTONY. When did she send thee?

DIOMEDES. Now, my lord.

ANTONY. Where is she?

DIOMEDES. Locked in her monument. She had a prophesying fear
Of what hath come to pass: for when she saw
(Which never shall be found) you did suspect
She had disposed with Caesar, and that your rage
Would not be purged, she sent you word she was dead;
But, fearing since how it might work, hath sent
Me to proclaim the truth; and I am come,
I dread, too late.

ANTONY. Too late, good Diomed: call my guard, I prithee.

DIOMEDES. What, ho, the emperor's guard! The guard, what, ho!
Come, your lord calls!

ANTONY. Bear me, good friends, where Cleopatra bides;
Tis the last service that I shall command you.

FIRST GUARD. Woe, woe are we, sir, you may not live to wear
All your true followers out.

ALL. Most heavy day!

ANTONY. Nay, good my fellows, do not please sharp fate
To grace it with your sorrows: bid that welcome
Which comes to punish us, and we punish it
Seeming to bear it lightly. Take me up:
I have led you oft: carry me now, good friends,
And have my thanks for all.

Scene 15—A Monument in the Grounds of Cleopatra's Palace

Cleopatra and her maids above

CLEOPATRA. O Charmian, I will never go from hence.

CHARMIAN. Be comforted, dear madam.

CLEOPATRA. No, I will not:
All strange and terrible events are welcome,
But comforts we despise; our size of sorrow,
Proportioned to our cause, must be as great
As that which makes it. *(Enter Diomedes below)*
How now! is he dead?

DIOMEDES. His death's upon him, but not dead.
Look out o' the other side your monument;
His guard have brought him thither.

Antony, borne by the Guard, appears below

CLEOPATRA. O Sun,
Burn the great sphere thou movest in! darkling stand

The varying shore o' the world. O Antony,
Antony, Antony ! Help, Charmian, help, Iras, help ;
Help, friends below ; let 's draw him hither.

ANTONY. Peace !
Not Caesar's valour hath o'erthrown Antony,
But Antony's hath triumphed on itself.

CLEOPATRA. So it should be, that none but Antony
Should conquer Antony ; but woe tis so !

ANTONY. I am dying, Egypt, dying ; only
I here importune death awhile, until
Of many thousand kisses the poor last
I lay upon thy lips.

CLEOPATRA. I dare not, dear—
Dear my lord, pardon—I dare not,
Lest I be taken : not the imperious show
Of the full-fortuned Caesar ever shall
Be brooched with me ; if knife, drugs, serpents, have
Edge, sting, or operation, I am safe :
Your wife Octavia, with her modest eyes, shall acquire no honour
Demuring upon me. But come, come, Antony,
(Help me, my women) we must draw thee up :
Assist, good friends.

ANTONY. O, quick, or I am gone.

CLEOPATRA. Here's sport indeed ! How heavy weighs my lord !
Our strength is all gone into heaviness,
That makes the weight : had I great Juno's power,
The strong-winged Mercury should fetch thee up,
And set thee by Jove's side. Yet come a little,
Wishers were ever fools ; O, come, come, come ;

They heave Antony aloft to Cleopatra

And welcome, welcome ! die where thou hast lived :
Quicken with kissing : had my lips that power,
Thus would I wear them out.

ALL. A heavy sight !

ANTONY. I am dying, Egypt, dying :
Give me some wine, and let me speak a little.

CLEOPATRA. No, let me speak ; and let me rail so high,
That the false housewife Fortune break her wheel,
Provoked by my offence.

ANTONY. One word, sweet queen :
Of Caesar seek your honour, with your safety. O !

CLEOPATRA. They do not go together.

ANTONY. Gentle, hear me :
None about Caesar trust but Proculeius.

CLEOPATRA. My resolution and my hands I'll trust;
None about Caesar.

ANTONY. The miserable change now at my end
Lament nor sorrow at; but please your thoughts
In feeding them with those my former fortunes
Wherein I lived, the greatest prince o' the world,
The noblest; and do now not basely die,
Not cowardly put off my helmet to
My countryman—a Roman by a Roman
Valiantly vanquished. Now my spirit is going;
I can no more.

CLEOPATRA. Noblest of men, woo 't die?
Hast thou no care of me? Shall I abide
In this dull world, which in thy absence is
No better than a sty? O, see, my women, *(He dies)*
The crown o' the earth doth melt. My lord!
O, withered is the garland of the war,
The soldier's star is fallen: young boys and girls
Are level now with men; the odds is gone,
And there is nothing left remarkable
Beneath the visiting moon. *(She faints)*

CHARMIAN. O, quietness, lady!

IRAS. She is dead too, our sovereign.

CHARMIAN. O madam, madam, madam!

IRAS. Royal Egypt, Empress!

CHARMIAN. Peace, peace, Iras!

CLEOPATRA. No more, but e'en a woman, and commanded
By such poor passion as the maid that milks
And does the meanest chares. It were for me
To throw my sceptre at the injurious gods;
To tell them that this world did equal theirs
Till they had stolen our jewel. All's but naught;
Patience is sottish, and impatience does
Become a dog that's mad: then is it sin
To rush into the secret house of death,
Ere death dare come to us? How do you, women?
What, what! good cheer! Why, how now, Charmian!
My noble girls! Ah, women, women, look,
Our lamp is spent, it's out! Good sirs, take heart:
We'll bury him; and then, what's brave, what's noble,
Let's do it after the high Roman fashion,
And make death proud to take us. Come, away:
This case of that huge spirit now is cold:
Ah, women, women! come; we have no friend
But resolution, and the briefest end.

ACT 5

Scene—Caesar's Camp in Alexandria

Enter Caesar with his Council of War

CAESAR. Go to him, Dolabella, bid him yield;
Being so frustrate, tell him he mocks
The pauses that he makes.

DOLABELLA. Caesar, I shall.

Enter Dercetas, with the sword of Antony

CAESAR. Wherefore is that? and what art thou that darest
Appear thus to us?

DERCETAS. I am called Dercetas;
Mark Antony I served, who best was worthy
Best to be served: whilst he stood up and spoke,
He was my master; and I wore my life
To spend upon his haters. If thou please
To take me to thee, as I was to him
I'll be to Caesar; if thou pleasest not,
I yield thee up my life.

CAESAR. What is't thou say'st?

DERCETAS. I say, O Caesar, Antony is dead.

CAESAR. The breaking of so great a thing should make
A greater crack: the round world
Should have shook lions into civil streets,
And citizens to their dens: the death of Antony
Is not a single doom; in the name lay
A moiety of the world.

DERCETAS. He is dead, Caesar;
Not by a public minister of justice,
Nor by a hired knife; but that self-hand,
Which writ his honour in the acts it did,
Hath, with the courage which the heart did lend it,
Splitted the heart. This is his sword;
I robbed his wound of it; behold it stained
With his most noble blood.

CAESAR. Look you sad, friends?
The gods rebuke me, but it is tidings
To wash the eyes of kings.

AGRIPPA. And strange it is,
That nature must compel us to lament
Our most persisted deeds.

MECAENAS. His taints and honours waged equal with him.

AGRIPPA. A rarer spirit never
Did steer humanity : but you, gods, will give us
Some faults to make us men. Caesar is touched.

MECAENAS. When such a spacious mirror's set before him
He needs must see himself.

CAESAR. O Antony !
I have followed thee to this ; but we do lance
Diseases in our bodies : I must perforce
Have shown to thee such a declining day,
Or look on thine ; we could not stall together
In the whole world : but yet let me lament,
With tears as sovereign as the blood of hearts,
That thou, my brother, my competitor
In top of all design, my mate in empire,
Friend and companion in the front of war,
The arm of mine own body, and the heart
Where mine his thoughts did kindle—that our stars,
Unreconciliable, should divide
Our equalness to this. Hear me, good friends—
But I will tell you at some meeter season.

Enter an Egyptian

The business of this man looks out of him ;
We'll hear him what he says. Whence are you ?

EGYPTIAN. A poor Egyptian yet. The queen my mistress,
Confined in all she has, her monument,
Of thy intents desires instruction,
That she preparedly may frame herself
To the way she's forced to.

CAESAR. Bid her have good heart :
She soon shall know of us, by some of ours,
How honourable and how kindly we
Determine for her ; for Caesar cannot live
To be ungentle.

EGYPTIAN. So the gods preserve thee !

CAESAR. Come hither, Proculeius. Go and say
We purpose her no shame : give her what comforts
The quality of her passion shall require,
Lest, in her greatness, by some mortal stroke
She do defeat us ; for her life in Rome
Would be eternal in our triumph : go,
And with your speediest bring us what she says,
And how you find of her.

PROCULEIUS. Caesar, I shall.

CAESAR. Go with me to my tent, where you shall see
How hardly I was drawn into this war;
How calm and gentle I proceeded still
In all my writings: go with me, and see
What I can show in this.

Scene 2—A Room in Cleopatra's Monument

CLEOPATRA. My desolation does begin to make
A better life. Tis paltry to be Caesar;
Not being Fortune, he's but Fortune's knave,
A minister of her will: and it is great
To do that thing that ends all other deeds.

Caesar's ambassadors reach the monument

PROCULEIUS. Caesar sends greeting to the Queen of Egypt;
And bids thee study on what fair demands
Thou mean'st to have him grant thee.

CLEOPATRA. What's thy name?

PROCULEIUS. My name is Proculeius.

CLEOPATRA. Antony
Did tell me of you, bade me trust you; but
I do not greatly care to be deceived,
That have no use for trusting. If your master
Would have a queen his beggar, you must tell him
That majesty, to keep decorum, must
No less beg than a kingdom: if he please
To give me conquered Egypt for my son,
He gives me so much of mine own, as I
Will kneel to him with thanks.

PROCULEIUS. Be of good cheer;
You're fallen into a princely hand, fear nothing:
Make your full reference freely to my lord,
Who is so full of grace that it flows over
On all that need: let me report to him
Your sweet dependency; and you shall find
A conqueror that will pray in aid for kindness,
Where he for grace is kneeled to.

CLEOPATRA. Pray you, tell him
I am his fortune's vassal, and I send him
The greatness he has got. I hourly learn
A doctrine of obedience; and would gladly
Look him i' the face.

PROCULEIUS. This I'll report, dear lady.
Have comfort, for I know your plight is pitied
Of him that caused it.

Here Guards climb the monument and take Cleopatra by surprise

GALLUS. Guard her till Caesar come.

CHARMIAN. O Cleopatra ! thou art taken, queen.

CLEOPATRA. Quick, quick, good hands. *(Drawing a dagger)*

PROCULEIUS. Hold, worthy lady, hold. *(He disarms her)*
Do not yourself such wrong, who are in this
Relieved, but not betrayed.

CLEOPATRA. What, of death too,
That rids our dogs of languish ?

PROCULEIUS. Cleopatra, do not abuse my master's bounty by
The undoing of yourself : let the world see
His nobleness well acted, which your death
Will never let come forth.

CLEOPATRA. Where art thou, Death ?
Come hither, come ! come, come, and take a queen
Worth many babes and beggars !

PROCULEIUS. O, temperance, lady !

CLEOPATRA. Sir, I will eat no meat, I'll not drink, sir ;
If idle talk will once be necessary,
I'll not sleep neither : this mortal house I'll ruin,
Do Caesar what he can. Know, sir, that I
Will not wait pinioned at your master's court ;
Nor once be chastised with the sober eye
Of dull Octavia. Shall they hoist me up
And show me to the shouting varletry
Of censuring Rome ? Rather a ditch in Egypt
Be gentle grave unto me ! Rather make
My country's high pyramids my gibbet,
And hang me up in chains !

PROCULEIUS. You do extend
These thoughts of horror further than you shall
Find cause in Caesar.

DOLABELLA *(sent by Caesar)*. Proculeius,
What thou hast done thy master Caesar knows,
And he hath sent for thee : for the queen,
I'll take her to my guard.

PROCULEIUS. So, Dolabella,
It shall content me best : be gentle to her.

DOLABELLA. Most noble empress, you have heard of me ?

CLEOPATRA. I cannot tell.

DOLABELLA. Assuredly you know me.

CLEOPATRA. No matter, sir, what I have heard or known.
You laugh when boys or women tell their dreams ;
Is't not your trick ?

DOLABELLA. I understand not, madam.

CLEOPATRA. I dreamed there was an Emperor Antony:
O, such another sleep, that I might see
But such another man!

DOLABELLA. If it might please ye—

CLEOPATRA. His face was as the heavens; and therein stuck
A sun and moon, which kept their course, and lighted
The little O, the earth.

DOLABELLA. Most sovereign creature—

CLEOPATRA. His legs bestrid the ocean: his reared arm
Crested the world: his voice was propertied
As all the tunèd spheres, and that to friends;
But when he meant to quail and shake the orb,
He was as rattling thunder. For his bounty,
There was no winter in't; an autumn 'twas
That grew the more by reaping: in his livery
Walked crowns and crownets; realms and islands were
As plates dropped from his pocket.

DOLABELLA. Cleopatra!

CLEOPATRA. Think you there was, or might be, such a man
As this I dreamed of?

DOLABELLA. Gentle madam, no.

CLEOPATRA. You lie, up to the hearing of the gods.
But, if there be, or ever were, one such,
It's past the size of dreaming: nature wants stuff
To vie strange forms with fancy; yet to imagine
An Antony were nature's piece 'gainst fancy,
Condemning shadows quite.

DOLABELLA. Hear me, good madam.
Your loss is as yourself, great; and you bear it
As answering to the weight: would I might never
O'ertake pursued success, but I do feel,
By the rebound of yours, a grief that smites
My very heart at root.

CLEOPATRA. I thank you, sir.
Know you what Caesar means to do with me?

DOLABELLA. I am loth to tell you what I would you knew.

CLEOPATRA. Nay, pray you, sir—

DOLABELLA. Though he be honourable,—

CLEOPATRA. He'll lead me, then, in triumph?

DOLABELLA. Madam, he will; I know 't.

Trumpets and shout within: enter Caesar and his train

CAESAR. Which is the Queen of Egypt ?

DOLABELLA. It is the emperor, madam. *(Cleopatra kneels)*

CAESAR. Arise, you shall not kneel :
I pray you, rise ; rise, Egypt.

CLEOPATRA. Sir, the gods
Will have it thus ; my master and my lord
I must obey.

CAESAR. Take to you no hard thoughts :
The record of what injuries you did us,
Though written in our flesh, we shall remember
As things but done by chance.

CLEOPATRA. Sole sir o' the world,
I cannot project mine own cause so well
To make it clear ; but do confess I have
Been laden with like frailties which before
Have often shamed our sex.

CAESAR. Cleopatra, know,
We will extenuate rather than enforce :
If you apply yourself to our intents,
Which towards you are most gentle, you shall find
A benefit in this change ; but if you seek
To lay on me a cruelty, by taking
Antony's course, you shall bereave yourself
Of my good purposes, and put your children
To that destruction which I'll guard them from
If thereon you rely. I'll take my leave.

CLEOPATRA. And may, through all the world : tis yours ; and we,
Your scutcheons and your signs of conquest, shall
Hang in what place you please. Here, my good lord.

CAESAR. You shall advise me in all for Cleopatra.

CLEOPATRA. This is the brief of money, plate, and jewels,
I am possessed of : tis exactly valued ;
Not petty things admitted. Where's Seleucus ?

SELEUCUS. Here, madam.

CLEOPATRA. This is my treasurer : let him speak, my lord,
Upon his peril, that I have reserved
To myself nothing. Speak the truth, Seleucus.

SELEUCUS. Madam,
I had rather seal my lips, than, to my peril,
Speak that which is not.

CLEOPATRA. What have I kept back ?

SELEUCUS. Enough to purchase what you have made known.

CAESAR. Nay, blush not, Cleopatra; I approve
Your wisdom in the deed.

CLEOPATRA. See, Caesar! O, behold,
How pomp is followed! mine will now be yours;
And, should we shift estates, yours would be mine.
The ingratitude of this Seleucus does
Even make me wild: O slave, of no more trust
Than love that's hired! What, goest thou back? thou shalt
Go back, I warrant thee; but I'll catch thine eyes,
Though they had wings; slave, soulless villain, dog!
O rarely base!

CAESAR. Good queen, let us entreat you.

CLEOPATRA. O Caesar, what a wounding shame is this,
That thou vouchsafing here to visit me,
Doing the honour of thy lordliness
To one so meek, that mine own servant should
Parcel the sum of my disgraces by
Addition of his envy! Say, good Caesar,
That I some lady trifles have reserved,
Immoment toys, things of such dignity
As we greet modern friends withal; and say,
Some nobler token I have kept apart
For Livia and Octavia, to induce
Their mediation; must I be unfolded
With one that I have bred? The gods! it smites me
Beneath the fall I have. Prithee *(to Seleucus)*, go hence;
Or I shall show the cinders of my spirits
Through the ashes of my chance: wert thou a man,
Thou wouldst have mercy on me.

CAESAR. Forbear, Seleucus.

CLEOPATRA. Be it known, that we, the greatest, are misthought
For things that others do; and, when we fall,
We answer others' merits in our name,
Are therefore to be pitied.

CAESAR. Cleopatra,
Not what you have reserved, nor what acknowledged,
Put we i' the roll of conquest: still be 't yours,
Bestow it at your pleasure; and believe,
Caesar's no merchant, to make prize with you
Of things that merchants sold. Therefore be cheered;
Make not your thoughts your prisons: no, dear queen;
For we intend so to dispose you as
Yourself shall give us counsel. Feed, and sleep:

Our care and pity is so much upon you
That we remain your friend ; and so, adieu.

CLEOPATRA. My master, and my lord !

CAESAR. Not so. Adieu. *(Caesar and his train leave)*

CLEOPATRA. He words me, girls, he words me, that I should not
Be noble to myself : but, hark thee, Charmian *(whispering)*.

IRAS. Finish, good lady ; the bright day is done,
And we are for the dark.

CLEOPATRA. Hie thee again :
I have spoke already, and it is provided ;
Go put it to the haste.

CHARMIAN. Madam, I will.

DOLABELLA *(returning)*. Where is the queen ?

CHARMIAN. Behold, sir !

CLEOPATRA. Dolabella !

DOLABELLA. Madam, as thereto sworn by your command,
Which my love makes religion to obey,
I tell you this : Caesar through Syria
Intends his journey ; and within three days
You with your children will he send before :
Make your best use of this : I have performed
Your pleasure and my promise.

CLEOPATRA. Dolabella, I shall remain your debtor.

DOLABELLA. I your servant.
Adieu, good queen ; I must attend on Caesar.

CLEOPATRA. Farewell, and thanks. Now, Iras, what think'st thou ?
Thou, an Egyptian puppet, shalt be shown
In Rome, as well as I : mechanic slaves
With greasy aprons, rules, and hammers, shall
Uplift us to the view ; in their thick breaths,
Rank of gross diet, shall we be enclouded,
And forced to drink their vapour.

IRAS. I'll never see 't ; for, I am sure, my nails
Are stronger than mine eyes.

CLEOPATRA. Why, that's the way
To fool their preparation, and to conquer
Their most absurd intents. *(Charmian returns)*
Now, Charmian !
Show me, my women, like a queen ; go fetch
My best attires : I am again for Cydnus,
To meet Mark Antony : sirrah Iras, go.
Now, noble Charmian, we'll dispatch indeed ;

And, when thou hast done this chare, I'll give thee leave
To play till Doomsday. Bring our crown and all.
Wherefore's this noise ?

GUARDSMAN *(entering)*. Here is a rural fellow
That will not be denied your highness' presence :
He brings you figs.

CLEOPATRA. Let him come in. What poor an instrument
May do a noble deed ! he brings me liberty.
My resolution's placed, and I have nothing
Of woman in me : now from head to foot
I am marble-constant : now the fleeting moon
No planet is of mine.

Guardsman returns with Clown bringing in a basket

GUARDSMAN. This is the man.

CLEOPATRA. Avoid, and leave him. *(Guardsman goes)*
Hast thou the pretty worm of Nilus there,
That kills and pains not ?

CLOWN. Truly, I have him : but I would not be the party that should desire you to touch him, for his biting is immortal; those that do die of it do seldom or never recover.

CLEOPATRA. Rememberest thou any that have died on 't ?

CLOWN. Very many, men and women too. I heard of one of them no longer than yesterday : a very honest woman, but something given to lie ; as a woman should not do, but in the way of honesty : how she died of the biting of it, what pain she felt : truly, she makes a very good report.

CLEOPATRA. Get thee hence ; farewell.

Enter Iras bearing robe and crown

CLEOPATRA. Give me my robe, put on my crown ; I have
Immortal longings in me : now no more
The juice of Egypt's grape shall moist this lip :
Yare, yare, good Iras ; quick. Methinks I hear
Antony call ; I see him rouse himself
To praise my noble act ; I hear him mock
The luck of Caesar, which the gods give men
To excuse their after wrath : husband, I come :
Now to that name my courage prove my title !
I am fire and air ; my other elements
I give to baser life. So ; have you done ?
Come then, and take the last warmth of my lips.
Farewell, kind Charmian ; Iras, long farewell.

She kisses them, and Iras falls and dies

Have I the aspic in my lips? Dost fall?
If thou and nature can so gently part
The stroke of death is as a lover's pinch,
Which hurts and is desired. Dost thou lie still?
If thus thou vanishest, thou tell'st the world
It is not worth leave-taking.

CHARMIAN. Dissolve, thick cloud, and rain; that I may say,
The gods themselves do weep!

CLEOPATRA. This proves me base:
If she first meet the curlèd Antony,
He'll make demand of her, and spend that kiss
Which is my heaven to have. Come, thou mortal wretch (*to an asp, which she applies to her breast*),
With thy sharp teeth this knot intrinsicate
Of life at once untie: poor venomous fool,
Be angry, and dispatch.

CHARMIAN. O eastern star!

CLEOPATRA. Peace, peace!
Dost thou not see my baby at my breast!

CHARMIAN. O, break! O, break!

CLEOPATRA. As sweet as balm, as soft as air, as gentle—
O Antony! Nay, I will take thee too (*applying another asp*).
What should I stay— (*She dies*)

CHARMIAN. In this vile world? So, fare thee well.
Now boast thee, death, in thy possession lies
A lass unparalleled. Downy windows, close;
And golden Phoebus never be beheld
Of eyes again so royal! Your crown's awry;
I'll mend it, and then play. (*The Guards rush in*)

FIRST GUARD. Where is the queen?

CHARMIAN. Speak softly, wake her not.

FIRST GUARD. Caesar hath sent—

CHARMIAN. Too slow a messenger. (*She applies an asp*)
O, come apace, dispatch! I partly feel thee.

FIRST GUARD. Approach, ho! All 's not well: Caesar's beguiled.

SECOND GUARD. There's Dolabella sent from Caesar; call him.

FIRST GUARD. What work is here! Charmian, is this well done?

CHARMIAN. It is well done, and fitting for a princess
Descended of so many royal kings. Ah, soldier! (*She dies*)

DOLABELLA (*approaching*). How goes it here?

SECOND GUARD. All dead.

DOLABELLA. Caesar, thy thoughts
Touch their effects in this: thyself art coming
To see performed the dreaded act which thou
So sought'st to hinder.

A noise within and a shout: enter Caesar and all his train, marching

DOLABELLA. O sir, you are too sure an augurer:
That you did fear is done.

CAESAR. Bravest at the last,
She levelled at our purposes, and, being royal,
Took her own way. The manner of their deaths?
I do not see them bleed.

DOLABELLA. Who was last with them?

FIRST GUARD. A simple countryman, that brought her figs:
This was his basket.

CAESAR. Poisoned, then.

FIRST GUARD. O Caesar,
This Charmian lived but now; she stood and spake:
I found her trimming up the diadem
On her dead mistress; tremblingly she stood
And on the sudden dropped.

CAESAR. O noble weakness!
If they had swallowed poison, 'twould appear
By external swelling: but she looks like sleep,
As she would catch another Antony
In her strong toil of grace.

DOLABELLA. Here, on her breast,
There is a vent of blood and something blown:
The like is on her arm.

FIRST GUARD. This is an aspic's trail.

CAESAR. Most probable
That so she died, for her physician tells me
She hath pursued conclusions infinite
Of easy ways to die. Take up her bed,
And bear her women from the monument.
She shall be buried by her Antony.
No grave upon the earth shall clip in it
A pair so famous. High events as these
Strike those that make them, and their story is
No less in pity than his glory which
Brought them to be lamented. Our army shall
In solemn show attend this funeral;
And then to Rome. Come, Dolabella, see
High order in this great solemnity.

The Story of Richard the Second

THERE is something in this play that will be remembered to the end of time. If England were to pass away the dying speech of John o' Gaunt would carry on its memory and its spirit.

WE see Shakespeare here at the beginning of the great time when he gave to the world that series of historical plays which brought him from John o' Gaunt, his typical Englishman, to Henry the Fifth, his patriot king. He is at his very best in these great plays of kings, and his love of England stirs us to the depths.

IT must have seemed to most people a strange thing that Shakespeare, who lived through the days of the Spanish Armada, has not a word for that event in all his plays ; nor does he mention Francis Drake. He seems to have been unmoved by the events which made the spacious days of Elizabeth famous for all time. It may be that they gave the stage no chance ; it was easier to make a pageantry of kings and queens. Certain it is that Shakespeare loved to see his country great and strong; the fervour of his patriotism in these plays has in it the glow of a passionate faith. It comes from Shakespeare's heart.

WHEN John o' Gaunt lay dying in his house in Holborn King Richard the Second was wasting the resources of the land. He was sowing the seeds of ruin and decay. A thousand flatterers sat within his crown, and he was England's landlord, not her King. So the passionate protest poured from the lips of the dying Gaunt, who saw

> This royal throne of kings, this sceptered isle,
> This land of such dear souls, this dear dear land,

leased out like a farm by his brother's son. The vision and the prophecy are lost on such a king. Old Gaunt is not yet in his grave when the King seizes all his lands to feed his wars. Bolingbroke he has sent into exile, and, blind in his folly, Richard goes his pitiful way.

IT is the way of doom, the fall of a king from the height of his throne to such depths of shame that even when he is most contemptible we feel some pity for him. Down, down he goes, gathering hatred and contempt about him, losing friends and kindred, and all those aids a fallen king so sorely needs. The exiled Bolingbroke becomes the hope of all those whom the tyrannous system of government has robbed, and Bolingbroke returns, the hero of a clamouring land.

WHAT must the king do now ? It is one of the most pathetic scenes in Shakespeare, the more pathetic when we remember the sanctity of kingship in those days. Bolingbroke has in him elements of greatness, and he is clever ; Richard has in him all the elements of weakness, and he is a fool. Yet who could not weep to hear him offering his kingdom for a little grave, " a little little grave, an obscure grave " ?

HE is soon to find it, and we may hope he found in it a little of that peace of which he robbed his land.

THE PLAYERS

Richard, King of England. Weak and capricious, governing badly.

John of Gaunt, Duke of Lancaster, the aged uncle of the King. Bold, outspoken, patriotic; Shakespeare's typical Englishman.

Duke of York, uncle to the King. Weak in action, but very loyal to whatever king may reign.

Henry Bolingbroke, son of Gaunt, first Duke of Hereford, then of Lancaster; then King Henry IV. Clever and ambitious.

Duke of Aumerle, son of York, and a supporter of the King.

Thomas Mowbray, Duke of Norfolk, enemy of Bolingbroke.

Duke of Surrey, a supporter of the King.

Earl of Salisbury, a supporter of the King.

Lord Berkeley, a nobleman supporting the King.

Bushy, Bagot, and Green, servants to Richard.

Earl of Northumberland, a supporter of Bolingbroke.

Henry Percy, son of Northumberland, known as Hotspur.

Lord Ross, a supporter of Bolingbroke.

Lord Willoughby, a supporter of Bolingbroke.

Lord Fitzwater, a supporter of Bolingbroke.

Bishop of Carlisle, an honest man, loyal to the King.

Abbot of Westminster, a loyal supporter of Richard.

Sir Stephen Scroop, a supporter of the King.

Sir Pierce of Exton, a follower of Bolingbroke.

Queen of King Richard, neglected but faithful.

Duchess of York, aunt of Bolingbroke, mother of Aumerle.

Duchess of Gloucester, widow of Richard's murdered uncle.

Lord marshal, captain of a band of Welshmen, heralds, gardeners, lords, a messenger, a keeper, a groom, and other attendants.

SCENES—In England and Wales. TIME—1398 to 1400.

King Richard the Second

ACT 1

Scene 1—King Richard's Palace in London

Enter Richard and John of Gaunt

RICHARD. Old John of Gaunt, time-honoured Lancaster,
Hast thou, according to thy oath and bond,
Brought hither Henry Hereford thy bold son,
Here to make good the boisterous late appeal,
Which then our leisure would not let us hear,
Against the Duke of Norfolk, Thomas Mowbray ?

GAUNT. I have, my liege.

RICHARD. Tell me, moreover, hast thou sounded him,
If he appeal the duke on ancient malice ;
Or worthily, as a good subject should,
On some known ground of treachery in him ?

GAUNT. As near as I could sift him on that argument,
On some apparent danger seen in him
Aimed at your highness, no inveterate malice.

RICHARD. Then call them to our presence ; face to face,
And frowning brow to brow ; ourselves will hear
The accuser and the accusèd freely speak :
High-stomached are they both, and full of ire,
In rage deaf as the sea, hasty as fire.

Enter Bolingbroke and Mowbray

BOLINGBROKE. Many years of happy days befall
My gracious sovereign, my most loving liege !

MOWBRAY. Each day still better other's happiness ;
Until the heavens, envying earth's good hap,
Add an immortal title to your crown !

RICHARD. We thank you both : yet one but flatters us,
As well appeareth by the cause you come,
Namely, to appeal each other of high treason.
Cousin of Hereford, what dost thou object
Against the Duke of Norfolk, Thomas Mowbray ?

BOLINGBROKE. First, heaven be the record to my speech!
In the devotion of a subject's love,
Tendering the precious safety of my prince.
Now, Thomas Mowbray, do I turn to thee,
And mark my greeting well; for what I speak
My body shall make good upon this earth,
Or my divine soul answer it in heaven.
Thou art a traitor and a miscreant,
Too good to be so and too bad to live,
Since the more fair and crystal is the sky,
The uglier seem the clouds that in it fly.

MOWBRAY. Let not my cold words here accuse my zeal.
Setting aside his high blood's royalty,
And let him be no kinsman to my liege,
I do defy him, and I spit at him;
Call him a slanderous coward and a villain:
Which to maintain I would allow him odds,
And meet him, were I tied to run afoot
Even to the frozen ridges of the Alps,
Or any other ground inhabitable,
Wherever Englishman durst set his foot.
Meantime let this defend my loyalty:
By all my hopes, most falsely doth he lie.

Bolingbroke declares the occasions of his charge of treachery against Mowbray, which Mowbray indignantly denies. The King intervenes for peace.

RICHARD. Wrath-kindled gentlemen, be ruled by me;
Forget, forgive; conclude and be agreed;
Our doctors say this is no month to bleed.
Good uncle, let this end where it began;
We'll calm the Duke of Norfolk, you your son.

GAUNT. To be a make-peace shall become my age:
Throw down, my son, the Duke of Norfolk's gage.

RICHARD. And, Norfolk, throw down his.

GAUNT. When, Harry, when?
Obedience bids I should not bid again.

RICHARD. Norfolk, throw down, we bid; there is no boot.

MOWBRAY. Myself, I throw, dread sovereign, at thy foot.
My life thou shalt command, but not my shame:
The one my duty owes; but my fair name,
Despite of death that lives upon my grave,
To dark dishonour's use thou shalt not have.

RICHARD. Rage must be withstood.
Give me his gage: lions make leopards tame.

MOWBRAY. Yea, but not change his spots: take but my shame,
And I resign my gage. My dear dear lord,
The purest treasure mortal times afford
Is spotless reputation: that away,
Men are but gilded loam or painted clay.
A jewel in a ten times barred-up chest
Is a bold spirit in a loyal breast.
Mine honour is my life; both grow in one;
Take honour from me and my life is done:
Then, dear my liege, mine honour let me try;
In that I live and for that will I die.

RICHARD. Cousin, throw up your gage; do you begin.

BOLINGBROKE. O, God defend my soul from such deep sin!

RICHARD. We were not born to sue, but to command;
Which, since we cannot do to make you friends,
Be ready, as your lives shall answer it,
At Coventry, upon Saint Lambert's day:
There shall your swords and lances arbitrate
The swelling difference of your settled hate.

Scene 2—The Duke of Lancaster's Palace

Enter John of Gaunt with the Duchess of Gloucester

GAUNT. Alas, the part I had in Gloucester's blood
Doth more solicit me than your exclaims
To stir against the butchers of his life!
But since correction lieth in those hands
Which made the fault that we cannot correct,
Put we our quarrel to the will of heaven.

DUCHESS. Finds brotherhood in thee no sharper spur?
Hath love in thy old blood no living fire?
Ah, Gaunt, his blood was thine! thou dost consent
In some large measure to thy father's death
In that thou seest thy wretched brother die,
Who was the model of thy father's life.
Call it not patience, Gaunt; it is despair:
That which in mean men we entitle patience
Is pale cold cowardice in noble breasts.

GAUNT. God's is the quarrel; for God's substitute,
His deputy anointed in His sight,
Hath caused his death: the which if wrongfully
Let heaven revenge; for I may never lift
An angry arm against His minister.

DUCHESS. Where then, alas, may I complain myself?

GAUNT. To God, the widow's champion and defence.

Duchess of Gloucester. Why, then, I will.
Farewell, old Gaunt: thy sometimes brother's wife
With her companion grief must end her life.

Gaunt. Sister, farewell; I must to Coventry:
As much good stay with thee as go with me!

Duchess of Gloucester. Desolate, desolate, will I hence and die:
The last leave of thee takes my weeping eye.

Scene 3—The Arena at Coventry

Bolingbroke and Mowbray are to fight. The trumpets sound, and the King enters with his nobles. Mowbray appears in arms, with a Herald.

Richard. Marshal, demand of yonder champion
The cause of his arrival here in arms:
Ask him his name and orderly proceed
To swear him in the justice of his cause.

Marshal. In God's name and the king's, say who thou art
And why thou comest thus knightly clad in arms,
Against what man thou comest, and what thy quarrel:
Speak truly, on thy knighthood and thy oath;
As so defend thee heaven and thy valour!

Mowbray. My name is Thomas Mowbray, Duke of Norfolk;
Who hither come engagèd by my oath—
Which God defend a knight should violate!—
Both to defend my loyalty and truth
To God, my king, and my succeeding issue,
Against the Duke of Hereford that appeals me;
And, by the grace of God and this mine arm,
To prove him, in defending of myself,
A traitor to my God, my king, and me:
And as I truly fight, defend me heaven!

Trumpets sound. Enter Bolingbroke in armour, with a Herald.

Richard. Marshal, ask yonder knight in arms
Both who he is and why he cometh hither
Thus plated in habiliments of war,
And formally, according to our law,
Depose him in the justice of his cause.

Marshal. What is thy name? and wherefore comest thou hither,
Before King Richard in his royal lists?
Against whom comest thou? and what's thy quarrel?
Speak like a true knight, so defend thee heaven!

Bolingbroke. Harry of Hereford, Lancaster and Derby
Am I; who ready here do stand in arms,
To prove, by God's grace and my body's valour,
In lists, on Thomas Mowbray, Duke of Norfolk,

That he is a traitor, foul and dangerous,
To God of heaven, King Richard, and to me;
And as I truly fight, defend me heaven!
Lord marshal, let me kiss my sovereign's hand,
And bow my knee before his majesty,
For Mowbray and myself are like two men
That vow a long and weary pilgrimage;
Then let us take a ceremonious leave
And loving farewell of our several friends.

MARSHAL. The appellant in all duty greets your highness,
And craves to kiss your hand and take his leave.

RICHARD. We will descend and fold him in our arms.
Cousin of Hereford, as thy cause is right,
So be thy fortune in this royal fight!
Farewell, my blood; which if today thou shed,
Lament we may, but not revenge thee dead.

MOWBRAY. However God or fortune cast my lot,
There lives or dies, true to King Richard's throne,
A loyal, just, and upright gentleman:
Never did captive with a freer heart
Cast off his chains of bondage and embrace
His golden uncontrolled enfranchisement,
More than my dancing soul doth celebrate
This feast of battle with mine adversary.
Most mighty liege, and my companion peers,
Take from my mouth the wish of happy years:
As gentle and as jocund as to jest
Go I to fight: truth hath a quiet breast.

RICHARD. Farewell, my lord: securely I espy
Virtue with valour couchèd in thine eye.
Order the trial, marshal, and begin.

MARSHAL. Sound, trumpets; and set forward, combatants.

A charge is sounded, but the King stays the combat by suddenly throwing down his truncheon.

MARSHAL. Stay, the king hath thrown his warder down.

RICHARD. Let them lay by their helmets and their spears,
And both return back to their chairs again:
Withdraw with us: and let the trumpets sound
While we return these dukes what we decree.
Draw near,
And list what with our council we have done.
For that our kingdom's earth should not be soiled
With that dear blood which it hath fosterèd;
And for our eyes do hate the dire aspect
Of civil wounds ploughed up with neighbours' sword;

Therefore, we banish you our territories.
You, cousin Hereford, upon pain of life,
Till twice five summers have enriched our fields
Shall not regreet our fair dominions,
But tread the stranger paths of banishment.

Bolingbroke. Your will be done: this must my comfort be,
That sun that warms you here shall shine on me;
And those his golden beams to you here lent
Shall point on me and gild my banishment.

Richard. Norfolk, for thee remains a heavier doom,
Which I with some unwillingness pronounce:
The sly slow hours shall not determinate
The dateless limit of thy dear exile;
The hopeless word of *never to return*
Breathe I against thee, upon pain of life.

Mowbray. A heavy sentence, my most sovereign liege,
And all unlooked for from your highness' mouth:
The language I have learned these forty years,
My native English, now I must forego:
And now my tongue's use is to me no more
Than an unstringèd viol or a harp,
Or like a cunning instrument cased up,
Or, being open, put into his hands
That knows no touch to tune the harmony.
I am too old to fawn upon a nurse,
Too far in years to be a pupil now:
What is thy sentence then but speechless death,
Which robs my tongue from breathing native breath?

Richard. It boots thee not to be compassionate:
After our sentence plaining comes too late.

Mowbray. Then thus I turn me from my country's light,
To dwell in solemn shades of endless night.
Farewell, my liege. Now no way can I stray;
Save back to England, all the world's my way.

Richard. Uncle, even in the glasses of thine eyes
I see thy grievèd heart: thy sad aspèct
Hath from the number of his banished years
Plucked four away. *(To Bolingbroke)* Six frozen winters spent,
Return with welcome home from banishment.

Bolingbroke. How long a time lies in one little word!
Four lagging winters and four wanton springs
End in a word: such is the breath of kings.

Gaunt. I thank my liege, that in regard of me
He shortens four years of my son's exile:
But little vantage shall I reap thereby,

For, ere the six years that he hath to spend
Can change their moons and bring their times about,
My oil-dried lamp and time-bewasted light
Shall be extinct with age and endless night;
My inch of taper will be burnt and done,
And blindfold death not let me see my son.

RICHARD. Why, uncle, thou hast many years to live.

GAUNT. But not a minute, king, that thou canst give:
Shorten my days thou canst with sullen sorrow,
And pluck nights from me, but not lend a morrow;
Thou canst help time to furrow me with age,
But stop no wrinkle in his pilgrimage;
Thy word is current with him for my death,
But dead, thy kingdom cannot buy my breath.

RICHARD. Thy son is banished upon good advice.
Cousin, farewell; and, uncle, bid him so;
Six years we banish him, and he shall go. *(The King leaves)*

GAUNT. O, to what purpose dost thou hoard thy words,
That thou return'st no greeting to thy friends?

BOLINGBROKE. I have too few to take my leave of you,
When the tongue's office should be prodigal
To breathe the abundant dolour of the heart.

GAUNT. Thy grief is but thy absence for a time.

BOLINGBROKE. Joy absent, grief is present for that time.

GAUNT. What is six winters? they are quickly gone.

BOLINGBROKE. To men in joy; but grief makes one hour ten.

GAUNT. All places that the eye of heaven visits
Are to a wise man ports and happy havens.
Teach thy necessity to reason thus;
There is no virtue like necessity.
Think not the king did banish thee,
But thou the king. Woe doth the heavier sit,
Where it perceives it is but faintly borne.
Go, say I sent thee forth to purchase honour
And not the king exiled thee; or suppose
Devouring pestilence hangs in our air
And thou art flying to a fresher clime:
Look, what thy soul holds dear, imagine it
To lie that way thou goest, not whence thou comest:
Suppose the singing birds musicians,
The flowers fair ladies, and thy steps no more
Than a delightful measure or a dance;
For gnarling sorrow hath less power to bite
The man that mocks at it and sets it light.

BOLINGBROKE. O, who can hold a fire in his hand
By thinking on the frosty Caucasus ?
Or cloy the hungry edge of appetite
By bare imagination of a feast ?
Or wallow naked in December snow
By thinking on fantastic summer's heat ?

GAUNT. Come, come, my son, I'll bring thee on thy way :
Had I thy youth and cause, I would not stay.

BOLINGBROKE. Then, England's ground, farewell; sweet soil, adieu;
My mother and my nurse, that bears me yet !
Where'er I wander, boast of this I can,
Though banished, yet a trueborn Englishman.

Scene 4—The Court

The Duke of Aumerle reports to the King that Hereford has left the realm, and Richard reflects on the exile's popularity with the common folk.

RICHARD. How he did seem to dive into their hearts
With humble and familiar courtesy !
What reverence he did throw away on slaves,
Wooing poor craftsmen with the craft of smiles !
Off goes his bonnet to an oyster-wench ;
A brace of draymen bid God-speed him well
And had the tribute of his supple knee,
With *Thanks, my countrymen, my loving friends* ;
As were our England in reversion his,
And he our subjects' next degree in hope.

GREEN. Well, he is gone ; and with him go these thoughts.
Now for the rebels which stand out in Ireland.

RICHARD. We will ourself in person to this war :
And (for our coffers, with too great a court
And liberal largess, are grown somewhat light)
We are enforced to farm our royal realm,
The revenue whereof shall furnish us
For our affairs in hand.

BUSHY *(entering)*. Old John of Gaunt is grievous sick, my lord,
Suddenly taken ; and hath sent post haste
To entreat your majesty to visit him.

RICHARD. Now put it, God, in the physician's mind
To help him to his grave immediately !
The lining of his coffers shall make coats
To deck our soldiers for these Irish wars.
Come, gentlemen, let's all go visit him :
Pray God we may make haste, and come too late !

ACT 2

Scene 1—Ely House

John of Gaunt is dying: York is with him

GAUNT. Will the king come, that I may breathe my last
In wholesome counsel to his unstaid youth ?

YORK. Vex not yourself, nor strive not with your breath ;
For all in vain comes counsel to his ear.

GAUNT. O, but they say the tongues of dying men
Enforce attention like deep harmony :
Where words are scarce they are seldom spent in vain,
For they breathe truth that breathe their words in pain.
He that no more must say is listened more
Than they whom youth and ease have taught to glose ;
More are men's ends marked than their lives before :
The setting sun, and music at the close,
As the last taste of sweets, is sweetest last,
Writ in remembrance more than things long past :
Though Richard my life's counsel would not hear,
My death's sad tale may yet undeaf his ear.

YORK. No ; it is stopped with other flattering sounds.
Direct not him whose way himself will choose :
Tis breath thou lack'st, and that breath wilt thou lose.

GAUNT. Methinks I am a prophet new inspired
And thus expiring do foretell of him :
His rash fierce blaze of riot cannot last,
For violent fires soon burn out themselves ;
Small showers last long, but sudden storms are short :
He tires betimes that spurs too fast betimes ;
With eager feeding food doth choke the feeder.
Light vanity, insatiate cormorant,
Consuming means, soon preys upon itself.
This royal throne of kings, this sceptered isle,
This earth of majesty, this seat of Mars,
This other Eden, demi-paradise,
This fortress built by Nature for herself
Against infection and the hand of war,
This happy breed of men, this little world,
This precious stone set in the silver sea,
Which serves it in the office of a wall
Or as a moat defensive to a house,
Against the envy of less happier lands,
This blessed plot, this earth, this realm, this England,
This land of such dear souls, this dear dear land,

Dear for her reputation through the world,
Is now leased out (I die pronouncing it),
Like to a tenement or pelting farm:
England, bound in with the triumphant sea,
Whose rocky shore beats back the envious siege
Of watery Neptune, is now bound in with shame,
With inky blots and rotten parchment bonds:
That England, that was wont to conquer others,
Hath made a shameful conquest of itself.
Ah, would the scandal vanish with my life,
How happy then were my ensuing death!

Enter the King and Queen, with lords

YORK. The king is come: deal mildly with his youth,
For young hot colts being raged do rage the more.

QUEEN. How fares our noble uncle, Lancaster?

RICHARD. What comfort, man? how is't with aged Gaunt?

GAUNT. O, how that name befits my composition!
Old Gaunt indeed, and gaunt in being old.

RICHARD. Can sick men play so nicely with their names?

GAUNT. No, misery makes sport to mock itself:
Since thou dost seek to kill my name in me,
I mock my name, great king, to flatter thee.

RICHARD. Should dying men flatter with those that live?

GAUNT. No, no, men living flatter those that die.
Now He that made me knows I see thee ill;
Thy death-bed is no lesser than thy land
Wherein thou liest in reputation sick;
And thou, too careless patient as thou art,
Commit'st thy anointed body to the cure
Of those physicians that first wounded thee:
A thousand flatterers sit within thy crown,
Whose compass is no bigger than thy head;
And yet, incagèd in so small a verge,
The waste is no whit lesser than thy land.
O, had thy grandsire with a prophet's eye
Seen how his son's son should destroy his sons,
From forth thy reach he would have laid thy shame.
Why, cousin, wert thou regent of the world,
It were a shame to let this land by lease;
Landlord of England art thou now, not king.
Thy state of law is bondslave to the law,
And thou—

RICHARD. A lunatic lean-witted fool,
Presuming on an ague's privilege,

Darest with thy frozen admonition
Make pale our cheek.
Wert thou not brother to great Edward's son,
This tongue that runs so roundly in thy head
Should run thy head from thy unreverent shoulders.

GAUNT. O, spare me not, my brother Edward's son,
Join with the present sickness that I have;
And thy unkindness be like crookèd age,
To crop at once a too long withered flower.
Live in thy shame, but die not shame with thee!
These words hereafter thy tormentors be!
Convey me to my bed, then to my grave:
Love they to live that love and honour have.

He is borne off by his Attendants

RICHARD. And let them die that age and sullens have;
For both hast thou, and both become the grave.

YORK. I do beseech your majesty, impute his words
To wayward sickliness and age in him:
He loves you, on my life, and holds you dear
As Harry Duke of Hereford, were he here.

RICHARD. Right, you say true: as Hereford's love, so his;
As theirs, so mine; and all be as it is.

Northumberland, entering, announces that Gaunt is dead, whereupon the King proclaims that the possessions of the dead man's family are forfeit to the Crown. York protests indignantly against this crime, but the King persists and declares that he will leave at once for the Irish wars, for which Gaunt's estate will pay. He goes, and the rest remain to discuss Richard's lawless seizures, his alienation of peers and commons, and the deplorable condition to which he has brought the country. Northumberland then confides to his friends that the Duke of Hereford, with a band of friends and three thousand armed men, is crossing from Brittany, and they agree to meet him at his landing-place.

Scene 2—Windsor Castle

Enter the Queen, with Bushy and Bagot

BUSHY. Madam, your majesty is too much sad:
You promised, when you parted with the king,
To lay aside life-harming heaviness
And entertain a cheerful disposition.

QUEEN. To please the king I did; to please myself
I cannot do it; yet I know no cause
Why I should welcome such a guest as grief,
Save bidding farewell to so sweet a guest
As my sweet Richard; yet again, methinks,

Some unborn sorrow, ripe in fortune's womb,
Is coming towards me, and my inward soul
With nothing trembles : at some thing it grieves
More than with parting from my lord the king.

BUSHY. Each substance of a grief hath twenty shadows,
Which shows like grief itself, but is not so.

QUEEN. It may be so ; but yet my inward soul
Persuades me it is otherwise : howe'er it be,
I cannot but be sad. *(Enter Green in haste)*

GREEN. God save your majesty ! and well met, gentlemen :
I hope the king is not yet shipped for Ireland.

QUEEN. Why hopest thou so ?

GREEN. The banished Bolingbroke repeals himself,
And with uplifted arms is safe arrived
At Ravenspurgh.

QUEEN. Now God in heaven forbid !

GREEN. Ah, madam, tis too true : and that is worse,
The Lord Northumberland, his son young Henry Percy,
The Lords of Ross, Beaumond, and Willoughby,
With all their powerful friends, are fled to him.

BUSHY. Why have you not proclaimed Northumberland
And all the rest revolted faction traitors ?

GREEN. We have : whereupon the Earl of Worcester
Hath broke his staff, resigned his stewardship,
And all the household servants fled with him
To Bolingbroke. Here comes the Duke of York.

QUEEN. With signs of war about his aged neck :
O, full of careful business are his looks !
Uncle, for God's sake, speak comfortable words.

YORK. Should I do so I should belie my thoughts :
Comfort's in heaven, and we are on the earth,
Where nothing lives but crosses, cares, and grief.
Your husband, he is gone to save far off,
Whilst others come to make him lose at home :
Here am I left to underprop his land,
Who, weak with age, cannot support myself :
Now comes the sick hour that his surfeit made ;
Now shall he try his friends that flattered him.

SERVANT *(entering)*. My lord, your son was gone before I came.

YORK. He was ? Why, so ! go all which way it will !
The nobles they are fled, the commons they are cold,
And will, I fear, revolt on Hereford's side.
Sirrah, get thee to Plashy, to my sister Gloucester ;
Bid her send me presently a thousand pounds :
Hold, take my ring.

SERVANT. My lord, I had forgot to tell your lordship,
Today, as I came by, I callèd there;
But I shall grieve you to report the rest.

YORK. What is't, knave?

SERVANT. An hour before I came the duchess died.

YORK. God for his mercy! what a tide of woes
Comes rushing on this woeful land at once!
I know not what to do: I would to God,
So my untruth had not provoked him to it,
The king had cut off my head with my brother's.
How shall we do for money for these wars?
Gentlemen, will you go muster men?
If I know how or which way to order these affairs
Thus thrust disorderly into my hands,
Never believe me. Both are my kinsmen:
The one is my sovereign, whom both my oath
And duty bid defend; the other again
Is my kinsman, whom the king hath wronged,
Whom conscience and my kindred bid to right.
Well, somewhat we must do.
Gentlemen, go, muster up your men. *(He leaves with the Queen)*

GREEN. Well, I will for refuge straight to Bristol castle:
The Earl of Wiltshire is already there.

BUSHY. Thither will I with you; for little office
The hateful commons will perform for us,
Except like curs to tear us all to pieces.
Will you go along with us?

BAGOT. No; I will to Ireland to his majesty.
Farewell: if heart's presages be not vain,
We three here part that ne'er shall meet again.

BUSHY. That's as York thrives to beat back Bolingbroke.

GREEN. Alas, poor duke! the task he undertakes
Is numbering sands and drinking oceans dry;
Where one on his side fights, thousands will fly.
Farewell at once, for once, for all, and ever.

Scene 3—In the wilds of Gloucestershire

Enter Bolingbroke and Northumberland, with forces

BOLINGBROKE. How far is it, my lord, to Berkeley now?

NORTHUMBERLAND. Believe me, noble lord,
I am a stranger here in Gloucestershire;
These high wild hills and rough uneven ways
Draw out our miles, and make them wearisome;
And yet your fair discourse hath been as sugar,
Making the hard way sweet and delectable.

BOLINGBROKE. Of much less value is my company
Than your good words. But who comes here ?

NORTHUMBERLAND. It is my son, young Harry Percy.
Harry *(now approaching)*, how fares your uncle ?

PERCY. I had thought, my lord, to have learned his health of you.

NORTHUMBERLAND. Why, is he not with the queen ?

PERCY. No, my good lord ; he hath forsook the court,
Broken his staff of office and dispersed
The household of the king.

NORTHUMBERLAND. What was his reason ?
He was not so resolved when last we spake together.

PERCY. Because your lordship was proclaimèd traitor.
But he, my lord, is gone to Ravenspurgh,
To offer service to the Duke of Hereford,
And sent me over by Berkeley to discover
What power the Duke of York had levied there ;
Then with directions to repair to Ravenspurgh.

NORTHUMBERLAND. Have you forgot the Duke of Hereford, boy ?

PERCY. No, my good lord, for that is not forgot
Which ne'er I did remember : to my knowledge
I never in my life did look on him.

NORTHUMBERLAND. Then learn to know him now ; this is the duke.

PERCY. My gracious lord, I tender you my service,
Such as it is, being tender, raw, and young ;
Which elder days shall ripen and confirm
To more approvèd service and desert.

BOLINGBROKE. I thank thee, gentle Percy ; and be sure
I count myself in nothing else so happy
As in a soul remembering my good friends.

NORTHUMBERLAND. How far is it to Berkeley ? and what stir
Keeps good old York there with his men of war ?

PERCY. There stands the castle, by yon tuft of trees,
Manned with three hundred men, as I have heard ;
And in it are the Lords of York, Berkeley, and Seymour ;
None else of name and noble estimate.

NORTHUMBERLAND. Here come the Lords of Ross and Willoughby.

BOLINGBROKE. Welcome, my lords. I wot your love pursues
A banished traitor : all my treasury
Is yet but unfelt thanks, which more enriched
Shall be your love and labour's recompense.

ROSS. Your presence makes us rich, most noble lord.

BOLINGBROKE. But who comes here ?

NORTHUMBERLAND. It is my Lord of Berkeley, as I guess.

BERKELEY. My Lord of Hereford, my message is to you.

BOLINGBROKE. My lord, my answer is—to Lancaster;
And I am come to seek that name in England;
And I must find that title in your tongue,
Before I make reply to aught you say.

BERKELEY. Mistake me not, my lord; tis not my meaning
To raze one title of your honour out:
To you, my lord, I come, what lord you will,
From the most gracious regent of this land,
The Duke of York, to know what pricks you on
To take advantage of the absent time
And fright our native peace with self-born arms.

BOLINGBROKE. I shall not need transport my words by you;
Here comes his grace in person. My noble uncle! *(He kneels)*

YORK. Show me thy humble heart, and not thy knee,
Whose duty is deceivable and false.

BOLINGBROKE. My gracious uncle—

YORK. Grace me no grace, nor uncle me no uncle:
I am no traitor's uncle; and that word *grace*
In an ungracious mouth is but profane.
Why have those banished and forbidden legs
Dared once to touch a dust of England's ground?
But then more *why?* why have they dared to march
So many miles upon her peaceful bosom,
Frighting her pale-faced villages with war
And ostentation of despisèd arms?
Comest thou because the anointed king is hence?
Why, foolish boy, the king is left behind,
And in my loyal bosom lies his power.
Were I but now the lord of such hot youth
As when brave Gaunt, thy father, and myself
Rescued the Black Prince, that young Mars of men,
From forth the ranks of many thousand French,
O, then how quickly should this arm of mine,
Now prisoner to the palsy, chastise thee
And minister correction to thy fault!

BOLINGBROKE. My gracious uncle, let me know my fault:
On what condition stands it and wherein?

YORK. Even in condition of the worst degree,
In gross rebellion and detested treason:
Thou art a banished man, and here art come
Before the expiration of thy time,
In braving arms against thy sovereign.

BOLINGBROKE. As I was banished, I was banished Hereford;
But as I come, I come for Lancaster.

And, noble uncle, I beseech your grace
Look on my wrongs with an indifferent eye:
You are my father, for methinks in you
I see old Gaunt alive; O, then, my father,
Will you permit that I shall stand condemned
A wandering vagabond; my rights and royalties
Plucked from my arms perforce and given away
To upstart unthrifts? Wherefore was I born?
My father's goods are all distrained and sold,
And these and all are all amiss employed.
What would you have me do? I am a subject,
And I challenge law: attorneys are denied me;
And therefore personally I lay my claim
To my inheritance of free descent.

NORTHUMBERLAND. The noble duke hath been too much abused.

ROSS. It stands your grace upon to do him right.

YORK. My lords of England, let me tell you this:
I have had feeling of my cousin's wrongs
And laboured all I could to do him right;
But in this kind to come, in braving arms,
Be his own carver and cut out his way,
To find out right with wrong, it may not be;
And you that do abet him in this kind
Cherish rebellion and are rebels all.

NORTHUMBERLAND. The noble duke hath sworn his coming is
But for his own; and for the right of that
We all have strongly sworn to give him aid;
And let him ne'er see joy that breaks that oath!

YORK. Well, well, I see the issue of these arms:
I cannot mend it, I must needs confess,
Because my power is weak and all ill left:
But if I could, by Him that gave me life
I would attach you all and make you stoop
Unto the sovereign mercy of the king;
But since I cannot, be it known to you
I do remain as neuter. So, fare you well;
Unless you please to enter in the castle
And there repose you for this night.

BOLINGBROKE. An offer, uncle, that we will accept:
But we must win your grace to go with us
To Bristol castle, which they say is held
By Bushy, Bagot, and their complices,
The caterpillars of the commonwealth,
Which I have sworn to weed and pluck away.

YORK. It may be I will go with you: but yet I'll pause;
For I am loth to break our country's laws.
Nor friends nor foes, to me welcome you are:
Things past redress are now with me past care.

Scene 4—A Camp in Wales

The action is advanced by a captain's communication that the Welsh army awaiting Richard's return from Ireland, weary of delay and believing the King dead, has broken up and scattered. Salisbury, left alone, receives signs that appear to foretell the ruin of the King.

ACT 3

Scene 1—Before the Castle at Bristol: Bushy and Green captive

BOLINGBROKE. Bring forth these men.
Bushy and Green, I will not vex your souls
(Since presently your souls must part your bodies)
With too much urging your pernicious lives,
For 'twere no charity; yet, to wash your blood
From off my hands, here in the view of men
I will unfold some causes of your deaths.
You have misled a prince, a royal king,
A happy gentleman in blood and lineaments,
By you unhappied and disfigured clean:
You have in manner with your sinful hours
Made a divorce betwixt his queen and him.
Myself, a prince by fortune of my birth,
Near to the king in blood, and near in love
Till you did make him misinterpret me,
Have stooped my neck under your injuries,
And sighed my English breath in foreign clouds,
Eating the bitter bread of banishment,
Whilst you have fed upon my signories,
Disparked my parks and felled my forest woods,
From my own windows torn my household coat,
Razed out my impress, leaving me no sign,
Save men's opinions and my living blood,
To show the world I am a gentleman.
This and much more, much more than twice all this,
Condemns you to the death.

BUSHY. More welcome is the stroke of death to me
Than Bolingbroke to England. Lords, farewell.

GREEN. My comfort is that heaven will take our souls
And plague injustice with the pains of hell.

BOLINGBROKE. My Lord Northumberland, see them dispatched.

Scene 2—In sight of a Castle on the Welsh Coast

Trumpets sound and colours fly, while Richard enters with friends

RICHARD. I weep for joy
To stand upon my kingdom once again.
Dear earth, I do salute thee with my hand,
Though rebels wound thee with their horses' hoofs:
As a long-parted mother with her child
Plays fondly with her tears and smiles in meeting,
So, weeping, smiling, greet I thee, my earth,
And do thee favours with my royal hands.

CARLISLE. Fear not, my lord: that Power that made you king
Hath power to keep you king in spite of all.
The means that heaven yields must be embraced,
And not neglected.

AUMERLE. He means, my lord, that we are too remiss;
Whilst Bolingbroke, through our security,
Grows strong and great in substance and in power.

RICHARD. Discomfortable cousin! know'st thou not
That when the searching eye of heaven is hid
Behind the globe that lights the lower world,
Then thieves and robbers range abroad unseen;
But when from under this terrestrial ball
He fires the proud tops of the eastern pines,
Then murders, treasons, and detested sins,
The cloak of night being plucked from off their backs,
Stand bare and naked, trembling at themselves?
So when this thief, this traitor, Bolingbroke,
Who all this while hath revelled in the night
Whilst we were wandering with the antipodes,
Shall see us rising in our throne, the east,
His treasons will sit blushing in his face,
Not able to endure the sight of day,
But self-affrighted tremble at his sin.
Not all the water in the rough rude sea
Can wash the balm from an anointed king;
The breath of worldly men cannot depose
The deputy elected by the Lord:
For every man that Bolingbroke hath pressed
To lift shrewd steel against our golden crown,
God for his Richard hath in heavenly pay
A glorious angel: then, if angels fight,
Weak men must fall, for heaven still guards the right.

Enter the Earl of Salisbury

Welcome, my lord: how far off lies your power?

SALISBURY. Nor near nor farther off, my gracious lord,
Than this weak arm: discomfort guides my tongue
And bids me speak of nothing but despair.
One day too late, I fear me, noble lord,
Hath clouded all thy happy days on earth:
O, call back yesterday, bid time return,
And thou shalt have twelve thousand fighting men!
Today, today, unhappy day, too late,
O'erthrows thy joys, friends, fortune, and thy state;
For all the Welshmen, hearing thou wert dead,
Are gone to Bolingbroke, dispersed and fled.

AUMERLE. Comfort, my liege: why looks your grace so pale?

RICHARD. But now the blood of twenty thousand men
Did triumph in my face, and they are fled;
And, till so much blood thither come again,
Have I not reason to look pale and dead?
All souls that will be safe fly from my side,
For time hath set a blot upon my pride.

AUMERLE. Comfort, my liege; remember who you are.

RICHARD. I had forgot myself: am I not king?
Awake, thou coward majesty! thou sleepest.
Is not the king's name twenty thousand names?
Arm, arm, my name! a puny subject strikes
At thy great glory. Look not to the ground,
Ye favourites of a king: are we not high?
High be our thoughts: I know my uncle York
Hath power enough to serve our turn. But who comes here?

SCROOP *(entering)*. More health and happiness betide my liege
Than can my care-tuned tongue deliver him!

RICHARD. Mine ear is open and my heart prepared:
The worst is worldly loss thou canst unfold.
Say, is my kingdom lost? why, 'twas my care;
And what loss is it to be rid of care?
Strives Bolingbroke to be as great as we?
Greater he shall not be; if he serve God,
We'll serve Him too and be his fellow so.
Revolt our subjects? That we cannot mend;
They break their faith to God as well as us.
Cry woe, destruction, ruin, and decay;
The worst is death, and death will have his day.

SCROOP. Glad am I that your highness is so armed
To bear the tidings of calamity.
Like an unseasonable stormy day,
Which makes the silver rivers drown their shores,
As if the world were all dissolved to tears,

So high above his limits swells the rage
Of Bolingbroke, covering your fearful land
With hard bright steel and hearts harder than steel.
White-beards have armed their thin and hairless scalps
Against thy majesty ; boys, with women's voices,
Strive to speak big and clap their female joints
In stiff unwieldy arms against thy crown :
Thy very beadsmen learn to bend their bows
Of double-fatal yew against thy state ;
Yea, distaff-women manage rusty bills
Against thy seat : both young and old rebel,
And all goes worse than I have power to tell.

RICHARD. Too well, too well thou tell'st a tale so ill.
Where is the Earl of Wiltshire ? where is Bagot ?
What is become of Bushy ? where is Green ?
I warrant they have made peace with Bolingbroke.

SCROOP. Peace have they made with him indeed, my lord.

RICHARD. O villains, vipers, cursed without redemption !
Dogs, easily won to fawn on any man !
Snakes, in my heart-blood warmed, that sting my heart !
Three Judases, each one thrice worse than Judas !

SCROOP. Sweet love, I see, changing his property,
Turns to the sourest and most deadly hate :
Again uncurse their souls ; their peace is made
With heads and not with hands : those whom you curse
Have felt the worst of death's destroying wound
And lie full low, graved in the hollow ground.

AUMERLE. Are Bushy, Green, and the Earl of Wiltshire dead ?

SCROOP. Ay, all of them at Bristol lost their heads.

AUMERLE. Where is the duke my father with his power ?

RICHARD. No matter where ; of comfort no man speak :
Let's talk of graves, of worms and epitaphs ;
Make dust our paper and with rainy eyes
Write sorrow on the bosom of the earth ;
Let's choose executors and talk of wills :
And yet not so, for what can we bequeath
Save our deposèd bodies to the ground ?
Our lands, our lives, and all are Bolingbroke's,
And nothing can we call our own but death
And that small model of the barren earth
Which serves as paste and cover to our bones.
For God's sake, let us sit upon the ground
And tell sad stories of the death of kings :
How some have been deposed ; some slain in war ;
Some haunted by the ghosts they have deposed ;

Some poisoned by their wives; some sleeping killed;
All murdered: for within the hollow crown
That rounds the mortal temples of a king
Keeps Death his court, and there the Antic sits,
Scoffing his state and grinning at his pomp,
Allowing him a breath, a little scene,
To monarchise, be feared, and kill with looks,
Infusing him with self and vain conceit,
As if this flesh which walls about our life
Were brass impregnable, and, humoured thus,
Comes at the last and with a little pin
Bores through his castle wall, and *Farewell king!*
Cover your heads and mock not flesh and blood
With solemn reverence: throw away respect,
Tradition, form, and ceremonious duty,
For you have but mistook me all this while:
I live with bread like you, feel want,
Taste grief, need friends: subjected thus,
How can you say to me, I am a king?

CARLISLE. My lord, wise men ne'er sit and wail their woes,
But presently prevent the ways to wail.
To fear the foe, since fear oppresseth strength,
Gives in your weakness strength unto your foe,
And so your follies fight against yourself.
Fear, and be slain; no worse can come to fight:
And fight and die is death destroying death;
Where fearing dying pays death servile breath.

AUMERLE. My father hath a power; inquire of him,
And learn to make a body of a limb.

RICHARD. Thou chidest me well: proud Bolingbroke, I come
To change blows with thee for our day of doom.
Say, Scroop, where lies our uncle with his power?
Speak sweetly, man, although thy looks be sour.

SCROOP. Men judge by the complexion of the sky
The state and inclination of the day:
So may you by my dull and heavy eye,
My tongue hath but a heavier tale to say.
I play the torturer, by small and small
To lengthen out the worst that must be spoken:
Your uncle York is joined with Bolingbroke,
And all your northern castles yielded up,
And all your southern gentlemen in arms
Upon his party.

RICHARD. Thou hast said enough.
Beshrew thee, cousin *(to Aumerle)*, which didst lead me forth
Of that sweet way I was in to despair!

What say you now ? what comfort have we now ?
By heaven, I'll hate him everlastingly
That bids me be of comfort any more.
Go to Flint castle : there I'll pine away ;
A king, woe's slave, shall kingly woe obey.
That power I have, discharge ; and let them go
To ear the land that hath some hope to grow,
For I have none : let no man speak again
To alter this, for counsel is but vain.

AUMERLE. My liege, one word.

RICHARD. He does me double wrong
That wounds me with the flatteries of his tongue.
Discharge my followers : let them hence away,
From Richard's night to Bolingbroke's fair day.

Scene 3—Before Flint Castle in Wales

Enter Bolingbroke, York, and Northumberland

BOLINGBROKE. What, will not this castle yield ?

PERCY. The castle royally is manned, my lord,
Against thy entrance.

BOLINGBROKE. Royally !
Why, it contains no king ?

PERCY. Yes, my good lord,
It doth contain a king ; King Richard lies
Within the limits of yon lime and stone.

BOLINGBROKE. Noble lords,
Go to the rude ribs of that ancient castle ;
Through brazen trumpet send the breath of parley
Into his ruined ears, and thus deliver :
Henry Bolingbroke
On both his knees doth kiss King Richard's hand
And sends allegiance and true faith of heart
To his most royal person, hither come
Even at his feet to lay my arms and power,
Provided that my banishment repealed
And lands restored again be freely granted :
If not, I'll use the advantage of my power
And lay the summer's dust with showers of blood
Rained from the wounds of slaughtered Englishmen :
The which, how far off from the mind of Bolingbroke
It is such crimson tempest should bedrench
The fresh green lap of fair King Richard's land,
My stooping duty tenderly shall show.
Go, signify as much, while here we march
Upon the grassy carpet of this plain.

Let's march without the noise of threatening drum,
That from this castle's tattered battlements
Our fair appointments may be well perused.

The King appears on the Castle wall

March on, and mark King Richard how he looks.
See, see, King Richard doth himself appear,
As doth the blushing discontented sun
From out the fiery portal of the east,
When he perceives the envious clouds are bent
To dim his glory and to stain the track
Of his bright passage to the Occident.

YORK. Yet looks he like a king: behold, his eye,
As bright as is the eagle's, lightens forth
Controlling majesty: alack, alack, for woe,
That any harm should stain so fair a show!

RICHARD. We are amazed; and thus long have we stood
To watch the fearful bending of thy knee,
Because we thought ourself thy lawful king:
And if we be, how dare thy joints forget
To pay their awful duty to our presence?
If we be not, show us the hand of God
That hath dismissed us from our stewardship;
For well we know, no hand of blood and bone
Can grip the sacred handle of our sceptre,
Unless he do profane, steal, or usurp.
And though you think that all, as you have done,
Have torn their souls by turning them from us,
And we are barren and bereft of friends,
Yet know, my master, God omnipotent,
Is mustering in his clouds on our behalf
Armies of pestilence; and they shall strike
Your children yet unborn and unbegot,
That lift your vassal hands against my head
And threat the glory of my precious crown.
Tell Bolingbroke (for yond methinks he stands)
That every stride he makes upon my land
Is dangerous treason: he is come to open
The purple testament of bleeding war;
But ere the crown he looks for live in peace,
Ten thousand crowns of mothers' sons
Shall ill become the flower of England's face,
Change the complexion of her maid-pale peace
To scarlet indignation and bedew
Her pastures' grass with faithful English blood.

NORTHUMBERLAND. The king of heaven forbid our lord the king
Should so with civil and uncivil arms

Be rushed upon ! Thy thrice noble cousin
Harry Bolingbroke doth humbly kiss thy hand ;
And by the honourable tomb he swears,
That stands upon your royal grandsire's bones,
And by the buried hand of warlike Gaunt,
And by the worth and honour of himself,
Comprising all that may be sworn or said,
His coming hither hath no further scope
Than for his lineal royalties, and to beg
Enfranchisement immediate on his knees :
Which on thy royal party granted once,
His glittering arms he will commend to rust,
His barbèd steeds to stables, and his heart
To faithful service of your majesty.
This swears he, as he is a prince, is just ;
And, as I am a gentleman, I credit him.

RICHARD. Northumberland, say thus the king returns :
His noble cousin is right welcome hither ;
And all the number of his fair demands
Shall be accomplished without contradiction.
With all the gracious utterance thou hast
Speak to his gentle hearing kind commends.
(To Aumerle) We do debase ourselves, cousin, do we not,
To look so poorly and to speak so fair ?
Shall we call back Northumberland, and send
Defiance to the traitor, and so die ?

AUMERLE. No, good my lord ; let's fight with gentle words
Till time lend friends and friends their helpful swords.

RICHARD. O God, O God ! that e'er this tongue of mine,
That laid the sentence of dread banishment
On yon proud man, should take it off again
With words of sooth ! O that I were as great
As is my grief, or lesser than my name !

AUMERLE. Northumberland comes back from Bolingbroke.

RICHARD. What must the king do now ? Must he submit ?
The king shall do it. Must he be deposed ?
The king shall be contented. Must he lose
The name of king ? O' God's name, let it go :
I'll give my jewels for a set of beads,
My gorgeous palace for a hermitage,
My gay apparel for an almsman's gown,
My figured goblets for a dish of wood,
My sceptre for a palmer's walking-staff,
My subjects for a pair of carvèd saints,

And my large kingdom for a little grave,
A little little grave, an obscure grave;
Or I'll be buried in the king's highway,
Some way of common trade, where subjects' feet
May hourly trample on their sovereign's head,
For on my heart they tread now whilst I live,
And, buried once, why not upon my head?
Aumerle, thou weep'st, my tender-hearted cousin!
We'll make foul weather with despisèd tears.
Most mighty prince, my Lord Northumberland,
What says King Bolingbroke? Will his majesty
Give Richard leave to live till Richard die?

NORTHUMBERLAND. My lord, in the base court he doth attend
To speak with you; may it please you to come down?

RICHARD. In the base court? Base court, where kings grow base,
To come at traitors' calls and do them grace.
In the base court? Come down? Down, court! down, king!
For night-owls shriek where mounting larks should sing.

The King descends

BOLINGBROKE. Stand all apart. And show fair duty to his majesty.
My gracious lord *(kneeling)*——

RICHARD. Fair cousin, you debase your princely knee
To make the base earth proud with kissing it:
Me rather had my heart might feel your love
Than my unpleased eye see your courtesy.
Up, cousin, up; your heart is up, I know,
Thus high at least, although your knee be low.

BOLINGBROKE. My gracious lord, I come but for mine own.

RICHARD. Your own is yours, and I am yours, and all.

BOLINGBROKE. So far be mine, my most redoubted lord,
As my true service shall deserve your love.

RICHARD. Well you deserve: they well deserve to have,
That know the strong'st and surest way to get.
Uncle, give me your hands: nay, dry your eyes;
Tears show their love, but want their remedies.
Cousin, I am too young to be your father,
Though you are old enough to be my heir.
What you will have, I'll give, and willing too;
For do we must what force will have us do.
Set on towards London, cousin, is it so?

BOLINGBROKE. Yea, my good lord.

RICHARD. Then I must not say no.

Scene 4—The Duke of York's Garden at Langley

Enter the Queen and two Ladies

QUEEN. What sport shall we devise here in this garden,
To drive away the heavy thought of care?

LADY. Madam, we'll play at bowls.

QUEEN. Twill make me think the world is full of rubs,
And that my fortune runs against the bias.

LADY. Madam, we'll dance.

QUEEN. My legs can keep no measure in delight,
When my poor heart no measure keeps in grief:
Therefore, no dancing, girl; some other sport.

LADY. Madam, we'll tell tales.

QUEEN. Of sorrow or of joy?

LADY. Of either, madam.

QUEEN. Of neither, girl:
For if of joy, being altogether wanting,
It doth remember me the more of sorrow;
Or if of grief, being altogether sad,
It adds more sorrow to my want of joy:
For what I have I need not to repeat;
And what I want it boots not to complain.

LADY. Madam, I'll sing.

QUEEN. Tis well that thou hast cause;
But thou shouldst please me better wouldst thou weep.

LADY. I could weep, madam, would it do you good.

QUEEN. And I could sing, would weeping do me good,
And never borrow any tear of thee.

The Gardener comes with two Servants

But stay, here come the gardeners:
Let's step into the shadow of these trees.
My wretchedness unto a row of pins
They'll talk of state, for every one doth so
Against a change; woe is forerun with woe.

GARDENER. Go, bind thou up yon dangling apricocks,
Which, like unruly children, make their sire
Stoop with oppression of their prodigal weight:
Give some supportance to the bending twigs.
Go thou, and like an executioner,
Cut off the heads of too fast growing sprays,
That look too lofty in our commonwealth:
All must be even in our government.
You thus employed, I will go root away
The noisome weeds, which without profit suck
The soil's fertility from wholesome flowers.

SERVANT. Why should we in the compass of a pale
Keep law and form and due proportion,
Showing, as in a model, our firm estate,
When our sea-wallèd garden, the whole land,
Is full of weeds, her fairest flowers choked up,
Her fruit-trees all unpruned, her hedges ruined,
Her knots disordered and her wholesome herbs
Swarming with caterpillars?

GARDENER. Hold thy peace:
He that hath suffered this disordered spring
Hath now himself met with the fall of leaf:
The weeds which his broad-spreading leaves did shelter
That seemed in eating him to hold him up,
Are plucked up root and all by Bolingbroke,
I mean the Earl of Wiltshire, Bushy, Green.

SERVANT. What, are they dead?

GARDENER. They are; and Bolingbroke
Hath seized the wasteful king. O, what pity is it
That he had not so trimmed and dressed his land
As we this garden! We at time of year
Do wound the bark, the skin of our fruit-trees,
Lest, being over-proud in sap and blood,
With too much riches it confound itself:
Had he done so to great and growing men,
They might have lived to bear and he to taste
Their fruits of duty: superfluous branches
We lop away, that bearing boughs may live:
Had he done so, himself had borne the crown,
Which waste of idle hours hath quite thrown down.

SERVANT. What, think you then the king shall be deposed?

GARDENER. Depressed he is already, and deposed
Tis doubt he will be: letters came last night
To a dear friend of the good Duke of York's,
That tell black tidings.

QUEEN. O, I am pressed to death through want of speaking!
Thou, old Adam's likeness, set to dress this garden,
How dares thy harsh rude tongue sound this unpleasing news?
What Eve, what serpent, hath suggested thee
To make a second fall of cursèd man?
Why dost thou say King Richard is deposed?
Darest thou, thou little better thing than earth,
Divine his downfall? Say, where, when, and how,
Camest thou by this ill tidings? speak, thou wretch.

GARDENER. Pardon me, madam: little joy have I
To breathe this news; yet what I say is true.

King Richard, he is in the mighty hold
Of Bolingbroke: their fortunes both are weighed:
In your lord's scale is nothing but himself,
And some few vanities that make him light;
But in the balance of great Bolingbroke,
Besides himself, are all the English peers,
And with that odds he weighs King Richard down.
Post you to London, and you will find it so;
I speak no more than everyone doth know.

QUEEN. Gardener, for telling me these news of woe,
Pray God the plants thou graft'st may never grow. *(She goes)*

GARDENER. Poor queen! so that thy state might be no worse,
I would my skill were subject to thy curse.
Here did she fall a tear; here in this place
I'll set a bank of rue, sour herb of grace:
Rue, even for ruth, here shortly shall be seen,
In the remembrance of a weeping queen.

ACT 4

Scene 1—Westminster Hall

Enter Bolingbroke, Aumerle, Northumberland, Carlisle, the Abbot of Westminster, and others. There is some discussion on Gloucester's death, during which Carlisle announces that Mowbray has died in Venice, giving

His body to that pleasant country's earth,
And his pure soul unto his captain Christ,
Under whose colours he had fought so long.

York declares that Richard has adopted Bolingbroke his heir and resigned the throne, which Henry the Fourth will now ascend. The Bishop of Carlisle passionately protests and is arrested. York leaves and returns with Richard.

RICHARD. Alack, why am I sent for to a king,
Before I have shook off the regal thoughts
Wherewith I reigned? I hardly yet have learned
To insinuate, flatter, bow, and bend my limbs:
Give sorrow leave awhile to tutor me
To this submission. Yet I well remember
The favours of these men: were they not mine?
Did they not sometime cry, *All hail!* to me?
So Judas did to Christ: but he, in twelve,
Found truth in all but one; I, in twelve thousand, none.
God save the king! Will no man say Amen?
Am I both priest and clerk? Well then, Amen.
God save the king! although I be not he;
And yet Amen, if heaven do think him me.
To do what service am I sent for hither?

YORK. To do that office of thine own good will
Which tired majesty did make thee offer,
The resignation of thy state and crown
To Henry Bolingbroke.

RICHARD. Give me the crown. Here, cousin, seize the crown;
Here cousin;
On this side my hand, and on that side yours.
Now is this golden crown like a deep well
That owes two buckets, filling one another,
The emptier ever dancing in the air,
The other down, unseen and full of water:
That bucket down and full of tears am I,
Drinking my griefs, whilst you mount up on high.

BOLINGBROKE. I thought you had been willing to resign.

RICHARD. My crown I am; but still my griefs are mine:
You may my glories and my state depose,
But not my griefs; still am I king of those.

BOLINGBROKE. Part of your cares you give me with your crown.

RICHARD. Your cares set up do not pluck my cares down.

BOLINGBROKE. Are you contented to resign the crown?

RICHARD. Ay, no; no, ay; for I must nothing be;
Therefore no no, for I resign to thee.
I give this heavy weight from off my head
And this unwieldy sceptre from my hand,
The pride of kingly sway from out my heart;
With mine own tears I wash away my balm,
With mine own hands I give away my crown,
With mine own tongue deny my sacred state,
With mine own breath release all duty's rites:
All pomp and majesty I do forswear;
My manors, rents, *revenues* I forego;
My acts, decrees, and statutes I deny:
God pardon all oaths that are broke to me!
God keep all vows unbroke that swear to thee!
Make me, that nothing have, with nothing grieved,
And thou with all pleased that hast all achieved!
Long mayst thou live in Richard's seat to sit,
And soon lie Richard in an earthy pit!
God save King Harry, unkinged Richard says,
And send him many years of sunshine days!
What more remains?

NORTHUMBERLAND. No more, but that you read
These accusations and these grievous crimes
Committed by your person and your followers
Against the state and profit of this land;

That, by confessing them, the souls of men
May deem that you are worthily deposed.

RICHARD. Must I do so? and must I ravel out
My weaved-up folly? Gentle Northumberland,
If thy offences were upon record,
Would it not shame thee in so fair a troop
To read a lecture of them?

NORTHUMBERLAND. My lord, dispatch; read o'er these articles.

RICHARD. Mine eyes are full of tears, I cannot see;
And yet salt water blinds them not so much
But they can see a sort of traitors here.
Nay, if I turn mine eyes upon myself,
I find myself a traitor with the rest;
For I have given here my soul's consent
To undeck the pompous body of a king;
Made glory base and sovereignty a slave,
Proud majesty a subject, state a peasant.

NORTHUMBERLAND. My lord—

RICHARD. No lord of thine, thou haught insulting man,
Nor no man's lord; I have no name, no title,
No, not that name was given me at the font,
But tis usurped: alack the heavy day,
That I have worn so many winters out,
And know not now what name to call myself!
O that I were a mockery king of snow,
Standing before the sun of Bolingbroke,
To melt myself away in water-drops!
Good king, great king, and yet not greatly good,
An if my word be sterling yet in England,
Let it command a mirror hither straight,
That it may show me what a face I have,
Since it is bankrupt of his majesty.

BOLINGBROKE. Go some of you and fetch a looking-glass.

RICHARD. Give me the glass, and therein will I read.
No deeper wrinkles yet? hath sorrow struck
So many blows upon this face of mine
And made no deeper wounds? O flattering glass,
Like to my followers in prosperity,
Thou dost beguile me! Was this face the face
That every day under his household roof
Did keep ten thousand men! Was this the face
That, like the sun, did make beholders wink?
Was this the face that faced so many follies,
And was at last out-faced by Bolingbroke?

A brittle glory shineth in this face :
As brittle as the glory is the face ;

He dashes the glass to the ground

For there it is, cracked in a hundred shivers.
Mark, silent king, the moral of this sport,
How soon my sorrow hath destroyed my face.

BOLINGBROKE. The shadow of your sorrow hath destroyed
The shadow of your face.
Go, some of you convey him to the Tower.

RICHARD. O, good ! convey ? Conveyers are you all,
That rise thus nimbly by a true king's fall. *(He leaves)*

BOLINGBROKE. On Wednesday next we solemnly set down
Our coronation : lords, prepare yourselves.

The Court departs

ABBOT OF WESTMINSTER. A woeful pageant have we here beheld.

CARLISLE. The woe's to come ; the children yet unborn
Shall feel this day as sharp to them as thorn.

AUMERLE. You holy clergymen, is there no plot
To rid the realm of this pernicious blot ?

ABBOT. My lord,
Before I freely speak my mind herein,
You shall not only take the sacrament
To bury mine intents, but also to effect
Whatever I shall happen to devise.
I see your brows are full of discontent,
Your hearts of sorrow and your eyes of tears :
Come home with me to supper ; and I'll lay
A plot shall show us all a merry day.

ACT 5

Scene 1—A Street leading to the Tower

Enter the Queen and her Ladies

QUEEN. This way the king will come ; this is the way
To Julius Caesar's ill-erected tower,
To whose flint bosom my condemnèd lord
Is doomed a prisoner by proud Bolingbroke :
Here let us rest, if this rebellious earth
Have any resting for her true king's queen.

Richard approaches with his Guard

But soft, but see, or rather do not see,
My fair rose wither : yet look up, behold,
That you in pity may dissolve to dew,
And wash him fresh again with true-love tears.

RICHARD. Join not with grief, fair woman, do not so,
To make my end too sudden: learn, good soul,
To think our former state a happy dream;
From which awaked, the truth of what we are
Shows us but this: I am sworn brother, sweet,
To grim Necessity, and he and I
Will keep a league till death. Hie thee to France
And cloister thee in some religious house:
Our holy lives must win a new world's crown,
Which our profane hours here have stricken down.

QUEEN. What, is my Richard both in shape and mind
Transformed and weakened? Hath Bolingbroke deposed
Thine intellect? Hath he been in thy heart?
The lion dying thrusteth forth his paw,
And wounds the earth, if nothing else, with rage
To be o'erpowered; and wilt thou, pupil-like,
Take thy correction mildly, kiss the rod,
And fawn on rage with base humility,
Which art a lion and a king of beasts?

RICHARD. A king of beasts, indeed; if aught but beasts,
I had been still a happy king of men.
Good sometime queen, prepare thee hence for France:
Think I am dead and that even here thou takest,
As from my deathbed, thy last living leave.
In winter's tedious nights sit by the fire
With good old folks and let them tell thee tales
Of woeful ages long ago betid;
And ere thou bid Good-night, to quit their griefs,
Tell thou the lamentable tale of me
And send the hearers weeping to their beds.

Enter Northumberland

NORTHUMBERLAND. My lord, the mind of Bolingbroke is changed;
You must to Pomfret, not unto the Tower.
And, madam, there is order ta'en for you;
With all swift speed you must away to France.

RICHARD. Northumberland, thou ladder wherewithal
The mounting Bolingbroke ascends my throne,
The time shall not be many hours of age
More than it is ere foul sin gathering head
Shall break into corruption: thou shalt think,
Though he divide the realm and give thee half,
It is too little, helping him to all;
And he shall think that thou, which know'st the way
To plant unrightful kings, wilt know again,
Being ne'er so little urged, another way
To pluck him headlong from the usurped throne.

The love of wicked men converts to fear;
That fear to hate, and hate turns one or both
To worthy danger and deservèd death.

NORTHUMBERLAND. My guilt be on my head, and there an end.
Take leave and part; for you must part forthwith.

RICHARD. Doubly divorced! Bad men, you violate
A twofold marriage, 'twixt my crown and me,
And then betwixt me and my married wife.
Let me unkiss the oath 'twixt thee and me;
And yet not so, for with a kiss 'twas made.
Part us, Northumberland; I towards the north,
Where shivering cold and sickness pines the clime;
My wife to France: from whence, set forth in pomp,
She came adornèd hither like sweet May,
Sent back like Hallowmas, or short'st of day.

QUEEN. And must we be divided? Must we part?

RICHARD. Ay, hand from hand, my love, and heart from heart.

QUEEN. Banish us both and send the king with me.

NORTHUMBERLAND. That were some love but little policy.

QUEEN. Then whither he goes, thither let me go.

RICHARD. So two, together weeping, make one woe.
Weep thou for me in France, I for thee here;
Better far off than near, be ne'er the near.
Go, count thy way with sighs; I mine with groans.

QUEEN. So longest way shall have the longest moans.

RICHARD. Come, come, in wooing sorrow let's be brief,
Since, wedding it, there is such length in grief:
One kiss shall stop our mouths, and dumbly part;
Thus give I mine, and thus take I thy heart.
We make woe wanton with this fond delay:
Once more, adieu: the rest let sorrow say.

Scene 2—The Duke of York's Palace

Enter the Duke and Duchess

DUCHESS OF YORK. My lord, you told me you would tell the rest,
When weeping made you break the story off,
Of our two cousins coming into London.

YORK. Where did I leave?

DUCHESS OF YORK. At that sad stop, my lord,
Where rude misgoverned hands from windows' tops
Threw dust and rubbish on King Richard's head.

YORK. Then, as I said, the duke, great Bolingbroke,
Mounted upon a hot and fiery steed
Which his aspiring rider seemed to know,

With slow but stately pace kept on his course,
Whilst all tongues cried *God save thee, Bolingbroke!*
You would have thought the very windows spake,
So many greedy looks of young and old
Through casements darted their desiring eyes
Upon his visage, and that all the walls
With painted imagery had said at once
Jesu preserve thee! welcome, Bolingbroke!
Whilst he, from the one side to the other turning,
Bareheaded, lower than his proud steed's neck,
Bespake them thus; *I thank you, countrymen*:
And thus still doing, thus he passed along.

DUCHESS. Alack, poor Richard! where rode he the whilst?

YORK. As in a theatre, the eyes of men,
After a well-graced actor leaves the stage,
Are idly bent on him that enters next,
Thinking his prattle to be tedious;
Even so, or with much more contempt, men's eyes
Did scowl on gentle Richard; no man cried *God save him!*
No joyful tongue gave him his welcome home:
But dust was thrown upon his sacred head,
Which with such gentle sorrow he shook off,
His face still combating with tears and smiles,
The badges of his grief and patience,
That had not God, for some strong purpose, steeled
The hearts of men, they must perforce have melted
And barbarism itself have pitied him.
But heaven hath a hand in these events,
To whose high will we bound our calm contents.
To Bolingbroke are we sworn subjects now,
Whose state and honour I for aye allow.

DUCHESS OF YORK. Here comes my son Aumerle.

YORK. Aumerle that was;
But that is lost for being Richard's friend,
And, madam, you must call him Rutland now:
I am in parliament pledge for his truth
And lasting fealty to the new-made king.

DUCHESS OF YORK. Welcome, my son: who are the violets now
That strew the green lap of the new come spring?

AUMERLE. Madam, I know not, nor I greatly care not:
God knows I had as lief be none as one.

YORK. Well, bear you well in this new spring of time,
Lest you be cropped before you come to prime.
What seal is that that hangs without thy bosom?
Yea, look'st thou pale? let me see the writing.

AUMERLE. My lord, tis nothing.

YORK. No matter, then, who see it.

AUMERLE. I do beseech your grace to pardon me :
It is a matter of small consequence,
Which for some reasons I would not have seen.

YORK. Which for some reasons, sir, I mean to see.

He plucks it out of his bosom and reads it

Treason ! foul treason ! Villain ! traitor ! slave !
Ho ! who is within there ? Saddle my horse.
God for his mercy, what treachery is here !
Now, by mine honour, by my life, my troth,
I will appeach the villain.

DUCHESS OF YORK. What is the matter ?

YORK. Peace, foolish woman.

DUCHESS OF YORK. I will not peace. What is the matter, Aumerle ?

AUMERLE. Good mother, be content ; it is no more
Than my poor life must answer.

DUCHESS OF YORK. Thy life answer !
Why, York, what wilt thou do ?
Wilt thou not hide the trespass of thine own ?
Have we more sons ? or are we like to have ?
And wilt thou pluck my fair son from mine age,
And rob me of a happy mother's name ?
Is he not like thee ? Is he not thine own ?

YORK. Thou fond mad woman,
Wilt thou conceal this dark conspiracy ?
A dozen of them here have ta'en the sacrament,
To kill the king at Oxford.

DUCHESS OF YORK. He shall be none ;
We'll keep him here : then what is that to him ?

YORK. Away, fond woman ! were he twenty times my son
I would appeach him. Make way, unruly woman ! *(He rushes out)*

DUCHESS. After, Aumerle ! mount thee upon his horse ;
Spur post, and get before him to the king,
And beg thy pardon ere he do accuse thee.
I'll not be long behind ; though I be old,
I doubt not but to ride as fast as York :
And never will I rise up from the ground
Till Bolingbroke hath pardoned thee.

Scene 3—Windsor Castle : Bolingbroke as King with Lords

BOLINGBROKE. Can no man tell me of my unthrifty son ?
Tis full three months since I did see him last :
If any plague hang over us, tis he.

I would to God, my lords, he might be found:
Inquire at London, 'mongst the taverns there,
For there, they say, he daily doth frequent,
With unrestrainèd loose companions,
Even such, they say, as stand in narrow lanes,
And beat our watch, and rob our passengers;
Which he, young wanton and effeminate boy,
Takes on the point of honour to support
So dissolute a crew, as dissolute as desperate; yet through both
I see some sparks of better hope, which elder years
May happily bring forth. But who comes here?

AUMERLE *(entering)*. Where is the king?

BOLINGBROKE. What means our cousin, that he stares and looks
So wildly?

AUMERLE. God save your grace! I do beseech your majesty,
To have some conference with your grace alone.

BOLINGBROKE. Withdraw yourselves, and leave us here alone.
What is the matter with our cousin now?

AUMERLE. For ever may my knees grow to the earth,
My tongue cleave to my roof within my mouth,
Unless a pardon ere I rise or speak.

BOLINGBROKE. Intended or committed was this fault?
If on the first, how heinous e'er it be,
To win thy after-love I pardon thee.

AUMERLE. Then give me leave that I may turn the key,
That no man enter till my tale be done.

BOLINGBROKE. Have thy desire.

York arrives at the door and knocks loudly

YORK. My liege, beware; look to thyself;
Thou hast a traitor in thy presence there.
Open the door, secure, foolhardy king:
Shall I for love speak treason to thy face?
Open the door, or I will break it open. *(The door is opened)*

BOLINGBROKE. What is the matter, uncle? speak;
Recover breath; tell us how near is danger,
That we may arm us to encounter it.

YORK. Peruse this writing here, and thou shalt know
The treason that my haste forbids me show.

AUMERLE. Remember, as thou read'st, thy promise passed:
I do repent me; read not my name there;
My heart is not confederate with my hand.

YORK. It was, villain, ere thy hand did set it down.
I tore it from the traitor's bosom, king;
Fear, and not love, begets his penitence:
Forget to pity him, lest thy pity prove
A serpent that will sting thee to the heart.

BOLINGBROKE. O heinous, strong, and bold conspiracy!
O loyal father of a treacherous son!

The Duchess of York knocks loudly

DUCHESS OF YORK. What ho, my liege! for God's sake, let me in.

BOLINGBROKE. What shrill-voiced suppliant makes this eager cry?

DUCHESS OF YORK. A woman, and thy aunt, great king; tis I.
Speak with me, pity me, open the door:
A beggar begs that never begged before.

BOLINGBROKE. Our scene is altered from a serious thing,
And now changed to *The Beggar and the King.*
My dangerous cousin, let your mother in:
I know she is come to pray for your foul sin.

DUCHESS OF YORK *(kneeling).* O king, believe not this hard-hearted man!
Love loving not itself none other can.

BOLINGBROKE. Rise up, good aunt.

DUCHESS OF YORK. Not yet, I thee beseech:
For ever will I walk upon my knees,
And never see day that the happy sees,
Till thou give joy; until thou bid me joy,
By pardoning Rutland, my transgressing boy.

AUMERLE. Unto my mother's prayers I bend my knee.

BOLINGBROKE. Good aunt, stand up.

DUCHESS OF YORK. Nay, do not say, *stand up*;
Say *pardon* first, and afterwards *stand up.*
An if I were thy nurse, thy tongue to teach,
Pardon should be the first word of thy speech.
I never longed to hear a word till now;
Say *pardon,* king; let pity teach thee how:
The word is short, but not so short as sweet;
No word like *pardon* for kings' mouths so meet.

YORK. Speak it in French, king; say, *pardonnez-moi.*

DUCHESS OF YORK. Dost thou teach Pardon pardon to destroy?
Ah, my sour husband, my hard-hearted lord,
That set'st the word itself against the word!
Speak *pardon* as tis current in our land;
The chopping French we do not understand.

BOLINGBROKE. Good aunt, stand up.

DUCHESS OF YORK. I do not sue to stand;
Pardon is all the suit I have in hand.

BOLINGBROKE. I pardon him, as God shall pardon me.

DUCHESS OF YORK. O happy vantage of a kneeling knee!
Yet am I sick for fear: speak it again;
Twice saying *pardon* doth not pardon twain,
But makes one pardon strong.

BOLINGBROKE. With all my heart I pardon him.

DUCHESS OF YORK. A god on earth thou art.

BOLINGBROKE. But for the rest of that consorted crew,
Destruction straight shall dog them at the heels.
Good uncle, help to order several powers
To Oxford, or where'er these traitors are:
They shall not live within this world, I swear.
Uncle, farewell: and, cousin too, adieu:
Your mother well hath prayed, and prove you true.

DUCHESS OF YORK. Come, my old son: I pray God make thee new.

Scene 4—Windsor Castle

Enter Sir Pierce of Exton with his servant

EXTON. Didst thou not mark the king, what words he spake,
Have I no friend will rid me of this living fear?
Was it not so?

SERVANT. These were his very words.

EXTON. *Have I no friend?* quoth he: he spake it twice,
And urged it twice together, did he not?

SERVANT. He did.

EXTON. And speaking it, he wistly looked on me;
As who should say, *I would thou wert the man*
That would divorce this terror from my heart;
Meaning the king at Pomfret. Come, let's go:
I am the king's friend, and will rid his foe.

Scene 5—King Richard at Pomfret Castle

RICHARD *(alone)*. Music do I hear?
Ha, ha! keep time: how sour sweet music is
When time is broke and no proportion kept!
So is it in the music of men's lives.

And here have I the daintiness of ear
To check time broke in a disordered string;
But for the concord of my state and time
Had not an ear to hear my true time broke.
I wasted time, and now doth time waste me.
This music mads me; let it sound no more;
For though it have helped madmen to their wits,
In me it seems it will make wise men mad.
Yet blessing on his heart that gives it me!
For tis a sign of love; and love to Richard
Is a strange brooch in this all-hating world.

A Groom of the Stable comes in

GROOM. Hail, royal prince!

RICHARD. Thanks, noble peer;
The cheapest of us is ten groats too dear.
What art thou? and how comest thou hither,
Where no man ever comes but that sad dog
That brings me food to make misfortune live?

GROOM. I was a poor groom of thy stable, king,
When thou wert king; who, travelling towards York,
With much ado at length have gotten leave
To look upon my sometime royal master's face.
O, how it yearned my heart when I beheld
In London streets, that coronation day,
When Bolingbroke rode on roan Barbary,
That horse that thou so often hast bestrid,
That horse that I so carefully have dressed!

RICHARD. Rode he on Barbary? Tell me, gentle friend,
How went he under him?

GROOM. So proudly as if he disdained the ground.

RICHARD. So proud that Bolingbroke was on his back!
That jade hath ate bread from my royal hand;
This hand hath made him proud with clapping him.
Would he not stumble? Would he not fall down,
Since pride must have a fall, and break the neck
Of that proud man that did usurp his back?
Forgiveness, horse! why do I rail on thee,
Since thou, created to be awed by man,
Wast born to bear? I was not made a horse,
And yet I bear a burthen like an ass,
Spurred, galled, and tired by jauncing Bolingbroke.

Enter Keeper with a dish

KEEPER. Fellow, give place ; here is no longer stay.

RICHARD. If thou love me, tis time thou wert away.

GROOM *(going)*. What my tongue dares not, that my heart shall say.

KEEPER. My lord, will 't please you to fall to ?

RICHARD. Taste of it first, as thou art wont to do.

KEEPER. My lord, I dare not : Sir Pierce of Exton, who lately came from the king, commands the contrary.

RICHARD. The devil take Henry of Lancaster and thee !
Patience is stale, and I am weary of it.

Richard sets upon the keeper and beats him, when Exton enters with his servants, armed. Snatching an axe from one of them, Richard kills both servants, when Exton strikes him down and he dies, saying :

Mount, mount, my soul ! thy seat is up on high ;
Whilst my gross flesh sinks downward, here to die.

Scene 6—Windsor Castle

Bolingbroke and York are present with lords when Sir Pierce of Exton enters with attendants bearing a coffin.

EXTON. Great king, within this coffin I present
Thy buried fear : herein all breathless lies
The mightiest of thy greatest enemies,
Richard of Bordeaux, by me hither brought.

BOLINGBROKE. Exton, I thank thee not ; for thou hast wrought
A deed of slander with thy fatal hand
Upon my head and all this famous land.

EXTON. From your own mouth, my lord, did I this deed.

BOLINGBROKE. They love not poison that do poison need,
Nor do I thee.
The guilt of conscience take thou for thy labour,
But neither my good word nor princely favour :
With Cain go wander through the shades of night,
And never show thy head by day nor light.
Lords, I protest, my soul is full of woe,
That blood should sprinkle me to make me grow :
Come, mourn with me for that I do lament,
And put on sullen black incontinent :
I'll make a voyage to the Holy Land,
To wash this blood off from my guilty hand :
March sadly after ; grace my mournings here ;
In weeping after this untimely bier.

The Story of Richard the Third

FOR three hundred years this play, rapid, compact, and powerful, has remained one of the most popular tragedies in the English tongue.

THE theme is appalling. It is a story of wickedness such as has rarely been clothed in human form. King Richard wades through slaughter to his throne, and falls fighting with ten murders on his conscience. In using crime as a stepping-stone to power, Macbeth is a novice compared with him.

SUBSTANTIALLY, though not exactly, the play is actual history. The man Richard was as he is presented by Shakespeare. Murder was nothing to him; if a man stood in his path the man must go, and killing was the easy way. He was by far the cleverest man in the England of his day, and he was determined to be king. He had won popularity as a governor of Northern England, and on this popularity his power was based. He used it as his stepping-stone on the way to the throne.

WE can hardly believe the scenes through which the play moves on. He murders a king, and the widow, setting aside her mourning, is at his feet. It is his way, and he is impenitent in his villainies. In the very opening lines of the play we see the inmost mind of this misshapen, cynical, ambitious, cruel man. Richard never deceives himself for a moment. He plans from first to last his campaign to win a throne. His villainy is cool and determined; he knows the price he must pay and he pays it, and his confidence in his own powers of invention and deception knows no tremor.

THE play moves swiftly on through all this tragedy, through tragic scenes at times familiar to us all, such as that of the death of the little princes in the Tower. Only a style bold and robust could present such a monster as Richard to the world.

THIS play will do no harm to those who talk stupidly of the good old days. Here are the sort of things that happened in those days, not among the common people but in the full light of the throne. This play pictures the savage rivalries that were not uncommon in royal circles in the days before popular government began. We cannot imagine today such kings as John, or Richard the Third, or Henry the Eighth, but they were kings of England, monsters though they were. So thin was the veneer of civilisation that murder was accepted as the whim of a ruling man. *Off with his head* came from the lips of an English king as readily as *Kill me that fat citizen* came from the lips of a Roman Emperor. Rivals were dogs in their way.

ALWAYS, on such men, retribution falls, and it tracks this man at last on Bosworth Field, where he dies with his back to the wall, fighting and unrepentant, so bringing to an end a grim and terrible story which only Shakespeare's genius has made into great drama.

THE PLAYERS

Edward the Fourth, who dies pledging enemies to forgiveness.

Edward, Prince of Wales, the uncrowned Edward the Fifth; murdered in the Tower with his brother.

Richard, Duke of York, a clever boy; murdered in the Tower with his brother.

Duke of Clarence, brother of Richard the Third; murdered.

Richard, Duke of Gloucester, becoming Richard the Third. Crooked, crippled, cruel, but clever, active, and unafraid.

Cardinal Bourchier, Archbishop of Canterbury.

Thomas Rotherham, Archbishop of York.

Henry, Earl of Richmond, becoming Henry the Seventh, victor of Bosworth Field.

John Morton, Bishop of Ely; a supporter of Richmond.

Duke of Buckingham, the closest friend of Richard; executed.

Duke of Norfolk, a supporter of Richard.

Earl of Surrey, son of Norfolk, and supporter of Richard.

Earl Rivers, brother of King Edward's Queen.

Lord Grey, son of King Edward's Queen Elizabeth; executed.

Marquis of Dorset, son of King Edward's Queen Elizabeth.

Sir Thomas Vaughan, friend of Elizabeth; executed.

Lord Hastings, a supposed friend of Richard; executed.

Lord Stanley, also called Earl of Derby, a supporter of Richmond.

Earl of Oxford, a supporter of Richmond.

Sir Walter Herbert, loyal to Richmond.

Sir Robert Brakenbury, Lieutenant of the Tower of London.

Sir James Tyrrel, a procurer of murderers.

Sir Richard Ratcliff, an attendant on Richard.

Sir William Catesby, an attendant on Richard.

Lord Lovel, an attendant on Richard.

Sir Christopher Urswick, a priest, with another priest.

Lord Mayor of London, a time-server.

Elizabeth, Queen of Edward the Fourth.

Margaret, widow of King Henry the Sixth.

Margaret Plantagenet, daughter of the Duke of Clarence.

Lady Anne, widow of Henry the Sixth's son Edward, and afterwards the unhappy wife of King Richard.

Duchess of York, mother of Richard the Third and Edward the Fourth.

Sheriff, ghosts, lords, citizens, murderers, soldiers.

SCENE—England

King Richard the Third

ACT 1

Scene 1—A Street in London : Duke of Gloucester alone

GLOUCESTER. Now is the winter of our discontent
Made glorious summer by this sun of York ;
And all the clouds that loured upon our house
In the deep bosom of the ocean buried.
Now are our brows bound with victorious wreaths ;
Our bruisèd arms hung up for monuments,
Our stern alarums changed to merry meetings,
Our dreadful marches to delightful measures.
Grim-visaged war hath smoothed his wrinkled front ;
And now, instead of mounting barbèd steeds
To fright the souls of fearful adversaries,
He capers nimbly in a lady's chamber
To the luxurious pleasing of a lute.
But I, that am not shaped for sportive tricks,
Nor made to court an amorous looking-glass ;
I, that am rudely stamped, and want love's majesty
To strut before a wanton ambling nymph ;
I, that am curtailed of this fair proportion,
Cheated of feature by dissembling nature,
Deformed, unfinished, sent before my time
Into this breathing world, scarce half made up,
And that so lamely and unfashionable
That dogs bark at me as I halt by them ;
Why, I, in this weak piping time of peace,
Have no delight to pass away the time,
Unless to spy my shadow in the sun
And *des*cant on mine own deformity :
And therefore, since I cannot prove a lover,
To entertain these fair well-spoken days,
I am determinèd to prove a villain
And hate the idle pleasures of these days.
Plots have I raised, inductions dangerous,
By drunken prophecies, libels, and dreams,

To set my brother Clarence and the king
In deadly hate the one against the other:
And if King Edward be as true and just
As I am subtle, false, and treacherous,
This day should Clarence closely be mewed up,
About a prophecy, which says that G
Of Edward's heirs the murderer shall be.
Dive, thoughts, down to my soul: here Clarence comes.

Enter Clarence, guarded, with Brakenbury

Brother, good day: what means this armèd guard
That waits upon your grace?

CLARENCE. His majesty,
Tendering my person's safety, hath appointed
This conduct to convey me to the Tower.

Clarence declares himself innocent of offence, except that his name begins with the G said by a stupid legend to be fatal to Edward's heirs. Gloucester suggests that the King is not to blame, but the Queen and her brother, who, he says, have been responsible for the imprisonment of Hastings, now released. Brakenbury stops the conversation, and Clarence passes on, leaving Gloucester to his sinister meditations.

GLOUCESTER. Go, tread the path that thou shalt ne'er return,
Simple, plain Clarence! I do love thee so,
That I will shortly send thy soul to heaven,
If heaven will take the present at our hands.
But who comes here? The new-delivered Hastings?

HASTINGS *(entering)*. Good time of day unto my gracious lord!

GLOUCESTER. As much unto my good lord chamberlain!
Well are you welcome to the open air.
How hath your lordship brooked imprisonment?

HASTINGS. With patience, noble lord, as prisoners must:
But I shall live, my lord, to give them thanks
That were the cause of my imprisonment.

GLOUCESTER. No doubt, no doubt; and so shall Clarence too;
For they that were your enemies are his,
And have prevailed as much on him as you.

HASTINGS. More pity that the eagle should be mewed,
While kites and buzzards prey at liberty.

GLOUCESTER. What news abroad?

HASTINGS. No news so bad abroad as this at home;
The king is sickly, weak, and melancholy,
And his physicians fear him mightily.

GLOUCESTER. Now, by Saint Paul, this news is bad indeed.
O, he hath kept an evil diet long,
And overmuch consumed his royal person:

Tis very grievous to be thought upon.
What, is he in his bed ?

HASTINGS. He is. *(Hastings goes)*

GLOUCESTER *(alone)*. Go you before, and I will follow you.
He cannot live, I hope, and must not die
Till George be packed with post-horse up to heaven.
I'll in, to urge his hatred more to Clarence,
With lies well steeled with weighty arguments ;
And, if I fail not in my deep intent,
Clarence hath not another day to live :
Which done, God take King Edward to his mercy,
And leave the world for me to bustle in !
For then I'll marry Warwick's youngest daughter.
What though I killed her husband and her father ?
The readiest way to make the wench amends
Is to become her husband and her father :
The which will I ; not all so much for love
As for another secret close intent,
By marrying her which I must reach unto.
But yet I run before my horse to market :
Clarence still breathes ; Edward still lives and reigns :
When they are gone, then must I count my gains.

Scene 2—Another Street in London

A Guard bearing the body of Henry the Sixth, Lady Anne as mourner

ANNE. Set down, set down your honourable load,
If honour may be shrouded in a hearse,
Whilst I awhile obsequiously lament
The untimely fall of virtuous Lancaster.
Poor key-cold figure of a holy king !
Pale ashes of the house of Lancaster !
Thou bloodless remnant of that royal blood !
Be it lawful that I invocate thy ghost,
To hear the lamentations of poor Anne,
Wife to thy Edward, to thy slaughtered son,
Stabbed by the selfsame hand that made these wounds !
Cursed be the hand that made these fatal holes !
Cursed be the heart that had the heart to do it !
Cursèd the blood that let this blood from hence !
More direful hap betide that hated wretch,
That makes us wretched by the death of thee,
Than I can wish to adders, spiders, toads,
Or any creeping venomed thing that lives !
If ever he have wife, let her be made
As miserable by the death of him
As I am made by my poor lord and thee !

GLOUCESTER. Stay, you that bear the corse, and set it down.

ANNE. What black magician conjures up this fiend
To stop devoted charitable deeds ?

GLOUCESTER. Villains, set down the corse ; or, by Saint Paul,
I'll make a corse of him that disobeys.

GENTLEMAN. My lord, stand back, and let the coffin pass.

GLOUCESTER. Unmannered dog ! stand thou, when I command :
Advance thy halberd higher than my breast,
Or, by Saint Paul, I'll strike thee to my foot,
And spurn upon thee, beggar, for thy boldness.

ANNE. What, do you tremble ? Are you all afraid ?
(To Gloucester) Avaunt, thou dreadful minister of hell!
Thou hadst but power over his mortal body,
His soul thou canst not have ; therefore, be gone.

GLOUCESTER. Sweet saint, for charity, be not so curst.

It is hardly possible that the dialogue which follows can be historical. It opens with Anne's passionate denunciation of Gloucester for his crimes, and ends with her acceptance of him as a husband. She is wooed and won beside the bier of her father-in-law, King Henry the Sixth, and Gloucester now craves a favour.

ANNE. What is it ?

GLOUCESTER. That it would please thee leave these sad designs
To him that hath more cause to be a mourner,
And presently repair to Crosby Place ;
Where, after I have solemnly interred
At Chertsey monastery this noble king,
And wet his grave with my repentant tears,
I will with all expedient duty see you :
For divers unknown reasons, I beseech you,
Grant me this boon.

ANNE. With all my heart ; and much it joys me too,
To see you are become so penitent. *(She leaves him alone)*

GLOUCESTER *(to himself)*. Was ever woman in this humour wooed ?
Was ever woman in this humour won ?
I'll have her ; but I will not keep her long.
What ! I, that killed her husband and his father,
To take her in her heart's extremest hate,
With curses in her mouth, tears in her eyes,
The bleeding witness of her hatred by ;
Having God, her conscience, and these bars against me,
And I nothing to back my suit at all
But the plain devil and dissembling looks,
And yet to win her, all the world to nothing !
Ha !
Hath she forgot already that brave prince,

Edward, her lord, whom I, some three months since,
Stabbed in my angry mood at Tewkesbury ?
A sweeter and a lovelier gentleman,
Framed in the prodigality of nature,
Young, valiant, wise, and, no doubt, right royal,
The spacious world cannot again afford :
And will she yet debase her eyes on me,
That cropped the golden prime of this sweet prince ?
On me whose all not equals Edward's moiety ?
On me that halt and am unshapen thus ?
My dukedom to a beggarly denier,
I do mistake my person all this while :
Upon my life, she finds, although I cannot,
Myself to be a marvellous proper man.
I'll be at charges for a looking-glass,
And entertain some score or two of tailors,
To study fashions to adorn my body :
Since I am crept in favour with myself,
I will maintain it with some little cost.
But first I'll turn yon fellow in his grave ;
And then return lamenting to my love.
Shine out, fair sun, till I have bought a glass,
That I may see my shadow as I pass.

Scene 3—The Palace

Enter Queen Elizabeth, Lord Rivers, and Lord Grey

RIVERS. Have patience, madam : there's no doubt his majesty
Will soon recover his accustomed health.

GREY. In that you brook it ill, it makes him worse :
Therefore, for God's sake, entertain good comfort,
And cheer his grace with quick and merry words.

QUEEN ELIZABETH. If he were dead, what would betide of me ?

RIVERS. No other harm but loss of such a lord.

QUEEN ELIZABETH. The loss of such a lord includes all harm.

GREY. The heavens have blessed you with a goodly son,
To be your comforter when he is gone.

QUEEN ELIZABETH. Oh, he is young, and his minority
Is put unto the trust of Richard Gloucester,
A man that loves not me, nor none of you.

RIVERS. Is it concluded he shall be protector ?

QUEEN ELIZABETH. It is determined, not concluded yet :
But so it must be if the king miscarry.

GREY. Here come the lords of Buckingham and Derby.

BUCKINGHAM. Good time of day unto your royal grace !

RIVERS. Saw you the king today, my Lord of Derby ?

STANLEY. But now the Duke of Buckingham and I
Are come from visiting his majesty.

QUEEN ELIZABETH. What likelihood of his amendment, lords?

BUCKINGHAM. Madam, good hope; his grace speaks cheerfully.

QUEEN ELIZABETH. God grant him health! Did you confer with him?

BUCKINGHAM. Madam, we did: he desires to make atonement
Betwixt the Duke of Gloucester and your brothers,
And betwixt them and my lord chamberlain;
And sent to warn them to his royal presence.

QUEEN ELIZABETH. Would all were well! but that will never be:
I fear our happiness is at the highest.

Enter Gloucester, Hastings, and Dorset

GLOUCESTER. They do me wrong, and I will not endure it:
Who are they that complain unto the king,
That I, forsooth, am stern and love them not?
By holy Paul, they love his grace but lightly
That fill his ears with such dissentious rumours.
Because I cannot flatter and speak fair,
Smile in men's faces, smooth, deceive, and cog,
Duck with French nods and apish courtesy,
I must be held a rancorous enemy.
Cannot a plain man live and think no harm,
But thus his simple truth must be abused
By silken, sly, insinuating Jacks?

RIVERS. To whom in all this presence speaks your grace?

GLOUCESTER. To thee, that hast nor honesty nor grace.
When have I injured thee? When done thee wrong?
Or thee? or thee? or any of your faction?
A plague upon you all! His royal person
(Whom God preserve better than you would wish!)
Cannot be quiet scarce a breathing-while,
But you must trouble him with lewd complaints.

QUEEN ELIZABETH. Brother of Gloucester, you mistake the matter.
The king, of his own royal disposition,
And not provoked by any suitor else,
Aiming, belike, at your interior hatred,
Which in your outward actions shows itself
Against my kindred, brothers, and myself,
Makes him to send, that thereby he may gather
The ground of your ill-will, and so remove it.

GLOUCESTER. I cannot tell: the world is grown so bad
That wrens make prey where eagles dare not perch:
Since every Jack became a gentleman,
There's many a gentle person made a Jack.

QUEEN ELIZABETH. Come, come, we know your meaning, brother Gloucester;
You envy my advancement and my friends':
God grant we never may have need of you!

GLOUCESTER. Meantime, God grants that we have need of you:
Our brother is imprisoned by your means,
Myself disgraced, and the nobility
Held in contempt; whilst many fair promotions
Are daily given to ennoble those
That scarce, some two days since, were worth a noble.

QUEEN ELIZABETH. By Him that raised me to this careful height
From that contented hap which I enjoyed,
I never did incense his majesty
Against the Duke of Clarence, but have been
An earnest advocate to plead for him.
My lord, you do me shameful injury,
Falsely to draw me in these vile suspects.
My Lord of Gloucester, I have too long borne
Your blunt upbraidings and your bitter scoffs:
By heaven, I will acquaint his majesty
With those gross taunts I often have endured.
I had rather be a country servant-maid
Than a great queen, with this condition,
To be thus taunted, scorned, and baited at:
Small joy have I in being England's queen.

Enter Queen Margaret, behind

QUEEN MARGARET. And lessened be that small, God, I beseech thee!
Thy honour, state, and seat is due to me.

GLOUCESTER. What! threat you me with telling of the king?
Tell him, and spare not: look, what I have said
I will avouch in presence of the king:
I dare adventure to be sent to the Tower.
Tis time to speak; my pains are quite forgot.

QUEEN MARGARET. Out, devil! I remember them too well:
Thou slewest my husband Henry in the Tower,
And Edward, my poor son, at Tewkesbury.

GLOUCESTER. Ere you were queen, yea, or your husband king,
I was a pack-horse in his great affairs;
A weeder-out of his proud adversaries,
A liberal rewarder of his friends:
To royalise his blood I spilt mine own.

QUEEN MARGARET. Yea, and much better blood than his or thine.

GLOUCESTER. In all which time you and your husband Grey
Were factious for the house of Lancaster;

And, Rivers, so were you. Was not your husband
In Margaret's battle at Saint Albans slain?
Let me put in your minds, if you forget,
What you have been ere now, and what you are;
Withal, what I have been, and what I am.

QUEEN MARGARET. A murderous villain, and so still thou art.

GLOUCESTER. Poor Clarence did forsake his father, Warwick;
Yea, and forswore himself—which Jesu pardon!—

QUEEN MARGARET. Which God revenge!

GLOUCESTER. To fight on Edward's party for the crown;
And for his meed, poor lord, he is mewed up.
I would to God my heart were flint, like Edward's;
Or Edward's soft and pitiful, like mine:
I am too childish-foolish for this world.

RIVERS. My Lord of Gloucester, in those busy days
Which here you urge to prove us enemies,
We followed then our lord, our lawful king:
So should we you, if you should be our king.

GLOUCESTER. If I should be! I had rather be a pedlar:
Far be it from my heart, the thought of it!

QUEEN ELIZABETH. As little joy, my lord, as you suppose
You should enjoy, were you this country's king,
As little joy may you suppose in me,
That I enjoy, being the queen thereof.

QUEEN MARGARET. Hear me, you wrangling pirates, that fall out,
Which of you trembles not that looks on me?
A husband and a son thou owest to me;
And thou a kingdom; all of you allegiance;
The sorrow that I have by right is yours,
And all the pleasures you usurp are mine.
God, I pray him,
That none of you may live your natural age,
But be by unlooked accident cut off!

GLOUCESTER. Have done thy charm, thou hateful withered hag!

QUEEN MARGARET. And leave out thee? stay, dog, for thou shalt hear me.
If heaven have any grievous plague in store
Exceeding those that I can wish upon thee,
O, let them keep it till thy sins be ripe,
And then hurl down their indignation
On thee, the troubler of the poor world's peace!
The worm of conscience still begnaw thy soul!
Thy friends suspect for traitors while thou livest,
And take deep traitors for thy dearest friends!

No sleep close up that deadly eye of thine,
Unless it be whilst some tormenting dream
Affrights thee, thou rag of honour ! thou detested—

HASTINGS. False-boding woman, end thy frantic curse,
Lest to thy harm thou move our patience.

MARGARET. Foul shame upon you ! you have all moved mine.

RIVERS. Were you well served you would be taught your duty.

QUEEN MARGARET. To serve me well you all should do me duty,
Teach me to be your queen, and you my subjects :
O, serve me well, and teach yourselves that duty !

DORSET. Dispute not with her ; she is lunatic.

QUEEN MARGARET. Peace, master marquess, you are malapert :
Your fire-new stamp of honour is scarce current.
O, that your young nobility could judge,
What 'twere to lose it, and be miserable !
They that stand high have many blasts to shake them ;
And if they fall they dash themselves to pieces.

GLOUCESTER. Good counsel, marry : learn it, learn it, marquess.

DORSET. It toucheth you, my lord, as much as me.

GLOUCESTER. Yea, and much more : but I was born so high,
Our aery buildeth in the cedar's top,
And dallies with the wind and scorns the sun.

QUEEN MARGARET. And turns the sun to shade ; alas ! alas !
Witness my son, now in the shade of death ;
Whose bright out-shining beams thy cloudy wrath
Hath in eternal darkness folded up.
Your aery buildeth in our aery's nest.
O God, that seest it, do not suffer it ;
As it was won with blood, lost be it so !

BUCKINGHAM. Have done ! for shame, if not for charity.

QUEEN MARGARET. Urge neither charity nor shame to me :
Uncharitably with me have you dealt,
And shamefully by you my hopes are butchered.
My charity is outrage, life my shame ;
And in that shame still live my sorrow's rage !

BUCKINGHAM. Have done, have done.

QUEEN MARGARET. O princely Buckingham, I'll kiss thy hand,
In sign of league and amity with thee :
Now fair befall thee and thy noble house !
Thy garments are not spotted with our blood,
Nor thou within the compass of my curse.

BUCKINGHAM. Nor no one here ; for curses never pass
The lips of those that breathe them in the air.

QUEEN MARGARET. I'll not believe but they ascend the sky,
And there awake God's gentle-sleeping peace.
O Buckingham, take heed of yonder dog!
Look, when he fawns, he bites; and when he bites,
His venom tooth will rankle to the death:
Have not to do with him, beware of him;
Sin, death, and hell have set their marks on him,
And all their ministers attend on him. *(She goes)*

HASTINGS. My hair doth stand on end to hear her curses.

RIVERS. And so doth mine: I muse why she's at liberty.

GLOUCESTER. I cannot blame her: by God's holy mother,
She hath had too much wrong; and I repent
My part thereof that I have done to her.

QUEEN ELIZABETH. I never did her any, to my knowledge.

GLOUCESTER. But you have all the vantage of her wrong.

CATESBY *(entering)*. Madam, his majesty doth call for you;
And for your grace; and you, my noble lords.

QUEEN ELIZABETH. Catesby, we come. Lords, will you go with us?

RIVERS. Madam, we will attend your grace.

GLOUCESTER *(left alone)*. I do the wrong, and first begin to brawl.
The secret mischiefs that I set abroach
I lay unto the grievous charge of others.
Clarence, whom I, indeed, have laid in darkness,
I do beweep to many simple gulls;
Namely, to Hastings, Derby, Buckingham;
And say it is the queen and her allies
That stir the king against the duke my brother.
Now, they believe it; and withal whet me
To be revenged on Rivers, Vaughan, Grey:
But then I sigh; and, with a piece of scripture,
Tell them that God bids us do good for evil:
And thus I clothe my naked villainy
With old odd ends stolen out of holy writ;
And seem a saint, when most I play the devil.

Two murderers enter

But, soft! here come my executioners.
How now, my hardy, stout resolvèd mates!
Are you now going to dispatch this deed?

MURDERER. We are, my lord; and come to have the warrant,
That we may be admitted where he is.

GLOUCESTER. Well thought upon; I have it here about me.
When you have done, repair to Crosby Place.
But, sirs, be sudden in the execution,
Withal obdurate, do not hear him plead;

For Clarence is well-spoken, and perhaps
May move your hearts to pity, if you mark him.

MURDERER. Fear not, my lord, we will not stand to prate ;
We come to use our hands and not our tongues.

GLOUCESTER. Your eyes drop millstones when fools' eyes drop tears :
I like you, lads ; about your business straight.

Scene 4—The Tower of London : Clarence and Brakenbury

BRAKENBURY. Why looks your grace so heavily today ?

CLARENCE. O, I have passed a miserable night,
So full of ugly sights, of ghastly dreams,
That, as I am a Christian faithful man,
I would not spend another such a night,
Though 'twere to buy a world of happy days,
So full of dismal terror was the time !
Lord, Lord ! methought, what pain it was to drown !
What dreadful noise of waters in mine ears !
What ugly sights of death within mine eyes !
Methought I saw a thousand fearful wrecks ;
Ten thousand men that fishes gnawed upon ;
Wedges of gold, great anchors, heaps of pearl,
Inestimable stones, unvalued jewels,
All scattered in the bottom of the sea :
Some lay in dead men's skulls ; and, in those holes
Where eyes did once inhabit, there were crept,
As 'twere in scorn of eyes, reflecting gems,
Which wooed the slimy bottom of the deep,
And mocked the dead bones that lay scattered by.
O, then began the tempest to my soul,
Who passed, methought, the melancholy flood,
With that grim ferryman which poets write of,
Unto the kingdom of perpetual night.
O Brakenbury, I have done those things,
Which now bear evidence against my soul,
For Edward's sake ; and see how he requites me !
O God ! if my deep prayers cannot appease thee,
But thou wilt be avenged on my misdeeds,
Yet execute thy wrath in me alone,
O, spare my guiltless wife and my poor children !
I pray thee, gentle keeper, stay by me ;
My soul is heavy, and I fain would sleep.

BRAKENBURY. I will, my lord : God give your grace good rest !

As he sleeps the two murderers enter

MURDERER. Ho! who's here?

BRAKENBURY. In God's name what are you?

MURDERER. I would speak with Clarence.

BRAKENBURY. Yea, are you so brief?

SECOND MURDERER. Show him our commission; talk no more.

BRAKENBURY *(reading)*. I am, in this, commanded to deliver
The noble Duke of Clarence to your hands:
I will not reason what is meant hereby,
Because I will be guiltless of the meaning.
Here are the keys, there sits the duke asleep:
I'll to the king.

FIRST MURDERER. Do so, it is a point of wisdom: fare you well. *(Brakenbury leaves)*

SECOND MURDERER. What, shall we stab him as he sleeps?

FIRST MURDERER. No; then he will say 'twas done cowardly when he wakes.

SECOND MURDERER. When he wakes! Why, fool, he shall never wake till the Judgment Day.

FIRST MURDERER. Why, then he will say we stabbed him sleeping.

SECOND MURDERER. The urging of that word *judgment* hath bred a kind of remorse in me.

FIRST MURDERER. What, art thou afraid?

SECOND MURDERER. Not to kill him, having a warrant for it; but to be damned for killing him, from which no warrant can defend us.

FIRST MURDERER. I thought thou hadst been resolute.

SECOND MURDERER. So I am, to let him live.

FIRST MURDERER. Back to the Duke of Gloucester; tell him so.

SECOND MURDERER. I pray thee, stay a while: I hope my holy humour will change; 'twas wont to hold me but while one would tell twenty.

FIRST MURDERER. Remember our reward, when the deed is done.

SECOND MURDERER. Zounds, he dies: I had forgot the reward.

FIRST MURDERER. Where is thy conscience now?

SECOND MURDERER. In the Duke of Gloucester's purse.

FIRST MURDERER. So when he opens his purse to give us our reward, thy conscience flies out.

SECOND MURDERER. Let it go; there's few or none will entertain it. I'll not meddle with it: it is a dangerous thing. It makes a man a coward. A man cannot steal but it accuseth him. He cannot swear but it checks him. Tis a blushing shamefast spirit that mutinies in a man's bosom. It fills one full of obstacles; it made me once restore a purse of gold that I found. It beggars any man that keeps it. It is turned out of all towns and cities for a dangerous thing; and every man that means to live well endeavours to trust to himself and to live without it.

FIRST MURDERER. Zounds, it is even now at my elbow, persuading me not to kill the duke. Hark! he stirs; shall I strike?

Clarence awakes to find himself at the mercy of two ruffians, with whom he pleads in vain. They kill him, and as they carry the body away one of them, fearful at what he has done, exclaims:

A frightful deed, and desperately dispatched!
How fain, like Pilate, would I wash my hands
Of this most grievous guilty murder done!

FIRST MURDERER. How now! what mean'st thou, that thou help'st me not?
By heavens, the duke shall know how slack thou art!

SECOND MURDERER. I would he knew that I had saved his brother!
Take thou the fee, and tell him what I say;
For I repent me that the duke is slain. *(He goes)*

FIRST MURDERER. So do not I: go, coward as thou art.
Now must I hide his body in some hole,
Until the duke take order for his burial:
And when I have my meed, I must away;
For this will out, and here I must not stay.

ACT 2

Scene 1—The Palace

Enter King Edward, ill, with his Queen and lords

KING EDWARD. Why, so: now have I done a good day's work:
You peers, continue this united league:
I every day expect an embassage
From my Redeemer to redeem me hence;
And now in peace my soul shall part to heaven,
Since I have set my friends at peace on earth.
Rivers and Hastings, take each other's hand;
Dissemble not your hatred, swear your love.

RIVERS. By heaven, my heart is purged from grudging hate;
And with my hand I seal my true heart's love.

HASTINGS. So thrive I, as I truly swear the like!

KING EDWARD. Take heed you dally not before your king;
Lest he that is the supreme King of kings
Confound your hidden falsehood, and award
Either of you to be the other's end.

HASTINGS. So prosper I, as I swear perfect love!

RIVERS. And I, as I love Hastings with my heart!

KING EDWARD. Madam, yourself are not exempt in this,
Nor your son Dorset, Buckingham, nor you ;
You have been factious one against the other.
Wife, love Lord Hastings, let him kiss your hand ;
And what you do, do it unfeignedly.

QUEEN ELIZABETH. Here, Hastings ; I will never more remember
Our former hatred, so thrive I and mine !

EDWARD. Dorset, embrace him ; Hastings, love lord marquess.

DORSET. This interchange of love, I here protest,
Upon my part shall be inviolable.

HASTINGS. And so swear I, my lord.

KING EDWARD. Now, princely Buckingham, seal thou this league
With thy embracements to my wife's allies,
And make me happy in your unity.

BUCKINGHAM *(to the Queen)*. Whenever Buckingham doth turn his hate
On you or yours, but with all duteous love
Doth cherish you and yours, God punish me
With hate in those where I expect most love !
When I have most need to employ a friend,
And most assurèd that he is a friend,
Deep, hollow, treacherous, and full of guile,
Be he unto me ! this do I beg of God,
When I am cold in zeal to you or yours.

KING EDWARD. A pleasing cordial, princely Buckingham,
Is this thy vow unto my sickly heart.
There wanteth now our brother Gloucester here,
To make the perfect period of this peace.

BUCKINGHAM. And, in good time, here comes the noble duke.

GLOUCESTER. Good-morrow to my sovereign king and queen ;
And, princely peers, a happy time of day !

KING EDWARD. Happy, indeed, as we have spent the day.
Brother, we have done deeds of charity ;
Made peace of enmity, fair love of hate,
Between these swelling wrong-incensèd peers.

GLOUCESTER. A blessèd labour, my most sovereign liege :
Amongst this princely heap, if any here,
By false intelligence, or wrong surmise,
Hold me a foe ;
If I unwittingly, or in my rage,
Have aught committed that is hardly borne
By any in this presence, I desire
To reconcile me to his friendly peace :
Tis death to me to be at enmity ;
I hate it, and desire all good men's love.

I do not know that Englishman alive
With whom my soul is any jot at odds
More than the infant that is born tonight:
I thank my God for my humility.

QUEEN ELIZABETH. A holy day shall this be kept hereafter:
I would to God all strifes were well compounded.
My sovereign liege, I do beseech your majesty
To take our brother Clarence to your grace.

GLOUCESTER. Why, madam, have I offered love for this,
To be so flouted in this royal presence?
Who knows not that the noble duke is dead?
You do him injury to scorn his corse.

They all start with astonishment

RIVERS. Who knows not he is dead! Who knows he is?

QUEEN ELIZABETH. All-seeing heaven, what a world is this!

BUCKINGHAM. Look I so pale, Lord Dorset, as the rest?

DORSET. Ay, my good lord; and no one in this presence
But his red colour hath forsook his cheeks.

KING EDWARD. Is Clarence dead? The order was reversed.

GLOUCESTER. But he, poor soul, by your first order died,
And that a wingèd Mercury did bear;
Some tardy cripple bore the countermand,
That came too lag to see him buried.
God grant that some, less noble and less loyal,
Nearer in thoughts, but not in blood,
Deserve not worse than wretched Clarence did,
And yet go current from suspicion!

STANLEY *(entering)*. A boon, my sovereign, for my service done!

KING EDWARD. I pray thee, peace: my soul is full of sorrow.

STANLEY. I will not rise, unless your highness hear me.

KING EDWARD. Then speak at once what is it thou demand'st.

STANLEY. The forfeit, sovereign, of my servant's life;
Who slew today a riotous gentleman
Lately attendant on the Duke of Norfolk.

KING EDWARD. Have I a tongue to doom my brother's death,
And shall the same give pardon to a slave?
My brother slew no man; his fault was thought,
And yet his punishment was cruel death.
Who sued to me for him? Who, in my rage,
Kneeled at my feet, and bade me be advised?
Who spake of brotherhood? Who spake of love?
Who told me how the poor soul did forsake
The mighty Warwick, and did fight for me?
Who told me, in the field by Tewkesbury,

When Oxford had me down, he rescued me,
And said, *Dear brother, live, and be a king* ?
Who told me, when we both lay in the field
Frozen almost to death, how he did lap me
Even in his own garments, and gave himself,
All thin and naked, to the numb cold night ?
All this from my remembrance brutish wrath
Sinfully plucked, and not a man of you
Had so much grace to put it in my mind.
But when your carters or your waiting-vassals
Have done a drunken slaughter, and defaced
The precious image of our dear Redeemer,
You straight are on your knees for pardon, pardon ;
And I, unjustly too, must grant it you :
But for my brother not a man would speak,
Nor I, ungracious, speak unto myself
For him, poor soul. The proudest of you all
Have been beholding to him in his life ;
Yet none of you would once plead for his life.
O God, I fear thy justice will take hold
On me, and you, and mine, and yours for this !

The King and Queen leave, with others

GLOUCESTER. This is the fruit of rashness ! Marked you not
How that the guilty kindred of the queen
Looked pale when they did hear of Clarence' death ?
O, they did urge it still unto the king !
God will revenge it. But come, let us in,
To comfort Edward with our company.

Scene 2—A Room in the Palace

This scene shows the Duchess of York grieving for the death of her son Edward the Fourth, and the Queen Elizabeth grieving for him as her husband, while the children of Clarence grieve for their father, and the Queen's brother, Rivers, urges that they must at once bring the young King to London from Ludlow and have him crowned. Meantime Gloucester and his friend Buckingham begin to plot how they can

Part the queen's proud kindred from the king,

as a first step towards enthroning Gloucester in place of young Edward.

Scene 3—A Street in London

Citizens anxiously discuss the death of the King and its consequences. Will the King's son reign ? Full of danger is the Duke of Gloucester.

Scene 4—The Palace

The young Duke of York, the Duchess of York, Queen Elizabeth, and the Archbishop of York, are discussing the coming of the young Prince Edward.

ARCHBISHOP. Last night, I hear, they lay at Northampton ;
At Stony Stratford will they be tonight :
Tomorrow, or next day, they will be here.

DUCHESS. I long with all my heart to see the prince:
I hope he is much grown since last I saw him.

QUEEN ELIZABETH. But I hear, no; they say my son of York
Hath almost overta'en him in his growth.

YORK. Ay, mother; but I would not have it so.

DUCHESS. Why, my young cousin, it is good to grow.

YORK. Grandam, one night, as we did sit at supper,
My uncle Rivers talked how I did grow
More than my brother: *Ay*, quoth my uncle Gloucester,
Small herbs have grace, great weeds do grow apace:
And since, methinks, I would not grow so fast,
Because sweet flowers are slow and weeds make haste.

DUCHESS. Good faith, good faith, the saying did not hold
In him that did object the same to thee:
He was the wretched'st thing when he was young,
So long a-growing and so leisurely,
That, if this rule were true, he should be gracious.

ARCHBISHOP. Why, madam, so, no doubt, he is.

DUCHESS. I hope he is; but yet let mothers doubt.

YORK. Now, by my troth, if I had been remembered,
I could have given my uncle's grace a flout,
To touch his growth nearer than he touched mine.

DUCHESS. How, my pretty York? I pray thee, let me hear it.

YORK. Marry, they say my uncle grew so fast
That he could gnaw a crust at two hours old:
Twas full two years ere I could get a tooth.

A messenger now arrives with the news that the Queen's relatives. Rivers and Grey, have been sent as prisoners to Pomfret. Then, taking alarm, the Queen, her mother-in-law, and little York, all seek sanctuary at Westminster Abbey, whither the Archbishop conducts them.

ACT 3

Scene 1—A Street in London

Enter the young Prince, the Dukes of Gloucester and Buckingham, and others

BUCKINGHAM. Welcome, sweet prince, to London, to your chamber.

GLOUCESTER. Welcome, dear cousin, my thoughts' sovereign:
The weary way hath made you melancholy.

PRINCE. No, uncle; but our crosses on the way
Have made it tedious, wearisome, and heavy:
I want more uncles here to welcome me.

GLOUCESTER. Sweet prince, the untainted virtue of your years
Hath not yet dived into the world's deceit:
Nor more can you distinguish of a man

Than of his outward show ; which, God he knows,
Seldom or never jumpeth with the heart.
Those uncles which you want were dangerous ;
Your grace attended to their sugared words,
But looked not on the poison of their hearts :
God keep you from them, and from such false friends !

PRINCE. God keep me from false friends ! but they were none.

GLOUCESTER. My lord, the mayor of London comes to greet you.

Enter the Lord Mayor and his train

MAYOR. God bless your grace with health and happy days !

PRINCE. I thank you, good my lord ; and thank you all.
I thought my mother, and my brother York,
Would long ere this have met us on the way :
Fie, what a slug is Hastings, that he comes not
To tell us whether they will come or no ! *(Enter Lord Hastings)*

BUCKINGHAM. And, in good time, here comes the sweating lord.

PRINCE. Welcome, my lord : what, will our mother come ?

HASTINGS. On what occasion, God he knows, not I,
The queen your mother, and your brother York,
Have taken sanctuary : the tender prince
Would fain have come with me to meet your grace,
But by his mother was perforce withheld.

BUCKINGHAM. Fie, what an indirect and peevish course
Is this of hers ! Lord cardinal, will your grace
Persuade the queen to send the Duke of York
Unto his princely brother presently ?
If she deny, Lord Hastings, go with him,
And from her jealous arms pluck him perforce.

HASTINGS. I go, my lord.

PRINCE. Good lords, make all the speedy haste you may. *(They go)*
Say, uncle Gloucester, if our brother come,
Where shall we sojourn till our coronation ?

GLOUCESTER. Where it seems best unto your royal self.
If I may counsel you, some day or two
Your highness shall repose you at the Tower :
Then where you please, and shall be thought most fit
For your best health and recreation.

PRINCE. I do not like the Tower, of any place.
Did Julius Caesar build that place, my lord ?

BUCKINGHAM. He did, my gracious lord, begin that place,
Which, since, succeeding ages have re-edified.

PRINCE. Is it upon recòrd, or else reported
Successively from age to age, he built it ?

BUCKINGHAM. Upon recòrd, my gracious lord.

PRINCE. But say, my lord, it were not registered,
Methinks the truth should live from age to age,
As 'twere retailed to all posterity,
Even to the general all-ending day.

GLOUCESTER *(aside)*. So wise, so young, they say, do never live long.

PRINCE. That Julius Caesar was a famous man ;
With what his valour did enrich his wit,
His wit set down to make his valour live :
Death makes no conquest of this conqueror ;
For now he lives in fame, though not in life.
I'll tell you what, my cousin Buckingham—

BUCKINGHAM. What, my gracious lord ?

PRINCE. An if I live until I be a man,
I'll win our ancient right in France again,
Or die a soldier, as I lived a king.

GLOUCESTER *(aside)*. Short summers lightly have a forward spring.

Enter young York, Hastings, and the Cardinal

BUCKINGHAM. Now, in good time, here comes the Duke of York.

PRINCE. Richard of York ! how fares our loving brother ?

YORK. Well, my dread lord ; so must I call you now.

PRINCE. Ay, brother, to our grief, as it is yours :
Too late he died that might have kept that title,
Which by his death hath lost much majesty.

GLOUCESTER. How fares our cousin, noble Lord of York ?

YORK. I thank you, gentle uncle. O, my lord,
You said that idle weeds are fast in growth :
The prince my brother hath outgrown me far.

GLOUCESTER. He hath, my lord.

YORK. And therefore is he idle ?

GLOUCESTER. O, my fair cousin, I must not say so.

YORK. I pray thee, uncle, give me this dagger.

GLOUCESTER. My dagger, little cousin ? with all my heart.

PRINCE. A beggar, brother ?

YORK. Of my kind uncle, that I know will give,
And being a toy which it is no grief to give.

GLOUCESTER. A greater gift than that I'll give my cousin.

YORK. A greater gift ! O, that's the sword to it.

GLOUCESTER. Ay, gentle cousin, were it light enough.

YORK. O, then, I see you will part but with light gifts ;
In weightier things you'll say a beggar Nay.

GLOUCESTER. It is too heavy for your grace to wear.

YORK. I weigh it lightly, were it heavier.

GLOUCESTER. What, would you have my weapon, little man?

YORK. I would that I might thank you as you call me.

GLOUCESTER. How?

YORK. Little.

BUCKINGHAM. With what a sharp-provided wit he reasons!

GLOUCESTER. My lord, will't please you pass along?
Myself and my good cousin Buckingham
Will to your mother, to entreat of her
To meet you at the Tower and welcome you.

YORK. What, will you go unto the Tower, my lord?

PRINCE. My lord protector needs will have it so.

YORK. I shall not sleep in quiet at the Tower.

PRINCE. But come, my lord.

All but Gloucester, Buckingham, and Catesby go

BUCKINGHAM. Think you, my lord, this little prating York
Was not incensèd by his subtle mother
To taunt and scorn you thus opprobriously?

GLOUCESTER. No doubt, no doubt: O, tis a parlous boy;
Bold, quick, ingenious, forward, capable:
He is all the mother's, from the top to toe.

BUCKINGHAM. Well, let them rest. Come hither, Catesby.
Thou art sworn as deeply to effect what we intend
As closely to conceal what we impart:
Thou know'st our reasons urged upon the way;
What think'st thou? is it not an easy matter
To make William Lord Hastings of our mind,
For the instalment of this noble duke
In the seat royal of this famous isle?

CATESBY. He for his father's sake so loves the prince,
That he will not be won to aught against him.

BUCKINGHAM. What think'st thou, then, of Stanley? what will he?

CATESBY. He will do all in all as Hastings doth.

BUCKINGHAM. Well, then, no more but this: go, gentle Catesby,
And, as it were far off, sound thou Lord Hastings,
How he doth stand affected to our purpose;
And summon him tomorrow to the Tower,
To sit about the coronation.
If thou dost find him tractable to us,
Encourage him, and show him all our reasons:
If he be leaden, icy-cold, unwilling,
Be thou so too; and so break off your talk,
And give us notice of his inclination:
For we tomorrow hold divided councils,
Wherein thyself shalt highly be employed.

GLOUCESTER. Commend me to Lord William: tell him, Catesby,
His ancient knot of dangerous adversaries
Tomorrow are let blood at Pomfret Castle.

BUCKINGHAM. Good Catesby, go, effect this business soundly.

Catesby leaves

BUCKINGHAM. Now, my lord, what shall we do, if we perceive
Lord Hastings will not yield to our complots?

GLOUCESTER. Chop off his head, man; somewhat we will do:
And, look, when I am king, claim thou of me
The earldom of Hereford, and the movables
Whereof the king my brother stood possessed.

BUCKINGHAM. I'll claim that promise at your grace's hands.

GLOUCESTER. And look to have it yielded with all willingness.

Scene 2—At the House of Lord Hastings

MESSENGER. What, ho! my lord!

HASTINGS *(within)*. Who knocks at the door?

MESSENGER. A messenger from the Lord Stanley.

HASTINGS *(entering)*. What is 't o'clock?

MESSENGER. Upon the stroke of four.

HASTINGS. Cannot thy master sleep these tedious nights?

MESSENGER. So it should seem by that I have to say.
First, he commends him to your noble lordship.

HASTINGS. And then?

MESSENGER. And then he sends you word
He dreamt tonight the boar had razed his helm:
Besides, he says there are two councils held;
And that may be determined at the one
Which may make you and him to rue at the other.
Therefore he sends to know your lordship's pleasure,
If presently you will take horse with him,
And with all speed post with him toward the north,
To shun the danger that his soul divines.

HASTINGS. Go, fellow, go, return unto thy lord;
Bid him not fear the separate councils:
His honour and myself are at the one,
And at the other is my servant Catesby;
Where nothing can proceed that toucheth us
Whereof I shall not have intelligence.
Tell him his fears are shallow, wanting instance:
And for his dreams, I wonder he is so fond
To trust the mockery of unquiet slumbers:
To fly the boar before the boar pursues,
Were to incense the boar to follow us

And make pursuit where he did mean no chase.
Go, bid thy master rise and come to me.

The messenger leaves and Catesby enters

CATESBY. Many good-morrows to my noble lord!

HASTINGS. Good-morrow, Catesby; you are early stirring:
What news, what news, in this our tottering State?

CATESBY. It is a reeling world, indeed, my lord;
And I believe 'twill never stand upright
Till Richard wear the garland of the realm.

HASTINGS. How! wear the garland! dost thou mean the crown?

CATESBY. Ay, my good lord.

HASTINGS. I'll have this crown of mine cut from my shoulders
Ere I will see the crown so foul misplaced.
But canst thou guess that he doth aim at it?

CATESBY. Ay, on my life; and hopes to find you forward
Upon his party for the gain thereof:
And thereupon he sends you this good news,
That this same very day your enemies,
The kindred of the queen, must die at Pomfret.

HASTINGS. Indeed, I am no mourner for that news,
Because they have been still mine enemies:
But, that I'll give my voice on Richard's side,
To bar my master's heirs in true descent,
God knows I will not do it, to the death.

CATESBY. God keep your lordship in that gracious mind!

HASTINGS. But I shall laugh at this a twelvemonth hence,
That they who brought me in my master's hate,
I live to look upon their tragedy.
Ere a fortnight make me elder,
I'll send some packing that yet think not on it.

CATESBY. Tis a vile thing to die, my gracious lord,
When men are unprepared and look not for it.

HASTINGS. O monstrous, monstrous! and so falls it out
With Rivers, Vaughan, Grey: and so 'twill do
With some men else, who think themselves as safe
As thou and I; who, as thou know'st, are dear
To princely Richard and to Buckingham.

CATESBY. The princes both make high account of you.

HASTINGS. I know they do; and I have well deserved it.

STANLEY. My lord, Good-morrow; Good-morrow, Catesby:
You may jest on, but, by the holy rood,
I do not like these several councils, I.

HASTINGS. My lord,
I hold my life as dear as you do yours;
And never in my life, I do protest,
Was it more precious to me than tis now:
Think you, but that I know our state secure,
I would be so triumphant as I am?

STANLEY. The lords at Pomfret, when they rode from London,
Were jocund, and supposed their state was sure,
And they indeed had no cause to mistrust;
But yet, you see, how soon the day o'ercast.
This sudden stab of rancour I misdoubt:
Pray God, I say, I prove a needless coward!
What, shall we toward the Tower? The day is spent.

HASTINGS. Come, come, have with you. Wot you what, my lord?
Today the lords you talk of are beheaded.

STANLEY. They, for their truth, might better wear their heads
Than some that have accused them wear their hats.
But come, my lord, let us away.

Enter a Pursuivant

HASTINGS. Go on before; I'll talk with this good fellow.
How now, sirrah, how goes the world with thee?

PURSUIVANT. The better that your lordship please to ask.

HASTINGS. I tell thee, man, tis better with me now
Than when I met thee last where now we meet:
Then was I going prisoner to the Tower,
By the suggestion of the queen's allies;
But now, I tell thee (keep it to thyself),
This day those enemies are put to death,
And I in better state than e'er I was.

PURSUIVANT. God hold it, to your honour's good content!

PRIEST. Well met, my lord; I am glad to see your honour.

HASTINGS. I thank thee, good Sir John, with all my heart.

BUCKINGHAM *(entering)*. What, talking with a priest, lord chamberlain?
Your friends at Pomfret, they do need the priest;
Your honour hath no shriving work in hand.

HASTINGS. Good faith, and when I met this holy man,
Those men you talk of came into my mind.
What, go you toward the Tower?

BUCKINGHAM. I do, my lord; but long I shall not stay:
I shall return before your lordship thence.

HASTINGS. Tis like enough, for I stay dinner there.

BUCKINGHAM *(aside)*. And supper too, although thou know'st it not.
Come, will you go?

HASTINGS. I'll wait upon your lordship.

Scene 3—Pomfret Castle

Sir Richard Ratcliff leading Rivers, Grey, and Vaughan to their doom

RATCLIFF. Come, bring forth the prisoners.

RIVERS. Sir Richard Ratcliff, let me tell thee this:
Today shalt thou behold a subject die
For truth, for duty, and for loyalty.

GREY. God keep the prince from all the pack of you!

VAUGHAN. You live that shall cry woe for this hereafter.

RATCLIFF. Dispatch; the limit of your lives is out.

RIVERS. O Pomfret, Pomfret! O thou blood-stained prison,
Fatal and ominous to noble peers!
Within the guilty closure of thy walls
Richard the Second here was hacked to death;
And, for more slander to thy dismal seat,
We give thee up our guiltless blood to drink.

GREY. Now Margaret's curse is fallen upon our heads,
For standing by when Richard stabbed her son.

RIVERS. Then cursed she Hastings, then cursed she Buckingham,
Then cursed she Richard. O, remember, God,
To hear her prayers for them, as now for us!
And for my sister and her princely sons,
Be satisfied, dear God, with our true blood,
Which, as thou know'st, unjustly must be spilt.

RATCLIFF. Make haste; the hour of death is expiate.

RIVERS. Come Grey, come Vaughan, let us all embrace;
And take our leave, until we meet in heaven.

Scene 4—The Tower of London: a Conference

Enter Buckingham, Stanley, Hastings, Bishop of Ely, and others

HASTINGS. My lords, at once: the cause why we are met
Is to determine of the coronation.
In God's name, speak: when is the royal day?

BUCKINGHAM. Are all things fitting for that royal time?

STANLEY. It is, and wants but nomination.

ELY. Tomorrow, then, I judge a happy day.

BUCKINGHAM. Who knows the lord protector's mind herein?
Who is most inward with the royal duke?

ELY. Your grace, we think, should soonest know his mind.

BUCKINGHAM. Who, I, my lord! we know each other's faces.
But for our hearts, he knows no more of mine
Than I of yours;
Nor I no more of his than you of mine.
Lord Hastings, you and he are near in love.

HASTINGS. I thank his grace, I know he loves me well;
But, for his purpose in the coronation,
I have not sounded him, nor he delivered
His gracious pleasure any way therein:
But you, my noble lords, may name the time;
And in the duke's behalf I'll give my voice,
Which, I presume, he'll take in gentle part.

ELY. Now, in good time, here comes the duke himself.

GLOUCESTER. My noble lords and cousins all, Good-morrow.
I have been long a sleeper; but I hope
My absence doth neglect no great designs,
Which by my presence might have been concluded.

BUCKINGHAM. Had not you come upon your cue, my lord,
William Lord Hastings had pronounced your part
(I mean, your voice)—for crowning of the king.

GLOUCESTER. Than my Lord Hastings no man might be bolder;
His lordship knows me well, and loves me well.

HASTINGS. I thank your grace.

GLOUCESTER. My lord of Ely! When I was last in Holborn,
I saw good strawberries in your garden there:
I do beseech you send for some of them.

ELY. Marry, and will, my lord, with all my heart. *(He goes)*

GLOUCESTER. Cousin of Buckingham, a word with you.
(Aside) Catesby hath sounded Hastings in our business,
And finds the testy gentleman so hot,
As he will lose his head ere give consent
His master's son, as worshipful he terms it,
Shall lose the royalty of England's throne.

BUCKINGHAM. Withdraw you hence, my lord, I'll follow you.

They leave, and presently return

GLOUCESTER. I pray you all, tell me what they deserve
That do conspire my death with devilish plots
Of witchcraft, and that have prevailed
Upon my body with their hellish charms?

HASTINGS. The tender love I bear your grace, my lord,
Makes me most forward in this noble presence
To doom the offenders—whatsoever they be:
I say, my lord, they have deservèd death.

GLOUCESTER. Then be your eyes the witness of this ill:
See how I am bewitched; behold mine arm

Is, like a blasted sapling, withered up :
And this is Edward's wife, that monstrous witch,
That by her witchcraft thus hath markèd me.

HASTINGS. If she has done this thing, my gracious lord—

GLOUCESTER. If! Tellest thou me of *ifs*? Thou art a traitor :
Off with his head! Now, by Saint Paul, I swear
I will not dine until I see the same.
Lovel and Ratcliff, look that it be done :
The rest, that love me, rise and follow me.

All but Hastings, Ratcliff, and Lovel leave

HASTINGS. Woe, woe for England! not a whit for me.
O Margaret, Margaret, now thy heavy curse
Is lighted on poor Hastings' wretched head!

RATCLIFF. Dispatch, my lord; the duke would be at dinner:
Make a short shrift; he longs to see your head.

HASTINGS. O momentary grace of mortal men,
Which we more hunt for than the grace of God!
Who builds his hopes in air of your good looks
Lives like a drunken sailor on a mast,
Ready, with every nod, to tumble down
Into the fatal bowels of the deep.

LOVEL. Come, come, dispatch; tis bootless to exclaim.

HASTINGS. O wretched Richard! miserable England!
I prophesy the fearfull'st time to thee
That ever wretched age hath looked upon.
Come, lead me to the block; bear him my head :
They smile at me that shortly shall be dead.

Scene 5—The Tower Walls : Gloucester and Buckingham

GLOUCESTER. Come, cousin, canst thou quake, and change thy colour,
Murder thy breath in the middle of a word,
And then begin again, and stop again,
As if thou wert distraught and mad with terror?

BUCKINGHAM. Tut, I can counterfeit the deep tragedian;
Speak and look back, and pry on every side,
Tremble and start at wagging of a straw,
Intending deep suspicion : ghastly looks
Are at my service, like enforcèd smiles;
And both are ready in their offices,
At any time, to grace my stratagems.
But what, is Catesby gone?

GLOUCESTER. He is; and, see, he brings the mayor along.

BUCKINGHAM. Lord mayor, the reason we have sent—

GLOUCESTER. Look back, defend thee, here are enemies.

BUCKINGHAM. God and our innocency defend and guard us!
GLOUCESTER. Be patient, they are friends, Ratcliff and Lovel.

Enter Lovel and Ratcliff, bearing the head of Hastings

LOVEL. Here is the head of that ignoble traitor,
The dangerous and unsuspected Hastings.
GLOUCESTER. So dear I loved the man that I must weep.
I took him for the plainest harmless creature
That breathed upon this earth a Christian;
Made him my book, wherein my soul recorded
The history of all her secret thoughts.
BUCKINGHAM. Well, well, he was the covert'st sheltered traitor
That ever lived.
Would you imagine, or almost believe,
Were't not that, by great preservation,
We live to tell it you, the subtle traitor
This day had plotted in the council-house
To murder me and my good Lord of Gloucester?
MAYOR. What, had he so?
GLOUCESTER. What, think you we are Turks or infidels?
Or that we would, against the form of law,
Proceed thus rashly to the villain's death,
But that the extreme peril of the case,
The peace of England and our person's safety,
Enforced us to this execution?
Yet had not we determined he should die,
Until your lordship came to see his death;
Which now the loving haste of these our friends,
Somewhat against our meaning, have prevented:
Because, my lord, we would have had you heard
The traitor speak, and timorously confess
The manner and the purpose of his treason;
That you might well have signified the same
Unto the citizens, who haply may
Misconstrue us in him and wail his death.
MAYOR. But, my good lord, your grace's word shall serve,
As well as I had seen and heard him speak:
And doubt you not, right noble princes both,
But I'll acquaint our duteous citizens
With all your just proceedings in this cause.
GLOUCESTER. And to that end we wished your lordship here,
To avoid the carping censures of the world.
BUCKINGHAM. But since you come too late of our intents,
Yet witness what you hear we did intend:
And so, my good lord mayor, we bid farewell.

Gloucester then sends Buckingham into the city to "play the orator" and convince the crowd that Edward's children had no right to the crown.

Scene 6—A Street: A Scrivener reading a Paper

SCRIVENER. This is the indictment of the good Lord Hastings;
Which in a set hand fairly is engrossed,
That it may be this day read over in Paul's.
And mark how well the sequel hangs together:
Eleven hours I spent to write it over,
For yesternight by Catesby was it brought me;
The precedent was full as long a-doing:
And yet within these five hours lived Lord Hastings,
Untainted, unexamined, free, at liberty.
Here's a good world the while! Why, who's so gross,
That seeth not this palpable device?
Yet who's so bold but says he sees it not?
Bad is the world; and all will come to nought,
When such bad dealing must be seen in thought.

Scene 7—Baynard's Castle: Gloucester and Buckingham meet

GLOUCESTER. How now, my lord, what say the citizens?
BUCKINGHAM. Now, by the holy mother of our Lord,
The citizens are mum, say not a word.
GLOUCESTER. Touched you the question of Edward's children?
BUCKINGHAM. I did.
Laid open all your victories in Scotland,
Your discipline in war, wisdom in peace,
Your bounty, virtue, fair humility;
Indeed, left nothing fitting for the purpose
Untouched, or slightly handled, in discourse:
And when mine oratory grew to an end,
I bid them that did love their country's good
Cry *God save Richard, England's royal king!*
GLOUCESTER. Ah! and did they so?
BUCKINGHAM. No, so God help me, they spake not a word;
But, like dumb statuas or breathing stones,
Gazed on each other, and looked deadly pale:
Which when I saw, I reprehended them;
And asked the mayor what meant this wilful silence:
His answer was the people were not wont
To be spoke to but by the recorder.
Then he was urged to tell my tale again,
Thus saith the duke, thus hath the duke inferred;
But nothing spake in warrant from himself.
When he had done, some followers of mine won,
At the lower end of the hall, hurled up their caps,
And some ten voices cried *God save King Richard!*
And thus I took the vantage of those few,
Thanks, gentle citizens and friends, quoth I;

This general applause and loving shout
Argues your wisdoms and your love to Richard :
And even here brake off, and came away.

GLOUCESTER. What tongueless blocks were they! Would they not speak ?

BUCKINGHAM. No, by my troth, my lord.

GLOUCESTER. Will not the mayor then and his brethren come ?

BUCKINGHAM. The mayor is here at hand : intend some fear ;
Be not you spoke with, but by mighty suit :
And look you get a prayer-book in your hand,
And stand betwixt two churchmen, good my lord ;
For on that ground I'll build a holy *des*cant :
And be not easily won to our request.

Gloucester retires, and when the Mayor and citizens arrive the servant brings word that the Duke is at prayer and fears the assemblage of the unexpected citizens. Buckingham, seeking to impress the Mayor with the religious and retiring habit of Gloucester, sends a second message of entreaty, whereupon the Duke attends, escorted by bishops.

MAYOR. See, where he stands between two clergymen !

BUCKINGHAM. Two props of virtue for a Christian prince,
To stay him from the fall of vanity :
And, see, a book of prayer in his hand,
True ornaments to know a holy man.
Famous Plantagenet, most gracious prince,
Lend favourable ears to our request ;
And pardon us the interruption
Of thy devotion and right Christian zeal.

GLOUCESTER. My lord, there needs no such apology :
I rather do beseech you pardon me,
Who, earnest in the service of my God,
Neglect the visitation of my friends.
But, leaving this, what is your grace's pleasure ?

BUCKINGHAM. Even that, I hope, which pleaseth God above,
And all good men of this ungoverned isle.

GLOUCESTER. I do suspect I have done some offence
That seems disgracious in the city's eyes,
And that you come to reprehend my ignorance.

BUCKINGHAM. You have, my lord : would it might please your grace,
At our entreaties, to amend that fault !

GLOUCESTER. Else wherefore breathe I in a Christian land ?

BUCKINGHAM. Then know, it is your fault that you resign
The supreme seat, the throne majestical,
The sceptered office of your ancestors,

Your state of fortune and your due of birth,
The lineal glory of your royal house,
To the corruption of a blemished stock:
Whilst, in the mildness of your sleepy thoughts
Which here we waken to our country's good,
This noble isle doth want her proper limbs;
Her face defaced with scars of infamy,
Her royal stock graft with ignoble plants,
And almost shouldered in the swallowing gulf
Of blind forgetfulness and dark oblivion.
Which to recure, we heartily solicit
Your gracious self to take on you the charge
And kingly government of this your land;
Not as protector, steward substitute,
Or lowly factor for another's gain;
But as successively from blood to blood,
Your right of birth, your empery, your own.

GLOUCESTER. I know not whether to depart in silence,
Or bitterly to speak in your reproof,
Best fitteth my degree or your condition:
If not to answer, you might haply think
Tongue-tied ambition, not replying, yielded
To bear the golden yoke of sovereignty,
Which fondly you would here impose on me;
If to reprove you for this suit of yours,
So seasoned with your faithful love to me,
Then, on the other side, I checked my friends.
Therefore, to speak, and to avoid the first,
And then, in speaking, not to incur the last,
Definitively thus I answer you.
Your love deserves my thanks; but my desert
Unmeritable shuns your high request.
First, if all obstacles were cut away,
And that my path were even to the crown,
As my ripe revenue and due by birth;
Yet so much is my poverty of spirit,
So mighty and so many my defects,
As I had rather hide me from my greatness,
Being a barque to brook no mighty sea,
Than in my greatness covet to be hid,
And in the vapour of my glory smothered.
But, God be thankèd, there's no need of me,
The royal tree hath left us royal fruit,
Which, mellowed by the stealing hours of time,
Will well become the seat of majesty,
And make, no doubt, us happy by his reign.
On him I lay what you would lay on me,

The right and fortune of his happy stars;
Which God defend that I should wring from him!

With masterly hypocrisy Buckingham pretends to see religious scruples in Richard's refusal, but begs him to take the throne and bless the land and redeem it from the corruption of the times. Still feigning great reluctance, Gloucester at last yields, and accepts the prize for which he has been so pitilessly striving.

BUCKINGHAM. Then I salute you with this kingly title:
Long live Richard, England's royal king!

MAYOR AND CITIZENS. Amen.

BUCKINGHAM. Tomorrow will it please you to be crowned?

GLOUCESTER. Even when you please, since you will have it so.

BUCKINGHAM. Tomorrow, then, we will attend your grace:
And so most joyfully we take our leave.

GLOUCESTER. Come, let us to our holy task again
Farewell, good cousin; farewell, gentle friends.

ACT 4

Scene 1—Before the Tower

Enter on one side, Queen Elizabeth, Duchess of York, and Marquis of Dorset; on the other, Anne and Lady Margaret Plantagenet.

DUCHESS. Who meets us here? My niece Plantagenet
Led in the hand of her kind aunt of Gloucester!
Now, for my life, she's wandering to the Tower,
On pure heart's love to greet the tender princes.
Daughter, well met.

ANNE. God give your graces both
A happy and a joyful time of day!

QUEEN ELIZABETH. As much to you, good sister! Whither away?

ANNE. No farther than the Tower; and, as I guess,
Upon the like devotion as yourselves,
To gratulate the gentle princes there.

QUEEN ELIZABETH. Kind sister, thanks: we'll enter all together.
And, in good time, here the lieutenant comes.
Master lieutenant, pray you, by your leave,
How doth the prince, and my young son of York?

BRAKENBURY. Right well, dear madam. By your patience,
I may not suffer you to visit them;
The king hath straitly charged the contrary.

QUEEN ELIZABETH. The king! why, who's that?

BRAKENBURY. I cry you mercy: I mean the lord protector.

QUEEN ELIZABETH. The Lord protect him from that kingly title!
Hath he set bounds betwixt their love and me?
I am their mother; who should keep me from them?

DUCHESS. I am their father's mother; I will see them.

ANNE. Their aunt I am in law, in love their mother:
Then bring me to their sights; I'll bear thy blame
And take thy office from thee, on my peril.

BRAKENBURY. No, madam, no; I may not leave it so:
I am bound by oath, and therefore pardon me. *(He goes)*

STANLEY *(entering)*. Let me but meet you, ladies, one hour hence,
And I'll salute your grace of York as mother,
And reverend looker on, of two fair queens.
(To Anne) Come, madam, you must straight to Westminster,
There to be crownèd Richard's royal queen.

QUEEN ELIZABETH. O, cut my lace in sunder, that my pent heart
May have some scope to beat, or else I swoon
With this dead-killing news!

ANNE. Despiteful tidings! O unpleasing news!

DORSET. Be of good cheer: mother, how fares your grace?

QUEEN ELIZABETH. O Dorset, speak not to me, get thee hence!
Death and destruction dog thee at the heels;
Thy mother's name is ominous to children.
If thou wilt outstrip death, go cross the seas,
Go, hie thee, hie thee from this slaughter-house,
Lest thou increase the number of the dead,
And make me die the thrall of Margaret's curse,
Nor mother, wife, nor England's counted queen.

STANLEY. Full of wise care is this your counsel, madam.
Take all the swift advantage of the hours;
You shall have letters from me to my son
To meet you on the way, and welcome you.
Be not ta'en tardy by unwise delay.
Come, madam, come; I in all haste was sent.

ANNE. And I in all unwillingness will go.
I would to God that the inclusive verge
Of golden metal that must round my brow
Were red-hot steel, to sear me to the brain!
Anointed let me be with deadly venom,
And die ere men can say *God save the queen!*

QUEEN ELIZABETH. Go, go, poor soul, I envy not thy glory.

ANNE. No! why? When he that is my husband now
Came to me, as I followed Henry's corse,
When scarce the blood was well washed from his hands
Which issued from my other angel husband
And that dead saint which then I weeping followed;
O, when, I say, I looked on Richard's face,
This was my wish: *Be thou* (quoth I) *accursed,*

For making me, so young, so old a widow!
And, when thou wed'st, let sorrow haunt thy bed;
And be thy wife, if any be so mad,
As miserable by the life of thee
As thou hast made me by my dear lord's death!
Lo, ere I can repeat this curse again,
Even in so short a space, my woman's heart
Grossly grew captive to his honey words
And proved the subject of my own soul's curse,
Which ever since hath kept my eyes from rest.
For never yet one hour in his bed
Have I enjoyed the golden dew of sleep,
But have been wakèd by his timorous dreams.
Besides, he hates me for my father Warwick;
And will, no doubt, shortly be rid of me.

QUEEN ELIZABETH. Poor heart, adieu! I pity thy complaining.

ANNE. No more than from my soul I mourn for yours.

QUEEN ELIZABETH. Farewell, thou woeful welcomer of glory!

ANNE. Adieu, poor soul, that takest thy leave of it!

DUCHESS *(to Dorset)*. Go thou to Richmond, and good fortune guide thee!
(To Anne) Go thou to Richard, and good angels guard thee!
(To Queen Elizabeth) Go thou to sanctuary, and good thoughts possess thee!
I to my grave, where peace and rest lie with me!

QUEEN ELIZABETH. Stay, yet look back with me unto the Tower.
Pity, you ancient stones, those tender babes
Whom envy hath immured within your walls!
Rough cradle for such little pretty ones!
Rude ragged nurse, old sullen playfellow
For tender princes, use my babies well!
So foolish sorrow bids your stones farewell.

Scene 2—The Palace

Enter Richard crowned, with Buckingham, Catesby, and others

KING RICHARD. Stand all apart. Cousin of Buckingham!

BUCKINGHAM. My gracious sovereign?

KING RICHARD *(ascending the throne)*. Give me thy hand. Thus high, by thy advice
And thy assistance, is King Richard seated:
But shall we wear these honours for a day?
Or shall they last, and we rejoice in them?

BUCKINGHAM. Still live they and for ever may they last!

KING RICHARD. O Buckingham, now do I play the touch,
To try if thou be current gold indeed:
Young Edward lives: think now what I would say.

BUCKINGHAM. Say on, my loving lord.

KING RICHARD. Why, Buckingham, I say, I would be king.

BUCKINGHAM. Why, so you are, my thrice-renownèd liege.

RICHARD. Ha! am I king? tis so: but Edward lives.

BUCKINGHAM. True, noble prince.

KING RICHARD. O bitter consequence:
That Edward still should live! *True, noble Prince!*
Cousin, thou wert not wont to be so dull:
Shall I be plain? I wish the princes dead;
And I would have it suddenly performed.
What sayest thou? speak suddenly; be brief.

BUCKINGHAM. Your grace may do your pleasure.

KING RICHARD. Tut, tut, thou art all ice, thy kindness freezeth:
Say, have I thy consent that they shall die?

BUCKINGHAM. Give me some breath, some little pause, my lord,
Before I positively speak herein:
I will resolve your grace immediately. *(He goes)*

CATESBY *(aside)*. The king is angry: see, he bites the lip.

KING RICHARD. I will converse with iron-witted fools
And unrespective boys: none are for me
That look into me with considerate eyes:
High-reaching Buckingham grows circumspect.
Boy!

PAGE. My lord?

KING RICHARD. Know'st thou not any whom corrupting gold
Would tempt unto a close exploit of death?

PAGE. My lord, I know a discontented gentleman,
Whose humble means match not his haughty mind:
Gold were as good as twenty orators,
And will, no doubt, tempt him to anything.

KING RICHARD. What is his name?

PAGE. His name, my lord, is Tyrrel.

KING RICHARD. I partly know the man: go, call him hither.
The deep-revolving witty Buckingham
No more shall be the neighbour to my counsel:
Hath he so long held out with me untired,
And stops he now for breath? *(Here Stanley comes)*
How now! what news with you?

STANLEY. My lord, I hear the Marquis Dorset's fled
To Richmond, in those parts where he abides.

KING RICHARD. Catesby!

CATESBY. My lord?

KING RICHARD. Rumour it abroad
That Anne, my wife, is sick and like to die:

I will take order for her keeping close.
Inquire me out some mean-born gentleman,
Whom I will marry straight to Clarence's daughter:
The boy is foolish, and I fear not him.
Look, how thou dream'st! I say again, give out
That Anne my wife is sick and like to die:
About it; for it stands me much upon,
To stop all hopes whose growth may damage me.

Catesby leaves and the Page returns with Tyrrel

Is thy name Tyrrel?

TYRREL. James Tyrrel, and your most obedient subject.

KING RICHARD. Art thou, indeed?

TYRREL. Prove me, my gracious sovereign.

KING RICHARD. Darest thou resolve to kill a friend of mine?

TYRREL. Ay, my lord,
But I had rather kill two enemies.

KING RICHARD. Why, there thou hast it: two deep enemies,
Foes to my rest and my sweet sleep's disturbers
Are they that I would have thee deal upon:
Tyrrel, I mean those princes in the Tower.

TYRREL. Let me have open means to come to them
And soon I'll rid you from the fear of them.

KING. Thou sing'st sweet music. Hark, come hither, Tyrrel:
Go, by this token: rise, and lend thine ear:
There is no more but so: say it is done,
And I will love thee, and prefer thee too.

TYRREL. Tis done, my gracious lord.

KING RICHARD. Shall we hear from thee, Tyrrel, ere we sleep?

TYRREL. Ye shall, my lord. *(He leaves)*

BUCKINGHAM *(entering).* My lord, I have considered in my mind
The late demand that you did sound me in.

KING RICHARD. Well, let that pass. Dorset is fled to Richmond.

BUCKINGHAM. I hear that news, my lord.

KING RICHARD. Stanley, he is your wife's son: well look to it.

BUCKINGHAM. My lord, I claim your gift, my due by promise,
For which your honour and your faith is pawned;
The earldom of Hereford and the movables
The which you promisèd I should possess.

KING RICHARD. Stanley, look to your wife: if she convey
Letters to Richmond, you shall answer it.

BUCKINGHAM. What says your highness to my just demand?

KING RICHARD. As I remember, Henry the Sixth
Did prophesy that Richmond should be king,
When Richmond was a little peevish boy.

BUCKINGHAM. My lord, your promise for the earldom!

KING RICHARD. Ay, what's o'clock?

BUCKINGHAM. I am thus bold to put your grace in mind
Of what you promised me.

KING RICHARD. I am not in the giving vein today.

BUCKINGHAM. Why, then resolve me whether you will or no.

KING RICHARD. Tut, tut,
Thou troublest me; I am not in the vein.

All but Buckingham go

BUCKINGHAM. Is it even so? Rewards he my true service
With such deep contempt? Made I him king for this?
O, let me think on Hastings, and be gone
To Brecknock, while my fearful head is on!

Scene 3—The Palace

TYRREL *(entering)*. The tyrranous and accursèd deed is done,
The most arch act of piteous massacre
That ever yet this land was guilty of.
Dighton and Forrest, whom I did suborn
To do this ruthless piece of butchery,
Melting with tenderness and kind compassion
Wept like two children in their deaths' sad stories.
Lo, thus (quoth Dighton) *lay those tender babes:*
Thus, thus (quoth Forrest) *girdling one another*
Within their innocent alabaster arms:
Their lips were four red roses on a stalk,
Which in their summer beauty kissed each other.
A book of prayers on their pillow lay;
Which once (quoth Forrest) *almost changed my mind;*
But O! the devil (there the villain stopped,
Whilst Dighton thus told on): *We smothered*
The most replenishèd sweet work of nature,
That from the prime creation e'er she framed.
Thus both are gone with conscience and remorse;
They could not speak; and so I left them both.

Enter King Richard

KING RICHARD. Kind Tyrrel, am I happy in thy news?

TYRREL. If to have done the thing you gave in charge
Beget your happiness, be happy then,
For it is done, my lord.

KING RICHARD. But didst thou see them dead?

TYRREL. I did, my lord.

KING RICHARD. And buried, gentle Tyrrel?

TYRREL. The chaplain of the Tower hath buried them;
But how or in what place I do not know.

KING RICHARD. Come to me, Tyrrel, soon after supper,
And thou shalt tell the process of their death.
Meantime, but think how I may do thee good,
And be inheritor of thy desire.
Farewell till soon. *(Tyrrel leaves)*
The son of Clarence have I pent up close;
His daughter meanly have I matched in marriage;
The sons of Edward sleep in Abraham's bosom,
And Anne my wife hath bid the world Good-night.
Now, for I know the Breton Richmond aims
At young Elizabeth, my brother's daughter,
And, by that knot, looks proudly o'er the crown,
To her I go, a jolly thriving wooer.

CATESBY *(entering)*. My lord!

KING RICHARD. Good news or bad, that thou comest in so bluntly?

CATESBY. Bad news, my lord: Ely is fled to Richmond;
And Buckingham, backed with the hardy Welshmen,
Is in the field, and still his power increaseth.

KING RICHARD. Ely with Richmond troubles me more near
Than Buckingham and his rash-levied army.
Come, I have heard that fearful commenting
Is leaden servitor to dull delay;
Delay leads impotent and snail-paced beggary:
Then fiery expedition be my wing.
Come, muster men: my counsel is my shield;
We must be brief when traitors brave the field.

Scene 4—Before the Palace

Queen Margaret enters alone, murmuring her griefs, tempered with satisfaction that retribution attends her enemies. Accompanied by the Duchess of York, Queen Elizabeth appears bewailing the fate of her little sons. All three tell over their sorrows and apportion blame in a frenzy of lamentation, which sounds the deepest note of tragedy. As Margaret passes out Richard enters, with drums and music, and his progress is arrested by the Duchess, his mother.

RICHARD. Who intercepts my expedition?

DUCHESS. O, she that might have intercepted thee
By strangling thee.

QUEEN ELIZABETH. Hidest thou that forehead with a golden crown,
Where should be graven, if that right were right,
The slaughter of the prince that owed that crown,
And the dire death of my two sons and brothers?
Tell me, thou villain slave, Where are my children?

DUCHESS. Thou toad, thou toad, where is thy brother Clarence?
And little Ned Plantagenet, his son?

QUEEN ELIZABETH. Where is kind Hastings, Rivers, Vaughan, Grey?

KING RICHARD. A flourish, trumpets! strike alarum, drums!
Let not the heavens hear these tell-tale women
Rail on the Lord's anointed: strike, I say! *(Trumpets sound)*
Either be patient, and entreat me fair,
Or with the clamorous report of war
Thus will I drown your exclamations.

DUCHESS. Art thou my son? O let me speak?
I will be mild and gentle in my speech.

KING RICHARD. And brief, good mother; for I am in haste.

DUCHESS. Art thou so hasty? I have stayed for thee,
God knows, in anguish, pain, and agony.

KING RICHARD. And came I not at last to comfort you?

DUCHESS. No, by the holy rood, thou know'st it well,
Thou camest on earth to make the earth my hell.
Tetchy and wayward was thy infancy;
Thy schooldays frightful, desperate, wild, and furious,
Thy prime of manhood daring, bold, and venturous,
Thy age confirmed, proud, subtle, treacherous,
More mild, but yet more harmful, kind in hatred.
What comfortable hour canst thou name,
That ever graced me in thy company?

KING RICHARD. If I be so disgracious in your sight,
Let me march on, and not offend your grace.
Strike up the drum.

DUCHESS. I prithee, hear me speak.

KING RICHARD. You speak too bitterly.

DUCHESS. Hear me a word;
For I shall never speak to thee again.

KING RICHARD. So.

DUCHESS. Either thou wilt die, by God's just ordinance,
Ere from this war thou turn a conqueror,
Or I with grief and extreme age shall perish
And never look upon thy face again.
Therefore take with thee my most heavy curse;
Which, in the day of battle, tire thee more
Than all the complete armour that thou wear'st!
My prayers on the adverse party fight;
And there the little souls of Edward's children
Whisper the spirits of thine enemies
And promise them success and victory. *(She goes)*

QUEEN ELIZABETH. Though far more cause, yet much less spirit to curse
Abides in me; I say, Amen to all.

KING RICHARD. Stay, madam; I must speak a word with you.

QUEEN ELIZABETH. I have no more sons of the royal blood
For thee to murder: for my daughters, Richard,
They shall be praying nuns, not weeping queens;
And therefore level not to hit their lives.

KING RICHARD. You have a daughter called Elizabeth,
Virtuous and fair, royal and gracious.

QUEEN ELIZABETH. And must she die for this? O, let her live,
And I'll corrupt her manners, stain her beauty,
Throw over her the veil of infamy,
So she may live unscarred of bleeding slaughter.

KING RICHARD. All unavoided is the doom of destiny.

QUEEN ELIZABETH. True, when avoided grace makes destiny:
My babes were destined to a fairer death
If grace had blessed thee with a fairer life.

KING RICHARD. You speak as if that I had slain my cousins.

QUEEN ELIZABETH. Cousins, indeed; and by their uncle cozened
Of comfort, kingdom, kindred, freedom, life.
Whose hand soever lanced their tender hearts,
Thy head, all indirectly, gave direction:
No doubt the murderous knife was dull and blunt
Till it was whetted on thy stone-hard heart.

KING RICHARD. Madam, so thrive I in my enterprise
As I intend more good to you and yours
Than ever you or yours were by me wronged!

QUEEN ELIZABETH. What good is covered with the face of heaven,
To be discovered, that can do me good?

KING RICHARD. The advancement of your children, gentle lady.

QUEEN ELIZABETH. Up to some scaffold, there to lose their heads?

KING RICHARD. No, to the dignity and height of honour,
The high imperial type of this earth's glory.

QUEEN ELIZABETH. Flatter my sorrows with report of it;
Tell me what state, what dignity, what honour,
Canst thou demise to any child of mine?

KING RICHARD. Even all I have; yea, and myself and all,
Will I withal endow a child of thine;
So in the Lethe of thy angry soul
Thou drown the sad remembrance of those wrongs
Which thou supposest I have done to thee.

QUEEN ELIZABETH. Be brief, lest that the process of thy kindness
Last longer telling than thy kindness' date.

King Richard. Then know that from my soul I love thy daughter,
And mean to make her queen of England.

Queen Elizabeth. Say then, who dost thou mean shall be her king?

King Richard. Even he that makes her queen; who should be else?

Queen Elizabeth. What, thou?

King Richard. I, even I: what think you of it, madam?

Queen Elizabeth. How canst thou woo her?

King Richard. That would I learn of you,
As one that are best acquainted with her humour.

Queen Elizabeth. And wilt thou learn of me?

King Richard. Madam, with all my heart.

Queen Elizabeth. Send to her, by the man that slew her brothers,
A pair of bleeding hearts; thereon engrave
Edward and York; then haply she will weep;
Therefore present to her—as sometime Margaret
Did to thy father, steeped in Rutland's blood—
A handkerchief; which, say to her, did drain
The purple sap from her sweet brother's body,
And bid her dry her weeping eyes therewith.
If this inducement force her not to love,
Send her a story of thy noble acts;
Tell her thou madest away her uncle Clarence,
Her uncle Rivers; yea, and, for her sake,
Made'st quick conveyance with her good aunt Anne.

Untouched by the catalogue of crimes for which the Queen indicts him, Richard pleads vehemently. She has lost a son who should have been a King, he reminds her; she shall have a Queen for her daughter and a son-in-law for King, while her brother Dorset shall stand next the throne. The rebellion of Buckingham shall be broken, and the union he proposes will be for the general good. The Queen pours bitter reproaches upon him, but Richard reminds her that though he pleads he can command, and at last achieves another of his triumphs, for the helpless Queen surrenders.

Queen Elizabeth. Shall I be tempted of the devil thus?

King Richard. Ay, if the devil tempt thee to do good.

Queen Elizabeth. Shall I forget myself to be myself?

King Richard. Ay, if yourself's remembrance wrong yourself.

Queen Elizabeth. Shall I go win my daughter to thy will?

King Richard. And be a happy mother by the deed.

Queen Elizabeth. I go. Write to me very shortly,
And you shall understand from me her mind.

KING RICHARD. Bear her my true love's kiss; and so, farewell.
(Aside as she goes) Relenting fool, and shallow, changing woman!

Ratcliff and Catesby enter

RATCLIFF. My gracious sovereign, on the western coast
Rideth a puissant navy; to the shore
Throng many doubtful hollow-hearted friends,
Unarmed, and unresolved to beat them back:
Tis thought that Richmond is their admiral;
And there they hull, expecting but the aid
Of Buckingham to welcome them ashore.

KING RICHARD. Some light-foot friend post to the Duke of Norfolk:
Ratcliff, thyself, or Catesby; where is he?

CATESBY. Here, my lord.

KING RICHARD. Fly to the duke. Bid him levy straight
The greatest strength and power he can make,
And meet me presently at Salisbury.

Catesby goes and Stanley enters

How now, what news with you?

STANLEY. Richmond is on the seas.

KING RICHARD. There let him sink, and be the seas on him!
White-livered runagate, what doth he there?

STANLEY. I know not, mighty sovereign, but by guess.

KING RICHARD. Well, sir, as you guess, as you guess?

STANLEY. Stirred up by Dorset, Buckingham, and Ely,
He makes for England, there to claim the crown.

KING RICHARD. Is the chair empty? Is the sword unswayed?
Is the king dead? the empire unpossessed?
What heir of York is there alive but we?
And who is England's king but great York's heir?
Then, tell me, what doth he upon the sea?

STANLEY. Unless for that, my liege, I cannot guess.

KING RICHARD. Unless for that he comes to be your liege,
You cannot guess wherefore the Welshman comes.
Thou wilt revolt, and fly to him, I fear.

STANLEY. No, mighty liege; therefore mistrust me not.

KING RICHARD. Where is thy power, then, to beat him back?
Where are thy tenants and thy followers?
Are they not now upon the western shore,
Safe-conducting the rebels from their ships?

STANLEY. No, my good lord, my friends are in the north.

KING RICHARD. Cold friends to Richard: what do they in the north
When they should serve their sovereign in the west?

STANLEY. They have not been commanded, mighty sovereign:
Please it your majesty to give me leave,
I'll muster up my friends, and meet your grace
Where and what time your majesty shall please.

KING RICHARD. Ay, ay, thou wouldst be gone to join with Richmond:
I will not trust you, sir.

STANLEY. Most mighty sovereign,
You have no cause to hold my friendship doubtful:
I never was nor never will be false.

KING RICHARD. Well,
Go muster men; but, hear you, leave behind
Your son, George Stanley: look your faith be firm,
Or else his head's assurance is but frail.

STANLEY. So deal with him as I prove true to you.

As Stanley goes a messenger comes

MESSENGER. My gracious sovereign, now in Devonshire,
As I by friends am well advertisèd,
Sir Edward Courtney, and the haughty prelate
Bishop of Exeter, his brother there,
With many more confederates, are in arms.

ANOTHER MESSENGER. My liege, in Kent the Guildfords are in arms,
And every hour more competitors
Flock to their aid, and still their power increaseth.

THIRD MESSENGER. The army of the Duke of Buckingham—

KING RICHARD. Out on you, owls! nothing but songs of death?
Take that *(striking him)* until thou bring me better news.

MESSENGER. The news I have to tell your majesty
Is that by sudden floods and fall of waters,
Buckingham's army is dispersed and scattered;
And he himself wandered away alone,
No man knows whither.

KING RICHARD. I cry thee mercy!
There is my purse to cure that blow of thine.
Hath any well-advisèd friend proclaimed
Reward to him that brings the traitor in?

MESSENGER. Such proclamation hath been made, my liege.

FOURTH MESSENGER. Sir Thomas Lovel and Lord Marquis Dorset,
Tis said, my liege, in Yorkshire are in arms.
Yet this good comfort bring I to your grace,
The Breton navy is dispersed by tempest:
Richmond, in Dorsetshire, sent out a boat
Unto the shore, to ask those on the banks

If they were his assistants, yea or no;
Who answered him they came from Buckingham
Upon his party: he, mistrusting them,
Hoised sail and made away for Brittany.

KING RICHARD. March on, march on, since we are up in arms;
If not to fight with foreign enemies,
Yet to beat down these rebels here at home.

CATESBY *(returning)*. My liege, the Duke of Buckingham is taken;
That is the best news: that the Earl of Richmond
Is with a mighty power landed at Milford,
Is colder tidings, yet they must be told.

KING RICHARD. Away towards Salisbury! while we reason here
A royal battle might be won and lost:
Someone take order Buckingham be brought
To Salisbury; the rest march on with me.

Scene 5—At Lord Stanley's House

STANLEY. Sir Christopher Urswick, tell Richmond this from me:
My son George Stanley is franked up in hold:
If I revolt, off goes young George's head;
The fear of that withholds my present aid.
Return unto thy lord; commend me to him:
Tell him the queen hath heartily consented
He shall espouse Elizabeth her daughter.
These letters will resolve him of my mind.
Farewell.

ACT 5

Scene 1—An Open Place in Salisbury

Buckingham is led out to execution. The King has refused to see him, and in his despair he recalls the crimes and treacheries to which he has allowed himself to be a party in order to serve the King, and accepts the doom which he confesses he deserves.

Scene 2—The Camp near Tamworth

Enter Richmond and his supporters, with drums and colours

RICHMOND. Fellows in arms, and my most loving friends,
Bruised underneath the yoke of tyranny,
Thus far into the bowels of the land
Have we marched on without impediment;
And here receive we from our father Stanley
Lines of fair comfort and encouragement.
In God's name, cheerly on, courageous friends,
To reap the harvest of perpetual peace
By this one trial of sharp war.

OXFORD. Every man's conscience is a thousand swords,
To fight against that cursèd homicide.

HERBERT. I doubt not but his friends will fly to us.

BLUNT. He hath no friends but who are friends for fear,
Which in his greatest need will shrink from him.

RICHMOND. All for our vantage. Then, in God's name, march:
True hope is swift, and flies with swallow's wings;
Kings it makes gods, and meaner creatures kings.

Scene 3—Bosworth Field

Enter King Richard with noblemen, pitching tents

KING RICHARD. Here pitch our tents, even here in Bosworth field.
My Lord of Surrey, why look you so sad?

SURREY. My heart is ten times lighter than my looks.

KING RICHARD. My Lord of Norfolk—

NORFOLK. Here, most gracious liege.

KING RICHARD. Norfolk, we must have knocks; ha! must we not?

NORFOLK. We must both give and take, my gracious lord.

KING RICHARD. Up with my tent there! Here will I lie tonight;
But where tomorrow? Well, all's one for that.
Who hath descried the number of the foe?

NORFOLK. Six or seven thousand is their utmost power.

KING RICHARD. Why, our battalion trebles that account:
Besides, the king's name is a tower of strength,
Which they upon the adverse party want.
Up with my tent there! Valiant gentlemen,
Let us survey the vantage of the field;
Call for some men of sound direction:
Let's want no discipline, make no delay,
For, lords, tomorrow is a busy day.

Enter Richmond with supporters, pitching tents

RICHMOND. The weary sun hath made a golden set,
And, by the bright track of his fiery car,
Gives signal of a goodly day tomorrow.
Sir William Brandon, you shall bear my standard.
Give me some ink and paper in my tent:
I'll draw the form and model of our battle,
Limit each leader to his several charge,
And part in just proportion our small strength.
My Lord of Oxford, you, Sir William Brandon,
And you, Sir Walter Herbert, stay with me.
The Earl of Pembroke keeps his regiment:
Good Captain Blunt, bear my Good-night to him,
And by the second hour in the morning
Desire the earl to see me in my tent:

Yet one thing more, good Blunt, before thou goest,
Where is Lord Stanley quartered, dost thou know ?

BLUNT. Unless I have mista'en his colours much,
Which well I am assured I have not done,
His regiment lies half a mile at least
South from the mighty power of the king.

RICHMOND. If without peril it be possible,
Good Captain Blunt, bear my Good-night to him,
And give him from me this most needful scroll.

BLUNT. Upon my life, my lord, I'll undertake it ;
And so, God give you quiet rest tonight !

RICHMOND. Good-night, good Captain Blunt. Come, gentlemen,
Let us consult upon tomorrow's business :
Into our tent ; the air is raw and cold.

King Richard enters his tent with Norfolk, Catesby, and Ratcliff

KING RICHARD. What is 't o'clock ?

CATESBY. It's supper-time, my lord ; it's nine o'clock.

KING RICHARD. I will not sup tonight.
Give me some ink and paper.
Is all my armour laid into my tent ?

CATESBY. It is, my liege ; and all things are in readiness.

KING RICHARD. Good Norfolk, hie thee to thy charge ;
Use careful watch, choose trusty sentinels.

NORFOLK. I go, my lord.

KING RICHARD. Stir with the lark tomorrow, gentle Norfolk.

NORFOLK. I warrant you, my lord.

KING RICHARD. Catesby !

CATESBY. My Lord !

KING RICHARD. Send out a pursuivant at arms
To Stanley's regiment ; bid him bring his power
Before sunrising, lest his son George fall
Into the blind cave of eternal night. *(Catesby goes)*
Fill me a bowl of wine. Give me a watch.
Saddle white Surrey for the field tomorrow.
Look that my staves be sound, and not too heavy.
Ratcliff !

RATCLIFF. My lord !

RICHARD. Saw'st thou the melancholy Lord Northumberland ?

RATCLIFF. Thomas the Earl of Surrey, and himself,
Much about cock-shut time, from troop to troop
Went through the army, cheering up the soldiers.

KING RICHARD. So, I am satisfied. Give me a bowl of wine :
I have not that alacrity of spirit,

Nor cheer of mind, that I was wont to have.
Set it down. Is ink and paper ready?

RATCLIFF. It is, my lord.

KING RICHARD. Bid my guard watch; leave me.
Ratcliff, about the mid of night come to my tent
And help to arm me. Leave me, I say. *(He sleeps)*

Enter Stanley to Richmond in his tent

STANLEY. Fortune and victory sit on thy helm!

RICHMOND. All comfort that the dark night can afford
Be to thy person, noble father-in-law!
Tell me, how fares our loving mother?

STANLEY. I, by attorney, bless thee from thy mother,
Who prays continually for Richmond's good:
So much for that. The silent hours steal on,
And flaky darkness breaks within the east.
In brief (for so the season bids us be),
Prepare thy battle early in the morning,
And put thy fortune to the arbitrement
Of war.
I, as I may (that which I would I cannot),
With best advantage will deceive the time,
And aid thee in this doubtful shock of arms:
But on thy side I may not be too forward,
Lest, being seen, thy brother, tender George,
Be executed in his father's sight.
Farewell: the leisure and the fearful time
Cuts off the ceremonious vows of love
And ample interchange of sweet discourse,
Which so long sundered friends should dwell upon:
God give us leisure for these rites of love!
Once more, adieu: be valiant, and speed well!

RICHMOND. Good lords, conduct him to his regiment:
I'll strive, with troubled thoughts, to take a nap,
Lest leaden slumber peise me down tomorrow,
When I should mount with wings of victory:
Once more Good-night, kind lords and gentlemen.

All go, leaving Richmond alone, praying:

O Thou whose captain I account myself,
Look on my forces with a gracious eye;
Put in their hands thy bruising irons of wrath,
That they may crush down with a heavy fall
The usurping helmets of our adversaries!
Make us thy ministers of chastisement,
That we may praise thee in the victory!
To thee I do commend my watchful soul,

Ere I let fall the windows of mine eyes:
Sleeping and waking, O, defend me still! *(He sleeps)*

Ghost of Prince Edward appears to both sleepers

GHOST *(to Richard).* Let me sit heavy on thy soul tomorrow!
Think how thou stab'dst me in my prime of youth!
(To Richmond) Be cheerful, Richmond, for the wrongèd souls
Of butchered princes fight in thy behalf:
King Henry's issue, Richmond, comforts thee.

Ghost of Henry the Sixth

(*To Richard*) Think on the Tower and me: despair, and die!
Harry the Sixth bids thee despair and die!
(To Richmond) Virtuous and holy, be thou conqueror!
Harry, that prophesied thou shouldst be king,
Doth comfort thee in thy sleep.

Ghost of Clarence

(To Richard) Tomorrow in the battle think on me,
And fall thy edgeless sword: despair, and die!
(To Richmond) Thou offspring of the house of Lancaster,
The wrongèd heirs of York do pray for thee:
Good angels guard thy battle!

Ghosts of Rivers, Grey, and Vaughan

(To Richard) Let me sit heavy on thy soul tomorrow,
Rivers, that died at Pomfret! despair, and die!
Think upon Grey, and let thy soul despair!
Think upon Vaughan, and, with guilty fear,
Let fall thy lance: despair, and die!
(To Richmond) Awake, and think our wrongs in Richard's bosom
Will conquer him! awake, and win the day!

Ghost of Hastings

(To Richard) Think on Lord Hastings: despair, and die!
(To Richmond) Quiet untroubled soul, awake, awake!
Arm, fight, and conquer, for fair England's sake!

Ghosts of the two young Princes

(To Richard) Dream on thy cousins smothered in the Tower:
Let us be lead within thy bosom, Richard.
And weigh thee down to ruin, shame, and death!
Thy nephews' souls bid thee despair and die!
(To Richmond) Sleep, Richmond, sleep in peace and wake in joy;
Good angels guard thee from the boar's annoy!

Ghost of Lady Anne

(To Richard) Richard, thy wife, that wretched Anne thy wife,
That never slept a quiet hour with thee,
Now fills thy sleep with perturbations:
Tomorrow in the battle think on me,
And fall thy edgeless sword: despair, and die!

(To Richmond) Thou quiet soul, sleep thou a quiet sleep ;
Dream of success and happy victory !
Thy adversary's wife doth pray for thee.

Ghost of Buckingham

(To Richard) The first was I that helped thee to the crown ;
The last was I that felt thy tyranny :
O, in the battle think on Buckingham,
And die in terror of thy guiltiness !
Fainting, despair ; despairing, yield thy breath !
(To Richmond) I died for hope ere I could lend thee aid :
But cheer thy heart, and be thou not dismayed :
God and good angels fight on Richmond's side ;
And Richard falls in height of all his pride.

The Ghosts vanish, and King Richard starts out of his dream

KING RICHARD. Give me another horse : bind up my wounds.
Have mercy, Jesu ! Soft ! I did but dream.
O coward conscience, how dost thou afflict me !
The lights burn blue. It is now dead midnight.
Cold fearful drops stand on my trembling flesh.
Methought the souls of all that I had murdered
Came to my tent ; and every one did threat
Tomorrow's vengeance on the head of Richard.
Zounds ! who is there ?

RATCLIFF. Ratcliff, my lord ; tis I. The early village-cock
Hath twice done salutation to the morn ;
Your friends are up, and buckle on their armour.

KING RICHARD. O Ratcliff, I have dreamed a fearful dream !
What thinkest thou, will our friends prove all true ?

RATCLIFF. No doubt, my lord.

KING RICHARD. O Ratcliff, I fear, I fear—

RATCLIFF. Nay, good my lord, be not afraid of shadows.

KING RICHARD. By the apostle Paul, shadows tonight
Have struck more terror to the soul of Richard
Than can the substance of ten thousand soldiers
Armèd in proof, and led by shallow Richmond.
It is not yet near day. Come, go with me ;
Under our tents I'll play the eavesdropper,
To see if any mean to shrink from me.

Enter the Lords to Richmond, sitting in his tent

LORDS. Good-morrow, Richmond !

RICHMOND. Cry mercy, lords and watchful gentlemen,
That you have ta'en a tardy sluggard here.

LORDS. How have you slept, my lord ?

RICHMOND. The sweetest sleep and fairest-boding dreams
That ever entered in a drowsy head,

Have I since your departure had, my lords.
Methought their souls whose bodies Richard murdered
Came to my tent, and cried on victory:
I promise you my soul is very jocund
In the remembrance of so fair a dream.
How far into the morning is it, lords?

LORDS. Upon the stroke of four.

RICHMOND. Why, then tis time to arm and give direction.

His oration to his Soldiers

More than I have said, loving countrymen,
The leisure and enforcement of the time
Forbids to dwell upon: yet remember this,
God and our good cause fight upon our side;
The prayers of holy saints and wrongèd souls,
Like high-reared bulwarks, stand before our faces;
Richard except, those whom we fight against
Had rather have us win than him they follow:
For what is he they follow? truly, gentlemen,
A tyrant and a homicide;
Onè raised in blood, and one in blood established;
One that made means to come by what he hath,
And slaughtered those that were the means to help him;
One that hath ever been God's enemy:
Then, if you fight against God's enemy,
God will in justice ward you as his soldiers;
If you do sweat to put a tyrant down
You sleep in peace, the tyrant being slain;
If you do fight in safeguard of your wives
Your wives shall welcome home the conquerors;
If you do free your children from the sword
Your children's children quit it in your age.
Then, in the name of God and all these rights,
Advance your standards, draw your willing swords.
For me, the ransom of my bold attempt
Shall be this cold corpse on the earth's cold face;
But, if I thrive, the gain of my attempt
The least of you shall share his part thereof.
Sound drums and trumpets boldly and cheerfully;
God and saint George! Richmond and victory!

Enter King Richard, Ratcliff, Attendants, and Forces

KING RICHARD. What said Northumberland as touching Richmond?

RATCLIFF. That he was never trainèd up in arms.

KING RICHARD. He said the truth; and what said Surrey then?

RATCLIFF. He smiled and said *The better for our purpose.*

King Richard. He was in the right. Give me a calendar.
Who saw the sun today?

Ratcliff. Not I, my lord.

King Richard. Then he disdains to shine; for by the book
He should have braved the east an hour ago:
A black day will it be to somebody.
The sun will not be seen today;
The sky doth frown and lour upon our army.
I would these dewy tears were from the ground.
Not shine today! Why, what is that to me
More than to Richmond? for the selfsame heaven
That frowns on me looks sadly upon him.

Norfolk comes in, running

Norfolk. Arm, arm, my lord; the foe vaunts in the field.

King Richard. Come, bustle, bustle; caparison my horse.
Call up Lord Stanley, bid him bring his power:
I will lead forth my soldiers to the plain,
And thus my battle shall be orderèd:
My foreward shall be drawn out all in length,
Consisting equally of horse and foot;
Our archers shall be placèd in the midst:
John Duke of Norfolk, Thomas Earl of Surrey,
Shall have the leading of this foot and horse.
They thus directed, we will follow
In the main battle, whose puissance on either side
Shall be well wingèd with our chiefest horse.
This, and Saint George to boot! What think'st thou, Norfolk?

Norfolk. A good direction, warlike sovereign.
This found I on my tent this morning.

He shows the King a paper and the King reads:

Jockey of Norfolk, be not too bold,
For Dickon thy master is bought and sold.

King Richard. A thing devisèd by the enemy.
Go, gentlemen, every man unto his charge:
Let not our babbling dreams affright our souls:
Conscience is but a word that cowards use,
Devised at first to keep the strong in awe:
Our strong arms be our conscience, swords our law.
March on, join bravely, let us to 't pell-mell;
If not to heaven, then hand in hand to hell.

His oration to his Army

What shall I say more than I have inferred?
Remember whom you are to cope withal;
A sort of vagabonds, rascals, and runaways,
A scum of Bretons, and base lackey peasants,

Whom their o'er-cloyèd country vomits forth
To desperate ventures and assured destruction.
You sleeping safe, they bring to you unrest ;
You having lands, and blest with beauteous wives,
They would restrain the one, distain the other.
And who doth lead them but a paltry fellow,
Long kept in Bretagne at our mother's cost ?
A milk-sop, one that never in his life
Felt so much cold as over shoes in snow ?
Let's whip these stragglers o'er the seas again ;
Lash hence these overweening rags of France,
These famished beggars, weary of their lives ;
Who, but for dreaming on this fond exploit,
For want of means, poor rats, had hanged themselves :
If we be conquered, let men conquer us,
And not these Bretons, whom our fathers
Have in their own land beaten, bobbed, and thumped,
And in recòrd left them the heirs of shame.
Hark ! I hear their drum.
Fight, gentlemen of England ! fight, bold yeomen !
Draw, archers, draw your arrows to the head !
Spur your proud horses hard, and ride in blood ;
Amaze the welkin with your broken staves !

Enter a Messenger

What says Lord Stanley ? will he bring his power ?

MESSENGER. My lord, he doth deny to come.

KING RICHARD. Off with his son George's head !

NORFOLK. My lord, the enemy is past the marsh :
After the battle let George Stanley die.

KING RICHARD. A thousand hearts are great within my bosom :
Advance our standards, set upon our foes ;
Our ancient word of courage, fair Saint George,
Inspire us with the spleen of fiery dragons !
Upon them ! Victory sits on our helms.

Scene 4—The Battlefield

CATESBY. Rescue, my lord of Norfolk, rescue, rescue !
The king enacts more wonders than a man,
Daring an opposite to every danger :
His horse is slain, and all on foot he fights,
Seeking for Richmond in the throat of death.
Rescue, fair lord, or else the day is lost !

Enter King Richard

KING RICHARD. A horse ! a horse ! my kingdom for a horse !

CATESBY. Withdraw, my lord ; I'll help you to a horse.

KING RICHARD. Slave, I have set my life upon a cast,

And I will stand the hazard of the die:
I think there be six Richmonds in the field;
Five have I slain today instead of him.
A horse! a horse! my kingdom for a horse!

Scene 5—Another part of the Field

Richard and Richmond meet and go out fighting, Richmond returning, followed by Stanley carrying the Crown.

RICHMOND. God and your arms be praised, victorious friends;
The day is ours, the dog is dead.

STANLEY. Courageous Richmond, well hast thou acquit thee.
Lo, here, this long-usurpèd royalty
From the dead temples of this cursèd wretch
Have I plucked off, to grace thy brows withal:
Wear it, enjoy it, and make much of it.

RICHMOND. Great God of heaven, say Amen to all!
But, tell me, is young George Stanley living?

STANLEY. He is, my lord, and safe in Leicester town;
Whither, if it please you, we may now withdraw us.

RICHMOND. What men of name are slain on either side?

STANLEY. John Duke of Norfolk, Walter Lord Ferrers,
Sir Robert Brakenbury, and Sir William Brandon.

RICHMOND. Inter their bodies as becomes their births:
Proclaim a pardon to the soldiers fled
That in submission will return to us:
And then, as we have ta'en the sacrament,
We will unite the white rose and the red:
Smile heaven upon this fair conjunction,
That long have frowned upon their enmity!
What traitor hears me and says not Amen?
England hath long been mad, and scarred herself;
The brother blindly shed the brother's blood,
The father rashly slaughtered his own son,
The son, compelled, been butcher to the sire:
All this divided York and Lancaster,
Divided in their dire division,
O, now, let Richmond and Elizabeth,
The true succeeders of each royal house,
By God's fair ordinance conjoin together!
And let their heirs, God, if thy will be so,
Enrich the time to come with smooth-faced peace,
With smiling plenty and fair prosperous days!
Abate the edge of traitors, gracious Lord;
Let them not live to taste this land's increase
That would with treason wound this fair land's peace!
Now civil wounds are stopped, peace lives again:
That she may long live here, God say Amen!

The Story of The Taming of the Shrew

THE story of The Taming of the Shrew is a queer example of an old play which was popular long before Shakespeare; less than half the play is supposed to be his own.

THE subject of the play was a favourite idea with very early dramatists on the Continent. The idea of the conquest of a self-willed and scolding woman was supposed in those days to be a very humorous subject, and dramatists played with it until audiences must have tired. It was like the silly jokes of our music-halls not many years ago, when they used to make fun of the mother-in-law or the drunken husband. They were the ready targets of the humour of the music-hall artists of the last generation, who introduced them so tiresomely that they brought their stage into contempt.

SHAKESPEARE, of course, in taking an old play and patching it up as his own, raises this hackneyed theme to a distinction of his own, and his version of The Taming of the Shrew holds his audience by its vigorous movement. We find ourselves forgetting that so much of the story is sordid and blatant. We enjoy the rollicking fun of it, knowing that it is all to end well.

TWO themes are loosely interwoven in the play. One is the sordid wooing of Bianca, an Italian lady, by several suitors who woo her for her money's sake; the other is the extraordinary wooing of Bianca's sister Katharina by Petruchio, who finds her a shrew and transforms her into a gentle and obedient wife. Shakespeare's treatment of the first theme is taken almost bodily from an old play, where it is treated in a tame and stilted style, but he treats the relation between Petruchio and Katharina with great vigour, and it is this that gives the play the life that has preserved it. It has always been popular—perhaps because its theme, though worn threadbare in old days, has been more unusual in modern times, and the play has for us a freshness of its own.

IT has an unusual opening, with the old device of an Introduction, making it a play within a play. A merry lord and his hunting friends, coming upon a drunken tinker, put him to bed in a fine house, and when he comes to his senses persuade him that he is a lord, and that the life he remembers has been a dream. He is offered the play for his entertainment, and it is acted before him. We hear no more of Christopher Sly the tinker, and in the great fun of the play we forget his existence.

THE play comes casually into Shakespeare as a piece of theatrical revision between his earliest work for the stage and the more ambitious writing which gave him his incomparable fame.

THE PLAYERS

In the Introduction

A Lord, a countryman who loves a practical joke.

Christopher Sly, a drunken tinker, with some sense of humour.

Hostess, page, players, huntsmen, and servants.

In the Play

Baptista, a rich gentleman of Padua with two daughters.

Vincentio, an old gentleman of Pisa.

Lucentio, son of Vincentio, in love with Bianca.

Petruchio, a gentleman of Verona, a suitor of Katharina. Forward, bold, ironical, caring nothing what others think.

Grumio, a humorous servant of Petruchio.

Curtis, another servant of Petruchio.

Tranio, a servant of Lucentio.

Biondello, another servant of Lucentio.

Gremio, a suitor of Bianca.

Hortensio, also in love with Bianca.

Katharina, the shrew, eldest daughter of Baptista ; self-willed and violent, jealous of her mild sister Bianca. Not so strong a character as she thinks she is.

Bianca, the younger sister of Katharina.

A pedant, a widow, a tailor, a haberdasher, and servants.

Scene—Padua and the country house of Petruchio

Taming of the Shrew

INTRODUCTION

Scene 1—Before an Alehouse on a Heath

Enter the Hostess with Christopher Sly

HOSTESS. A pair of stocks, you rogue!

SLY. Ye are a baggage: the Slys are no rogues; look in the chronicles; we came in with Richard Conqueror.

HOSTESS. You will not pay for the glasses you have burst?

SLY. No, not a denier.

HOSTESS. I know my remedy; I must go fetch the third-borough constable.

SLY. I'll answer him by law: I'll not budge an inch, boy: let him come, and kindly. *(He falls asleep)*

Enter a Lord from hunting, with his train

LORD. Huntsman, I charge thee, tender well my hounds:
Tomorrow I intend to hunt again.

HUNTSMAN. I will, my lord.

LORD. What's here? One dead, or drunk? See, doth he breathe?

HUNTSMAN. He breathes, my lord. Were he not warmed with ale,
This were a bed but cold to sleep so soundly.

LORD. O monstrous beast! how like a swine he lies!
Grim death, how foul and loathsome is thine image!
Sirs, I will practise on this drunken man.
What think you—if he were conveyed to bed,
Wrapped in sweet clothes, rings put upon his fingers,
A most delicious banquet by his bed,
And brave attendants near him when he wakes,
Would not the beggar then forget himself?

HUNTSMAN. It would seem strange unto him when he waked.

LORD. Then take him up and manage well the jest:
Carry him gently to my fairest chamber
And hang it round with all my merry pictures:
Balm his foul head in warm distillèd waters

And burn sweet wood to make the lodging sweet:
Procure me music ready when he wakes,
To make a dulcet and a heavenly sound;
And if he chance to speak, be ready straight
And with a low submissive reverence
Say *What is it your honour will command?*
Let one attend him with a silver basin
Full of rose-water and bestrewed with flowers;
Another bear the ewer, the third a diaper,
And say *Will't please your lordship cool your hands?*
Someone be ready with a costly suit
And ask him what apparel he will wear;
Another tell him of his hounds and horse,
And that his lady mourns at his disease:
Persuade him that he hath been lunatic,
And when he says he is say that he dreams,
For he is nothing but a mighty lord.
This do and do it kindly, gentle sirs:
It will be pastime passing excellent,
If it be husbanded with modesty.
Take him up gently and to bed with him;
And each one to his office when he wakes.

They carry out Sly and a trumpet sounds

The trumpets herald the approach of strolling players. The lord welcomes them to act in the presence of the awakened Christopher, of whose condition he does not inform them. Then a page is sent off to array himself as a woman, pretending to be the loving wife of the tinker, upon whom she is to shower tears with the aid of an onion hidden in a handkerchief.

Scene 2—A Bedroom in the Nobleman's House

Sly *(waking up)*. For God's sake, a pot of small ale.

First Servant. Will't please your lordship drink a cup of sack?

Second. Will't please your honour taste of these conserves?

Third Servant. What raiment will your honour wear today?

Sly. I am Christophero Sly; call not me *honour* nor *lordship*: I ne'er drank sack in my life; and if you give me any conserves give me conserves of beef. Ne'er ask me what raiment I'll wear, for I have no more doublets than backs, no more stockings than legs, nor no more shoes than feet; nay, sometime more feet than shoes, or such shoes as my toes look through the overleather.

Lord. Heaven cease this idle humour in your honour!
O, that a mighty man of such descent,
Of such possessions and so high esteem,
Should be infusèd with so foul a spirit!

Sly. What, would you make me mad? Am not I Christopher Sly, old Sly's son of Burton Heath, by birth a pedlar, by education a card-maker, by transmutation a bear-herd, and now by present profession a tinker? Ask Marian Hacket, the fat ale-wife of Wincot, if she know me not: if she say I am not fourteen pence on the score for sheer ale score me up for the lyingest knave in Christendom.

THIRD SERVANT. O, this it is that makes your lady mourn!

SECOND SERVANT. O, this is it that makes your servants droop!

LORD. Hence comes it that your kindred shuns your house,
As beaten hence by your strange lunacy.
O noble lord, bethink thee of thy birth,
Call home thy ancient thoughts from banishment
And banish hence these abject lowly dreams.
Look how thy servants do attend on thee,
Each in his office ready at thy beck.
Wilt thou have music? hark! *(Music)* Apollo plays
And twenty cagèd nightingales do sing.
Or wilt thou sleep? we'll have thee to a couch.
Say thou wilt walk; we will bestrew the ground.
Or wilt thou ride? thy horses shall be trapped,
Their harness studded all with gold and pearl.
Dost thou love hawking? Thou hast hawks will soar
Above the morning lark. Or wilt thou hunt?
Thy hounds shall make the welkin answer them
And fetch shrill echoes from the hollow earth.

SERVANT. Say thou wilt course; thy greyhounds are as swift
As breathèd stags, ay, fleeter than the roe.

SECOND SERVANT. Dost thou love pictures? we will fetch thee straight
Adonis painted by a running brook,
And Cytherea all in sedges hid.

LORD. Thou art a lord and nothing but a lord:
Thou hast a lady far more beautiful
Than any woman in this waning age.

SLY. Am I a lord? And have I such a lady?
Or do I dream—or have I dreamed till now?
I do not sleep: I see, I hear, I speak;
I smell sweet savours and I feel soft things:
Upon my life, I am a lord indeed
And not a tinker nor Christophero Sly.
Well, bring our lady hither to our sight;
And once again, a pot o' the smallest ale.

SERVANT. Will't please your mightiness to wash your hands?
O, how we joy to see your wit restored!
O, that once more you knew but what you are!
These fifteen years you have been in a dream;
Or when you waked, so waked as if you slept.

SLY. These fifteen years! by my fay, a goodly nap.
But did I never speak of all that time?

FIRST SERVANT. O, yes, my lord, but very idle words:
For though you lay here in this goodly chamber,
Yet would you say ye were beaten out of door;
And rail upon the hostess of the house;
Sometimes you would call out for Cicely Hacket.

SLY. Ay, the woman's maid of the house.

THIRD SERVANT. Why, sir, you know no house nor no such maid,
Nor no such men as you have reckoned up,
As Stephen Sly and old John Naps of Greece
And Peter Turph and Henry Pimpernell
And twenty more such names and men as these
Which never were nor no man ever saw.

SLY. Now Lord be thankèd for my good amends!

Enter the Page as a lady, with attendants

PAGE. How fares my noble lord?

SLY. Marry, I fare well; for here is cheer enough.
Where is my wife?

PAGE. Here, noble lord: what is thy will with her?

SLY. Are you my wife and will not call me husband?
My men should call me *lord*: I am your goodman.

PAGE. My husband and my lord, my lord and husband;
I am your wife in all obedience.

SLY. Madam wife, they say that I have dreamed
And slept above some fifteen year or more.

PAGE. Ay, and the time seems thirty unto me.

MESSENGER. Your honour's players, hearing your amendment,
Are come to play a pleasant comedy;
For so your doctors hold it very meet,
Seeing too much sadness hath congealed your blood,
And melancholy is the nurse of frenzy:
Therefore they thought it good you hear a play
And frame your mind to mirth and merriment,
Which bars a thousand harms and lengthens life.

SLY. Marry, I will; let them play it. We'll see 't. Come, madam wife, sit by my side and let the world slip; we shall ne'er be younger.

ACT 1

Scene 1—A Public Place in Padua: Lucentio and his man Tranio

LUCENTIO. Tranio, since for the great desire I had
To see fair Padua, nursery of arts,
I am arrived for fruitful Lombardy,
The pleasant garden of great Italy;

And by my father's love and leave am armed
With his goodwill and thy good company,
My trusty servant, well approved in all,
Here let us breathe and haply institute
A course of learning and ingenious studies.
Tell me thy mind; for I have Pisa left
And am to Padua come, as he that leaves
A shallow plash to plunge him in the deep
And with satiety seeks to quench his thirst.

TRANIO. Pardon, gentle master mine,
I am in all affected as yourself;
Glad that you thus continue your resolve
To suck the sweets of sweet philosophy.
Only, good master, while we do admire
This virtue and this moral discipline,
Let's be no stoics nor no stocks, I pray;
In brief, sir, study what you most affect.

LUCENTIO. Gramercies, Tranio, well dost thou advise.
But stay awhile: what company is this?

TRANIO. Master, some show to welcome us to town.

Enter Baptista, Katharina, Bianca, Gremio, and Hortensio. Lucentio and Tranio stand aside.

BAPTISTA. Gentlemen, importune me no further,
For how I firmly am resolved you know;
That is, not to bestow my youngest daughter
Before I have a husband for the elder:
If either of you both love Katharina,
Because I know you well and love you well,
Leave shall you have to court her at your pleasure.

GREMIO *(aside)*. To cart her rather: she's too rough for me.
There, there, Hortensio, will you any wife?

KATHARINA. I pray you, sir, is it your will
To make a stale of me amongst these mates?

HORTENSIO. Mates, maid! how mean you that? no mates for you,
Unless you were of gentler, milder mould.
From all such devils, good Lord deliver us!

GREMIO. And me too, good Lord!

TRANIO. Hush, master! here's some good pastime toward:
That wench is stark mad or wonderful froward.

LUCENTIO. But in the other's silence do I see
Maid's mild behaviour and sobriety.
Peace, Tranio!

TRANIO. Well said, master; mum! and gaze your fill.

BAPTISTA. Gentlemen, that I may soon make good
What I have said, Bianca, get you in:
And let it not displease thee, good Bianca,
For I will love thee ne'er the less, my girl.

KATHARINA. A pretty pet!

BIANCA. Sister, content you in my discontent.
Sir, to your pleasure humbly I subscribe:
My books and instruments shall be my company.

LUCENTIO. Hark, Tranio! thou may'st hear Minerva speak.

HORTENSIO. Signior Baptista, will you be so strange?
Sorry am I that our goodwill effects
Bianca's grief.

GREMIO. Why will you mew her up, Signior Baptista,
And make her bear the penance of her sister's tongue?

BAPTISTA. Gentlemen, content ye; I am resolved:
Go in, Bianca: *(She goes)*
And for I know she taketh most delight
In music, instruments, and poetry,
Schoolmasters will I keep within my house,
Fit to instruct her youth. If you, Hortensio,
Or Signior Gremio, you, know any such,
Prefer them hither; for to cunning men
I will be very kind, and liberal
To mine own children in good bringing up:
And so farewell. Katharina, you may stay;
For I have more to commune with Bianca.

KATHARINA. Why, and I trust I may go too, may I not? What, shall I be appointed hours, as though, belike, I knew not what to take, and what to leave, ha? *(She follows)*

HORTENSIO. Tush, Gremio, though it pass your patience and mine to endure her loud alarums, why, man, there be good fellows in the world, an a man could light on them, would take her with all faults, and money enough.

GREMIO. I cannot tell; but I had as lief take her dowry with this condition, to be whipped at the high cross every morning.

HORTENSIO. Faith, as you say, there's small choice in rotten apples. But come; since this bar in law makes us friends, it shall be so far forth friendly maintained till by helping Baptista's eldest daughter to a husband we set his youngest free for a husband, and then have to 't afresh. Sweet Bianca! He that runs fastest gets the ring. How say you, Signior Gremio?

GREMIO. I am agreed; and would I had given him the best horse in Padua to begin his wooing that would thoroughly woo her, wed her, and rid the house of her! Come on. *(They go)*

TRANIO *(coming forward)*. I pray, sir, tell me, is it possible
That love should of a sudden take such hold ?

LUCENTIO. O Tranio, till I found it to be true,
I never thought it possible or likely ;
But see, while idly I stood looking on,
I found the effect of love in idleness,
And now in plainness do confess to thee,
That art to me as secret and as dear
As Anna to the queen of Carthage was,
Tranio, I burn, I pine, I perish, Tranio,
If I achieve not this young modest girl.
Counsel me, Tranio, for I know thou canst ;
Assist me, Tranio, for I know thou wilt.

TRANIO. Master, it is no time to chide you now ;
Affection is not rated from the heart :
If love have touched you, nought remains but so,
Buy yourself off as cheaply as you can.
I pray, awake, sir : thus it stands :
Her eldest sister is so curst and shrewd
That till the father rid his hands of her,
Master, your love must live a maid at home ;
And therefore has he closely mewed her up,
Because she will not be annoyed with suitors.

LUCENTIO. Ah, Tranio, what a cruel father's he !
But art thou not advised, he took some care
To get her cunning schoolmasters to instruct her ?

TRANIO. Ay, marry, am I, sir.
You will be schoolmaster
And undertake the teaching of the maid !
That's your device ?

LUCENTIO. It is : may it be done ?

TRANIO. Not possible ; for who shall bear your part,
And be in Padua here Vincentio's son,
Keep house and ply his book, welcome his friends,
Visit his countrymen and banquet them ?

As neither of them is known in Padua the two agree to exchange identities, Tranio to be the master and Lucentio his servant. When Biondello, the other servant, arrives he is told that the change is necessary to disguise Lucentio and save him from arrest for something he pretends to have done.

LUCENTIO. And not a jot of Tranio in your mouth :
Tranio is changed into Lucentio.

BIONDELLO. The better for him : would I were so too !

TRANIO. So could I, faith, boy, to have the next wish after,
That Lucentio indeed had Baptista's youngest daughter.
But, sirrah, not for my sake, but your master's, I advise
You use your manners discreetly in all kind of companies:
When I am alone, why, then I am Tranio;
But in all places else your master Lucéntio.

LUCENTIO. Tranio, let's go: one thing more rests, that thyself make one among these wooers: if thou ask me why, my reasons are both good and weighty.

A SERVANT *(to Sly). My lord, you nod; you do not mind the play.*

SLY. *Yes, by Saint Anne, do I. A good matter, surely: comes there any more of it?*

PAGE. *My lord, tis but begun.*

SLY. *Tis a very excellent piece of work, madam lady; would 'twere done!*

Scene 2—Before Hortensio's house: Petruchio with Grumio

PETRUCHIO. Verona, for a while I take my leave,
To see my friends in Padua, but of all
My best belovèd and approvèd friend,
Hortensio; and I trow this is his house.

While they are talking Hortensio appears and recognises Petruchio

HORTENSIO. Sweet friend, what happy gale
Blows you to Padua here from old Verona?

PETRUCHIO. Such wind as scatters young men through the world
To seek their fortunes farther than at home
Where small experience grows.
Signior Hortensio, thus it stands with me:
Antonio, my father, is deceased;
And I have thrust myself into this maze,
Haply to wive and thrive as best I may:
Crowns in my purse I have and goods at home,
And so am come abroad to see the world.

HORTENSIO. Petruchio, shall I then come roundly to thee
And wish thee to a shrewd ill-favoured wife?
Thou'dst thank me but a little for my counsel:
And yet I'll promise thee she shall be rich
And very rich: but thou'rt too much my friend,
And I'll not wish thee to her.

PETRUCHIO. Signior Hortensio, 'twixt such friends as we
Few words suffice; and therefore, if thou know
One rich enough to be Petruchio's wife,
As wealth is burden of my wooing dance,
Be she as foul as was Florentius' love,
As old as Sibyl, and as curst and shrewd

As Socrates' Xanthippe, or a worse,
She moves me not, or not removes, at least,
Affection's edge in me, were she as rough
As are the swelling Adriatic seas :
I come to wive it wealthily in Padua ;
If wealthily, then happily in Padua.

GRUMIO. Nay, look you, sir, he tells you flatly what his mind is : why, give him gold enough and marry him to a puppet, or an old trot with ne'er a tooth in her head, though she have as many diseases as two and fifty horses : why, nothing comes amiss, so money comes withal.

HORTENSIO. Petruchio, since we are stepped thus far in,
I will continue that I broached in jest.
I can, Petruchio, help thee to a wife
With wealth enough, and young and beauteous,
Brought up as best becomes a gentlewoman :
Her only fault, and that is faults enough,
Is that she is intolerable curst
And shrewd and froward, so beyond all measure
That, were my state far worser than it is,
I would not wed her for a mine of gold.

PETRUCHIO. Hortensio, peace ! thou know'st not gold's effect :
Tell me her father's name and tis enough ;
For I will woo her, though she chide as loud
As thunder when the clouds in autumn crack.

HORTENSIO. Her father is Baptista Minola,
An affable and courteous gentleman :
Her name is Katharina Minola,
Renowned in Padua for her scolding tongue.

PETRUCHIO. I will not sleep, Hortensio, till I see her ;
And therefore let me be thus bold with you
To give you over at this first encounter,
Unless you will accompany me thither.

GRUMIO. I pray you, sir, let him go while the humour lasts. O' my word, an she knew him as well as I do she would think scolding would do little good upon him.

HORTENSIO. Tarry, Petruchio, I must go with thee,
For in Baptista's keep my treasure is :
He hath the jewel of my life in hold,
His youngest daughter, beautiful Bianca.
Supposing it a thing impossible,
For those defects I have before rehearsed,
That ever Katharina will be wooed,
Therefore this order hath Baptista ta'en,
That none shall have access unto Bianca

Till Katharine the curst have got a husband.
Now shall my friend Petruchio do me grace,
And offer me disguised in sober robes
To old Baptista as a schoolmaster
Well seen in music, to instruct Bianca;
That so I may, by this device, at least
Have leave and leisure to make love to her
And unsuspected court her by herself.

GRUMIO. Here's no knavery! See, to beguile the old folks, how the young folks lay their heads together!

Enter Gremio, and Lucentio disguised and carrying books

Master, master, look about you: who goes there, ha?

HORTENSIO. Peace, Grumio! it is the rival of my love.
Petruchio, stand by a while.

GRUMIO. A proper stripling and an amorous! *(They step aside)*

GREMIO *(to Lucentio)*. O, very well; I have perused the note.
Hark you, sir; I'll have them very fairly bound:
All books of love, see that at any hand;
And see you read no other lectures to her:
You understand me. Take your paper too,
And let me have them very well perfumed:
For she is sweeter than perfume itself
To whom they go to. What will you read to her?

LUCENTIO. Whate'er I read to her, I'll plead for you
As for my patron, stand you so assured,
As firmly as yourself were still in place:
Yea, and perhaps with more successful words
Than you, unless you were a scholar, sir.

GREMIO. O this learning, what a thing it is!

GRUMIO. O this woodcock, what an ass it is!

PETRUCHIO. Peace, sirrah!

HORTENSIO. Grumio, mum! God save you, Signior Gremio.

GREMIO. And you are well met, Signior Hortensio.
Trow you whither I am going? To Baptista Minola.
I promised to inquire carefully
About a schoolmaster for the fair Bianca:
And by good fortune I have lighted well
On this young man, for learning and behaviour
Fit for her turn, well read in poetry,
And other books, good ones, I warrant ye.

HORTENSIO. Tis well; and I have met a gentleman
Hath promised me to help me to another,
A fine musician to instruct our mistress;
So shall I no whit be behind in duty
To fair Bianca, so beloved of me.

GREMIO. Beloved of me; and that my deeds shall prove.

HORTENSIO. Gremio, tis now no time to vent our love:
Listen to me, and if you speak me fair,
I'll tell you news indifferent good for either.
Here is a gentleman whom by chance I met,
Upon agreement from us to his liking,
Will undertake to woo curst Katharine,
Yea, and to marry her if her dowry please.

GREMIO. So said, so done, is well.
Hortensio, have you told him all her faults?

PETRUCHIO. I know she is an irksome brawling scold:
If that be all, masters, I hear no harm.

GREMIO. But will you woo this wild-cat?

PETRUCHIO. Will I live?
Why came I hither but to that intent?
Think you a little din can daunt mine ears?
Have I not in my time heard lions roar?
Have I not heard the sea puffed up with winds
Rage like an angry boar chafèd with sweat?
Have I not heard great ordnance in the field,
And heaven's artillery thunder in the skies?
Have I not in a pitchèd battle heard
Loud 'larums, neighing steeds, and trumpets clang?
And do you tell me of a woman's tongue?

Enter Tranio, bravely apparelled, with Biondello

TRANIO. Gentlemen, God save you. If I may be bold,
Tell me, I beseech you, which is the readiest way
To the house of Signior Baptista Minola?

BIONDELLO. He that has the two fair daughters: is 't he you mean?

TRANIO. Even he, Biondello.

GREMIO. Hark you, sir; you mean not her to woo?

TRANIO. Perhaps, him and her, sir: what have you to do?

PETRUCHIO. Not her that chides, sir, at any hand, I pray.

TRANIO. I love no chiders, sir. Biondello, let's away.

HORTENSIO. Sir, a word ere you go;
Are you a suitor to the maid you talk of, yea or no?

TRANIO. And if I be, sir, is it any offence?

GREMIO. No; if without more words you will get you hence.

TRANIO. Why, sir, I pray, are not the streets as free
For me as for you?

GREMIO. But so is not she.

TRANIO. For what reason, I beseech you?

GREMIO. For this reason, if you'll know,
That she's the choice love of Signior Gremio.

HORTENSIO. That she's the chosen of Signior Hortensio.

TRANIO. Softly, my masters! if you be gentlemen,
Do me this right; hear me with patience.
Baptista is a noble gentleman,
To whom my father is not all unknown;
And were his daughter fairer than she is
She may more suitors have and me for one.

HORTENSIO. Let me be so bold as ask you,
Did you yet ever see Baptista's daughter?

TRANIO. No, sir; but hear I do that he hath two,
The one as famous for a scolding tongue
As is the other for beauteous modesty.

PETRUCHIO. Sir, sir, the first's for me; let her go by.

GREMIO. Yea, leave that labour to great Hercules.

PETRUCHIO. Sir, understand you this of me in sooth:
The youngest daughter whom you hearken for
Her father keeps from all access of suitors,
And will not promise her to any man
Until the elder sister first be wed:
The younger then is free, and not before.

ACT 2

Scene 1—A Room in Baptista's house at Padua

BIANCA. Good sister, wrong me not, nor wrong yourself,
To make a bondmaid and a slave of me;
That I disdain: but for these other gawds,
Unbind my hands, I'll pull them off myself,
Yea, all my raiment, to my petticoat;
Or what you will command me will I do,
So well I know my duty to my elders.

KATHARINA. Of all thy suitors, here I charge thee, tell
Whom thou lovest best: see thou dissemble not.

BIANCA. Believe me, sister, of all the men alive
I never yet beheld that special face
Which I could fancy more than any other.

KATHARINA. Minion, thou liest. Is 't not Hortensio?

BIANCA. If you affect him, sister, here I swear
I'll plead for you myself, but you shall have him.

KATHARINA. O then, belike, you fancy riches more:
You will have Gremio to keep you fair.

She strikes Bianca as Baptista enters

BAPTISTA. Why, how now, dame! whence grows this insolence?
Bianca, stand aside. Poor girl! she weeps.
Go ply thy needle; meddle not with her.

For shame, thou hilding of a devilish spirit,
Why dost thou wrong her that did ne'er wrong thee?
When did she cross thee with a bitter word?

KATHARINA. Her silence flouts me, and I'll be revenged.

She approaches Bianca

BAPTISTA. What, in my sight? Bianca, get thee in. *(Bianca goes)*

KATHARINA. What, will you not suffer me? Nay, now I see
She is your treasure, she must have a husband;
I must dance barefoot on her wedding-day.
Talk not to me: I will go sit and weep
Till I can find occasion of revenge.

BAPTISTA. Was ever gentleman thus grieved as I?
But who comes here? *(Katharina goes)*

Enter Gremio, Lucentio as a poor man, Petruchio, with Hortensio as a musician, and Tranio, with Biondello bearing a lute and books.

GREMIO. Good-morrow, neighbour Baptista.

BAPTISTA. Good-morrow, neighbour Gremio. God save you, gentlemen.

PETRUCHIO. And you, good sir! Pray, have you not a daughter
Called Katharina, fair and virtuous?

BAPTISTA. I have a daughter, sir, called Katharina.

GREMIO. You are too blunt; go to it orderly.

PETRUCHIO. You wrong me, Signior Gremio; give me leave.
I am a gentleman of Verona, sir,
That, hearing of her beauty and her wit,
Her affability and bashful modesty,
Her wondrous qualities and mild behaviour,
Am bold to show myself a forward guest
Within your house to make mine eye my witness
Of that report which I so oft have heard.
And, for an entrance to my entertainment,
I do present you with a man of mine *(presenting Hortensio)*,
Cunning in music and the mathematics,
To instruct her fully in those sciences,
Whereof I know she is not ignorant.
His name is Licio, born in Mantua.

BAPTISTA. You're welcome, sir; and he, for your good sake.
But for my daughter Katharine, this I know,
She is not for your turn, the more my grief.

PETRUCHIO. I see you do not mean to part with her,
Or else you like not of my company.

BAPTISTA. Mistake me not; I speak but as I find.
Whence are you, sir? what may I call your name?

PETRUCHIO. Petruchio is my name; Antonio's son,
A man well known throughout all Italy.

BAPTISTA. I know him well: you are welcome for his sake.

GREMIO. Saving your tale, Petruchio, I pray,
Let us, that are poor petitioners, speak too.

PETRUCHIO. O, pardon me, Signior Gremio; I would fain be doing.

GREMIO. I doubt it not, sir; but you will curse your wooing. Neighbour, this is a gift very grateful, I am sure of it. To express the like kindness, myself, that have been more kindly beholding to you than any, freely give unto you this young scholar *(presenting Lucentio)*, that hath been long studying at Rheims; as cunning in Greek, Latin, and other languages as the other in music and mathematics. His name is Cambio; pray, accept his service.

BAPTISTA. A thousand thanks, Signior Gremio. Welcome, good Cambio. But, gentle sir *(to Tranio)*, methinks you walk like a stranger: may I be so bold to know the cause of your coming?

TRANIO. Pardon me, sir, the boldness is mine own,
That, being a stranger in this city here,
Do make myself a suitor to your daughter,
Unto Bianca, fair and virtuous.
Nor is your firm resolve unknown to me,
In the preferment of the eldest sister.
This liberty is all that I request,
That, upon knowledge of my parentage,
I may have welcome 'mongst the rest that woo
And free access and favour as the rest:
And, toward the education of your daughters,
I here bestow a simple instrument,
And this small packet of Greek and Latin books.

BAPTISTA. Lucentio is your name; of whence, I pray?

TRANIO. Of Pisa, sir; son to Vincentio.

BAPTISTA. A mighty man of Pisa; by report
I know him well: you are very welcome, sir.
Take you the lute, and you the set of books;
You shall go see your pupils presently.

A servant takes them to Baptista's daughters

(To Petruchio) We will go walk a little in the orchard,
And then to dinner. You are passing welcome,
And so I pray you all to think yourselves.

PETRUCHIO. Signior Baptista, my business asketh haste,
And every day I cannot come to woo.
You knew my father well, and in him me,
Left solely heir to all his lands and goods,
Which I have bettered rather than decreased:
Then tell me, if I get your daughter's love,
What dowry shall I have with her to wife?

BAPTISTA. After my death the one half of my lands,
And in possession twenty thousand crowns.

PETRUCHIO. And, for that dowry, I'll assure her of
Her widowhood, be it that she survive me,
In all my lands and leases whatsoever:
Let specialties be therefore drawn between us,
That covenants may be kept on either hand.

BAPTISTA. Ay, when the special thing is well obtained,
That is, her love; for that is all in all.

PETRUCHIO. Why, that is nothing; for I tell you, father,
I am as peremptory as she proud-minded;
And where two raging fires meet together
They do consume the thing that feeds their fury:
Though little fire grows great with little wind,
Yet extreme gusts will blow out fire and all:
So I to her and so she yields to me;
For I am rough and woo not like a babe.

BAPTISTA. Well mayst thou woo, and happy be thy speed!

Hortensio runs in with his head bandaged

How now, my friend! why dost thou look so pale?

HORTENSIO. For fear, I promise you, if I look pale.

BAPTISTA. What, will my daughter prove a good musician?

HORTENSIO. I think she'll sooner prove a soldier:
Iron may hold with her, but never lutes.

BAPTISTA. Why, then thou canst not break her to the lute?

HORTENSIO. Why, no; for she hath broke the lute to me.
I did but tell her she mistook her frets,
And bowed her hand to teach her fingering;
When, with a most impatient devilish spirit,
Frets, call you these? (quoth she). *I'll fume with them.*
And with that word she struck me on the head,
And through the instrument my pate made way;
And there I stood amazèd for a while,
As on a pillory, looking through the lute;
While she did call me rascal fiddler
And twangling Jack; with twenty such vile terms,
As had she studied to misuse me so.

PETRUCHIO. Now, by the world, it is a lusty wench;
I love her ten times more than e'er I did:
O, how I long to have some chat with her!

BAPTISTA. Well, go with me and be not so discomfited:
Proceed in practice with my younger daughter;
She's apt to learn and thankful for good turns.
Signior Petruchio, will you go with us,
Or shall I send my daughter Kate to you?

PETRUCHIO. I pray you do. I will attend her here *(they go)*,
And woo her with some spirit when she comes.
Say that she rail; why then I'll tell her plain
She sings as sweetly as a nightingale.
Say that she frown; I'll say she looks as clear
As morning roses newly washed with dew.
Say she be mute and will not speak a word;
Then I'll commend her volubility,
And say she uttereth piercing eloquence.
If she do bid me pack I'll give her thanks,
As though she bid me stay by her a week:
If she deny to wed I'll crave the day
When I shall ask the banns and when be married.
But here she comes; and now, Petruchio, speak.
Good-morrow, Kate; for that's your name, I hear.

KATHARINA. Well have you heard, but something hard of hearing:
They call me Katharine that do talk of me.

PETRUCHIO. You lie, in faith; for you are called plain Kate,
And bonny Kate and sometimes Kate the curst;
But Kate, the prettiest Kate in Christendom,
Take this of me, Kate of my consolation:
Hearing thy mildness praised in every town,
Thy virtues spoke of, and thy beauty sounded,
Yet not so deeply as to thee belongs,
Myself am moved to woo thee for my wife.

KATHARINA. Moved! In good time: let him that moved you hither
Remove you hence.

PETRUCHIO. Come, come, you wasp; i' faith, you are too angry.
Good Kate, I am a gentleman.

KATHARINA. That I'll try *(striking him)*.

PETRUCHIO. I swear I'll cuff you if you strike again.

KATHARINA. So may you lose your arms:
If you strike me you are no gentleman.

PETRUCHIO. Nay, come, Kate, come; you must not look so sour.

KATHARINA. It is my fashion, when I see a crab.

PETRUCHIO. Nay, hear you, Kate: in sooth you scape not so.

KATHARINA. I chafe you if I tarry: let me go.

PETRUCHIO. No, not a whit: I find you passing gentle.
Twas told me you were rough and coy and sullen,
And now I find report a very liar,
For thou art pleasant, gamesome, passing courteous,
But slow in speech, yet sweet as springtime flowers:
Thou canst not frown, thou canst not look askance,
Nor bite the lip, as angry wenches will,
Nor hast thou pleasure to be cross in talk,

But thou with mildness entertain'st thy wooers,
With gentle conference, soft, and affable.
Why does the world report that Kate doth limp ?
O slanderous world ! Kate like the hazel-twig
Is straight and slender and as brown in hue
As hazel nuts, and sweeter than the kernels.
O, let me see thee walk : thou dost not halt.

KATHARINA. Go, fool, and whom thou keep'st, command.

PETRUCHIO. Did ever Dian so become a grove
As Kate this chamber with her princely gait ?

KATHARINA. Where did you study all this goodly speech ?

PETRUCHIO. It is extempore, from my mother-wit :
And therefore, setting all this chat aside,
Thus in plain terms : your father hath consented
That you shall be my wife ; your dowry 'greed on ;
And, will you, nill you, I will marry you.
Now, Kate, I am a husband for your turn ;
For, by this light, whereby I see thy beauty,
Thy beauty that doth make me like thee well,
Thou must be married to no man but me ;
For I am he am born to tame you, Kate.
Here comes your father : never make denial ;
I must and will have Katharine to my wife.

BAPTISTA *(returning with Gremio)*. Now, Signior Petruchio, how speed you with my daughter ?

PETRUCHIO. How but well, sir ? how but well ?

BAPTISTA. Why, how now, daughter Katharine ! in your dumps ?

KATHARINA. Call you me daughter ? now, I promise you,
You have showed a tender fatherly regard
To wish me wed to one half lunatic,
A madcap ruffian and a swearing Jack,
That thinks with oaths to face the matter out.

PETRUCHIO. Father, tis thus : yourself and all the world,
That talked of her, have talked amiss of her :
If she be curst it is for policy,
For she's not froward, but modest as the dove ;
She is not hot, but temperate as the morn ;
And to conclude, we have 'greed so well together,
That upon Sunday is the wedding-day.

KATHARINA. I'll see thee hanged on Sunday first.

GREMIO. Hark, Petruchio ; she says she'll see thee hanged first.

PETRUCHIO. Be patient, gentlemen ; I choose her for myself ;
If she and I be pleased, what's that to you ?
Tis bargained 'twixt us twain, being alone,
That she shall still be curst in company.

I tell you, tis incredible to believe
How much she loves me : O, the kindest Kate !
She hung about my neck ; and kiss on kiss
She vied so fast, protesting oath on oath,
That in a twink she won me to her love.
Give me thy hand, Kate : I will unto Venice,
To buy apparel 'gainst the wedding-day.
Provide the feast, father, and bid the guests ;
I will be sure my Katharine shall be fine.

BAPTISTA. I know not what to say : but give me your hands ;
God send you joy, Petruchio ! tis a match.

PETRUCHIO. Father, and wife, and gentlemen, adieu ;
I will to Venice ; Sunday comes apace :
We will have rings and things and fine array ;
And kiss me, Kate, we will be married o' Sunday.

Petruchio and Katharina go separately

GREMIO. Was ever match clapped up so suddenly ?

BAPTISTA. Faith, gentlemen, now I play a merchant's part,
And venture madly on a desperate mart.

Baptista proceeds to bargain with the suitors for the hand of his daughter Bianca. Gremio offers a generous dower, but Tranio, impersonating Lucentio, outbids him, and his offer is accepted on the condition that the offer is sustained by Lucentio's father Vincentio. If that assurance is forthcoming the marriage is fixed for the Sunday following Kate's marriage. If the bargain fails Gremio is to be the bridegroom.

ACT 3

Scene 1—Baptista's House

Enter Lucentio, Hortensio, and Bianca

LUCENTIO. Fiddler, forbear ; you grow too forward, sir :
Have you so soon forgot the entertainment
Her sister Katharine welcomed you withal ?

HORTENSIO. But, wrangling pedant, this is
The patroness of heavenly harmony :
Then give me leave to have prerogative ;
And when in music we have spent an hour
Your lecture shall have leisure for as much.

LUCENTIO. Preposterous ass, that never read so far
To know the cause why music was ordained !
Was it not to refresh the mind of man
After his studies or his usual pain ?
Then give me leave to read philosophy,
And, while I pause, serve in your harmony.

HORTENSIO. Sirrah, I will not bear these braves of thine.

BIANCA. Why, gentlemen, you do me double wrong,
To strive for that which resteth in my choice :
I am no breeching scholar in the schools ;
I'll not be tied to hours nor 'pointed times,
But learn my lessons as I please myself.
And, to cut off all strife, here sit we down :
Take you your instrument, play you the whiles ;
His lecture will be done ere you have tuned.
Where left we last ?

Bianca resumes her Latin studies with Lucentio, who mingles courtship with her studies and reveals who he is, while Hortensio tunes his instrument for a music lesson. Hortensio pleads his cause under cover of the music lesson. Each is watchfully jealous of the other. A servant enters.

SERVANT. Mistress, your father prays you leave your books
And help to dress your sister's chamber up :
You know tomorrow is the wedding-day.

BIANCA. Farewell, sweet masters both ; I must be gone.

Scene 2—Baptista's House

Baptista with his daughters, Lucentio, Tranio, and Gremio

BAPTISTA. Signior Lucentio, this is the 'pointed day
That Katharine and Petruchio should be married,
And yet we hear not of our son-in-law.
What will be said ? What mockery will it be,
To want the bridegroom when the priest attends
To speak the ceremonial rites of marriage !

KATHARINA. No shame but mine : I must, forsooth, be forced
To give my hand opposed against my heart
Unto a mad-brain rudesby full of spleen,
Who wooed in haste and means to wed at leisure.
I told you, I, he was a frantic fool,
Hiding his bitter jests in blunt behaviour :
And, to be noted for a merry man,
He'll woo a thousand, 'point the day of marriage,
Make feasts, invite friends, and proclaim the banns,
Yet never means to wed where he hath wooed.
Now must the world point at poor Katharine,
And say, *Lo, there is mad Petruchio's wife,*
If it would please him come and marry her !

TRANIO. Patience, good Katharine, and Baptista too.
Upon my life, Petruchio means but well,
Whatever fortune stays him from his word :
Though he be blunt, I know him passing wise ;
Though he be merry, yet withal he's honest.

KATHARINA. Would Katharine had never seen him though !

She goes out weeping, followed by all but her father

BAPTISTA. Go, girl; I cannot blame thee now to weep;
For such an injury would vex a very saint,
Much more a shrew of thy impatient humour.

BIONDELLO *(entering)*. Master, master! news, old news, and such news as you never heard of!

BAPTISTA. Is it new and old too? How may that be?

BIONDELLO. Why, Petruchio is coming in a new hat and an old jerkin, a pair of old breeches thrice turned, a pair of boots that have been candle-cases, one buckled, another laced, an old rusty sword ta'en out of the town-armoury, with a broken hilt; his horse hipped with an old mothy saddle.

BAPTISTA. Who comes with him?

BIONDELLO. O, sir, his lackey, for all the world caparisoned like the horse; with a linen stock on one leg and a kersey boot-hose on the other, gartered with a red and blue list; an old hat; a very monster in apparel, and not like a Christian footboy or a gentleman's lackey.

TRANIO. Tis some odd humour pricks him to this fashion;
Yet oftentimes he goes but mean-apparelled.

BAPTISTA. I am glad he's come, howsoe'er he comes.

PETRUCHIO *(approaching with Grumio)*. Come, where be these gallants? Who's at home?

BAPTISTA. You are welcome, sir.

PETRUCHIO. And yet I come not well.

TRANIO. Not so well apparelled as I wish you were.

PETRUCHIO. But where is Kate? Where is my lovely bride?
How does my father? Gentles, methinks you frown:
And wherefore gaze this goodly company,
As if they saw some wondrous monument,
Some comet or unusual prodigy?

BAPTISTA. Why, sir, you know this is your wedding-day:
First were we sad, fearing you would not come;
Now sadder, that you come so unprovided.
Fie, doff this habit, shame to your estate,
An eye-sore to our solemn festival!

TRANIO. And tell us what occasion of import
Hath all so long detained you from your wife,
And sent you hither so unlike yourself.

PETRUCHIO. Tedious it were to tell, and harsh to hear:
Sufficeth, I am come to keep my word,
Though in some part enforcèd to digress;
Which, at more leisure, I will so excuse
As you shall well be satisfied withal.
But where is Kate? I stay too long from her:
The morning wears, tis time we were at church.

TRANIO. See not your bride in these unreverent robes :
Go to my chamber ; put on clothes of mine.

PETRUCHIO. Not I, believe me : thus I'll visit her.

BAPTISTA. But thus, I trust, you will not marry her.

PETRUCHIO. Good sooth, even thus ; therefore ha' done with words :
To me she's married, not unto my clothes.
But what a fool am I to chat with you,
When I should bid good-morrow to my bride,
And seal the title with a lovely kiss ! *(He goes)*

TRANIO. He hath some meaning in his mad attire :
We will persuade him, be it possible,
To put on better ere he go to church.

BAPTISTA. I'll after him, and see the event of this.

Enter Gremio, and Baptista returning from the wedding

TRANIO. Signior Gremio, came you from the church ?

GREMIO. As willingly as e'er I came from school.

TRANIO. And is the bride and bridegroom coming home ?

GREMIO. A bridegroom say you ? tis a groom indeed,
A grumbling groom, and that the girl shall find.

TRANIO. Curster than she ? why, tis impossible.

GREMIO. Tut, she's a lamb, a dove, a fool to him !
I'll tell you, Sir Lucentio : when the priest
Should ask if Katharine should be his wife
He swore so loud that, all-amazed, the priest let fall the book ;
And, as he stooped again to take it up,
The mad-brained bridegroom took him such a cuff
That down fell priest and book and book and priest.

TRANIO. What said the wench when he rose again ?

GREMIO. Trembled and shook ; for why, he stamped and swore,
As if the vicar meant to cozen him.
But after many ceremonies done
He calls for wine : *A health !* quoth he, as if
He had been aboard, carousing to his mates
After a storm ; quaffed off the muscadel
And threw the sops all in the sexton's face.
This done, he took the bride about the neck
And kissed her lips with such a clamorous smack
That at the parting all the church did echo :
And I, seeing this, came thence for very shame ;
And after me, I know, the rout is coming.
Such a mad marriage never was before :
Hark, hark ! I hear the minstrels play.

Music plays, while Petruchio, Katharina, Baptista, and others enter

PETRUCHIO. Gentlemen and friends, I thank you for your pains:
I know you think to dine with me today,
And have prepared great store of wedding cheer;
But so it is, my haste doth call me hence,
And therefore here I mean to take my leave.

BAPTISTA. Is 't possible you will away tonight?

PETRUCHIO. I must away today, before night come:
Make it no wonder; if you knew my business
You would entreat me rather go than stay.
And, honest company, I thank you all,
That have beheld me give away myself
To this most patient, sweet, and virtuous wife:
Dine with my father, drink a health to me;
For I must hence; and farewell to you all.

TRANIO. Let us entreat you stay till after dinner.

PETRUCHIO. It may not be.

GREMIO. Let me entreat you.

PETRUCHIO. It cannot be.

KATHARINA. Let me entreat you.

PETRUCHIO. I am content.

KATHARINA. Are you content to stay?

PETRUCHIO. I am content you shall entreat me stay;
But yet not stay, entreat me how you can.

KATHARINA. Now, if you love me, stay.

PETRUCHIO. Grumio, my horse.

KATHARINA. Nay, then, do what thou canst, I will not go today;
No, nor tomorrow, not till I please myself.
The door is open, sir; there lies your way.
You may be jogging whiles your boots are green;
For me, I'll not be gone till I please myself:
Tis like you'll prove a jolly surly groom,
That take it on you at the first so roundly.

PETRUCHIO. O Kate, content thee; prithee, be not angry.

KATHARINA. I will be angry: what hast thou to do?
Father, be quiet: he shall stay my leisure.
Gentlemen, forward to the bridal dinner:
I see a woman may be made a fool,
If she had not a spirit to resist.

PETRUCHIO. They shall go forward, Kate, at thy command.
Obey the bride, you that attend on her;
Go to the feast, revel and domineer,
Be mad and merry, or go hang yourselves:
But for my bonny Kate, she must with me.
Nay, look not big, nor stamp, nor stare, nor fret;

I will be master of what is mine own:
She is my goods, my chattels; she is my house,
My household stuff, my field, my barn,
My horse, my ox, my ass, my anything;
And here she stands, touch her whoever dare.
Fear not, sweet wench, they shall not touch thee, Kate:
I'll buckler thee against a million. *(They go)*

BAPTISTA. Nay, let them go, a couple of quiet ones.

GREMIO. Went they not quickly I should die with laughing.

TRANIO. Of all mad matches never was the like.

LUCENTIO. Mistress, what's your opinion of your sister?

BIANCA. That, being mad herself, she's madly mated.

GREMIO. I warrant him, Petruchio is Kated.

BAPTISTA. Neighbours and friends, though bride and bridegroom wants
For to supply the places at the table,
You know there wants no junkets at the feast.
Lucentio, you shall supply the bridegroom's place;
And let Bianca take her sister's room.

TRANIO. Shall sweet Bianca practise how to bride it?

BAPTISTA. She shall, Lucentio. Come, gentlemen, let's go.

ACT 4

Scene 1—Petruchio's Country House

GRUMIO. Fie, fie on all tired jades, on all mad masters and all foul ways! Was ever man so beaten? Was ever man so rayed? Was ever man so weary? I am sent before to make a fire. Holla, ho! Curtis.

CURTIS. Who is that calls so coldly?

GRUMIO. A piece of ice: if thou doubt it thou mayst slide from my shoulder to my heel with no greater a run but my head and my neck. A fire, good Curtis.

CURTIS. Is my master and his wife coming, Grumio?

GRUMIO. O, ay, Curtis, ay: and therefore fire; cast on no water.

CURTIS. Is she so hot a shrew as she's reported?

GRUMIO. She was, good Curtis, before this frost: but, thou knowest, winter tames man, woman, and beast, for it hath tamed my old master and my new mistress and myself, fellow Curtis. But wilt thou make a fire, or shall I complain on thee to our mistress, whose hand thou shalt soon feel, to thy cold comfort, for being slow?

CURTIS. I prithee, good Grumio, tell me, how goes the world?

GRUMIO. A cold world, Curtis, in every office but thine; and therefore fire: do thy duty, for my master and mistress are almost frozen to death.

CURTIS. There's fire ready; and therefore, good Grumio, news.

GRUMIO. Where's the cook? Is supper ready, the house trimmed, rushes strewed, cobwebs swept; the serving-men in their new fustian, their white stockings, and every officer his wedding-garment on? Be the jacks fair within, the jills fair without, the carpets laid, and everything in order?

CURTIS. All ready; and therefore, I pray thee, news.

GRUMIO. My horse is tired, my master and mistress fallen out. But what talk I of this? Call forth Nathaniel, Joseph, Nicholas, Philip, Walter, Sugarsop, and the rest: let their heads be sleekly combed, their blue coats brushed, and their garters of an indifferent knit: let them curtsey with their left legs and not presume to touch a hair of my master's horse-tail till they kiss their hands. Are they all ready?

CURTIS. They are.

GRUMIO. Call them forth. *(The servants enter)*

NATHANIEL. Welcome home, Grumio!

PHILIP. How now, Grumio!

JOSEPH. What, Grumio!

NICHOLAS. Fellow Grumio!

NATHANIEL. How now, old lad?

GRUMIO. Welcome, you; how now, you; what, you; fellow, you; and thus much for greeting. Now, my spruce companions, is all ready, and all things neat?

NATHANIEL. All things are ready. How near is our master?

GRUMIO. E'en at hand, alighted by this; and therefore be not— Silence! I hear my master.

PETRUCHIO. Where be these knaves? What, no man at door
To hold my stirrup nor to take my horse!
Where is Nathaniel, Gregory, Philip?

ALL SERVANTS. Here, here, sir: here, sir.

PETRUCHIO. Here, sir! here, sir! here, sir! here, sir!
You logger-headed and unpolished grooms!
What, no attendance? no regard? no duty?
Where is the foolish knave I sent before?

GRUMIO. Here, sir; as foolish as I was before.

PETRUCHIO. You peasant swain! you malt-horse drudge!
Did I not bid thee meet me in the park,
And bring along these rascal knaves with thee?

GRUMIO. Nathaniel's coat, sir, was not fully made,
And Gabriel's pumps were all unpinked i' the heel;
There was no link to colour Peter's hat,
And Walter's dagger was not come from sheathing:
There were none fine but Adam, Ralph, and Gregory;

The rest were ragged, old, and beggarly;
Yet, as they are, here are they come to meet you.

PETRUCHIO. Go, rascals, go, and fetch my supper in.
Sit down, Kate, and welcome. Good, sweet Kate, be merry.

The servants bring in food

(To servants) Off with my boots, you rogues! you villains, when?
Out, you rogue! you pluck my foot awry:
Take that, and mend the plucking off the other *(striking him)*.
Be merry, Kate. Some water, here; what, ho!
Where's my spaniel Troilus? Sirrah, get you hence,
And bid my cousin Ferdinand come hither:
One, Kate, that you must kiss, and be acquainted with.
Where are my slippers? Shall I have some water?
Come, Kate, and wash, and welcome heartily.
You villain; will you let it fall? *(striking him)*.

KATHARINA. Patience, I pray you; 'twas a fault unwilling.

PETRUCHIO. A beetle-headed, flap-eared knave!
Come, Kate, sit down; I know you have a stomach.
Will you give thanks, sweet Kate; or else shall I?
What's this? Tis burnt; and so is all the meat.
What dogs are these! Where is the rascal cook?
How durst you, villains, bring it from the dresser,
And serve it thus to me that love it not?
There, take it to you, trenchers, cups, and all:
You heedless joltheads and unmannered slaves!

He throws the things at them

What, do you grumble? I'll be with you straight.

KATHARINA. I pray you, husband, be not so disquiet:
The meat was well, if you were so contented.

PETRUCHIO. I tell thee, Kate, 'twas burnt and dried away;
And I expressly am forbid to touch it,
For it engenders choler, planteth anger;
And better 'twere that both of us did fast
Than feed it with such over-roasted flesh.
Be patient; tomorrow 't shall be mended,
And, for this night, we'll fast for company:
Come, I will bring thee to thy bridal chamber.

They go, and the servants enter

NATHANIEL. Peter, didst ever see the like?

PETER. He kills her in her own humour.

GRUMIO. Where is he?

CURTIS. In her chamber, making a sermon to her;
And rails, and swears, and rates, that she, poor soul,
Knows not which way to stand, to look, to speak,

And sits as one new-risen from a dream.
Away, away! for he is coming hither. *(They go)*

PETRUCHIO *(to himself)*. Thus have I politicly begun my reign,
And tis my hope to end successfully.
My falcon now is sharp and passing empty,
And till she stoop she must not be full-gorged.
She ate no meat today, nor none shall eat;
Last night she slept not, nor tonight she shall not;
As with the meat, some undeservèd fault
I'll find about the making of the bed;
And here I'll fling the pillow, there the bolster,
This way the coverlet, another way the sheets:
Ay, and amid this hurly I intend
That all is done in reverent care of her;
And in conclusion she shall watch all night:
And if she chance to nod I'll rail and brawl
And with the clamour keep her still awake.
This is a way to kill a wife with kindness;
And thus I'll curb her mad and headstrong humour.
He that knows better how to tame a shrew,
Now let him speak: tis charity to show.

Scene 2—Before Baptista's House: Tranio and Hortensio

TRANIO. Is 't possible, friend Licio, that Mistress Bianca
Doth fancy any other but Lucentio?
I tell you, sir, she bears me fair in hand.

HORTENSIO. Sir, to satisfy you in what I have said,
Stand by and mark the manner of his teaching.

Bianca and Lucentio enter

LUCENTIO. Now, mistress, profit you in what you read?

BIANCA. What, master, read you? First resolve me that.

LUCENTIO. I read that I profess, the Art to Love.

BIANCA. And may you prove, sir, master of your art!

LUCENTIO. While you, sweet dear, prove mistress of my heart!

HORTENSIO. Quick proceeders, marry! Now, tell me, I pray,
You that durst swear that your mistress Bianca
Loved none in the world so well as Lucentio.

TRANIO. O despiteful love! unconstant womankind!
I tell thee, Licio, this is wonderful.

HORTENSIO. Mistake no more: I am not Licio,
Nor a musician, as I seem to be;
But one that scorn to live in this disguise,
For such a one as leaves a gentleman,
And makes a god of such a cullion:
Know, sir, that I am called Hortensio.

TRANIO. Signior Hortensio, I have often heard
Of your entire affection to Bianca;
And, since mine eyes are witness of her lightness,
I will with you, if you be so contented,
Forswear Bianca and her love for ever.

HORTENSIO. See how they kiss and court! Signior Lucentio,
Here is my hand, and here I firmly vow
Never to woo her more, but do forswear her,
As one unworthy all the former favours
That I have fondly flattered her withal.

TRANIO. And here I take the like unfeignèd oath
Never to marry with her though she would entreat.

HORTENSIO. Would all the world but he had quite forsworn!
For me, that I may surely keep mine oath,
I will be married to a wealthy widow
Ere three days pass, which hath as long loved me
As I have loved this proud disdainful haggard.
And so farewell, Signior Lucentio.
Kindness in women, not their beauteous looks,
Shall win my love: and so I take my leave.

BIANCA. But have you both forsworn me?

TRANIO. Mistress, we have.

Tranio arranges with a Pedant that he shall be dressed up as Vincentio, father of Lucentio, and while impersonating him shall give to Baptista the assurance he needs respecting Bianca's marriage dower.

Scene 3—A Room in Petruchio's House: Katharina and Grumio

GRUMIO. No, no, forsooth; I dare not for my life.

KATHARINA. The more my wrong, the more his spite appears:
What, did he marry me to famish me?
Beggars that come unto my father's door
Upon entreaty have a present alms;
If not, elsewhere they meet with charity:
But I, who never knew how to entreat,
Nor never needed that I should entreat,
Am starved for meat, giddy for lack of sleep,
With oaths kept waking and with brawling fed:
And that which spites me more than all these wants,
He does it under name of perfect love;
As who should say, if I should sleep or eat,
Twere deadly sickness or else present death.
I prithee go and get me some repast.

GRUMIO. What say you to a piece of beef and mustard?

KATHARINA. A dish that I do love to feed upon.

GRUMIO. Ay, but the mustard is too hot a little.

KATHARINA. Why then, the beef, and let the mustard rest.

GRUMIO. Nay then, I will not: you shall have the mustard,
Or else you get no beef of Grumio.

KATHARINA. Then both, or one, or anything thou wilt.

GRUMIO. Why then, the mustard without the beef.

KATHARINA. Go, get thee gone, thou false deluding slave,
That feed'st me with the very name of meat:
Sorrow on thee and all the pack of you,
That triumph thus upon my misery!
Go, get thee gone, I say.

Enter Petruchio with a dish of meat, followed by Hortensio

PETRUCHIO. How fares my Kate? What, sweeting, all amort?
Pluck up thy spirits; look cheerfully upon me.
Here, love; thou see'st how diligent I am
To dress thy meat myself and bring it thee:
I am sure, sweet Kate, this kindness merits thanks.
What, not a word? Nay, then thou lovest it not;
And all my pains is sorted to no proof.
Here, take away this dish.

KATHARINA. I pray you, let it stand.

PETRUCHIO. The poorest service is repaid with thanks;
And so shall mine, before you touch the meat.

KATHARINA. I thank you, sir.

HORTENSIO. Signior Petruchio, fie! you are to blame.
Come, Mistress Kate, I'll bear you company.

PETRUCHIO *(aside)*. Eat it up all, Hortensio, if thou lovest me.
Much good do it unto thy gentle heart!
Kate, eat apace: and now, my honey love,
Will we return unto thy father's house
And revel it as bravely as the best,
With silken coats and caps and golden rings,
With ruffs and cuffs and fardingales and things;
With scarfs and fans and double change of bravery,
With amber bracelets, beads, and all this knavery.
What, hast thou dined? The tailor stays thy leisure,
To deck thy body with his ruffling treasure.
Come, tailor, let us see these ornaments;
Lay forth the gown. *(Enter Haberdasher.)* What news with you, sir?

HABERDASHER. Here is the cap your worship did bespeak.

PETRUCHIO. Why, this was moulded on a porringer;
A velvet dish: fie, fie! tis lewd and filthy:

Why, tis a cockle or a walnut-shell,
A knack, a toy, a trick, a baby's cap:
Away with it! Come, let me have a bigger.

KATHARINA. I'll have no bigger: this doth fit the time,
And gentlewomen wear such caps as these.

PETRUCHIO. When you are gentle, you shall have one too.

KATHARINA. Why, sir, I trust I may have leave to speak,
And speak I will: I am no child, no babe:
Your betters have endured me say my mind,
And, if you cannot, best you stop your ears.
My tongue will tell the anger of my heart,
Or else my heart concealing it will break,
And, rather than it shall, I will be free
Even to the uttermost, as I please, in words.

PETRUCHIO. Why, thou say'st true; it is a paltry cap:
I love thee well, in that thou likest it not.

KATHARINA. Love me or love me not, I like the cap;
And it I will have, or I will have none. *(Haberdasher goes)*

PETRUCHIO. Thy gown? why, ay: come, tailor, let us see 't.
O mercy, God! what masquing stuff is here?
What's this? a sleeve? tis like a demi-cannon:
What, up and down, carved like an apple-tart?
Here's snip and nip and cut and slish and slash,
Like to a censer in a barber's shop:
Why, what, i' devil's name, tailor, call'st thou this?

TAILOR. You bid me make it orderly and well,
According to the fashion and the time.

PETRUCHIO. Marry, and did; but, if you be remembered,
I did not bid you mar it to the time.
Go, hop me over every kennel home,
For you shall hop without my custom, sir:
I'll none of it: hence! make your best of it.

KATHARINA. I never saw a better-fashioned gown,
More quaint, more pleasing, nor more commendable:
Belike you mean to make a puppet of me.

PETRUCHIO. Why, true: he means to make a puppet of thee.

TAILOR. She says your worship means to make a puppet of her.

PETRUCHIO. O monstrous arrogance! Thou liest, thou thread,
thou thimble,
Thou yard, three-quarters, half-yard, quarter, nail!
Braved in mine own house with a skein of thread?
Away, thou rag, thou quantity, thou remnant;
I tell thee, I, that thou hast marred her gown.

Tailor. Your worship is deceived; the gown is made
Just as my master had direction:
Grumio gave order how it should be done.

Grumio. I gave him no order; I gave him the stuff.

Tailor. But how did you desire it should be made?

Grumio. Marry, sir, with needle and thread.

Tailor. But did you not request to have it cut?

Grumio. Thou hast faced many things.

Tailor. I have.

Grumio. Face not me: thou hast braved many men; brave not me; I will neither be faced nor braved. I say unto thee, I bid thy master cut out the gown; but I did not bid him cut it to pieces.

Tailor. Why, here is the note of the fashion to testify.

Petruchio. Read it.

Tailor *(reading)*. *A loose-bodied gown—*

Grumio. Master, if ever I said loose-bodied gown sew me in the skirts of it, and beat me to death with a bottom of brown thread: I said a gown.

Tailor *(reading)*. *With a small compassed cape—*

Grumio. I confess the cape.

Tailor. *With a trunk sleeve—*

Grumio. I confess two sleeves.

Tailor *(reading)*. *The sleeves curiously cut—*

Petruchio. Ay, there's the villainy.
Well, sir, in brief, the gown is not for me.
(Aside) Hortensio, say thou wilt see the tailor paid.
Go take it hence; be gone, and say no more.

Hortensio. Tailor, I'll pay thee for thy gown tomorrow:
Take no unkindness of his hasty words:
Away! I say; commend me to thy master. *(Tailor goes)*

Petruchio. Well, come, my Kate; we will unto your father's,
Even in these honest mean habiliments:
Our purses shall be proud, our garments poor;
For tis the mind that makes the body rich;
And as the sun breaks through the darkest clouds,
So honour peereth in the meanest habit.
What, is the jay more precious than the lark
Because his feathers are more beautiful?
Or is the adder better than the eel
Because his painted skin contents the eye?
O, no, good Kate; neither art thou the worse
For this poor furniture and mean array.
If thou account'st it shame, lay it on me,

And therefore frolic: we will hence forthwith,
To feast and sport us at thy father's house.
Go, call my men, and let us straight to him;
And bring our horses unto Long-lane end;
There will we mount, and thither walk on foot.
Let's see; I think tis now some seven o'clock,
And well we may come there by dinner-time.

KATHARINA. I dare assure you, sir, tis almost two;
And 'twill be supper-time ere you come there.

PETRUCHIO. It shall be seven ere I go to horse:
Look, what I speak, or do, or think to do,
You are still crossing it. Sirs, let 't alone:
I will not go today; and ere I do
It shall be what o'clock I say it is.

HORTENSIO *(aside)*. Why, so this gallant will command the sun.

In Scene 4 of Act 4 the Pedant, impersonating Vincentio, is introduced satisfactorily to Baptista, who accepts his guarantee of Lucentio's dower (believing still that Tranio is Lucentio); but to make sure of Bianca the real Lucentio has arranged with her that he and she shall at once be privately married. Meantime the Pedant is busy in Tranio's house (that is, Lucentio's) making legal arrangements about the money.

Scene 5—On a Public Road

Petruchio and Katharina, with Hortensio and Servants

PETRUCHIO. Come on, i' God's name; once more toward our father's.
Good Lord, how bright and goodly shines the moon!

KATHARINA. The moon! the sun: it is not moonlight now.

PETRUCHIO. I say it is the moon that shines so bright.

KATHARINA. I know it is the sun that shines so bright.

PETRUCHIO. Now, by my mother's son, and that's myself,
It shall be moon, or star, or what I list,
Or ere I journey to your father's house.
Go on, and fetch our horses back again.
Evermore crossed and crossed; nothing but crossed!

HORTENSIO. Say as he says, or we shall never go.

KATHARINA. Forward, I pray, since we have come so far,
And be it moon, or sun, or what you please:
An if you please to call it a rush-candle,
Henceforth I vow it shall be so for me.

PETRUCHIO. I say it is the moon.

KATHARINA. I know it is the moon.

PETRUCHIO. Nay, then you lie: it is the blessed sun.

KATHARINA. Then, God be blessed, it is the blessed sun:
What you will have it named, even that it is;
And so it shall be so for Katharine.

HORTENSIO. Petruchio, go thy ways; the field is won.

PETRUCHIO. But, soft, company is coming here. *(Vincentio enters)*
Good-morrow, gentle mistress *(to Vincentio)*: where away?
Tell me, sweet Kate, and tell me truly too,
Hast thou beheld a fresher gentlewoman?
Such war of white and red within her cheeks!
What stars do spangle heaven with such beauty
As those two eyes become that heavenly face?
Fair lovely maid, once more good day to thee.
Sweet Kate, embrace her for her beauty's sake.

HORTENSIO. A' will make the man mad, to make a woman of him.

KATHARINA. Young budding virgin, fair and fresh and sweet,
Whither away, or where is thy abode?
Happy the parents of so fair a child.

PETRUCHIO. Why, how now, Kate! I hope thou art not mad:
This is a man, old, wrinkled, faded, withered,
And not a maiden, as thou say'st he is.

KATHARINA. Pardon, old father, my mistaking eyes,
That have been so bedazzled with the sun
That everything I look on seemeth green:
Now I perceive thou art a reverend father;
Pardon, I pray thee, for my mad mistaking.

PETRUCHIO. Do, good old grandsire; and withal make known
Which way thou travellest: if along with us
We shall be joyful of thy company.

VINCENTIO. Fair sir, and you my merry mistress,
That with your strange encounter much amazèd me,
My name is called Vincentio; my dwelling Pisa;
And bound I am to Padua; there to visit
A son of mine, which long I have not seen.

PETRUCHIO. What is his name?

VINCENTIO. Lucentio, gentle sir.

PETRUCHIO. Happily met; the happier for thy son.
And now by law, as well as reverend age,
I may entitle thee my loving father:
The sister to my wife, this gentlewoman,
Thy son by this hath married. Wonder not,
Nor be not grieved: she is of good esteem,
Her dowry wealthy, and of worthy birth;
Beside, so qualified as may beseem
The spouse of any noble gentleman.
Let me embrace with old Vincentio,

And wander we to see thy honest son,
Who will of thy arrival be full joyous.

VINCENTIO. But is this true ? or is it else your pleasure,
Like pleasant travellers, to break a jest
Upon the company you overtake ?

HORTENSIO. I do assure thee, father, so it is.

PETRUCHIO. Come, go along, and see the truth hereof ;
For our first merriment hath made thee jealous.

ACT 5

Scene 1—Before Lucentio's House

The arrival of Vincentio with Petruchio and Kate before the house of Lucentio in Padua leads to a riot of merry confusion. Lucentio and Bianca, accompanied by Biondello, have stolen away to be married. Vincentio demands his son ; the Pedant declares that he is Vincentio and father of Lucentio ; Biondello, returning from the wedding, repudiates Vincentio and is beaten for his audacity. Next Tranio, still acting as Lucentio, becomes involved, and the real Vincentio, seeing himself and his son personated, becomes so violent that Baptista thinks him a lunatic or an impostor, and calls for the police. At this moment Lucentio and Bianca appear and confront their lawful parents. Father and son greet each other, whereupon the other agents in the plot hastily run away. The two fathers accept the situation, vowing punishment, but all proceed happily towards the wedding feast, and the scene closes with the complete surrender of Katharina to Petruchio.

KATHARINA. Husband, let's follow to see the end of this ado.

PETRUCHIO. First kiss me, Kate, and we will.

KATHARINA. What, in the midst of the street ?

PETRUCHIO. What, art thou ashamed of me ?

KATHARINA. No, sir, God forbid ; but ashamed to kiss.

PETRUCHIO. Why, then let's home again. Come, sirrah, let's away.

KATHARINA. Nay, I will give thee a kiss ; now pray thee, love, stay.

PETRUCHIO. Is not this well ? Come, my sweet Kate :
Better once than never, for never too late.

Scene 2—A Banquet at Lucentio's House

LUCENTIO. At last, though long, our jarring notes agree :
And time it is, when raging war is done,
To smile at scapes and perils overblown.
My fair Bianca, bid my father welcome,
While I with selfsame kindness welcome thine.
Brother Petruchio, sister Katharina,
And thou, Hortensio, with thy loving widow,
Feast with the best, and welcome to my house.
Pray you, sit down,
For now we sit to chat as well as eat.

PETRUCHIO. Nothing but sit and sit, and eat and eat!

BAPTISTA. Padua affords this kindness, son Petruchio.

PETRUCHIO. Padua affords nothing but what is kind.

HORTENSIO. For both our sakes I would that word were true.

PETRUCHIO. Now, for my life, Hortensio fears his widow.

WIDOW. Then never trust me if I be afeard.

PETRUCHIO. You are very sensible, and yet you miss my sense:
I mean Hortensio is afeard of you.

WIDOW. He that is giddy thinks the world turns round.

KATHARINA. *He that is giddy thinks the world turns round:*
I pray you, tell me what you meant by that.

WIDOW. Your husband, being troubled with a shrew,
Measures my husband's sorrow by his woe. *(The ladies go)*

BAPTISTA. In good sadness, son Petruchio,
I think thou hast the veriest shrew of all.

PETRUCHIO. Well, I say No: and therefore for assurance
Let's each one send unto his wife;
And he whose wife is most obedient
To come at first when he doth send for her,
Shall win the wager which we will propose.

HORTENSIO. Content. What is the wager?

LUCENTIO. Twenty crowns.

PETRUCHIO. Twenty crowns!
I'll venture so much of my hawk or hound,
But twenty times so much upon my wife.

LUCENTIO. A hundred then.

HORTENSIO. Content.

PETRUCHIO. A match! tis done.

HORTENSIO. Who shall begin?

LUCENTIO. That will I.
Go, Biondello, bid your mistress come to me.

BIONDELLO. I go.

BAPTISTA. Son, I'll be your half Bianca comes.

LUCENTIO. I'll have no halves; I'll bear it all myself.

BIONDELLO *(returning)*. Sir, my mistress sends you word
That she is busy and she cannot come.

PETRUCHIO. How! she is busy and she cannot come!
Is that an answer?

GREMIO. Ay, and a kind one too:
Pray God, sir, your wife send you not a worse.

PETRUCHIO. I hope, better.

HORTENSIO. Sirrah Biondello, go and entreat my wife
To come to me forthwith.

PETRUCHIO. O, ho! entreat her!
Nay, then she must needs come.

HORTENSIO. I am afraid, sir, do what you can, yours will not be entreated.

BIONDELLO *(returning)*. She says you have some goodly jest in hand:
She will not come; she bids you come to her.

PETRUCHIO. Worse and worse; she will not come!
Sirrah Grumio, go to your mistress;
Say I command her come to me.

HORTENSIO. I know her answer. She will not.

PETRUCHIO. The fouler fortune mine, and there an end.

BAPTISTA. Now, by my holidame, here comes Katharina!

KATHARINA. What is your will, sir, that you send for me?

PETRUCHIO. Where is your sister, and Hortensio's wife?

KATHARINA. They sit conferring by the parlour fire.

PETRUCHIO. Go, fetch them hither: if they deny to come,
Swinge me them soundly forth unto their husbands:
Away, I say, and bring them hither straight. *(She goes meekly)*

LUCENTIO. Here is a wonder, if you talk of a wonder.

HORTENSIO. And so it is: I wonder what it bodes.

PETRUCHIO. Marry, peace it bodes, and love and quiet life,
An awful rule and right supremacy;
And, to be short, what not that's sweet and happy?

BAPTISTA. Now, fair befal thee, good Petruchio!
The wager thou hast won; and I will add
Unto their losses twenty thousand crowns,
Another dowry to another daughter,
For she is changed, as she had never been.

PETRUCHIO. Nay, I will win my wager better yet
And show more sign of her obedience,
Her new-built virtue and obedience.
See where she comes, and brings your froward wives
As prisoners to her womanly persuasion.

Enter Katharina, Bianca, and Widow

Katharine, that cap of yours becomes you not:
Off with that bauble, throw it under-foot.

WIDOW. Lord, let me never have a cause to sigh,
Till I be brought to such a silly pass!

BIANCA. Fie! what a foolish duty call you this?

Lucentio. I would your duty were as foolish too:
The wisdom of your duty, fair Bianca,
Hath cost me a hundred crowns since supper-time.

Bianca. The more fool you, for laying on my duty.

Petruchio. Katharine, I charge thee, tell these headstrong women
What duty they do owe their lords and husbands.

Widow. Come, come, you're mocking: we will have no telling.

Petruchio. Come on, I say; and first begin with her.

Katharina. Fie, fie! unknit that threatening unkind brow,
And dart not scornful glances from those eyes
To wound thy lord, thy king, thy governor:
It blots thy beauty as frosts do bite the meads,
Confounds thy fame as whirlwinds shake fair buds,
And in no sense is meet or amiable.
A woman moved is like a fountain troubled,
Muddy, ill-seeming, thick, bereft of beauty;
And while it is so none so dry or thirsty
Will deign to sip or touch one drop of it.
Thy husband is thy lord, thy life, thy keeper,
Thy head, thy sovereign; one that cares for thee,
And for thy maintenance commits his body
To painful labour both by sea and land,
To watch the night in storms, the day in cold,
Whilst thou liest warm at home, secure and safe;
And craves no other tribute at thy hands
But love, fair looks, and true obedience;
Too little payment for so great a debt.
Such duty as the subject owes the prince
Even such a woman oweth to her husband;
I am ashamed that women are so simple
To offer war where they should kneel for peace,
Or seek for rule, supremacy, and sway,
When they are bound to serve, love, and obey.
Why are our bodies soft and weak and smooth,
Unapt to toil and trouble in the world,
But that our soft conditions and our hearts
Should well agree with our external parts?
Come, come, you froward and unable worms!
My mind hath been as big as one of yours,
My heart as great, my reason haply more,
To bandy word for word and frown for frown;
But now I see our lances are but straws,
Our strength as weak, our weakness past compare,
That seeming to be most which we indeed least are.

Petruchio. Why, there's a wench! Come on, and kiss me, Kate.

The Story of Henry the Eighth

It pleased Shakespeare to please the great Elizabeth by setting her father in a piece of splendid pageantry, but not even the glory that Shakespeare sets about the throne can hide the cruelty of our Bluebeard king. He took wives when he wanted them, and killed them when he tired of them.

We see it all beginning here, for this play centres round the noble figure of Queen Katharine. Through it runs her passionate plea for justice, but it runs in vain, for pitted against her is the soulless scheming of two of the most astonishing men who have moved across the political stage of our country.

Nothing could stand in the way of this most selfish king. Nothing could stand in the way of this most selfish cardinal, the Ipswich butcher's son who rose to a glory that almost dimmed the King's. It is the clashing of these forces—the great wrong done to Katharine and her noble vindication, the masterly hypocrisy of the King and the ambitious self-seeking of Wolsey—that gives Shakespeare his opportunity in this play which is not entirely his.

It belongs to a group of plays which Shakespeare never finished, but handed over to the company he was connected with, who handed them to John Fletcher to finish. So it comes about that the play is unequal; with scenes loosely connected over a wide stretch of time. The points of concentration, into which Shakespeare puts some of his greatest speeches, are the trial of Katharine and the fall of Wolsey.

Every schoolboy knows how Wolsey fell: is it not all in one of the most famous orations ever recited in a schoolroom? This cardinal's ambition has carried him too far; the proud man's reign is over. He has served a king made of the same uncertain stuff as he himself, and there is something in the final scene which reminds us of the last meeting of another King Henry with Falstaff.

Henry the Eighth goes his way; he has his Anne Boleyn and nothing matters: Wolsey, who once trod the ways of glory, goes out of his great world, his robe "and his integrity to Heaven" all he dare call his own. Somewhere at an abbey far away they took him in:

> An old man, broken with the storms of State,
> Is come to lay his weary bones among ye;
> Give him a little earth for charity!

So he died. And so, in another quiet, far-off place, another died. Calling for music while she sat meditating "on that celestial harmony I go to," Queen Katharine sends her last message to the Court:

> Remember me in all humility unto his highness,
> Say his long trouble now is passing
> Out of this world.

Henry the Eighth and Anne Boleyn lived on—she, at any rate, not dreaming of what was soon to come.

THE PLAYERS

King Henry the Eighth, before and after his second marriage.

Cardinal Wolsey, just before and after his fall from power.

Cardinal Campeius, sent from Rome to act with Wolsey.

Capucius, Ambassador from the Emperor Charles the Fifth.

Cranmer, Archbishop of Canterbury, friendly to Anne Boleyn.

Dukes of Norfolk and Suffolk, noblemen at Court.

Earl of Surrey, a prominent courtier.

Duke of Buckingham, an opponent of Wolsey. The Cardinal sweeps him from his path.

The Lord Chamberlain and the Lord Chancellor.

Gardiner, Bishop of Winchester, an opponent of Cranmer.

The Bishop of Lincoln.

Lords Abergavenny and Sands, opponents of Wolsey.

Sir Henry Guildford and Sir Thomas Lovell, courtiers.

Sir Anthony Denny and Sir Nicholas Vaux, courtiers.

Thomas Cromwell, the faithful servant of Wolsey, and of the King afterwards.

Griffith, gentleman-usher to Queen Katharine, faithful and devoted to her.

Surveyor to the Duke of Buckingham.

Three Gentlemen about the Court who retail its news.

Sergeant-at-Arms, a doorkeeper, a porter, a crier, and a page.

Queen Katharine, the faithful but wronged wife of the King.

Anne Boleyn, Katharine's Maid of Honour, afterwards Queen.

An Old Lady, familiar with Anne Boleyn before her marriage.

Patience, a woman attending Queen Katharine.

Brandon, lords, scribes, officers, guards, attendants.

SCENES—London, Westminster, and Kimbolton

King Henry the Eighth

THE PROLOGUE

I COME no more to make you laugh: things now,
That bear a weighty and a serious brow,
Sad, high, and working, full of state and woe,
Such noble scenes as draw the eye to flow,
We now present. Those that can pity, here
May, if they think it well, let fall a tear;
The subject will deserve it. Such as give
Their money out of hope they may believe,
May here find truth too. Those that come to see
Only a show or two, and so agree
The play may pass, if they be still and willing,
I'll undertake may see away their shilling
Richly in two short hours. Only they
That come to hear a merry vulgar play,
A noise of targets, or to see a fellow
In a long motley coat guarded with yellow,
Will be deceived.
Be sad, as we would make ye: think ye see
The very persons of our noble story
As they were living; think you see them great,
And followed with the general throng and sweat
Of thousand friends; then, in a moment, see
How soon this mightiness meets misery:
And, if you can be merry then, I'll say
A man may weep upon his wedding day.

ACT 1

Scene 1—An Outer Chamber in the Palace

The Duke of Norfolk, the Duke of Buckingham, and Lord Abergavenny discuss the meeting of the English and French Kings on the Field of the Cloth of Gold, and the part Wolsey played there. Buckingham is scornful of the Cardinal, and Norfolk warns him to beware, for the Cardinal is malicious as well as powerful. Buckingham says he will declare Wolsey's treason to the King.

NORFOLK. Say not treasonous.

BUCKINGHAM. To the king I'll say 't.

Brandon with the Sergeant-at-Arms here enters

SERGEANT. My lord the Duke of Buckingham, and Earl
Of Hereford, Stafford, and Northampton, I
Arrest thee of high treason, in the name
Of our most sovereign king.

BUCKINGHAM. Lo, you, my lord,
The net has fallen upon me!

BRANDON. I am sorry
To see you ta'en from liberty, to look on
The business present: tis his highness' pleasure
You shall to the Tower.

BUCKINGHAM. It will help me nothing to plead mine innocence;
The will of heaven be done.
O my Lord Abergavenny, fare you well!

BRANDON. Nay, he must bear you company. The king
Is pleased you shall to the Tower, till you know
How he determines further.

ABERGAVENNY. As the duke said, the will of heaven be done.

BRANDON. Here is a warrant from
The king to attach Lord Montacute; and the bodies
Of the duke's confessor, John de la Car,
One Gilbert Peck, his chancellor—

BUCKINGHAM. So, so; these are the limbs o' the plot: no more, I hope.

BRANDON. A monk o' the Chartreux.

BUCKINGHAM. O, Nicholas Hopkins?

BRANDON. He.

BUCKINGHAM. My surveyor is false; the o'er-great cardinal
Hath showed him gold; my life is spanned already:
I am the shadow of poor Buckingham,
Whose figure even this instant cloud puts on,
By darkening my clear sun. My lord, farewell.

Scene 2—The Council Chamber

The King enters, leaning on the Cardinal's shoulder

KING. My life itself, and the best heart of it,
Thanks you for this great care: I stood i' the level
Of a full-charged confederacy, and give thanks
To you that choked it. Let be called before us
That gentleman of Buckingham's; in person
I'll hear him his confessions justify;
And point by point the treasons of his master
He shall again relate.

A noise within, crying Room for the Queen, who enters and kneels. The King rises, kisses her, and places her by him.

QUEEN KATHARINE. Nay, we must longer kneel: I am a suitor.

KING. Arise, and take place by us: half your suit
Never name to us; you have half our power:
The other moiety, ere you ask, is given;
Repeat your will and take it.

QUEEN KATHARINE. Thank your majesty.
That you would love yourself, and in that love
Not unconsidered leave your honour, nor
The dignity of your office, is the point
Of my petition.

KING. Lady mine, proceed.

QUEEN KATHARINE. I am solicited that your subjects
Are in great grievance: there have been commissions
Sent down among 'em which hath flawed the heart
Of all their loyalties: wherein, although,
My good lord cardinal, they vent reproaches
Most bitterly on you, as putter on
Of these exactions, yet the king our master
(Whose honour heaven shield from soil!), even he escapes not
Language unmannerly, yea, such which breaks
The sides of loyalty, and almost appears
In loud rebellion.

NORFOLK. Not almost appears,
It doth appear; for, upon these taxations,
The clothiers all, not able to maintain
The many to them longing, have put off
The spinsters, carders, fullers, weavers, who,
Unfit for other life, compelled by hunger
And lack of other means, are all in uproar,
And danger serves among them.

KING. Taxation!
Wherein? and what taxation? My lord cardinal,
You that are blamed for it alike with us,
Know you of this taxation?

WOLSEY. Please you, sir,
I know but of a single part in aught
Pertains to the State.

QUEEN KATHARINE. No, my lord,
You know no more than others; but you frame
Things that are known alike, which are not wholesome.
These exactions,
Whereof my sovereign would have note, they are
Most pestilent to the hearing; and, to bear 'em,
The back is sacrifice to the load. They say
They are devised by you; or else you suffer
Too hard an exclamation.

KING. Still exaction!
The nature of it? In what kind, let's know,
Is this exaction?

QUEEN KATHARINE. I am much too venturous
In tempting of your patience; but am boldened

Under your promised pardon. The subjects' grief
Comes through commissions, which compel from each
The sixth part of his substance, to be levied
Without delay ; and the pretence for this
Is named, your wars in France : this makes bold mouths :
Tongues spit their duties out, and cold hearts freeze
Allegiance in them ; their curses now
Live where their prayers did : and it's come to pass,
This tractable obedience is a slave
To each incensèd will. I would your highness
Would give it quick consideration, for
There is no primer business.

KING. By my life, this is against our pleasure.

WOLSEY. And for me,
I have no further gone in this than by
A single voice ; and that not passed me but
By learned approbation of the judges. If I am
Traduced by ignorant tongues, which neither know
My faculties nor person, yet will be
The chronicles of my doing, let me say
Tis but the fate of place, and the rough brake
That virtue must go through. We must not stint
Our necessary actions in the fear
To cope malicious censurers. If we stand still,
In fear our motion will be mocked or carped at,
We should take root here where we sit, or sit
State-statues only.

KING. Things done well,
And with a care, exempt themselves from fear ;
Things done without example, in their issue
Are to be feared. Have you a precedent
Of this commission ? I believe, not any.
We must not rend our subjects from our laws,
And stick them in our will. Sixth part of each ?
A trembling contribution ! Why, we take
From every tree lop, bark, and part o' the timber,
And, though we leave it with a root, thus hacked,
The air will drink the sap. To every county
Where this is questioned send our letters, with
Free pardon to each man that has denied
The force of this commission : pray, look to 't.

WOLSEY *(to the Secretary)*. A word with you.
Let there be letters writ to every shire
Of the king's grace and pardon. Let it be noised
That through our intercession this revokement
And pardon comes : I shall anon advise you.

QUEEN KATHARINE. I am sorry that the Duke of Buckingham
Is run in your displeasure.

KING. It grieves many:
The gentleman is learned, and a most rare speaker;
To nature none more bound; his training such
That he may furnish and instruct great teachers
And never seek for aid out of himself. Yet see,
When these so noble benefits shall prove
Not well disposed, the mind growing once corrupt,
They turn to vicious forms, ten times more ugly
Than ever they were fair. This man so complete,
Who was enrolled 'mongst wonders, and when we,
Almost with ravished listening, could not find
His hour of speech a minute—he, my lady,
Hath into monstrous habits put the graces
That once were his, and is become as black
As if besmeared in hell. Sit by us; you shall hear
Things to strike honour sad.

A Surveyor enters and is summoned to speak of Buckingham

Speak freely.

SURVEYOR. First, it was usual with him, every day
It would infect his speech, that if the king
Should without issue die, he'll carry it so
To make the sceptre his: these very words
I've heard him utter to his son-in-law,
Lord Abergavenny, to whom by oath he menaced
Revenge upon the cardinal.

QUEEN KATHARINE. If I know you well,
You were the duke's surveyor, and lost your office
On the complaint o' the tenants: take good heed
You charge not in your spleen a noble person
And spoil your nobler soul: I say, take heed.

SURVEYOR. On my soul, I'll speak but truth.
I told my lord the duke that 'twas dangerous for him
To ruminate on this so far, until
It forged him some design, which, being believed,
It was much like to do: he answered, *Tush,*
It can do me no damage; adding further
That, had the king in his last sickness failed,
The cardinal's and Sir Thomas Lovell's heads
Should have gone off.

KING. Ha! what, so rank? Ah ha!
There's mischief in this man. A giant traitor!

WOLSEY. Now, madam, may his highness live in freedom,
And this man out of prison?

Queen Katharine. God mend all!

King. Call him to present trial: if he may
Find mercy in the law, tis his; if none,
Let him not seek 't of us: by day and night,
He's traitor to the height.

Scenes 3 and 4

In Scene 3 the Lord Chamberlain and Lord Sands talk of the fashions that have come from France since the Kings have met, and disapprove such innovations. Scene 4 shows a masked ball at the Cardinal's mansion at which King Henry meets Anne Boleyn and is attracted by her.

ACT 2

Scene 1—A Street in Westminster

First Gentleman. Whither away so fast?

Second Gentleman. O, God save ye!
Even to the hall, to hear what shall become
Of the great Duke of Buckingham.

First Gentleman. I'll save you that labour, sir.
I'll tell you in a little. The great duke
Came to the bar; where to his accusations
He pleaded still not guilty and alleged
Many sharp reasons to defeat the law.
The king's attorney on the contrary
Urged on the examinations, proofs, confessions
Of divers witnesses; which the duke fain
Would have flung from him, but, indeed, he could not:
And so his peers, upon this evidence,
Have found him guilty of high treason. Much
He spoke, and learnedly, for life; but all
Was either pitied in him or forgotten.

Second Gentleman. After all this, how did he bear himself?

First. When he was brought again to the bar, to hear
His knell rung out, his judgment, he was stirred
With such an agony, he sweat extremely,
And something spoke in choler, ill, and hasty:
But he fell to himself again, and sweetly
In all the rest showed a most noble patience.

Second Gentleman. I do not think he fears death.

First Gentleman. Sure, he does not:
He never was so womanish; the cause
He may a little grieve at.

Second Gentleman. Certainly the cardinal is the end of this.

First Gentleman. Tis likely, by all conjectures.

Second Gentleman. All the commons
Hate him perniciously, and, o' my conscience,

Wish him ten fathom deep: this duke as much
They love and dote on; call him bounteous Buckingham,
The mirror of all courtesy—

FIRST GENTLEMAN. Stay there, sir,
And see the noble ruined man you speak of.

Buckingham is led out to execution

SECOND GENTLEMAN. Let's stand close, and behold him.

BUCKINGHAM. All good people,
You that thus far have come to pity me,
Hear what I say, and then go home and lose me.
I have this day received a traitor's judgment,
And by that name must die: yet heaven bear witness,
And if I have a conscience, let it sink me,
Even as the axe falls, if I be not faithful!
You few that loved me,
And dare be bold to weep for Buckingham,
His noble friends and fellows, whom to leave
Is only bitter to him, only dying,
Go with me, like good angels, to my end;
And, as the long divorce of steel falls on me,
Make of your prayers one sweet sacrifice,
And lift my soul to heaven. Lead on, o' God's name.

LOVELL. I do beseech your grace, for charity,
If ever any malice in your heart
Were hid against me, now to forgive me frankly.

BUCKINGHAM. Sir Thomas Lovell, I as free forgive you
As I would be forgiven: I forgive all;
There cannot be those numberless offences
Gainst me that I cannot take peace with: no black envy
Shall mark my grave. Commend me to his grace;
And, if he speak of Buckingham, pray, tell him
You met him half in heaven: my vows and prayers
Yet are the king's; and, till my soul forsake,
Shall cry for blessings on him: may he live
Longer than I have time to tell his years!
And when old time shall lead him to his end,
Goodness and he fill up one monument!

VAUX. The duke is coming: see the barge be ready;
And fit it with such furniture as suits
The greatness of his person.

BUCKINGHAM. Nay, Sir Nicholas, my state now will but mock me.
When I came hither I was lord high constable
And Duke of Buckingham; now, poor Edward Bohun:
Yet I am richer than my base accusers,
That never knew what truth meant.

My noble father, Henry of Buckingham,
Flying for succour to his servant Banister,
Being distressed, was by that wretch betrayed,
And without trial fell. I had my trial,
And, must needs say, a noble one; which makes me
A little happier than my wretched father:
Yet thus far we are one in fortunes: both
Fell by our servants, by those men we loved most;
A most unnatural and faithless service!
Heaven has an end in all: yet, you that hear me,
This from a dying man receive as certain:
Where you are liberal of your loves and counsels
Be sure you be not loose; for those you make friends
And give your hearts to, when they once perceive
The least rub in your fortunes, fall away
Like water from ye, never found again
But where they mean to sink ye. All good people,
Pray for me! I must now forsake ye: the last hour
Of my long weary life is come upon me.
Farewell:
And when you would say something that is sad,
Speak how I fell. I have done: and God forgive me!

He goes to his doom

First Gentleman. O, this is full of pity! Sir, it calls,
I fear, too many curses on their heads
That were the authors.

Second Gentleman. If the duke be guiltless
Tis full of woe: yet I can give you inkling
Of an ensuing evil, if it fall, greater than this.

First. Good angels keep it from us! What may it be?

Second. Did you not of late days hear a buzzing of a separation
Between the king and Katharine? Either the cardinal,
Or some about him near, have, out of malice
To the good queen, possessed him with a scruple
That will undo her: to confirm this too,
Cardinal Campeius is arrived, and lately;
As all think, for this business.

First Gentleman. Tis the cardinal;
And merely to revenge him on the emperor
For not bestowing on him, at his asking,
The archbishopric of Toledo, this is purposed.

Second. I think you have hit the mark: but is't not cruel
That she should feel the smart of this? The cardinal
Will have his will, and she must fall.

First. Tis woeful. We are too open here to argue this;
Let's think in private more.

Scene 2—An Ante-chamber in the Palace

The Lord Chamberlain meets the Dukes of Norfolk and Suffolk

NORFOLK. Well met, my lord chamberlain.

LORD CHAMBERLAIN. Good day to both your graces.

SUFFOLK. How is the king employed ?

LORD CHAMBERLAIN. I left him full of sad thoughts and troubles.

NORFOLK. What's the cause ?

LORD CHAMBERLAIN. It seems the marriage with his brother's wife
Has crept too near his conscience.

SUFFOLK. No, his conscience has crept too near another lady.

NORFOLK. Tis so.
This is the cardinal's doing, the king-cardinal :
That blind priest, like the eldest son of fortune,
Turns what he list. The king will know him one day.

SUFFOLK. Pray God he do ! he'll never know himself else.

NORFOLK. How holily he works in all his business !
And with what zeal ! for, now he has cracked the league
Between us and the emperor, the queen's great nephew,
He dives into the king's soul, and there scatters
Dangers, doubts, wringing of the conscience,
Fears, and despairs ; and all these for his marriage :
And out of all these to restore the king,
He counsels a divorce ; a loss of her
That, like a jewel, has hung twenty years
About his neck, yet never lost her lustre ;
Of her that loves him with that excellence
That angels love good men with.

LORD CHAMBERLAIN. Every true heart weeps for 't.
Heaven will open
The king's eyes, that so long have slept upon
This bold bad man.

SUFFOLK. And free us from his slavery.

NORFOLK. We had need pray,
And heartily, for our deliverance,
Or this imperious man will work us all
From princes into pages.

SUFFOLK. For me, my lords,
I love him not nor fear him.

NORFOLK. Let's in ;
And with some other business put the king
From these sad thoughts, that work too much upon him.
My lord, you'll bear us company ?

LORD CHAMBERLAIN. Excuse me;
The king has sent me otherwhere: besides,
You'll find a most unfit time to disturb him.

A curtain is drawn and the King is seen as if deep in thought. The two Cardinals appear, and Norfolk and Suffolk are rudely dismissed.

WOLSEY. Your grace has given a precedent of wisdom
Above all princes, in committing freely
Your scruple to the voice of Christendom:
Who can be angry now? what envy reach you?
The Spaniard, tied by blood and favour to her,
Must now confess, if they have any goodness,
The trial just and noble. All the clerks,
I mean the learned ones, in Christian kingdoms
Have their free voices: Rome, the nurse of judgment,
Invited by your noble self, hath sent
One general tongue unto us, this good man,
This just and learned priest, Cardinal Campeius;
Whom once more I present unto your highness.

KING. And once more in mine arms I bid him welcome,
And thank the holy conclave for their loves:
They have sent me such a man I would have wished for.

CAMPEIUS. Your grace must needs deserve all strangers' loves,
You are so noble. To your highness' hand
I tender my commission; by whose virtue,
The court of Rome commanding, you, my lord
Cardinal of York, are joined with me their servant
In the unpartial judging of this business.

KING. Two equal men. The queen shall be acquainted
Forthwith for what you come.

WOLSEY. I know your majesty has always loved her
So dear in heart, not to deny her that
A woman of less place might ask by law:
Scholars allowed freely to argue for her.

KING. Ay, and the best she shall have; and my favour
To him that does best: God forbid else.

The King calls for his new secretary Gardiner, whom he finds "a fit fellow." Gardiner whispers his thanks to Wolsey for the appointment and declares he will "ever be commanded." Campeius asks Wolsey if it is true that his treatment had driven Gardiner's predecessor to madness, and Wolsey answers that the man was a fool, for he would needs be virtuous. But, as to Gardiner, "that good fellow"

If I command him, follows my appointment:
I will have none so near else.

KING. Deliver this with modesty to the queen. *(Gardiner goes)*
The most convenient place that I can think of
For such receipt of learning is Blackfriars;
There ye shall meet about this weighty business.
My Wolsey, see it furnished. O, my lord,
Would it not grieve an able man to leave
So sweet a queen? But, conscience, conscience!
O, tis a tender place; and I must leave her.

Scene 3—A Room in the Queen's Apartments

Enter Anne Boleyn and an Old Lady

ANNE. His highness having lived so long with her, and she
So good a lady that no tongue could ever
Pronounce dishonour of her, O, now, after
So many courses of the sun enthroned,
Still growing in a majesty and pomp, the which
To leave a thousandfold more bitter than
Tis sweet at first to acquire—after this process,
To give her the avaunt! It is a pity
Would move a monster.

OLD LADY. Hearts of most hard temper melt and lament for her.

ANNE. O, God's will! much better
She ne'er had known pomp: though 't be temporal.

OLD LADY. Alas, poor lady! She's a stranger now again.

ANNE. So much the more
Must pity drop upon her. Verily,
I swear, tis better to be lowly born,
And range with humble livers in content,
Than to be perked up in a glistering grief,
And wear a golden sorrow.

OLD LADY. Our content is our best having.

ANNE. By my troth I would not be a queen.

OLD LADY. Beshrew me, I would.
You, that have so fair parts of woman on you,
Have too a woman's heart; which ever yet
Affected eminence, wealth, sovereignty,
Which, to say sooth, are blessings.

ANNE. Nay, good troth.

OLD LADY. Yes, troth, and troth; you would not be a queen?

ANNE. No, not for all the riches under heaven.
I swear again, I would not be a queen for all the world.

OLD LADY. Lo, who comes here?

LORD CHAMBERLAIN. Good-morrow, ladies. What were 't worth to know
The secret of your conference?

ANNE. Our mistress' sorrows we were pitying.

LORD CHAMBERLAIN. It was a gentle business, and becoming
The action of good women: there is hope
All will be well.

ANNE. Now, I pray God, amen!

CHAMBERLAIN. You bear a gentle mind, and heavenly blessings
Follow such creatures. The king's majesty
Commends his good opinion of you, and
Does purpose honour to you no less flowing
Than Marchioness of Pembroke; to which title
A thousand pound a year, annual support,
Out of his grace he adds.

ANNE. I do not know
What kind of my obedience I should tender;
More than my all is nothing. Beseech your lordship,
Vouchsafe to speak my thanks and my obedience,
As from a blushing handmaid, to his highness.

CHAMBERLAIN. Lady, I shall not fail to approve the fair conceit
The king hath of you. I'll to the king,
And say I spoke with you. *(Lord Chamberlain leaves)*

ANNE. My honoured lord.

OLD LADY. Why, this it is; see, see!
I have been begging sixteen years in court,
Am yet a courtier beggarly; and you, O fate!
Have your mouth filled up before you open it.

ANNE. This is strange to me.

OLD LADY. How tastes it? Is it bitter? Forty pence, no.
There was a lady once (tis an old story)
That would not be a queen, that would she not,
For all the mud in Egypt: have you heard it?

ANNE. Come, you are pleasant.

OLD LADY. With your theme I could
O'ermount the lark. The Marchioness of Pembroke!
A thousand pounds a year for pure respect!
No other obligation! By my life,
That promises more thousands.

ANNE. Good lady,
Make yourself mirth with your particular fancy,
And leave me out on 't.
It faints me to think what follows.
The queen is comfortless, and we forgetful
In our long absence: pray, do not deliver
What here you've heard to her.

OLD LADY. What do you think me?

Scene 4—A Hall in Blackfriars

In a Hall in Blackfriars an Inquiry is being held, before the King, Cardinals, the Archbishop of Canterbury, and four Bishops, with Noblemen, Priests, Ushers, and a Crier in attendance, to decide whether the marriage of the King with Queen Katharine is valid or not. The Queen rises from her seat, kneels at the King's feet, and speaks.

QUEEN KATHARINE. Sir, I desire you do me right and justice,
And to bestow your pity on me : for
I am a most poor woman, and a stranger
Born out of your dominions ; having here
No judge indifferent, nor no more assurance
Of equal friendship and proceeding. Alas, sir,
In what have I offended you ? What cause
Hath my behaviour given to your displeasure,
That thus you should proceed to put me off
And take your good grace from me ? Heaven witness,
I have been to you a true and humble wife,
At all times to your will conformable ;
Ever in fear to kindle your dislike,
Yea, subject to your countenance, glad or sorry
As I saw it inclined : when was the hour
I ever contradicted your desire,
Or made it not mine too ? Or which of your friends
Have I not strove to love, although I knew
He were mine enemy ? What friend of mine
That had to him derived your anger, did I
Continue in my liking ? Nay, gave notice
He was from thence discharged ? Sir, call to mind
That I have been your wife, in this obedience,
Upward of twenty years, and have been blest
With many children by you : if, in the course
And process of this time, you can report,
And prove it too, against mine honour aught,
My bond to wedlock, or my love and duty,
Against your sacred person, in God's name
Turn me away ; and let the foul'st contempt
Shut door upon me, and so give me up
To the sharpest kind of justice. Please you, sir,
The king, your father, was reputed for
A prince most prudent, of an excellent
And unmatched wit and judgment : Ferdinand
My father, king of Spain, was reckoned one
The wisest prince that there had reigned by many
A year before : it is not to be questioned
That they had gathered a wise council to them
Of every realm, that did debate this business,
Who deemed our marriage lawful : wherefore I humbly

Beseech you, sir, to spare me, till I may
Be by my friends in Spain advised ; whose counsel
I will implore : if not, i' the name of God,
Your pleasure be fulfilled !

WOLSEY. You have here, lady,
And of your choice, these reverend fathers ; men
Of singular integrity and learning,
Yea, the elect o' the land, who are assembled to plead your cause.

CAMPEIUS. His grace
Hath spoken well and justly : therefore, madam,
It's fit this royal session do proceed ;
And that, without delay, their arguments be heard.

QUEEN KATHARINE. Lord Cardinal, to you I speak.

WOLSEY. Your pleasure, madam ?

QUEEN KATHARINE. Sir, I am about to weep ; but, thinking that
We were a queen, or long have dreamed so, certain
The daughter of a king, my drops of tears
I'll turn to sparks of fire.

WOLSEY. Be patient yet.

QUEEN KATHARINE. I will, when you are humble ; nay, before,
Or God will punish me. I do believe,
Induced by potent circumstances, that
You are mine enemy, and make my challenge
You shall not be my judge : for it is you
Have blown this coal betwixt my lord and me,
Which God's dew quench ! Therefore I say again,
I utterly abhor, yea, from my soul
Refuse you for my judge ; whom, yet once more,
I hold my most malicious foe, and think not
At all a friend to truth.

WOLSEY. Madam, you do me wrong :
I have no spleen against you ; nor injustice
For you or any. I do beseech
You, gracious madam, to unthink your speaking
And to say so no more.

QUEEN KATHARINE. My lord, my lord,
I am a simple woman, much too weak
To oppose your cunning. You're meek and humble-mouthed ;
You sign your place and calling, in full seeming,
With meekness and humility ; but your heart
Is crammed with arrogancy, spleen, and pride.
You have, by fortune and his highness' favours,
Gone slightly o'er low steps, and now are mounted
Where powers are your retainers, and your words,
Domestics to you, serve your will as 't please

Yourself pronounce their office. I must tell you,
You tender more your person's honour than
Your high profession spiritual: that again
I do refuse you for my judge; and here,
Before you all, appeal unto the pope,
To bring my whole cause 'fore his holiness,
And to be judged by him.

She curtsies to the King and offers to go

CAMPEIUS. The queen is obstinate,
Stubborn to justice, apt to accuse it, and
Disdainful to be tried by 't: tis not well.
She's going away.

KING. Call her again.

CRIER. Katharine Queen of England, come into the court.

GRIFFITH. Madam, you are called back.

QUEEN. What need you note it? Pray you, keep your way:
When you are called, return. Now the Lord help!
They vex me past my patience! Pray you, pass on:
I will not tarry; no, nor evermore
Upon this business my appearance make
In any of their courts. *(She leaves with her attendants)*

KING. Go thy ways, Kate:
That man i' the world who shall report he has
A better wife, let him in nought be trusted,
For speaking false in that: thou art, alone,
If thy rare qualities, sweet gentleness,
Thy meekness saint-like, wife-like government,
Obeying in commanding, and thy parts
Sovereign and pious else, could speak thee out,
The queen of earthly queens: she's noble born,
And like her true nobility she has
Carried herself towards me.

WOLSEY. Most gracious sir,
In humblest manner I require your highness,
That it shall please you to declare, in hearing
Of all these ears, whether ever I
Did broach this business to your highness; or
Laid any scruple in your way, which might
Induce you to the question on 't? or ever
Have to you spake one least word that might
Be to the prejudice of her present state?

KING. My lord cardinal,
I do excuse you; yea, upon mine honour,
I free you from 't. You are not to be taught
That you have many enemies, that know not

Why they are so, but, like to village curs,
Bark when their fellows do: by some of these
The queen is put in anger. You're excused:
But will you be more justified? You ever
Have wished the sleeping of this business; never desired
It to be stirred; but oft have hindered, oft,
The passages made toward it: on my honour,
I speak my good lord cardinal to this point,
And thus far clear him. Now, what moved me to 't,
I will be bold with time and your attention:
Then mark the inducement. Thus it came; give heed to 't.
My conscience first received a tenderness,
Scruple, and prick, on certain speeches uttered
By the Bishop of Bayonne, then French ambassador;
Who had been hither sent on the debating
A marriage 'twixt the Duke of Orleans and
Our daughter Mary: i' the progress of this business,
Ere a determinate resolution, he
(I mean the bishop) did require a respite,
Wherein he might the king his lord ad*ver*tise
Respecting this our marriage with the dowager,
Sometimes our brother's wife. This respite shook
The bosom of my conscience, entered me,
Yea, with a splitting power, and made to tremble
The region of my breast. First, methought
I stood not in the smile of heaven; that my kingdom,
Well worthy the best heir o' the world, should not
Be gladded in 't by me: then follows, that
I weighed the danger which my realms stood in
By this my issue's fail; and that gave to me
Many a groaning throe. Thus hulling in
The wild sea of my conscience, I did steer
Toward this remedy, whereupon we are
Now present here together; that's to say,
I meant to rectify my conscience. I then moved you,
My Lord of Canterbury; and got your leave
To make this present summons. Therefore, go on;
For no dislike i' the world against the person
Of the good queen, but the sharp thorny points
Of my allegèd reasons, drive this forward:
Prove but our marriage lawful, by my life
And kingly dignity, we are contented
To wear our mortal state to come with her,
Katharine our queen, before the primest creature
That's paragoned o' the world.

CAMPEIUS. So please your highness,
The queen being absent, tis a needful fitness

That we adjourn this court till further day:
Meanwhile must be an earnest motion
Made to the queen, to call back her appeal
She intends unto his holiness.

KING *(aside)*. I may perceive
These cardinals trifle with me: I abhor
This dilatory sloth and tricks of Rome.
My learned and well-belovèd servant, Cranmer,
Prithee, return: with thy approach, I know,
My comfort comes along. Break up the court:
I say, Set on.

ACT 3

Scene 1—The Queen's Apartments: the Queen and her Women sewing

QUEEN. Take thy lute, wench: my soul grows sad with troubles;
Sing, and disperse 'em, if thou can'st: leave working.

SONG BY ONE OF THE WOMEN

Orpheus with his lute made trees,
And the mountain tops that freeze,
Bow themselves when he did sing:
To his music plants and flowers
Ever sprung; as sun and showers
There had made a lasting spring.

Everything that heard him play,
Even the billows of the sea,
Hung their heads, and then lay by.
In sweet music is such art,
Killing care and grief of heart
Fall asleep or, hearing, die.

Here a gentleman enters to announce two Cardinals

QUEEN KATHARINE. Pray their graces
To come near. What can be their business
With me, a poor weak woman, fallen from favour?
I do not like their coming. Now I think on 't,
They should be good men; but all hoods make not monks.

Enter the two Cardinals, Wolsey and Campeius

WOLSEY. Peace to your highness!

QUEEN KATHARINE. Your graces find me here part of a housewife,
I would be all, against the worst may happen.
What are your pleasures with me, reverend lords?

WOLSEY. May it please you, noble madam, to withdraw
Into your private chamber, we shall give you
The full cause of our coming.

QUEEN KATHARINE. Speak it here;
There's nothing I have done yet, o' my conscience,
Deserves a corner: would all other women

Could speak this with as free a soul as I do!
My lords, I care not if my actions
Were tried by every tongue, every eye saw 'em,
Envy and base opinion set against 'em,
I know my life so even. If your business
Seek me out, and that way I am wife in,
Out with it boldly: truth loves open dealing.

WOLSEY. *Tanta est erga te mentis integritas, regina serenissima—*

QUEEN KATHARINE. O, good my lord, no Latin;
I am not such a truant since my coming
As not to know the language I have lived in:
A strange tongue makes my cause more strange, suspicious;
Pray, speak in English: here are some will thank you,
If you speak truth, for their poor mistress' sake;
Believe me, she has had much wrong: lord cardinal,
The willing'st sin I ever yet committed
May be absolved in English.

WOLSEY. Noble lady,
I am sorry my integrity should breed
So deep suspicion, where all faith was meant.
We come not by the way of accusation,
To taint that honour every good tongue blesses,
Nor to betray you any way to sorrow,
You have too much, good lady; but to know
How you stand minded in the weighty difference
Between the king and you; and to deliver,
Like free and honest men, our just opinions
And comforts to your cause.

QUEEN. My lords, I thank you both for your good wills;
Ye speak like honest men; pray God ye prove so!
But how to make ye suddenly an answer,
In such a point of weight, so near mine honour
(More near my life, I fear) with my weak wit,
And to such men of gravity and learning,
In truth, I know not. I was set at work
Among my maids; full little, God knows, looking
Either for such men or such business.
Let me have time and counsel for my cause:
Alas, I am a woman, friendless, hopeless!

WOLSEY. Madam, you wrong the king's love with these fears:
Your hopes and friends are infinite.

QUEEN KATHARINE. In England
But little for my profit: can you think, lords,
That any Englishman dare give me counsel?
Or be a known friend, 'gainst his highness' pleasure,

Though he be grown so desperate to be honest,
And live a subject? Nay, forsooth, my friends,
They that must weigh out my afflictions,
They that my trust must grow to, live not here:
They are, as all my other comforts, far hence
In mine own country, lords.

CAMPEIUS. I would your grace
Would leave your griefs, and take my counsel.

QUEEN KATHARINE. How, sir?

CAMPEIUS. Put your main cause into the king's protection;
He's loving and most gracious: 'twill be much
Both for your honour better and your cause;
For if the trial of the law o'ertake ye,
You'll part away disgraced.

QUEEN KATHARINE. Ye tell me what ye wish for both—my ruin:
Is this your Christian counsel? Out upon ye!
Heaven is above all yet; there sits a Judge
That no king can corrupt.

CAMPEIUS. Your rage mistakes us.

QUEEN KATHARINE. The more shame for ye: holy men I thought ye,
Upon my soul, two reverend cardinal virtues;
But cardinal sins and hollow hearts I fear ye:
Mend 'em, for shame, my lords. Is this your comfort?
The cordial that ye bring a wretched lady,
A woman lost among ye, laughed at, scorned?
I will not wish ye half my miseries;
I have more charity: but say, I warned ye;
Take heed, for heaven's sake, take heed, lest at once
The burthen of my sorrows fall upon ye.

WOLSEY. Madam, this is a mere distraction;
You turn the good we offer into envy.

QUEEN KATHARINE. Ye turn me into nothing: woe upon ye
And all such false professors! would you have me
(If you have any justice, any pity;
If ye be anything but churchmen's habits)
Put my sick cause into his hands that hates me?
That banished me his love too long ago? I am old, my lords,
And all the fellowship I hold now with him
Is only my obedience. What can happen
To me above this wretchedness?
Have I lived thus long a wife, a true one?
A woman, I dare say without vain-glory,
Never yet branded with suspicion?
Have I with all my full affections
Still met the king? loved him next heaven? obeyed him?

Been, out of fondness, superstitious to him ?
Almost forgot my prayers to content him ?
And am I thus rewarded ? Tis not well, lords.
Bring me a constant woman to her husband,
One that ne'er dreamed a joy beyond his pleasure,
And to that woman, when she has done most,
Yet will I add an honour, a great patience.

WOLSEY. Madam, you wander from the good we aim at.

QUEEN KATHARINE. My lord, I dare not make myself so guilty,
To give up willingly that noble title
Your master wed me to : nothing but death
Shall e'er divorce my dignities.
Would I had never trod this English earth,
Or felt the flatteries that grow upon it !
Ye have angels' faces, but heaven knows your hearts.
What will become of me now, wretched lady !
I am the most unhappy woman living.
Alas, poor wenches, where are now your fortunes !
Shipwrecked upon a kingdom, where no pity,
No friends, no hope ; no kindred weep for me ;
Almost no grave allowed me : like the lily,
That once was mistress of the field and flourished,
I'll hang my head and perish.

WOLSEY. If your grace
Could but be brought to know our ends are honest,
You'd feel more comfort : why should we, good lady,
Upon what cause, wrong you ? alas, our places,
The way of our profession, is against it :
We are to cure such sorrows, not to sow 'em.
For goodness' sake, consider what you do ;
How you may hurt yourself, ay, utterly
Grow from the king's acquaintance, by this carriage.
The hearts of princes kiss obedience,
So much they love it ; but to stubborn spirits
They swell, and grow as terrible as storms.
I know you have a gentle, noble temper,
A soul as even as a calm : pray, think us
Those we profess, peace-makers, friends, and servants.

CAMPEIUS. Madam, you'll find it so. You wrong your virtues
With these weak women's fears : a noble spirit,
As yours was put into you, ever casts
Such doubts, as false coin, from it. The king loves you ;
Beware you lose it not : for us, if you please
To trust us in your business, we are ready
To use our utmost studies in your service.

QUEEN. Do what ye will, my lords: and, pray, forgive me,
If I have used myself unmannerly;
You know I am a woman, lacking wit
To make a seemly answer to such persons.
Pray, do my service to his majesty:
He has my heart yet; and shall have my prayers
While I shall have my life. Come, reverend fathers,
Bestow your counsels on me; she now begs
That little thought, when she set footing here,
She should have bought her dignities so dear.

Scene 2—Outside the King's Apartment

Enter Norfolk, Surrey, Suffolk, and the Lord Chamberlain

The three nobles hotly denounce Wolsey's disdainful treatment of the peers, and Norfolk declares that now is the time to combine against him, for he is losing favour. Henry has discovered a letter written by the Cardinal urging the Pope to delay the divorce as the King's affections incline to Anne Boleyn. Wolsey is too late, says the Lord Chamberlain, for Henry has already secretly married Anne with the help of Cranmer. Wolsey draws near, accompanied by his secretary Cromwell.

NORFOLK. Observe, observe, he's moody.
WOLSEY *(approaching)*. The packet, Cromwell,
Gave 't you the king?
CROMWELL. To his own hand.
WOLSEY. Looked he o' the inside of the paper?
CROMWELL. Presently
He did unseal them: and the first he viewed,
He did it with a serious mind; a heed
Was in his countenance. You he bade
Attend him here this morning.
WOLSEY. Is he ready to come abroad?
CROMWELL. I think by this he is.
WOLSEY. Leave me awhile.
(Aside) It shall be to the Duchess of Alençon,
The French king's sister: he shall marry her.
Anne Boleyn! No; I'll no Anne Boleyns for him:
There's more in 't than fair visage. Boleyn!
No, we'll no Boleyns.

Enter the King, reading a schedule, and Lovell, unseen by Wolsey

SUFFOLK. The king, the king!
KING. What piles of wealth hath he accumulated
To his own portion! and what expense by the hour
Seems to flow from him! How, i' the name of thrift,
Does he rake this together! Now, my lords,
Saw you the cardinal?

NORFOLK. My lord, we have
Stood here observing him: some strange commotion
Is in his brain: he bites his lip, and starts;
Stops on a sudden, looks upon the ground,
Then lays his finger on his temple; straight
Springs out into fast gait; then stops again,
Strikes his breast hard, and anon he casts
His eye against the moon: in most strange postures
We have seen him set himself.

KING. It may well be;
There is a mutiny in's mind. This morning
Papers of State he sent me to peruse,
As I required: and wot you what I found?
Forsooth, an inventory, thus importing;
The several parcels of his plate, his treasure,
Rich stuffs, and ornaments of household; which
I find at such proud rate that it out-speaks
Possession of a subject.

NORFOLK. It's heaven's will:
Some spirit put this paper in the packet,
To bless your eye withal.

KING. If we did think
His contemplation were above the earth,
And fixed on spiritual object, he should still
Dwell in his musings: but I am afraid
His thinkings are below the moon.

WOLSEY *(looking up)*. Heaven forgive me! Ever God bless your highness!

KING. Good my lord,
You are full of heavenly stuff, and bear the inventory
Of your best graces in your mind; the which
You were now running o'er: you have scarce time
To steal from spiritual leisure a brief span
To keep your earthly audit: sure, in that
I deem you an ill husband, and am glad
To have you therein my companion.

WOLSEY. Sir, for holy offices I have a time; a time
To think upon the part of business which
I bear i' the State; and nature does require
Her times of preservation, which perforce
I, her frail son, amongst my brethren mortal,
Must give my tendance to.

KING. You have said well,
And tis a kind of good deed to say well:
And yet words are no deeds. My father loved you:

He said he did ; and with his deed did crown
His word upon you. Since I had my office,
I have kept you next my heart ; have not alone
Employed you where high profits might come home,
But pared my present havings, to bestow
My bounties upon you.

WOLSEY. *(Aside)* What should this mean ?

KING. Have I not made you
The prime man of the State ? I pray you, tell me,
If what I now pronounce you have found true :
And, if you may confess it, say withal,
If you are bound to us or no. What say you ?

WOLSEY. My sovereign, I confess your royal graces,
Showered on me daily, have been more than could
My studied purposes requite ; which went
Beyond all man's endeavours : my endeavours
Have ever come too short of my desires,
Yet filed with my abilities : mine own ends
Have been mine so that evermore they pointed
To the good of your most sacred person and
The profit of the State. For your great graces
Heaped upon me, poor undeserver, I
Can nothing render but allegiant thanks,
My prayers to heaven for you, my loyalty
(Which ever has and ever shall be growing),
Till death, that winter, kill it.

KING. Fairly answered :
A loyal and obedient subject is
Therein illustrated : the honour of it
Does pay the act of it ; as, i' the contrary,
The foulness is the punishment. I presume
That, as my hand has opened bounty to you,
My heart dropped love, my power rained honour, more
On you than any ; so your hand and heart,
Your brain, and every function of your power,
Should be more to me, your friend, than any.

WOLSEY. I do profess
That for your highness' good I ever laboured
More than mine own.

KING. Tis nobly spoken :
Take notice, lords, he has a loyal breast,
For you have seen him open 't. Read o'er this *(giving him papers)* ;
And after, this : and then to breakfast with
What appetite you have.

The King leaves with his nobles, frowning on Wolsey

WOLSEY. What should this mean ?
What sudden anger's this ? how have I reaped it ?
He parted frowning from me, as if ruin
Leaped from his eyes : so looks the chafèd lion
Upon the daring huntsman that has galled him ;
Then makes him nothing. I must read this paper ;
I fear the story of his anger. Tis so ;
This paper has undone me : tis the account
Of all that world of wealth I have drawn together
For mine own ends ; indeed, to gain the popedom,
And fee my friends in Rome. O negligence !
Fit for a fool to fall by : what cross devil
Made me put this main secret in the packet
I sent the king ? Is there no way to cure this ?
No new device to beat this from his brains ?
I know 'twill stir him strongly ; yet I know
A way, if it take right, in spite of fortune
Will bring me off again. What's this ? *To the Pope !*
The letter, as I live, with all the business
I writ to 's holiness. Nay then, farewell !
I have touched the highest point of all my greatness ;
And, from that full meridian of my glory,
I haste now to my setting : I shall fall
Like a bright exhalation in the evening,
And no man see me more.

The Lord Chamberlain returns with the nobles

NORFOLK. Hear the king's pleasure, cardinal : who commands you
To render up the great seal presently
Into our hands.

WOLSEY. Where's your commission, lords ? words cannot carry
Authority so weighty. Now I feel
Of what coarse metal ye are moulded, envy :
How eagerly ye follow my disgraces,
As if it fed ye ! and how sleek and wanton
Ye appear in everything may bring my ruin !
Follow your envious courses, men of malice ;
You have Christian warrant for 'em, and, no doubt,
In time will find their fit rewards. That seal,
You ask with such a violence, the king,
Mine and your master, with his own hand gave me ;
Bade me enjoy it, with the place and honours,
During my life ; and, to confirm his goodness,
Tied it by letters-patent : now, who'll take it ?

SURREY. The king that gave it.

WOLSEY. It must be himself, then.

SURREY. Thou art a proud traitor, priest.

WOLSEY. Proud lord, thou liest:
Within these forty hours Surrey durst better
Have burnt that tongue than said so.

SURREY. Thy ambition,
Thou scarlet sin, robbed this bewailing land
Of noble Buckingham, my father-in-law:
The heads of all thy brother cardinals,
With thee and all thy best parts bound together,
Weighed not a hair of his. Plague of your policy!
You sent me deputy for Ireland;
Far from his succour, from the king, from all
That might have mercy on the fault thou gavest him;
Whilst your great goodness, out of holy pity,
Absolved him with an axe.

WOLSEY. This, and all else
This talking lord can lay upon my credit,
I answer is most false. The duke by law
Found his deserts: how innocent I was
From any private malice in his end,
His noble jury and foul cause can witness.
If I loved many words, lord, I should tell you
You have as little honesty as honour.

SURREY. By my soul,
Your long coat, priest, protects you; thou shouldst feel
My sword i' the life-blood of thee else. My lords,
Can ye endure to hear this arrogance?
And from this fellow?

WOLSEY. All goodness is poison to thy stomach.

SURREY. Yes, that goodness
Of gleaning all the land's wealth into one,
Into your own hands, cardinal, by extortion.
Now, if you can blush and cry *guilty*, cardinal,
You'll show a little honesty.

WOLSEY. Speak on, sir; if I blush,
It is to see a nobleman want manners.

Surrey, Norfolk, and Suffolk then tell how the Cardinal tried to be the Papal legate without the King's sanction; how he had in letters given himself preference before the King; had acted as an ambassador to the Emperor without the King's knowledge, and had taken with him the great seal of the kingdom, had concluded a foreign alliance, and had his hat stamped on the King's coins. Besides, he had sent bribes to Rome.

LORD CHAMBERLAIN. O my lord,
Press not a falling man too far! tis virtue:
His faults lie open to the laws; let them,
Not you, correct him. My heart weeps to see him
So little of his great self.

SUFFOLK. Lord cardinal, the king's further pleasure is,
That a writ be sued against you
To forfeit all your goods, lands, tenements,
Chattels, and whatsoever, and to be
Out of the king's protection. This is my charge.

NORFOLK. And so we'll leave you to your meditations
How to live better. For your stubborn answer
About the giving back the great seal to us,
The king shall know it, and, no doubt, shall thank you.
So fare you well, my little good lord cardinal.

WOLSEY. Farewell! a long farewell, to all my greatness!
This is the state of man: today he puts forth
The tender leaves of hopes; tomorrow blossoms,
And bears his blushing honours thick upon him;
The third day comes a frost, a killing frost,
And, when he thinks, good easy man, full surely
His greatness is a-ripening, nips his root,
And then he falls, as I do. I have ventured,
Like little wanton boys that swim on bladders,
This many summers in a sea of glory,
But far beyond my depth: my high-blown pride
At length broke under me and now has left me,
Weary and old with service, to the mercy
Of a rude stream, that must for ever hide me.
Vain pomp and glory of this world, I hate ye:
I feel my heart new opened. O, how wretched
Is that poor man that hangs on princes' favours!
There is, betwixt that smile we would aspire to,
That sweet aspect of princes, and their ruin,
More pangs and fears than wars or women have;
And when he falls, he falls like Lucifer,
Never to hope again.

Cromwell enters and stands amazed

Why, how now, Cromwell!

CROMWELL. I have no power to speak, sir.

WOLSEY. What, amazed
At my misfortunes? Can thy spirit wonder
A great man should decline? Nay, an you weep,
I am fallen indeed.

CROMWELL. How does your grace?

WOLSEY. Why, well;
Never so truly happy, my good Cromwell.
I know myself now; and I feel within me
A peace above all earthly dignities,
A still and quiet conscience. The king has cured me

(I humbly thank his grace), and from these shoulders,
These ruined pillars, out of pity, taken
A load would sink a navy, too much honour:
O, tis a burthen, Cromwell, tis a burthen
Too heavy for a man that hopes for heaven!

CROMWELL. I am glad your grace has made that right use of it.

WOLSEY. I hope I have: I am able now, methinks,
Out of a fortitude of soul I feel,
To endure more miseries and greater far
Than my weak-hearted enemies dare offer.
What news abroad?

CROMWELL. The heaviest and the worst
Is your displeasure with the king.
The next is that Sir Thomas More is chosen
Lord Chancellor in your place.

WOLSEY. That's somewhat sudden:
But he's a learnèd man. May he continue
Long in his highness' favour, and do justice
For truth's sake and his conscience; that his bones,
When he has run his course and sleeps in blessings,
May have a tomb of orphans' tears wept on 'em!
What more?

CROMWELL. That Cranmer is returned with welcome,
Installed lord archbishop of Canterbury.

WOLSEY. That's news indeed.

CROMWELL. Last, that the Lady Anne,
Whom the king hath in secrecy long married,
This day was viewed in open as his queen,
Going to chapel; and the voice is now
Only about her coronation.

WOLSEY. There was the weight that pulled me down. O Cromwell,
The king has gone beyond me: all my glories
In that one woman I have lost for ever:
No sun shall ever usher forth mine honours,
Or gild again the noble troops that waited
Upon my smiles. Go, get thee from me, Cromwell;
I am a poor fallen man, unworthy now
To be thy lord and master: seek the king;
That sun, I pray, may never set! I have told him
What and how true thou art: he will advance thee;
Some little memory of me will stir him
(I know his noble nature) not to let
Thy hopeful service perish too: good Cromwell,
Neglect him not; make use now, and provide
For thine own future safety.

CROMWELL. O my lord,
Must I, then, leave you ? must I needs forego
So good, so noble, and so true a master ?
Bear witness, all that have not hearts of iron,
With what a sorrow Cromwell leaves his lord.
The king shall have my service ; but my prayers
For ever and for ever shall be yours.

WOLSEY. Cromwell, I did not think to shed a tear
In all my miseries ; but thou hast forced me,
Out of thy honest truth, to play the woman.
Let's dry our eyes : and thus far hear me, Cromwell ;
And when I am forgotten, as I shall be,
And sleep in dull cold marble, where no mention
Of me more must be heard of, say I taught thee,
Say Wolsey, that once trod the ways of glory,
And sounded all the depths and shoals of honour,
Found thee a way, out of his wreck, to rise in ;
A sure and safe one, though thy master missed it.
Mark but my fall, and that that ruined me.
Cromwell, I charge thee, fling away ambition :
By that sin fell the angels ; how can man, then,
The image of his Maker, hope to win by it ?
Love thyself last : cherish those hearts that hate thee ;
Corruption wins not more than honesty.
Still in thy right hand carry gentle peace,
To silence envious tongues. Be just, and fear not :
Let all the ends thou aim'st at be thy country's,
Thy God's, and truth's ; then if thou fall'st, O Cromwell,
Thou fall'st a blessed martyr ! Serve the king ;
And prithee, lead me in :
There take an inventory of all I have,
To the last penny ; tis the king's : my robe,
And my integrity to heaven, is all
I dare now call mine own. O Cromwell, Cromwell !
Had I but served my God with half the zeal
I served my king, he would not in mine age
Have left me naked to mine enemies.

CROMWELL. Good sir, have patience.

WOLSEY. So I have. Farewell
The hopes of court ! my hopes in heaven do dwell.

ACT 4

Scene 1—A Street in Westminster

FIRST GENTLEMAN. You're well met once again.

SECOND GENTLEMAN. So are you.

FIRST. You come to take your stand here, and behold
The Lady Anne pass from her coronation ?

SECOND GENTLEMAN. Tis all my business. At our last encounter
The Duke of Buckingham came from his trial.

FIRST GENTLEMAN. Tis very true: but that time offered sorrow;
This, general joy.

SECOND GENTLEMAN. Tis well: the citizens,
I am sure, have shown at full their royal minds
In celebration of this day with shows,
Pageants and sights of honour.

FIRST GENTLEMAN. Never greater,
Nor, I'll assure you, better taken, sir.

SECOND GENTLEMAN. I beseech you, what's become of Katharine,
The princess dowager? how goes her business?

FIRST GENTLEMAN. That I can tell you. The Archbishop
Of Canterbury, accompanied with other
Learned and reverend fathers of his order,
Held a late court at Dunstable, six miles off
From Ampthill where the princess lay; to which
She was often cited by them, but appeared not:
And, to be short, for not appearance and
The king's late scruple, she was divorced,
And the late marriage made of none effect:
Since which she was removed to Kimbolton,
Where she remains now sick.

SECOND GENTLEMAN. Alas, good lady!
The trumpets sound: stand close, the queen is coming.

The order of the gorgeous Coronation of the new Queen, Anne Boleyn, is then described by the First, Second, and Third Gentlemen, and we learn that Cranmer and Thomas Cromwell have received advancement.

Scene 2—At Kimbolton

Katharine, attended by Griffith, and Patience, her gentlewoman

GRIFFITH. How does your grace?

KATHARINE. O Griffith, sick to death! Reach a chair:
So; now, methinks, I feel a little ease.
Didst thou not tell me, Griffith, as thou led'st me,
That the great child of honour, Cardinal Wolsey,
Was dead?

GRIFFITH. Yes, madam; but I think your grace,
Out of the pain you suffered, gave no ear to 't.

KATHARINE. Prithee, good Griffith, tell me how he died:
If well, he stepped before me, happily
For my example.

GRIFFITH. Well, the voice goes, madam:
For after the stout Earl Northumberland
Arrested him at York, and brought him forward,

As a man sorely tainted, to his answer,
He fell sick suddenly, and grew so ill
He could not sit his mule.

KATHARINE. Alas, poor man!

GRIFFITH. At last, with easy roads, he came to Leicester,
Lodged in the abbey; where the reverend abbot,
With all his covent, honourably received him;
To whom he gave these words, *O, father abbot,*
An old man, broken with the storms of State,
Is come to lay his weary bones among ye;
Give him a little earth for charity!
So went to bed; where eagerly his sickness
Pursued him still: and, three nights after this,
About the hour of eight, which he himself
Foretold should be his last, full of repentance,
Continual meditations, tears, and sorrows,
He gave his honours to the world again,
His blessed part to heaven, and slept in peace.

KATHARINE. So may he rest; his faults lie gently on him!
Yet thus far, Griffith, give me leave to speak him,
And yet with charity. He was a man
Of an unbounded stomach, ever ranking
Himself with princes; one that, by suggestion,
Tied all the kingdom: simony was fair play;
His own opinion was his law: i' the presence
He would say untruths, and be ever double
Both in his words and meaning: he was never,
But where he meant to ruin, pitiful:
His promises were, as he then was, mighty,
But his performance, as he is now, nothing:
Of his own body he was ill, and gave
The clergy ill example.

GRIFFITH. Noble madam,
Men's evil manners live in brass; their virtues
We write in water. May it please your highness
To hear me speak his good now?

KATHARINE. Yes, good Griffith; I were malicious else.

GRIFFITH. This cardinal,
Though from an humble stock, undoubtedly
Was fashioned to much honour from his cradle.
He was a scholar, and a ripe and good one;
Exceeding wise, fair-spoken, and persuading:
Lofty and sour to them that loved him not,
But to those men that sought him sweet as summer.
And though he were unsatisfied in getting,
Which was a sin, yet in bestowing, madam,

He was most princely: ever witness for him
Those twins of learning that he raised in you,
Ipswich and Oxford! one of which fell with him,
Unwilling to outlive the good that did it;
The other, though unfinished, yet so famous,
So excellent in art, and still so rising,
That Christendom shall ever speak his virtue.
His overthrow heaped happiness upon him;
For then, and not till then, he felt himself,
And found the blessedness of being little:
And, to add greater honours to his age
Than man could give him, he died fearing God.

KATHARINE. After my death I wish no other herald,
No other speaker of my living actions,
To keep mine honour from corruption,
But such an honest chronicler as Griffith.
Whom I most hated living, thou hast made me,
With thy religious truth and modesty,
Now in his ashes honour: peace be with him!
Patience, be near me still; and set me lower:
I have not long to trouble thee. Good Griffith,
Cause the musicians play me that sad note
I named my knell, whilst I sit meditating
On that celestial harmony I go to. *(Sad and solemn music)*

GRIFFITH. She is asleep: good wench, let's sit down quiet,
For fear we wake her: softly, gentle Patience.

In her sleep the sorrowful Queen has a vision of six white-robed figures about her, offering her garlands of bays and palms, and she wakes holding up her hands with signs of rejoicing as they vanish.

KATHARINE. Spirits of peace, where are ye? are ye all gone,
And leave me here in wretchedness behind ye?

GRIFFITH. Madam, we are here.

KATHARINE. It is not you I call for; saw ye none enter since I slept?

GRIFFITH. None, madam.

KATHARINE. No? Saw you not, even now, a blessed troop
Invite me to a banquet; whose bright faces
Cast thousand beams upon me, like the sun?
They promised me eternal happiness,
And brought me garlands, Griffith, which I feel
I am not worthy yet to wear: I shall, assuredly.

GRIFFITH. I am most joyful, madam, such good dreams
Possess your fancy.

KATHARINE. Bid the music leave,
They are harsh and heavy to me.

PATIENCE. Do you note
How much her grace is altered on the sudden?
How long her face is drawn? how pale she looks,
And of an earthy cold? Mark her eyes!

GRIFFITH. She is going, wench: pray, pray.

PATIENCE. Heaven comfort her!

MESSENGER *(entering in haste)*. An 't like your grace—

KATHARINE. You are a saucy fellow:
Deserve we no more reverence?

MESSENGER. I humbly do entreat your highness' pardon;
My haste made me unmannerly. There is staying
A gentleman sent from the king to see you.

KATHARINE. Admit him entrance, Griffith; but this fellow
Let me ne'er see again.

He dismisses the messenger, and returns with Capucius

If my sight fail not,
You should be lord ambassador from the emperor,
My royal nephew, and your name Capucius.

CAPUCIUS. Madam, the same; your servant.

KATHARINE. O, my lord,
The times and titles now are altered strangely
With me since first you knew me. But, I pray you,
What is your pleasure with me?

CAPUCIUS. Noble lady,
First, mine own service to your grace; the next,
The king's request that I would visit you;
Who grieves much for your weakness, and by me
Sends you his princely commendations,
And heartily entreats you take good comfort.

KATHARINE. O my good lord, that comfort comes too late;
Tis like a pardon after execution:
That gentle physic, given in time, had cured me;
But now I am past all comforts here but prayers.
How does his highness?

CAPUCIUS. Madam, in good health.

KATHARINE. So may he ever do! and ever flourish,
When I shall dwell with worms, and my poor name
Banished the kingdom! Patience, is that letter
I caused you write yet sent away?

PATIENCE. No, madam. *(Giving it to Katharine)*

KATHARINE. Sir, I most humbly pray you to deliver
This to my lord the king, in which I have commended to his goodness
The model of our chaste loves, his young daughter:
The dews of heaven fall thick in blessings on her!
Beseeching him to give her virtuous breeding

(She is young, and of a noble modest nature,
I hope she will deserve well), and a little
To love her for her mother's sake, that loved him,
Heaven knows how dearly. My next poor petition
Is that his noble grace would have some pity
Upon my wretched women, that so long
Have followed both my fortunes faithfully :
Of which there is not one but will deserve,
For virtue and true beauty of the soul,
For honesty and decent carriage,
A right good husband, let him be a noble :
And, sure, those men are happy that shall have 'em.
The last is for my men ; they are the poorest,
But poverty could never draw 'em from me ;
That they may have their wages duly paid 'em,
And something over to remember me by ;
If heaven had pleased to have given me longer life
And able means, we had not parted thus.
These are the whole contents : and, good my lord,
By that you love the dearest in this world,
As you wish Christian peace to souls departed,
Stand these poor people's friend, and urge the king
To do me this last right.

CAPUCIUS. By heaven, I will,
Or let me lose the fashion of a man !

KATHARINE. I thank you, honest lord. Remember me
In all humility unto his highness :
Say his long trouble now is passing
Out of this world ; tell him in death I blessed him,
For so I will. Mine eyes grow dim. Farewell,
My lord. Griffith, farewell. Nay, Patience,
You must not leave me yet : I must to bed ;
Call in more women. When I am dead, good wench,
Let me be used with honour : strew me over
With maiden flowers, that all the world may know
I was a chaste wife to my grave : embalm me,
Then lay me forth : although unqueened, yet like
A queen, and daughter to a king, inter me.
I can no more.

ACT 5

The Fifth Act traces a conspiracy at Court against Archbishop Cranmer, whom they charge with heresy. Many join in it, but the King firmly supports the Archbishop, and he triumphs over his enemies, who had sought to commit him to the Tower. It is Cranmer who, in the last scene, when Anne Boleyn's daughter, Princess Elizabeth, is christened, closes the Play with a prophecy of her future greatness as a Queen.

CRANMER *(to the King)*. Let me speak, sir,
For heaven now bids me; and the words I utter
Let none think flattery, for they'll find 'em truth.
This royal infant (heaven still move about her!)
Though in her cradle, yet now promises
Upon this land a thousand thousand blessings,
Which time shall bring to ripeness: she shall be
A pattern to all princes living with her,
And all that shall succeed: Saba was never
More covetous of wisdom and fair virtue
Than this pure soul shall be: all princely graces,
That mould up such a mighty piece as this is,
With all the virtues that attend the good,
Shall still be doubled on her: truth shall nurse her,
Holy and heavenly thoughts still counsel her:
She shall be loved and feared: her own shall bless her;
Her foes shake like a field of beaten corn,
And hang their heads with sorrow: good grows with her:
In her days every man shall eat in safety,
Under his own vine, what he plants; and sing
The merry songs of peace to all his neighbours:
God shall be truly known; and those about her
From her shall read the perfect ways of honour,
And by those claim their greatness, not by blood.

KING. Thou speakest wonders.

CRANMER. She shall be, to the happiness of England,
An aged princess; many days shall see her,
And yet no day without a deed to crown it.
Would I had known no more! but she must die,
She must, the saints must have her; yet a virgin,
A most unspotted lily shall she pass,
And all the world shall mourn her.

KING. O lord archbishop,
Thou hast made me now a man! Never, before
This happy child, did I get anything:
This oracle of comfort has so pleased me,
That when I am in heaven I shall desire
To see what this child does, and praise my Maker.
I thank ye all. To you, my good lord mayor,
And your good brethren, I am much beholding;
I have received much honour by your presence,
And ye shall find me thankful. Lead the way, lords:
Ye must all see the queen, and she must thank ye,
She will be sick else. This day no man think
He has business at his house, for all shall stay:
This little one shall make it holiday.

The Story of Othello

WITH Macbeth and King Lear the pitiful tale of Othello completes the trio of Shakespeare's greatest tragedies. It is one of the most powerful and terrible studies of jealousy in all our literature.

OTHELLO is a Moor in Venice, a generous and honest man in love and friendship. Incapable of deceit himself, he is incapable of suspecting it in others, but the seeds of jealousy sown in his impulsive nature destroy the natural balance of his character. His finer qualities fail him, and the simple Othello is a changed man. His simple but passionate Oriental mind flares up with anger and injustice. He is torn by doubt and racked by anguish. He sees nothing but treachery where all is well, and where belief should have been his instinctive duty. He is at the mercy of a lie told to destroy him.

IAGO, Othello's standard-bearer as we should call him, his Ancient as they called him then, is matchless in Shakespeare as a human instrument of devilry. In almost the first line of the play he is seeking vengeance for some imaginary wrong, and he pursues it with almost incredible malevolence to the end. He is himself a victim of jealousy, jealousy of ambition directed against the frank, genial, loyal, but superficial Cassio. Imagining himself wronged, he sets out to ruin Cassio by striking at the happiness of an almost perfect union of hearts.

THE development of Iago's plot is managed with the poet's utmost skill. Iago makes us feel at times that if Satan's throne were vacant he could fill it easily, and yet, as he moves step by step along his ruthless way, he is all unsuspected, so ingenious are his trickeries, so single-hearted is the pure Othello.

THE tragedy moves on until the heart is almost breaking, yet never once until too late does the truth dawn on Othello's mind. His innocence of the plot being woven about him is matched only by the innocence of the victim of it all, the glorious Desdemona, who loved him for the dangers he had passed and loved him through all the danger she is in. Shakespeare has no nobler character than hers; she is true till death. In the face of the vilest accusations she never for a moment loses the delicacy and modesty that have made her one of the most beloved of all the women of Shakespeare. She loves Othello while his love for her is wavering and failing.

AS for Othello, we see his noble nature consumed and wrecked. His love for Desdemona is almost a religion; when faith in Desdemona goes the world for him is done.

SO this long tragedy draws to its end, in a scene that has moved the hearts of men since it was acted first in Whitehall in the seventeenth century. Its poignancy is intense; we see the powers of evil wreck two noble lives and break two noble hearts. It is a dark piece of life, painted by one of the master artists of the world.

THE PLAYERS

Duke of Venice, a gentle-minded ruler.

Othello, a nobleman of Morocco, serving Venice as a general; secretly married to Desdemona. Too honest to suspect deceit in a false friend who poisons his mind.

Brabantio, a Senator; the impetuous father of Desdemona.

Gratiano, brother of Brabantio.

Lodovico, kinsman of Brabantio.

Cassio, lieutenant to Othello; victim of Iago's treachery.

Iago, ancient (or ensign) to Othello; the master mind and villain of the play.

Roderigo, a young Venetian, vicious and credulous; the dupe of Iago.

Montano, governing Cyprus for Venice before Othello's arrival.

Desdemona, daughter of Brabantio. She "loved Othello for the dangers he had passed."

Emilia, the trustful wife of Iago, attending Desdemona.

Bianca, a companion of Cassio.

Senators, sailors, officers, musicians, attendants, and a herald.

SCENES—In Venice and at a seaport in Cyprus

Othello, the Moor of Venice

ACT 1

Scene 1—A Street in Venice : Roderigo and Iago

RODERIGO. Tush ! never tell me ; I take it much unkindly
That thou, Iago, who hast had my purse
As if the strings were thine, shouldst know of this.

IAGO. If ever I did dream of such a matter,
Abhor me.

RODERIGO. Thou told'st me thou didst hold him in thy hate.

IAGO. Despise me if I do not. Three great ones of the city,
In personal suit to make me his lieutenant,
Off-capped to him : and, by the faith of man,
I know my price, I am worth no worse a place ;
But he, as loving his own pride and purposes,
Evades them, with a bombast circumstance
Horribly stuffed with epithets of war,
And, in conclusion,
Nonsuits my mediators ; for, *Certes*, says he,
I have already chose my officer.
And what was he ?
Forsooth, a great arithmetician,
One Michael Cassio, a Florentine,
That never set a squadron in the field,
Nor the division of a battle knows
More than a spinster ; mere prattle, without practice,
Is all his soldiership. But he, sir, had the election :
And I, of whom his eyes had seen the proof
At Rhodes, at Cyprus, and on other grounds
Christian and heathen, must be be-lee'd and calmed
By debitor and creditor : this counter-caster,
He, in good time, must his lieutenant be,
And I (God bless the mark !) his Moorship's ancient.

RODERIGO. By heaven, I rather would have been his hangman.

IAGO. Why, there's no remedy ; tis the curse of service,
Preferment goes by letter and affection,
And not by old gradation, where each second
Stood heir to the first. Now, sir, be judge yourself,
Whether I in any just term am affined
To love the Moor.

RODERIGO. I would not follow him then.

IAGO. O, sir, content you ;
I follow him to serve my turn upon him :
We cannot all be masters, nor all masters
Cannot be truly followed. You shall mark
Many a duteous and knee-crooking knave,
That, doting on his own obsequious bondage,
Wears out his time, much like his master's ass,
For nought but provender, and when he's old, cashiered :
Whip me such honest knaves. Others there are
Who, trimmed in forms and visages of duty,
Keep yet their hearts attending on themselves,
And, throwing but shows of service on their lords,
Do well thrive by them, and when they have lined their coats
Do themselves homage : these fellows have some soul ;
And such a one do I profess myself. For, sir,
It is as sure as you are Roderigo,
Were I the Moor, I would not be Iago :
In following him, I follow but myself ;
Heaven is my judge, not I for love and duty,
But seeming so, for my peculiar end :
For when my outward action doth demonstrate
The native act and figure of my heart
In compliment extern, tis not long after
But I will wear my heart upon my sleeve
For daws to peck at : I am not what I am.

Roderigo has been a suitor for the hand of Desdemona, and Iago now persuades him to wake Brabantio and tell him that Othello has stolen his daughter. Desdemona is declared to be missing, and her angry father takes steps to bring Othello before the Senate. Iago proves that Desdemona and Othello are secretly married, sees the fire of mischief well alight, and steals away to his master Othello.

Scene 2—A Street in Venice

Enter Othello and Iago with Attendants carrying torches

IAGO. Though in the trade of war I have slain men,
Yet do I hold it very stuff o' the conscience
To do no contrived murder : I lack iniquity
Sometimes to do me service : nine or ten times
I had thought to have yerked him here under the ribs.

OTHELLO. Tis better as it is.

IAGO. Nay, but he prated,
And spoke such scurvy and provoking terms
Against your honour
That, with the little godliness I have,
I did full hard forbear him.

Be assured of this, he will divorce you;
Or put upon you what restraint and grievance
The law, with all his might to enforce it on,
Will give him cable.

OTHELLO. Let him do his spite:
My services which I have done the signiory
Shall out-tongue his complaints. Tis yet to know
(Which, when I know that boasting is an honour,
I shall promulgate), I fetch my life and being
From men of royal siege, and my demerits
May speak unbonneted to as proud a fortune
As this that I have reached: for know, Iago,
But that I love the gentle Desdemona,
I would not my unhoused free condition
Put into circumscription and confine
For the sea's worth. But, look! what lights come yond?

IAGO. Those are the raisèd father and his friends:
You were best go in.

OTHELLO. Not I: I must be found:
My parts, my title, and my perfect soul
Shall manifest me rightly. Is it they?

IAGO. By Janus, I think no.

Enter Cassio, and certain officers with torches

OTHELLO. The servants of the duke, and my lieutenant.
The goodness of the night upon you, friends!
What is the news?

CASSIO. The duke does greet you, general,
And he requires your haste-post-haste appearance,
Even on the instant.

OTHELLO. What is the matter, think you?

CASSIO. Something from Cyprus, as I may divine:
It is a business of some heat: the galleys
Have sent a dozen sequent messengers
This very night at one another's heels,
And many of the consuls, raised and met,
Are at the duke's already: you have been hotly called for;
When being not at your lodging to be found
The Senate hath sent about three several quests
To search you out.

OTHELLO. Tis well I am found by you.

Enter Brabantio, Roderigo, and officers with torches and weapons

OTHELLO. Holla! stand there!

RODERIGO. Signior, it is the Moor.

BRABANTIO. Down with him, thief!

Both sides draw swords

IAGO. You, Roderigo ! come, sir, I am for you.

OTHELLO. Keep up your bright swords, for the dew will rust them.
Good signior, you shall more command with years
Than with your weapons.

BRABANTIO. O thou foul thief, where hast thou stowed my daughter ?
Cursed as thou art, thou hast enchanted her ;
For I'll refer me to all things of sense,
If she in chains of magic were not bound,
Whether a maid so tender, fair, and happy,
So opposite to marriage that she shunned
The wealthy curlèd darlings of our nation,
Would ever have, to incur a general mock,
Run from her guardage to the sooty bosom
Of such a thing as thou, to fear, not to delight.
Judge me the world, if tis not
That thou hast practised on her with foul charms ;
Tis probable and palpable to thinking.
I therefore apprehend and do attach thee
For an abuser of the world, a practiser
Of arts inhibited and out of warrant.
Lay hold upon him : if he do resist,
Subdue him at his peril.

OTHELLO. Hold your hands :
Were it my cue to fight, I should have known it
Without a prompter. Where will you that I go
To answer this your charge ?

BRABANTIO. To prison, till fit time
Of law and course of direct session
Call thee to answer.

OTHELLO. What if I do obey ?
How may the duke be therewith satisfied,
Whose messengers are here about my side,
Upon some present business of the State
To bring me to him ?

FIRST OFFICER. Tis true, most worthy signior ;
The duke's in council, and your noble self,
I am sure, is sent for.

BRABANTIO. How ! the duke in council !
In this time of the night ! Bring him away :
Mine's not an idle cause : the duke himself,
Or any of my brothers of the State
Cannot but feel this wrong as 'twere their own.
For if such actions may have passage free,
Bond-slaves and pagans shall our statesmen be.

Scene 3—A Council Chamber

The Duke and the Senators are sitting at a table, alarmed by the news that the Turks are making for Cyprus. They are discussing the matter when "here come Brabantio and the valiant Moor" with Iago and Roderigo.

DUKE. Valiant Othello, we must straight employ you
Against the general enemy Ottoman.
(To Brabantio) I did not see you ; welcome, gentle signior ;
We lacked your counsel and your help tonight.

BRABANTIO. So did I yours. Good your grace, pardon me ;
Neither my place nor aught I heard of business
Hath raised me from my bed, nor doth the general care
Take hold on me, for my particular grief
Is of so flood-gate and o'erbearing nature
That it engluts and swallows other sorrows
And it is still itself.

DUKE. Why, what's the matter ?

BRABANTIO. My daughter ! O, my daughter !

DUKE AND SENATORS. Dead ?

BRABANTIO. Ay, to me ;
She is abused, stolen from me, and corrupted
By spells and medicines bought of mountebanks ;
For nature so preposterously to err,
Being not deficient, blind, or lame of sense,
Sans witchcraft could not.

DUKE. Whoe'er he be that in this foul proceeding
Hath thus beguiled your daughter of herself
And you of her, the rigid book of law
You shall yourself read in the bitter letter
After your own sense, yea, though our proper son
Stood in your action.

BRABANTIO. Humbly I thank your grace.
Here is the man, this Moor, whom now, it seems,
Your special mandate for the State affairs
Hath hither brought.

DUKE AND SENATORS. We are very sorry for 't.
(To Othello) What in your own part can you say to this ?

OTHELLO. Most potent, grave, and reverend signiors,
My very noble and approved good masters,
That I have ta'en away this old man's daughter,
It is most true ; true, I have married her :
The very head and front of my offending
Hath this extent, no more. Rude am I in my speech,
And little blessed with the soft phrase of peace,
For since these arms of mine had seven years' pith,
Till now some nine moons wasted, they have used
Their dearest action in the tented field,

And little of this great world can I speak,
More than pertains to feats of broil and battle,
And therefore little shall I grace my cause
In speaking for myself. Yet, by your gracious patience,
I will a round unvarnished tale deliver
Of my whole course of love; what drugs, what charms,
What conjuration and what mighty magic,
For such proceeding I am charged withal,
I won his daughter.

BRABANTIO. A maiden never bold;
Of spirit so still and quiet that her motion
Blushed at herself; and she, in spite of nature,
Of years, of country, credit, everything,
To fall in love with what she feared to look on!
It is a judgment maimed and most imperfect
That will confess perfection so could err
Against all rules of nature. I therefore vouch again
That with some mixtures powerful o'er the blood,
Or with some dram conjured to this effect,
He wrought upon her.

DUKE. To vouch this is no proof,
Without more wider and more overt test
Than these thin habits and poor likelihoods
Of modern seeming do prefer against him.

FIRST SENATOR. But, Othello, speak:
Did you by indirect and forcèd courses
Subdue and poison this young maid's affections?
Or came it by request and such fair question
As soul to soul affordeth?

OTHELLO. I do beseech you,
Send for the lady to the Sagittary,
And let her speak of me before her father:
If you do find me foul in her report,
The trust, the office I do hold of you,
Not only take away, but let your sentence
Even fall upon my life.

DUKE. Fetch Desdemona hither.

OTHELLO. Ancient, conduct them; you best know the place.

Iago goes

And, till she come, as truly as to heaven
I do confess the vices of my blood,
So justly to your grave ears I'll present
How I did thrive in this fair lady's love,
And she in mine.

DUKE. Say it, Othello.

OTHELLO. Her father loved me; oft invited me;
Still questioned me the story of my life,
From year to year, the battles, sieges, fortunes,
That I have passed.
I ran it through, even from my boyish days,
To the very moment that he bade me tell it;
Wherein I spake of most disastrous chances,
Of moving accidents by flood and field,
Of hairbreadth scapes in the imminent deadly breach,
Of being taken by the insolent foe
And sold to slavery, of my redemption thence
And portance in my travels' history:
Wherein of caverns vast and deserts idle,
Rough quarries, rocks and hills whose heads touch heaven,
It was my hint to speak—such was the process;
And of the cannibals that each other eat,
The Anthropophagi, and men whose heads
Do grow beneath their shoulders. This to hear
Would Desdemona seriously incline:
But still the house affairs would draw her thence:
Which ever as she could with haste dispatch,
She'd come again, and with a greedy ear
Devour up my discourse: which I observing,
Took once a pliant hour, and found good means
To draw from her a prayer of earnest heart
That I would all my pilgrimage dilate,
Whereof by parcels she had something heard,
But not intentively: I did consent,
And often did beguile her of her tears,
When I did speak of some distressful stroke
That my youth suffered. My story being done,
She gave me for my pains a world of sighs:
She swore, in faith, 'twas strange, 'twas passing strange,
Twas pitiful, 'twas wondrous pitiful:
She wished she had not heard it, yet she wished
That heaven had made her such a man: she thanked me,
And bade me, if I had a friend that loved her,
I should but teach him how to tell my story,
And that would woo her. Upon this hint I spake:
She loved me for the dangers I had passed,
And I loved her that she did pity them.
This only is the witchcraft I have used:
Here comes the lady; let her witness it.

Enter Desdemona, Iago, and Attendants

DUKE. I think this tale would win my daughter too.
Good Brabantio,

Take up this mangled matter at the best:
Men do their broken weapons rather use
Than their bare hands.

BRABANTIO. I pray you, hear her speak:
If she confess that she was half the wooer,
Destruction on my head if my bad blame
Light on the man! Come hither, gentle mistress:
Do you perceive in all this noble company
Where most you owe obedience?

DESDEMONA. My noble father,
I do perceive here a divided duty:
To you I am bound for life and education;
My life and education both do learn me
How to respect you; you are the lord of duty;
I am hitherto your daughter. But here's my husband,
And so much duty as my mother showed
To you, preferring you before her father,
So much I challenge that I may profess
Due to the Moor my lord.

BRABANTIO. God be wi' you! I have done.
Please it your grace, on to the State affairs.
Come hither, Moor:
I here do give thee that with all my heart
Which, but thou hast already, with all my heart
I would keep from thee. For your sake, jewel,
I am glad at soul I have no other child;
For thy escape would teach me tyranny,
To hang clogs on them. I have done, my lord.

DUKE. Let me speak like yourself, and lay a sentence.
When remedies are past, the griefs are ended
By seeing the worst, which late on hopes depended.
To mourn a mischief that is past and gone
Is the next way to draw new mischief on.
The robbed that smiles steals something from the thief;
He robs himself that spends a bootless grief.

BRABANTIO. So let the Turk of Cyprus us beguile;
We lose it not, so long as we can smile.
These sentences, to sugar, or to gall,
Being strong on both sides, are equivocal:
But words are words; I never yet did hear
That the bruised heart was piercèd through the ear.
I humbly beseech you, proceed to the affairs of State.

DUKE. The Turk with a most mighty preparation makes for Cyprus. Othello, the fortitude of the place is best known to you; and though we have there a substitute of most allowed sufficiency, yet opinion, a sovereign mistress of effects, throws a safer voice on you: you must therefore be content to sully the gloss of your new fortunes with this more stubborn and boisterous expedition.

OTHELLO. The tyrant custom, most grave senators,
Hath made the flinty and steel couch of war
My thrice-driven bed of down: I do confess
A natural and prompt alacrity
I find in hardness, and do undertake
These present wars against the Ottomites.

Othello "must away tonight," and Desdemona is permitted to go with him. Roderigo, filled with rage and misery, threatens to drown himself. Iago scoffs at him. Iago and Emilia are to accompany Desdemona to Cyprus, and Roderigo is invited to join them. Desdemona, says Iago, will soon tire of Othello, and Roderigo may hope to win her. Roderigo agrees, and leaves Iago chuckling over a knavery well launched.

ACT 2

Scene 1—A Seaport in Cyprus

A great storm is raging, and Montano, Governor of Cyprus, is looking out to sea anxiously, fearing for Othello. Messengers report that the storm has shattered the Turkish fleet, and Cassio, Othello's lieutenant, who lands in safety, reports that Iago and Desdemona together in one ship and Othello in another are sailing through the storm, Iago's vessel being near at hand. Who is Desdemona? asks Montano.

CASSIO. She that I spake of, our great captain's captain,
Left in the conduct of the bold Iago,
Whose footing here anticipates our thoughts
At se'nnight's speed. Great Jove, Othello guard,
And swell his sail with thine own powerful breath,
That he may bless this bay with his tall ship,
And bring all Cyprus comfort!

Enter Desdemona, Emilia, Iago, Roderigo, and attendants

O, behold, the riches of the ship is come on shore!
Ye men of Cyprus, let her have your knees.
Hail to thee, lady! and the grace of heaven,
Before, behind thee, and on every hand,
Enwheel thee round!

DESDEMONA. I thank you, valiant Cassio.
What tidings can you tell me of my lord?

CASSIO. He is not yet arrived: nor know I aught
But that he's well and will be shortly here.

DESDEMONA. O, but I fear—How lost you company?

CASSIO. The great contention of the sea and skies
Parted our fellowship—But, hark!
Lo, where he comes!

OTHELLO *(entering)*. O my fair warrior!

DESDEMONA. My dear Othello!

OTHELLO. It gives me wonder great as my content
To see you here before me. O my soul's joy!
If after every tempest come such calms,
May the winds blow till they have wakened death!

DESDEMONA. The heavens forbid
But that our loves and comforts should increase,
Even as our days do grow!

OTHELLO. Amen to that, sweet powers!
I cannot speak enough of this content;
It stops me here; it is too much of joy:
And this, and this *(kissing her)*, the greatest discords be
That e'er our hearts shall make!

IAGO *(aside)*. O, you are well tuned now!
But I'll set down the pegs that make this music,
As honest as I am.

OTHELLO. Come, let us to the castle.
News, friends; our wars are done, the Turks are drowned.
How does my old acquaintance of this isle?
Honey, you shall be well desired in Cyprus;
I have found great love amongst them. O my sweet,
I prattle out of fashion, and I dote
In mine own comforts. I prithee, good Iago,
Go to the bay and disembark my coffers:
Bring thou the master to the citadel;
He is a good one, and his worthiness
Does challenge much respect. Come, Desdemona,
Once more, well met at Cyprus.

Othello, Desdemona, and Attendants go, leaving Iago and Roderigo

IAGO. Do thou meet me presently at the harbour. Come hither. If thou be'st valiant, list me. The lieutenant tonight watches on the court of guard: first, I must tell thee this—Desdemona is directly in love with him.

Iago's jealous mind imagines that Othello and Cassio are in love with his wife Emilia, and he decides to strike at Cassio through Roderigo, who agrees to provoke a quarrel with Cassio and leave it to Iago to incite a riot, which will pain and anger the law-abiding Othello.

Scene 2—A Proclamation in the Street

HERALD. It is Othello's pleasure, our noble and valiant general, that every man put himself into triumph; some to dance, some to make bonfires, each man to what sport and revels his addiction leads him. All offices are open, and there is full liberty of feasting from this present hour of five till the bell have told eleven. Heaven bless the isle of Cyprus and our noble general Othello!

Scene 3—A Hall in the Castle

Enter Othello, Desdemona, and Cassio

OTHELLO. Good Michael, look you to the guard tonight:
Let's teach ourselves that honourable stop,
Not to outsport discretion.

CASSIO. Iago hath direction what to do;
But, notwithstanding, with my personal eye
Will I look to 't.

OTHELLO. Iago is most honest.
Michael, Good-night: tomorrow with your earliest
Let me have speech with you. Come, my dear love.

He leaves with Desdemona as Iago enters

CASSIO. Welcome, Iago; we must to the watch.

IAGO. Not this hour, lieutenant; tis not yet ten o' the clock. Our general cast us thus early for the love of his Desdemona.

CASSIO. She's a most exquisite lady. She is indeed perfection.

IAGO. Well, happiness to their marriage. Come, lieutenant, I have a stoup of wine; and here without are a brace of Cyprus gallants that would fain have a measure to the health of black Othello.

CASSIO. Not tonight, good Iago: I have very poor and unhappy brains for drinking; I could well wish courtesy would invent some other custom of entertainment.

IAGO. O, they are our friends; but one cup: I'll drink for you.

Iago, much against Cassio's will, tempts Cassio to drink in company with Montano and other gentlemen of Cyprus. A quarrel with Roderigo leads to fighting in which Montano is wounded, while Roderigo, prompted by Iago, runs out crying Mutiny, to ring the alarm bell of the city. Othello bursts in upon this scene indignantly.

OTHELLO. Hold, for your lives!

IAGO. Hold, ho! Lieutenant—sir—Montano—gentlemen,
Have you forgot all sense of place and duty?
Hold, the General speaks to you: hold, hold, for shame!

OTHELLO. Why, how now, ho! from whence ariseth this?
For Christian shame, put by this barbarous brawl:
He that stirs next to carve for his own rage
Holds his soul light; he dies upon his motion.
Silence that dreadful bell: it frights the isle
From her propriety. What is the matter, masters?
Honest Iago, that look'st dead with grieving,
Speak, who began this? on thy love, I charge thee.

IAGO. I do not know: friends all but now, and then,
As if some planet had unwitted men,
Swords out, and tilting one at other's breast.

OTHELLO. How comes it, Michael, you are thus forgot?

CASSIO. I pray you, pardon me; I cannot speak.

OTHELLO. Worthy Montano, you were wont be civil;
The gravity and stillness of your youth
The world hath noted, and your name is great
In mouths of wisest censure: what's the matter,
That you unlace your reputation thus
And spend your rich opinion for the name
Of a night-brawler?

MONTANO. Worthy Othello, I am hurt to danger:
Your officer, Iago, can inform you
Of all that I do know: nor know I aught
By me that's said or done amiss this night.

OTHELLO. Now, by heaven,
My blood begins my safer guides to rule,
And passion, having my best judgment collied,
Assays to lead the way: if I once stir,
Or do but lift this arm, the best of you
Shall sink in my rebuke. Give me to know
How this foul rout began, who set it on;
And he that is approved in this offence,
Though he had twinned with me, both at a birth,
Shall lose me. Iago, who began 't?

IAGO. Thus it is, general.
Montano and myself being in speech,
There comes a fellow crying out for help:
And Cassio following him with determined sword,
To execute upon him. Sir, this gentleman
Steps in to Cassio, and entreats his pause:
Myself the crying fellow did pursue,
Lest by his clamour (as it so fell out)
The town might fall in fright: he, swift of foot,
Outran my purpose; and I returned the rather
For that I heard the clink and fall of swords,
And Cassio high in oath; which till tonight
I ne'er might say before. When I came back
(For this was brief) I found them close together,
At blow and thrust; even as again they were
When you yourself did part them.
More of this matter cannot I report:
But men are men; the best sometimes forget:
Though Cassio did some little wrong to him,
As men in rage strike those that wish them best,
Yet surely Cassio, I believe, received
From him that fled some strange indignity,
Which patience could not pass.

OTHELLO. I know, Iago,
Thy honesty and love doth mince this matter,
Making it light to Cassio. Cassio, I love thee;
But never more be officer of mine.

DESDEMONA *(entering)*. What's the matter?

OTHELLO. All's well now;
Come, Desdemona: tis the soldiers' life
To have their balmy slumbers waked with strife.

All but Iago and Cassio leave

IAGO. What, are you hurt, lieutenant?

CASSIO. Ay, past all surgery.

IAGO. Marry, heaven forbid!

CASSIO. Reputation, reputation, reputation! O, I have lost my reputation! I have lost the immortal part of myself. My reputation, Iago, my reputation!

IAGO. As I am an honest man, I thought you had received some bodily wound; there is more sense in that than in reputation. Reputation is an idle and most false imposition, oft got without merit, and lost without deserving: you have lost no reputation at all, unless you repute yourself such a loser. What, man! there are ways to recover the general again: you are but now cast in his mood, a punishment more in policy than in malice; even so as one would beat his offenceless dog to affright an imperious lion: sue to him again, and he's yours.

CASSIO. I will rather sue to be despised than to deceive so good a commander with so slight, so drunken, and so indiscreet an officer. Drunk? and speak parrot? and squabble? swagger? swear? and discourse fustian with one's own shadow? O thou invisible spirit of wine, if thou hast no name to be known by let us call thee Devil!

IAGO. What was he that you followed with your sword? What had he done to you?

CASSIO. I know not.

IAGO. Is't possible?

CASSIO. I remember a mass of things, but nothing distinctly; a quarrel, but nothing wherefore. O God, that men should put an enemy in their mouths to steal away their brains, that we should, with joy, pleasance, revel, and applause, transform ourselves into beasts!

IAGO. Come, you are too severe a moraler: as the time, the place, and the condition of this country stands, I could heartily wish this had not befallen; but, since it is as it is, mend it for your own good.

CASSIO. I will ask him for my place again; he shall tell me I am a drunkard! Had I as many mouths as Hydra such an answer would stop them all. To be now a sensible man, by and by a fool, and presently a beast! O strange!

With venomous cunning Iago moulds the guileless Cassio to his will. He suggests that Cassio should seek the goodwill of Desdemona who will plead for him with Othello. Cassio is willing, and Iago rejoices at the opportunity to poison the mind of Othello by misrepresenting the nature of the meeting between Desdemona and Cassio. In the meantime Roderigo complains that he has been beaten by Cassio, has spent all his money, and regrets having left Venice.

ACT 3

Scene 1—Before the Castle: Cassio and Musicians

CASSIO. Masters, play here; I will content your pains;
Something that's brief; and bid *Good-morrow, general.* *(Music)*

CLOWN. Masters, here's money for you: and the general so likes your music, that he desires you, for love's sake, to make no more noise with it.

FIRST MUSICIAN. Well, sir, we will not.

CLOWN. If you have any music that may not be heard, to 't again: but, as they say, to hear music the general does not greatly care.

FIRST MUSICIAN. We have none such, sir.

CLOWN. Then put up your pipes in your bag, for I'll away: go; vanish into air; away!

CASSIO *(to Clown)*. Dost thou hear, my honest friend?

CLOWN. No, I hear not your honest friend; I hear you.

CASSIO. Prithee, keep up thy quillets. There's a poor piece of gold for thee: if the gentlewoman that attends the general's wife be stirring, tell her there's one Cassio entreats her a little favour of speech: wilt thou do this?

CLOWN. She is stirring, sir: if she will stir hither, I shall seem to notify unto her.

CASSIO. Do, good my friend. *(Clown leaves)*

IAGO *(entering)*. You have not been a-bed, then?

CASSIO. Why, no; the day had broke
Before we parted. I have made bold, Iago,
To send in to your wife: my suit to her
Is that she will to virtuous Desdemona
Procure me some access.

IAGO. I'll send her to you presently;
And I'll devise a mean to draw the Moor
Out of the way, that your converse and business
May be more free.

CASSIO. I humbly thank you for 't. I never knew
A Florentine more kind and honest.

Iago goes and Emilia enters

EMILIA. Good-morrow, good lieutenant: I am sorry
For your displeasure, but all will sure be well.
The general and his wife are talking of it,
And she speaks for you stoutly: the Moor replies
That he you hurt is of great fame in Cyprus
And great affinity, and that in wholesome wisdom
He might not but refuse you, but he protests he loves you
And needs no other suitor but his likings
To take the safest occasion by the front
To bring you in again.

CASSIO. Yet, I beseech you,
If you think fit, or that it may be done,
Give me advantage of some brief discourse
With Desdemona alone.

EMILIA. Pray you, come in:
I will bestow you where you will have time
To speak your bosom freely.

CASSIO. I am much bound to you.

Scene 2—A Room in the Castle

In this brief scene Othello leaves to view a fortification, while Iago goes to deliver letters.

Scene 3—The Garden of the Castle

Enter Desdemona, Cassio, and Emilia

DESDEMONA. Be thou assured, good Cassio, I will do
All my abilities in thy behalf.

EMILIA. Good madam, do: I warrant it grieves my husband
As if the case were his.

DESDEMONA. O, that's an honest fellow. Do not doubt, Cassio,
But I will have my lord and you again
As friendly as you were.

CASSIO. Bounteous madam,
Whatever shall become of Michael Cassio,
He's never anything but your true servant.

DESDEMONA. I know 't; I thank you. You do love my lord:
You have known him long; and be you well assured
He shall in strangeness stand no farther off
Than in a politic distance.

CASSIO. Ay, but, lady,
That policy may either last so long,
Or feed upon such nice and waterish diet,
Or breed itself so out of circumstance,
That, I being absent and my place supplied,
My general will forget my love and service.

DESDEMONA. Do not doubt that; before Emilia here
I give thee warrant of thy place: assure thee,
If I do vow a friendship, I'll perform it
To the last article: my lord shall never rest;
I'll watch him tame and talk him out of patience;
I'll intermingle everything he does
With Cassio's suit: therefore be merry, Cassio;
For thy solicitor shall rather die
Than give thy cause away.

EMILIA. Madam, here comes my lord.

CASSIO. Madam, I'll take my leave.

DESDEMONA. Why, stay, and hear me speak.

CASSIO. Madam, not now: I am very ill at ease,
Unfit for mine own purposes.

DESDEMONA. Well, do your discretion.

Cassio leaves as Othello and Iago enter

IAGO. Ha! I like not that.

OTHELLO. What dost thou say?

IAGO. Nothing, my lord: or if—I know not what.

OTHELLO. Was not that Cassio parted from my wife?

IAGO. Cassio, my lord! No, sure, I cannot think it,
That he would steal away so guilty-like,
Seeing you coming.

OTHELLO. I do believe 'twas he.

DESDEMONA. How now, my lord!
I have been talking with a suitor here,
A man that languishes in your displeasure.

OTHELLO. Who is 't you mean?

DESDEMONA. Why, your lieutenant, Cassio. Good my lord,
If I have any grace or power to move you,
His present reconciliation take;
For if he be not one that truly loves you,
That errs in ignorance and not in cunning,
I have no judgment in an honest face:
I prithee, call him back.

OTHELLO. Went he hence now?

DESDEMONA. Ay, sooth; so humbled
That he hath left part of his grief with me,
To suffer with him. Good love, call him back.

OTHELLO. Not now, sweet Desdemona; some other time.

DESDEMONA. But shall 't be shortly?

OTHELLO. The sooner, sweet, for you.

DESDEMONA. Shall 't be tonight at supper?

OTHELLO. No, not tonight.

DESDEMONA. Tomorrow dinner, then ?

OTHELLO. I shall not dine at home ;
I meet the captains at the citadel.

DESDEMONA. Why, then, tomorrow night ; or Tuesday morn ;
On Tuesday noon, or night ; on Wednesday morn :
I prithee, name the time, but let it not
Exceed three days : in faith, he's penitent :
When shall he come ?
Tell me, Othello : I wonder in my soul
What you would ask me that I should deny.

OTHELLO. Prithee, no more : let him come when he will ;
I will deny thee nothing.

DESDEMONA. Why, this is not a boon ;
Tis as I should entreat you wear your gloves,
Or feed on nourishing dishes, or keep you warm ;
Nay, when I have a suit
Wherein I mean to touch your love indeed,
It shall be full of poise and difficult weight
And fearful to be granted.

OTHELLO. I will deny thee nothing :
Whereon, I do beseech thee, grant me this,
To leave me but a little to myself.

DESDEMONA. Shall I deny you ? no : farewell, my lord.

OTHELLO. Farewell, my Desdemona : I'll come to thee straight.

DESDEMONA. Emilia, come. Be as your fancies teach you ;
Whate'er you be, I am obedient. *(Desdemona and Emilia go)*

OTHELLO. Excellent wretch ! Perdition catch my soul,
But I do love thee, and when I love thee not
Chaos is come again.

IAGO. My noble lord—

OTHELLO. What dost thou say, Iago ?

IAGO. Did Michael Cassio, when you wooed my lady,
Know of your love ?

OTHELLO. He did, from first to last : why dost thou ask ?

IAGO. But for a satisfaction of my thought ;
No further harm.

OTHELLO. Why of thy thought, Iago ?

IAGO. I did not think he had been acquainted with her.

OTHELLO. O, yes ; and went between us very oft.

IAGO. Indeed !

OTHELLO. Indeed ! ay, indeed : discern'st thou aught in that ?
Is he not honest ?

IAGO. Honest, my lord !

OTHELLO. Honest! ay, honest.

IAGO. My lord, for aught I know.

OTHELLO. What dost thou think?

IAGO. Think, my lord!

OTHELLO. Think, my lord! By heaven, he echoes me,
As if there were some monster in his thought
Too hideous to be shown. Thou dost mean something:
I heard thee say even now thou likedst not that,
When Cassio left my wife. What didst not like?
And when I told thee he was of my counsel
In my whole course of wooing, thou criedst *Indeed!*
And didst contract and purse thy brow together,
As if thou then hadst shut up in thy brain
Some horrible conceit: if thou dost love me,
Show me thy thought.

IAGO. My lord, you know I love you.

OTHELLO. I think thou dost;
And, for I know thou'rt full of love and honesty,
And weigh'st thy words before thou givest them breath,
Therefore these stops of thine fright me the more:

IAGO. For Michael Cassio,
I dare be sworn I think that he is honest.

OTHELLO. I think so too. Yet there's more in this:
I prithee, speak to me as to thy thinkings,
As thou dost ruminate, and give thy worst of thoughts
The worst of words.

IAGO. Good my lord, pardon me:
Though I am bound to every act of duty,
I am not bound to that all slaves are free to.
Utter my thoughts? Why, say they are vile and false;
As where's that palace whereinto foul things
Sometimes intrude not? Who has a breast so pure,
But some uncleanly apprehensions
Keep leets and law-days and in session sit
With meditations lawful?

OTHELLO. Thou dost conspire against thy friend, Iago,
If thou but think'st him wronged and makest his ear
A stranger to thy thoughts.

IAGO. I do beseech you—
It were not for your quiet nor your good,
Nor for my manhood, honesty, or wisdom,
To let you know my thoughts.

OTHELLO. What dost thou mean?

IAGO. Good name in man and woman, dear my lord,
Is the immediate jewel of their souls:

Who steals my purse steals trash ; tis something, nothing ;
Twas mine, tis his, and has been slave to thousands ;
But he that filches from me my good name
Robs me of that which not enriches him
And makes me poor indeed.

OTHELLO. By heaven, I'll know thy thoughts.

IAGO. You cannot, if my heart were in your hand ;
Nor shall not, whilst tis in my custody.

OTHELLO. Ha !

IAGO. O, beware, my lord, of jealousy ;
It is the green-eyed monster which doth mock
The meat it feeds on.
O, what desperate minutes tells he o'er
Who dotes, yet doubts, suspects, yet strongly loves !

OTHELLO. O misery !
Good heaven, the souls of all my tribe defend
From jealousy ! Why, why is this ?
Think'st thou I'd make a life of jealousy,
To follow still the changes of the moon
With fresh suspicions ? No ; to be once in doubt
Is once to be resolved. Tis not to make me jealous
To say my wife is fair, feeds well, loves company,
Is free of speech, sings, plays, and dances well ;
Where virtue is, these are more virtuous :
Nor from mine own weak merits will I draw
The smallest fear or doubt of her revolt ;
For she had eyes, and chose me. No, Iago ;
I'll see before I doubt ; when I doubt, prove ;
And on the proof there is no more but this :
Away at once with love or jealousy !

IAGO. I am glad of it, for now I shall have reason
To show the love and duty that I bear you
With franker spirit : therefore, as I am bound,
Receive it from me. I speak not yet of proof.
Look to your wife ; observe her well with Cassio ;
Wear your eye thus, not jealous nor secure :
I would not have your free and noble nature,
Out of self-bounty, be abused ; look to 't.
But I am much to blame ;
I humbly do beseech you of your pardon
For too much loving you.

OTHELLO. I am bound to thee for ever.

IAGO. I see this hath a little dashed your spirits.

OTHELLO. Not a jot, not a jot.

IAGO. I' faith, I fear it has.
I hope you will consider what is spoke
Comes from my love. But I do see you're moved:
I am to pray you not to strain my speech
To grosser issues nor to larger reach
Than to suspicion.

OTHELLO. I will not.

IAGO. Should you do so, my lord,
My speech should fall into such vile success
As my thoughts aim not at. Cassio's my worthy friend—
My lord, I see you're moved.

OTHELLO. No, not much moved:
I do not think but Desdemona's honest.

IAGO. Long live she so! and long live you to think so!

OTHELLO. Farewell, farewell:
If more thou dost perceive, let me know more;
Set on thy wife to observe: leave me, Iago.

IAGO *(going)*. My lord, I take my leave.

OTHELLO. Why did I marry? This honest creature doubtless
Sees and knows more, much more, than he unfolds.

IAGO *(returning)*. My lord, I would I might entreat your honour
To scan this thing no further; leave it to time:
Though it be fit that Cassio have his place,
For, sure, he fills it up with great ability,
Yet, if you please to hold him off awhile,
You shall by that perceive him and his means:
Note, if your lady strain his entertainment
With any strong or vehement importunity:
Much will be seen in that. In the meantime
Let me be thought too busy in my fears,
And hold her free, I do beseech your honour.

OTHELLO. Fear not my government.

IAGO. I once more take my leave.

OTHELLO *(alone)*. This fellow's of exceeding honesty,
And knows all qualities, with a learnèd spirit,
Of human feelings. O curse of marriage,
That we can call these delicate creatures ours,
And not their appetites! I had rather be a toad,
And live upon the vapour of a dungeon,
Than keep a corner in the thing I love
For others' uses. Desdemona comes:
If she be false, O, then heaven mocks itself!
I'll not believe 't.

DESDEMONA *(entering with Emilia)*. How now, my dear Othello!
Your dinner, and the generous islanders
By you invited, do attend your presence.

OTHELLO. I am to blame.

DESDEMONA. Why do you speak so faintly?
Are you not well?

OTHELLO. I have a pain upon my forehead here.

DESDEMONA. 'Faith, that's with watching: 'twill away again:
Let me but bind it hard, within this hour
It will be well.

OTHELLO. Your napkin is too little:
Let it alone. Come, I'll go in with you.

He puts the handkerchief from him, and it drops

DESDEMONA. I am very sorry that you are not well.

Othello and Desdemona go

EMILIA. I am glad I have found this napkin:
This was her first remembrance from the Moor:
My wayward husband hath a hundred times
Wooed me to steal it; but she so loves the token,
For he conjured her she should ever keep it,
That she reserves it evermore about her
To kiss and talk to. I'll have the work ta'en out,
And give 't Iago: what he will do with it
Heaven knows, not I;
I nothing but to please his fantasy.

IAGO *(entering)*. How now! What do you here alone?

EMILIA. Do not you chide; I have a thing for you.

IAGO. A thing for me? It is a common thing—

EMILIA. Ha!

IAGO. To have a foolish wife.

EMILIA. O, is that all? What will you give me now
For that same handkerchief?

IAGO. What handkerchief?

EMILIA. Why, that the Moor first gave to Desdemona;
That which so often you did bid me steal.

IAGO. Hast stolen it from her?

EMILIA. No, 'faith; she let it drop by negligence,
And, to the advantage, I, being here, took 't up.
Look, here it is.

IAGO. A good wench; give it me.

EMILIA. What will you do with 't, that you have been so earnest
To have me filch it ?

IAGO *(snatching it)*. Why, what's that to you ?

EMILIA. If it be not for some purpose of import,
Give 't me again : poor lady, she'll run mad
When she shall lack it.

IAGO. I have use for it. Go, leave me. *(She goes)*
I will in Cassio's lodging lose this napkin,
And let him find it. Trifles light as air
Are to the jealous confirmations strong
As proofs of holy writ : this may do something.
The Moor already changes with my poison :
Dangerous conceits are, in their natures, poisons,
Which at the first are scarce found to distaste,
But with a little act upon the blood,
Burn like the mines of sulphur. I did say so :
Look, where he comes !

OTHELLO *(entering)*. Ha ! ha ! false to me ?

IAGO. Why, how now, general ! no more of that.

OTHELLO. Avaunt ! be gone ! thou hast set me on the rack :
I swear tis better to be much abused
Than but to know 't a little.

IAGO. How now, my lord !

OTHELLO. What sense had I of her stolen hours ?
I saw 't not, thought it not, it harmed not me :
I slept the next night well, was free and merry ;
I found not Cassio's kisses on her lips :
He that is robbed, not wanting what is stolen,
Let him not know 't and he's not robbed at all.

IAGO. I am sorry to hear this.

OTHELLO. O, now, for ever
Farewell the tranquil mind ! farewell content !
Farewell the plumèd troop, and the big wars,
That make ambition virtue ! O, farewell !
Farewell the neighing steed, and the shrill trump,
The spirit-stirring drum, the ear-piercing fife,
The royal banner, and all quality,
Pride, pomp, and circumstance of glorious war !
Farewell ! Othello's occupation's gone !

IAGO. Is 't possible, my lord ?

OTHELLO. Villain, be sure thou prove my love untrue,
Be sure of it ; give me the ocular proof,
Or, by the worth of man's eternal soul,

Thou hadst been better have been born a dog
Than answer my waked wrath !

IAGO. Is 't come to this ?

OTHELLO. Make me to see 't ; or, at the least, so prove it
That the probation bear no hinge nor loop
To hang a doubt on ; or woe upon thy life !
If thou dost slander her and torture me,
Never pray more ; abandon all remorse ;
On horror's head horrors accumulate ;
Do deeds to make heaven weep, all earth amazed ;
For nothing canst thou to damnation add
Greater than that.

IAGO. O grace ! O heaven forgive me !
Are you a man ? Have you a soul or sense ?
God be wi' you ; take mine office. O wretched fool,
That livest to make thine honesty a vice !
O monstrous world ! Take note, take note, O world,
To be direct and honest is not safe.
I thank you for this profit ; and from hence
I'll love no friend, since love breeds such offence.

OTHELLO. Nay, stay : thou shouldst be honest.

IAGO. I should be wise, for honesty's a fool
And loses that it works for.

OTHELLO. By the world,
I think my wife be honest and think she is not ;
I think that thou art just and think thou art not.
I'll have some proof. Her name, that was as fresh
As Dian's visage, is now begrimed and black
As mine own face. If there be cords, or knives,
Poison, or fire, or suffocating streams,
I'll not endure it. Would I were satisfied !

IAGO. I see, sir, you are eaten up with passion :
I do repent me that I put it to you.
You would be satisfied ?

OTHELLO. Would ! nay, I will.
Give me a living reason she's disloyal.

IAGO. I do not like the office :
But, since I am entered in this cause so far,
Pricked to 't by foolish honesty and love,
I will go on. I lay with Cassio lately,
And, being troubled with a raging tooth,
I could not sleep.
There are a kind of men so loose of soul
That in their sleeps will mutter their affairs :
One of this kind is Cassio :

In sleep I heard him say, *Sweet Desdemona,*
Let us be wary, let us hide our loves ;
And then, sir, would he grip and wring my hand,
Cry *O sweet creature !* and then
Cried *Cursed fate that gave thee to the Moor !*

OTHELLO. O monstrous ! monstrous !

IAGO. Nay, this was but his dream.

OTHELLO. But this denoted a foregone conclusion :
Tis a shrewd doubt, though it be but a dream.

IAGO. And this may help to thicken other proofs
That do demonstrate thinly.

OTHELLO. I'll tear her all to pieces.

IAGO. Nay, but be wise : yet we see nothing done ;
She may be honest yet. Tell me but this,
Have you not sometimes seen a handkerchief
Spotted with strawberries in your wife's hand ?

OTHELLO. I gave her such a one ; 'twas my first gift.

IAGO. I know not that ; but such a handkerchief
(I am sure it was your wife's) did I today
See Cassio wipe his beard with.

OTHELLO. If it be that—

IAGO. If it be that, or any that was hers,
It speaks against her with the other proofs.

OTHELLO. O, that the slave had forty thousand lives !
One is too poor, too weak for my revenge.
Now do I see tis true. Look here, Iago ;
All my fond love thus do I blow to heaven.
Tis gone.
Arise, black vengeance, from thy hollow cell !
Yield up, O love, thy crown and hearted throne
To tyrannous hate ! Swell, bosom, with thy fraught,
For tis of aspics' tongues !

IAGO. Yet be content.

OTHELLO. O, blood, blood, blood !

IAGO. Patience, I say ; your mind perhaps may change.

OTHELLO. Never, Iago. Like to the Pontic sea,
Whose icy current and compulsive course
Ne'er feels retiring ebb, but keeps due on
To the Propontic and the Hellespont,
Even so my desperate thoughts, with violent pace,
Shall ne'er look back, ne'er ebb to humble love,

Till that a capable and wide revenge
Swallow them up. Now, by yond marble heaven,
In the due reverence of a sacred vow
I here engage my words. *(He kneels)*

IAGO. Do not rise yet. *(Iago kneels)*
Witness, you ever-burning lights above,
You elements that clip us round about,
Witness that here Iago doth give up
The execution of his wit, hands, heart,
To wronged Othello's service! *(They rise)*

OTHELLO. I greet thy love,
Not with vain thanks, but with acceptance bounteous,
And will upon the instant put thee to 't:
Within these three days let me hear thee say
That Cassio's not alive.

IAGO. My friend is dead; tis done at your request:
But let her live.

OTHELLO. Curse her, lewd minx! O, curse her!
Come, go with me apart; I will withdraw,
To furnish me with some swift means of death
For the fair devil. Now art thou my lieutenant.

IAGO. I am your own for ever.

Scene 4—Before the Castle: Desdemona, Emilia, and Clown

DESDEMONA. Do you know, sirrah, where Lieutenant Cassio lies? Seek him, bid him come hither: tell him I have moved my lord on his behalf, and hope all will be well.

CLOWN. To do this is within the compass of man's wit; and therefore I will attempt the doing it.

DESDEMONA. Where should I lose that handkerchief, Emilia?

EMILIA. I know not, madam.

DESDEMONA. Believe me, I had rather have lost my purse
Full of crusadoes: and, but my noble Moor
Is true of mind and made of no such baseness
As jealous creatures are, it were enough
To put him to ill thinking.

EMILIA. Is he not jealous?

DESDEMONA. Who, he? I think the sun where he was born
Drew all such humours from him.

EMILIA. Look, where he comes.

DESDEMONA. I will not leave him now till Cassio
Be called to him. How is 't with you, my lord?

OTHELLO. Well, my good lady. How do you, Desdemona?

DESDEMONA. Well, my good lord.

OTHELLO. Give me your hand: this hand is moist, my lady.

DESDEMONA. It yet hath felt no age nor known no sorrow.

OTHELLO. This argues fruitfulness and liberal heart:
Hot, hot, and moist: this hand of yours requires
A sequester from liberty, fasting, and prayer,
Much castigation, exercise devout;
For here's a young and sweating devil here,
That commonly rebels. Tis a good hand,
A frank one.

DESDEMONA. You may, indeed, say so;
For 'twas that hand that gave away my heart.

OTHELLO. A liberal hand: the hearts of old gave hands;
But our new heraldry is hands, not hearts.

DESDEMONA. I cannot speak of this. Come now, your promise.

OTHELLO. What promise, chuck?

DESDEMONA. I have sent to bid Cassio come speak with you.

OTHELLO. I have a salt and sorry rheum offends me;
Lend me thy handkerchief.

DESDEMONA. Here, my lord.

OTHELLO. That which I gave you.

DESDEMONA. I have it not about me.

OTHELLO. Not?

DESDEMONA. No, indeed, my lord.

OTHELLO. That is a fault. That handkerchief
Did an Egyptian to my mother give;
She was a charmer, and could almost read
The thoughts of people: she told her, while she kept it,
Twould make her amiable and subdue my father
Entirely to her love, but if she lost it
Or made a gift of it, my father's eye
Should hold her loathèd and his spirits should hunt
After new fancies: she, dying, gave it me,
And bade me, when my fate would have me wive,
To give it her. I did so: and take heed on 't;
Make it a darling like your precious eye;
To lose 't or give 't away were such perdition
As nothing else could match.

DESDEMONA. Is 't possible?

OTHELLO. Tis true: there's magic in the web of it:
A sibyl, that had numbered in the world
The sun to course two hundred compasses,

In her prophetic fury sewed the work;
The worms were hallowed that did breed the silk;
And it was dyed in mummy which the skilful
Conserved of maidens' hearts.

DESDEMONA. Indeed! is 't true?

OTHELLO. Most veritable; therefore look to 't well.

DESDEMONA. Then would to God that I had never seen 't!

OTHELLO. Ha! wherefore?

DESDEMONA. Why do you speak so startingly and rash?

OTHELLO. Is 't lost? is 't gone? speak, is it out o' the way?

DESDEMONA. Heaven bless us!

OTHELLO. Say you?

DESDEMONA. It is not lost; but what an if it were?

OTHELLO. How!

DESDEMONA. I say, it is not lost.

OTHELLO. Fetch 't, let me see 't.

DESDEMONA. Why, so I can, sir, but I will not now.
This is a trick to put me from my suit:
Pray you, let Cassio be received again.

OTHELLO. Fetch me the handkerchief: my mind misgives.

DESDEMONA. Come, come;
You'll never meet a more sufficient man.

OTHELLO. The handkerchief!

DESDEMONA. I pray, talk me of Cassio.

OTHELLO. The handkerchief!

DESDEMONA. A man that all his time
Hath founded his good fortunes on your love,
Shared dangers with you—

OTHELLO. The handkerchief!

DESDEMONA. In sooth, you are to blame.

OTHELLO. Away! *(He goes)*

EMILIA. Is not this man jealous?

DESDEMONA. I ne'er saw this before.
Sure, there's some wonder in this handkerchief:
I am most unhappy in the loss of it.

Iago urges Cassio to press Desdemona to continue to plead for him, and Desdemona replies that some strange emotion moves Othello, and she must wait. As Desdemona goes out, Bianca, who loves Cassio, appears. Cassio gives her a handkerchief he has found in his chamber. Cassio goes, having decided on a personal interview with Othello.

ACT 4

Scene 1—Before the Castle at Cyprus

As Iago reminds him of the handkerchief and talks of confessions, Othello, believing all Iago's inventions, is seized with uncontrollable passion and falls in a fit. Cassio appears.

CASSIO. What's the matter ?
IAGO. My lord is fallen into an epilepsy :
This is his second fit ; he had one yesterday.
CASSIO. Rub him about the temples.
IAGO. No, forbear ;
The lethargy must have his quiet course :
If not, he foams at mouth and by and by
Breaks out to savage madness. Look, he stirs :
Do you withdraw yourself a little while,
He will recover straight : when he is gone,
I would on great occasion speak with you. *(Cassio goes)*
How is it, general ? have you not hurt your head ?
OTHELLO. Dost thou mock me ?
IAGO. I mock you ! no, by heaven.
Would you would bear your fortune like a man !
OTHELLO. Did he confess it ?
IAGO. Good sir, be a man.
OTHELLO. O, thou art wise ; tis certain.
IAGO. Stand you awhile apart ;
Confine yourself but in a patient list.
Whilst you were here o'erwhelmèd with your grief—
A passion most unsuiting such a man—
Cassio came hither : I shifted him away,
Bade him anon return and here speak with me ;
The which he promised. Do but encave yourself,
And mark the fleers, the gibes, and notable scorns
That dwell in every region of his face ;
For I will make him tell the tale anew ;
I say, but mark his gesture.

With Othello concealed but within hearing, Iago urges Cassio to talk of Bianca, whose affection Cassio does not return, and of whom he speaks mockingly. Othello, not hearing the name, thinks it is Desdemona he is discussing. Bianca appears, flaunting the handkerchief Cassio gave her. Othello recognises it as one he gave to Desdemona, and as the others go he comes from his hiding-place denouncing Cassio and musing on the character of Desdemona.

OTHELLO. I would have him nine years a-killing. A fine woman ! a fair woman ! a sweet woman !

IAGO. Nay, you must forget that.

OTHELLO. Ay, let her rot, and perish, for she shall not live: no, my heart is turned to stone; I strike it and it hurts my hand. O, the world hath not a sweeter creature.

IAGO. Nay, that's not your way.

OTHELLO. Hang her! I do but say what she is: so delicate with her needle: an admirable musician: O! she will sing the savageness out of a bear: of so high and plenteous wit and invention—

IAGO. She's the worse for all this.

OTHELLO. O, a thousand thousand times: and then, of so gentle a condition!

IAGO. Ay, too gentle.

OTHELLO. Nay, that's certain: but yet the pity of it, Iago! O Iago, the pity of it, Iago!

IAGO. If you are so fond over her iniquity, give her patent to offend; for, if it touch not you, it comes near nobody.

OTHELLO. I will chop her into messes!

IAGO. O, tis foul in her.

OTHELLO. With mine officer!

IAGO. That's fouler.

OTHELLO. Get me some poison, Iago; this night: I'll not expostulate with her, lest her beauty unprovide my mind.

IAGO. Do it not with poison; strangle her in her bed.

OTHELLO. Good, good: the justice of it pleases: very good.

IAGO. And for Cassio, let me be his undertaker: you shall hear more by midnight.

OTHELLO. Excellent good. What trumpet is that?

IAGO. Something from Venice, sure. Tis Lodovico
Come from the duke: and, see, your wife is with him.

At this point Lodovico, a kinsman of Desdemona, arrives with a letter from Venice recalling Othello now that the war is ended, and appointing Cassio to succeed him in Cyprus. Desdemona, coming in, begs Lodovico to intercede between Cassio and Othello. But Othello is now more and more inflamed by suspicion, so that he speaks vilely of her and strikes her, to the consternation of Lodovico and his attendants.

Scene 2—A Room in the Castle: Othello and Emilia

OTHELLO. You have seen nothing then?

EMILIA. Nor ever heard, nor ever did suspect.

OTHELLO. Yes, you have seen Cassio and her together.

EMILIA. But then I saw no harm, and then I heard
Each syllable that breath made up between them.

OTHELLO. What, did they never whisper?

EMILIA. Never, my lord.

OTHELLO. Nor send you out o' the way?

EMILIA. Never.

OTHELLO. To fetch her fan, her gloves, her mask, nor nothing ?

EMILIA. Never, my lord.

OTHELLO. That's strange.

EMILIA. I durst, my lord, to wager she is honest,
Lay down my soul at stake : if you think other
Remove your thought ; it doth abuse your bosom,
If any wretch have put this in your head
Let heaven requite it with the serpent's curse !
For, if she be not honest, chaste, and true,
There's no man happy ; the purest of their wives
Is foul as slander.

OTHELLO. Bid her come hither : go. *(Emilia goes)*
And yet she'll kneel and pray ; I have seen her do 't.

DESDEMONA *(entering)*. My lord, what is your will ?

OTHELLO. Pray, chuck, come hither.

DESDEMONA. What is your pleasure ?

OTHELLO. Let me see your eyes ; look in my face.

DESDEMONA. What horrible fancy's this ?
Upon my knees, what doth your speech import ?
I understand a fury in your words,
But not the words.

OTHELLO. Why, what art thou ?

DESDEMONA. Your wife, my lord ; your true
And loyal wife.

OTHELLO. Come, swear it, swear thou art honest.

DESDEMONA. Heaven doth truly know it.

OTHELLO. Heaven truly knows that thou art false as hell.

DESDEMONA. To whom, my lord ? With whom ? How am I false ?

OTHELLO. O Desdemona ! away ! away ! away !

DESDEMONA. Alas the heavy day ! Why do you weep ?
Am I the motive of these tears, my lord ?
If haply you my father do suspect
An instrument of this your calling back,
Lay not your blame on me : if you have lost him,
Why, I have lost him too.

OTHELLO. Had it pleased heaven
To try me with affliction ; had they rained
All kinds of sores and shames on my bare head,
Steeped me in poverty to the very lips,
Given to captivity me and my utmost hopes,
I should have found in some place of my soul
A drop of patience : but, alas, to make me

A fixèd figure for the time of scorn
To point his slow unmoving finger at!
Yet could I bear that too; well, very well:
But there, where I have garnered up my heart,
Where either I must live or bear no life;
The fountain from the which my current runs,
Or else dries up; to be discarded thence!
Or keep it as a cistern for foul toads!
Turn thy complexion there,
Patience, thou young and rose-lipped cherubin;
Ay, there, look grim as hell!

DESDEMONA. I hope my noble lord esteems me honest!

OTHELLO. O! ay! as summer flies are in the shambles. O thou weed!
Who art so lovely fair and smell'st so sweet
That the sense aches at thee, would thou hadst ne'er been born!

DESDEMONA. Alas, what ignorant sin have I committed?

OTHELLO. Committed! O thou public commoner!
I should make very forges of my cheeks,
That would to cinders burn up modesty,
Did I but speak thy deeds.

DESDEMONA. By heaven, you do me wrong.

OTHELLO. I cry you mercy, then:
I took you for that cunning one of Venice
That married with Othello. You, mistress *(raising his voice)*,
That have the office opposite to Saint Peter,
And keep the gate of hell! *(Emilia enters.)* You, you, ay, you!
We have done our course; there's money for your pains:
I pray you, turn the key and keep our counsel.

After Othello's withdrawal Desdemona and Emilia hold pitiful conference. Iago enters, and Emilia fiercely denounces the knave, to her unknown, who has started all this suspicion. Iago professes horror at so base a betrayal, and when Desdemona pleads with him to counsel her he answers:

Tis but his humour;
The business of the State does him offence
And he does chide with you.

The women go, and Roderigo comes in railing against Iago, who beguiles him afresh, tells him Cassio is to govern Cyprus, and persuades him to seek advancement by killing Cassio.

RODERIGO. And that you would have me to do?

IAGO. Ay, if you dare do yourself a profit and a right. He knows not yet of his honourable fortune. If you will watch his going, which I will fashion to fall out between twelve and one, you may take him at your pleasure: I will be near to second your attempt, and he shall fall between us. Come, stand not amazed at it, but go along with me; I will show you such a necessity in his death that you shall think yourself bound to put it on him. It is now high supper-time, and the night grows to waste: about it.

RODERIGO. I will hear further reason for this.

IAGO. And you shall be satisfied.

Scene 3—A Room in the Castle

Enter Othello, Lodovico, Desdemona, Emilia, and Attendants

LODOVICO. I do beseech you, sir, trouble yourself no further.

OTHELLO. O, pardon me; 'twill do me good to walk.

LODOVICO. Madam, Good-night; I humbly thank your ladyship.

DESDEMONA. Your honour is most welcome.

OTHELLO. Will you walk, sir?
O, Desdemona—

DESDEMONA. My lord?

OTHELLO. Get you to bed on the instant; I will be returned forthwith: dismiss your attendant there: look it be done.

DESDEMONA. I will, my lord. *(She is left alone with Emilia)*

EMILIA. How goes it now? He looks gentler than he did.

DESDEMONA. He says he will return:
He hath commanded me to go to bed,
And bade me to dismiss you.

EMILIA. Dismiss me!

DESDEMONA. It was his bidding; therefore, good Emilia,
Give me my nightly wearing, and adieu:
We must not now displease him.

EMILIA. I would you had never seen him!

DESDEMONA. So would not I: my love doth so approve him
That even his stubbornness, his checks, his frowns
(Prithee, unpin me) have grace and favour in them.

EMILIA. I have laid those wedding sheets you bade me on the bed.

DESDEMONA. All's one. Good faith, how foolish are our minds!
If I do die before thee, prithee, shroud me
In one of those same sheets.

EMILIA. Come, come, you talk.

DESDEMONA. My mother had a maid called Barbara:
She was in love, and he she loved proved mad
And did forsake her: she had a song of *willow*;
An old thing 'twas, but it expressed her fortune,
And she died singing it: that song tonight
Will not go from my mind; I have much to do
But to go hang my head all at one side,
And sing it like poor Barbara. Prithee, dispatch.

EMILIA. Shall I go fetch your night-gown?

DESDEMONA. No, unpin me here. *(She sings)*

The poor soul sat sighing by a sycamore tree,
Sing all a green willow ;
Her hand on her bosom, her head on her knee,
Sing willow, willow, willow ;
The fresh streams ran by her, and murmured her moans ;
Sing willow, willow, willow ;
Her salt tears fell from her, and softened the stones—

Prithee, hie thee ; he'll come anon :
Hark ! who is 't that knocks ?

EMILIA. It's the wind.

DESDEMONA *(singing)*. *I called my love false love ;*
but what said he then ?
Sing willow, willow, willow.
So, get thee gone ; Good-night. O, these men, these men !

ACT 5

Scene 1—A Street in Cyprus

IAGO *(to Roderigo)*. Here, stand behind this bulk ; straight will he come :
Wear thy good rapier bare, and put it home :
Quick, quick ; fear nothing ; I'll be at thy elbow :
It makes us or it mars us ; think on that,
And fix most firm thy resolution.

RODERIGO. Be near at hand ; I may miscarry in 't.

IAGO. Here, at thy hand : be bold, and take thy stand. *(Iago hides)*

RODERIGO. I have no great devotion to the deed ;
And yet he hath given me satisfying reasons :
Tis but a man gone. Forth, my sword : he dies.

IAGO. I have rubbed this young quat almost to the sense,
And he grows angry. Now, whether he kill Cassio,
Or Cassio him, or each do kill the other,
Every way makes my gain : live Roderigo,
He calls me to a restitution large
Of gold and jewels that I bobbed from him,
As gifts to Desdemona ;
It must not be : if Cassio do remain,
He hath a daily beauty in his life
That makes me ugly ; and, besides, the Moor
May unfold me to him ; there stand I in much peril :
No, he must die. But so : I hear him coming. *(Cassio enters)*

RODERIGO. I know his gait, tis he. Villain, thou diest !

He attacks Cassio

CASSIO. That thrust had been mine enemy indeed,
But that my coat is better than thou know'st :
I will make proof of thine. *(He draws, and wounds Roderigo)*

RODERIGO. O, I am slain!

Iago from behind wounds Cassio in the leg and flees

CASSIO. I am maimed for ever. Help, ho! murder! *(He falls)*

OTHELLO *(entering)*. The voice of Cassio: Iago keeps his word.

RODERIGO. O, villain that I am!

OTHELLO. It is even so.

CASSIO. O, help, ho! light! a surgeon!

OTHELLO. Tis he: O brave Iago, honest and just,
That hast such noble sense of thy friend's wrong!
Thou teachest me.

Othello goes and Lodovico and Gratiano appear

CASSIO. What, ho! no watch? no passage? murder! murder!

GRATIANO. Tis some mischance; the cry is very direful.

CASSIO. O, help!

LODOVICO. Hark!

RODERIGO. O wretched villain!

LODOVICO. Two or three groan: it is a heavy night:
These may be counterfeits: let's think 't unsafe
To come in to the cry without more help.

RODERIGO. Nobody come? then shall I bleed to death.

LODOVICO. Hark! *(Iago approaches with a light)*

GRATIANO. Here's one comes in his shirt, with light and weapons.

IAGO. Who's there? Whose noise is this that cries on murder?

LODOVICO. We do not know.

IAGO. Did not you hear a cry?

CASSIO. Here, here! for heaven's sake, help me!

IAGO. What's the matter?
What are you here that cry so grievously?

CASSIO. Iago? O, I am spoiled, undone by villains!
Give me some help.

IAGO. O me, lieutenant! What villains have done this?

CASSIO. I think that one of them is hereabout,
And cannot make away.

IAGO. O treacherous villains!

RODERIGO. O, help me here!

CASSIO. That's one of them.

IAGO. O murderous slave! O villain! *(He stabs Roderigo)*

RODERIGO. O curst Iago! O inhuman dog!

IAGO. Kill men i' the dark! Where be these thieves?
How silent is this town! Ho! murder! murder!
What may you be? Are you of good or evil?

LODOVICO. As you shall prove us, praise us.

IAGO. Signior Lodovico?

LODOVICO. He, sir.

IAGO. I cry you mercy. Here's Cassio hurt by villains.

GRATIANO. Cassio!

IAGO. How is 't, brother!

CASSIO. My leg is cut in two.

IAGO. Marry, heaven forbid!
Light, gentlemen: I'll bind it with my shirt.

BIANCA *(entering)*. What is the matter, ho? who is 't that cried?

IAGO. Who is 't that cried!

BIANCA. O my dear Cassio! my sweet Cassio!
O Cassio, Cassio, Cassio!

IAGO. Cassio, may you suspect
Who they should be that have thus mangled you?

CASSIO. No.

GRATIANO. I am sorry to find you thus: I have been to seek you.

IAGO. Lend me a garter. So. O, for a chair,
To bear him easily hence!

BIANCA. Alas, he faints! O Cassio, Cassio, Cassio!

IAGO. Patience awhile, good Cassio. Come, come;
Lend me a light. Know we this face or no?
Alas, my friend and my dear countryman
Roderigo! no: yes, sure: O heaven! Roderigo.

GRATIANO. What, of Venice?

IAGO. Even he, sir: did you know him?

GRATIANO. Know him! ay.

IAGO. Signior Gratiano? I cry you gentle pardon;
These accidents must excuse my manners,
That so neglected you.

GRATIANO. I am glad to see you.

IAGO. How do you, Cassio? O, a chair, a chair!

GRATIANO. Roderigo!

IAGO. He, he, tis he. Some good man bear him.
I'll fetch the general's surgeon.
He that lies slain here, Cassio,
Was my dear friend: what malice was between you?

CASSIO. None in the world; nor do I know the man.

EMILIA *(entering)*. Alas, what's the matter? what's the matter, husband?

IAGO. Cassio hath here been set on in the dark
By Roderigo and fellows that are scaped:
He's almost slain, and Roderigo dead.

EMILIA. Alas, good gentleman! alas, good Cassio!

IAGO. Emilia, run you to the citadel,
And tell my lord and lady what hath happed. This is the night
That either makes me or fordoes me quite.

Scene 2—A Bedchamber in the Castle : Desdemona asleep

OTHELLO *(entering)*. It is the cause, it is the cause, my soul,
Let me not name it to you, you chaste stars !
It is the cause. Yet I'll not shed her blood ;
Nor scar that whiter skin of hers than snow,
And smooth as monumental alabaster :
Yet she must die, else she'll betray more men.
Put out the light, and then put out the light :
If I quench thee, thou flaming minister,
I can again thy former light restore,
Should I repent me : but once put out *thy* light,
Thou cunning'st pattern of excelling nature,
I know not where is that Promethean heat
That can thy light relume. When I have plucked the rose,
I cannot give it vital growth again,
It must needs wither : I'll smell it on the tree. *(He kisses her)*
Ah, balmy breath, that dost almost persuade
Justice to break her sword ! One more, one more.
Be thus when thou art dead, and I will kill thee,
And love thee after. One more, and this the last :
So sweet was ne'er so fatal. I must weep,
But they are cruel tears : this sorrow's heavenly ;
It strikes where it doth love. She wakes.

DESDEMONA. Who's there ? Othello ?

OTHELLO. Ay, Desdemona.

DESDEMONA. Will you come to bed, my lord ?

OTHELLO. Have you prayed tonight, Desdemona ?

DESDEMONA. Ay, my lord.

OTHELLO. If you bethink yourself of any crime
Unreconciled as yet to heaven and grace,
Solicit for it straight.

DESDEMONA. Alas, my lord, what do you mean by that ?

OTHELLO. Well, do it, and be brief ; I will walk by :
I would not kill thy unpreparèd spirit ;
No ; heaven forfend ! I would not kill thy soul.

DESDEMONA. Talk you of killing ?

OTHELLO. Ay, I do.

DESDEMONA. Then heaven have mercy on me !

OTHELLO. Amen, with all my heart !

DESDEMONA. If you say so, I hope you will not kill me,
And yet I fear you ; for you are fatal then

When your eyes roll so; why I should fear I know not,
Since guiltiness I know not; but yet I feel I fear.

OTHELLO. Think on thy sins.

DESDEMONA. They are loves I bear to you.

OTHELLO. Ay, and for that thou diest.

DESDEMONA. That death's unnatural that kills for loving.
Alas, why gnaw you so your nether lip?
Some fearful passion shakes your very frame.

OTHELLO. Peace, and be still!

DESDEMONA. I will so. What's the matter?

OTHELLO. That handkerchief which I so loved and gave thee
Thou gavest to Cassio.

DESDEMONA. No, by my life and soul!
Send for the man, and ask him.

OTHELLO. Sweet soul, take heed,
Take heed of perjury; thou art on thy deathbed.

DESDEMONA. Ay, but not yet to die.

OTHELLO. Yes, presently:
Therefore confess thee freely of thy sin,
For to deny each article with oath
Cannot remove nor choke the strong conception
That I do groan withal. Thou art to die.

DESDEMONA. Then Lord have mercy on me!

OTHELLO. I say, amen.

DESDEMONA. And have you mercy too! I never did
Offend you in my life; never loved Cassio
But with such general warranty of heaven
As I might love; I never gave him token.

OTHELLO. By heaven, I saw my handkerchief in 's hand.
O perjured woman! thou dost stone my heart,
And makest me call what I intend to do
A murder, which I thought a sacrifice:
I saw the handkerchief.

DESDEMONA. He found it then;
I never gave it him: send for him hither;
Let him confess a truth.

OTHELLO. No, his mouth is stopped.

DESDEMONA. O! my fear interprets: what, is he dead?

OTHELLO. Had all his hairs been lives, my great revenge
Had stomach for them all.

DESDEMONA. Alas! he is betrayed and I undone.

OTHELLO. Out, traitor! weep'st thou for him to my face?

DESDEMONA. O, banish me, my lord, but kill me not!

OTHELLO. Down!

DESDEMONA. Kill me tomorrow: let me live tonight!

OTHELLO. Nay, if you strive—

DESDEMONA. But half an hour!

OTHELLO. Being done, there is no pause.

DESDEMONA. But while I say one prayer!

OTHELLO. It is too late. *(He stifles her)*

EMILIA *(within)*. My lord, my lord! what, ho! my lord, my lord!

OTHELLO. What noise is this? Not dead? not yet quite dead?
I that am cruel am yet merciful;
I would not have thee linger in thy pain: so, so.

EMILIA *(within)*. What, ho! my lord, my lord!

OTHELLO. Who's there?

EMILIA. O, good my lord, I would speak a word with you!

OTHELLO. Yes: tis Emilia. By and by. She's dead.
Tis like she comes to speak of Cassio's death.
The noise was here. Ha! no more moving?
Still as the grave. Shall she come in? were 't good?
I think she stirs again: no. What's best to do?
If she come in, she'll sure speak to my wife:
My wife! my wife! what wife? I have no wife.
O, insupportable! O heavy hour!
Methinks it should be now a huge eclipse
Of sun and moon, and that the affrighted globe
Should yawn at alteration.

EMILIA *(within)*. I do beseech you
That I may speak with you, O, good my lord!

OTHELLO. I had forgot thee: O, come in, Emilia:
Soft; by and by. Let me the curtains draw.
Where art thou? *(He unlocks the door)*

EMILIA. O, my good lord, yonder's foul murder done!

OTHELLO. What, now?

EMILIA. But now, my lord.

OTHELLO. It is the very error of the moon;
She comes more nearer earth than she was wont,
And makes men mad.

EMILIA. Cassio, my lord, hath killed a young Venetian
Called Roderigo.

OTHELLO. Roderigo killed!
And Cassio killed!

EMILIA. No, Cassio is not killed.

OTHELLO. Not Cassio killed! then murder's out of tune,
And sweet revenge grows harsh.

DESDEMONA. O, falsely, falsely murdered!

EMILIA. Alas, what cry is that?
OTHELLO. That! what?
EMILIA. Out, and alas! that was my lady's voice.
Help! help, ho! help! O lady, speak again!
Sweet Desdemona! O sweet mistress, speak!
DESDEMONA. A guiltless death I die.
EMILIA. O, who hath done this deed?
DESDEMONA. Nobody; I myself. Farewell:
Commend me to my kind lord: O, farewell! *(She dies)*
OTHELLO. Why, how should she be murdered?
EMILIA. Alas, who knows?
OTHELLO. You heard her say herself it was not I.
EMILIA. She said so: I must needs report the truth.
OTHELLO. She's, like a liar, gone to burning hell:
Twas I that killed her.
EMILIA. O, the more angel she,
And you the blacker devil!
OTHELLO. She was false as water.
EMILIA. Thou art rash as fire, to say
That she was false: O, she was heavenly true!
OTHELLO. O, I were lost beneath all depth in hell,
But that I did proceed upon just grounds
To this extremity. Thy husband knew it all.
EMILIA. My husband!
OTHELLO. Thy husband.
EMILIA. That she was false?
OTHELLO. Ay, with Cassio. Nay, had she been true,
If heaven would make me such another world
Of one entire and perfect chrysolite,
I'd not have sold her for it.
EMILIA. My husband!
OTHELLO. Ay, 'twas he that told me first:
An honest man he is, and hates the slime
That sticks on filthy deeds.
EMILIA. My husband!
OTHELLO. What needs this iteration, woman? I say thy husband.
EMILIA. O mistress, villainy hath made mocks with love!
My husband say that she was false!
OTHELLO. He, woman;
I say thy husband: dost understand the word?
My friend, thy husband, honest, honest Iago.
EMILIA. If he say so, may his pernicious soul
Rot half a grain a day! he lies to the heart:
She was too fond of her most filthy bargain.

OTHELLO. Ha!

EMILIA. Do thy worst:
This deed of thine is no more worthy heaven
Than thou wast worthy her.

OTHELLO. Peace, you were best.

EMILIA. Thou hast not half that power to do me harm
As I have to be hurt. O gull! O dolt!
As ignorant as dirt! thou hast done a deed—
I care not for thy sword; I'll make thee known
Though I lost twenty lives—Help! help, ho! help!
The Moor hath killed my mistress! Murder! murder!

Enter Montano, Gratiano, Iago, and others

MONTANO. What is the matter? How now, General!

EMILIA. O, are you come, Iago? you have done well,
That men must lay their murders on your neck.

GRATIANO. What is the matter?

EMILIA. Disprove this villain, if thou be'st a man:
He says thou told'st him that his wife was false:
I know thou didst not, thou'rt not such a villain:
Speak, for my heart is full.

IAGO. I told him what I thought, and told no more
Than what he found himself was apt and true.

EMILIA. But did you ever tell him she was false?

IAGO. I did.

EMILIA. You told a lie; an odious lie;
Upon my soul a lie, a wicked lie.
She false with Cassio!—did you say with Cassio?

IAGO. With Cassio, mistress. Go to, charm your tongue.

EMILIA. I will not charm my tongue; I am bound to speak:
My mistress here lies murdered in her bed—

ALL. O heavens forfend!

EMILIA. And your reports have set the murder on.

OTHELLO. Nay, stare not, masters: it is true, indeed.

GRATIANO. Tis a strange truth.

MONTANO. O monstrous act!

EMILIA. Villainy, villainy, villainy!
I think upon 't, I think: I smell 't: O villainy!
I thought so then: I'll kill myself for grief:
O villainy, villainy!

IAGO. What, are you mad? I charge you, get you home.

EMILIA. Good gentlemen, let me have leave to speak:
Tis proper I obey him, but not now.
Perchance, Iago, I will ne'er go home.

Othello. O! O! O! *(He falls on the bed)*

Emilia. Nay, lay thee down and roar;
For thou hast killed the sweetest innocent
That e'er did lift up eye.

Othello *(rising)*. O, she was foul!
I scarce did know you, uncle; there lies your niece
Whose breath, indeed, these hands have newly stopped:
I know this act shows horrible and grim.

Gratiano. Poor Desdemona! I am glad thy father's dead:
Thy match was mortal to him, and pure grief
Shore his old thread in twain: did he live now,
This sight would make him do a desperate turn,
Yea, curse his better angel from his side
And fall to reprobation.

Othello. Tis pitiful; but Cassio confessed,
And she did gratify his amorous works
With that recognizance and pledge of love
Which I first gave her; I saw it in his hand:
It was a handkerchief, an antique token
My father gave my mother.

Emilia. O heaven! O heavenly powers!

Iago. Come, hold your peace.

Emilia. Twill out, 'twill out: I peace!
No, I will speak as liberal as the north:
Let heaven and men and devils, let them all,
All, all, cry shame against me, yet I'll speak.

Iago. Be wise, and get you home.

Emilia. I will not.
O thou dull Moor! that handkerchief thou speak'st of
I found by fortune and did give my husband;
For often, with a solemn earnestness,
More than indeed belonged to such a trifle,
He begged of me to steal it. She give it Cassio! no alas! I found it,
And I did give 't my husband.

Iago. Filth, thou liest!

Emilia. By heaven, I do not, I do not, gentlemen.
O murderous coxcomb! What should such a fool
Do with so good a woman?

Othello. Are there no stones in heaven
But what serve for the thunder? Precious villain!

He runs at Iago; Iago from behind stabs Emilia and flees

Gratiano. The woman falls; sure, he hath killed his wife.

Emilia. Ay, ay: O, lay me by my mistress' side.

Gratiano. He's gone, but his wife's killed.

MONTANO. Tis a notorious villain. Take you this weapon,
Which I have here recovered from the Moor:
Come, guard the door without; let him not pass
But kill him rather.

OTHELLO. I am not valiant neither,
But every puny whipster gets my sword.
But why should honour outlive honesty?
Let it go all.

EMILIA. What did thy song bode, lady?
Hark, canst thou hear me? I will play the swan,
And die in music. *Willow, willow, willow.*
Moor, she was chaste; she loved thee, cruel Moor;
So come my soul to bliss, as I speak true;
So speaking as I think, I die, I die. *(She dies)*

OTHELLO. I have another weapon in this chamber;
It is a sword of Spain, the ice-brook's temper:
O, here it is.

GRATIANO *(within)*. If thou attempt it, it will cost thee dear.

OTHELLO. Look in upon me then and speak with me,
Or, naked as I am, I will assault thee.

GRATIANO *(entering)*. What is the matter?

OTHELLO. Behold, I have a weapon;
A better never did itself sustain
Upon a soldier's thigh: I have seen the day,
That, with this little arm and this good sword,
I have made my way through more impediments
Than twenty times your stop: but, O vain boast!
Who can control his fate? tis not so now.
Be not afraid, though you do see me weaponed;
Here is my journey's end, here is my butt,
And very sea-mark of my utmost sail.
Do you go back dismayed? tis a lost fear;
Man but a rush against Othello's breast,
And he retires. Where should Othello go?
Now, how dost thou look now? O ill-starred wench!
Pale as thy smock! when we shall meet at compt,
This look of thine will hurl my soul from heaven,
And fiends will snatch at it. Cold, cold, my girl!
Even like thy chastity. O cursèd slave!
Whip me, ye devils,
From the possession of this heavenly sight!
Blow me about in winds! roast me in sulphur!
Wash me in steep-down gulfs of liquid fire!
O Desdemona! Desdemona! dead!
O! O! O!

Cassio is borne in on a chair and Iago as a prisoner

LODOVICO. Where is this rash and most unfortunate man?

OTHELLO. That's he that was Othello: here I am.

LODOVICO. Where is that viper? bring the villain forth.

OTHELLO. I look down towards his feet; but that's a fable.
If that thou be'st a devil, I cannot kill thee. *(Wounds Iago)*

LODOVICO. Wrench his sword from him.

IAGO. I bleed, sir; but not killed.

OTHELLO. I am not sorry neither: I'd have thee live;
For, in my sense, tis happiness to die.

LODOVICO. O thou Othello, that wert once so good,
Fallen in the practice of a cursèd slave,
What shall be said to thee?

OTHELLO. Why, anything:
An honourable murderer, if you will;
For nought I did in hate, but all in honour.

LODOVICO. This wretch hath part confessed his villainy:
Did you and he consent in Cassio's death?

OTHELLO. Ay.

CASSIO. Dear general, I never gave you cause.

OTHELLO. I do believe it, and I ask you pardon.
Will you, I pray, demand that demi-devil
Why he hath thus ensnared my soul and body?

IAGO. Demand me nothing: what you know, you know:
From this time forth I never will speak word.

LODOVICO. What, not to pray?

GRATIANO. Torments will ope your lips.

OTHELLO. Well, thou dost best.

LODOVICO. Sir, you shall understand what hath befallen,
Which, as I think, you know not. Here is a letter
Found in the pocket of the slain Roderigo;
And here another: the one of them imports
The death of Cassio to be undertook
By Roderigo.

OTHELLO. O villain! O the pernicious caitiff!
How came you, Cassio, by that handkerchief
That was my wife's?

CASSIO. I found it in my chamber:
And he himself confessed but even now
That there he dropped it for a special purpose
Which wrought to his desire.

OTHELLO. O fool! fool! fool!

CASSIO. There is besides in Roderigo's letter,
How he upbraids Iago, that he made him
Brave me upon the watch; whereon it came

That I was cast: and even but now he spake,
After long seeming dead, Iago hurt him,
Iago set him on.

LODOVICO. You must forsake this room, and go with us:
Your power and your command is taken off,
And Cassio rules in Cyprus. For this slave,
If there be any cunning cruelty
That can torment him much and hold him long,
It shall be his. You shall close prisoner rest,
Till that the nature of your fault be known
To the Venetian State. Come, bring him away.

OTHELLO. Soft you; a word or two before you go.
I have done the State some service, and they know 't.
No more of that. I pray you, in your letters,
When you shall these unlucky deeds relate,
Speak of me as I am; nothing extenuate,
Nor set down aught in malice: then must you speak
Of one that loved not wisely but too well;
Of one not easily jealous, but being wrought
Perplexed in the extreme; of one whose hand,
Like the base Indian, threw a pearl away
Richer than all his tribe; of one whose subdued eyes,
Albeit unused to the melting mood,
Drop tears as fast as the Arabian trees
Their medi*ci*nal gum. Set you down this;
And say besides that in Aleppo once,
Where a malignant and a turbaned Turk
Beat a Venetian and traduced the State,
I took by the throat the dog, and smote him, thus.
I kissed thee ere I killed thee: no way but this;
Killing myself, to die upon a kiss.

He kisses Desdemona and dies by her side

CASSIO. This did I fear, but thought he had no weapon;
For he was great of heart.

LODOVICO *(to Iago)*. O Spartan dog,
More fell than anguish, hunger, or the sea!
Look on the tragic loading of this bed;
This is thy work: the object poisons sight;
Let it be hid. Gratiano, keep the house,
And seize upon the fortunes of the Moor,
For they succeed on you. To you, lord governor,
Remains the censure of this hellish villain;
The time, the place, the torture: O, enforce it!
Myself will straight aboard; and to the State
This heavy act with heavy heart relate.

The Story of Coriolanus

CORIOLANUS takes us farther back in time than any other Shakespeare play: it goes back to the dim mists of Rome in the early years of the fifth century before Christianity. It is based on a legend Shakespeare found in Plutarch, and the poet wrote the play late in his writing life, a year or two before he left London.

IT is unlike any other play in Shakespeare, and is probably very little read. It has much stir and vigour, but its interest is remote, and its subject belongs rather to politics than to the drama. It is difficult to imagine the play holding an audience. It is the study of an autocrat who scorns the people; it touches the whole controversy of autocracy and democracy without taking sides.

THE play pictures Rome at a time when the government of the city was passing from the rule of a group of patrician senators into the hands of the mass of the people. Coriolanus belongs to the class which sees power passing from it, and he sees with a bitter resentment the acquiring of power by the people. It is not too much to say that he hates the very thought of the people; he is not only an autocrat; he is what we should now call a snob. It is not possible for us to sympathise with him, but most of us will probably think him no worse than the two tribunes who seek to break his power.

THE ordinary citizens are described in the play as an easily impressed crowd, flattered, moulded, and led by the tribunes they have chosen, who hate the senators as Coriolanus hates the people. Among them, and among the patricians who had been looked upon as natural rulers, class feeling is equally strong, and it comes to its height when Coriolanus is nominated Consul.

CORIOLANUS is back from the wars full of wounds and honours, and his election as Consul is almost a certainty. But he will not pay the price the mob expects for its support, and his scorn of the crowd, expressed in contemptuous action and unbridled speech, causes the clash on which the play turns. The harsh pride and headstrong egotism of Coriolanus arouse the bitterest resentment in the crowd.

WE must not think of Coriolanus as a typical Roman. He was made what he was by an ambitious mother. Neither of them cares for others, and neither is a good Roman. Nor are their enemies good Romans; they are tricky politicians, making catspaws of less clever people, whom they deceive. It is a play of Rome before she had become powerful in the world, and it has not the true Roman spirit. It shows us the falsehood of extremes; it shows us that the real patriots are not those who make most noise or catch most readily the public eye. We see the real Romans quietly putting in a word here and there, and we see the doom that comes everywhere from the clash between the two blind tyrannies of an autocracy and a mob. It is a lesson never out of date, and it is the moral of this powerful play.

THE PLAYERS

Caius Marcius (Coriolanus), a brave Roman soldier, dreaded by the enemies of Rome, but hated by the Roman crowd because he was proud, arrogant, and scornful to them.

Cominius, Roman Consul. A general under whom Coriolanus served before becoming Consul.

Titus Lartius, a Roman general, friendly to Coriolanus.

Menenius, an aged Roman patrician, staunch friend of Coriolanus, and popular with the crowd.

Brutus, Roman tribune elected by the people.

Sicinius, another Roman tribune of the people.

Marcius, son of Coriolanus, a young boy.

Tullus Aufidius, the general of the Volscians, enemies of Rome. He is repeatedly defeated by Coriolanus.

First Citizen, a mob orator, against Coriolanus.

Second Citizen, a moderate man who asks for fair play.

Volumnia, mother of Coriolanus, who has built up his pride and encouraged his warlike ambition.

Virgilia, wife of Coriolanus, a quiet peaceful woman.

Valeria, a friend of the family of Coriolanus.

A gentlewoman attending on Virgilia.

A lieutenant to Aufidius in the Volscian army.

Conspirators with Aufidius.

A Volscian citizen of Antium.

Senators, patricians, and citizens of both States.

Aediles (executive officials), soldiers, messengers, servants, attendants, and a herald.

SCENE—Rome and round about; Corioli and round about: Antium, the town of Aufidius.

The Tragedy of Coriolanus

ACT 1

Scene 1—A Street in Rome : Citizens with Staves

FIRST CITIZEN. Before we proceed any further, hear me speak.

ALL. Speak, speak.

FIRST CITIZEN. You are all resolved rather to die than to famish ?

ALL. Resolved, resolved.

FIRST CITIZEN. First, you know Caius Marcius is chief enemy to the people.

ALL. We know 't, we know 't.

FIRST CITIZEN. Let us kill him, and we'll have corn at our own price. Is 't a verdict ?

ALL. No more talking on 't ; let it be done : away, away !

SECOND CITIZEN. One word, good citizens.

FIRST CITIZEN. We are accounted poor citizens ; the patricians, good. What authority surfeits on would relieve us : if they would yield us but the superfluity while it were wholesome, we might guess they relieved us humanely ; but they think we are too dear : the leanness that afflicts us, our misery, is as an inventory to particularise their abundance. Let us revenge this, for the gods know I speak this in hunger for bread, not in thirst for revenge.

SECOND CITIZEN. Would you proceed especially against Caius Marcius ?

ALL. Against him first ; he's a very dog to the commonalty.

SECOND CITIZEN. Consider you what services he has done ?

FIRST CITIZEN. Very well ; and could be content to give him good report for 't, but that he pays himself with being proud.

SECOND CITIZEN. Nay, but speak not maliciously.

FIRST CITIZEN. I say unto you, what he hath done famously he did it to that end : though soft-conscienced men can be content to say it was for his country, he did it to please his mother and to be partly proud ; which he is, even to the altitude of his virtue.

SECOND CITIZEN. What he cannot help in his nature you account a vice in him. You must in no way say he is covetous.

FIRST CITIZEN. If I must not, I need not be barren of accusations; he hath faults, with surplus, to tire in repetition. What shouts are these? The other side o' the city is risen: why stay we prating here? To the Capitol!

ALL. Come, come.

FIRST CITIZEN. Soft! who comes here? *(Enter Menenius Agrippa)*

SECOND CITIZEN. Worthy Menenius Agrippa; one that hath always loved the people.

FIRST CITIZEN. He's honest enough: would all the rest were so!

MENENIUS. What work's in hand? Where go you
With bats and clubs? The matter? Speak, I pray you.

FIRST CITIZEN. Our business is not unknown to the Senate; they have had inkling, this fortnight, what we intend to do, which now we'll show 'em in deeds. They shall know we have strong arms.

MENENIUS. Why, my good friends, mine honest neighbours,
Will you undo yourselves?

FIRST CITIZEN. We cannot, sir, we are undone already.

MENENIUS. I tell you, friends, most charitable care
Have the patricians of you. For your wants,
Your suffering in this dearth, you may as well
Strike at the heaven with your staves as lift them
Against the Roman State. For the dearth,
The gods, not the patricians, make it, and
Your knees to them, not arms, must help. Alack,
You are transported by calamity
Thither where more attends you, and you slander
The helms o' the State, who care for you like fathers,
When you curse them as enemies.

FIRST CITIZEN. Care for us! True, indeed! They ne'er cared for us yet: suffer us to famish, and their storehouses crammed with grain; make edicts for usury, to support usurers; repeal daily any wholesome act established against the rich, and provide more piercing statutes daily, to chain up and restrain the poor. If the wars eat us not up, they will; and there's all the love they bear us.

MENENIUS. There was a time when all the body's members
Rebelled against the belly; thus accused it:
That only like a gulf it did remain
I' the midst o' the body, idle and unactive,
Still cupboarding the viand, never bearing
Like labour with the rest; where the other instruments
Did see and hear, devise, instruct, walk, feel,
And, mutually participate, did minister
Unto the appetite and affection common
Of the whole body. The belly answered:

"True is it, my incorporate friends (quoth he),
That I receive the general food at first,
Which you do live upon ; and fit it is,
Because I am the storehouse and the shop
Of the whole body : but, if you do remember,
I send it through the rivers of your blood,
Even to the court, the heart, to the seat o' the brain ;
And, through the cranks and offices of man,
The strongest nerves and small inferior veins
From me receive that natural competency
Whereby they live." What say you to 't ?

FIRST CITIZEN. It was an answer : how apply you this ?

MENENIUS. The senators of Rome are this good belly,
And you the mutinous members. *(Caius Marcius approaches)*
Hail, noble Marcius !

MARCIUS. Thanks. What's the matter, you dissentious rogues ?

FIRST CITIZEN. We have ever your good word !

MARCIUS. What would you have, you curs,
That like nor peace nor war ? The one affrights you,
The other makes you proud. He that trusts to you,
Where he should find you lions, finds you hares ;
Where foxes, geese : you are no surer, no,
Than is the coal of fire upon the ice,
Or hailstone in the sun. Who deserves greatness
Deserves your hate ; and your affections are
A sick man's appetite, who desires most that
Which would increase his evil. He that depends
Upon your favours swims with fins of lead
And hews down oaks with rushes. Hang ye ! Trust ye ?
With every minute you do change a mind,
And call him noble that was now your hate,
Him vile that was your garland. What's the matter,
That in these several places of the city
You cry against the noble Senate, who,
Under the gods, keep you in awe, which else
Would feed on one another ? What's their seeking ?

MENENIUS. For corn at their own rates ; whereof, they say,
The city is well stored.

MARCIUS. Hang 'em ! They say !
They'll sit by the fire, and presume to know
What's done i' the Capitol. They say there's grain enough !
Would the nobility lay aside their ruth,
And let me use my sword, I'd make a quarry
With thousands of these quartered slaves, as high
As I could pick my lance.

MENENIUS. Nay, these are almost thoroughly persuaded;
For though abundantly they lack discretion,
Yet they are passing cowardly. But, I beseech you,
What says the other troop?

MARCIUS. They are dissolved: hang 'em!
They said they were a-hungry; sighed forth proverbs,
That hunger broke stone walls, that dogs must eat,
That meat was made for mouths, that the gods sent not
Corn for the rich men only: with these shreds
They vented their complainings; which being answered,
And a petition granted them, they threw their caps
As they would hang them on the horns o' the moon,
Shouting their emulation.

MENENIUS. What is granted them?

MARCIUS. Five tribunes to defend their vulgar wisdoms,
Of their own choice: one's Junius Brutus,
Sicinius Velutus, and I know not.
The rabble should have first unroofed the city
Ere so prevailed with me: it will in time
Win upon power and throw forth greater themes
For insurrection's arguing.

MENENIUS. This is strange.

MARCIUS. Go get you home, you fragments!

MESSENGER *(entering hastily)*. Where's Caius Marcius?

MARCIUS. Here: what's the matter?

MESSENGER. The news is, sir, the Volsces are in arms.

MARCIUS. I am glad on 't: then we shall ha' means to vent
Our musty superfluity. See, our best elders.

Enter Cominius, Lartius, and other Senators, with the two tribunes, Brutus and Sicinius.

FIRST SENATOR. Marcius, tis true that you have lately told us;
The Volsces are in arms.

MARCIUS. They have a leader,
Tullus Aufidius, that will put you to 't.
I sin in envying his nobility;
And were I anything but what I am,
I would wish me only he.

COMINIUS. You have fought together?

MARCIUS. Were half to half the world by the ears, and he
Upon my party, I'd revolt, to make
Only my wars with him: he is a lion
That I am proud to hunt.

FIRST SENATOR. Then, worthy Marcius,
Attend upon Cominius to these wars.

COMINIUS. It is your former promise.

MARCIUS. Sir, it is; and I am constant.

FIRST SENATOR. Your company to the Capitol, where I know
Our greatest friends attend us.
(To the Citizens) Hence to your homes; begone!

MARCIUS. Nay, let them follow:
The Volsces have much corn; take these rats thither
To gnaw their garners. Worshipful mutiners,
Your valour puts well forth: pray, follow.

Citizens steal away, leaving only Sicinius and Brutus

SICINIUS. Was ever man so proud as is this Marcius?

BRUTUS. He has no equal.

SICINIUS. When we were chosen tribunes for the people,

BRUTUS. Marked you his lip and eyes?

SICINIUS. Nay, but his taunts.

BRUTUS. Being moved, he will not spare to gird the gods.

SICINIUS. Bemock the modest moon. Such a nature,
Tickled with good success, disdains the shadow
Which he treads on at noon: but I do wonder
His insolence can brook to be commanded
Under Cominius.

BRUTUS. Fame, at the which he aims,
In whom already he's well graced, cannot
Better be held, nor more attained, than by
A place below the first: for what miscarries
Shall be the general's fault, though he perform
To the utmost of a man; and giddy censure
Will then cry out of Marcius "O, if he
Had borne the business!"

SICINIUS. Besides, if things go well,
Opinion, that so sticks on Marcius, shall
Of his demerits rob Cominius.

BRUTUS. Come:
Half all Cominius' honours are to Marcius,
Though Marcius earned them not; and all his faults
To Marcius shall be honours, though indeed
In aught he merit not.

SICINIUS. Let's hence, and hear how the dispatch is made.

Scene 2—The Senate-House at Corioli

FIRST SENATOR. So, your opinion is, Aufidius,
That they of Rome are entered in our counsels,
And know how we proceed.

Aufidius. Is it not yours?
Whatever has been thought on in this state,
That could be brought to bodily act ere Rome
Had circumvention? Tis not four days gone
Since I heard thence: these are the words: I think
I have the letter here: yes, here it is:
They have pressed a power, but it is not known
Whether for east or west: the dearth is great;
The people mutinous: and it is rumoured,
Cominius, Marcius your old enemy,
Who is of Rome worse hated than of you,
And Titus Lartius, a most valiant Roman,
These three lead on this preparation
Whither tis bent: most likely tis for you:
Consider of it.

First Senator. Our army's in the field:
We never yet made doubt but Rome was ready.

Aufidius. Nor did you think it folly
To keep your great pretences veiled till when
They needs must show themselves; which in the hatching,
It seemed, appeared to Rome. By the discovery
We shall be shortened in our aim, which was
To take in many towns ere almost Rome
Should know we were afoot.

Second Senator. Noble Aufidius,
Take your commission; hie you to your bands:
Let us alone to guard Corioli:
If they set down before 's, for the remove
Bring up your army: but I think you'll find
They've not prepared for us.

Aufidius. O, doubt not that;
I speak from certainties. Nay, more,
Some parcels of their power are forth already,
And only hitherward. I leave your honours.
If we and Caius Marcius chance to meet
Tis sworn between us we shall ever strike
Till one can do no more.

Scene 3—A Room in the House of Marcius

His mother and wife are sitting sewing

Volumnia. I pray you, daughter, sing, or express yourself in a more comfortable sort: if my son were my husband I should rejoice in that absence wherein he won honour. When yet he was but tender-bodied, I, considering how honour would become such a person, was pleased to let him seek danger where he was like to find fame. To a cruel war I sent him; from whence he returned, his brows bound with oak. Had I a dozen sons, each in my love alike, and none less dear than thine and my good Marcius, I had rather had eleven die nobly for their country than one voluptuously surfeit out of action.

VALERIA *(entering)*. How do you both? you are manifest housekeepers. What are you sewing here? A fine spot, in good faith. Come, lay aside your stitchery; I must have you play the idle huswife with me this afternoon.

VIRGILIA. Indeed, no, by your patience; I'll not over the threshold till my lord return from the wars.

VALERIA. Fie, you confine yourself most unreasonably. You would be another Penelope: yet they say all the yarn she spun in Ulysses' absence did but fill Ithaca full of moths.

VIRGILIA. No, good madam, pardon me; indeed, I will not forth.

VALERIA. In truth, I'll tell you excellent news of your husband.

VIRGILIA. O, good madam, there can be none yet.

VALERIA. Verily, I do not jest with you; there came news from him last night. I heard a senator speak it. Thus it is: the Volsces have an army forth, against whom Cominius the general is gone, with one part of our Roman power: your lord and Titus Lartius are set down before their city Corioli; they nothing doubt prevailing, and to make it brief wars.

VIRGILIA. Give me excuse, good madam; I will obey you in everything hereafter.

VALERIA. Well then, farewell.

Scene 4—Before Corioli

Enter, with drum and colours, Marcius, Titus Lartius, and Soldiers

MARCIUS. Yonder comes news. Say, has our general met the enemy?

MESSENGER *(arriving)*. They lie in view, but have not spoke as yet.

MARCIUS. How far off lie these armies?

MESSENGER. Within this mile and half.

MARCIUS. Then shall we hear their 'larum, and they ours.
Now, Mars, I prithee, make us quick in work,
That we with smoking swords may march from hence,
To help our fielded friends! Come, blow thy blast.
Tullus Aufidius, is he within your walls?

FIRST SENATOR. No, nor a man that fears you less than he,
That's lesser than a little. Hark, our drums
Are bringing forth our youth! We'll break our walls
Rather than they shall pound us up: our gates,
Which yet seem shut, we have but pinned with rushes;
They'll open of themselves. Hark you, far off!

There is Aufidius ; list what work he makes
Amongst your cloven army.

MARCIUS. O, they are at it !

LARTIUS. Their noise be our instruction. Ladders, ho !

Enter the army of the Volsces

MARCIUS. They fear us not, but issue forth their city.
Now put your shields before your hearts, and fight
With hearts more proof than shields. Advance, brave Titus :
They do disdain us much beyond our thoughts,
Which makes me sweat with wrath. Come on, my fellows :
He that retires, I'll take him for a Volsce,
And he shall feel mine edge.

The Romans are beaten back to their trenches ; re-enter Marcius, raging

MARCIUS. All the contagion of the south light on you,
You shames of Rome ! You souls of geese,
That bear the shapes of men, how have you run
From slaves that apes would beat !
All hurt behind ; backs red, and faces pale
With flight and agued fear ! Mend, and charge home,
Or, by the fires of heaven, I'll leave the foe,
And make my wars on you : look to 't : come on ;
If you'll stand fast, we'll beat them to their wives.

The Volsces fly and Marcius follows them to the gates

So, now the gates are ope : now prove good seconds :
Tis for the followers fortune widens them,
Not for the fliers : mark me, and do the like. *(He enters the gates)*

FIRST SOLDIER. Foolhardiness ; not I.

SECOND SOLDIER. Nor I. *(Marcius is shut in)*

FIRST SOLDIER. See, they have shut him in.

LARTIUS *(appearing)*. What is become of Marcius ?

FIRST SOLDIER. Following the fliers at the very heels,
With them he enters ; who, upon the sudden,
Clapped to their gates : he is himself alone,
To answer all the city.

LARTIUS. O noble fellow !
Who sensibly outdares his senseless sword,
And, when it bows, stands up ! Thou wast a soldier
Even to Cato's wish, not fierce and terrible
Only in strokes ; but, with thy grim looks and
The thunder-like percussion of thy sounds,
Thou madest thine enemies shake, as if the world
Were feverous and did tremble.

Re-enter Marcius, bleeding, assaulted by the enemy

FIRST SOLDIER. Look, sir.

LARTIUS. O, tis Marcius !
Let's fetch him off, or make remain alike.

They fight, and all enter the city

Scene 5—A Street in Corioli : Romans carrying spoils

FIRST ROMAN. This will I carry to Rome.

SECOND ROMAN. And I this.

THIRD ROMAN. A murrain on 't ! I took this for silver.

Enter Marcius and Lartius with a trumpet

MARCIUS. See here these movers that do prize their hours
At a cracked drachma ! Cushions, leaden spoons,
Irons of a doit, doublets that hangmen would
Bury with those that wore them, these base slaves,
Ere yet the fight be done, pack up : down with them !
And hark, what noise the general makes ! To him !
There is the man of my soul's hate, Aufidius,
Piercing our Romans : then, valiant Titus, take
Convenient numbers to make good the city ;
Whilst I, with those that have the spirit, will haste
To help Cominius.

LARTIUS. Worthy sir, thou bleed'st !

MARCIUS. My work hath yet not warmed me : fare you well :
The blood I drop is rather physical
Than dangerous to me : to Aufidius thus
I will appear, and fight.

LARTIUS. Now the fair goddess Fortune
Fall deep in love with thee ; and her great charms
Misguide thy opposers' swords ! Bold gentleman,
Prosperity be thy page !

MARCIUS. Thy friend no less
Than those she placeth highest ! So farewell. *(He goes)*

LARTIUS. Go sound thy trumpet in the market-place ;
Call thither all the officers o' the town,
Where they shall know our mind. Away !

Scene 6—Cominius in his Camp with Soldiers

COMINIUS. Breathe you, my friends : well fought : we are come off
Like Romans, neither foolish in our stands
Nor cowardly in retire : believe me, sirs,
We shall be charged again. Whiles we have struck,
By interims and conveying gusts we have heard
The charges of our friends. Ye Roman gods,
Lead their successes as we wish our own,
That both our powers, with smiling fronts encountering,
May give you thankful sacrifice !

MESSENGER *(arriving)*. The citizens of Corioli have issued,
And given to Lartius and to Marcius battle :

I saw our party to their trenches driven,
And then I came away.

COMINIUS. Who's yonder,
That does appear as he were flayed? O gods!
He has the stamp of Marcius.

MARCIUS *(appearing).* Come I too late?

COMINIUS. Ay, if you come not in the blood of others,
But mantled in your own.

MARCIUS. O, let me clip ye
In arms as sound as when I wooed.

COMINIUS. Flower of warriors! How is 't with Titus Lartius?

MARCIUS. As with a man busied about decrees:
Condemning some to death, and some to exile;
Ransoming him or pitying, threatening the other;
Holding Corioli in the name of Rome.

COMINIUS. Where is that slave
Which told me they had beat you to your trenches?
Where is he? Call him hither.

MARCIUS. Let him alone;
He did inform the truth: but for our gentlemen,
The common file (a plague! tribunes for them!),
The mouse ne'er shunned the cat as they did budge
From rascals worse than they.

COMINIUS. But how prevailed you?

MARCIUS. Will the time serve to tell? I do not think.
Where is the enemy? Are you lords o' the field?
If not, why cease till you are so?

COMINIUS. Marcius,
We have at disadvantage fought, and did
Retire to win our purpose.

MARCIUS. How lies their battle? know you on which side
They have placed their men of trust?

COMINIUS. As I guess, Marcius,
Their bands i' the vanguard are the Antiates,
Of their best trust; o'er them Aufidius,
Their very heart of hope.

MARCIUS. I do beseech you,
By all the battles wherein we have fought,
By the blood we have shed together, by the vows
We have made to endure friends, that you directly
Set me against Aufidius and his Antiates;
And that you not delay the present, but,
Filling the air with swords advanced and darts,
We prove this very hour.

COMINIUS. Though I could wish
You were conducted to a gentle bath,
And balms applied to you, yet dare I never
Deny your asking: take your choice of those
That best can aid your action.

MARCIUS. Those are they that most are willing.
If any think brave death outweighs bad life,
And that his country's dearer than himself,
Let him alone, or so many so minded,
Wave thus, to express his disposition,
And follow Marcius. *(All shout and wave swords.)* A certain number,
Though thanks to all, must I select from all: the rest
Shall bear the business in some other fight,
As cause will be obeyed. Please you to march,
And four shall quickly draw out my command,
Which men are best inclined.

COMINIUS. March on, my fellows.

Scene 7—At the Gates of Corioli

LARTIUS. So, let the ports be guarded: keep your duties,
As I have set them down. If I do send, dispatch
Those centuries to our aid; the rest will serve
For a short holding: if we lose the field
We cannot keep the town.

LIEUTENANT. Fear not our care, sir.

LARTIUS. Hence, and shut your gates upon 's.
Our guider, come; to the Roman camp conduct us.

Scene 8—A Field between the two Camps: Marcius and Aufidius meet

MARCIUS. I'll fight with none but thee; for I do hate thee
Worse than a promise-breaker.

AUFIDIUS. We hate alike:
Not Afric owns a serpent I abhor
More than thy fame and envy. Fix thy foot.

MARCIUS. Let the first budger die the other's slave,
And the gods doom him after!

AUFIDIUS. If I fly, Marcius, holloa me like a hare.

MARCIUS. Within these three hours, Tullus,
Alone I fought in your Corioli walls,
And made what work I pleased: tis not *my* blood
Wherein thou seest me masked; for thy revenge
Wrench up thy power to the highest.

AUFIDIUS. Wert thou the Hector
That was the whip of your bragged progeny,
Thou shouldst not 'scape me here.

They fight, and Volsces come to the aid of Aufidius, Marcius fighting on

Scene 9—The Roman Camp : Marcius with his Arm in a Scarf

COMINIUS *(to Marcius)*. If I should tell thee o'er this thy day's work,
Thou'lt not believe thy deeds : but I'll report it,
Where senators shall mingle tears with smiles ;
Where great patricians shall attend, and shrug,
I' the end admire ; where ladies shall be frighted,
And, gladly quaked, hear more ; where the dull tribunes,
That, with the fusty plebeians, hate thine honours,
Shall say against their hearts *We thank the gods*
Our Rome hath such a soldier.

LARTIUS *(entering with his forces)*. O general,
Here is the steed, we the caparison :
Hadst thou beheld—

MARCIUS. Pray now, no more : my mother,
Who has a charter to extol her blood,
When she does praise me grieves me. I have done
As you have done ; that's what I can : induced
As you have been ; that's for my country :
He that has but effected his goodwill
Hath overta'en mine act.

COMINIUS. You shall not be
The grave of your deserving ; Rome must know
The value of her own : 'twere a concealment
Worse than a theft, no less than a traducement,
To hide your doings ; therefore, I beseech you,
(In sign of what you are, not to reward
What you have done) before our army hear me.

MARCIUS. I have some wounds upon me, and they smart
To hear themselves remembered.

COMINIUS. Should they not,
Well might they fester 'gainst ingratitude,
And tent themselves with death. Of all the horses,
Whereof we have ta'en good, and good store, of all
The treasure in this field achieved and city,
We render you the tenth.

MARCIUS. I thank you, general ;
But cannot make my heart consent to take
A bribe to pay my sword : I do refuse it,
And stand upon my common part with those
That have beheld the doing.

COMINIUS. Too modest are you ;
More cruel to your good report than grateful
To us that give you truly : by your patience,
If 'gainst yourself you be incensed, we'll put you,
Like one that means his proper harm, in manacles,

Then reason safely with you. Therefore, be it known,
As to us, to all the world, that Caius Marcius
Wears this war's garland: in token of the which
My noble steed, known to the camp, I give him,
With all his trim belonging; and from this time,
For what he did before Corioli, call him,
With all the applause and clamour of the host,
CAIUS MARCIUS CORIOLANUS. Bear
The addition nobly ever! *(Trumpets sound)*

ALL. Caius Marcius Coriolanus!

CORIOLANUS. I will go wash;
And when my face is fair you shall perceive
Whether I blush, or no: howbeit, I thank you:
I mean to stride your steed.

COMINIUS. So, to our tent;
Where, ere we do repose us, we will write
To Rome of our success.

CORIOLANUS. The gods begin to mock me. I, that now
Refused most princely gifts, am bound to beg.

COMINIUS. Take 't; tis yours. What is 't?

CORIOLANUS. I sometime lay here in Corioli
At a poor man's house; he used me kindly:
He cried to me; I saw him prisoner;
But then Aufidius was within my view,
And wrath o'erwhelmed my pity: I request you
To give my poor host freedom.

COMINIUS. O, well begged!
Were he the butcher of my son he should
Be free as is the wind. Deliver him, Titus.

Scene 10—The Camp of the Volsces: enter Aufidius with Soldiers

AUFIDIUS. The town is ta'en!

SOLDIER. Twill be delivered back on good condition.

AUFIDIUS. Condition!
I would I were a Roman; for I cannot,
Being a Volsce, be that I am. Condition!
What good condition can a treaty find
I' the part that is at mercy? Five times, Marcius,
I have fought with thee; so often hast thou beat me;
And wouldst do so, I think, should we encounter
As often as we eat. By the elements,
If e'er again I meet him beard to beard,
He's mine, or I am his: mine emulation
Hath not that honour in 't it had; for where
I thought to crush him in an equal force,

True sword to sword, I'll potch at him some way,
Or wrath or craft may get him.

SOLDIER. He's the devil.

AUFIDIUS. Bolder, though not so subtle. My valour's poisoned
With only suffering stain by him; for him
Shall fly out of itself: nor sleep nor sanctuary,
Being naked, sick, nor fane nor Capitol,
The prayers of priests nor times of sacrifice,
Embarquements all of fury, shall lift up
Their rotten privilege and custom 'gainst
My hate to Marcius: where I find him, were it
At home, upon my brother's guard, even there,
Against the hospitable canon, would I
Wash my fierce hand in 's heart. Go you to the city;
Learn how tis held, and what they are that must
Be hostages for Rome.

SOLDIER. I shall, sir.

ACT 2

Scene 1—A Public Place in Rome: enter Menenius, with the two Tribunes

MENENIUS. The augurer tells me we shall have news tonight.

BRUTUS. Good or bad?

MENENIUS. Not according to the prayer of the people, for they love not Marcius.

SICINIUS. Nature teaches beasts to know their friends.

MENENIUS. This is strange now: do you two know how you are censured here in the city? You blame Marcius for being proud?

BRUTUS. We do it not alone, sir.

MENENIUS. I know you can do very little alone; for your helps are many, or else your actions would grow wondrous single: your abilities are too infant-like for doing much alone. You talk of pride: O that you could turn your eyes toward the napes of your necks, and make but an interior survey of your good selves! O that you could!

BOTH. What then, sir?

MENENIUS. Why, then you should discover a brace of unmeriting, proud, violent, testy magistrates, alias fools, as any in Rome.

The tribunes step aside, while Volumnia, Virgilia, and Valeria enter

VOLUMNIA. Honourable Menenius, my boy Marcius approaches; for the love of Juno, let's go.

MENENIUS. Ha! Marcius coming home?

VOLUMNIA. Ay, worthy Menenius; and with most prosperous approbation. Look, here's a letter from him: the State hath another, his wife another; and, I think, there's one at home for you.

MENENIUS. A letter for me! It gives me an estate of seven years' health. Is he not wounded? He was wont to come home wounded.

VIRGILIA. O, no, no, no.

VOLUMNIA. O, he is wounded; I thank the gods for 't.

MENENIUS. So do I too, if it be not too much: brings a' victory in his pocket? The wounds become him.

VOLUMNIA. On his brows: Menenius, he comes the third time home with the oaken garland.

MENENIUS. Has he disciplined Aufidius soundly?

VOLUMNIA. Titus Lartius writes they fought together, but Aufidius got off. Good ladies, let's go. Yes, yes, yes; the Senate has letters from the General, wherein he gives my son the whole name of the war: he hath in this action outdone his former deeds.

VALERIA. In troth, there's wondrous things spoke of him.

VIRGILIA. The gods grant them true!

MENENIUS. True! I'll be sworn they are true. Where is he wounded? *(To the Tribunes*: God save your good worships! Marcius is coming home: he has more cause to be proud.) Where is he wounded?

VOLUMNIA. I' the shoulder and i' the left arm: there will be large cicatrices to show the people, when he shall stand for his place. He received in the repulse of Tarquin seven hurts i' the body.

MENENIUS. There's nine that I know.

VOLUMNIA. He had, before this last expedition, twenty-five wounds upon him.

MENENIUS. Now it's twenty-seven: every gash was an enemy's grave. Hark! the trumpets.

Trumpets sound, and Coriolanus enters crowned with an oak garland

HERALD. Know, Rome, that all alone Marcius did fight
Within Corioli gates: where he hath won,
With fame, a name to Caius Marcius; these
In honour follows Coriolanus.
Welcome to Rome, renownèd Coriolanus!

ALL. Welcome to Rome, renownèd Coriolanus!

CORIOLANUS. No more of this, it does offend my heart;
Pray now, no more.

COMINIUS. Look, sir, your mother!

CORIOLANUS. O, you have, I know, petitioned all the gods
For my prosperity! *(He kneels)*

VOLUMNIA. Nay, my good soldier, up;
My gentle Marcius, worthy Caius, and
By deed-achieving honour newly named,
(What is it?) Coriolanus must I call thee?
But, O, thy wife!

CORIOLANUS. My gracious silence, hail!
Wouldst thou have laughed had I come coffined home,
Thou weep'st to see me triumph? Ah, my dear,
Such eyes the widows in Corioli wear,
And mothers that lack sons.

MENENIUS. Now, the gods crown thee!

CORIOLANUS. And live you yet? *(To Valeria)* O my sweet lady, pardon.

VOLUMNIA. I know not where to turn: O welcome home:
And welcome, General: and ye're welcome all.

MENENIUS. A hundred thousand welcomes. I could weep,
And I could laugh; I am light and heavy. Welcome:
A curse begin at very root on 's heart,
That is not glad to see thee! You are three
That Rome should dote on: yet, by the faith of men,
We have some old crab-trees here at home that will not
Be grafted to your relish. Yet welcome, warriors.

CORIOLANUS *(to Volumnia and Virgilia)*. Your hand, and yours:
Ere in our own house I do shade my head,
The good patricians must be visited;
From whom I have received not only greetings,
But with them change of honours.

VOLUMNIA. I have lived
To see inherited my very wishes
And the buildings of my fancy: only
There's one thing wanting, which I doubt not but
Our Rome will cast upon thee.

CORIOLANUS. Know, good mother,
I had rather be their servant in my way
Than sway with them in theirs.

COMINIUS. On, to the Capitol!

They go, and the two tribunes come forward

BRUTUS. All tongues speak of him, and the bleared sights
Are spectacled to see him. Such a pother,
As if that whatsoever god who leads him
Were slily crept into his human powers,
And gave him graceful posture.

SICINIUS. I warrant him consul.

BRUTUS. Then our office may, during his power, go sleep.
I heard him swear,
Were he to stand for consul, never would he
Appear i' the market-place, nor on him put
The napless vesture of humility,
Nor showing, as the manner is, his wounds
To the people, beg their stinking breaths.

SICINIUS. Tis right.

BRUTUS. It was his word: O, he would miss it rather
Than carry it but by the suit of the gentry to him,
And the desire of the nobles.

SICINIUS. I wish no better
Than have him hold that purpose and to put it
In execution.

BRUTUS. Tis most like he will.

SICINIUS. It shall be to him then, as our good wills,
A sure destruction.

BRUTUS. So it must fall out
To him or our authorities. For an end,
We must suggest the people in what hatred
He still hath held them; that to 's power he would
Have made them mules, silenced their pleaders and
Dispropertied their freedoms; holding them,
In human action and capacity,
Of no more soul nor fitness for the world
Than camels in the war, who have their provand
Only for bearing burthens, and sore blows
For sinking under them.

SICINIUS. This, as you say, suggested
At some time when his soaring insolence
Shall touch the people (which time shall not want,
If he be put upon 't; and that's as easy
As to set dogs on sheep) will be his fire
To kindle their dry stubble; and their blaze
Shall darken him for ever.

MESSENGER. You are sent for to the Capitol. Tis thought
That Marcius shall be consul.
I have seen the dumb men throng to see him and
The blind to hear him speak: matrons flung gloves,
Ladies and maids their scarfs and handkerchers,
Upon him as he passed: the nobles bended,
As to Jove's statue, and the commons made
A shower and thunder with their caps and shouts:
I never saw the like.

BRUTUS. Let's to the Capitol,
And carry with us ears and eyes for the time,
But hearts for the event.

Scene 2—The Capitol

FIRST OFFICER. Come, come, they are almost here. How many stand for consulships?

SECOND OFFICER. Three, they say: but tis thought of every one Coriolanus will carry it.

First Officer. That's a brave fellow; but he's vengeance proud, and loves not the common people.

Second Officer. He hath deserved worthily of his country—

First Officer. No more of him; make way, they are coming.

Enter Senators, headed by Cominius, and accompanied by the tribunes

Menenius. Having determined of the Volsces and
To send for Titus Lartius, it remains,
As the main point of this our after-meeting,
To gratify his noble service that
Hath thus stood for his country: therefore, please you,
Most reverend and grave elders, to desire
The present consul, and last general
In our well-found successes, to report
A little of that worthy work performed
By Caius Marcius Coriolanus; whom
We met here, both to thank and to remember
With honours like himself.

First Senator. Speak, good Cominius.

Cominius. I shall lack voice: the deeds of Coriolanus
Should not be uttered feebly. It is held
That valour is the chiefest virtue and
Most dignifies the haver: if it be,
The man I speak of cannot in the world
Be singly counterpoised. At sixteen years,
When Tarquin made a head for Rome, he fought
Beyond the mark of others: our then dictator,
Whom with all praise I point at, saw him fight,
When with his Amazonian chin he drove
The bristled lips before him: he bestrid
An o'er-pressed Roman, and i' the consul's view
Slew three opposers: Tarquin's self he met,
And struck him on his knee: in that day's feats,
When he might act the woman in the scene,
He proved best man i' the field, and for his meed
Was brow-bound with the oak. His pupil age
Man-entered thus, he waxèd like a sea;
And, in the brunt of seventeen battles since,
He lurched all swords of the garland. For this last,
Before and in Corioli, let me say,
I cannot speak him home: he stopped the fliers;
And by his rare example made the coward
Turn terror into sport: as weeds before
A vessel under sail, so men obeyed,
And fell below his stem: alone he entered
The mortal gate of the city, aidless came off,

And with a sudden re-enforcement struck
Corioli like a planet: now all's his:
When, by and by, the din of war gan pierce
His ready sense; then straight his doubled spirit
Re-quickened what in flesh was fatigate,
And to the battle came he; where he did
Run reeking o'er the lives of men, as if
'Twere a perpetual spoil; and till we called
Both field and city ours he never stood
To ease his breast with panting.

MENENIUS. Worthy man!

FIRST SENATOR. He cannot but with measure fit the honours
Which we devise him.

COMINIUS. Our spoils he kicked at,
And looked upon things precious as they were
The common muck of the world: he covets less
Than misery itself would give.

MENENIUS. He's right noble: let him be called for. *(He comes)*
The Senate, Coriolanus, are well pleased
To make thee consul.

CORIOLANUS. I do owe them still my life and services.

MENENIUS. It then remains that you do speak to the people.

CORIOLANUS. I do beseech you
Let me o'erleap that custom, for I cannot
Put on the gown, stand naked, and entreat them,
For my wounds' sake, to give their suffrage: please you
That I may pass this doing.

SICINIUS. Sir, the people
Must have their voices; neither will they bate
One jot of ceremony.

MENENIUS. Put them not to 't:
Pray you, go fit you to the custom, and
Take to you, as your predecessors have,
Your honour with your form.

CORIOLANUS. It is a part
That I shall blush in acting, and might well
Be taken from the people.

BRUTUS. Mark you that?

CORIOLANUS. To brag unto them, thus I did, and thus;
Show them the unaching scars which I should hide,
As if I had received them for the hire
Of their breath only!

MENENIUS. Do not stand upon 't.
We recommend to you, tribunes of the people,

Our purpose to them: and to our noble consul
Wish we all joy and honour.

SENATORS. To Coriolanus come all joy and honour!

Flourish of cornets. All but Sicinius and Brutus leave

BRUTUS. You see how he intends to use the people.

SICINIUS. May they perceive 's intent! He will require them,
As if he did contemn what he requested
Should be in them to give.

Scene 3—The Forum

FIRST CITIZEN. Once, if he do require our voices, we ought not to deny him.

SECOND CITIZEN. We may, sir, if we will.

THIRD CITIZEN. I say, if he would incline to the people, there was never a worthier man.

Enter Coriolanus in a gown of humility, with Menenius

Here he comes, and in the gown of humility: mark his behaviour. We are not to stay all together, but to come by him where he stands, by ones, by twos, and by threes. He's to make his requests by particulars, wherein every one of us has a single honour, in giving him our own voices with our own tongues: therefore follow me, and I'll direct you how you shall go by him. *(Citizens leave)*

MENENIUS. O sir, you are not right: have you not known
The worthiest men have done 't?

CORIOLANUS. What must I say?
I pray, sir (Plague upon 't! I cannot bring
My tongue to such a pace). *Look, sir, my wounds!*
I got them in my country's service, when
Some certain of your brethren roared, and ran
From the noise of our own drums.

MENENIUS. O me, the gods!
You must not speak of that: you must desire them
To think upon you.

CORIOLANUS. Think upon me! hang 'em!
I would they would forget me.

MENENIUS. You'll mar all:
I'll leave you: pray you, speak in wholesome manner.

CORIOLANUS. Bid them wash their faces,
And keep their teeth clean.
You know the cause, sir, of my standing here.

THIRD CITIZEN. We do, sir; tell us what hath brought you to 't.

CORIOLANUS. Mine own desert!

SECOND CITIZEN. Your own desert!

CORIOLANUS. Ay, but not mine own desire.

THIRD CITIZEN. How! not your own desire!

CORIOLANUS. No, sir, 'twas never my desire yet to trouble the poor with begging.

THIRD CITIZEN. You must think, if we give you anything, we hope to gain by you.

CORIOLANUS. Well then, I pray, your price o' the consulship?

FIRST CITIZEN. The price is to ask it kindly.

CORIOLANUS. Kindly! Sir, I pray, let me have it, I have wounds to show you, which shall be yours in private. Your good voice, sir; what say you?

SECOND CITIZEN. You shall have it, worthy sir.

CORIOLANUS. A match, sir. There's in all two worthy voices begged. I have your alms: adieu.

THIRD CITIZEN. But this is something odd.

SECOND CITIZEN. An 'twere to give again—but tis no matter.

The three Citizens leave and two others enter

CORIOLANUS. Pray you now, if it may stand with the tune of your voices that I may be consul, I have here the customary gown.

FOURTH CITIZEN. You have deserved nobly of your country, and you have not desired nobly.

CORIOLANUS. Your enigma?

FOURTH CITIZEN. You have been a scourge to her enemies, you have been a rod to her friends; you have not indeed loved the common people.

CORIOLANUS. You should account me the more virtuous that I have not been common in my love.

FIFTH CITIZEN. We hope to find you our friend; and therefore give you our voices heartily.

FOURTH CITIZEN. You have received many wounds for your country.

CORIOLANUS. I will not seal your knowledge with showing them. I will make much of your voices, and so trouble you no farther.

BOTH CITIZENS. The gods give you joy, sir, heartily! *(They go)*

CORIOLANUS. Most sweet voices!
Better it is to die, better to starve,
Than crave the hire which first we do deserve.
Why in this woolvish toge should I stand here,
To beg of Hob and Dick that do appear,
Their needless vouches? Custom calls me to it:
What custom wills, in all things should we do it,
The dust on antique time would lie unswept,
And mountainous error be too highly heaped
For truth to o'er-peer. Rather than fool it so,
Let the high office and the honour go

To one that would do thus. I am half through:
The one part suffered, the other will I do.
Here come more voices. *(Citizens appear)*
Your voices: for your voices I have fought;
Watched for your voices; for your voices bear
Of wounds two dozen odd; battles thrice six
I have seen, and heard of; for your voices have
Done many things, some less, some more: your voices:
Indeed, I would be consul.

SIXTH CITIZEN. He has done nobly, and cannot go without any honest man's voice.

SEVENTH CITIZEN. Therefore let him be consul: the gods give him joy, and make him good friend to the people!

ALL. Amen, amen. God save thee, noble consul! *(They go)*

CORIOLANUS. Worthy voices!

Re-enter Menenius, with Brutus and Sicinius

MENENIUS. You have stood your limitation; and the tribunes
Endue you with the people's voice: remains
That, in the official marks invested, you
Anon do meet the Senate.

CORIOLANUS. May I change these garments?

SICINIUS. You may, sir.

CORIOLANUS. That I'll straight do, and, knowing myself again,
Repair to the Senate House.

SICINIUS. Fare you well.

Perplexed by the attitude of Coriolanus, the citizens are incited by Sicinius and Brutus to denounce him for high-handed contempt. Counselled by the tribunes, they resolve to march to the Senate House and to withdraw their support, so compelling the Senate to defeat his election.

ACT 3

Scene 1—A Street in Rome

Enter Coriolanus, with Senators and Patricians

While on the way to the Senate House Coriolanus learns that Aufidius is leading the Volsces to war again, breathing vengeance against him. The talk is interrupted by the entry of Sicinius and Brutus, who forbid him further progress, saying that the people, realising his scorn and enmity towards them, have withdrawn their support for his election. He has flouted and mocked them, and denounced their claim to free corn, so the people will not have him; he shall not be made Consul.

CORIOLANUS. Tell me of corn!
This was my speech, and I will speak 't again—

MENENIUS. Not now, not now.

FIRST SENATOR. Not in this heat, sir, now.

CORIOLANUS. Now, as I live, I will. My nobler friends,
I crave their pardons :
For the mutable, rank-scented many, let them
Regard me as I do not flatter, and
Therein behold themselves : I say again,
In soothing them, we nourish 'gainst our Senate
The cockle of rebellion, insolence, sedition,
Which we ourselves have ploughed for, sowed, and scattered,
By mingling them with us, the honoured number ;
Who lack not virtue, no, nor power, but that
Which they have given to beggars.

BRUTUS. You speak o' the people,
As if you were a god to punish, not a man of their infirmity.

SICINIUS. Twere well we let the people know 't.

MENENIUS. What, what ? his choler ?

CORIOLANUS. Choler ! Were I as patient as the midnight sleep,
By Jove, 'twould be my mind !

SICINIUS. It is a mind that shall remain a poison where it is,
Not poison any further.

CORIOLANUS. Shall remain !
Here you this Triton of the minnows, mark you
His absolute *shall* ?
O good but most unwise patricians ! Why,
You grave but reckless senators, have you thus
Given Hydra here to choose an officer,
That with his peremptory *shall*, being but
The horn and noise o' the monster's, wants not spirit
To say he'll turn your current in a ditch,
And make your channel his ? By Jove himself,
It makes the consuls base ! and my soul aches
To know, when two authorities are up,
Neither supreme, how soon confusion
May enter 'twixt the gap of both and take
The one by the other.

COMINIUS. Well, on to the market-place.

CORIOLANUS. Whoever gave that counsel, to give forth
The corn o' the storehouse gratis, as 'twas used
Sometime in Greece—

MENENIUS. Well, well, no more of that.

CORIOLANUS. Though there the people had more absolute power,
I say they nourished disobedience, fed
The ruin of the State.

BRUTUS. Why, shall the people give
One that speaks thus their voice ?

CORIOLANUS. I'll give my reasons,
More worthier than their voices. They know the corn
Was not our recompense, resting well assured
They ne'er did service for 't : being pressed to the war,
Even when the navel of the State was touched,
They would not thread the gates. This kind of service
Did not deserve corn gratis : being i' the war,
Their mutinies and revolts, wherein they showed
Most valour, spoke not for them. We debase
The nature of our seats, and make the rabble
Call our cares fears, which will in time
Break ope the locks o' the Senate, and bring in
The crows to peck the eagles.

MENENIUS. Come, enough.

BRUTUS. Enough, with over measure.

SICINIUS. Has spoken like a traitor, and shall answer
As traitors do.

CORIOLANUS. Thou wretch, despite o'erwhelm thee!
What should the people do with these bald tribunes?

BRUTUS. Manifest treason!

SICINIUS. This a consul? No.

BRUTUS. The aediles, ho! Let him be apprehended. *(The Aediles, or executive officials, appear.)*

SICINIUS. Go, call the people, in whose name myself
Attach thee as a traitorous innovator,
A foe to the public weal : obey, I charge thee,
And follow to thine answer.

The scornful defiance of the mob by Coriolanus enables the tribunes to bring about a situation in which it is easy and natural for them to order that he shall be arrested and cast to death from the Tarpeian rock. A violent conflict follows, in which Coriolanus and his friends put the guards and citizens to flight. Coriolanus is then persuaded to retire to his house, and to leave the matter to be composed in the Senate by the wisdom of Menenius. The tribunes return with added numbers, and now insist on vengeance against Coriolanus.

MENENIUS. Hear me speak :
As I do know the consul's worthiness,
So can I name his faults—

SICINIUS. Consul! what consul?

MENENIUS. The consul Coriolanus.

BRUTUS. He consul!

CITIZENS. No, no, no, no, no.

MENENIUS. If, by the tribunes' leave, and yours, good people,
I may be heard, I would crave a word or two ;

The which shall turn you to no further harm
Than so much loss of time.

SICINIUS. Speak briefly then,
For we are peremptory to dispatch
This viperous traitor: to eject him hence
Were but one danger, and to keep him here
Our certain death: therefore it is decreed
He dies tonight.

MENENIUS. Now the good gods forbid
That our renownèd Rome, whose gratitude
Towards her deservèd children is enrolled
In Jove's own book, like an unnatural dam
Should now eat up her own!

SICINIUS. He's a disease that must be cut away.

MENENIUS. O, he's a limb that has but a disease;
Mortal, to cut it off; to cure it, easy.
What has he done to Rome that's worthy death?
Killing our enemies, the blood he hath lost—
Which, I dare vouch, is more than that he hath
By many an ounce—he dropped it for his country;
And what is left, to lose it by his country
Were to us all that do 't and suffer it
A brand to the end o' the world.

BRUTUS. We'll hear no more.
Pursue him to his house, and pluck him thence;
Lest his infection, being of catching nature,
Spread further.

MENENIUS. One word more, one word. Proceed by process,
Lest parties, as he is beloved, break out,
And sack great Rome with Romans.

SICINIUS. What do ye talk?
Have we not had a taste of his obedience?
Our aediles smote? ourselves resisted? Come.

MENENIUS. Consider this: he has been bred i' the wars
Since he could draw a sword, and is ill schooled
In bolted language; meal and bran together
He throws without distinction. Give me leave,
I'll go to him, and undertake to bring him
Where he shall answer, by a lawful form,
In peace, to his utmost peril.

FIRST SENATOR. Noble tribunes,
It is the humane way.

SICINIUS. Noble Menenius,
Be you then as the people's officer.
Masters, lay down your weapons.

BRUTUS. Go not home.

SICINIUS. Meet on the market-place. We'll attend you there:
Where, if you bring not Marcius, we'll proceed
In our first way.

MENENIUS. I'll bring him to you.
(To the Senators) Let me desire your company: he must come,
Or what is worse will follow.

FIRST SENATOR. Pray you, let's to him.

Scene 2—A Room in the House of Coriolanus

Coriolanus is besought by his mother, Cominius, and also by Menenius, to meet the people, to conciliate them, and repent what he has spoken. "For them? (cries he). I cannot do it to the gods; must I then do it to them?" In vain Volumnia counsels wisdom, but when, altering her tone, she declares that his courage is of her, and that she will die with him, his affection prevails over his pride and he consents to meet the people "mildly." Menenius, urging him to please the people, warns him that the tribunes have now prepared yet stronger accusations.

Scene 3—The Forum

BRUTUS. In this point charge him home, that he affects
Tyrannical power: if he evade us there,
Enforce him with his envy to the people,
And that the spoil got on the Antiates
Was ne'er distributed. What, will he come?

AEDILE *(entering)*. He's coming.

SICINIUS. Have you a catalogue
Of all the voices that we have procured,
Set down by the poll?

AEDILE. I have; tis ready.

SICINIUS. Assemble presently the people hither:
And when they hear me say *It shall be so*
I' the right and strength o' the commons, be it either
For death, for fine, or banishment, then let them,
If I say fine, cry *Fine*, if death, cry *Death*,
Insisting on the old prerogative
And power i' the truth o' the cause.

BRUTUS. And when such time they have begun to cry,
Let them not cease, but with a din confused
Enforce the present execution
Of what we chance to sentence.

SICINIUS. Make them be strong, and ready for this hint,
When we shall hap to give 't them.

BRUTUS. Go about it.
Put him to choler straight: he hath been used

Ever to conquer and to have his worth
Of contradiction: being once chafed, he cannot
Be reined again to temperance; then he speaks
What's in his heart; and that is there which looks
With us to break his neck.

Enter Coriolanus with Senators and Patricians

MENENIUS. Calmly, I do beseech you.

CORIOLANUS. Ay, as an ostler, that for the poorest piece
Will bear the knave by the volume. The honoured gods
Keep Rome in safety, and the chairs of justice
Supplied with worthy men! plant love among us!
Throng our large temples with the shows of peace,
And not our streets with war!

FIRST SENATOR. Amen, amen.

MENENIUS. A noble wish. *(Aedile comes with Citizens)*

SICINIUS. Draw near, ye people.

AEDILE. List to your tribunes; audience: peace, I say!

CORIOLANUS. First, hear me speak.

BOTH TRIBUNES. Well, say. Peace, ho!

CORIOLANUS. Shall I be charged no further than this present?
Must all determine here?

SICINIUS. I do demand,
If you submit you to the people's voices,
Allow their officers, and are content
To suffer lawful censure for such faults
As shall be proved upon you.

CORIOLANUS. I am content.

MENENIUS. Lo, citizens, he says he is content:
The warlike service he has done, consider; think
Upon the wounds his body bears, which show
Like graves i' the holy churchyard.

CORIOLANUS. Scratches with briers,
Scars to move laughter only.

MENENIUS. Consider further,
That when he speaks not like a citizen,
You find him like a soldier: do not take
His rougher accents for malicious sounds,
But, as I say, such as become a soldier
Rather than envy you.

CORIOLANUS. What is the matter
That, being passed for consul with full voice,
I am so dishonoured that the very hour
You take it off again?

SICINIUS. We charge you, that you have contrived to take
From Rome all seasoned office, and to wind
Yourself into a power tyrannical;
For which you are a traitor to the people.

CORIOLANUS. How! traitor!

MENENIUS. Nay, temperately; your promise.

CORIOLANUS. The fires i' the lowest hell fold in the people!
Call me their traitor! Thou injurious tribune!
Within thine eyes sat twenty thousand deaths,
In thy hands clutched as many millions, in
Thy lying tongue both numbers, I would say
Thou liest unto thee with a voice as free
As I do pray the gods.

SICINIUS. Mark you this, people?

CITIZENS. To the rock, to the rock with him!

SICINIUS. Peace!
We need not put new matter to his charge:
What you have seen him do and heard him speak,
Beating your officers, cursing yourselves,
Opposing laws with strokes, and here defying
Those whose great power must try him; even this,
So criminal and in such capital kind,
Deserves the extremest death.

BRUTUS. But since he hath served well for Rome—

CORIOLANUS. What, do you prate of service?

BRUTUS. I talk of that, that know it.

CORIOLANUS. You?

MENENIUS. Is this the promise that you made your mother?

COMINIUS. Know, I pray you—

CORIOLANUS. I'll know no further:
Let them pronounce the steep Tarpeian death,
Vagabond exile, flaying, pent to linger
But with a grain a day, I would not buy
Their mercy at the price of one fair word,
Nor check my courage for what they can give,
To have 't with saying *Good-morrow*.

SICINIUS. For that he has,
As much as in him lies, from time to time
Envied against the people, seeking means
To pluck away their power, as now at last
Given hostile strokes, and that not in the presence
Of dreaded justice, but on the ministers
That do distribute it; in the name o' the people,

And in the power of us the tribunes, we,
Even from this instant, banish him our city,
In peril of precipitation
From off the rock Tarpeian, never more
To enter our Rome gates: i' the people's name,
I say it shall be so.

CITIZENS. It shall be so, it shall be so; let him away:
He's banished, and it shall be so.

COMINIUS. Hear me, my masters, and my common friends—

SICINIUS. He's sentenced; no more hearing.

COMINIUS. Let me speak:
I have been consul, and can show for Rome
Her enemies' marks upon me. I do love
My country's good with a respect more tender,
More holy and profound, than mine own life—

BRUTUS. There's no more to be said, but he is banished,
As enemy to the people and his country:
It shall be so.

CITIZENS. It shall be so, it shall be so.

CORIOLANUS. You common cry of curs! whose breath I hate
As reek o' the rotten fens, whose loves I prize
As the dead carcasses of unburied men
That do corrupt my air, I banish you;
And here remain with your uncertainty!
Let every feeble rumour shake your hearts!
Your enemies, with nodding of their plumes,
Fan you into despair! Have the power still
To banish your defenders; till at length
Your ignorance deliver you as most
Abated captives to some nation
That won you without blows! Despising,
For you, the city, thus I turn my back:
There is a world elsewhere. *(He leaves with his friends)*

AEDILE. The people's enemy is gone, is gone!

CITIZENS. Our enemy is banished! he is gone! Hoo! hoo!

They all shout and throw up their caps

SICINIUS. Go, see him out at gates, and follow him,
As he hath followed you, with all despite;
Give him deserved vexation. Let a guard
Attend us through the city.

CITIZENS. Come, come, let's see him out at gates; come.
The gods preserve our noble tribunes! Come.

ACT 4

Scene 1—One of the Gates of Rome

Coriolanus takes leave of his friends

CORIOLANUS. Come, leave your tears ; a brief farewell : the beast
With many heads butts me away. Nay, mother,
Where is your ancient courage ? you were used
To say extremity was the trier of spirits ;
That common chances common men could bear ;
You were used to load me
With precepts that would make invincible
The heart that conned them.

VIRGILIA. O heavens ! O heavens !

CORIOLANUS. Nay, I prithee, woman—

VOLUMNIA. Now the red pestilence strike all trades in Rome,
And occupations perish !

CORIOLANUS. What, what, what !
I shall be loved when I am lacked. Nay, mother.
Resume that spirit, when you were wont to say,
If you had been the wife of Hercules,
Six of his labours you'd have done, and saved
Your husband so much sweat. Cominius,
Droop not ; adieu. Farewell, my wife, my mother.
I'll do well yet. Thou old and true Menenius,
Thy tears are salter than a younger man's
And venomous to thine eyes. My sometime general,
I have seen thee stern, and thou hast oft beheld
Heart-hardening spectacles ; tell these sad women,
Tis fond to wail inevitable strokes,
As tis to laugh at 'em. My mother, you wot well
My hazards still have been your solace : and
Believe 't not lightly—though I go alone,
Like to a lonely dragon, that his fen
Makes feared and talked of more than seen—your son
Will or exceed the common, or be caught
With cautelous baits and practice.

VOLUMNIA. My first son,
Whither wilt thou go ? Take good Cominius
With thee awhile : determine on some course,
More than a wild exposure to each chance
That starts i' the way before thee.

COMINIUS. I'll follow thee a month, devise with thee
Where thou shalt rest, that thou mayst hear of us
And we of thee.

CORIOLANUS. Fare ye well :
Thou hast years upon thee ; and thou art too full

Of the war's surfeits, to go rove with one
That's yet unbruised : bring me but out at gate.
Come, my sweet wife, my dearest mother, and
My friends of noble touch, when I am forth
Bid me farewell, and smile. I pray you, come.
While I remain above the ground, you shall
Hear from me still, and never of me aught
But what is like me formerly.

MENENIUS. That's worthily
As any ear can hear. Come, let's not weep.
If I could shake off but one seven years
From these old arms and legs, by the good gods,
I'd with thee every foot.

CORIOLANUS. Give me thy hand : come.

Scene 2—A Street near the Gate of Rome

Returning to their homes, the sorrowing friends of Coriolanus meet Sicinius and Brutus, disappointed of their hope to heap ignominy upon the exile. They are fiercely denounced by Volumnia, whose wrath they fear, and hurry from the scene, revealing in their conversation that the Roman nobles are incensed at the action against Coriolanus.

Scene 3—A Highway between Rome and Antium

On the highway between Rome and Antium, where Aufidius has his headquarters, a Roman and a Volsce meet, and the first tells the other of the state of affairs in Rome. Sore at the banishment of Coriolanus, the nobles are prepared to seize all power from the Citizens, civil strife is threatened in the capital, and the time is opportune for Aufidius, in the absence of Coriolanus, to strike another blow at Rome. The Volsce departs to bear the strange news he has heard to Aufidius.

Scene 4—The House of Aufidius in Antium

Coriolanus enters, disguised and muffled, in mean apparel

CORIOLANUS. A goodly city is this Antium. City,
Tis I that made thy widows : many an heir
Of these fair edifices 'fore my wars
Have I heard groan and drop : then know me not;
Lest that thy wives with spits, and boys with stones,
In puny battle slay me. *(To Citizen, entering)* Save you, sir.

CITIZEN. And you.

CORIOLANUS. Direct me, if it be your will,
Where great Aufidius lies : is he in Antium ?

CITIZEN. He is, and feasts the nobles of the State
At his house this night.

CORIOLANUS. Which is his house, beseech you ?

CITIZEN. This, here, before you.

CORIOLANUS. Thank you, sir: farewell. *(Citizen goes)*
O world, thy slippery turns! Friends now fast sworn,
Whose double bosoms seem to wear one heart,
Whose hours, whose bed, whose meal and exercise
Are still together, who twin as 'twere, in love
Unseparable, shall within this hour,
On a dissension of a doit, break out
To bitterest enmity: so fellest foes shall grow dear friends
And interjoin their issues. So with me:
My birthplace hate I, and my love's upon
This enemy town. I'll enter: if he slay me,
He does fair justice; if he give me way
I'll do his country service.

Scene 5—A Hall in the House of Aufidius

Music is playing when Coriolanus enters, met by a servant

CORIOLANUS. A goodly house: the feast smells well; but I
Appear not like a guest

FIRST SERVANT. What would you have, friend? whence are you? Here's no place for you: pray, go to the door.

CORIOLANUS *(going)*. I have deserved no better entertainment, In being Coriolanus.

SECOND SERVANT *(entering)*. Whence are you, sir? Has the porter his eyes in his head, that he gives entrance to such companions? Pray, get you out.

CORIOLANUS. Away!

SECOND SERVANT. Get you away.

CORIOLANUS. Now thou'rt troublesome.

THIRD SERVANT *(entering)*. What fellow's this?

FIRST SERVANT. A strange one as ever I looked on; I cannot get him out o' the house: prithee, call my master to him.

THIRD SERVANT. What have you to do here, fellow? Pray you, avoid the house.

CORIOLANUS. Let me but stand; I will not hurt your hearth.

THIRD SERVANT. What are you?

CORIOLANUS. A gentleman.

THIRD SERVANT. A marvellous poor one.

CORIOLANUS. True, so I am.

THIRD SERVANT. Pray you, poor gentleman, take up some other station; here's no place for you; pray you, avoid: come.

CORIOLANUS. Follow your function, go, and batten on cold bits.

THIRD SERVANT. What, you will not? Prithee, tell my master what a strange guest he has here.

SECOND SERVANT. And I shall.

AUFIDIUS *(entering)*. Where is this fellow?

SECOND SERVANT. Here, sir: I'd have beaten him like a dog, but for disturbing the lords within.

AUFIDIUS. Whence comest thou? What wouldst thou? Thy name?

CORIOLANUS *(unmuffling)*. If, Tullus,
Not yet thou knowest me, and, seeing me, dost not
Think me for the man I am, necessity
Commands me name myself.

AUFIDIUS. What is thy name?

CORIOLANUS. A name unmusical to the Volscian's ears,
And harsh in sound to thine.

AUFIDIUS. Say what's thy name!
Thou hast a grim appearance, and thy face
Bears a command in 't; though thy tackle's torn,
Thou show'st a noble vessel: what's thy name?

CORIOLANUS. Prepare thy brow to frown: know'st thou me yet?

AUFIDIUS. I know thee not; thy name?

CORIOLANUS. My name is Caius Marcius, who hath done
To thee particularly, and to all the Volsces,
Great hurt and mischief; thereto witness may
My surname, Coriolanus: the painful service,
The extreme dangers, and the drops of blood
Shed for my thankless country, are requited
But with that surname.
The cruelty and envy of the people,
Permitted by our dastard nobles, who
Have all forsook me, hath devoured the rest;
And suffered me by the voice of slaves to be
Whooped out of Rome. Now, this extremity
Hath brought me to thy hearth: not out of hope
(Mistake me not) to save my life, for if
I had feared death, of all the men i' the world
I would have 'voided thee; but in mere spite,
To be full quit of those my banishers,
Stand I before thee here. Then if thou hast
A heart of wreak in thee, thou wilt revenge
Thine own particular wrongs, and stop those maims
Of shame seen through thy country, speed thee straight,
And make my misery serve thy turn: so use it
That my revengeful services may prove
As benefits to thee; for I will fight
Against my cankered country with the spleen
Of all the under fiends. But if so be
Thou darest not this, and that to prove more fortunes
Thou'rt tired, then, in a word, I also am

Longer to live most weary, and present
My throat to thee and to thy ancient malice;
Which not to cut would show thee but a fool,
Since I have ever followed thee with hate,
Drawn tuns of blood out of thy country's breast,
And cannot live but to thy shame, unless
It be to do thee service.

AUFIDIUS. O Marcius, Marcius!
Each word thou hast spoke hath weeded from my heart
A root of ancient envy. If Jupiter
Should from yond cloud speak divine things,
And say *Tis true*, I'd not believe them more
Than thee, all noble Marcius. Let me twine
Mine arms about that body, where against
My grainèd ash a hundred times hath broke,
And scarred the moon with splinters: here I clip
The anvil of my sword, and do contest
As hotly and as nobly with thy love
As ever in ambitious strength I did
Contend against thy valour. Know thou first,
I loved the maid I married; never man
Sighed truer breath; but that I see thee here,
Thou noble thing! more dances my rapt heart
Than when I first my wedded mistress saw
Bestride my threshold. Why, thou Mars! I tell thee,
We have a power on foot; and I had purpose
Once more to hew thy target from thy brawn,
Or lose mine arm for 't: thou hast beat me out
Twelve several times, and I have nightly since
Dreamt of encounters 'twixt thyself and me;
We have been down together in my sleep,
Unbuckling helms, fisting each other's throat;
And waked half dead with nothing. Worthy Marcius,
Had we no quarrel else to Rome but that
Thou art thence banished, we would muster all
From twelve to seventy, and pouring war
Into the bowels of ungrateful Rome,
Like a bold flood o'er-beat. O, come, go in,
And take our friendly senators by the hands,
Who now are here, taking their leaves of me,
Who am prepared against your territories,
Though not for Rome itself.

CORIOLANUS. You bless me, gods!

AUFIDIUS. Therefore, most absolute sir, if thou wilt have
The leading of thine own revenges, take
The one half of my commission, and set down—

As best thou art experienced, since thou know'st
Thy country's strength and weakness—thine own ways;
Whether to knock against the gates of Rome,
Or rudely visit them in parts remote,
To fright them, ere destroy. But come in:
Let me commend thee first to those that shall
Say yea to thy desires. A thousand welcomes!
And more a friend than e'er an enemy;
Yet, Marcius, that was much. Your hand: most welcome!

Scene 6—A Public Place in Rome

Sicinius and Brutus encounter Menenius in the street, boast of the peaceful state of Rome, and tauntingly suggest that all is well since the expulsion of Coriolanus. An Aedile enters to tell of the Volscian armies having entered Roman territory. Brutus declares the tidings false, but news comes next that Coriolanus leads one of the hostile forces and Aufidius the other, each with terrible success. Citizens break into lamentation over the absence of the exile, and the only hope seems to be an appeal to the returning Coriolanus. The crowd departs, lamenting.

FIRST CITIZEN. The gods be good to us! Come, masters, let's home. I ever said we were i' the wrong when we banished him.

SECOND CITIZEN. So did we all. But, come, let's home.

BRUTUS. I do not like this news.

SICINIUS. Nor I.

BRUTUS. Let's to the Capitol: would half my wealth
Would buy this for a lie!

Scene 7—Aufidius in Camp near Rome

AUFIDIUS. Do they still fly to the Roman?

LIEUTENANT. I do not know what witchcraft's in him, but
Your soldiers use him as the grace 'fore meat,
Their talk at table and their thanks at end;
And you are darkened in this action, sir,
Even by your own.

AUFIDIUS. I cannot help it now,
Unless, by using means, I lame the foot
Of our design. He bears himself more proudlier,
Even to my person, than I thought he would
When first I did embrace him: yet his nature
In that's no changeling; and I must excuse
What cannot be amended.

LIEUTENANT. Yet I wish, sir—
I mean for your particular—you had not
Joined in commission with him; but either

Had borne the action of yourself, or else
To him had left it solely.

AUFIDIUS. I understand thee well; and be thou sure,
When he shall come to his account, he knows not
What I can urge against him. Although it seems,
And so he thinks, and is no less apparent
To the vulgar eye, that he bears all things fairly,
And shows good husbandry for the Volscian State,
Fights dragon-like, and does achieve as soon
As draw his sword, yet he hath left undone
That which shall break his neck or hazard mine,
Whene'er we come to our account.

LIEUTENANT. Sir, I beseech you, think you he'll carry Rome?

AUFIDIUS. All places yield to him ere he sits down;
And the nobility of Rome are his:
The senators and patricians love him too:
The tribunes are no soldiers; and their people
Will be as rash in the repeal as hasty
To expel him thence. I think he'll be to Rome
As is the osprey to the fish, who takes it
By sovereignty of nature.
Come, let's away. When, Caius, Rome is thine,
Thou art poor'st of all; then shortly art thou mine.

ACT 5

Scene 1—A Public Place in Rome: enter Senators and Tribunes

MENENIUS. No, I'll not go: you hear what he hath said
Which was sometime his general, who loved him
In a most dear particular. He called me father,
But what o' that? Go, you that banished him;
A mile before his tent fall down, and knee
The way into his mercy: nay, if he coyed
To hear Cominius speak, I'll keep at home.

COMINIUS. He would not seem to know me.

MENENIUS. Do you hear?

COMINIUS. Yet one time he did call me by my name:
I urged our old acquaintance, and the drops
That we have bled together. Coriolanus
He would not answer to: forbade all names;
He was a kind of nothing, titleless,
Till he had forged himself a name o' the fire
Of burning Rome.

MENENIUS. Why, so: you have made good work!
A pair of tribunes that have racked for Rome,
To make coals cheap: a noble memory!

COMINIUS. I minded him how royal 'twas to pardon
When it was less expected: he replied
It was a bare petition of a State
To one whom they had punished.

MENENIUS. Very well: could he say less?

COMINIUS. I offered to awaken his regard
For 's private friends: his answer to me was,
He could not stay to pick them in a pile
Of noisome musty chaff: he said 'twas folly,
For one poor grain or two, to leave unburnt,
And still to nose the offence.

MENENIUS. For one poor grain or two!
I am one of those; his mother, wife, his child,
And this brave fellow too, we are the grains:
You are the musty chaff, and you are smelt
Above the moon: we must be burnt for you.

SICINIUS. Nay, pray, be patient: if you refuse your aid
In this so never-needed help, yet do not
Upbraid 's with our distress. But sure, if you
Would be your country's pleader, your good tongue,
More than the instant army we can make,
Might stop our countryman.

MENENIUS. No, I'll not meddle.

SICINIUS. Pray you, go to him.

MENENIUS. What should I do?

BRUTUS. Only make trial what your love can do
For Rome, towards Marcius.

MENENIUS. Well, and say that Marcius
Return me, as Cominius is returned,
Unheard; what then?

SICINIUS. Yet your goodwill
Must have that thanks from Rome, after the measure
As you intended well.

MENENIUS. I'll undertake it.
I think he'll hear me. Yet, to bite his lip
And hum at good Cominius much hurts me.

BRUTUS. You know the very road into his kindness
And cannot lose your way.

MENENIUS. Good faith, I'll prove him,
Speed how it will. I shall ere long have knowledge
Of my success.

COMINIUS. He'll never hear him.
I tell you he does sit in gold, his eye
Red as 'twould burn Rome; and his injury

The gaoler to his pity. I kneeled before him:
Twas very faintly he said *Rise*; dismissed me
Thus, with his speechless hand: what he would do
He sent in writing after me; what he would not,
Bound with an oath to yield to his conditions:
So that all hope is vain,
Unless his noble mother, and his wife,
Who, as I hear, mean to solicit him
For mercy to his country. Therefore, let's hence,
And with our fair entreaties haste them on.

Scene 2—The Volscian Camp before Rome: Two Sentinels on guard. Menenius comes

FIRST SENTINEL. Stay: whence are you?

SECOND SENTINEL. Stand, and go back.

MENENIUS. I am an officer of State, and come
To speak with Coriolanus.

FIRST SENTINEL. You may not pass, you must return: our general
Will no more hear.

SECOND SENTINEL. You'll see your Rome embraced with fire before
You'll speak with Coriolanus.

MENENIUS. Good my friends,
If you have heard your general talk of Rome,
And of his friends there, it is lots to blanks
My name hath touched your ears: it is Menenius.

FIRST SENTINEL. Be it so; go back: the virtue of your name
Is not here passable.

MENENIUS. I tell thee, fellow,
Thy general is my lover: I have been
The book of his good acts; therefore, fellow,
I must have leave to pass.

While Menenius is disputing with the Sentinels, Coriolanus enters accompanied by Aufidius, but is deaf to the appeal of his old friend.

MENENIUS. The glorious gods sit in hourly synod about thy particular prosperity, and love thee no worse than thy old father Menenius does! O my son, my son! thou art preparing fire for us; look thee, here's water to quench it. I was hardly moved to come to thee; but, being assured none but myself could move thee, I have been blown out of your gates with sighs; and conjure thee to pardon Rome and thy petitionary countrymen. The good gods assuage thy wrath, and turn the dregs of it upon this varlet here—this, who, like a block, hath denied my access to thee.

CORIOLANUS. Away!

MENENIUS. How! away!

CORIOLANUS. Wife, mother, child, I know not. My affairs
Are servanted to others. Therefore be gone.
Mine ears against your suits are stronger than
Your gates against my force. Yet, for I loved thee,
Take this along *(giving him a letter)*; I writ it for thy sake,
And would have sent it. Another word, Menenius,
I will not hear thee speak. This man, Aufidius,
Was my beloved in Rome: yet thou behold'st.

AUFIDIUS. You keep a constant temper.

Coriolanus and Aufidius go

FIRST SENTINEL. Now, sir, is your name Menenius?

SECOND SENTINEL. Tis a spell, you see, of much power: you know the way home again.

FIRST SENTINEL. Do you hear how we are shent for keeping your greatness back?

SECOND SENTINEL. What cause, do you think, I have to swoon?

MENENIUS. I neither care for the world nor your general. He that hath a will to die by himself fears it not from another: let your general do his worst. For you, be that you are, long; and your misery increase with your age! I say to you, as I was said to, Away!

FIRST SENTINEL. A noble fellow, I warrant him.

SECOND SENTINEL. The worthy fellow is our general: he's the rock, the oak not to be wind-shaken.

Scene 3—Coriolanus in his Tent with Aufidius

CORIOLANUS. We will before the walls of Rome tomorrow
Set down our host. My partner in this action,
You must report to the Volscian lords how plainly
I have borne this business.

AUFIDIUS. Only their ends
You have respected; stopped your ears against
The general suit of Rome; never admitted
A private whisper, no, not with such friends
That thought them sure of you.

CORIOLANUS. This last old man,
Whom with a cracked heart I have sent to Rome,
Loved me above the measure of a father,
Nay, godded me indeed. Their latest refuge
Was to send him, for whose old love I have,
Though I showed sourly to him, once more offered
The first conditions, which they did refuse
And cannot now accept; to grace him only
That thought he could do more, a very little
I have yielded to: fresh embassies and suits,

Nor from the State nor private friends, hereafter
Will I lend ear to. Ha ! what shout is this ?
Shall I be tempted to infringe my vow
In the same time tis made ? I will not.

The mother and wife of Coriolanus enter in mourning, with his young son Marcius and their friend Valeria

My wife comes foremost. But out, affection !
All bond and privilege of nature, break !
Let it be virtuous to be obstinate.
What is that curtsey worth ? or those doves' eyes
Which can make gods forsworn ? I melt, and am not
Of stronger earth than others. My mother bows,
As if Olympus to a molehill should
In supplication nod : and my young boy
Hath an aspect of intercession, which
Great nature cries *Deny not.* Let the Volsces
Plough Rome and harrow Italy : I'll never
Be such a gosling to obey instinct ; but stand,
As if a man were author of himself
And knew no other kin.

VIRGILIA. My lord and husband !

CORIOLANUS. These eyes are not the same I wore in Rome.

VIRGILIA. The sorrow that delivers us thus changed
Makes you think so.

CORIOLANUS. Like a dull actor now
I have forgot my part and I am out,
Even to a full disgrace. Best of my flesh,
Forgive my tyranny ; but do not say
For that *Forgive our Romans.* O, a kiss
Long as my exile, sweet as my revenge !
Now, by the jealous queen of heaven, that kiss
I carried from thee, dear, and my true lip
Hath virgined it e'er since. You gods ! I prate,
And the most noble mother of the world
Leave unsaluted : sink, my knee, i' the earth *(kneeling)* ;
Of thy deep duty more impression show
Than that of common sons.

VOLUMNIA. O, stand up blest !
Whilst, with no softer cushion than the flint,
I kneel before thee, and unproperly
Show duty, as mistaken all this while
Between the child and parent.

CORIOLANUS. What is this ?
Your knees to me ? To your corrected son ?

VOLUMNIA. Thou art my warrior;
I helped to frame thee. Do you know this lady?

CORIOLANUS. The noble sister of Publicola,
The moon of Rome; chaste as the icicle
That's curdied by the frost from purest snow
And hangs on Dian's temple: dear Valeria!

VOLUMNIA *(leading in his son)*. This is a poor epitome of yours,
Which by the interpretation of full time
May show like all yourself.

CORIOLANUS. The god of soldiers,
With the consent of supreme Jove, inform
Thy thoughts with nobleness, that thou mayst prove
To shame unvulnerable.

VOLUMNIA *(to young Marcius)*. Your knee, sirrah.

CORIOLANUS. That's my brave boy!

VOLUMNIA. Even he, your wife, this lady, and myself
Are suitors to you.

CORIOLANUS. I beseech you, peace:
Or, if you'd ask, remember this before:
The thing I have forsworn to grant may never
Be held by your denials. Do not bid me
Dismiss my soldiers, or capitulate
Again with Rome's mechanics: tell me not
Wherein I seem unnatural: desire not
To allay my rages and revenges with
Your colder reasons.

VOLUMNIA. O, no more, no more!
You have said you will not grant us anything;
For we have nothing else to ask, but that
Which you deny already: yet we will ask,
That, if you fail in our request, the blame
May hang upon your hardness.

CORIOLANUS. Aufidius, and you Volsces, mark; for we'll
Hear nought from Rome in private. Your request?

VOLUMNIA. Should we be silent and not speak, our raiment
And state of bodies would bewray what life
We have led since thy exile. Think with thyself
How more unfortunate than all living women
Are we come hither; since that thy sight, which should
Make our eyes flow with joy, hearts dance with comforts,
Constrains them weep and shake with fear and sorrow;
Making the mother, wife, and child, to see
The son, the husband, and the father, tearing
His country's bowels out. Either thou
Must, as a foreign recreant, be led

With manacles through our streets, or else
Triumphantly tread on thy country's ruin
And bear the palm for having bravely shed
Thy wife and children's blood. For myself, son,
I purpose not to wait on fortune till
These wars determine : if I cannot persuade thee
Rather to show a noble grace to both parts
Than seek the end of one, thou shalt no sooner
March to assault thy country than to tread—
Trust to 't, thou shalt not—on thy mother,
That brought thee to this world.

VIRGILIA. Ay, and mine,
That brought you forth this boy, to keep your name
Living to time.

BOY. A' shall not tread on me ;
I'll run away till I am bigger, but then I'll fight.

CORIOLANUS. Not of a woman's tenderness to be,
Requires nor child nor woman's face to see.
I have sat too long. *(Rising)*

VOLUMNIA. Nay, go not from us thus.
If it were so that our request did tend
To save the Romans, thereby to destroy
The Volsces whom you serve, you might condemn us
As poisonous of your honour : no ; our suit
Is that you reconcile them : while the Volsces
May say *This mercy we have showed*, the Romans,
This we received ; and each in either side
Give the All-hail to thee, and cry *Be blest*
For making up this peace ! Thou know'st, great son,
The end of war's uncertain, but this certain,
That if thou conquer Rome the benefit
Which thou shalt thereby reap is such a name
Whose repetition will be dogged with curses ;
Whose chronicle thus writ : *The man was noble,*
But with his last attempt he wiped it out,
Destroyed his country, and his name remains
To the ensuing age abhorred. Speak to me, son :
Thou hast affected the fine strains of honour,
To imitate the graces of the gods.
Why dost thou not speak ?
Think'st thou it honourable for a noble man
Still to remember wrongs ? Daughter, speak you :
He cares not for your weeping. Speak thou, boy :
Perhaps thy childishness will move him more
Than can our reasons. There's no man in the world
More bound to 's mother, yet here he lets me prate

Like one i' the stocks. Thou hast never in thy life
Showed thy dear mother any courtesy;
When she, poor hen, fond of no second brood,
Has clucked thee to the wars, and safely home,
Loaden with honour. Say my request's unjust,
And spurn me back: but if it be not so
Thou art not honest, and the gods will plague thee,
That thou restrain'st from me the duty which
To a mother's part belongs. He turns away:
Down, ladies; let us shame him with our knees.
To his name Coriolanus belongs more pride
Than pity to our prayers. Down: an end;
This is the last: so we will home to Rome,
And die among our neighbours. Nay, behold 's:
This boy, that cannot tell what he would have,
But kneels and holds up hands for fellowship,
Does reason our petition with more strength
Than thou hast to deny 't. Come, let us go:
This fellow had a Volscian to his mother;
His wife is in Corioli, and his child
Like him by chance. Yet give us our dispatch:
I am hushed until our city be a-fire,
And then I'll speak a little.

CORIOLANUS *(holding her by the hand).* O mother, mother!
What have you done? Behold, the heavens do ope,
The gods look down, and this unnatural scene
They laugh at. O my mother, mother! O!
You have won a happy victory to Rome;
But, for your son, believe it, O, believe it,
Most dangerously you have with him prevailed,
If not most mortal to him. But let it come.
Aufidius, though I cannot make true wars,
I'll frame convenient peace. Now, good Aufidius,
Were you in my stead, would you have heard
A mother less, or granted less, Aufidius?

AUFIDIUS. I was moved withal.

CORIOLANUS. I dare be sworn you were:
And, sir, it is no little thing to make
Mine eyes to sweat compassion. But, good sir,
What peace you'll make, advise me: for my part,
I'll not to Rome, I'll back with you; and pray you,
Stand to me in this cause. O mother! wife!
But we will drink together. Ladies, you deserve
To have a temple built you: all the swords
In Italy, and her confederate arms,
Could not have made this peace.

Scene 4—A Public Place in Rome : Menenius and Sicinius

MENENIUS. See you yond coign o' the Capitol, yond corner-stone ?

SICINIUS. Why, what of that ?

MENENIUS. If it be possible for you to displace it with your little finger, there is some hope the ladies of Rome, especially his mother, may prevail with him. But I say there is no hope in 't : our throats are sentenced, and stay upon execution.

SICINIUS. Is 't possible that so short a time can alter the condition of a man ?

MENENIUS. There is difference between a grub and a butterfly; yet your butterfly was a grub. This Marcius is grown from man to dragon : he has wings ; he's more than a creeping thing.

SICINIUS. He loved his mother dearly.

MENENIUS. So did he me : and he no more remembers his mother now than an eight-year-old horse. The tartness of his face sours ripe grapes ; when he walks he moves like an engine, and the ground shrinks before his treading ; he is able to pierce a corslet with his eye ; talks like a knell, and his hum is a battery. He sits in his state as a thing made for Alexander. What he bids be done is finished with his bidding. He wants nothing of a god but eternity and a heaven to throne in.

SICINIUS. Yes, mercy, if you report him truly.

MENENIUS. I paint him in the character. Mark what mercy his mother shall bring from him : there is no more mercy in him than there is milk in a male tiger ; that shall our poor city find : and all this is long of you.

SICINIUS. The gods be good unto us !

MENENIUS. No, in such a case the gods will not be good unto us. When we banished him we respected not them ; and, he returning to break our necks, they respect not us. *(A messenger comes running)*

MESSENGER. Sir, if you'd save your life, fly to your house :
The plebeians have got your fellow-tribune,
And hale him up and down, all swearing, if
The Roman ladies bring not comfort home,
They'll give him death by inches.

ANOTHER MESSENGER. Good news, good news ; the ladies have prevailed,
The Volscians are dislodged, and Marcius gone :
A merrier day did never yet greet Rome,
No, not the expulsion of the Tarquins.

SICINIUS. Friend,
Art thou certain this is true ? Is it most certain ?

SECOND MESSENGER. As certain as I know the sun is fire :
Where have you lurked, that you make doubt of it ?

Ne'er through an arch so hurried the blown tide,
As the recomforted through the gates. Why, hark you!
The trumpets, sackbuts, psalteries, and fifes,
Tabors and cymbals and the shouting Romans,
Make the sun dance. Hark you!

MENENIUS. This is good news:
I will go meet the ladies. This Volumnia
Is worth of consuls, senators, patricians,
A city full; of tribunes, such as you,
A sea and land full. You have prayed well today:
This morning for ten thousand of your throats
I'd not have given a doit. Hark, how they joy!

SICINIUS. The gods bless you for your tidings.

Scene 5—A Street in Rome near the Gate

Enter two Senators with the women, followed by Patricians

FIRST SENATOR. Behold our patroness, the life of Rome!
Call all your tribes together, praise the gods,
And make triumphant fires; strew flowers before them:
Unshout the noise that banished Marcius,
Repeal him with the welcome of his mother;
Cry *Welcome, ladies, welcome!*

ALL. Welcome, ladies, welcome!

Scene 6—A Public Place in Corioli: Aufidius, with Attendants

AUFIDIUS. Go tell the lords o' the city I am here:
Deliver them this paper: having read it,
Bid them repair to the market-place, where I
Will vouch the truth of it. *(Enter three or four Conspirators)*

FIRST CONSPIRATOR. How is it with our general?

AUFIDIUS. Even so
As with a man by his own alms empoisoned,
And with his charity slain.

SECOND CONSPIRATOR. Most noble sir,
If you do hold the same intent wherein
You wished us parties, we'll deliver you
Of your great danger.

AUFIDIUS. Sir, I cannot tell:
We must proceed as we do find the people.

THIRD CONSPIRATOR. The people will remain uncertain whilst
Twixt you there's difference; but the fall of either
Makes the survivor heir of all.

AUFIDIUS. I know it,
And my pretext to strike at him admits
A good construction. I raised him, and I pawned
Mine honour for his truth. I took him,

Made him joint-servant with me, gave him way
In all his own desires, nay, let him choose
Out of my files, his projects to accomplish,
My best and freshest men, served his designments
In mine own person, helped to reap the fame
Which he did end all his; and took some pride
To do myself this wrong: till at the last
I seemed his follower.

FIRST CONSPIRATOR. The army marvelled at it, and in the last,
When he had carried Rome and that we looked
For no less spoil than glory—

AUFIDIUS. There was it:
For which my sinews shall be stretched upon him.
At a few drops of women's rheum, which are
As cheap as lies, he sold the blood and labour
Of our great action: therefore shall he die,
And I'll renew me in his fall. But hark!

Drums and trumpets sound, with great shouts of the people

FIRST CONSPIRATOR. Your native town you entered like a post,
And had no welcomes home; but he returns,
Splitting the air with noise.

SECOND CONSPIRATOR. And patient fools,
Whose children he hath slain, their base throats tear
With giving him glory.

THIRD CONSPIRATOR. Therefore, at your vantage,
Ere he express himself, or move the people
With what he would say, let him feel your sword.

AUFIDIUS. Say no more: here come the lords.

ALL THE LORDS. You are most welcome home.

AUFIDIUS. I have not deserved it.
But, worthy lords, have you with heed perused
What I have written to you?

FIRST LORD. And grieve to hear 't.
What faults he made before the last, I think
Might have found easy fines: but there to end
Where he was to begin, and give away
The benefit of our levies, answering us
With our own charge, making a treaty where
There was a yielding,—this admits no excuse.

AUFIDIUS. He approaches: you shall hear him.

Enter Coriolanus, marching with drum and colours

CORIOLANUS. Hail, lords! I am returned your soldier;
No more infected with my country's love
Than when I parted hence, but still subsisting

Under your great command. You are to know
That prosperously I have led your wars even to
The gates of Rome. Our spoils we have brought home
Do more than counterpoise a full third part
The charges of the action. We have made peace,
With no less honour to the Antiates
Than shame to the Romans: and we here deliver,
Subscribed by the consuls and patricians,
Together with the seal o' the Senate, what
We have compounded on.

AUFIDIUS. Read it not, noble lords,
But tell the traitor, in the highest degree
He hath abused your powers.

CORIOLANUS. Traitor! How now!

AUFIDIUS. Ay, traitor, Marcius!

CORIOLANUS. Marcius!

AUFIDIUS. Ay, Marcius, Caius Marcius: dost thou think
I'll grace thee with that robbery, thy stolen name
Coriolanus, in Corioli?
You lords and heads o' the State, perfidiously
He has betrayed your business, and given up,
For certain drops of salt, your city Rome.
I say *your city*, to his wife and mother;
Breaking his oath and resolution, like
A twist of rotten silk; never admitting
Counsel o' the war; but at his nurse's tears
He whined and roared away your victory;
That pages blushed at him, and men of heart
Looked wondering each at other.

CORIOLANUS. Hear'st thou, Mars?

AUFIDIUS. Name not the god, thou boy of tears!

CORIOLANUS. Ha!

AUFIDIUS. No more.

CORIOLANUS. Measureless liar, thou hast made my heart
Too great for what contains it. *Boy!* O slave!
Pardon me, lords, tis the first time that ever
I was forced to scold. Your judgments, my grave lords,
Must give this cur the lie.

FIRST LORD. Peace, both, and hear me speak.

CORIOLANUS. Cut me to pieces, Volsces; men and lads,
Stain all your edges on me. *Boy!* false hound!
If you have writ your annals true, tis there,
That, like an eagle in a dove-cote, I
Fluttered your Volscians in Corioli;
Alone I did it. *Boy!*

AUFIDIUS. Why, noble lords,
Will you be put in mind of his blind fortune,
Which was your shame, by this unholy braggart,
Fore your own eyes and ears?

ALL CONSPIRATORS. Let him die for 't.

SECOND LORD. Peace, ho! no outrage: peace!
The man is noble, and his fame folds in
This orb o' the earth. His last offences to us
Shall have judicious hearing. Stand, Aufidius,
And trouble not the peace.

CORIOLANUS. O that I had him,
With six Aufidiuses, or more, his tribe,
To use my lawful sword!

AUFIDIUS. Insolent villain!

The conspirators kill Coriolanus, and Aufidius stands on his body

LORDS. Hold, hold, hold, hold!

AUFIDIUS. My noble masters, hear me speak.

FIRST LORD. O Tullus—

SECOND LORD. Thou hast done a deed whereat valour will weep

THIRD LORD. Tread not upon him. Masters all, be quiet;
Put up your swords.

AUFIDIUS. My lords, when you shall know the great danger
Which this man's life did owe you, you'll rejoice
That he is thus cut off. Please it your honours
To call me to your Senate, I'll deliver
Myself your loyal servant, or endure
Your heaviest censure.

FIRST LORD. Bear from hence his body;
And mourn you for him: let him be regarded
As the most noble corse that ever herald
Did follow to his urn.

SECOND LORD. His own impatience
Takes from Aufidius a great part of blame.
Let's make the best of it.

AUFIDIUS. My rage is gone,
And I am struck with sorrow. Take him up:
Help, three o' the chiefest soldiers; I'll be one.
Beat thou the drum, that it speak mournfully:
Trail your steel pikes. Though in this city he
Hath widowed and unchilded many a one,
Which to this hour bewail the injury,
Yet he shall have a noble memory.

The dead march sounds while the body of Coriolanus is borne away

The Story of The Winter's Tale

THE WINTER'S TALE is one of Shakespeare's last plays and one of the best of all his stories. He is in his most gracious mood, as if he were sitting by the fire in the evening of his life, telling us a story.

HE took his plot from a novel written by a man of small mind, who saw Shakespeare rising into fame and did not like it—that Robert Greene who wrote of this young man from Warwickshire as "an upstart crow beautified with our feathers." Greene's romance was written before Shakespeare had written a word of his play, but immortality was beyond the power of Greene, and his tale is forgotten. It was the Upstart Crow who was to make The Winter's Tale live.

IT is a story pure and simple. The very name of the play suggests that Shakespeare recognises in it a touch of romantic exaggeration which must be accepted as a tale told by the fire on a winter's night, when improbable things are not scanned too closely. It has situations which are outside the bounds of reason but not outside the poet's licence; as we read this charming play we are willing to accept even the sudden frenzy of jealousy in Leontes and the keeping of a dramatic secret for sixteen years in the house of Paulina.

THE story runs with great smoothness, and most of the characters are fine. The tone of the play, apart from the senseless obsession of Leontes and the thieving of Autolycus, is singularly high-minded. With these two exceptions the characters are honest. Leontes is beyond the pale of understanding or forgiveness, but Autolycus is a merry rogue.

WE can have nothing but admiration for the other characters who hold the stage. They are thoroughly sound, loyal, and wise. Polixenes is a level-headed king, who only once gives way and soon recovers. Camillo is a fine and loyal fellow. Perdita and Florizel are exquisite, fitting well into light and dainty pastoral scenes, which Shakespeare clearly drew from his own memories of country life. Nothing could be better than the poetic feeling of the love scenes at the cottage; there are no lovers in Shakespeare whom we like more than these. Hermione, too, though slightly drawn, is admirable.

BUT it is Paulina who captures all our hearts. She is one of the best women in Shakespeare, consistent from the beginning to the end; one of Shakespeare's strongest women, and one of Wordsworth's too:

A perfect woman, nobly planned,
To warn, to comfort, and command.

WITHOUT her there would be no Winter's Tale; she is worth all the other characters of the play put together.

ONE small anomaly in this play has often been pointed out. It is said that the fact that Shakespeare gives Bohemia a sea-coast is a curious mark of his ignorance, but the fact is, whether Shakespeare knew it or not, that Bohemia once had a sea-coast.

THE PLAYERS

Leontes, King of Sicilia, giving way to sudden jealousy.

Mamillius, son of Leontes, who dies young.

Camillo, a lord of Sicilia, and the good genius of the Play.

Antigonus, Cleomenes, Dion, other lords of Sicilia.

Polixenes, King of Bohemia, and friend of Leontes.

Florizel, prince of Bohemia, in love with Perdita.

Archidamus, a lord of Bohemia.

An Old Shepherd, who finds and brings up Perdita.

Clown, a son of the Old Shepherd.

Autolycus, a barefaced but witty rogue.

Hermione, the innocent but suspected queen of Leontes.

Perdita, the lost daughter of Leontes and Hermione.

Paulina, wife of Antigonus, a woman of dignity and fine sense.

Emilia, a lady attending on Hermione.

A Mariner and a Gaoler.

Shepherdesses, lords, gentlemen, ladies, officers, servants.

SCENE—Sicilia and Bohemia

The Winter's Tale

ACT 1

Scene 1—The Palace of Leontes in Sicilia

ARCHIDAMUS. If you shall chance, Camillo, to visit Bohemia, on the like occasion whereon my services are now on foot, you shall see great difference betwixt our Bohemia and your Sicilia.

CAMILLO. I think, this coming summer, the King of Sicilia means to pay Bohemia the visitation which he justly owes him.

ARCHIDAMUS. Wherein our entertainment shall shame us we will be justified in our loves.

CAMILLO. Sicilia cannot show himself over-kind to Bohemia. They were trained together in their childhoods; and there rooted betwixt them then such an affection which cannot choose but branch now. The heavens continue their loves!

ARCHIDAMUS. I think there is not in the world either malice or matter to alter it. You have an unspeakable comfort of your young Prince Mamillius: it is a gentleman of the greatest promise that ever came into my note.

CAMILLO. I very well agree with you in the hopes of him. It is a gallant child; one that indeed makes old hearts fresh.

Scene 2—A State Room in the Palace

Enter Leontes, Polixenes, Hermione, Mamillius, Camillo, and Attendants

POLIXENES. Nine changes of the watery star have been
The shepherd's note since we have left our throne
Without a burden: time as long again
Would be filled up, my brother, with our thanks;
And yet we should for perpetuity
Go hence in debt.

LEONTES. Stay your thanks awhile,
And pay them when you part.

POLIXENES. Sir, that's tomorrow.
I am questioned by my fears of what may chance
Or breed upon our absence. Besides, I have stayed
To tire your royalty.

LEONTES. We are tougher, brother,
Than you can put us to 't.

POLIXENES. No longer stay.

LEONTES. One seven-night longer.

POLIXENES. Very sooth, tomorrow.

LEONTES. We'll part the time between 's then; and in that
I'll no gainsaying.

POLIXENES. Press me not, beseech you, so.
My affairs do even drag me homeward; which to hinder
Were in your love a whip to me; my stay
To you a charge and trouble: to save both,
Farewell, our brother.

The King, having failed to persuade Polixenes to stay, begs the Queen to add her pleading, and she succeeds. Thereupon Leontes is suspicious and suddenly jealous that the two are in love. He leaves them alone and observes their comings and goings, at length taking Camillo into counsel.

LEONTES. Ha' not you seen, Camillo, my wife is slippery?

CAMILLO. I would not be a stander-by, to hear
My sovereign mistress clouded so, without
My present vengeance taken: 'shrew my heart,
You never spoke what did become you less
Than this; which to reiterate were sin
As deep as that, though true.

LEONTES. Is whispering nothing?

CAMILLO. Good my lord, be cured
Of this diseased opinion, and betimes,
For tis most dangerous.

LEONTES. Say it be, tis true.

CAMILLO. No, no, my lord.

LEONTES. It is; you lie, you lie:
I say thou liest, Camillo, and I hate thee.

CAMILLO. Who does infect her?

LEONTES. Why, he that wears her like her medal, hanging
About his neck, Bohemia: who, if I
Had servants true about me, that bare eyes
To see alike mine honour as their profits,
Their own particular thrifts, they would do that
Which should undo more doing: ay, and thou,
His cupbearer (whom I from meaner form
Have benched and reared to worship, who mayst see
Plainly as heaven sees earth, and earth sees heaven,
How I am galled) mightst bespice a cup

To give mine enemy a lasting wink;
Which draught to me were cordial.

CAMILLO. Sir, my lord, I could do this, but I cannot
Believe this crack to be in my dread mistress,
So sovereignly being honourable.
I have loved thee—

LEONTES. Dost think I am so muddy, so unsettled,
To appoint myself in this vexation,
Give scandal to the blood o' the prince my son,
Who I do think is mine, and love as mine,
Without ripe moving to 't? Would I do this?

CAMILLO. I must believe you, sir:
I do; and will fetch off Bohemia for 't;
Provided that when he's removed, your highness
Will take again your queen as yours at first,
Even for your son's sake; and thereby for sealing
The injury of tongues in courts and kingdoms
Known and allied to yours.

LEONTES. Thou dost advise me
Even so as I mine own course have set down:
I'll give no blemish to her honour, none.

CAMILLO. My lord,
Go then; and with a countenance as clear
As friendship wears at feasts, keep with Bohemia,
And with your queen. I am his cupbearer;
If from me he have wholesome beverage,
Account me not your servant.

LEONTES. Do 't, and thou hast the one half of my heart;
Do 't not, thou split'st thine own.

CAMILLO. I'll do 't, my lord.

LEONTES. I will seem friendly, as thou hast advised me. *(He goes)*

CAMILLO. O miserable lady! But, for me,
What case stand I in? I must be the poisoner
Of good Polixenes, and my ground to do 't
Is the obedience to a master; one
Who, in rebellion with himself, will have
All that are his so too. To do this deed
Promotion follows. If I could find example
Of thousands that had struck anointed kings,
And flourished after, I'd not do 't; but since
Nor brass nor stone nor parchment bears not one,
Let villainy itself forswear 't. I must
Forsake the court: to do 't, or no, is certain
To me a break-neck. Happy star reign now!
Here comes Bohemia.

POLIXENES *(entering)*. This is strange: methinks
My favour here begins to warp. Not speak? Good-day, Camillo.

CAMILLO. Hail, most royal sir!

POLIXENES. What is the news i' the court?

CAMILLO. None rare, my lord.

POLIXENES. The king hath on him such a countenance
As he had lost some province and a region
Loved as he loves himself. Even now I met him
With customary compliment, when he,
Wafting his eyes to the contrary, and falling
A lip of much contempt, speeds from me, and
So leaves me to consider what is breeding
That changes thus his manners.

CAMILLO. I dare not know, my lord.

POLIXENES. How! dare not! do not! Do you know, and dare not
Be intelligent to me? Good Camillo,
Your changed complexions are to me a mirror
Which shows me mine changed too; for I must be
A party to this alteration, finding
Myself thus altered with 't.

CAMILLO. There is a sickness
Which puts some of us in distemper; but
I cannot name the disease, and it is caught
Of you that yet are well.

POLIXENES. How! caught of me?
Make me not sighted like the basilisk:
I have looked on thousands who have sped the better
By my regard, but killed none so. Camillo,
If you know aught which does behove my knowledge
Thereof to be informed, imprison it not
In ignorant concealment.

CAMILLO. I may not answer.

POLIXENES. A sickness caught of me, and yet I well!
I must be answered. Dost thou hear, Camillo?
I conjure thee that thou declare
What thou dost guess of harm
Is creeping toward me; how far off, how near;
Which way to be prevented if to be;
If not, how best to bear it.

CAMILLO. Sir, I will tell you,
Since I am charged in honour and by him
That I think honourable. Therefore mark my counsel,
Which must be even as swiftly followed as
I mean to utter it, or both yourself and me
Cry *lost* and so good-night!

Polixenes. On, good Camillo.

Camillo. I am appointed him to murder you.

Camillo then reveals to the King the purpose of Leontes, who believes himself betrayed by Hermione and Polixenes.

Polixenes. How should this grow?

Camillo. I know not: but I am sure tis safer to
Avoid what's grown than question how tis born.
If therefore you dare trust my honesty,
That lies enclosed in this trunk, which you
Shall bear along impawned, away tonight!
Your followers I will whisper to the business,
And will by twos and threes at several posterns
Clear them o' the city. For myself, I'll put
My fortunes to your service, which are here
By this discovery lost. Be not uncertain;
For, by the honour of my parents, I
Have uttered truth, which, if you seek to prove,
I dare not stand by; nor shall you be safer
Than one condemned by the king's own mouth, thereon
His execution sworn.

Polixenes. I do believe thee:
I saw his heart in 's face. Give me thy hand:
Be pilot to me and thy places shall
Still neighbour mine. My ships are ready and
My people did expect my hence departure
Two days ago. This jealousy
Is for a precious creature: as she's rare
Must it be great, and, as his person's mighty
Must it be violent, and, as he does conceive
He is dishonoured by a man which ever
Professed to him, why, his revenges must
In that be made more bitter. Come, Camillo;
I will respect thee as a father if
Thou bear'st my life off hence.

ACT 2

Scene 1—A Room in the Palace: Hermione and Mamillius

Hermione. Pray you, sit by us, and tell 's a tale.

Mamillius. Merry or sad shall't be?

Hermione. As merry as you will.

Mamillius. A sad tale's best for winter.
I have one of sprites and goblins.

Hermione. Let's have that, good sir.
Come on, sit down: come on, and do your best
To fright me with your sprites; you're powerful at it.

MAMILLIUS. There was a man—

HERMIONE. Nay, come, sit down; then on.

MAMILLIUS. Dwelt by a churchyard. I will tell it softly;
Yond crickets shall not hear it.

HERMIONE. Come on then, and give 't me in mine ear.

Enter Leontes and Antigonus with Lords

LEONTES. Was he met there? his train? Camillo with him?

FIRST LORD. Behind the tuft of pines I met them: never
Saw I men scour so on their way: I eyed them
Even to their ships.

LEONTES. Camillo was his help in this, his pandar:
There is a plot against my life, my crown;
All's true that is mistrusted: that false villain
Whom I employed was pre-employed by him:
He has discovered my design.
(To Hermione) Give me the boy: I am glad you did not nurse him:
Though he does bear some signs of me, yet you
Have too much blood in him.

HERMIONE. What is this? sport?

LEONTES. Bear the boy hence; he shall not come about her;
Away with him!

The King now accuses the Queen of unfaithfulness before the whole Court, and declares she is a traitor, with Camillo as a confederate. She declares she has no knowledge of why Polixenes and Camillo have gone away.

HERMIONE. How will this grieve you
When you shall come to clearer knowledge!
Gentle my lord,
You scarce can right me then to say you did mistake.

LEONTES. Away with her to prison!

HERMIONE. There's some ill planet reigns:
I must be patient till the heavens look
With an aspect more favourable. Good my lords,
I am not prone to weeping, as our sex
Commonly are; the want of which vain dew
Perchance shall dry your pities; but I have
That honourable grief lodged here which burns
Worse than tears drown. Adieu, my lord:
I never wished to see you sorry; now
I trust I shall. My women, come.

The Queen is led away, guarded

FIRST LORD. Beseech your highness call the queen again.

ANTIGONUS. Be certain what you do, sir, lest your justice
Prove violence, in the which three great ones suffer,
Yourself, your queen, your son.

FIRST LORD. For her, my lord,
I dare my life lay down, and will do 't, sir,
Please you to accept it—that the queen is spotless
I' the eyes of heaven and to you.

LEONTES. Hold your peaces!

FIRST LORD. Good my lord—

ANTIGONUS. It is for you we speak, not for ourselves.
You are abused, and by some putter-on
That will be cursed for 't; would I knew the villain.

LEONTES. Cease! no more.
You smell this business with a sense as cold
As is a dead man's nose; but I do see 't and feel 't.
We need no more of your advice: the matter,
The loss, the gain, the ordering on 't, is ours.

Leontes goes on to tell them that, though he needs no confirmation of his suspicions, he has sent Cleomenes and Dion to Apollo's temple to consult the Oracle, "for this business will raise us all."

ANTIGONUS *(aside)*. To laughter, as I take it,
If the good truth were known.

Scene 2—The outer Room of a Prison

Paulina, visiting the prison, learns from the Queen's gentlewomen that a daughter has been born to Hermione, and offers to take care of the child.

Scene 3—A Room in the Palace

Enter Leontes, Antigonus, Lords, and other Attendants

LEONTES. Nor night, nor day, no rest; it is but weakness
To bear the matter thus; mere weakness. If she were gone,
Given to the fire, a moiety of my rest
Might come to me again. Who's there?

FIRST ATTENDANT *(advancing)*. My lord?

LEONTES. How does the boy?

FIRST ATTENDANT. He took good rest tonight;
Tis hoped his sickness is discharged.

LEONTES. To see his nobleness!
Conceiving the dishonour of his mother,
He straight declined, drooped, took it deeply,
Fastened and fixed the shame on 't in himself,
Threw off his spirit, his appetite, his sleep,
And downright languished. Leave me solely: go,
See how he fares. *(Enter Paulina with a child)*

FIRST LORD. You must not enter.

PAULINA. Nay, rather, good my lords, be second to me:
Fear you his tyrannous passion more, alas,
Than the queen's life? a gracious innocent soul,
More free than he is jealous.

ANTIGONUS. That's enough.

ATTENDANT. Madam, he hath not slept tonight; commanded
None should come at him.

PAULINA. Not so hot, good sir;
I come to bring him sleep. Tis such as you,
That creep like shadows by him and do sigh
At each his needless heavings, such as you
Nourish the cause of his awaking: I
Do come with words medicinal as true,
Honest as either, to purge him of that humour
That presses him from sleep.

LEONTES. What noise there, ho?

PAULINA. No noise, my lord; but needful conference
About some gossips for your highness.

LEONTES. Away with that audacious lady! Antigonus,
I charged thee that she should not come about me.

ANTIGONUS. I told her so, my lord,
On your displeasure's peril, and on mine,
She should not visit you.

LEONTES. What! canst not rule her?

PAULINA. From all dishonesty he can: in this,
Unless he take the course that you have done,
Commit me for committing honour, trust it,
He shall not rule me. Good my liege, I come
From your good queen.

LEONTES. Good queen!

PAULINA. Good queen, my lord, good queen; I say, good queen.

LEONTES. Force her hence.

PAULINA. Let him that makes but trifles of his eyes
First hand me: on mine own accord I'll off;
But first I'll do my errand. The good queen,
For she is good, hath brought you forth a daughter:
Here tis; commends it to your blessing. *(Laying down the child)*

LEONTES. A mankind witch! Hence with her, out o' door:
Traitors! Will you not push her out?
This brat is none of mine;
I'll ha' thee burned.

PAULINA. I care not: it is a heretic that makes the fire,
Not she which burns in 't. I'll not call you tyrant,
But this most cruel usage of your queen,
Not able to produce more accusation
Than your own weak-hinged fancy, something savours
Of tyranny, and will ignoble make you,
Yea, scandalous to the world.

LEONTES. On your allegiance,
Out of the chamber with her! Were I a tyrant
Where were her life? She durst not call me so
If she did know me one. Away with her!

PAULINA. I pray you do not push me; I'll be gone.
Look to your babe, my lord; tis yours; Jove send her
A better guiding spirit! What need these hands?
You, that are thus so tender o'er his follies,
Will never do him good, not one of you.
So, so: farewell; we are gone.

LEONTES *(to Antigonus)*. Thou, traitor, hast set on thy wife to this.
My child! away with 't! Even thou, that hast
A heart so tender o'er it, take it hence
And see it instantly consumed with fire:
Even thou and none but thou. Take it up straight:
Within this hour bring me word tis done,
And by good testimony—or I'll seize thy life,
With what thou else call'st thine. If thou refuse
And wilt encounter with my wrath, say so;
Go, take it to the fire, for thou sett'st on thy wife.

ANTIGONUS. I did not, sir:
These lords, my noble fellows, if they please,
Can clear me in 't.

FIRST LORD. We can, my royal liege;
He is not guilty of her coming hither.

LEONTES. You are liars all.

FIRST LORD. Beseech your highness, give us better credit:
We have always truly served you, and beseech you
So to esteem of us; and on our knees we beg,
As recompense of our dear services
Past and to come, that you do change this purpose.

LEONTES. I am a feather for each wind that blows.
(To Antigonus) You, sir, come you hither.
What will you adventure
To save this brat's life?

ANTIGONUS. Anything, my lord, that my ability may undergo,
And nobleness impose: at least, thus much:
I'll pawn the little blood which I have left
To save the innocent: anything possible.

LEONTES. It shall be possible. Swear by this sword
Thou wilt perform my bidding.

ANTIGONUS. I will, my lord.

LEONTES. Mark and perform it (seest thou!), for the fail
Of any point in 't shall not only be

Death to thyself, but to thy lewd-tongued wife,
Whom for this time we pardon. We enjoin thee,
As thou art liegeman to us, that thou carry
This infant hence ; and that thou bear it
To some remote and desert place quite out
Of our dominions ; and that there thou leave it,
Without more mercy, to its own protection,
And favour of the climate. As by strange fortune
It came to us, I do in justice charge thee,
On thy soul's peril and thy body's torture,
That thou commend it strangely to some place,
Where chance may nurse or end it. Take it up.

ANTIGONUS. I swear to do this, though a present death
Had been more merciful. Come on, poor babe :
Some powerful spirit instruct the kites and ravens
To be thy nurses ! Wolves and bears, they say,
Casting their savageness aside have done
Like offices of pity. Sir, be prosperous
In more than this deed doth require ! And blessing
Against this cruelty fight on thy side,
Poor thing !

SERVANT *(entering)*. Please your highness, posts
From those you sent to the oracle are come
An hour since : Cleomenes and Dion,
Being well arrived from Delphos, are both landed,
Hasting to the court.

LEONTES. Twenty-three days
They have been absent : tis good speed ; foretells
The great Apollo suddenly will have
The truth of this appear. Prepare you, lords ;
Summon a session, that we may arraign
Our most disloyal lady ; for as she hath
Been publicly accused, so shall she have
A just and open trial. While she lives
My heart will be a burden to me. Leave me,
And think upon my bidding.

ACT 3

Scene 1—A Seaport in Sicilia

This scene shows Cleomenes and Dion, the messengers to the Oracle at the temple of Apollo, returning, praying that the message they bear (which is unknown to them) may be well for Hermione.

Scene 2—A Court of Justice in Sicilia

LEONTES. This sessions, to our great grief we pronounce,
Even pushes 'gainst our heart : the party tried

The daughter of a king, our wife, and one
Of us too much beloved. Let us be cleared
Of being tyrannous, since we so openly
Proceed in justice, which shall have due course,
Even to the guilt or the purgation.
Produce the prisoner.

OFFICER. It is his highness' pleasure that the queen
Appear in person here in court. Silence!

The Queen enters, guarded, Paulina and ladies attending, and an officer reads the indictment, which charges Hermione with being unfaithful, conspiring against the King, and aiding the escape of Camillo and Polixenes.

HERMIONE. Since what I am to say must be but that
Which contradicts my accusation, and
The testimony on my part no other
But what comes from myself, it shall scarce boot me
To say *Not guilty*: mine integrity
Being counted falsehood, shall, as I express it,
Be so received. But thus: if powers divine
Behold our human actions, as they do,
I doubt not then but innocence shall make
False accusation blush, and tyranny
Tremble at patience. You, my lord, best know,
My life hath been as chaste, as true,
As I am now unhappy.
For behold me, a great king's daughter,
The mother to a hopeful prince, here standing
To prate and talk of life and honour 'fore
Who please to come and hear. For life, I prize it
As I weigh grief, which I would spare: for honour,
Tis a derivative from me to mine,
And only that I stand for. I appeal
To your own conscience, sir, before Polixenes
Came to your court, how I was in your grace,
How merited to be so; since he came, if one jot beyond
The bound of honour, or in act or will
That way inclining, hardened be the hearts
Of all that hear me, and my near'st of kin
Cry fie upon my grave! For Polixenes,
With whom I am accused, I do confess
I loved him as in honour he required,
With such a kind of love as might become
A lady like me; with a love even such,
So and no other, as yourself commanded:
Which not to have done I think had been in me
Both disobedience and ingratitude

To you and toward your friend, whose love had spoke,
Even since it could speak, from an infant, freely
That it was yours. Now, for conspiracy,
I know not how it tastes, though it be dished
For me to try how : all I know of it
Is that Camillo was an honest man ;
And why he left your court, the gods themselves,
Wotting no more than I, are ignorant.

LEONTES. You knew of his departure, as you know
What you have undertaken in his absence.

HERMIONE. Sir, you speak a language that I understand not :
The crown and comfort of my life, your favour,
I do give lost ; for I do feel it gone,
But know not how it went. Now, my liege,
Tell me what blessings I have here alive,
That I should fear to die ? Therefore proceed.
But yet hear this. Mistake me not ; no life,
I prize it not a straw, but for mine honour,
I do refer me to the oracle : Apollo be my judge !

Enter Officers, with Cleomenes and Dion

OFFICER. You here shall swear upon this sword of justice,
That you, Cleomenes and Dion, have
Been both at Delphos, and from thence have brought
This sealed-up oracle, by the hand delivered
Of great Apollo's priest, and that since then
You have not dared to break the holy seal,
Nor read the secrets in 't. *(They swear)*

LEONTES. Break up the seals, and read.

OFFICER. *Hermione is chaste ; Polixenes blameless ; Camillo a true subject ; Leontes a jealous tyrant ; his innocent babe truly his ; and the king shall live without an heir if that which is lost be not found.*

LORDS. Now blessed be the great Apollo !

HERMIONE. Praised !

LEONTES. Hast thou read truth ?

OFFICER. Ay, my lord ; even so as it is here set down.

LEONTES. There is no truth at all i' the oracle :
The sessions shall proceed : this is mere falsehood.

SERVANT *(entering)*. My lord the king, the king !

LEONTES. What is the business ?

SERVANT. O sir ! I shall be hated to report it :
The prince your son, with mere conceit and fear
Of the queen's speed, is gone.

LEONTES. How ! gone !

SERVANT. Is dead.

LEONTES. Apollo's angry; and the heavens themselves
Do strike at my injustice. *(Hermione swoons.)* How now, there!

PAULINA. This news is mortal to the queen; look down,
And see what death is doing.

LEONTES. Take her hence:
Her heart is but o'ercharged; she will recover:
I have too much believed mine own suspicion:
Beseech you, tenderly apply to her
Some remedies for life.

Paulina and Ladies bear Hermione away

Apollo, pardon my great profaneness 'gainst thine oracle!
I'll reconcile me to Polixenes,
New woo my queen, recall the good Camillo,
Whom I proclaim a man of truth, of mercy;
For, being transported by my jealousies
To cruel thoughts and to revenge, I chose
Camillo for the minister to poison
My friend Polixenes: he, most humane
And filled with honour, to my kingly guest
Unclasped my practice, quit his fortunes here,
Which you knew great, and to the certain hazard
Of all uncertainties himself commended,
No richer than his honour: how he glisters
Through my rust! and how his piety
Does my deeds make the blacker!

PAULINA *(entering)*. Woe the while!
O, cut my lace, lest my heart, cracking it,
Break, too!

FIRST LORD. What fit is this, good lady?

PAULINA. What studied torments, tyrant, hast for me?
What wheels? racks? fires? What flaying? or what boiling
In leads, or oils? what old or newer torture
Must I receive, whose every word deserves
To taste of thy most worst? Thy tyranny,
Together working with thy jealousies,
(Fancies too weak for boys, too green and idle
For girls of nine), O! think what they have done,
And then run mad indeed, stark mad; for all
Thy bygone fooleries were but spices of it.
That thou betrayedst Polixenes, 'twas nothing;
That did but show thee of a fool; nor was 't much
Thou wouldst have poisoned good Camillo's honour
To have him kill a king; poor trespasses,
More monstrous standing by: whereof I reckon
The casting forth to crows thy baby daughter

To be or none or little ;
Nor is 't directly laid to thee, the death
Of the young prince, whose honourable thoughts
(Thoughts high for one so tender), cleft the heart.
This is not, no,
Laid to thy answer : but the last—O lords !
When I have said, cry, *Woe !*—the queen, the queen,
The sweetest, dearest creature's dead, and vengeance for 't
Not dropped down yet.

FIRST LORD. The higher powers forbid !

PAULINA. I say she's dead ; I'll swear 't : if word nor oath
Prevail not, go and see : if you can bring
Tincture or lustre in her lip, her eye,
Heat outwardly, or breath within, I'll serve you
As I would do the gods. But, O thou tyrant !
Do not repent these things, for they are heavier
Than all thy woes can stir ; therefore betake thee
To nothing but despair. A thousand knees
Ten thousand years together, naked, fasting,
Upon a barren mountain, and still winter
In storm perpetual, could not move the gods
To look that way thou wert.

LEONTES. Go on, go on ;
Thou canst not speak too much : I have deserved
All tongues to talk their bitterest.

FIRST LORD. Say no more :
Howe'er the business goes, you have made fault
I' the boldness of your speech.

PAULINA. I am sorry for 't :
All faults I make, when I shall come to know them,
I do repent. Alas ! I have showed too much
The rashness of a woman : he is touched
To the noble heart. What's gone and what's past help
Should be past grief : do not receive affliction
At my petition ; I beseech you, rather
Let me be punished, that have minded you
Of what you should forget. Now, good my liege,
Sir, royal sir, forgive a foolish woman :
The love I bore your queen (lo, fool again !),
I'll speak of her no more, nor of your children ;
I'll not remember you of my own lord,
Who is lost too : take your patience to you,
And I'll say nothing.

LEONTES. Thou didst speak but well
When most the truth. Prithee, bring me

To the dead bodies of my queen and son :
One grave shall be for both : upon them shall
The causes of their death appear, unto
Our shame perpetual. Once a day I'll visit
The chapel where they lie, and tears shed there
Shall be my recreation : so long as nature
Will bear up with this exercise, so long
I daily vow to use it. Come and lead me
Unto these sorrows.

Scene 3—A Desert Country near the Sea

This scene shows Antigonus landing on the coast of Bohemia (which has no coast today though once it had a seaboard for a short period). He has with him the child, whom he has named Perdita, and in this barren place he leaves the babe lying in the storm. On his way back to the ship he himself is killed by a bear, but the child is found by a shepherd, whose son (called the Clown in the play) has seen Antigonus killed. With the child a sum of gold has been left, and the shepherd decides to bring up the little one and keep the discovery a secret.

ACT 4

The Passing of Time

Time now appears as Chorus, as in the old Greek plays, and in a short speech we are told that sixteen years have passed since the events of the last act. Florizel, the son of King Polixenes, has now grown up, and so has Perdita, who is supposed to be a shepherd's daughter.

Scene 1—The Palace of Polixenes in Bohemia

POLIXENES. I pray thee, good Camillo, when sawest thou the Prince Florizel, my son ?

CAMILLO. Sir, it is three days since I saw the prince. What his happier affairs may be are to me unknown ; but I have missingly noted he is of late much retired from court, and is less frequent to his princely exercises.

POLIXENES. I have considered so much, Camillo, and with some care. I have this intelligence, that he is seldom from the house of a most homely shepherd, a man, they say, that from very nothing, and beyond the imagination of his neighbours, is grown into an unspeakable estate.

CAMILLO. I have heard, sir, of such a man, who hath a daughter of most rare note : the report of her is extended more than can be thought to begin from such a cottage.

POLIXENES. That's likewise part of my intelligence, but, I fear, the angle that plucks our son thither. Thou shalt accompany us to the place, where we will (not appearing what we are) have some question with the shepherd, from whose simplicity I think it not uneasy to get the cause of my son's resort thither. Prithee, be my partner in this business.

Scene 2—Near the Shepherd's Cottage : enter Autolycus, singing

When daffodils begin to peer,
With heigh ! the doxy, over the dale,
Why, then comes in the sweet o' the year ;
For the red blood reigns in the winter's pale.

The white sheet bleaching on the hedge,
With heigh ! the sweet birds, O, how they sing !
Doth set my thieving tooth on edge ;
For a quart of ale is a dish for a king.

The lark, that tirra-lirra chants,
With heigh ! with heigh ! the thrush and the jay,
Are summer songs for me and my aunts,
While we lie tumbling in the hay.

I have served Prince Florizel, and in my time wore three-pile, but now I am out of service. My traffic is sheets. My father named me Autolycus, who was likewise a snapper-up of unconsidered trifles. For the life to come, I sleep out the thought of it. A prize ! a prize !

The Clown, the shepherd's son, on his way to buy things needed for a sheep-shearing feast, is the prize Autolycus suddenly sees, and he at once begins to impose on the rustic's simplicity by pretending he has been stripped of his clothes, beaten, and clothed in rags by one Autolycus, of whom the Clown has heard as a great rogue. While the Clown is attending to him sympathetically Autolycus picks his pocket, and then, all unsuspected, goes on his way singing gaily :

Jog on, jog on, the footpath way,
And merrily hent the stile-a :
A merry heart goes all the day,
Your sad tires in a mile-a.

Scene 3—A Lawn at the Shepherd's Cottage : Florizel and Perdita

FLORIZEL. These your unusual weeds to each part of you
Do give a life : no shepherdess, but Flora
Peering in April's front. This your sheep-shearing
Is as a meeting of the petty gods,
And you the queen on 't.

PERDITA. Sir, my gracious lord, your high self,
The gracious mark o' the land, you have obscured
With a swain's wearing, and me, poor lowly maid,
Most goddess-like pranked up. But that our feasts
In every mess have folly, and the feeders
Digest it with a custom, I should blush
To see you so attired—swoon, I think,
To show myself a glass.

FLORIZEL. I bless the time
When my good falcon made her flight across
Thy father's ground.

PERDITA. Now, Jove afford you cause!
To me the difference forges dread; your greatness
Hath not been used to fear. Even now I tremble
To think, your father, by some accident,
Should pass this way as you did. O, the Fates!
How would he look, to see his work, so noble,
Vilely bound up? What would he say? Or how
Should I, in these my borrowed flaunts, behold
The sternness of his presence?

FLORIZEL. Apprehend nothing but jollity.

PERDITA. O! but, sir,
Your resolution cannot hold, when tis
Opposed, as it must be, by the power of the king.
One of these two must be necessities,
Which then will speak, that you must change this purpose,
Or I my life.

FLORIZEL. Thou dearest Perdita,
With these forced thoughts, I prithee, darken not
The mirth o' the feast: or I'll be thine, my fair,
Or not my father's; for I cannot be
Mine own, nor anything to any, if
I be not thine: to this I am most constant,
Though destiny say no. Be merry, gentle;
Strangle such thoughts as these with anything
That you behold the while. Your guests are coming:
Lift up your countenance, as it were the day
Of celebration of that nuptial which
We two have sworn shall come.

PERDITA. O lady Fortune, stand you auspicious!

FLORIZEL. See, your guests approach:
Address yourself to entertain them sprightly,
And let's be red with mirth.

Enter the Shepherd with Polixenes and Camillo disguised

SHEPHERD. Fie, daughter! when my old wife lived, upon
This day she was both pantler, butler, cook;
Both dame and servant; welcomed all, served all,
Would sing her song and dance her turn; now here,
At upper end o' the table, now i' the middle;
On his shoulder, and his; her face o' fire
With labour and the thing she took to quench it,
She would to each one sip. You are retired,
As if you were a feasted one and not

The hostess of the meeting: pray you, bid
These unknown friends to 's welcome; for it is
A way to make us better friends, more known.
Come, quench your blushes and present yourself
That which you are, mistress o' the feast: come on,
And bid us welcome to your sheep-shearing,
As your good flock shall prosper.

PERDITA *(to Polixenes)*. Sir, welcome:
It is my father's will I should take on me
The hostess-ship o' the day. *(To Camillo)* You're welcome, sir.
Give me those flowers there, Dorcas. Reverend sirs,
For you there's rosemary and rue; these keep
Seeming and savour all the winter long:
Grace and remembrance be to you both,
And welcome to our shearing!

POLIXENES. Shepherdess,
A fair one are you; well you fit our ages
With flowers of winter.

PERDITA. Sir, the year growing ancient,
Not yet on summer's death, nor on the birth
Of trembling winter, the fairest flowers o' the season
Are our carnations, and streaked gillyvors:
Of that kind our rustic garden's barren.
Here's flowers for you;
Hot lavender, mints, savory, marjoram;
The marigold, that goes to bed wi' the sun,
And with him rises weeping: these are flowers
Of middle summer, and I think they are given
To men of middle age. You're very welcome.

CAMILLO. I should leave grazing, were I of your flock,
And only live by gazing.

PERDITA. Out, alas!
You'd be so lean, that blasts of January
Would blow you through and through. Now, my fair'st friend,
I would I had some flowers o' the spring that might
Become your time of day; and yours, and yours:
O Proserpina!
For the flowers now that frighted thou let'st fall
From Dis's waggon! daffodils,
That come before the swallow dares, and take
The winds of March with beauty; violets dim,
But sweeter than the lids of Juno's eyes
Or Cytherea's breath; pale primroses,
That die unmarried, ere they can behold
Bright Phoebus in his strength; bold oxlips and
The crown imperial; lilies of all kinds,

The flower-de-luce being one! O! these I lack
To make you garlands of, and my sweet friend,
To strew him o'er and o'er! Come, take your flowers:
Methinks I play as I have seen them do
In Whitsun pastorals: sure this robe of mine
Does change my disposition.

FLORIZEL. What you do
Still betters what is done. When you speak, sweet,
I'd have you do it ever; when you sing
I'd have you buy and sell so; so give alms;
Pray so; and, for the ordering your affairs,
To sing them too: when you do dance I wish you
A wave o' the sea, that you might ever do
Nothing but that; move still, still so,
And own no other function: each your doing,
So singular in each particular,
Crowns what you are doing in the present deed,
That all your acts are queens.

PERDITA. O Doricles!
Your praises are too large: but that your youth,
And the true blood which fairly peeps through it,
Do plainly give you out an unstained shepherd,
With wisdom I might fear, my Doricles,
You wooed me the false way.

FLORIZEL. I think you have
As little skill to fear as I have purpose
To put you to 't. But, come; our dance, I pray.
Your hand, my Perdita: so turtles pair
That never mean to part.

PERDITA. I'll swear for 'em.

They dance to music, with shepherds and shepherdesses

POLIXENES. This is the prettiest low-born lass that ever
Ran on the green-sward: nothing she does or seems
But smacks of something greater than herself,
Too noble for this place.

CAMILLO. He tells her something
That makes her blood look out. Good sooth, she is
The queen of curds and cream.

POLIXENES. Pray, good shepherd, what fair swain is this
Which dances with your daughter?

SHEPHERD. They call him Doricles, and boasts himself
To have a worthy feeding; but I have it
Upon his own report and I believe it:
He looks like sooth. He says he loves my daughter:
I think so too; for never gazed the moon

Upon the water as he'll stand and read
As 'twere my daughter's eyes ; and, to be plain,
I think there is not half a kiss to choose
Who loves another best.

POLIXENES. She dances featly.

SHEPHERD. So she does anything, though I report it
That should be silent. If young Doricles
Do light upon her she shall bring him that
Which he not dreams of.

SERVANT *(entering)*. O master! if you did but hear the pedlar at the door, you would never dance again after a tabor and pipe ; no, the bagpipe could not move you. He sings several tunes faster than you'll tell money. He hath songs for man or woman, of all sizes ; no milliner can so fit his customers with gloves : he has the prettiest love-songs for maids. He hath ribands of all the colours in the rainbow; points more than all the lawyers in Bohemia can learnedly handle, though they come to him by the gross ; inkles, caddisses, cambrics, lawns : why, he sings 'em over as they were gods.

CLOWN. Prithee, bring him in, and let him approach singing.

Enter Autolycus singing

Lawn as white as driven snow ;
Cyprus black as e'er was crow ;
Gloves as sweet as damask roses ;
Masks for faces and for noses ;
Bugle-bracelet, necklace-amber,
Perfume for a lady's chamber ;
Golden quoifs and stomachers,
For my lads to give their dears ;
Pins and poking-sticks of steel ;
What maids lack from head to heel :
Come buy of me, come ; come buy, come buy ;
Buy, lads, or else your lasses cry : come, buy.

After more singing and dancing the conversation continues. Polixenes expresses surprise that Florizel has let the pedlar go without buying fancies for the object of his love, but Florizel declares that such trifles do not please Perdita, who has his heart.

FLORIZEL. Were I crowned the most imperial monarch,
Thereof most worthy, were I the fairest youth
That ever made eye swerve, had force and knowledge
More than was ever man's, I would not prize them
Without her love.

He asserts that they will marry, even without the consent of Florizel's father, who must be kept innocent of the whole matter. At this Polixenes becomes very angry, and reveals himself in a great passion.

POLIXENES. Mark your divorce, young sir,
Whom son I dare not call: thou art too base
To be acknowledged: thou a sceptre's heir,
That thus affect'st a sheep-hook!

Polixenes, cursing both his son and Perdita, takes his leave and the maid beseeches Florizel to leave her to her shepherd's life. She will milk her ewes and weep. But Florizel declares that not for Bohemia would he break his oath to his fair beloved, and begs Camillo to intervene on his behalf and assuage his father's passion. Camillo counsels him to go to Sicilia and present himself to Leontes.

FLORIZEL. I am bound to you. There is some sap in this.

CAMILLO. A course more promising
Than a wild dedication of yourselves
To unpathed waters, undreamed shores.

FLORIZEL. My good Camillo,
She is as forward of her breeding as
She is i' the rear o' her birth.

CAMILLO. I cannot say tis pity
She lacks instructions, for she seems a mistress
To most that teach.

PERDITA. Your pardon, sir; for this I'll blush you thanks.

As they talk aside Autolycus comes in

AUTOLYCUS. Ha, ha! what a fool Honesty is! and Trust, his sworn brother, a very simple gentleman! I have sold all my trumpery: not a counterfeit stone, not a riband, glass, pomander, brooch, table-book, ballad, knife, tape, glove, shoe-tie, bracelet, horn-ring, to keep my pack from fasting: they throng who should buy first, as if my trinkets had been hallowed and brought a benediction to the buyer, by which means I saw whose purse was best in picture; and what I saw to my good use I remembered.

The others come forward

CAMILLO. My letters, by this means being there
So soon as you arrive, shall clear that doubt.

FLORIZEL. And those that you'll procure from King Leontes—

CAMILLO. Shall satisfy your father.

PERDITA. Happy be you! All that you speak shows fair.

CAMILLO *(seeing Autolycus)*. Whom have we here?

AUTOLYCUS. I am a poor fellow, sir.

CAMILLO. Why, be so still; here's nobody will steal that from thee; yet for the outside of thy poverty we must make an exchange; therefore, discase thee instantly, and change garments with this gentleman.

AUTOLYCUS. I am a poor fellow, sir. Are you in earnest, sir? *(Aside)* I smell the trick on 't.

CAMILLO. Unbuckle, unbuckle.

Florizel and Autolycus change clothes and Perdita is disguised, the three then setting out for the sea, while Autolycus looks on and plans more knavery for their confusion.

CLOWN *(entering with Shepherd)*. See, see, what a man you are now! There is no other way but to tell the king she's a changeling and none of your flesh and blood. Show those things you found about her; this being done, let the law go whistle: I warrant you.

SHEPHERD. I will tell the king all, every word, yea, and his son's pranks too; who, I may say, is no honest man neither to his father nor to me, to go about to make me the king's brother-in-law.

CLOWN. Indeed, brother-in-law was the furthest off you could have been to him, and then your blood had been the dearer by I know not how much an ounce.

AUTOLYCUS *(aside)*. Very wisely, puppies!

SHEPHERD. Well, let us to the king.

CLOWN. Pray heartily he be at palace.

AUTOLYCUS *(aside)*. Though I am not naturally honest, I am so sometimes by chance. *(He takes off his false beard.)* How now, rustics! whither are you bound?

SHEPHERD. To the palace, an it like your worship.

AUTOLYCUS. Your affairs there, what, with whom?

CLOWN. We are but plain fellows, sir.

AUTOLYCUS. A lie; you are rough and hairy. Let me have no lying; it becomes none but tradesmen.

SHEPHERD. Are you a courtier, an 't like you, sir?

AUTOLYCUS. Whether it like me or no, I am a courtier. Seest thou not the air of the court in these enfoldings? hath not my gait in it the measure of the court? I am courtier, and one that will either push on or pluck back thy business there: whereupon I command thee to open thy affair.

SHEPHERD. My business, sir, is to the king.

AUTOLYCUS. What advocate hast thou to him?

SHEPHERD. I know not, an 't like you.

AUTOLYCUS. How blessed are we that are not simple men!
Yet nature might have made me as these are,
Therefore I'll not disdain.

CLOWN. This cannot be but a great courtier.

SHEPHERD. His garments are rich, but he wears them not handsomely.

CLOWN. He seems to be the more noble in being fantastical: a great man, I'll warrant.

AUTOLYCUS. Wherefore that box?

SHEPHERD. Sir, there lies such secrets in this box which none must know but the king, and which he shall know within this hour if I may come to the speech of him.

AUTOLYCUS. Tell me, for you seem to be honest plain men, what you have to the king: being something gently considered I'll bring you where he is aboard, tender your persons to his presence, whisper him in your behalfs; and if it be in man besides the king to effect your suits, here is a man shall do it.

CLOWN. He seems to be of great authority: close with him, give him gold; though authority be a stubborn bear, yet he is oft led by the nose with gold. Show the inside of your purse to the outside of his hand, and no more ado.

SHEPHERD. An 't please you, sir, to undertake the business for us, here is that gold I have: I'll make it as much more and leave this young man in pawn till I bring it you.

AUTOLYCUS. After I have done what I have promised?

SHEPHERD. Ay, sir.

AUTOLYCUS. Well, give me the moiety. I will trust you. Walk before toward the seaside; go on the right hand; I will but look upon the hedge and follow you.

CLOWN. We are blessed in this man, as I may say, even blessed.

SHEPHERD. Let's before as he bids us. He was provided to do us good.

AUTOLYCUS. If I had a mind to be honest I see Fortune would not suffer me: she drops booties in my mouth. I will bring these two moles, these blind ones, aboard. To him will I present them: there may be matter in it.

ACT 5

Scene 1—A Room in the Palace of Leontes

The courtiers of Leontes now begin to suggest to him that he has long "performed a saint-like sorrow" for his Queen, and he might now fitly marry again. To that Paulina objects, and reminds him that the Oracle said he "should not have an heir till his lost child be found."

LEONTES. I'll have no wife, Paulina.

PAULINA. Will you swear
Never to marry but by my free leave?

LEONTES. Never, Paulina: so be blessed my spirit!

PAULINA. Then, good my lords, bear witness to his oath.

CLEOMENES. You tempt him over much.

PAULINA. Unless another, as like Hermione as is her picture,
Affront his eye.

CLEOMENES. Good madam—

PAULINA. I have done.
Yet, if my lord will marry, give me the office
To choose you a queen : she shall not be so young
As was your former, but she shall be such
As, walked your first queen's ghost, it should take joy
To see her in your arms.

LEONTES. My true Paulina,
We shall not marry till thou bidd'st us.

GENTLEMAN *(entering)*. One that gives out himself Prince Florizel,
Son of Polixenes, with his princess—she
The fairest I have yet beheld—desires access
To your high presence.

LEONTES. What with him ? What train ?

GENTLEMAN. But few, and those but mean.

LEONTES. His princess, say you, with him ?

GENTLEMAN. Ay, the most peerless piece of earth, I think,
That e'er the sun shone bright on.

LEONTES. Go, Cleomenes ;
Yourself, assisted with your honoured friends,
Bring them to our embracement. Still tis strange
He thus should steal upon us.

Cleomenes brings in Florizel, Perdita, and others

Most dearly welcome !
And you, fair princess—goddess ! O, alas !
I lost a couple, that 'twixt heaven and earth
Might thus have stood. What might I have been,
Might I a son and daughter now have looked on,
Such goodly things as you !

LORD *(entering)*. Most noble sir,
That which I shall report will bear no credit
Were not the proof so nigh. Please you, great sir,
Bohemia greets you from himself by me ;
Desires you to attach his son, who has
(His dignity and duty both cast off)
Fled from his father, from his hopes, and with
A shepherd's daughter.

LEONTES. Where's Bohemia ? Speak.

LORD. Here in your city ; I now come from him :
I speak amazedly, and it becomes
My marvel and my message. To your court
Whiles he was hastening (in the chase it seems
Of this fair couple) meets he on the way
The father of this seeming lady and

Her brother, having both their country quitted
With this young prince.

All are startled by this unexpected turn of events, and Leontes, expressing his sympathy with Perdita (in whom he has seen a resemblance to Hermione), leaves them to meet Polixenes and the two countrymen.

Scene 2—Before the Palace of Leontes

Autolycus meets courtiers who tell him what happened when the old shepherd told his story and opened his bundle, astonishing the King and Camillo ; how bonfires were lit because the King's daughter was found with the mantle of Hermione and her jewel about her neck ; how the two Kings had met with tears ; how the old shepherd had been thanked and his son had produced rings belonging to Antigonus ; how the ship had been wrecked so that no news of what happened had reached Sicilia ; how all were now going to Paulina's house to see a statue of Hermione by that rare Italian sculptor Julio Romano.

Scene 3—A Chapel in Paulina's House

Enter Leontes and Polixenes, Florizel and Perdita, Camillo and Paulina

LEONTES. O grave and good Paulina, the great comfort
That I have had of thee !
PAULINA. What, sovereign sir,
I did not well, I meant well. All my services
You have paid home ; but that you have vouchsafed,
With your crowned brother and these your contracted
Heirs of your kingdoms, my poor house to visit,
It is a surplus of your grace, which never
My life may last to answer.
LEONTES. O Paulina !
We honour you with trouble : but we came
To see the statue of our queen : your gallery
Have we passed through, but we saw not
That which my daughter came to look upon,
The statue of her mother.
PAULINA. As she lived peerless,
So her dead likeness, I do well believe
Excels whatever yet you looked upon
Or hand of man hath done ; therefore I keep it
Lonely, apart. But here it is : prepare
To see the life as lively mocked as ever
Still sleep mocked death : behold ! and say tis well.

Paulina draws back a curtain and reveals Hermione as a statue

LEONTES. Her natural posture !
Chide me, dear stone, that I may say, indeed
Thou art Hermione ; or rather, thou art she
In thy not chiding, for she was as tender

As infancy and grace. But yet, Paulina,
Hermione was not so much wrinkled; nothing
So aged as this seems.

POLIXENES. O! not by much.

PAULINA. So much the more our carver's excellence;
Which lets go by some sixteen years and makes her
As she lived now.

LEONTES. And now she might have done
So much to my good comfort, as it is
Now piercing to my soul. O! thus she stood,
Even with such life of majesty, warm life,
As now it coldly stands, when first I wooed her.
I am ashamed: does not the stone rebuke me
For being more stone than it? O, royal piece!
There's magic in thy majesty, which has
My evils conjured to remembrance, and
From thy admiring daughter took the spirits,
Standing like stone with thee.

PERDITA. And give me leave,
And do not say tis superstition, that
I kneel and then implore her blessing. Lady,
Dear queen, that ended when I but began,
Give me that hand of yours to kiss.

As they are all under the stress of great emotion at the powerful likeness of the statue, Paulina regrets having shown it, and is about to veil it when Leontes earnestly checks her.

LEONTES. Do not draw the curtain.

PAULINA. No longer shall you gaze on 't, lest your fancy
May think anon it moves.

LEONTES. Let be, let be!
Would I were dead, but that, methinks, already—
What was he that did make it? See, my lord,
Would you not deem it breathed, and that those veins
Did verily bear blood?

POLIXENES. Masterly done:
The very life seems warm upon her lip.

LEONTES. The fixure of her eye has motion in 't,
As we are mocked with art.

PAULINA. I'll draw the curtain;
My lord's almost so far transported that
He'll think anon it lives.

LEONTES. O sweet Paulina!
Make me to think so twenty years together:
No settled senses of the world can match
The pleasure of that madness. Let 't alone.

PAULINA. I am sorry, sir, I have thus far stirred you: but
I could afflict you further.

LEONTES. Do, Paulina;
For this affliction has a taste as sweet
As any cordial comfort. Still, methinks,
There is an air comes from her: what fine chisel
Could ever yet cut breath? Let no man mock me,
For I will kiss her.

PAULINA. Good my lord, forbear. Shall I draw the curtain?

LEONTES. No, not these twenty years.

PERDITA. So long could I stand by, a looker on.

PAULINA. Either forbear,
Quit presently the chapel, or resolve you
For more amazement. If you can behold it,
I'll make the statue move indeed, descend,
And take you by the hand; but then you'll think
(Which I protest against) I am assisted
By wicked powers.

LEONTES. What you can make her do,
I am content to look on: what to speak,
I am content to hear; for tis as easy
To make her speak as move.

PAULINA. It is required
You do awake your faith. Then, all stand still;
Or those that think it is unlawful business
I am about, let them depart.

LEONTES. Proceed: no foot shall stir.

PAULINA. Music, awake her: strike! *(Music sounds)*
Tis time; descend; be stone no more: approach;
Strike all that look upon with marvel. Come;
Bequeath to death your numbness, for from him
Dear life redeems you. You perceive she stirs!

Hermione comes down

Start not; her actions shall be holy as
You hear my spell is lawful: do not shun her
Until you see her die again, for then
You kill her double. Nay, present your hand:
When she was young you wooed her; now in age
Is she become the suitor!

LEONTES *(embracing her)*. O! she's warm.
If this be magic, let it be an art
Lawful as eating.

POLIXENES. She embraces him.

CAMILLO. She hangs about his neck:
If she pertain to life let her speak too.

POLIXENES. Ay; and make 't manifest where she has lived,
Or how stolen from the dead.

PAULINA. That she is living,
Were it but told you, should be hooted at
Like an old tale; but it appears she lives,
Though yet she speak not. Mark a little while.
Please you to interpose, fair madam: kneel
And pray your mother's blessing. Turn, good lady;
Our Perdita is found. *(Perdita kneels to Hermione)*

HERMIONE. You gods, look down,
And from your sacred vials pour your graces
Upon my daughter's head! Tell me, mine own,
Where hast thou been preserved? where lived? how found
Thy father's court? for thou shalt hear that I,
Knowing by Paulina that the oracle
Gave hope thou wast in being, have preserved
Myself to see the issue.

PAULINA. There's time enough for that;
Lest they desire upon this push to trouble
Your joys with like relation. Go together,
You precious winners all; your exultation
Partake to every one. I, an old turtle,
Will wing me to some withered bough, and there
My mate, that's never to be found again,
Lament till I am lost.

LEONTES. O! peace, Paulina.
Thou shouldst a husband take by my consent,
As I by thine a wife: this is a match,
And made between 's by vows. Thou hast found mine;
But how is to be questioned; for I saw her,
As I thought, dead, and have in vain said many
A prayer upon her grave. I'll not seek far
(For him, I partly know his mind) to find thee
An honourable husband. Come, Camillo,
And take her by the hand; whose worth and honesty
Is richly noted, and here justified
By us, a pair of kings. Let's from this place.
What! look upon my brother: both your pardons,
That e'er I put between your holy looks
My ill suspicion. This your son-in-law,
And son unto the king, whom heavens directing,
Is troth-plight to your daughter. Good Paulina,
Lead us from hence, where we may leisurely
Each one demand and answer to his part
Performed in this wide gap of time since first
We were dissevered. Hastily lead away.

Shakespeare at the Heart of England

Did it just happen, one wonders, that Shakespeare came to us out of the very heart of England, in the very dawning of her greatness, and at the very centre of her glory? Does it not seem, looking back through our immortal years, that it was written in the skies that Shakespeare should come when he did?

He came into this precious isle, set in the silver sea, at a point where Time and Place seemed to be meeting with some mighty work in hand. The world was filled with wonder; it was the very hour for an Imagination to be born. And for our greatest Englishman what place was there like Warwickshire? What glory could have stirred his soul like hers? He walked about unguessed at in the heart of this dear land.

It is not true that the glory of England is ended. It can never end while the hedges run along her country lanes, while the grass grows in her matchless fields, while her oaks and yews rise to the sky like sentinels of God. There never was a land more fit to be a Paradise.

We look upon our slums and think them foul: and foul they are, a shame that cries aloud; but we look upon our countryside on a summer's day and it is fit to be the Gate of Heaven. There is no corner of the whole wide Earth that matches it; if the prisoners of our towns could see it as it is they would give their lives that no ill should be allowed to come to it.

It may have been a chance that Shakespeare opened his eyes in the very centre of this loveliness, but in that case chance was fraught with wondrous consequence, for it was the beauty of the country round about him that printed the image of this land on his heart, to be transmitted from generation unto generation.

There are many Shakespeare mysteries, and one is where he spent the year between leaving Stratford and reaching London. Nobody knows. But any one of us may guess, and we may believe that he spent it in the countryside he loved so well, working in the villages, walking to the towns. He would stand enthralled by the quiet beauty of the country lanes. He would be delighted with the timbered cottages. He would stand on the old bridge of the Avon and think of the ages its smooth waters have been rolling on. He would pass from place to place in this enchanted land and see the vast cathedrals, and there would come into his mind the solemn sense of time, and of the spirit that moves behind men and things. He would begin to feel that there are more things in

Heaven and Earth than are dreamt of in our philosophy. He would take upon himself the mystery of things, the magical beauty of the world about him.

This mystery-year in Shakespeare's life was probably the most important year in his half-century. He was on his way to London to be crowned, and he came back king of the world. Between that day on which he left home with a heavy heart and his arrival a year later on the scene of his triumph, something must have happened. It is said he left Stratford because wild ways had got him into trouble, and he arrived in London with his future still in doubt. But the spirit had been born within him. He attached himself to a theatre, struggled as an actor, and in a year or two had laid the foundations of a career unequalled since the world began.

Is it not time that we who speak the tongue that Shakespeare spoke, a hundred millions of us scattered through the world, fixed on some holy place where we can pledge ourselves that, come what may, we will be faithful to our race? It would be a precious inspiration to us all if we would go as pilgrims to the cradle and the grave of Shakespeare, and see the country that he knew.

We should see indeed the country that he knew, for it is little changed. We can knock at the door of the house he was born in; we can go upstairs into the room in which he first saw the light. We can see the font in which they baptised him, just inside the doorway of the beautiful church in which he must have spent some of his most reflective hours. We can walk about the garden in which he played his first games with his mother. We can creep up the stairs into the attic where he slept with his brothers very near the old oak rafters. We can go down the street past the houses he saw on his way to school, and sit at a desk in his schoolroom. There is a desk he is said to have used; they show us a place where it is thought he sat. Certain we are that within these walls he learned a little Latin and less Greek. Here he learned to love books; here especially he loved a book which came back to his mind as he sat writing his last play.

The school is still as Shakespeare knew it; if he could come back and sit at his lessons he would notice hardly any change. It is surely one of the most thrilling rooms that this world has. And under it is another room that Shakespeare knew, one in which there may have come to him his first great dream. It was the old Guildhall when Shakespeare was a boy, and in it he saw his first play.

Does it not stir the imagination as we think of it? Here he probably saw an old play he was to rewrite, but little can he have thought that the day would come when he himself would play the king in it. At least sixteen companies of players came to Stratford while Shakespeare was a boy, and again and again he must have been enchanted with these spectacles. Sitting in this room, with the old oak beams and the lovely windows, the imagination dawning within him must have been moved by the drama of life as it was made to pass before his eyes. Could that small Guildhall hold the vasty fields of France, or might they cram within that wooden O the battlefield of Agincourt? How often, when his great days came, and he was shaping for the stage scenes that have thrilled men through the centuries, must he have thought of the plays he saw in this small room! Here his mind first thought of the stage; in the schoolroom upstairs he learned his first history. A dull Englishman must he be who could stand within these walls and not feel moved.

We feel indeed, wherever we move in Stratford, that we are on sacred ground. It is a precious piece of earth. Wherever we go Shakespeare was before us. We turn round a corner and in front of us stretches out a long line of Elizabethan England, all as Shakespeare saw it as far as we can see. We can stand in his garden and look up at the old red roofs that his eyes must have rested on a thousand times. This ring on the church door he must have touched and wondered at, for it had been there four hundred years when Shakespeare passed that way. He would stand on Clopton Bridge and watch the Avon winding through the trees and past the church.

But most of all, we think, he learned to love the mile walk through the fields to Shottery. There, just across the brook, was a bank where wild thyme grew, and a garden with rosemary and marigolds and lavender. He would open a gate and out to him would come Anne Hathaway, through this very door, along these very walks, or up the bank into the orchard there. For hundreds of years the Hathaways have lived in this fine house, and some of them are still about. It is perhaps the most intimate place that remains in Shakespeare's world. It is unspoiled; it is full of things he saw. There is an old carved bed that has never been out of the room for four hundred years. There is a table Shakespeare must have had his supper at, a wooden plate he may have eaten from, chairs he may have sat in, and, loveliest of all, there is still by the great fireplace the old settle on which he would sit with Anne Hathaway in the happiest hours of his youth. A little way off, in the Memorial Hall, is a brooch Anne Hathaway may have worn, and a pair of Shakespeare's gloves.

Those were his happy days, but they were not to last long. In some village round about Shakespeare married Anne Hathaway, and soon three children came. There was Susannah, who was to live to see her father's fame and to entertain a queen, and there were the twins, Judith and Hamnet. Judith was to marry the son of Shakespeare's friend Quiney, who wrote to him the only letter we have that he is known to have received ; and Hamnet lies in a little grave not far from his father and mother. Shakespeare was writing his plays in London when he lost his only son, who died before he was twelve.

We know nothing of the little son. There is no mark on his grave. But we know that he lies here near his twin sister where the Avon ripples past, and where, when his work was done, our greatest Englishman must have come to sit and think of the glory that passes away.

Shakespeare saw very little of this small son, for he left Anne Hathaway behind in Stratford with her three babies still almost rocking in their cradles. He had got himself into disgrace, it is said, by stealing a deer, and it was now that he wandered into the countryside alone. A very sad day it must have been for him walking over Clopton Bridge, the old bridge with its fifteen arches spanning the Avon still. He was leaving the home of his childhood, the town of his boyhood. He had lain in his cradle there with plague raging all about him. One in seven of all the people in the town had perished, but the house that sheltered the little Shakespeare was miraculously spared. His father had risen to prosperity and become a high official of the town, and had helped with a generous hand the hundreds of destitute left by the plague. Now the father had fallen on evil times : his fortunes had dwindled ; his civic dignities were taken from him ; he had lost his position of trust because he could not pay his taxes.

Shakespeare was going out into an unknown world. He was leaving behind the lanes and fields and the rivers that he loved, and we can imagine the flood of emotions surging within him as he passed out of sight of the spire of Stratford church. It is the next year of his life that we know nothing about, but it is the next ten years that make up a story as magical as anything that came from his pen. For in ten years Shakespeare was back in Stratford rich and famous. He re-established the family fortunes, put his father on his feet again, bought the biggest private house in the town, and stood among his own people as a favourite of the great. This Stratford boy had come to live in history with Elizabeth, the greatest Englishman and the greatest Englishwoman side by side.

We must believe that on his way to London Shakespeare would see the great sights of the country round about him. He must have marvelled at the peacefulness of England, seeing the powerful place it was taking among the nations of the world. While he was still at school Elizabeth had made a progress through Warwickshire to Kenilworth, and Shakespeare would be sure to go. He would have seen the Queen in that great pageantry, and now he would love to see Warwick again.

Its castle was at the height of its glory, looking, as Sir Walter Scott was to describe it centuries after, the fairest monument of ancient and chivalrous splendour uninjured by Time. Its foundations were laid by Alfred's daughter a thousand years ago ; passing through the winding road cut out of solid rock, we can still see the mound thrown up as a fortress by the daughter of our first great king. High above the hills of Warwick rise the castle towers, with walls eight feet thick, and from the summit Shakespeare would look out and see the green fields of this realm, this England.

His mind would be impressed with this great place as he walked about its spacious lawns, or stood on Warwick Bridge and saw the castle rising like a dream above the Avon ; and we may hope he had a chance to walk through its great rooms. He would feel the thrill of history as he walked about this house, for here came Elizabeth and Richard the Third, here came a King of England as a captive, and here came Shakespeare's patriot king as the guest of Richard Beauchamp. The very thought of that would thrill this boy from Stratford Grammar School. Who would not be thrilled by the thought of Richard Beauchamp sitting in Warwick Castle talking to Henry the Fifth ?

For Richard Beauchamp is a name to stir men with. We meet him again in a treasure-house where Shakespeare must have followed him, the Beauchamp Chapel. It is the chief glory of St. Mary's Church in Warwick and one of the priceless gems in England's crown of beauty. Richard Beauchamp never saw this wondrous place, but it was built in his name and with his fortune ; it was his money that carried on the work for twenty years. He saw three kings on the English throne. He lived through the reign of Henry the Fourth ; he looked on the wild youth of Henry the Fifth and saw him rise to be the idol of the English people ; and he lived long enough into the reign of Henry the Sixth to stain our flag with an infamy that Time will not forget. For it was this Richard Beauchamp, Earl of Warwick, lying here amid all this rich loveliness, with fourteen kinsmen and eighteen angels round his tomb, who burned Joan of Arc.

He died in Rouen as Joan did, but her ashes are blown about the fields of France and her tomb is in the hearts of men. He has this splendid tomb, we say, and here, it is true, he slept about two hundred years ; but it is recorded that the floor of the Beauchamp Chapel then fell in and Richard Beauchamp was seen again. There he lay in his sleep, fresh and perfect for a while, and then came a little wind and he was turned to dust, and the ladies of Warwick made rings with the locks of his hair. So that Richard Beauchamp is dust with Joan of Arc today, both scattered by the wind.

Yet we feel, as we look on this noble tomb crowned with his handsome effigy in brass, that such a sight must greatly have moved the traveller from Stratford. He must have thought how dark and strange are our human destinies. Perhaps, as he stood looking on this vision splendid, he seemed to hear Richard Beauchamp whispering :

Here I and sorrows sit ;
Here is my throne : bid kings come bow to it.

Within these walls there lies a man whom Shakespeare knew. He must have been at Shakespeare's funeral, for he was Recorder of Stratford at the time. He was one of two schoolboys at Shrewsbury. They loved each other, and about the time that Shakespeare walked to London they were fighting against Spain for Queen Elizabeth. One was in command, Fulke Greville, and he came home again ; the other died on the field, perishing from thirst but giving his cup of water to another. When Greville followed Philip Sidney in the course of time they laid him in the crypt of this splendid place, and round his tomb they set these words :

Here lies Fulke Greville,
servant to Queen Elizabeth,
Counsellor to King James,
friend to Sir Philip Sidney.

Perhaps they might have added Friend to William Shakespeare.

By the west gate of Warwick, which was then four centuries old, Shakespeare must have stopped to see the famous hospital Robert Dudley founded to house twelve men broken in the wars.

Shakespeare must have been many times to Warwick ; he must have known this splendid county well. It is not to be imagined that he lived within easy reach of Worcester and did not see it. He must have thought of Worcester and Warwick a hundred times as he sat writing his matchless pages of English history. For in Worcester, in one of the most impressive cathedral choirs in Europe, under the oldest royal effigy in England, lies what remains of King John.

Oh, what a goodly outside falsehood hath! Did ever a king so foul sleep in so sweet a place? Here lies a man who sold his country and his honour, whose infamy gave Shakespeare perhaps the most pathetic scene he ever put on paper:

Must you with hot irons burn out both mine eyes,
These eyes that never did nor never shall
So much as frown on you?

We can hardly help thinking, as we stand by this tomb, what Shakespeare himself must have thought when he wrote those last lines of King John. He must have thought that a land that could survive a king like that could endure anything; and his spirit stirred within him as his words rang out in those majestic lines:

This England never did, nor never shall,
Lie at the proud foot of a conqueror,
But when it first did help to wound itself.
Come the three corners of the world in arms
And we shall shock them. Nought shall make us rue
If England to itself do rest but true.

A step or two away from King John lies a chantry without a tomb. It is the beautiful chantry of Prince Arthur, the eldest son of Henry the Seventh. There are 88 figures in this little place, but no effigy of the prince. It was not well that too much should be made of him, for this was the beginning of a tale of a king who would have been well matched to lie with John at the foot of these steps. The death of the prince who sleeps in this chantry was the opportunity of our Bluebeard King. Henry the Eighth married his widow Katharine, she whom the royal butcher put away for Anne Boleyn (who was to be butchered in her turn), she whose maid sang to her with the lute that song which everybody knows:

Orpheus with his lute made trees,
And the mountain tops that freeze,
Bow themselves when he did sing.

Everything that heard him play,
Even the billows of the sea,
Hung their heads, and then lay by.

Perhaps there is not a single spot in Shakespeare's country, or in all England, where imagination runs as it does here, for if Prince Arthur had not died there would have been no Henry the Eighth, no Queen Elizabeth; there would have been no Reformation as we know it, the flow of the great tide of history would have gone some other way, and perhaps (who knows?) without the sympathy Elizabeth gave to players there might have been no Shakespeare.

We cannot follow Shakespeare everywhere ; we have no time to follow him to Tewkesbury and to Gloucester, and we must leave those ten great years in London. He acted, but fortunately for us all gave up acting, encouraging it perhaps in his little brother, whom he put into one of his companies and helped in many ways before he died. They buried him in Southwark Cathedral on the banks of the Thames, a stone's throw from the scene of Shakespeare's triumphs, and the grave is one of the few places in London where we can stand and know that Shakespeare let a tear fall there.

Once at least in every year Shakespeare would go back to Stratford, and the time came when he bought the best house in the town. In the end he went home to live there ; it was in 1611, and he was forty-seven.

He had begun to feel old long before. At the beginning of the century he wrote that he felt himself like a tree with the boughs shaking against the wind, " bare ruined choirs where late the sweet birds sang." But his work was not done. Shakespeare worked hard for one half of his life. We may think of his work as covering a quarter of a century, with the year 1600 half-way. There were twelve years of gaiety and romance, and twelve years of strength and peace. He was at the height of his power as the sixteenth century closed, when he gave the world Henry the Fifth. But even Shakespeare did not understand himself. He felt that in him men saw the twilight of a summer's day, yet his powers were to stay at their summit for twelve years more.

And then he came home. He said farewell to his old haunts, and to his friends in London Town. He took his last walks by the Thames before he went to take his last rest by the Avon. He would saunter for the last time through the nave of old St Paul's. He would stroll along the banks of the little River Fleet. He had been a quarter of a century away from home, and he who left with a heavy heart was going back with immortality. He was going back to his two barns and his two gardens. He was going to live with his wife and his two daughters. His father and mother were gone—they had died in the cottage he was born in, and were buried in the churchyard near his son.

To those who know what mothers endure for their children it is pleasant to remember that Shakespeare's mother lived to see him at the height of his fame, the richest man in his town and the proudest man in his country. There is a cottage at Wilmcote, outside Stratford, which Mary

Arden is thought to have lived in ; it was on her father's farm. There is the church where she married John Shakespeare, nestling among the trees of Aston Cantlow. We follow her to Stratford by the lanes she rode through as a happy bride, and we feel that the world owes her a debt that it has never paid.

It is sad that there should come into this story the sour-tempered old parson named Gastrell, but we cannot do without him. It happened that, a hundred and fifty years after Shakespeare, Parson Gastrell wanted a summer house to go to from his village of Frodsham in Cheshire, where he was vicar, and unhappily he bought Shakespeare's house. He quarrelled with everybody, for the Vicar of Frodsham had little of the spirit of his Master. He hated the people who peeped over his garden wall to see the mulberry tree that Shakespeare planted, and he cut the tree down and sold it as firewood. He quarrelled with the corporation about his taxes, and in his temper he pulled down the house to spite them. At last he left the town amid the ragings and cursings of its citizens, and so there passes out of the world one of the poorest little figures who ever strutted across its stage.

But nobody can take away from us this precious bit of earth where Shakespeare closed his life and fell asleep. We can stand in the very place where he died. Here are the foundations of the walls, and here is the house next door to his, in which his favourite daughter lived.

We know that we are standing on holy ground. This was his garden running down towards the Avon. Here is a mulberry tree descended from his own, grown from a slip that was saved ; and here are the foundations of a bay window looking out on the garden. At this window Shakespeare would sit and dream in those days of his peace. We like to think he may have come down here to work in quiet when he was writing his great tragedies. We do not know. But we may like to believe that when he had finished King Lear and his Roman plays, when he bade farewell to his tragic mood, he would sit at his window in Stratford and work on The Winter's Tale and Cymbeline ; and especially we should like to think that here he finished The Tempest, his farewell to the stage, and to the pen, and to that boundless world of wonder he had made his own.

There will always be something pathetic about The Tempest, for it is Shakespeare's last word to mankind. The bell was ringing in the tower across the street as it had rung out in his schooldays, and as it rings out still ; and as he sat at the window looking out on his garden his mind would run back to his boyhood. He was looking back on all that he had done; he was thinking of the wonder of it all. He saw once more the great scenes in the theatre, Elizabeth in her grand processions, King James in his palace, the glory of Warwick, Richard Beauchamp in his little chapel, the peace of the Avon and the rushing tide of life in London Town, the green fields of England, King Harry coming back from Agincourt, Brutus in his tent at Philippi, Shylock creeping in the shadows of the walls of Venice, Prospero with his mighty powers—he thought of it all. Where had they come from these children of his brain? Whither was he bound, now that his work was done?

The cloud-capped towers, the gorgeous palaces,
The solemn temples, the great globe itself,

were all dissolving, to leave not a rack behind. He felt that

We are such stuff
As dreams are made on, and our little life
Is rounded with a sleep.

He remembered a little book he used to love at school, with its majestic music of words flowing down the ages from Old Rome. It was running through his brain as he echoed it in Prospero's great speech to the powers from which he had drawn his magic:

This rough magic
I here abjure; and, when I have required
Some heavenly music (which even now I do)
To work mine end, I'll break my staff,
Bury it certain fathoms in the earth,
And, deeper than did ever plummet sound,
I'll drown my book.

Prospero laying down his powers is Shakespeare laying down his magic; in those last hours of his work he even took the name of Prospero from his old friend Ben Jonson.

We know little more of him, but we know that he lived on for five more years with his wife and his daughter Judith, and with Susannah happily married in a house just round the corner. He was rich and successful and famous; he had the three things that most men desire. But he seems to have spent his last years quietly among his own folk, in the countryside where he had begun his life without a thought of fame; and he would often go, we may be sure, out of his garden gate, across the lane, into the churchyard where his father and mother and his little lad were sleeping under the trees. The church had seen the first event in his famous life, but not his seven ages, for he had only reached his prime on that April day when they brought him here for his long rest. His wondrous life was rounded with a sleep at last. His eyes would see this lovely world no more, those eyes that Mrs Browning said had tears and laughter for all time. The boy who loved the Avon, the river that had heard his voice, reflected his face, felt his footsteps coming in the grass, had come to sleep on its bank.

Here he lies in this sacred earth, the dearest dust in England. He lies nameless before the altar, his wife on one side, his daughter on the other. Where we expect to find his name is something that we feel is all out of keeping in this solemn place. Here lies the master poet of the world, and on the stone above him is a brass with four lines which we feel are all unworthy to mark his tomb :

Good friend for Jesu's sake forbeare,
To digg the dust encloasèd heare :
Blest be the man that spares these stones,
And curst be he that moves my bones.

It is not impressive ; it does not sound like Shakespeare ; and it has saddened many a pilgrim to this place. We should have liked to have had here something from Milton :

What needs my Shakespeare for his honoured bones,
The labour of an age in pilèd stones ?
Thou in our wonder and astonishment
Hast built thyself a live-long monument.

Or something like the noble lines from Matthew Arnold's great sonnet :

And thou, who didst the stars and sunbeams know,
Self-schooled, self-scanned, self-honoured, self-secure,
Didst walk on earth unguessed at.

Best of all, perhaps, we should have liked something majestic from the plays themselves, let us say those lovely lines from Cymbeline, written in the quiet of Shakespeare's closing years :

Fear no more the heat o' the sun,
Nor the furious winter's rages ;
Thou thy worldly task hast done,
Home art gone, and ta'en thy wages.

And yet in this uncouth rhyme above his grave there is something to think about. The master poet of the world was home again, but his work was done. He was a plain man among his own people, and fame was nothing to him now. He had come back to rest in his town. Here lay his father and his mother and his only son, and soon he was to sleep among them. He remembered the gravedigger in Hamlet, throwing up a skull; he remembered that it had been poor Yorick: "A fellow of infinite jest, of most excellent fancy; he hath borne me on his back a thousand times; and now, how abhorred in my imagination it is! Here hung those lips that I knew. Where be your gibes, your songs, your flashes of merriment, that were wont to set the table on a roar?"

Shakespeare remembers it all, and he, who has always believed in hidden powers and never at any time been free from the superstitions of his age, remembers that not even the grave was sacred in those days, when bones were moved and put into a charnel house, into the charnel house down the steps by the altar of Stratford church, by the very spot where he was to lie. The thought of it is not to be borne, and so this Warwickshire lad come home again sits down and writes this verse to his own neighbours. He is not writing for the world that will come to worship at his grave, or for the centuries that will wonder at his plays: he is writing for vicars and sextons and grave-diggers, frightening them away from his bones.

And there he lies still as they laid him, our greatest Englishman sleeping in the very heart of the land he made immortal in the world. There are other spots he made famous in his life. There is the room he was born in, and the garden he died in. And what a host of memories gathers round that house in which he died! Susannah lived in it after him, and there this good daughter of Shakespeare, living through the Civil War, entertained Henrietta Maria and soldiers of the Puritan army. What a picture it is, Charles Stuart's wife and Shakespeare's daughter sitting by the fire before the Battle of Edgehill, and, when the battle was over, Shakespeare's daughter entertaining Cromwell's men, in the house where Shakespeare died.

But, of all the places touched by Shakespeare's magic, none can move us so, none can draw so many millions unto it, as this precious piece of earth in which he lies without a name. He needs no name whose fame is written in the skies.